Teacher's Guide

Mathematics II

Volume 1

Randall I. Charles
Basia Hall
Dan Kennedy
Laurie E. Bass
Allan E. Bellman
Sadie Chavis Bragg
William G. Handlin
Art Johnson
Stuart J. Murphy
Grant Wiggins

PEARSON

Boston, Massachusetts · Chandler, Arizona · Glenview, Illinois · Upper Saddle River, New Jersey

Acknowledgments appear on page Z25, which constitutes an extension of this copyright page.

PEARSON

ISBN-13: 978-0-13-323454-1
ISBN-10: 0-13-323454-1
6 17

Contents in Brief

Welcome to Pearson's ***Mathematics II***. This program was specifically developed to meet the Common Core State Standards for an integrated high school sequence. Each lesson focuses on specific Standards for Mathematical Content while the Standards for Mathematical Practice are woven throughout the course to help students build proficiency with these standards.

Series Authors

Randall I. Charles, Ph.D., is Professor Emeritus in the Department of Mathematics at San Jose State University, San Jose, California. He began his career as a high school mathematics teacher, and he was a mathematics supervisor for five years. Dr. Charles has been a member of several NCTM committees including the writing team for the Curriculum Focal Points. He is the former Vice President of the National Council of Supervisors of Mathematics. Much of his writing and research has been in the area of problem solving. He has authored more than 90 mathematics textbooks for kindergarten through college.

Dan Kennedy, Ph.D., is a classroom teacher and the Lupton Distinguished Professor of Mathematics at the Baylor School in Chattanooga, Tennessee. A frequent speaker at professional meetings on the subject of mathematics education reform, Dr. Kennedy has conducted more than 50 workshops and institutes for high school teachers. He is coauthor of textbooks in calculus and precalculus, and from 1990 to 1994 he chaired the College Board's AP Calculus Development Committee. He is a 1992 Tandy Technology Scholar and a 1995 Presidential Award winner.

Basia Hall currently serves as Manager of Instructional Programs for the Houston Independent School District. With 33 years of teaching experience, Ms. Hall has served as a department chair, instructional supervisor, school improvement facilitator, and professional development trainer. She has developed curricula for Algebra 1, Geometry, and Algebra 2 and co-developed the Texas state mathematics standards. A 1992 Presidential Awardee, Ms. Hall is past president of the Texas Association of Supervisors of Mathematics and is a state representative for the National Council of Supervisors of Mathematics (NCSM).

Consulting Authors

Stuart J. Murphy is a visual learning author and consultant. He is a champion of helping students develop visual learning skills so they become more successful students. He is the author of *MathStart,* a series of children's books that presents mathematical concepts in the context of stories, and *I See I Learn,* a Pre-Kindergarten and Kindergarten learning initiative that focuses on social and emotional skills. A graduate of the Rhode Island School of Design, he has worked extensively in educational publishing and has been on the authorship teams of a number of elementary and high school mathematics programs. He is a frequent presenter at meetings of the National Council of Teachers of Mathematics, the International Reading Association, and other professional organizations.

Grant Wiggins, Ed.D., is the President of Authentic Education in Hopewell, New Jersey. He earned his B.A. from St. John's College in Annapolis and his Ed.D. from Harvard University. Dr. Wiggins consults with schools, districts, and state education departments on a variety of reform matters; organizes conferences and workshops; and develops print materials and Web resources on curricular change. He is perhaps best known for being the coauthor, with Jay McTighe, of *Understanding by Design* and *The Understanding by Design Handbook*[1], the award-winning and highly successful materials on curriculum published by ASCD. His work has been supported by the Pew Charitable Trusts, the Geraldine R. Dodge Foundation, and the National Science Foundation.

[1]ASCD, publisher of the "Understanding by Design Handbook" co-authored by Grant Wiggins and registered owner of the trademark "Understanding by Design", has not authorized or sponsored this work and is in no way affiliated with Pearson or its products.

Program Authors

Algebra Topics

Allan E. Bellman, Ph.D., is an Associate Professor of Mathematics Education at the University of Mississippi. He previously taught at the University of California, Davis for 12 years and in public school in Montgomery County, Maryland for 31. He has been an instructor for both the Woodrow Wilson National Fellowship Foundation and the Texas Instruments' T^3 program. Dr. Bellman has expertise in the use of technology in education and assessment-driven instruction and speaks frequently on these topics. He is a recipient of the Tandy Award for Teaching Excellence and has twice been listed in Who's Who Among America's Teachers.

Sadie Chavis Bragg, Ed.D., is Senior Vice President of Academic Affairs and professor of mathematics at the Borough of Manhattan Community College of the City University of New York. She is a past president of the American Mathematical Association of Two-Year Colleges (AMATYC). In recognition for her service to the field of mathematics locally, statewide, nationally, and internationally, she was awarded AMATYC's most prestigious award, The Mathematics Excellence Award for 2010. Dr. Bragg has coauthored more than 60 mathematics textbooks for kindergarten through college.

William G. Handlin, Sr., is a classroom teacher and Department Chair of Mathematics and former Department Chair of Technology Applications at Spring Woods High School in Houston, Texas. Awarded Life Membership in the Texas Congress of Parents and Teachers for his contributions to the well-being of children, Mr. Handlin is also a frequent workshop and seminar leader in professional meetings.

Geometry Topics

Laurie E. Bass is a classroom teacher at the 9–12 division of the Ethical Culture Fieldston School in Riverdale, New York. A classroom teacher for more than 30 years, Ms. Bass has a wide base of teaching experience, ranging from Grade 6 through Advanced Placement Calculus. She was the recipient of a 2000 Honorable Mention for the Radio Shack National Teacher Awards. She has been a contributing writer for a number of publications, including software-based activities for the Algebra 1 classroom. Among her areas of special interest are cooperative learning for high school students and geometry exploration on the computer. Ms. Bass is a frequent presenter at local, regional, and national conferences.

Art Johnson, Ed.D., is a professor of mathematics education at Boston University. He is a mathematics educator with 32 years of public school teaching experience, a frequent speaker and workshop leader, and the recipient of a number of awards: the Tandy Prize for Teaching Excellence, the Presidential Award for Excellence in Mathematics Teaching, and New Hampshire Teacher of the Year. He was also profiled by the Disney Corporation in the American Teacher of the Year Program. Dr. Johnson has contributed 18 articles to NCTM journals and has authored over 50 books on various aspects of mathematics.

Program Components

Pearson's *Integrated High School Mathematics* offers an innovative hybrid instructional model that consists of digital delivery of content during instructional time, supplemented by a write-in student edition (WiSE), or worktext, in which students can record their understandings of the concepts presented as they work through the problems. The teacher's guide provides an easy-to-navigate walk-through for each lesson, just-in-time professional development, and point-of-use probing questions to maximize student thinking and learning.

Digital Features

The **digital courseware**, accessed through either *PearsonSuccessnet* or the Digital Lesson DVD, is the primary source of instructional content. Each lesson includes visually engaging and interactive problem situations from which students explore concepts and solidify their understandings of these concepts. Instruction can be further enhanced with the **robust math tools** and **dynamic activities** that are found within the Interactive Digital Path. Also available at *PearsonSuccessnet* is a full array of ancillary **teaching resources**, as well as a robust set of **assessment resources**.

Out of the classroom, students have full access to *PearsonSuccessnet*, from which they can log in to the digital courseware with all of the interactive instructional content as well as math homework tutor videos.

By scanning the QR codes on the first page of each lesson in the student worktext, students can access additional math videos developed by **Virtual Nerd**™.

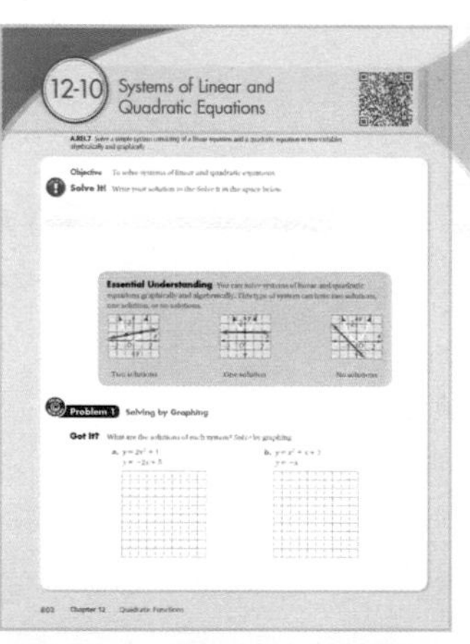

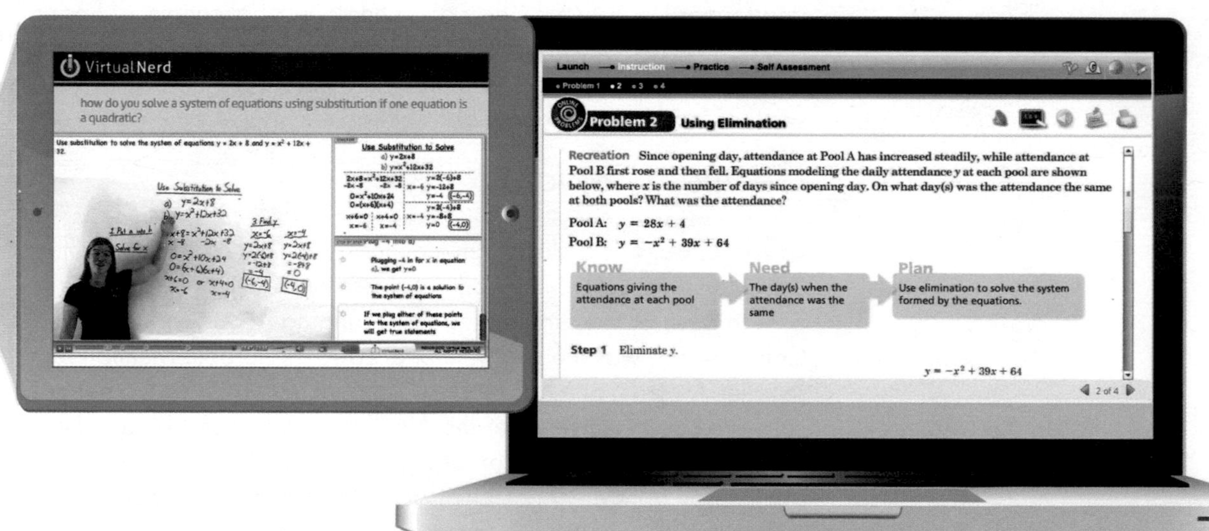

Look for these icons in the Interactive Digital Path!

For a full listing of all of the digital components, see page T8.

The *Solve It* presents an engaging, mathematical or real-world problem situation to get students ready to learn.

The main instruction for the program, the online problems are often interactive and visually rich.

Online practice and review is available at the the end-of-chapter.

Student-produced videos demonstrate engaging applications of math concepts.

Interactive online activities help to bring mathematics alive.

Online definitions for the new terms have audio explanations in both English and Spanish.

Print Components

The **Student Worktext** is a personalized learning journal and resource that students can refer back to throughout their high school studies. In the classroom, students record their work and solutions to problems and exercises, and as needed, their thinking about the exercises that follow each problem presented. At the end of each lesson, they will find homework exercises in the **More Practice and Problem Solving** section. The two-volume format provides slimmed-down, lighter student editions.

The student worktext is also available as an interactive etext online and on both iPad and Android tablets.

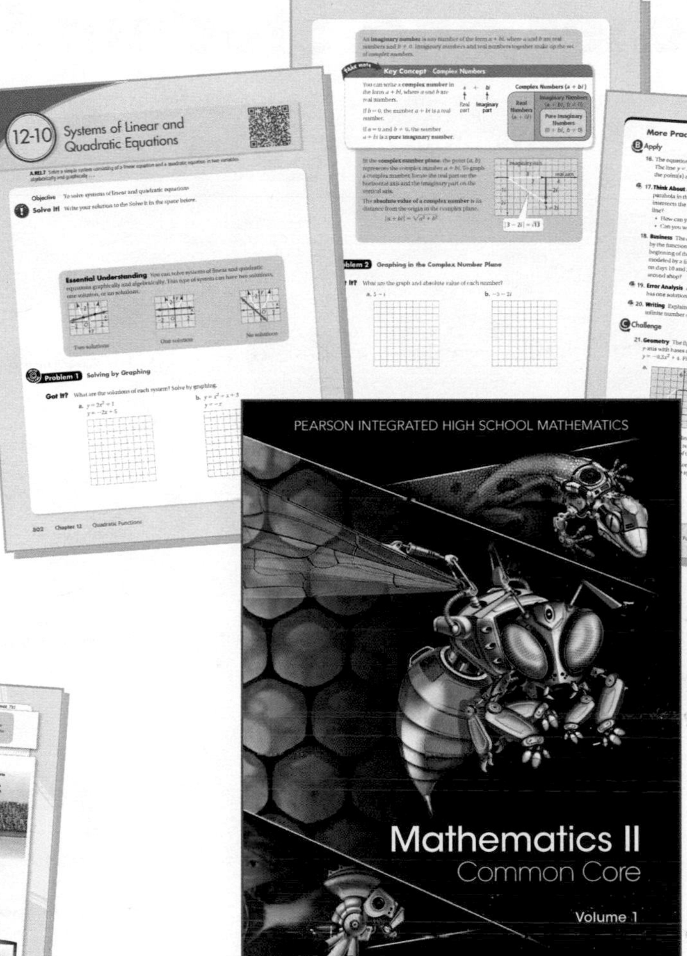

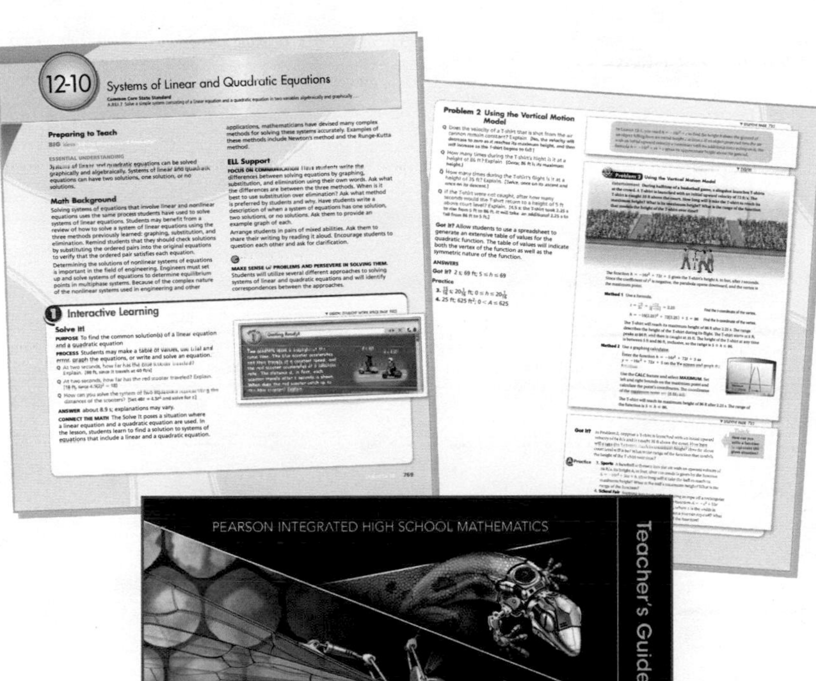

The **Teacher's Guide** provides a comprehensive resource for teachers to use in planning for and teaching lessons in the program. Each chapter includes a **Math Background** section that offers teachers an overview of the math concepts being presented. Lesson support has a side-by-side format that shows the student-facing material from either the digital courseware or the student worktext in the right column, with facilitating questions, teaching notes, and answers in the left column.

Teacher and Student Resources

	Component	Print	CD/ DVD	Online PearsonSuccessNet	Mobile iPad/Android
Student Resources	**Student Worktext**	√		√	√
	Digital Lessons DVD		√		
	Virtual Nerd™ Tutorial Videos			√	√
	Online Resources Practice, Problem Solving, and Test Prep Worksheets Homework Video Tutors in English and Spanish Multilingual Handbook (9 languages)			√	
Student and Teacher Resources	**Interactive Digital Path** Chapter Opening Videos Animated Lessons* Self-Assessments* Dynamic Activities* Math Tools* Key Concepts* Lesson Vocabulary and Glossary* MathXL® for School Interactive Practice			√	
Teacher Resources	**Teacher's Guide**	√		√	√
	Integrated High School Mathematics Implementation Guide	√		√	√
	Online Resources Lesson Resources: Leveled Practice, Reteaching, Enrichment, ELL/ Vocabulary Support, Problem Solving, Standardized Test Prep, Activities, Games, Puzzles, Daily Lesson Quiz Chapter Resources: Teaching with TI Technology, Find the Errors, Extended Constructed Response Tasks, Chapter Projects			√	
	Online Lesson Planner with Common Core State Standards			√	
	SuccessTracker Assessment System with Common Core State Standards			√	
	Assessment Resource Book Diagnostic Test, Lesson Quizzes, Chapter Tests, Benchmark Tests, End of Course Test	√		√	
	ExamView® Assessment Suite CD-ROM		√		
	Answers and Solutions DVD		√		

*also on Digital Lesson DVD

Assessment Resources

		Student Worktext	Pearson SuccessNet	CD/DVD	Assessment Resources book	Type
Course Level	Diagnostic Assessments • Screening Test • Entry Level Assessment • Diagnostic Tests	√	√		√	Diagnostic
	Summative Assessments • Quarter Test • Mid-Course Test • Final Test • End-of-Course Test	√	√		√	Summative
Chapter Level	Put It All Together	√	√			Formative
	Chapter Tests	√	√		√	Summative
	Benchmark Tests		√		√	Summative
	Chapter Projects		√			Summative
	Performance Tasks		√		√	Summative
Lesson Level	Get Ready	√	√			Diagnostic
	Got It?	√	√	√		Formative
	Lesson Check	√	√	√		Formative
	Lesson Quizzes	√	√	√	√	Formative
	Self-Assessment		√	√		Formative
	Standards Practice	√	√		√	Formative
Multi-Level Assessments	Math XL for School		√			Formative
	ExamView			√		Formative, Summative
	SuccessTracker		√			Formative, Summative

About This Program

Integrated High School Mathematics was developed to be taught with technology tools in the classroom, from a teacher presentation station and a projector, to a more optimal instructional environment that has reliable internet access and an interactive white board to project the lessons from the **Interactive Digital Path**. The **Student Worktext**, a 2-volume, write-in student edition, is designed to support daily classroom instruction. The **Teacher's Guide** is a useful resource for planning and instructional support.

In the Classroom

Teachers will make frequent use of the Interactive Digital Path to teach parts of lessons, in particular, the **Interactive Learning** and **Guided Instruction**. (See Lesson Structure on pages T12 through T13.)

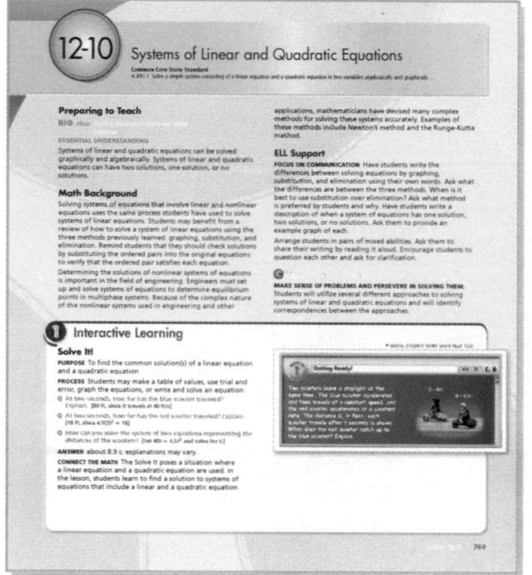

12-10 Systems of Linear and Quadratic Equations

Interactive Learning

Teacher's Guide

During instruction, the teacher can refer to the Teacher's Guide for probing questions, found at point-of-use.

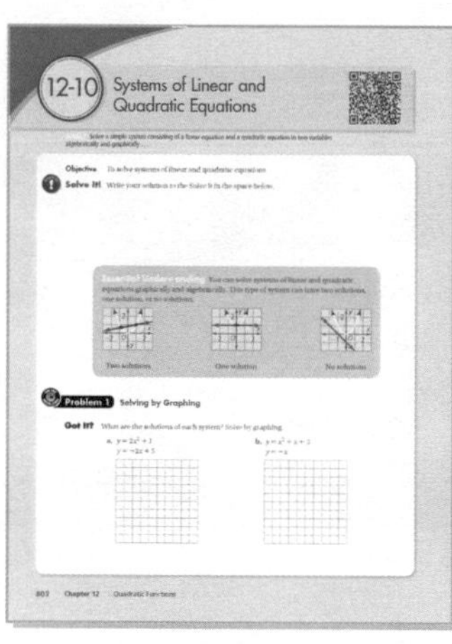

12-10 Systems of Linear and Quadratic Equations

Student Worktext

Students record their solutions to the *Solve It!* and *Got It?* exercises in their worktext. Students may also write down notes on concepts presented.

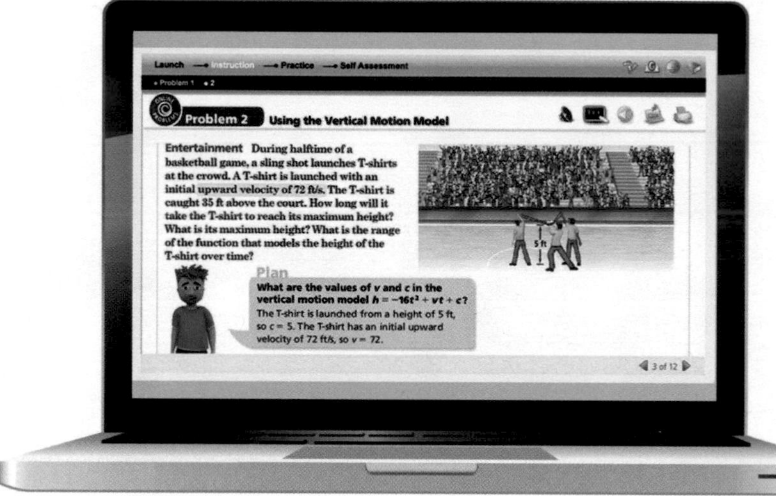

Interactive Digital Path

The teacher shows the *Solve It!* and Problems from the Interactive Digital Path or the Digital Lesson DVD and guides students to an understanding of the concepts.

Activity Labs, Technology Labs, and **Lesson Labs** are hands-on activities. These activities are not found in the Interactive Digital Path.

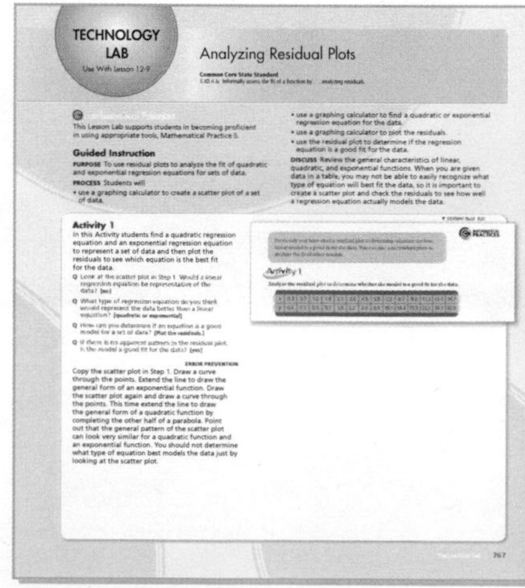

TECHNOLOGY LAB
Analyzing Residual Plots

Teacher's Guide

The Teacher's Guides offer teaching support that teachers may want to refer to during instruction.

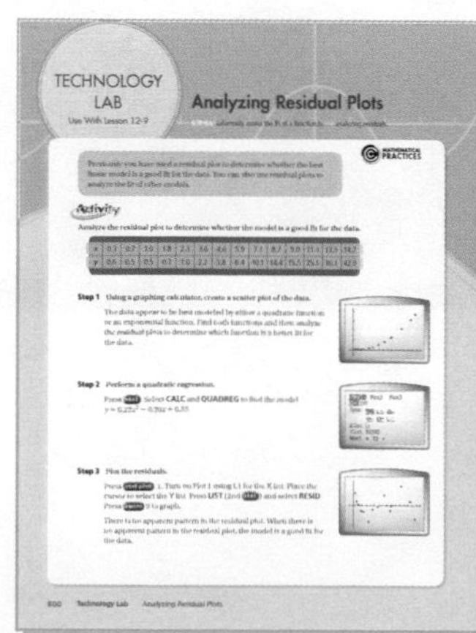

TECHNOLOGY LAB
Analyzing Residual Plots

Student Worktext

Students complete these activities in their Student Worktexts.

Out of the Classroom

Student Support

Students have full access to the Interactive Digital Path, including Animated Lessons, dynamic activities, and math tools, as well as other digital resources to support them in their learning out of the classroom. Using a smart phone or tablet with a camera, they can scan the QR code on the lesson opener in the worktext, which links to the appropriate Virtual Nerd™ video. These instructional videos support students as they complete their assigned homework exercises, found in their worktexts.

- By scanning the QR code, students can access an instructional video related to the lesson content.
- Students have individual log-ins to PearsonSuccessNet and can access it any time.
- Practice and Problem Solving exercises are found in the Student Worktext and on PearsonSuccessNet.

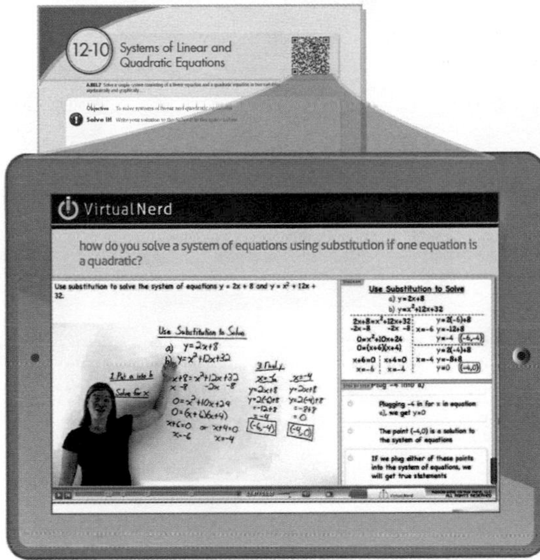

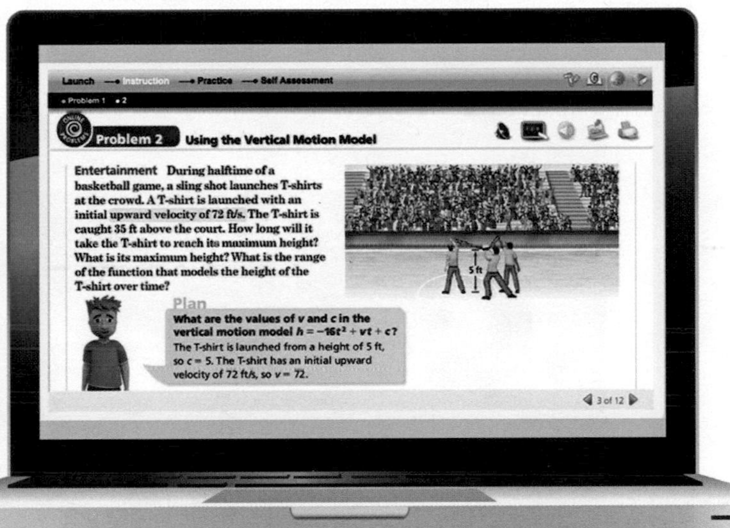

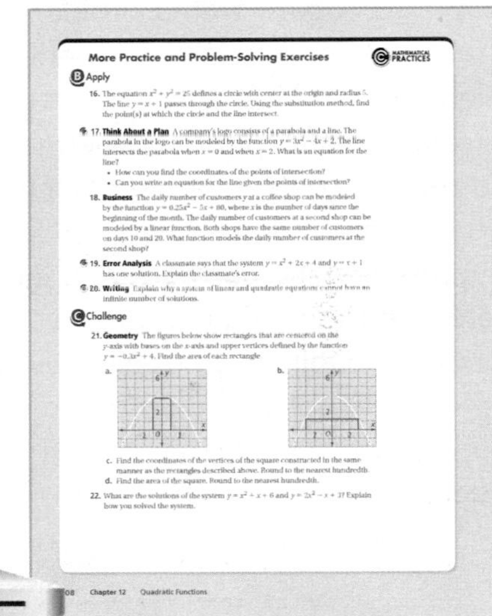

Teacher Support

Outside of the classroom, the Teacher's Guide can be the teacher's only needed resource for planning, comprehensive instructional support, formative assessment suggestions, and prescriptions for differentiation.

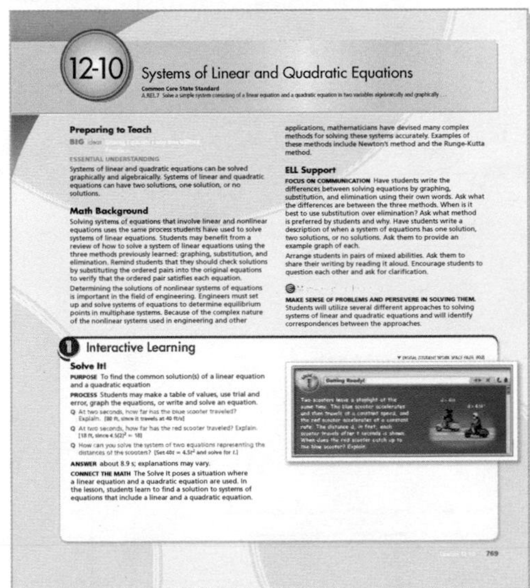

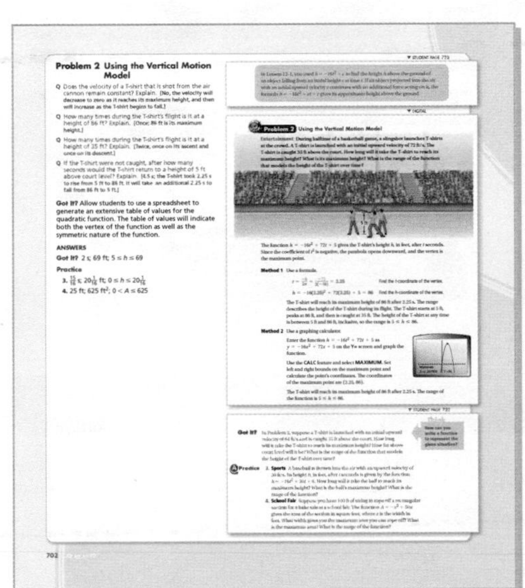

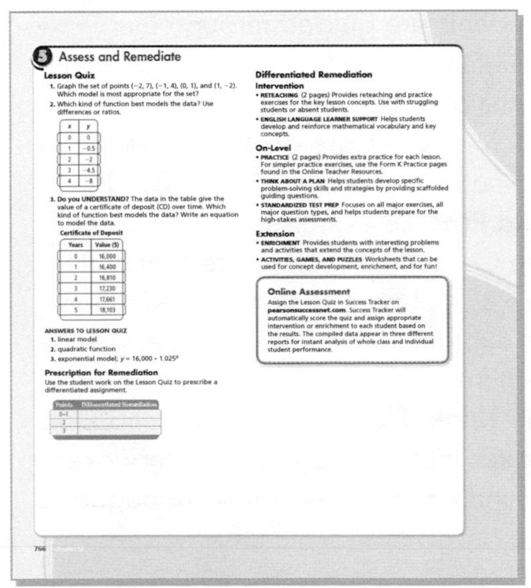

- Comprehensive instructional support is available at both the chapter and lesson level.
- Images of all instructional and assessment resources allow for one-stop planning.
- Formative assessment suggestions and prescriptions for differentiation are found in every lesson.

Lesson Structure

Pearson's *Integrated High School Mathematics* embraces the principles of Understanding by Design as developed by Grant Wiggins and Jay McTighe and published by the Association for Supervision and Curriculum Development (ASCD). The lessons are built around a **five-part lesson structure**: Interactive Learning, Guided Instruction, Lesson Check, Practice, and Assess and Remediate. These five parts help students to develop a deep conceptual understanding of the math concepts, provide opportunities for skill fluency, and facilitate student proficiency with reasoning and problem solving through application to real-world contexts.

1 Interactive Learning

Each lesson opens with a problem-based interactive learning experience called **Solve It!** This activity serves to activate students' prior knowledge and sets the context for the Essential Understanding for the lesson. Students are presented the **Solve It!** from the Interactive Digital Path and then work individually or in small groups to propose a solution plan and a solution, which they write in their student worktext.

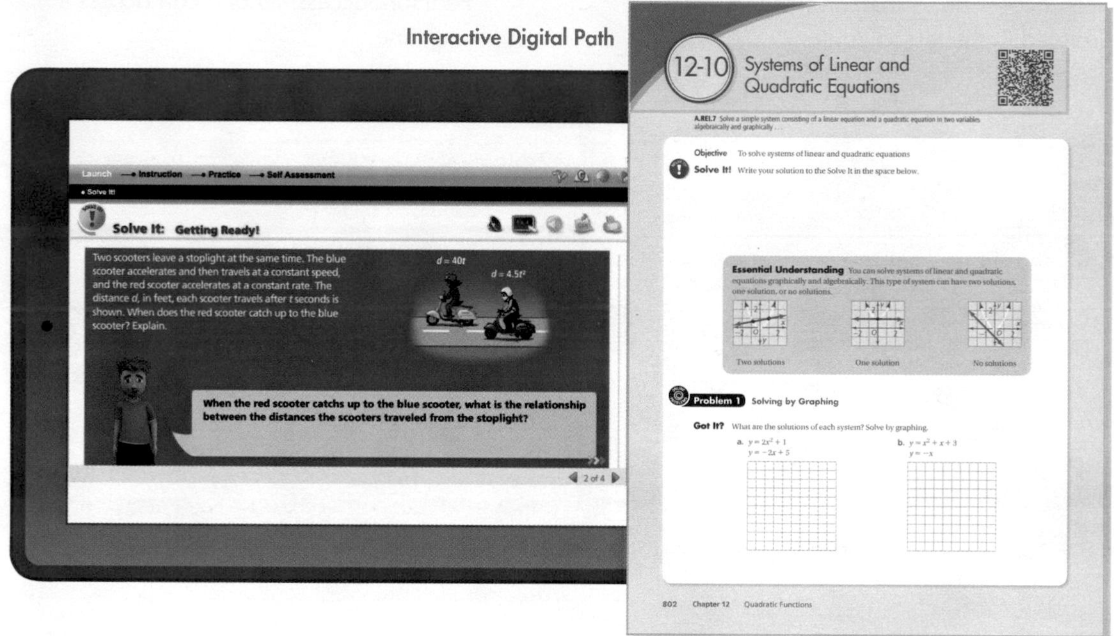

2 Guided Instruction

The Guided Instruction phase of the lesson is the heart of the lesson. Students are guided through the problems of the lesson, each of which focus on a key math concept. After each problem are opportunities for formative assessment in the **Got It?** and **Practice** exercises. Also part of the Guided Instruction are **Key Note** boxes that present concise definitions or explanations of math content. A key feature of the Guided Instruction are the **Think**, **Plan**, and **Know-Need-Plan** boxes that are part of the interwoven strand of reasoning found throughout the program.

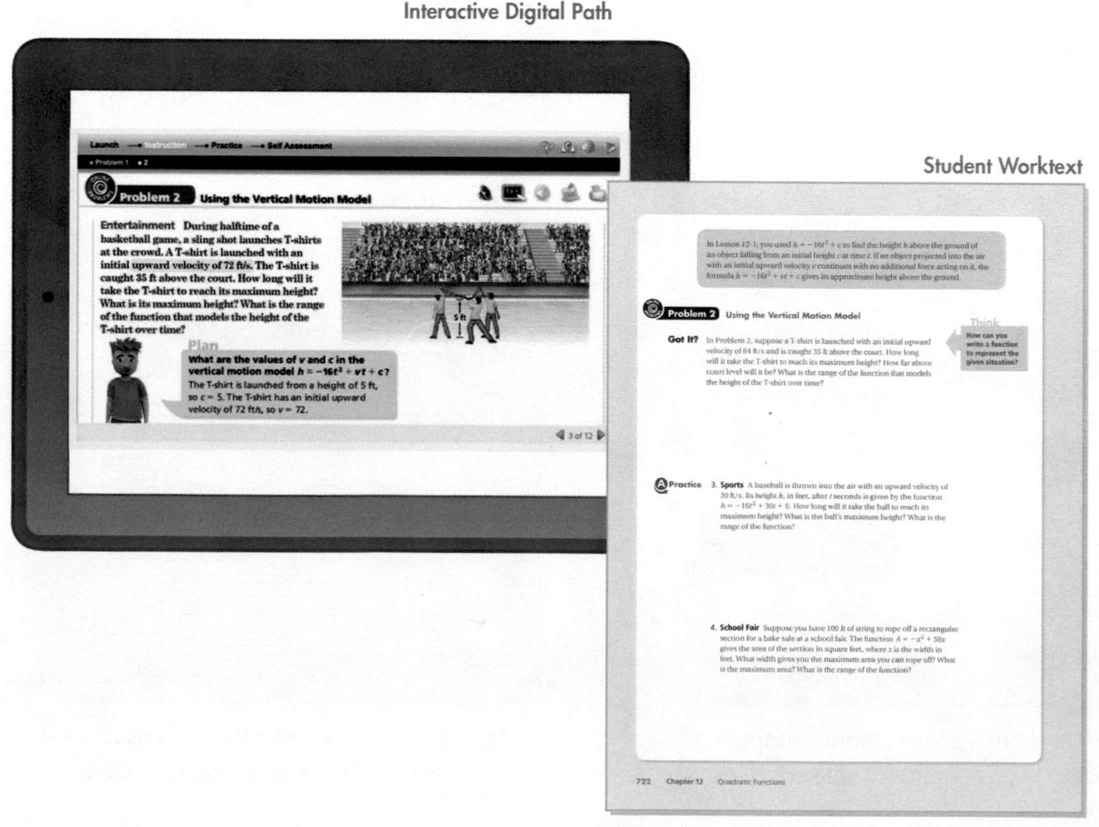

Student Worktext

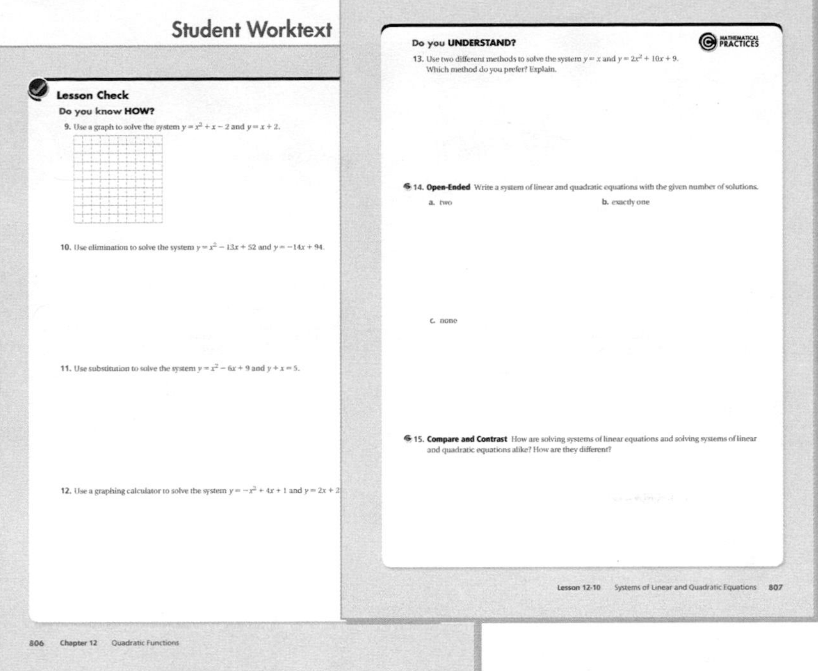
Lesson Check

Do you know HOW?

Do you UNDERSTAND?

Lesson 12-10 Systems of Linear and Quadratic Equations 807

806 Chapter 12 Quadratic Functions

Student Worktext

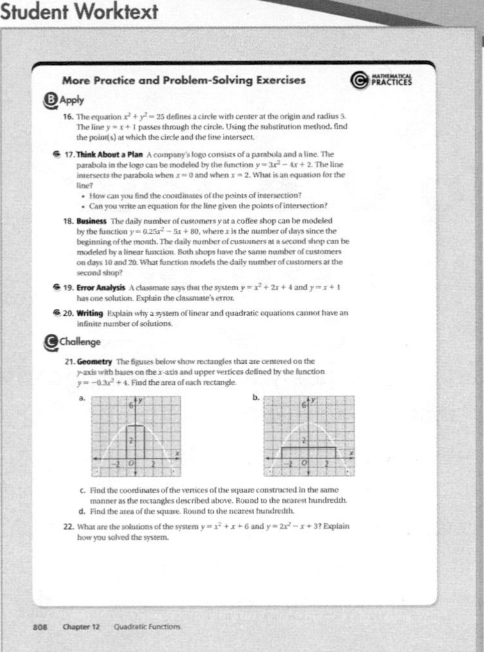
More Practice and Problem-Solving Exercises

Apply

Challenge

808 Chapter 12 Quadratic Functions

3 Lesson Check

The Lesson Check presents timely opportunities for assessing students' understanding of the lesson content. The **Do You Know HOW?** exercises assess students' procedural fluency while those in the **Do you UNDERSTAND?** section target students' understanding of mathematical structure and meaning. Students complete these exercises in their student worktext, providing them with a single resource to review key math concepts and skills.

4 Practice

The Practice phase affords students opportunities to solidify their procedural fluency and conceptual understanding of the lesson content. The exercises, found in both the Interactive Digital Path and the student worktext, are of three different types: practice, application, and challenge problems. Exercises with the Ⓖ logo have a particular emphasis on one or more of the Standards for Mathematical Practices.

5 Assess and Remediate

Each lesson ends with a Lesson Quiz and opportunities to provide differentiated instruction for students based on their quiz results.

Teachers will find in the Teacher's Guide personalized prescriptions based on a student's Lesson Quiz results. These prescriptions enable teachers to make data-driven decisions about assignments for intervention or extension.

Teachers may also choose to have students take the Lesson Quiz in SuccessTracker on PearsonSuccessnet. These online assessments are automatically scored and the appropriate intervention is assigned to each student.

Teacher's Guide

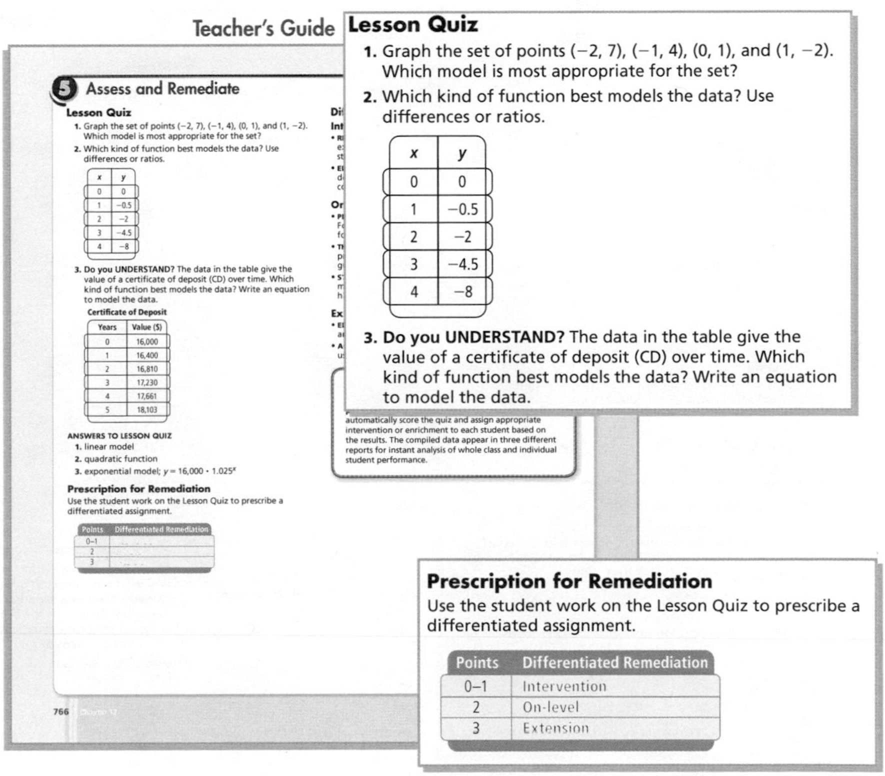
Lesson Quiz

1. Graph the set of points (−2, 7), (−1, 4), (0, 1), and (1, −2). Which model is most appropriate for the set?
2. Which kind of function best models the data? Use differences or ratios.

x	y
0	0
1	−0.5
2	−2
3	−4.5
4	−8

3. **Do you UNDERSTAND?** The data in the table give the value of a certificate of deposit (CD) over time. Which kind of function best models the data? Write an equation to model the data.

Certificate of Deposit

Years	Value ($)
0	16,000
1	16,400
2	16,810
3	17,230
4	17,661
5	18,103

ANSWERS TO LESSON QUIZ
1. linear model
2. quadratic function
3. exponential model; $y = 16{,}000 \cdot 1.025^x$

Prescription for Remediation

Use the student work on the Lesson Quiz to prescribe a differentiated assignment.

Points	Differentiated Remediation
0–1	Intervention
2	On-level
3	Extension

How To Use Your Teacher's Guide

Your Teacher's Guide also offers you easy-to-navigate teaching support for both planning and in-class instruction. For ease of planning with the different program components, the guide includes reduced images from both the Interactive Digital Path on PearsonSuccessnet and the student worktext. The student-facing elements will always be found in the right column with teaching notes, probing questions, and answers in the left column.

At the beginning of each chapter, you will find important resources to help you plan for instruction. The **Get Ready** page offers a diagnostic assessment you can use to determine your students' readiness for the math content of the chapter. On the page, you'll find a reduced student worktext page in the right column and the answers to the assessment in the left column.

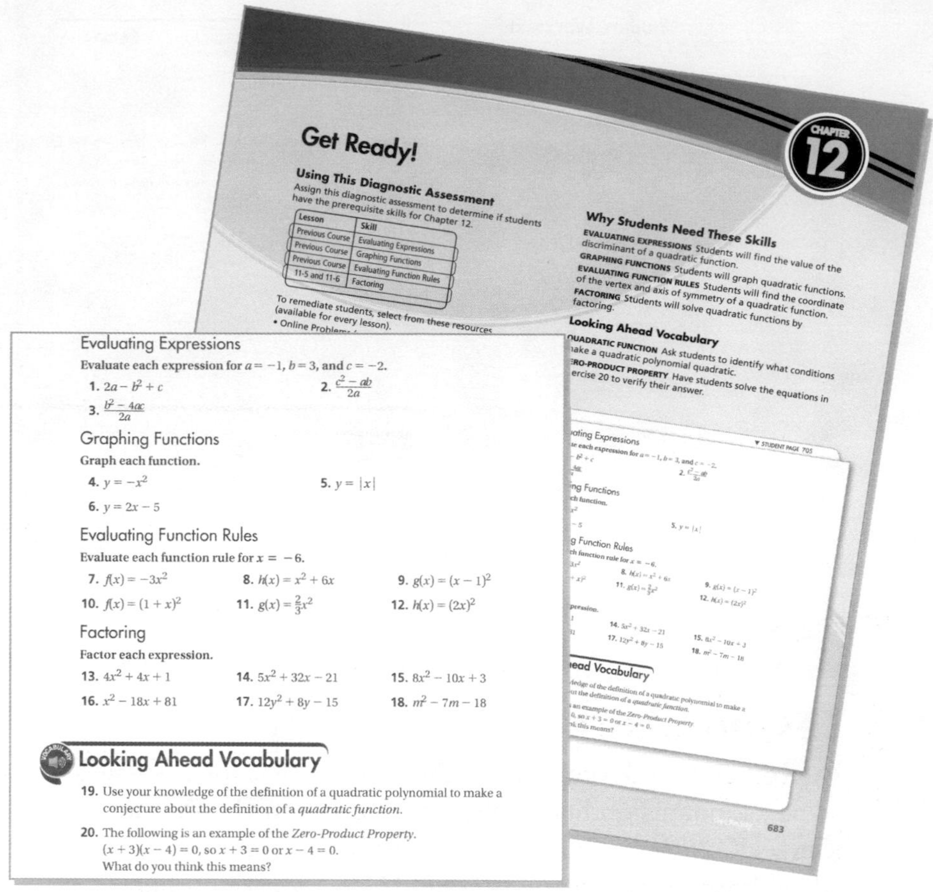

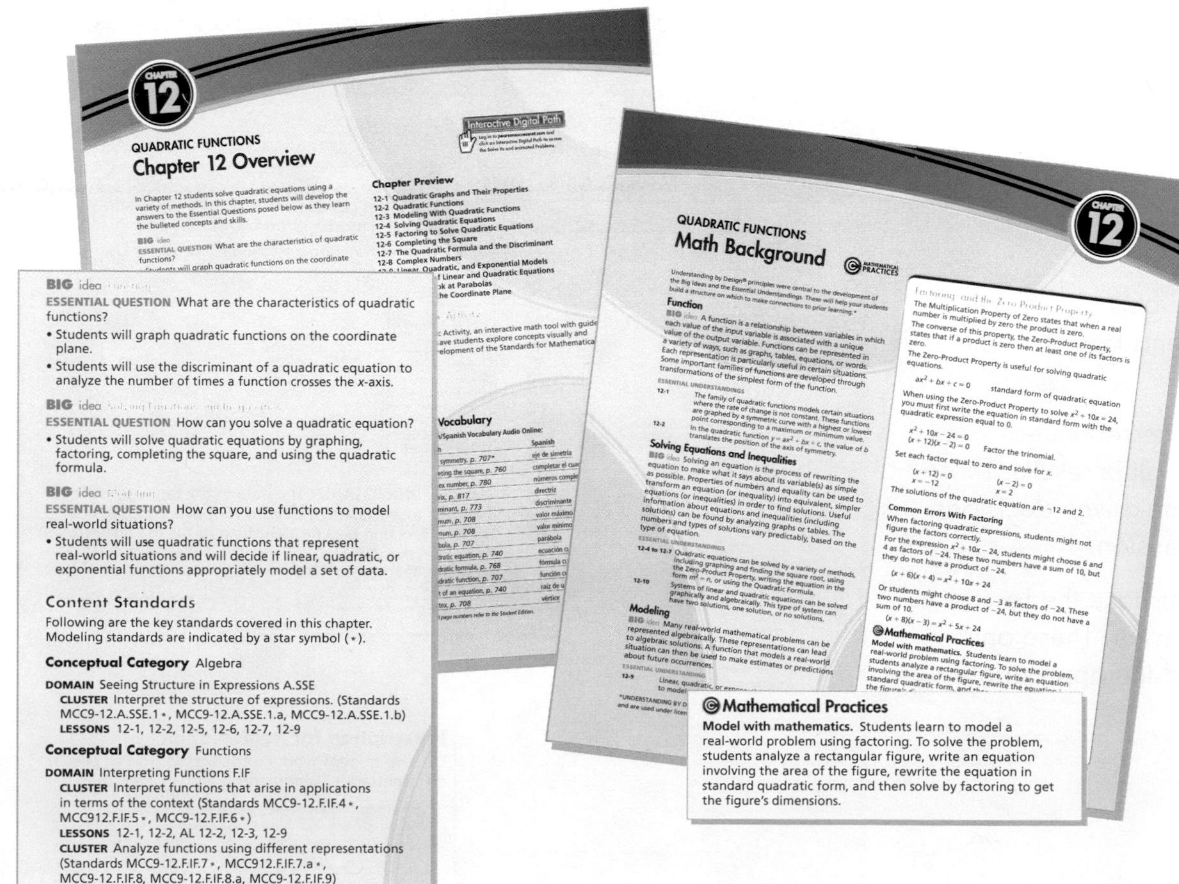

The **Chapter Overview** includes the Common Core State Standards addressed in the chapter, Essential Questions, Vocabulary, and a Chapter Preview, while the **Math Background** spread offers just-in-time professional development, including common student errors, and opportunities for developing proficiency with the Standards for Mathematical Practice.

Every lesson begins with just-in-time professional development for teachers. Teachers will find **Math Background** and **ELL Support** for each lesson.

Systems of Linear and Quadratic Equations

Common Core State Standard
A.REI.7 Solve a simple system consisting of a linear equation and a quadratic equation in two variables algebraically and graphically . . .

The **Common Core State Standard** addressed in the lesson listed under the lesson title.

Preparing to Teach

BIG ideas Solving Equations and Inequalities
Function

ESSENTIAL UNDERSTANDING

Systems of linear and quadratic equations can be solved graphically and algebraically. Systems of linear and quadratic equations can have two solutions, one solution, or no solutions.

Math Background

Solving systems of equations that involve linear and nonlinear equations uses the same process students have used to solve systems of linear equations. Students may benefit from a review of how to solve a system of linear equations using the three methods previously learned: graphing, substitution, and elimination. Remind students that they should check solutions by substituting the ordered pairs into the original equations to verify that the ordered pair satisfies each equation.

Determining the solutions of nonlinear systems of equations is important in the field of engineering. Engineers must set up and solve systems of equations to determine equilibrium points in multiphase systems. Because of the complex nature of the nonlinear systems used in engineering and other applications, mathematicians have devised many complex methods for solving these systems accurately. Examples of these methods include Newton's method and the Runge-Kutta method.

ELL Support

FOCUS ON COMMUNICATION Have students write the differences between solving equations by graphing, substitution, and elimination using their own words. Ask what the differences are between the three methods. When is it best to use substitution over elimination? Ask what method is preferred by students and why. Have students write a description of when a system of equations has one solution, two solutions, or no solutions. Ask them to provide an example graph of each.

Arrange students in pairs of mixed abilities. Ask them to share their writing by reading it aloud. Encourage students to question each other and ask for clarification.

Mathematical Practices

MAKE SENSE OF PROBLEMS AND PERSEVERE IN SOLVING THEM. Students will utilize several different approaches to solving systems of linear and quadratic equations and will identify correspondences between the approaches.

The ELL Support provides strategies to help **English Language Learners** maximize their learning.

1 Interactive Learning

Solve It!

PURPOSE To find the common solution(s) of a linear equation and a quadratic equation

PROCESS Students may make a table of values, use trial and error, graph the equations, or write and solve an equation.

Q At two seconds, how far has the blue scooter traveled? Explain. **[80 ft, since it travels at 40 ft/s]**

Q At two seconds, how far has the red scooter traveled? Explain. **[18 ft, since $4.5(2)^2 = 18$]**

Q How can you solve the system of two equations representing the distances of the scooters? **[Set $40t = 4.5t^2$ and solve for t.]**

ANSWER about 8.9 s; explanations may vary.

CONNECT THE MATH The Solve It poses a situation where a linear equation and a quadratic equation are used. In the lesson, students learn to find a solution to systems of equations that include a linear and a quadratic equation.

▼ DIGITAL (STUDENT WORK SPACE PAGE 802)

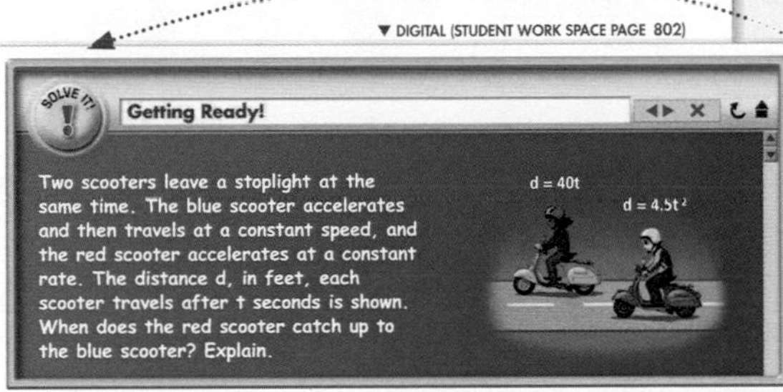

Getting Ready!
Two scooters leave a stoplight at the same time. The blue scooter accelerates and then travels at a constant speed, and the red scooter accelerates at a constant rate. The distance d, in feet, each scooter travels after t seconds is shown. When does the red scooter catch up to the blue scooter? Explain.
d = 40t
d = 4.5t²

Lesson 12-10 769

Above each image in the right column, you'll find a reference for the image. For the **Solve Its!**, you will note reference to both "digital" and "student workspace." This indicates that this feature is in the Interactive Digital Path and the student worktext.

Probing questions are set in blue to make them easier to find during instruction. These questions help teachers guide students to deep understanding of the concepts and greater proficiency with the **Standards for Mathematical Practice**.

How To Use Your Teacher's Guide *continued*

The **Guided Instruction** offers probing questions designed to help students develop deep conceptual understanding.

You'll find reduced images of all explanations of math concepts and **Essential Understandings** that students will see in their student worktext.

Each of the Problems in the **Interactive Digital Path** is shown in full to allow for one-stop planning.

There are probing or facilitating questions for many of the **Got It?** exercises.

Students are expected to work out their solutions to the **Got It?** and **Practice** exercises in their student worktext.

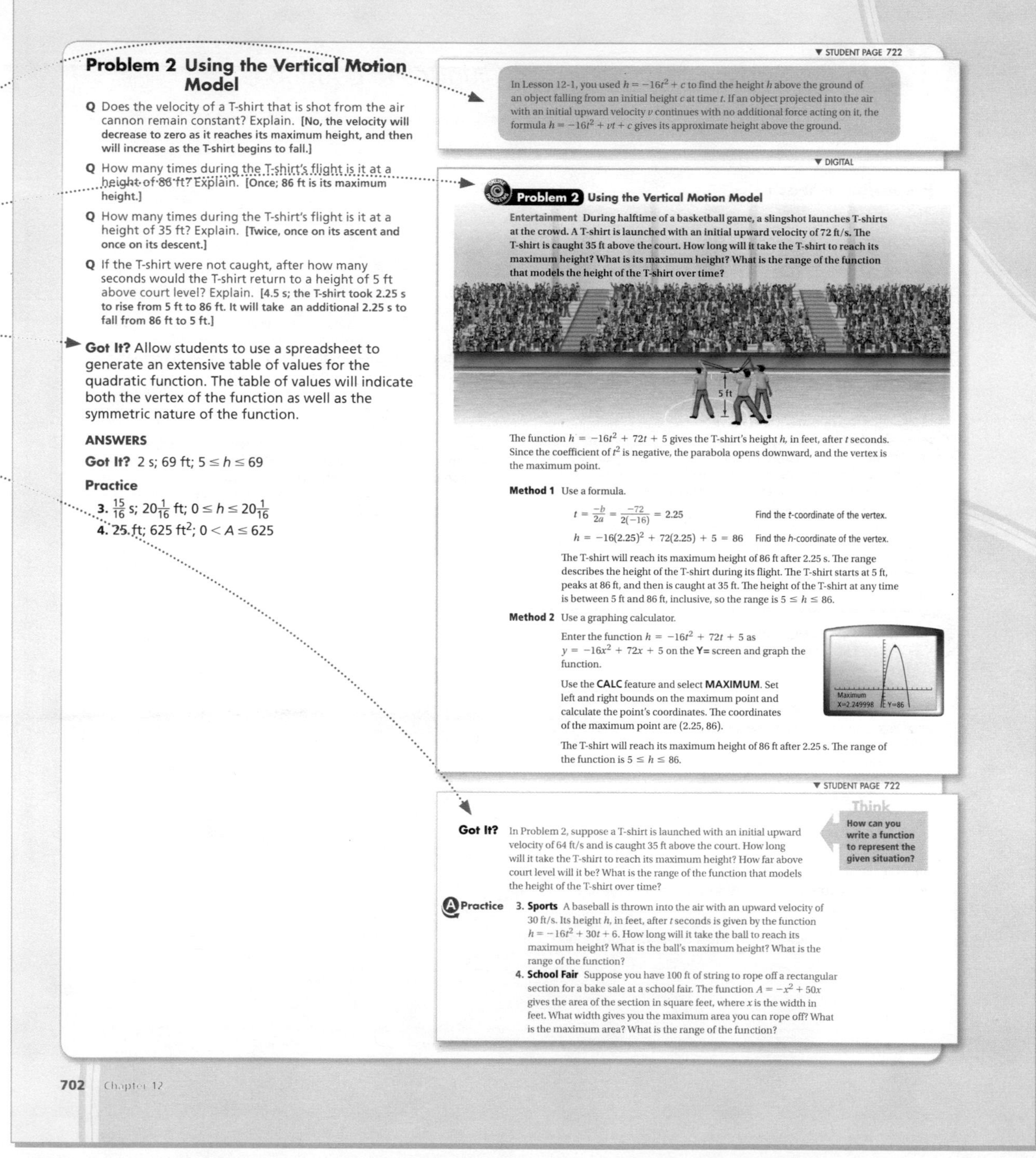

Problem 2 Using the Vertical Motion Model

Q Does the velocity of a T-shirt that is shot from the air cannon remain constant? Explain. **[No, the velocity will decrease to zero as it reaches its maximum height, and then will increase as the T-shirt begins to fall.]**

Q How many times during the T-shirt's flight is it at a height of 86 ft? Explain. **[Once; 86 ft is its maximum height.]**

Q How many times during the T-shirt's flight is it at a height of 35 ft? Explain. **[Twice, once on its ascent and once on its descent.]**

Q If the T-shirt were not caught, after how many seconds would the T-shirt return to a height of 5 ft above court level? Explain. **[4.5 s; the T-shirt took 2.25 s to rise from 5 ft to 86 ft. It will take an additional 2.25 s to fall from 86 ft to 5 ft.]**

Got It? Allow students to use a spreadsheet to generate an extensive table of values for the quadratic function. The table of values will indicate both the vertex of the function as well as the symmetric nature of the function.

ANSWERS

Got It? 2 s; 69 ft; $5 \le h \le 69$

Practice

3. $\frac{15}{16}$ s; $20\frac{1}{16}$ ft; $0 \le h \le 20\frac{1}{16}$
4. 25 ft; 625 ft^2; $0 < A \le 625$

▼ STUDENT PAGE 722

In Lesson 12-1, you used $h = -16t^2 + c$ to find the height h above the ground of an object falling from an initial height c at time t. If an object projected into the air with an initial upward velocity v continues with no additional force acting on it, the formula $h = -16t^2 + vt + c$ gives its approximate height above the ground.

▼ DIGITAL

Problem 2 **Using the Vertical Motion Model**

Entertainment **During halftime of a basketball game, a slingshot launches T-shirts at the crowd. A T-shirt is launched with an initial upward velocity of 72 ft/s. The T-shirt is caught 35 ft above the court. How long will it take the T-shirt to reach its maximum height? What is its maximum height? What is the range of the function that models the height of the T-shirt over time?**

The function $h = -16t^2 + 72t + 5$ gives the T-shirt's height h, in feet, after t seconds. Since the coefficient of t^2 is negative, the parabola opens downward, and the vertex is the maximum point.

Method 1 Use a formula.

$t = \frac{-b}{2a} = \frac{-72}{2(-16)} = 2.25$ Find the t-coordinate of the vertex.

$h = -16(2.25)^2 + 72(2.25) + 5 = 86$ Find the h-coordinate of the vertex.

The T-shirt will reach its maximum height of 86 ft after 2.25 s. The range describes the height of the T-shirt during its flight. The T-shirt starts at 5 ft, peaks at 86 ft, and then is caught at 35 ft. The height of the T-shirt at any time is between 5 ft and 86 ft, inclusive, so the range is $5 \le h \le 86$.

Method 2 Use a graphing calculator.

Enter the function $h = -16t^2 + 72t + 5$ as $y = -16x^2 + 72x + 5$ on the **Y=** screen and graph the function.

Use the **CALC** feature and select **MAXIMUM**. Set left and right bounds on the maximum point and calculate the point's coordinates. The coordinates of the maximum point are (2.25, 86).

The T-shirt will reach its maximum height of 86 ft after 2.25 s. The range of the function is $5 \le h \le 86$.

▼ STUDENT PAGE 722

Got It? In Problem 2, suppose a T-shirt is launched with an initial upward velocity of 64 ft/s and is caught 35 ft above the court. How long will it take the T-shirt to reach its maximum height? How far above court level will it be? What is the range of the function that models the height of the T-shirt over time?

Think
How can you write a function to represent the given situation?

Practice

3. **Sports** A baseball is thrown into the air with an upward velocity of 30 ft/s. Its height h, in feet, after t seconds is given by the function $h = -16t^2 + 30t + 6$. How long will it take the ball to reach its maximum height? What is the ball's maximum height? What is the range of the function?
4. **School Fair** Suppose you have 100 ft of string to rope off a rectangular section for a bake sale at a school fair. The function $A = -x^2 + 50x$ gives the area of the section in square feet, where x is the width in feet. What width gives you the maximum area you can rope off? What is the maximum area? What is the range of the function?

702 Chapter 12

Assign the **Lesson Check** and **Practice** exercises to determine how well your students have mastered the lesson content.

For each Practice section, you find an Assignment Guide and a **Homework Quick Check**. You will also find an alignment of the exercises to the Standards for Mathematical Practice.

Each **Think About a Plan** exercise has a student worksheet, available in the Teaching Resources on PearsonSuccessnet, that helps students structure and complete the problem-solving process.

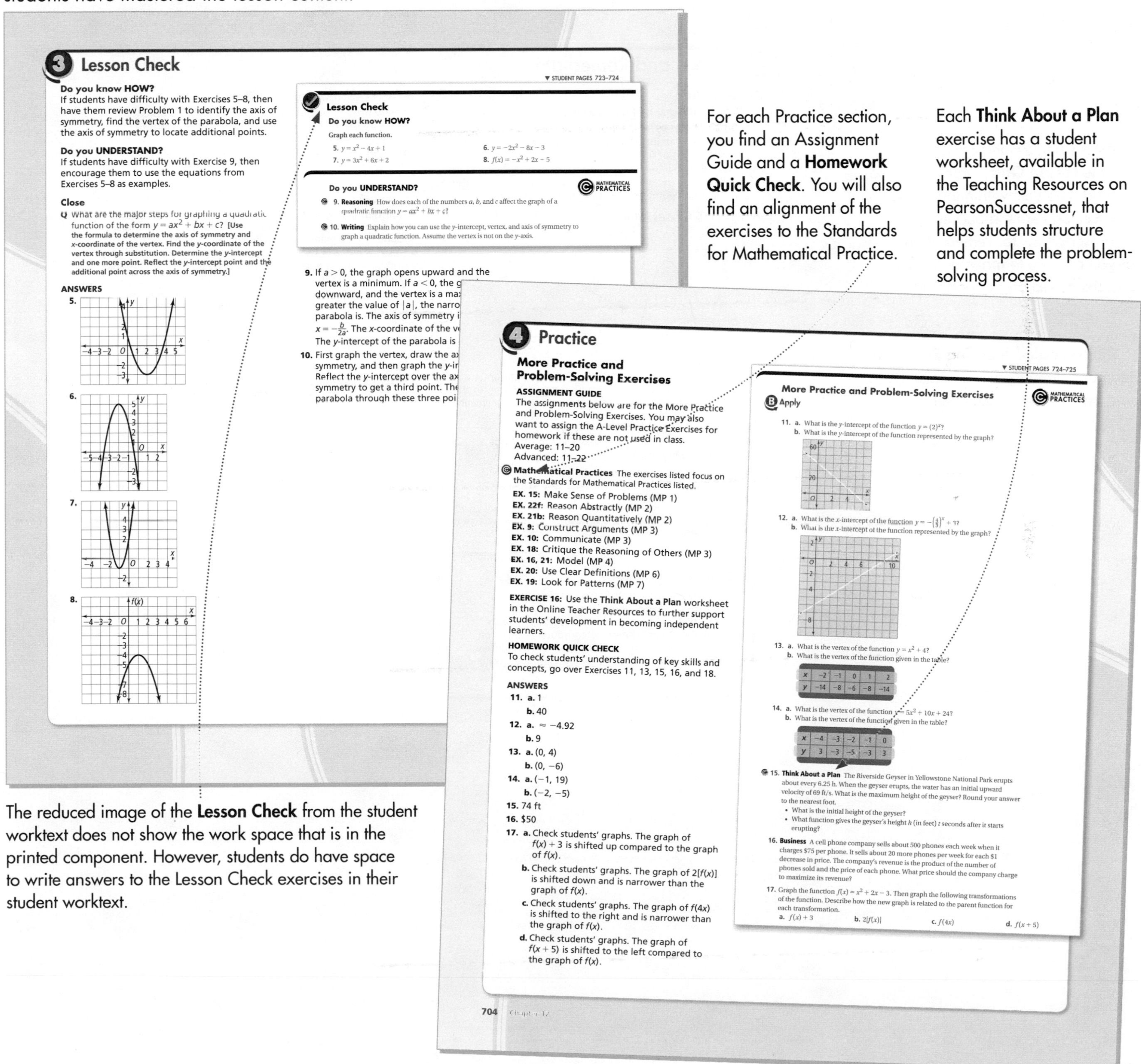

3 Lesson Check

Do you know HOW?
If students have difficulty with Exercises 5–8, then have them review Problem 1 to identify the axis of symmetry, find the vertex of the parabola, and use the axis of symmetry to locate additional points.

Do you UNDERSTAND?
If students have difficulty with Exercise 9, then encourage them to use the equations from Exercises 5–8 as examples.

Close

Q What are the major steps for graphing a quadratic function of the form $y = ax^2 + bx + c$? **[Use the formula to determine the axis of symmetry and x-coordinate of the vertex. Find the y-coordinate of the vertex through substitution. Determine the y-intercept and one more point. Reflect the y-intercept point and the additional point across the axis of symmetry.]**

ANSWERS

5.–8. [graphs]

▼ STUDENT PAGES 723–724

Lesson Check

Do you know HOW?

Graph each function.

5. $y = x^2 - 4x + 1$
6. $y = -2x^2 - 8x - 3$
7. $y = 3x^2 + 6x + 2$
8. $f(x) = -x^2 + 2x - 5$

Do you UNDERSTAND? MATHEMATICAL PRACTICES

9. **Reasoning** How does each of the numbers a, b, and c affect the graph of a quadratic function $y = ax^2 + bx + c$?

10. **Writing** Explain how you can use the y-intercept, vertex, and axis of symmetry to graph a quadratic function. Assume the vertex is not on the y-axis.

9. If $a > 0$, the graph opens upward and the vertex is a minimum. If $a < 0$, the g… downward, and the vertex is a ma… greater the value of $|a|$, the narro… parabola is. The axis of symmetry i… $x = -\frac{b}{2a}$. The x-coordinate of the v… The y-intercept of the parabola is …

10. First graph the vertex, draw the a… symmetry, and then graph the y-in… Reflect the y-intercept over the ax… symmetry to get a third point. The… parabola through these three poi…

4 Practice

More Practice and Problem-Solving Exercises

ASSIGNMENT GUIDE

The assignments below are for the More Practice and Problem-Solving Exercises. You may also want to assign the A-Level Practice Exercises for homework if these are not used in class.

Average: 11–20
Advanced: 11–22

Mathematical Practices The exercises listed focus on the Standards for Mathematical Practices listed.

EX. 15: Make Sense of Problems (MP 1)
EX. 22f: Reason Abstractly (MP 2)
EX. 21b: Reason Quantitatively (MP 2)
EX. 9: Construct Arguments (MP 3)
EX. 10: Communicate (MP 3)
EX. 18: Critique the Reasoning of Others (MP 3)
EX. 16, 21: Model (MP 4)
EX. 20: Use Clear Definitions (MP 6)
EX. 19: Look for Patterns (MP 7)

EXERCISE 16: Use the **Think About a Plan** worksheet in the Online Teacher Resources to further support students' development in becoming independent learners.

HOMEWORK QUICK CHECK
To check students' understanding of key skills and concepts, go over Exercises 11, 13, 15, 16, and 18.

ANSWERS

11. a. 1
b. 40
12. a. ≈ −4.92
b. 9
13. a. (0, 4)
b. (0, −6)
14. a. (−1, 19)
b. (−2, −5)
15. 74 ft
16. $50
17. a. Check students' graphs. The graph of $f(x) + 3$ is shifted up compared to the graph of $f(x)$.
b. Check students' graphs. The graph of $2[f(x)]$ is shifted down and is narrower than the graph of $f(x)$.
c. Check students' graphs. The graph of $f(4x)$ is shifted to the right and is narrower than the graph of $f(x)$.
d. Check students' graphs. The graph of $f(x + 5)$ is shifted to the left compared to the graph of $f(x)$.

▼ STUDENT PAGES 724–725

More Practice and Problem-Solving Exercises MATHEMATICAL PRACTICES

B Apply

11. a. What is the y-intercept of the function $y = (2)^x$?
b. What is the y-intercept of the function represented by the graph?

12. a. What is the x-intercept of the function $y = -\left(\frac{4}{3}\right)^x + 3$?
b. What is the x-intercept of the function represented by the graph?

13. a. What is the vertex of the function $y = x^2 + 4$?
b. What is the vertex of the function given in the table?

x	−2	−1	0	1	2
y	−14	−8	−6	−8	−14

14. a. What is the vertex of the function $y = 5x^2 + 10x + 24$?
b. What is the vertex of the function given in the table?

x	−4	−3	−2	−1	0
y	3	−3	−5	−3	3

15. **Think About a Plan** The Riverside Geyser in Yellowstone National Park erupts about every 6.25 h. When the geyser erupts, the water has an initial upward velocity of 69 ft/s. What is the maximum height of the geyser? Round your answer to the nearest foot.
- What is the initial height of the geyser?
- What function gives the geyser's height h (in feet) t seconds after it starts erupting?

16. **Business** A cell phone company sells about 500 phones each week when it charges $75 per phone. It sells about 20 more phones per week for each $1 decrease in price. The company's revenue is the product of the number of phones sold and the price of each phone. What price should the company charge to maximize its revenue?

17. Graph the function $f(x) = x^2 + 2x - 3$. Then graph the following transformations of the function. Describe how the new graph is related to the parent function for each transformation.
a. $f(x) + 3$ b. $2[f(x)]$ c. $f(4x)$ d. $f(x + 5)$

704 Chapter 12

The reduced image of the **Lesson Check** from the student worktext does not show the work space that is in the printed component. However, students do have space to write answers to the Lesson Check exercises in their student worktext.

The **Assess** and **Remediate** part of the lesson helps teachers to assign differentiated practice to students.

The Assess and Remediate pages show the **Lesson Quiz**, which can also be found as a PDF within the Teaching Resources on Pearson SuccessNet, and prescriptions for remediation that you can use to make data-driven decisions based on students' quiz scores.

The **Differentiated Teaching Resources** referenced on this page can also be found on Pearson SuccessNet.

5 Assess and Remediate

Lesson Quiz

1. What is the graph of the function $y = -x^2 + 4x + 1$?
2. **Do you UNDERSTAND?** Tyrone launches a toy rocket into the air with an initial upward velocity of 49 ft/s and an initial height of 0 ft. How long will it take the rocket to reach its maximum height? How high above the ground will it be? What is the range of the function? Why is there a maximum point on the graph of this function?

ANSWERS TO LESSON QUIZ

1.

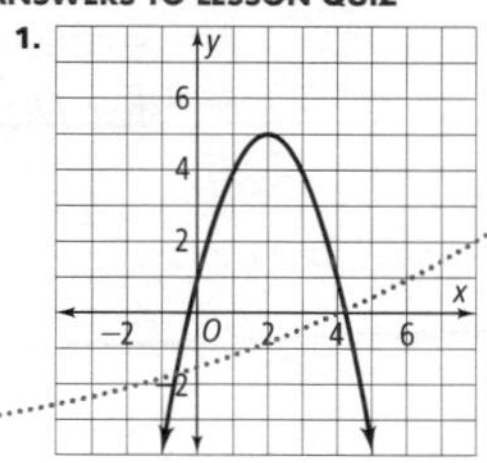

2. 1.53 s; 37.5 ft; $0 \le h \le 37.5$; The rocket will continue to travel upwards until gravity pulls it back to Earth, so there is a maximum point on the graph that opens downward.

Prescription for Remediation

Use the student work on the Lesson Quiz to prescribe a differentiated assignment.

Points	Differentiated Remediation
0	Intervention
1	On-level
2	Extension

Online Assessment

Assign the Lesson Quiz in Success Tracker on **pearsonsuccessnet.com.** Success Tracker will automatically score the quiz and assign appropriate intervention or enrichment to each student based on the results. The compiled data appear in three different reports for instant analysis of whole class and individual student performance.

Differentiated Remediation

- **RETEACHING** (2 pages) Provides reteaching and practice exercises for the key lesson concepts. Use with struggling students or absent students.
- **ENGLISH LANGUAGE LEARNER SUPPORT** Helps students develop and reinforce mathematical vocabulary and key concepts.

On-Level

- **PRACTICE** (2 pages) Provides extra practice for each lesson. For simpler practice exercises, use the Form K Practice pages found in the Online Teacher Resources.
- **THINK ABOUT A PLAN** Helps students develop specific problem-solving skills and strategies by providing scaffolded guiding questions.
- **STANDARDIZED TEST PREP** Focuses on all major exercises, all major question types, and helps students prepare for the high-stakes assessments.

Extension

- **ENRICHMENT** Provides students with interesting problems and activities that extend the concepts of the lesson.
- **ACTIVITIES, GAMES, AND PUZZLES** Worksheets that can be used for concept development, enrichment, and for fun!

706 Chapter 12

Each chapter ends with a **Chapter Review** and a **Pull It All Together**.

The **Pull It All Together** is a performance-based task that require students to draw on their understanding of important math concepts and their reasoning and problem-solving skills to complete the rich, multi-part task. These tasks can help students prepare for end-of-year performance-based assessments.

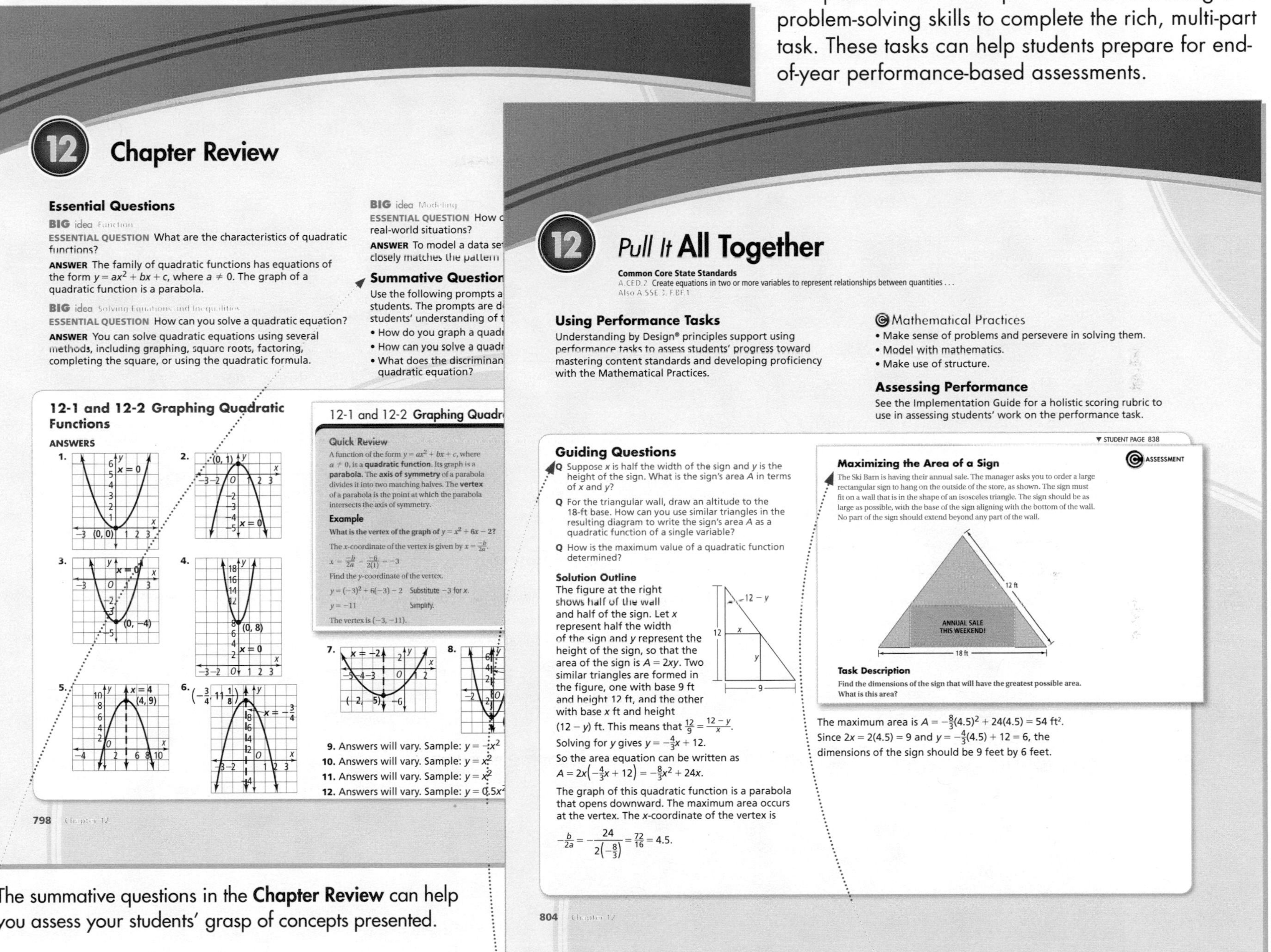

12 Chapter Review

Essential Questions

BIG idea Function

ESSENTIAL QUESTION What are the characteristics of quadratic functions?

ANSWER The family of quadratic functions has equations of the form $y = ax^2 + bx + c$, where $a \neq 0$. The graph of a quadratic function is a parabola.

BIG idea Solving Equations and Inequalities

ESSENTIAL QUESTION How can you solve a quadratic equation?

ANSWER You can solve quadratic equations using several methods, including graphing, square roots, factoring, completing the square, or using the quadratic formula.

BIG idea Modeling

ESSENTIAL QUESTION How c… real-world situations?

ANSWER To model a data se… closely matches the pattern…

Summative Question…

Use the following prompts a… students. The prompts are d… students' understanding of t…

- How do you graph a quadr…
- How can you solve a quadr…
- What does the discriminan… quadratic equation?

12-1 and 12-2 Graphing Quadratic Functions

ANSWERS

12-1 and 12-2 Graphing Quadr…

Quick Review

A function of the form $y = ax^2 + bx + c$, where $a \neq 0$, is a **quadratic function**. Its graph is a **parabola**. The **axis of symmetry** of a parabola divides it into two matching halves. The **vertex** of a parabola is the point at which the parabola intersects the axis of symmetry.

Example

What is the vertex of the graph of $y = x^2 + 6x - 2$?

The x-coordinate of the vertex is given by $x = \frac{-b}{2a}$.

$x = \frac{-b}{2a} = \frac{-6}{2(1)} = -3$

Find the y-coordinate of the vertex.

$y = (-3)^2 + 6(-3) - 2$ Substitute −3 for x.

$y = -11$ Simplify.

The vertex is $(-3, -11)$.

9. Answers will vary. Sample: $y = -x^2$
10. Answers will vary. Sample: $y = x^2$
11. Answers will vary. Sample: $y = x^2$
12. Answers will vary. Sample: $y = 0.5x^2$

798 Chapter 12

12 *Pull It* **All Together**

Common Core State Standards

A.CED.2 Create equations in two or more variables to represent relationships between quantities . . .

Also A.SSE.3, F.BF.1

Using Performance Tasks

Understanding by Design® principles support using performance tasks to assess students' progress toward mastering content standards and developing proficiency with the Mathematical Practices.

Mathematical Practices

- Make sense of problems and persevere in solving them.
- Model with mathematics.
- Make use of structure.

Assessing Performance

See the Implementation Guide for a holistic scoring rubric to use in assessing students' work on the performance task.

Guiding Questions

Q Suppose x is half the width of the sign and y is the height of the sign. What is the sign's area A in terms of x and y?

Q For the triangular wall, draw an altitude to the 18-ft base. How can you use similar triangles in the resulting diagram to write the sign's area A as a quadratic function of a single variable?

Q How is the maximum value of a quadratic function determined?

Solution Outline

The figure at the right shows half of the wall and half of the sign. Let x represent half the width of the sign and y represent the height of the sign, so that the area of the sign is $A = 2xy$. Two similar triangles are formed in the figure, one with base 9 ft and height 12 ft, and the other with base x ft and height $(12 - y)$ ft. This means that $\frac{12}{9} = \frac{12 - y}{x}$.

Solving for y gives $y = -\frac{4}{3}x + 12$.

So the area equation can be written as $A = 2x\left(-\frac{4}{3}x + 12\right) = -\frac{8}{3}x^2 + 24x$.

The graph of this quadratic function is a parabola that opens downward. The maximum area occurs at the vertex. The x-coordinate of the vertex is

$-\frac{b}{2a} = -\frac{24}{2\left(-\frac{8}{3}\right)} = \frac{72}{16} = 4.5.$

STUDENT PAGE 838

Maximizing the Area of a Sign

ASSESSMENT

The Ski Barn is having their annual sale. The manager asks you to order a large rectangular sign to hang on the outside of the store, as shown. The sign must fit on a wall that is in the shape of an isosceles triangle. The sign should be as large as possible, with the base of the sign aligning with the bottom of the wall. No part of the sign should extend beyond any part of the wall.

ANNUAL SALE THIS WEEKEND!

12 ft

18 ft

Task Description

Find the dimensions of the sign that will have the greatest possible area. What is this area?

The maximum area is $A = -\frac{8}{3}(4.5)^2 + 24(4.5) = 54$ ft². Since $2x = 2(4.5) = 9$ and $y = -\frac{4}{3}(4.5) + 12 = 6$, the dimensions of the sign should be 9 feet by 6 feet.

804 Chapter 12

The summative questions in the **Chapter Review** can help you assess your students' grasp of concepts presented.

You will find **guiding questions** throughout the course that you can ask students who have difficulty getting started or determining the next step.

You will notice a decrease in the level of scaffolding in these tasks throughout the course. Students are expected to solve progressively more complex tasks with fewer prompts.

Big Ideas and the Common Core

Chapter Title	Common Core Conceptual Categories and Domains	
1 Reasoning and Proof	Geometry	Congruence
2 Proving Theorems About Lines and Angles	Geometry	Congruence
3 Congruent Triangles	Geometry	Congruence Similarity, Right Triangles, and Trigonometry
4 Proving Theorems About Triangles	Geometry	Congruence Similarity, Right Triangles, and Trigonometry Circles
5 Proving Theorems About Quadrilaterals	Geometry	Congruence Similarity, Right Triangles, and Trigonometry
6 Similarity	Geometry	Congruence Similarity, Right Triangles, and Trigonometry
7 Right Triangles and Trigonometry	Geometry	Similarity, Right Triangles, and Trigonometry
8 Circles	Geometry	Circles
9 Surface Area and Volume	Geometry	Geometric Measurement and Dimension
10 Properties of Exponents With Rational Exponents	Number and Quantity	The Real Number System
11 Polynomials and Factoring	Algebra	Seeing Structure in Expressions Arithmetic with Polynomials and Rational Expressions
12 Quadratic Functions	Number and Quantity	The Complex Number System
	Algebra	Seeing Structure in Expressions Creating Equations Reasoning with Equations and Inequalities
	Functions	Interpreting Functions Building Functions
	Geometry	Expressing Geometric Properties with Equations
	Statistics and Probability	Interpreting Categorical and Quantitative Data
13 Probability	Statistics and Probability	Conditional Probability and the Rules of Probability
14 Other Types of Functions	Functions	Interpreting Functions Building Functions
15 Sequences and Series	Algebra	Seeing Structure in Expressions
	Function	Building Functions

The Big Ideas, the organizing structure of Pearson *Integrated High School Mathematics*, are closely aligned to the Conceptual Categories and Domains found in the Common Core State Standards.

Big Ideas	Essential Questions
Reasoning and Proof	How can you make a conjecture and prove that is it true?
Reasoning and Proof **Measurement** **Coordinate Geometry**	How can you prove that two lines are parallel or perpendicular? What is the sum of the measures of the angles of a triangle? How do you write an equation of a line in the coordinate plane?
Visualization **Reasoning and Proof**	How do you identify corresponding parts of congruent triangles How do you show that two triangles are congruent? How can you tell whether a triangle is isosceles or equilateral?
Coordinate Geometry **Measurement** **Reasoning and Proof**	How do you use coordinate geometry to find relationships within triangles? How do you solve problems that involve measurements of triangles? How do yo write indirect proofs?
Measurement **Reasoning and Proof** **Coordinate Geometry**	How can you find the sum of the measures of polygon angles? How can you classify quadrilaterals? How can you use coordinate geometry to prove general relationships?
Similarity **Reasoning and Proof** **Visualization**	How do you use proportions to find side lengths in similar polygons? How do you show two triangles are similar? How do you identify corresponding parts of similar triangles?
Measurement **Similarity**	How do you find a side length or angle measure in a right triangle? How do trigonometric ratios relate to similar right triangles?
Reasoning and Proof **Measurement** **Coordinate Geometry**	How can you prove relationships between angles and arcs in a circle? When lines intersect a circle, or within a circle, how do you find the measures of resulting angles, arcs, and segments? How do you find the equation of a circle in the coordinate plane?
Visualization **Measurement** **Coordinate Geometry**	How can you determine the intersection of a solid and a plane? How do you find the surface area and volume of a solid? How do the surface areas and volumes of similar solids compare?
Equivalence **Properties** **Function**	How can you represent numbers less than 1 using exponents? How can you simplify expressions involving exponents? What are the characteristics of exponential functions?
Equivalence **Properties**	Can two algebraic expressions that appear to be different be equivalent? How are properties of real numbers related to polynomials?
Solving Equations and Inequalities **Function** **Modeling**	How can you solve a quadratic equation? What are the characteristics of quadratic functions? How can you use functions to model real-world situations?
Probability **Data Representation** **Probability**	What is the difference between experimental probability and theoretical probability? What is a frequency table? What does it mean for an event to be random?
Modeling **Function**	How do you model a quantity that changes regularly over time by the same percentage? What are the characteristics of exponential functions? How do you combine functions using arithmetic operations?
Variable **Equivalence**	How can you represent the terms of a sequence explicitly? How can you represent them recursively? What are equivalent explicit and recursive definitions for an arithmetic sequence?

BIG ideas

These Big Ideas are the organizing ideas for the study of important areas of mathematics: algebra, geometry and statistics.

Stay connected! These Big Ideas will help you understand how the math you study in high school fits together.

Algebra

Properties

- In the transition from arithmetic to algebra, attention shifts from arithmetic operations (addition, subtraction, multiplication, and division) to the use of the *properties* of these operations.
- All of the facts of arithmetic and algebra follow from certain properties.

Variable

- Quantities are used to form expressions, equations, and inequalities.
- An expression refers to a quantity but does not make a statement about it. An equation (or an inequality) is a statement about the quantities it mentions.
- Using variables in place of numbers in equations (or inequalities) allows the statement of relationships among numbers that are unknown or unspecified.

Equivalence

- A single quantity may be represented by many different expressions.
- The facts about a quantity may be expressed by many different equations (or inequalities).

Solving Equations & Inequalities

- Solving an equation is the process of rewriting the equation to make what it says about its variable(s) as simple as possible.
- Properties of numbers and equality can be used to transform an equation (or inequality) into equivalent, simpler equations (or inequalities) in order to find solutions.
- Useful information about equations and inequalities (including solutions) can be found by analyzing graphs or tables.
- The numbers and types of solutions vary predictably, based on the type of equation.

Proportionality

- Two quantities are *proportional* if they have the same ratio in each instance where they are measured together.
- Two quantities are *inversely proportional* if they have the same product in each instance where they are measured together.

Function

- A function is a relationship between variables in which each value of the input variable is associated with a unique value of the output variable.
- Functions can be represented in a variety of ways, such as graphs, tables, equations, or words. Each representation is particularly useful in certain situations.
- Some important families of functions are developed through transformations of the simplest form of the function.
- New functions can be made from other functions by applying arithmetic operations or by applying one function to the output of another.

Modeling

- Many real-world mathematical problems can be represented algebraically. These representations can lead to algebraic solutions.
- A function that models a real-world situation can then be used to make estimates or predictions about future occurrences.

Statistics and Probability

Data Collection and Analysis

- Sampling techniques are used to gather data from real-world situations. If the data are representative of the larger population, inferences can be made about that population.
- Biased sampling techniques yield data unlikely to be representative of the larger population.
- Sets of numerical data are described using measures of central tendency and of dispersion.

Data Representation

- The most appropriate data representations depend on the type of data—quantitative or qualitative, and univariate or bivariate.
- Line plots, box plots, and histograms are different ways to show distribution of data over a possible range of values.

Probability

- Probability expresses the likelihood that a particular event will occur.
- Data can be used to calculate an experimental probability, and mathematical properties can be used to determine a theoretical probability.
- Either experimental or theoretical probability can be used to make predictions or decisions about future events.
- Various counting methods can be used to develop theoretical probabilities.

Geometry

Visualization

- Visualization can help you connect properties of real objects with two-dimensional drawings of these objects.

Transformations

- Transformations are mathematical functions that model concrete operations with figures.
- Transformations may be described geometrically or by coordinates.
- Symmetries of figures may be defined and classified by transformations.

Measurement

- Some attributes of geometric figures, such as length, area, volume, and angle measure, are measurable; units are used to describe these attributes.

Reasoning & Proof

- Definitions establish meanings and remove possible misunderstanding.
- Other truths are more complex and difficult to see. It is often possible to verify complex truths by reasoning from simpler ones by using deductive reasoning.

Similarity

- Two geometric figures are similar when corresponding lengths are proportional and corresponding angles are congruent.
- Areas of simlar figures are proportional to the squares of their corresponding lengths.
- Volumes of similar figures are proportional to the cubes of their corresponding lengths.

Coordinate Geometry

- A coordinate system on a line is a number line on which points are labeled, corresponding to the real numbers.
- A coordinate system in a plane is formed by two perpendicular number lines, called the x- and y-axes, and the quadrants they form. The coordinate plane can be used to graph many functions.
- It is possible to verify some complex truths using deductive reasoning in combination with Distance, Midpoint, and Slope formulas.

Common Core State Standards

The following shows the High School Standards for Mathematical Content that are taught in Pearson's *Mathematics II ©2014* and assessed in the PARCC End-of-Course Assessment for Mathematics II. Standards with ★ represent modeling standards.

Number and Quantity		Where to Find
The Real Number System		
Extend the properties of exponents to rational exponents		
N.RN.1	Explain how the definition of the meaning of rational exponents follows from extending the properties of integer exponents to those values, allowing for a notation for radicals in terms of rational exponents.	10-1, 10-2, 10-3, 10-4
N.RN.2	Rewrite expressions involving radicals and rational exponents using the properties of exponents.	10-4
Use properties of rational and irrational numbers		
N.RN.3	Explain why the sum or product of two rational numbers is rational; that the sum of a rational number and an irrational number is irrational; and that the product of a nonzero rational number and an irrational number is irrational.	AL[1] 10-4
Quantities		
Reason quantitatively and use units to solve problems		
N.Q.2	Define appropriate quantities for the purpose of descriptive modeling.	6-1, 9-1, 9-2
The Complex Number System		
Perform arithmetic operations with complex numbers		
N.CN.1	Know there is a complex number i such that $i^2 = -1$, and every complex number has the form $a + bi$ with a and b real.	12-8
N.CN.2	Use the relation $i^2 = -1$ and the commutative, associative, and distributive properties to add, subtract, and multiply complex numbers.	12-8
Use complex numbers in polynomial identities and equations		
N.CN.7	Solve quadratic equations with real coefficients that have complex solutions.	12-8

[1] AL = Activity Lab

Algebra		Where to Find
Seeing Structure in Expressions		
Interpret the structure of expressions		
A.SSE.1.b	Interpret expressions that represent a quantity in terms of its context. ★Interpret complicated expressions by viewing one or more of their parts as a single entity.	11-5, 11-6, 11-7, 11-8, 12-6, 12-7, 14-1
A.SSE.2	Use the structure of an expression to identify ways to rewrite it.	11-5, 11-6, 11-7, 11-8
Write expressions in equivalent forms to solve problems		
A.SSE.3.a	Choose and produce an equivalent form of an expression to reveal and explain properties of the quantity represented by the expression. ★Factor a quadratic expression to reveal the zeros of the function it defines.	12-5
A.SSE.3.b	Choose and produce an equivalent form of an expression to reveal and explain properties of the quantity represented by the expression. ★Complete the square in a quadratic expression to reveal the maximum or minimum value of the function it defines.	12-6
Arithmetic with Polynomials and Rational Expressions		
Perform arithmetic operations on polynomials		
A.APR.1	Understand that polynomials form a system analogous to the integers; namely, they are closed under the operations of addition, subtraction, and multiplication; add, subtract, and multiply polynomials.	11-1, 11-2, 11-3, 11-4
Creating Equations		
Create equations that describe numbers or relationships		
A.CED.1	Create equations and inequalities in one variable and use them to solve problems. *Include equations arising from linear and quadratic functions, and simple rational and exponential functions.*[1]	12-4, 12-5, 12-6, 12-7, LL 12-10, LL 14-1
A.CED.2	Create equations in two or more variables to represent relationships between quantities; graph equations on coordinate axes with labels and scales.	12-1, 12-2, 12-4, 12-5, 14-2
A.CED.4	Rearrange formulas to highlight a quantity of interest, using the same reasoning as in solving equations.	12-4, LL 12-4

Algebra (continued)		Where to Find
Reasoning with Equations and Inequalities		
Understand solving equations as a process of reasoning and explain the reasoning		
A.REI.1	Explain each step in solving a simple equation as following from the equality of numbers asserted at the previous step, starting from the assumption that the original equation has a solution. Construct a viable argument to justify a solution method.	12-4, 12-5, 12-6, 12-7
Solve equations and Inequalities in one variable		
A.REI.4.a	Solve quadratic equations in one variable. Use the method of completing the square to transform any quadratic equation in x into an equation of the form $(x - p)^2 = q$ that has the same solutions. Derive the quadratic formula from this form.	12-6, 12-7
A.REI.4.b	Solve quadratic equations in one variable. Solve quadratic equations by inspection (e.g., for $x^2 = 49$), taking square roots, completing the square, the quadratic formula and factoring, as appropriate to the initial form of the equation. Recognize when the quadratic formula gives complex solutions and write them as $a \pm bi$ for real numbers a and b.	12-4, 12-5, 12-6, 12-7, 12-8
Solve systems of equations		
A.REI.7	Solve a simple system consisting of a linear equation and a quadratic equation in two variables algebraically and graphically.	12-10

Functions		Where to Find
Interpreting Functions		
Interpret functions that arise in applications in terms of the context		
F.IF.4	For a function that models a relationship between two quantities, interpret key features of graphs and tables in terms of the quantities, and sketch graphs showing key features given a verbal description of the relationship. *Key features include: intercepts; intervals where the function is increasing, decreasing, positive, or negative; relative maximums and minimums; symmetries; end behavior; and periodicity.* ★	12-1, 12-2, 12-3, 12-9, 14-1, 14-2, 14-3
F.IF.5	Relate the domain of a function to its graph and, where applicable, to the quantitative relationship it describes.	12-1, 12-3
F.IF.6	Calculate and interpret the average rate of change of a function (presented symbolically or as a table) over a specified interval. Estimate the rate of change from a graph. ★	AL 12-2, 14-2

Functions (continued)		Where to Find
Analyze functions using different representations		
F.IF.7.a	Graph functions expressed symbolically and show key features of the graph, by hand in simple cases and using technology for more complicated cases. Graph linear and quadratic functions and show intercepts, maxima, and minima.	12-1, 12-2, 12-4
F.IF.7.b	Graph functions expressed symbolically and show key features of the graph, by hand in simple cases and using technology for more complicated cases. Graph square root, cube root, and piecewise-defined functions, including step functions and absolute value functions.	14-2, 14-3
F.IF.7.e	Graph functions expressed symbolically and show key features of the graph, by hand in simple cases and using technology for more complicated cases. Graph exponential and logarithmic functions, showing intercepts and end behavior, and trigonometric functions, showing period, midline, and amplitude.	14-1
F.IF.8.a	Write a function defined by an expression in different but equivalent forms to reveal and explain different properties of the function. Use the process of factoring and completing the square in a quadratic function to show zeros, extreme values, and symmetry of the graph, and interpret these in terms of a context.	12-5, 12-6
F.IF.8.b	Write a function defined by an expression in different but equivalent forms to reveal and explain different properties of the function. Use the properties of exponents to interpret expressions for exponential functions.	14-1, 14-2
F.IF.9	Compare properties of two functions each represented in a different way (algebraically, graphically, numerically in tables, or by verbal descriptions).	12-2
Building Functions		
Build a function that models a relationship between two quantities		
F.BF.1.a	Write a function that describes a relationship between two quantities. ★ Determine an explicit expression, a recursive process, or steps for calculation from a context.	12-2, 12-3, 15-1, 15-2, 15-3, 15-4
F.BF.1.b	Write a function that describes a relationship between two quantities. ★ Combine standard function types using arithmetic operations.	12-9, 14-4
Build new functions from existing functions		
F.BF.3	Identify the effect on the graph of replacing $f(x)$ by $f(x) + k$, $k\ f(x)$, $f(kx)$, and $f(x + k)$ for specific values of k (both positive and negative); find the value of k given the graphs. Experiment with cases and illustrate an explanation of the effects on the graph using technology. *Include recognizing even and odd functions from their graphs and algebraic expressions for them.*	12-1, TL 12-1, 12-2, 14-1, 14-2, 14-3

Geometry		Where to Find
Similarity, Right Triangles, and Trigonometry		
Understand similarity in terms of similarity transformations		
G.SRT.1.a	Verify experimentally the properties of dilations given by a center and a scale factor: A dilation takes a line not passing through the center of the dilation to a parallel line, and leaves a line passing through the center unchanged.	6-6, AL 6-6
G.SRT.1.b	Verify experimentally the properties of dilations given by a center and a scale factor: The dilation of a line segment is longer or shorter in the ratio given by the scale factor.	AL 6-6, 6-6
G.SRT.2	Given two figures, use the definition of similarity in terms of similarity transformations to decide if they are similar; explain using similarity transformations the meaning of similarity for triangles as the equality of all corresponding pairs of angles and the proportionality of all corresponding pairs of sides.	6-7
G.SRT.3	Use the properties of similarity transformations to establish the AA criterion for two triangles to be similar.	6-7
Prove theorems involving similarity		
G.SRT.4	Prove theorems about triangles. Theorems include: a line parallel to one side of a triangle divides the other two proportionally and conversely; the Pythagorean Theorem proved using triangle similarity.	6-5, 7-1
G.SRT.5	Use congruence and similarity criteria for triangles to solve problems and to Prove relationships in geometric figures.	3-2, 3-3, 3-4, 3-5, 3-6, 3-7, 4-1, 4-2, 4-4, 5-1, 5-2, 5-4, 5-5, 5-5, 5-6, 6-2, 6-3, 6-4
Define trigonometric ratios and solve problems involving right triangles		
G.SRT.6	Understand that by similarity, side ratios in right triangles are properties of the angles in the triangle, leading to definitions of trigonometric ratios for acute angles.	TL 7-3
G.SRT.7	Explain and use the relationship between the sine and cosine of complementary angles.	7-3
G.SRT.8	Use trigonometric ratios and the Pythagorean Theorem to solve right triangles in applied problems.	7-1, 7-2, 7-3, 7-4
Geometric Measurement and Dimension		
Explain volume formulas and use them to solve problems		
G.GMD.1	Give an informal argument for the formulas for the circumference of a circle, area of a circle, volume of a cylinder, pyramid, and cone. *Use dissection arguments, Cavalieri's principle, and informal limit arguments.*	AL 9-1, 9-3, AL 9-4, 9-4
G.GMD.3	Use volume formulas for cylinders, pyramids, cones, and spheres to solve problems. ★	9-3, 9-4, 9-5

Statistics and Probability		Where to Find
Interpreting Categorical and Quantitative Data		
Summarize, represent, and interpret data on two categorical and quantitative variables		
S.ID.6.a	Represent data on two quantitative variables on a scatter plot, and describe how the variables are related. Fit a function to the data; use functions fitted to data to solve problems in the context of the data. *Use given functions or choose a function suggested by the context. Emphasize linear and exponential models.*	12-3, 12-9
S.ID.6.b	Represent data on two quantitative variables on a scatter plot, and describe how the variables are related. informally assess the fit of a function by plotting and analyzing residuals.	TL 12-9
Conditional Probability and the Rules of Probability		
Understand independence and conditional probability and use them to interpret data		
S.CP.1	Describe events as subsets of a sample space (the set of outcomes) using characteristics (or categories) of the outcomes, or as unions, intersections, or complements of other events ("or," "and," "not").	13-1, 13-4
S.CP.2	Understand that two events *A* and *B* are independent if the probability of *A* and *B* occurring together is the product of their probabilities, and use this characterization to determine if they are independent.	13-4
S.CP.3	Understand the conditional probability of *A* given *B* as *P*(*A* and *B*)/*P*(*B*), and interpret independence of *A* and *B* as saying that the conditional probability of *A* given *B* is the same as the probability of *A*, and the conditional probability of *B* given *A* is the same as the probability of *B*.	13-6
S.CP.4	Construct and interpret two-way frequency tables of data when two categories are associated with each object being classified. Use the two-way table as a sample space to decide if events are independent and to approximate conditional probabilities.	13-5, 13-6
S.CP.5	Recognize and explain the concepts of conditional probability and independence in everyday language and everyday situations.	13-4, 13-6
Use the rules of probability to compute probabilities of compound events in a uniform probability model		
S.CP.6	Find the conditional probability of *A* given *B* as the fraction of *B*'s outcomes that also belong to *A*, and interpret the answer in terms of the model.	13-6
S.CP.7	Apply the Addition Rule, $P(A \text{ or } B) = P(A) + P(B) - P(A \text{ and } B)$, and interpret the answer in terms of the model.	13-4

Mathematics II *Pacing Guide*

This Pacing Guide is provided as a guide to help you customize your course. The suggested number of days for each chapter is based on a 45-minute class period and on a 90-minute block period.

		Common Core State Standards
Chapter 1 Reasoning and Proof		**Traditional 10 days; Block 5 days**
1-1	Basic Constructions	G.CO.12
1-2	Patterns and Inductive Reasoning	Prepares for G.CO.9, G.CO.10, G.CO.11
1-3	Conditional Statements	Prepares for G.CO.9, G.CO.10, G.CO.11
1-4	Biconditionals and Definitions	Prepares for G.CO.9, G.CO.10, G.CO.11
1-5	Deductive Reasoning	Prepares for G.CO.9, G.CO.10, G.CO.11
1-6	Reasoning in Algebra and Geometry	Prepares for G.CO.9, G.CO.10, G.CO.11
1-7	Proving Angles Congruent	G.CO.9
Chapter 2 Proving Theorems About Lines and Angles		**Traditional 9 days; Block 5 days**
2-1	Lines and Angles	Prepares for G.CO.9
2-2	Properties of Parallel Lines	G.CO.9
2-3	Proving Lines Parallel	G.CO.9
2-4	Parallel and Perpendicular Lines	G.CO.9
2-5	Parallel Lines and Triangles	G.CO.9, G.CO.10
2-6	Constructing Parallel and Perpendicular Lines	G.CO.12, G.CO.13
Chapter 3 Congruent Triangles		**Traditional 12 days; Block 6 days**
3-1	Congruent Figures	Prepares for G.CO.7, G.SRT.5
3-2	Triangle Congruence by SSS and SAS	G.SRT.5
3-3	Triangle Congruence by ASA and AAS	G.SRT.5
3-4	Using Corresponding Parts of Congruent Triangles	G.CO.12, G.SRT.5
	Activity Lab: Paper-Folding Conjectures	G.CO.12
3-5	Isosceles and Equilateral Triangles	G.CO.10, G.CO.13, G.SRT.5
3-6	Congruence in Right Triangles	G.CO10
3-7	Congruence in Overlapping Triangles	G.CO.10
	Lesson Lab: Review of Transformations	G.CO.6
3-8	Congruence Transformations	G.CO.6, G.CO.7, G.CO.8
Chapter 4 Proving Theorems About Triangles		**Traditional 10 days; Block 5 days**
4-1	Midsegments of Triangles	G.CO.10, G.SRT.5
4-2	Perpendicular and Angle Bisectors	G.CO.9, G.CO.12, G.SRT.5

	Common Core State Standards
4-3 Bisectors in Triangles	G.CO.10, G.C.3
4-4 Medians and Altitudes	G.CO.10, G.SRT.5
4-5 Indirect Proof	G.CO.10
4-6 Inequalities in One Triangle	G.CO.10
4-7 Inequalities in Two Triangles	G.CO.10
Chapter 5 Proving Theorems About Quadrilaterals	**Traditional 12 days; Block 6 days**
5-1 The Polygon Angle-Sum Theorems	G.CO.9, G.SRT.5
5-2 Properties of Parallelograms	G.CO.11, G.SRT.5
5-3 Proving That a Quadrilateral Is a Parallelogram	G.CO.11, G.SRT.5
5-4 Properties of Rhombuses, Rectangles, and Squares	G.CO.11, G.SRT.5
5-5 Conditions for Rhombuses, Rectangles, and Squares	G.CO.11, G.SRT.5
5-6 Trapezoids and Kites	G.CO.9, G.SRT.5
5-7 Applying Coordinate Geometry	G.CO.10, G.CO.11
5-8 Proofs Using Coordinate Geometry	G.CO.10, G.CO.11
Chapter 6 Similarity	**Traditional 10 days; Block 5 days**
6-1 Ratios and Proportions	N.Q.2, Prepares for G.SRT.5
6-2 Similar Polygons	G.SRT.5
6-3 Proving Triangles Similar	G.SRT.5, G.GPE.5
6-4 Similarity in Right Triangles	G.SRT.5, G.GPE.5
Technology Lab: Exploring Proportions in Triangles	G.CO.12, Prepares for G.SRT.4
6-5 Proportions in Triangles	G.SRT.4
Activity Lab: Exploring Dilations	G.SRT.1.a, G.SRT.1.b
6-6 Dilations	G.SRT.1.a, G.SRT.1.b
6-7 Similarity Transformations	G.SRT.2, G.SRT.3
Chapter 7 Right Triangles and Trigonometry	**Traditional 8 days; Block 4 days**
7-1 The Pythagorean Theorem and Its Converse	G.SRT.4, G.SRT.8
7-2 Special Right Triangles	G.SRT.8
Technology Lab: Exploring Trigonometric Ratios	G.SRT.6
7-3 Trigonometry	G.SRT.7, G.SRT.8
7-4 Angles of Elevation and Depression	G.SRT.8
7-5 Areas of Regular Polygons	A.SSE.1.b, G.CO.13
Chapter 8 Circles	**Traditional 10 days; Block 5 days**
8-1 Circles and Arcs	G.C.1, G.C.2, G.C.5
8-2 Areas of Circles and Sectors	G.C.5
Activity Lab: Circles and Radians	G.C.5

		Common Core State Standards
8-3	Tangent Lines	G.C.2
8-4	Chords and Arcs	G.C.2
8-5	Inscribed Angles	G.C.2, G.C.3
8-6	Angle Measures and Segment Lengths	G.C.2
Chapter 9 Surface Area and Volume		**Traditional 10 days; Block 5 days**
	Activity Lab: Exploring the Circumference and Area of a Circle	G.GMD.1
9-1	Surface Areas of Prisms and Cylinders	N.Q.2, G.MG.1
9-2	Surface Areas of Pyramids and Cones	N.Q.2, G.MG.1
9-3	Volumes of Prisms and Cylinders	G.GMD.1, G.GMD.2, G.GMD.3, G.MG.1
	Activity Lab: Finding Volume	G.GMD.1
9-4	Volumes of Pyramids and Cones	G.GMD.1, G.GMD.2, G.GMD.3, G.MG.1
9-5	Surface Areas and Volumes of Spheres	G.GMD.3, G.MG.1
Chapter 10 Properties of Exponents With Rational Exponents		**Traditional 6 days; Block 3 days**
10-1	Multiplying Powers With the Same Base	N.RN.1
10-2	More Multiplication Properties of Exponents	N.RN.1
10-3	Division Properties of Exponents	N.RN.1
10-4	Rational Exponents and Radicals	N.RN.1, N.RN.2
	Activity Lab: Operations With Rational and Irrational Numbers	N.RN.3
Chapter 11 Polynomials and Factoring		**Traditional 12 days; Block 6 days**
11-1	Adding and Subtracting Polynomials	A.APR.1
11-2	Multiplying and Factoring	A.APR.1
11-3	Multiplying Binomials	A.APR.1
11-4	Multiplying Special Cases	A.APR.1
11-5	Factoring $x^2 + bx + c$	A.SSE.1.a, A.SSE.1.b, A.SSE.2
11-6	Factoring $ax^2 + bx + c$	A.SSE.1.a, A.SSE.1.b, A.SSE.2
11-7	Factoring Special Cases	A.SSE.1.a, A.SSE.1.b, A.SSE.2
11-8	Factoring by Grouping	A.SSE.1.a, A.SSE.1.b, A.SSE.2
Chapter 12 Quadratic Functions		**Traditional 24 days; Block 12 days**
12-1	Quadratic Graphs and Their Properties	A.CED.2, F.IF.4, F.IF.5, F.IF.7.a, F.BF.3
	Technology Lab: Families of Quadratic Functions	F.IF.7, F.BF.3
12-2	Quadratic Functions	A.CED.2, F.IF.4, F.IF.7.a, F.IF.9, F.BF.1.a, F.BF.3
	Activity Lab: Rates of Increase	F.IF.6
12-3	Modeling With Quadratic Functions	N.Q.2, F.IF.4, F.IF.5, F.BF.1.a, S.ID.6.a
12-4	Solving Quadratic Equations	A.CED.1, A.CED.4, A.REI.1, A.REI.4.b

		Common Core State Standards
	Lesson Lab: Formulas With Quadratic Expressions	A.CED.4
12-5	Factoring to Solve Quadratic Equations	A.REI.1, A.REI.4, A.REI.4.b, F.IF.8.a
12-6	Completing the Square	A.SSE.1.b, A.CED.1, A.REI.4.a, A.REI.4.b, F.IF.8.a
12-7	The Quadratic Formula and the Discriminant	A.SSE.1.b, A.CED.1, A.REI.4.a, A.REI.4.b
12-8	Complex Numbers	N.CN.1, N.CN.2, N.CN.3, N.CN.7, A.REI.4.b
12-9	Linear, Quadratic, and Exponential Models	F.IF.4, F.BF.1.a, F.BF.1.b, F.LE.3, S.ID.6.a
	Technology Lab: Analyzing Residual Plots	S.ID.6.b
12-10	Systems of Linear and Quadratic Equations	A.REI.7
	Lesson Lab: Quadratic Inequalities	A.CED.1
12-11	A New Look at Parabolas	G.GPE.2, G.GPE.4
12-12	Circles in the Coordinate Plane	G.GPE.1, G.GPE.4
Chapter 13 Probability		**Traditional 10 days; Block 5 days**
13-1	Experimental and Theoretical Probability	S.CP.1
13-2	Probability Distributions and Frequency Tables	Prepares for S.CP.4, Prepares for S.CP.5
13-3	Permutations and Combinations	S.CP.9
13-4	Compound Probability	S.CP.1, S.CP.2, S.CP.5, S.CP.7
13-5	Probability Models	S.CP.4
13-6	Conditional Probability Formulas	S.CP.3, S.CP.4, S.CP.5, S.CP.6
13-7	Modeling Randomness	S.MD.6, S.MD.7
	Activity Lab: Probability and Decision Making	S.MD.7
Chapter 14 Other Types of Functions		**Traditional 7 days; Block 4 days**
14-1	Properties of Exponential Functions	A.SSE.1.b, A.SSE.3.c, F.IF.4, F.IF.7.e, F.IF.8.b
	Lesson Lab: Solving Exponential Equations and Inequalities	A.CED.1
14-2	Graphing Radical Functions	A.CED.2, F.IF.4, F.IF.6, F.IF.7.b, F.IF.8, F.BF.3
14-3	Piecewise Functions	F.IF.4, F.IF.7.b, F.BF.3
14-4	Combining Functions	F.BF.1.b
	Lesson Lab: Composition and Inverse Functions	F.BF.4.a
Chapter 15 Sequences and Series		**Traditional 8 days; Block 5 days**
15-1	Mathematical Patterns	F.BF.1.a
15-2	Arithmetic Sequences	F.BF.1.a
15-3	Geometric Sequences	F.BF.1.a
15-4	Arithmetic Series	F.BF.1.a
	Activity Lab: Geometry and Infinite Series	A.SSE.4
15-5	Geometric Series	A.SSE.4

1

Reasoning and Proof

Chapter 1

Geometry

Congruence

Experiment with transformations in the plane

Prove geometric theorems

Make geometric constructions

Proving Theorems About Lines and Angles

Chapter 2

Geometry

Congruence

Experiment with transformations in the plane

Prove geometric theorems

Make geometric constructions

Congruent Triangles

Chapter 3

Geometry
Congruence
- Understand congruence in terms of rigid motions
- Prove geometric theorems
- Make geometric constructions

Geometry
Similarity, Right Triangles, and Trigonometry
- Prove theorems involving similarity

Proving Theorems About Triangles

Chapter 4

Geometry
Congruence
Prove geometric theorems
Make geometric constructions

Geometry
Similarity, Right Triangles, and Trigonometry
Prove theorems involving similarity
Circles
Understand and apply theorems about circles

5

Proving Theorems About Quadrilaterals

Chapter 5

Geometry
Congruence
Prove geometric theorems

Geometry
Similarity, Right Triangles, and Trigonometry
Prove theorems involving similarity

Similarity

Chapter 6

Geometry
Congruence
Make geometric constructions
Similarity, Right Triangles, and Trigonometry
Understand similarity in terms of similarity transformations
Prove theorems involving similarity

Geometry
Expressing Geometric Properties with Equations
Use coordinates to prove simple geometric theorems algebraically

Right Triangles and Trigonometry

Chapter 7

Geometry
Congruence
Make geometric constructions

Geometry
Similarity, Right Triangles, and Trigonometry
Prove theorems involving similarity
Define trigonometric ratios and solve problems involving right triangles

Circles

Chapter 8

Geometry

Circles

Understand and apply theorems about circles

Find arc lengths and areas of sectors of circles

Surface Area and Volume

Chapter 9

Number and Quantity

Quantities

Reason quantitatively and use units to solve problems

Geometry

Geometric Measurement and Dimension

Explain volume formulas and use them to solve problems

Modeling with Geometry

Apply geometric concepts in modeling situations

Properties of Exponents With Rational Exponents

Chapter 10

Number and Quantity

The Real Number System

Extend the properties of exponents to rational exponents.

Use properties of rational and irrational numbers.

Polynomials and Factoring

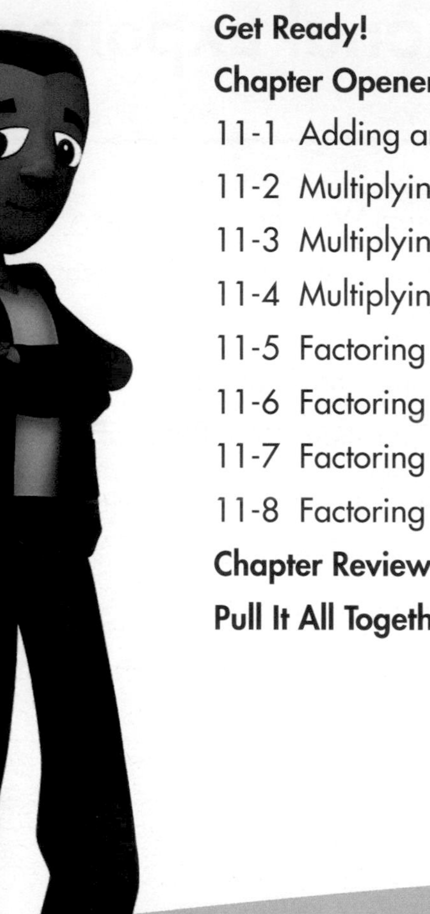

Chapter 11

Algebra

Seeing Structure in Expressions

Interpret the structure of expressions

Arithmetic with Polynomials and Rational Expressions

Perform arithmetic operations on polynomials

Quadratic Functions

Chapter 12

Number and Quantity

The Complex Number System

Perform arithmetic operations with complex numbers

Use complex numbers in polynomial identities and equations

Algebra

Seeing Structure in Expressions

Write expressions in equivalent forms to solve problems

Reasoning with Equations and Inequalities

Understand solving equations as a process of reasoning and explain the reasoning

Solve equations and inequalities in one variable

Functions

Building Functions

Build a function that models a relationship between two quantities

Build new functions from existing functions

Linear, Quadratic, and Exponential Functions

Construct and compare linear, quadratic, and exponential models and solve problems

Geometry

Expressing Geometric Properties with Equations

Use coordinates to prove simple geometric theorems algebraically

Probability

Chapter 13

Statistics and Probability
Conditional Probability and the Rules of Probability

Understand independence and conditional probability and use them to interpret data

Use the rules of probability to compute probabilities of compound events in a uniform probability model

Statistics and Probability
Using Probability to Make Decisions

Use probability to evaluate outcomes of decisions

Other Types of Functions

Chapter 14

Algebra

Seeing Structure in Expressions

Interpret the structure of expressions

Write expressions in equivalent forms to solve problems

Creating Equations

Create equations that describe numbers or relationships

Functions

Interpreting Functions

Interpret functions that arise in applications in terms of the context

Analyze functions using different representations

Building Functions

Build a function that models a relationship between two quantities

Build new functions from existing functions

Sequences and Series

Chapter 15

Algebra
Seeing Structure in Expressions
Write expressions in equivalent forms to solve problems

Functions
Building Functions
Build a function that models a relationship between two quantities

Get Ready!

Using This Diagnostic Assessment

Assign this diagnostic assessment to determine if students have the prerequisite skills for Chapter 1.

Lesson	Skill
Previous Course	Evaluating Expressions
Previous Course	Solving Equations
Previous Course	Segments and Angles

To remediate students, select from these resources (available for every lesson).

- Online Problems (pearsonsuccessnet.com)
- Reteaching (Online Teacher Resources)
- Practice (Online Teacher Resources)

Why Students Need These Skills

EVALUATING EXPRESSIONS Students will evaluate expressions to find counterexamples to conjectures.

SOLVING EQUATIONS Students will use equation-solving skills to evaluate numeric patterns, to determine angle measures, to assess conditional statements, to apply properties of equality, and to develop proof.

SEGMENTS AND ANGLES Students will need to know basic information about segments and angles in order to prove conjectures related to them.

Looking Ahead Vocabulary

HYPOTHESIS Ask students to give examples of how scientists test their hypotheses.

CONCLUSION Have students name other examples in real life that have conclusions.

DEDUCTIVE REASONING Read students a story that involves a mystery. Have them gather clues as you read.

ANSWERS

1. 50
2. −3
3. 25.5
4. 10.5
5. 15
6. 11
7. 7
8. 5
9. 6
10. 20
11. 18
12. $\angle ACD$, $\angle DCA$
13. 3
14. $m\angle 1 = 48$, $m\angle 2 = 42$
15. $\angle ADC$ and $\angle CDB$
16. $\angle 1$ and $\angle 2$
17. $\angle ADB$ or $\angle BDA$
18. Answers may vary. Sample: Similar: They are both statements you start with. Different: In geometry you do not try to prove the hypothesis of a statement.
19. Answers may vary. Sample: A conclusion in geometry answers questions raised by the hypothesis.
20. Answers may vary. Sample: In geometry we use deductive reasoning to draw conclusions from other information.

▼ STUDENT PAGE 1

Evaluating Expressions

Evaluate each expression for the given value of *x*.

1. $9x - 13$ for $x = 7$
2. $90 - 3x$ for $x = 31$
3. $\frac{1}{2}x + 14$ for $x = 23$

Solving Equations

Solve each equation.

4. $2x - 17 = 4$
5. $3x + 8 = 53$
6. $(10x + 5) + (6x - 1) = 180$
7. $14x = 2(5x + 14)$
8. $2(x + 4) = x + 13$
9. $7x + 5 = 5x + 17$
10. $(x + 21) + (2x + 9) = 90$
11. $2(3x - 4) + 10 = 5(x + 4)$

Segments and Angles

Use the figure at the right.

A, x + 8, D, 2x + 5, 1, 2, C, B

12. Name $\angle 1$ in two other ways.
13. If D is the midpoint of $\overline{AB}$, find the value of x.
14. If $\angle ACB$ is a right angle, $m\angle 1 = 4y$, and $m\angle 2 = 2y + 18$, find $m\angle 1$ and $m\angle 2$.
15. Name a pair of angles that form a linear pair.
16. Name a pair of adjacent angles that are not supplementary.
17. If $m\angle ADC + m\angle BDC = 180$, name the straight angle.

Looking Ahead Vocabulary

VOCABULARY

18. A scientist often makes an assumption, or *hypothesis*, about a scientific problem. Then the scientist uses experiments to test the *hypothesis* to see if it is true. How might a *hypothesis* in geometry be similar? How might it be different?
19. The *conclusion* of a novel answers questions raised by the story. How do you think the term *conclusion* applies in geometry?
20. A detective uses *deductive reasoning* to solve a case by gathering, combining, and analyzing clues. How might you use *deductive reasoning* in geometry?

CHAPTER
1

REASONING AND PROOF

Chapter 1 Overview

Interactive Digital Path
Log in to pearsonsuccessnet.com and click on Interactive Digital Path to access the Solve Its and animated Problems.

Chapter 1 introduces topics related to reasoning. Students will learn inductive and deductive reasoning. In this chapter, students will develop the answers to the Essential Question posed below as they learn the bulleted concepts and skills.

BIG idea Reasoning and Proof

ESSENTIAL QUESTION How can you make a conjecture and prove that it is true?

- Students will observe patterns leading to making conjectures.
- Students will solve equations giving their reasons for each step and connect this to simple proofs.
- Students will prove geometric relationships using given information, definitions, properties, postulates, and theorems.

Chapter Preview

1-1 Basic Constructions
1-2 Patterns and Inductive Reasoning
1-3 Conditional Statements
1-4 Biconditionals and Definitions
1-5 Deductive Reasoning
1-6 Reasoning in Algebra and Geometry
1-7 Proving Angles Congruent

DYNAMIC ACTIVITIES

Dynamic Activity

Use the Dynamic Activity, an interactive math tool with guided instruction, to have students explore concepts visually and support the development of the Standards for Mathematical Practice.

Content Standards

This chapter prepares students for the following standards.

Conceptual Category Geometry

DOMAIN Congruence G.CO
CLUSTER Prove geometric theorems (Standards G.CO.9, G.CO.10, G.CO.11) **LESSONS** 1-2, 1-3, 1-4, 1-5, 1-6

Following are the key standards covered in this chapter.

Conceptual Category Geometry

DOMAIN Congruence G.CO
CLUSTER Prove geometric theorems (Standard G.CO.9) **LESSON** 1-7
CLUSTER Make geometric constructions (Standard G.CO.12) **LESSON** 1-1

VOCABULARY

Vocabulary

English/Spanish Vocabulary Audio Online:

English	Spanish
biconditional, *p. 26**	bicondicional
conclusion, *p. 19*	conclusión
conditional, *p. 19*	condicional
conjecture, *p. 12*	conjetura
contrapositive, *p. 22*	contrapositivo
converse, *p. 22*	recíproco
deductive reasoning, *p. 34*	razonamiento deductivo
hypothesis, *p. 19*	hipótesis
inductive reasoning, *p. 11*	razonamiento inductivo
inverse, *p. 22*	inverso
negation, *p. 22*	negación
perpendicular bisector, *p. 5*	mediatriz
theorem, *p. 48*	teorema

**All page numbers refer to the Student Edition.*

CHAPTER 1 REASONING AND PROOF

Math Background

Understanding by Design® principles were central to the development of the Big Ideas and the Essential Understandings. These will help your students build a structure on which to make connections to prior learning.*

Reasoning and Proof

BIG idea Definitions establish meanings and remove possible misunderstanding. Other truths are more complex and difficult to see. It is often possible to verify complex truths by reasoning from simpler ones, using deductive reasoning.

ESSENTIAL UNDERSTANDINGS

1-2 Patterns in some number sequences and some sequences of geometric figures can be used to discover relationships.

1-3 Some mathematical relationships can be described using a variety of if-then statements.

1-4 A definition is good if it can be written as a biconditional.

1-5 Given true statements, deductive reasoning can be used to make a valid, or true, conclusion.

1-6 Algebraic properties of equality are used in geometry to solve problems and justify reasoning.

1-7 Given information, definitions, properties, postulates, and theorems can be used as reasons in a proof.

*UNDERSTANDING BY DESIGN® and UbD™ are trademarks of ASCD, and are used under license.

Inductive Reasoning

Inductive reasoning uses observed patterns to draw conclusions. With inductive reasoning you cannot be sure that your conclusion is valid. The patterns are assumed to continue. This is why the result of inductive reasoning is often called a conjecture.

For example, students might conjecture that the number sequence 1, 2, 4 will be continued with 8 and 16

$(1 \cdot 2 = 2, 2 \cdot 2 = 4, 4 \cdot 2 = 8, 8 \cdot 2 = 16)$.

The sequence can also be continued with 7 and 11

$(1 + 1 = 2, 2 + 2 = 4, 4 + 3 = 7, 7 + 4 = 11)$.

The rule for this sequence is *add 1, then add 2, then add 3, and so on.*

A *counterexample* disproves an inductive conjecture. A counterexample is a single example that shows that the conjecture is not true.

Common Errors With Inductive Reasoning

Students might conjecture by inductive reasoning without considering possible counterexamples.

For example, if three lines are randomly generated on a coordinate plane, the three lines may form a triangle, as shown below.

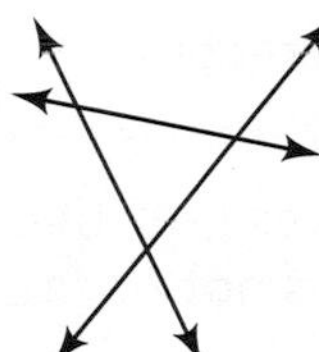

It is possible that such a triangle might be formed for each of thousands of attempts. It may be tempting to conjecture that three lines on the coordinate plane always form a triangle.

However the following counterexample is possible.

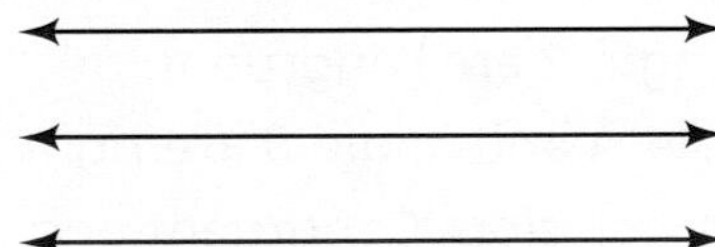

Mathematical Practices

Look for and make use of structure. Students become more mathematically proficient by finding patterns and using repeated reasoning to make predictions.

Math Background *(continued)*

Deductive Reasoning

Deductive reasoning uses given information, definitions, properties, postulates, and theorems to create a string of logically connected statements. The conclusion of deductive reasoning is valid as long as the methods used to draw the conclusion are correct. There are two universally accepted Laws of Logic that are presented in this chapter.

Law of Syllogism	Law of Detachment
If $p \longrightarrow q$ is true and $q \longrightarrow r$ is true, then $p \longrightarrow r$ is true.	If $p \longrightarrow q$ is true and p is true, then q is true.

Valid Arguments

An argument is only valid if the logic it uses is correct.

For example:

Premise: All rectangles are quadrilaterals.

Premise: A square is a rectangle.

Conclusion: A square is a quadrilateral.

This argument is valid because it uses the Law of Detachment.

Invalid Arguments

A conclusion that does not follow from the premises is invalid.

Premise: All rectangles are quadrilaterals.

Premise: A square is a rectangle.

Conclusion: A quadrilateral is a rectangle.

The Law of Detachment was not followed, and the conclusion is invalid: A quadrilateral is not necessarily a rectangle.

Common Errors With Deductive Reasoning

Students might incorrectly use the Law of Detachment. They may see that the conclusion of a statement is true and assume that the premise is true.

If two angles are right angles, then they are congruent.

Angle A and angle B are congruent.

Therefore, angle A and angle B are right angles.

This is not a valid conclusion. Congruent angles are not necessarily right angles.

Mathematical Practices

Construct viable arguments and critique the reasoning of others. Students learn to reason and construct arguments using laws of deductive thinking. They build up their skills and strategies through exposure to laws of logic and numerous examples.

Types of Proof

Proofs can be written in two-column, flow chart, or paragraph formats.

In a *two-column proof*, statements are listed in the first column and the reasons that justify them are listed in the second column.

Given: $-8x - 16 = 2x + 4$
Prove: $x = -2$

Statement	Reason
1) $-8x - 16 = 2x + 4$	**1)** Given
2) $-10x - 16 = 4$	**2)** Subtraction Property of Equality
3) $-10x = 20$	**3)** Addition Property of Equality
4) $x = -2$	**4)** Division Property of Equality

In a *flow proof*, statements are connected with arrows that indicate how one statement follows logically from another.

$-8x - 16 = 2x + 4$ → $-10x - 16 = 4$ → $-10x = 20$ → $x = -2$

Given; Subtraction Property of Equality; Addition Property of Equality; Division Property of Equality

A *paragraph proof* is a proof in paragraph form.

$-8x - 16 = 2x + 4$ is given. Subtract $2x$ from both sides to get $-10x - 16 = 4$. Then add 16 to both sides to get $-10x = 20$. Divide both sides by -10. So $x = -2$.

Common Errors With Proofs

Working with proofs is often a daunting task for many students. The number of mathematical properties, theorems, definitions, etc. can be overwhelming. Some students may benefit from working backward. Have them start with the statement they'd like to prove and identify what information is needed to get to that statement.

Mathematical Practices

Construct viable arguments and critique the reasoning of others. In writing proofs, students formalize their ability to make viable arguments supported by previously established results and stated assumptions. They also begin to see how algebraic properties tie in to geometric scenarios as they establish several angle-pair relationships.

1-1 Basic Constructions

Common Core State Standard
G.CO.12 Make formal geometric constructions with a variety of tools and methods (compass and straightedge . . .).

Preparing to Teach

ESSENTIAL UNDERSTANDING

Special geometric tools can be used to make a figure that is congruent to an original figure without measuring. Construction with straightedge and compass is more accurate than sketching and drawing.

Math Background

Euclidean constructions employ a compass and a straightedge. Students need to become comfortable using a straightedge for the purpose of drawing a straight line and, if a ruler is used, learn not to rely on the scale markings.

The techniques for constructing congruent figures in this lesson will be important skills in future lessons. Just as learning to write letters is a prerequisite for learning to write words, learning to construct congruent angles and segments is a prerequisite for learning to construct parallel and perpendicular lines in Chapter 2.

Three famous construction problems intrigued ancient Greek geometers and many others in more recent times: trisecting an angle, constructing a cube with double the volume, and constructing a square whose area is that of a given circle. No solutions were ever found, and many years passed before mathematicians proved that solutions do not exist.

ELL Support

FOCUS ON LANGUAGE Examine the word *perpendicular*. As an adjective, *perpendicular* means straight up and down or upright. Ask students for examples of things that are upright. Then ask students for synonyms for *perpendicular.* Remind students that a synonym is a word that means the same thing. Examples are *vertical, on two legs, standing, erect,* or *plumb*. Ask for antonyms, such as *horizontal* or *on four legs.*

Perpendicular can also be a noun meaning a tool for finding or marking a vertical line, or a line or plane at a right angle to another line or plane. The word comes from the Latin *perpendiculum* (plumb line) and from *perpendere* (balance carefully).

Lesson Vocabulary

- straightedge
- compass
- construction
- perpendicular lines
- perpendicular bisector

Mathematical Practices

USE APPROPRIATE TOOLS STRATEGICALLY. In addition to using rulers and protractors, students will use a compass to measure and draw line segments, angles, and bisectors of segments and angles.

Interactive Learning

Solve It!

PURPOSE To provide students with a method for constructing an angle bisector that requires only the use of a straightedge and compass

PROCESS Students may use visual judgment and their knowledge of congruent adjacent angles to determine the relationship in the question.

Q How many angles exist in the diagram after the fold is made? What are the names of the angles? **[3; ∠FGH, ∠FGJ, and ∠JGH]**

ANSWER $\overline{GJ}$ divides ∠*FGH* in exactly half; because the two halves of ∠*FGH* overlap each other exactly, you can conclude that ∠*FGJ* ≅ ∠*JGH* .

CONNECT THE MATH The method used in the Solve It for finding an angle bisector does not require the use of a measuring tool. This is one of the basic geometric constructions taught in this lesson.

▼ DIGITAL (STUDENT WORK SPACE PAGE 3)

Getting Ready!

Draw ∠FGH. Fold your paper so that $\overline{GH}$ lies on top of $\overline{GF}$. Unfold the paper. Label point J on the fold line in the interior of ∠FGH. How is $\overline{GJ}$ related to ∠FGH? How do you know?

2 Guided Instruction

Problem 1 Constructing Congruent Segments

Q In Step 1 can the distance between C and the arrowhead be shorter than the given segment? Explain. **[No, it needs to be longer than the given segment so that the arc will intersect the ray.]**

Got It? **SYNTHESIZING**
Point out to students that they are using the Segment Addition Postulate to complete this construction.

ANSWERS

Got It? X ——— Y

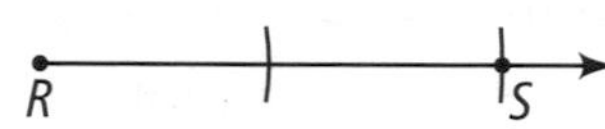

Practice

1.

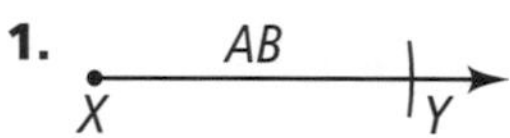

2.

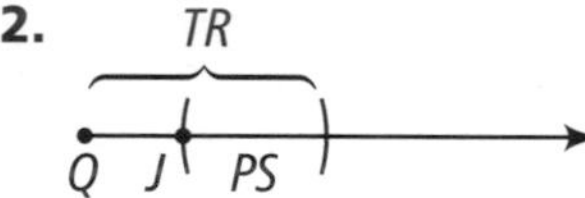

▼ STUDENT PAGE 3

In this lesson, you will learn another way to construct figures like the one in the Solve It.

Essential Understanding You can use special geometric tools to make a figure that is congruent to an original figure without measuring. This method is more accurate than sketching and drawing.

A **straightedge** is a ruler with no markings on it. A **compass** is a geometric tool used to draw circles and parts of circles called *arcs*. A **construction** is a geometric figure drawn using a straightedge and a compass.

▼ DIGITAL

Problem 1 **Constructing Congruent Segments**

Construct a segment congruent to a given segment.

Given: $\overline{AB}$

Construct: $\overline{CD}$ **so that** $\overline{CD} \cong \overline{AB}$

Step 1 Draw a ray with endpoint C.

Step 2 Open the compass to the length of $\overline{AB}$.

Step 3 With the same compass setting, put the compass point on point C. Draw an arc that intersects the ray. Label the point of intersection D.

$\overline{CD} \cong \overline{AB}$

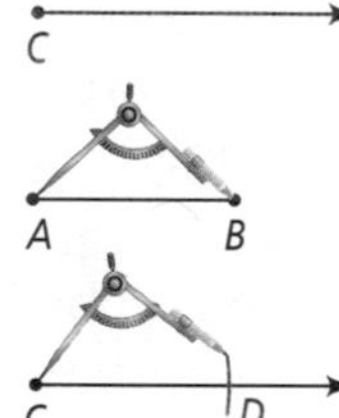

▼ STUDENT PAGES 3–4

Got It? Use a straightedge to draw $\overline{XY}$. Then construct $\overline{RS}$ so that $RS = 2XY$.

A Practice

1. Construct $\overline{XY}$ congruent to $\overline{AB}$.

   A ——— B

2. Construct $\overline{QJ}$ so that $QJ = TR - PS$.

   T ——— R P ——— S

Problem 2 Constructing Congruent Angles

Q If you repeat Steps 2 and 3 using a different compass setting than used originally, where will the two arcs in Step 4 intersect? **[The arcs will intersect somewhere on $\overrightarrow{ST}$.]**

Q How could you construct adjacent congruent angles? **[Instead of beginning with a new ray in Step 1, substitute $\overrightarrow{AB}$ for $\overrightarrow{SR}$ in the rest of the steps.]**

▼ DIGITAL

Problem 2 **Constructing Congruent Angles**

Construct an angle congruent to a given angle.

Given: $\angle A$

Construct: $\angle S$ **so that** $\angle S \cong \angle A$

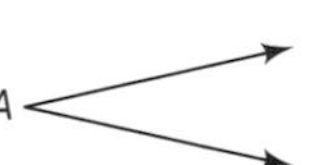

Step 1
Draw a ray with endpoint S.

Step 2
With the compass point on vertex A, draw an arc that intersects the sides of $\angle A$. Label the points of intersection B and C.

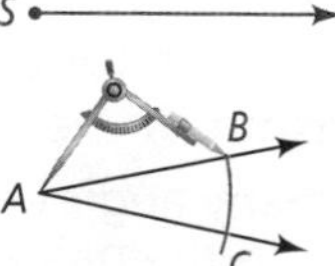

Step 3
With the same compass setting, put the compass point on point S. Draw an arc and label its point of intersection with the ray as R.

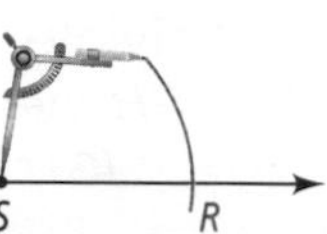

Step 4
Open the compass to the length BC. Keeping the same compass setting, put the compass point on R. Draw an arc to locate point T.

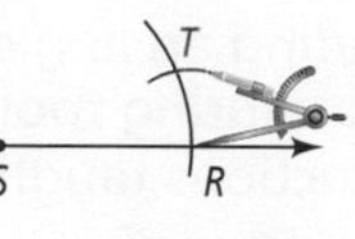

Step 5
Draw $\overrightarrow{ST}$.

$\angle S \cong \angle A$

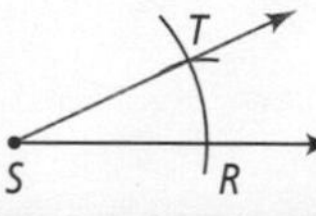

Got It?

Point out to students that the construction of the angle bisector of $\angle F$ is a byproduct of the construction of $\angle F$.

ANSWERS

Got It?

a.

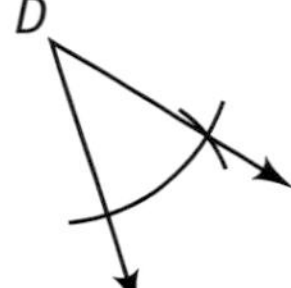

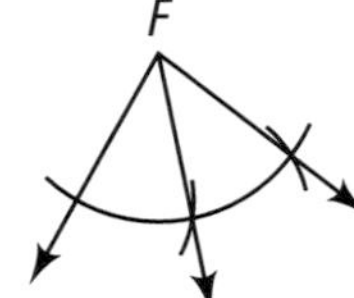

b. Answers may vary. Sample: You use a compass setting to copy a distance.

Practice

3. 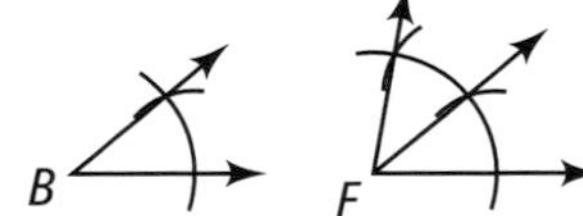

4.

Got It? **a.** Construct $\angle F$ so that $m\angle F = 2m\angle B$.

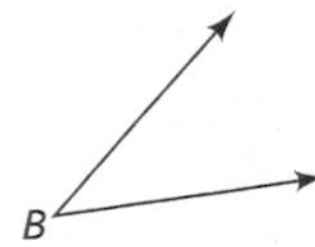

Think

Which postulate allows you to construct an angle with measure $2m\angle B$?

b. Reasoning How is constructing a congruent angle similar to constructing a congruent segment?

Practice **3.** Construct $\angle D$ so that $\angle D \cong \angle C$.

4. Construct $\angle F$ so that $m\angle F = 2m\angle C$.

C

Problem 3 Constructing the Perpendicular Bisector

Remind students that they worked with perpendicular lines and were also introduced to perpendicular bisectors in the context of reflections in a previous course.

Q What happens if you change the compass setting between Step 1 and Step 2? **[The intersections form a perpendicular line, but the line is not the bisector.]**

Q How can you use your compass to verify $\overline{AM} \cong \overline{MB}$? **[You can use your compass as a measuring tool to compare the lengths of the two segments.]**

Perpendicular lines are two lines that intersect to form right angles. The symbol $\perp$ means "is perpendicular to." In the diagram at the right, $\overleftrightarrow{AB} \perp \overleftrightarrow{CD}$ and $\overleftrightarrow{CD} \perp \overleftrightarrow{AB}$.

A **perpendicular bisector** of a segment is a line, segment, or ray that is perpendicular to the segment at its midpoint. In the diagram at the right, $\overleftrightarrow{EF}$ is the perpendicular bisector of $\overline{GH}$. The perpendicular bisector bisects the segment into two congruent segments. The construction in Problem 3 will show you how this works. You will justify the steps for this construction in Chapter 12, as well as for the other constructions in this lesson.

A D C B

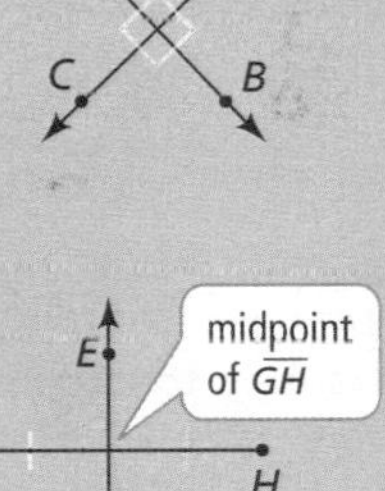

Problem 3 **Constructing the Perpendicular Bisector**

Construct the perpendicular bisector of a segment.

Given: $\overline{AB}$

Construct: $\overleftrightarrow{XY}$ so that $\overleftrightarrow{XY}$ is the perpendicular bisector of $\overline{AB}$

A B

Step 1
Put the compass point on point A and draw a long arc as shown. Be sure the opening is greater than $\frac{1}{2}AB$.

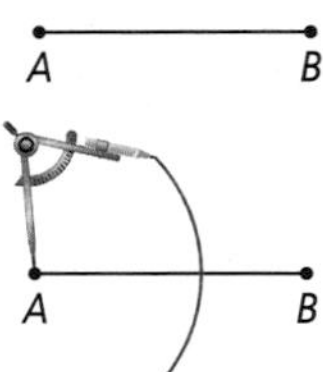

Step 2
With the same compass setting, put the compass point on point B and draw another long arc. Label the points where the two arcs intersect as X and Y.

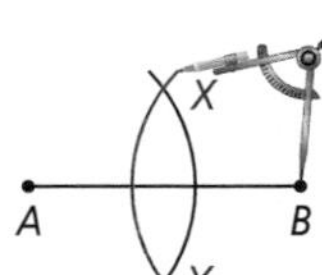

Step 3
Draw $\overleftrightarrow{XY}$. Label the point of intersection of $\overline{AB}$ and $\overleftrightarrow{XY}$ as M, the midpoint of $\overline{AB}$.

$\overleftrightarrow{XY} \perp \overline{AB}$ at midpoint M, so $\overleftrightarrow{XY}$ is the perpendicular bisector of $\overline{AB}$.

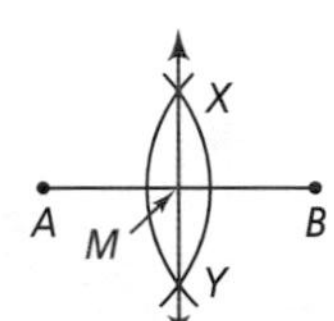

Problem 3 *continued*

Got It?

Encourage students to change the compass opening and repeat Steps 2 and 3 several times. Students will see that all of the pairs of arcs intersect on the perpendicular bisector.

ANSWERS

Got It?

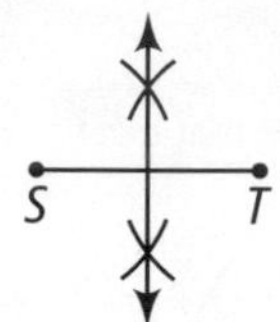

Practice

5.

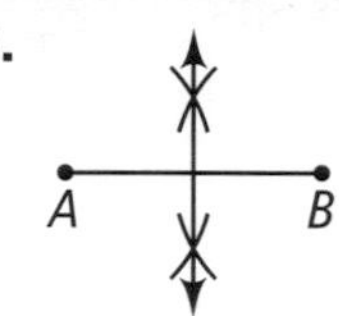

6.

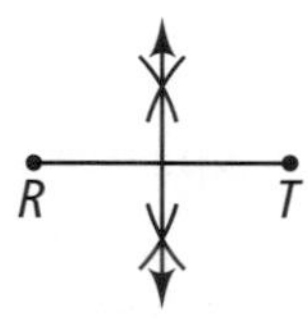

▼ STUDENT PAGE 6

Got It? Draw $\overline{ST}$. Construct its perpendicular bisector.

Think Why must the compass opening be greater than $\frac{1}{2}ST$?

A Practice **5.** Construct the perpendicular bisector of $\overline{AB}$.

6. Construct the perpendicular bisector of $\overline{TR}$.

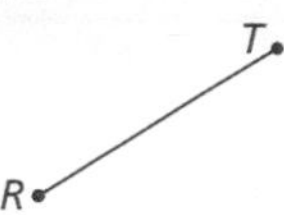

Problem 4 Constructing the Angle Bisector

Q How can you use your compass to verify $\angle BAD \cong \angle DAC$? **[You can use your compass as a measuring tool to compare the lengths of the two segments created by the intersections of the arc drawn in Step 1 with the bisector.]**

Q If the arcs in Step 2 are drawn such that the arcs lie to the left of vertex *A*, will their intersection also lie on the angle bisector? Explain. **[Yes, but it may be harder to draw an accurate angle bisector that way.]**

Got It? **VISUAL LEARNERS**

Students may find that they remember the construction steps more easily if they make a sketch of the desired outcome before beginning the construction.

ANSWERS

Got It?

X, P, Y, Z

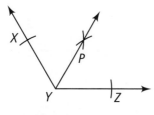

Practice

7.

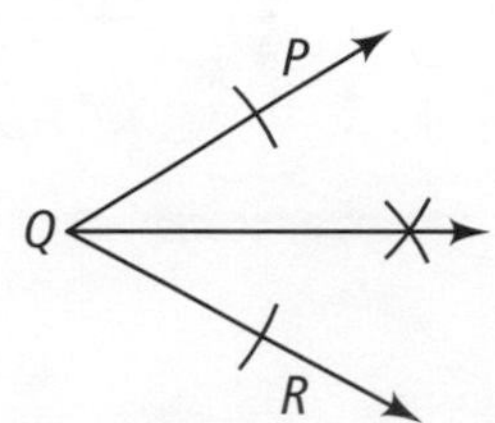

▼ DIGITAL

Problem 4 **Constructing the Angle Bisector**

Construct the bisector of an angle.

Given: $\angle A$

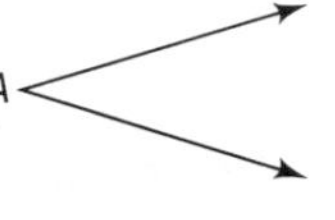

Construct: $\overrightarrow{AD}$, the bisector of $\angle A$

Step 1

Put the compass point on vertex *A*. Draw an arc that intersects the sides of $\angle A$. Label the points of intersection *B* and *C*.

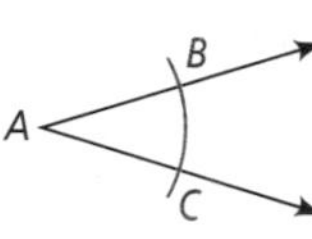

Step 2

Put the compass point on point *C* and draw an arc. With the same compass setting, draw an arc using point *B*. Be sure the arcs intersect. Label the point where the two arcs intersect as *D*.

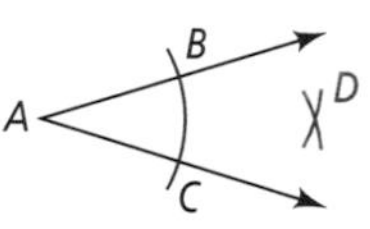

Step 3

Draw $\overrightarrow{AD}$.

$\overrightarrow{AD}$ is the bisector of $\angle CAB$.

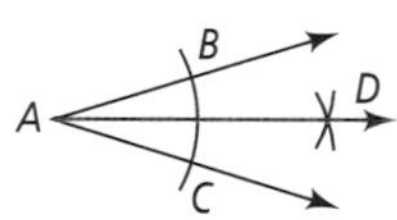

▼ STUDENT PAGE 7

Got It? Draw obtuse $\angle XYZ$. Then construct its bisector $\overrightarrow{YP}$.

A Practice **7.** Draw acute $\angle PQR$. Then construct its bisector.

3 Lesson Check

Do you know HOW?
If students have difficulty with Exercises 8, 9, and 10, then have them reference the steps in Problem 1, Problem 3, and Problem 4, respectively.

Do you UNDERSTAND?
If students have difficulty with Exercise 12, then ask them to sketch, draw, and construct a perpendicular bisector and an angle bisector and measure the accuracy of the results.

Close

Q How can you use the constructions learned in this lesson to create a 45° angle? **[Begin with a segment and construct its perpendicular bisector. Next, construct the angle bisector of one of the 90° angles that was created in Step 1. Each of the angles created by the angle bisector will measure 45°.]**

ANSWERS

8.

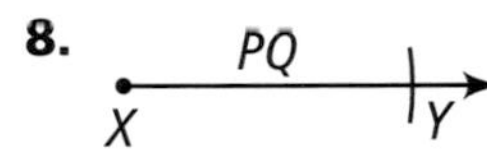

9.

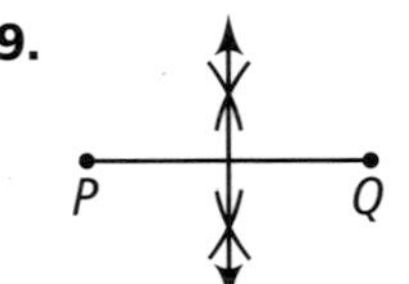

10.

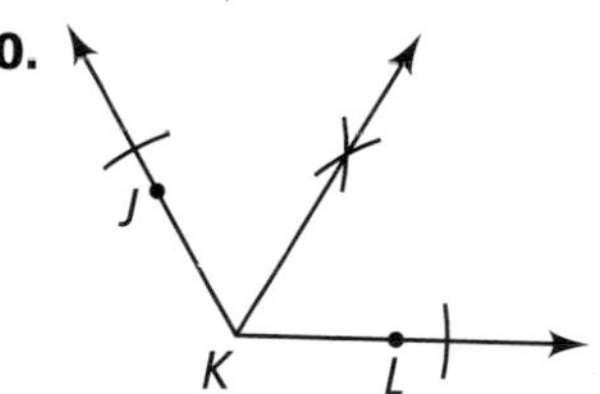

11. compass, straightedge

▼ STUDENT PAGES 7–9

Lesson Check

Do you know HOW?

8. Construct a segment congruent to $\overline{PQ}$.

9. Construct the perpendicular bisector of $\overline{PQ}$.

10. Draw an obtuse $\angle JKL$. Construct its bisector.

Do you UNDERSTAND?

11. Vocabulary What two tools do you use to make constructions?

12. Compare and Contrast Describe the difference in accuracy between sketching a figure, drawing a figure with a ruler and protractor, and constructing a figure. Explain.

13. Error Analysis Your friend constructs $\overleftrightarrow{XY}$ so that it is perpendicular to and contains the midpoint of $\overline{AB}$. He claims that $\overline{AB}$ is the perpendicular bisector of $\overline{XY}$. What is his error?

12. Answers may vary. Sample: When you sketch a figure, it does not require accurate measurements for angles and sides. When you draw a figure with a ruler and protractor, you use measurements to determine the lengths of sides or the sizes of angles. When you construct a figure, the only tools you use are a compass and straightedge. A construction is the most accurate of the three methods.

13. Since $\overleftrightarrow{XY}$ is $\perp$ to and contains the midpoint of $\overline{AB}$, then $\overleftrightarrow{XY}$ is the $\perp$ bis. of $\overline{AB}$, not the other way around.

4 Practice

More Practice and Problem-Solving Exercises

ASSIGNMENT GUIDE
The assignments below are for the More Practice and Problem-Solving Exercises. You may also want to assign the A-Level Practice Exercises for homework if these are not used in class.
Average: 14–29
Advanced: 14–32

Mathematical Practices The exercises listed focus on the Standards for Mathematical Practices listed.

EX. 17: Persevere in Solving Problems (MP 1)
EX. 28, 31: Construct Arguments (MP 3)
EX. 13: Critique the Reasoning of Others (MP 3)
EX. 12, 22: Use Appropriate Tools (MP 5)
EX. 16: Use Structure (MP 7)

▼ STUDENT PAGE 9

More Practice and Problem-Solving Exercises

Apply

Sketch the figure described. Explain how to construct it. Then do the construction.

14. $\overrightarrow{XY} \perp \overrightarrow{YZ}$

15. $\overrightarrow{ST}$ bisects right $\angle PSQ$.

16. Compare and Contrast How is constructing an angle bisector similar to constructing a perpendicular bisector?

EXERCISE 23: Use the **Think About a Plan** worksheet in the Online Teacher Resources to further support students' development in becoming independent learners.

HOMEWORK QUICK CHECK
To check students' understanding of key skills and concepts, go over Exercises 14, 15, 17, 22, and 23.

ANSWERS

14. Answers may vary. Sample:

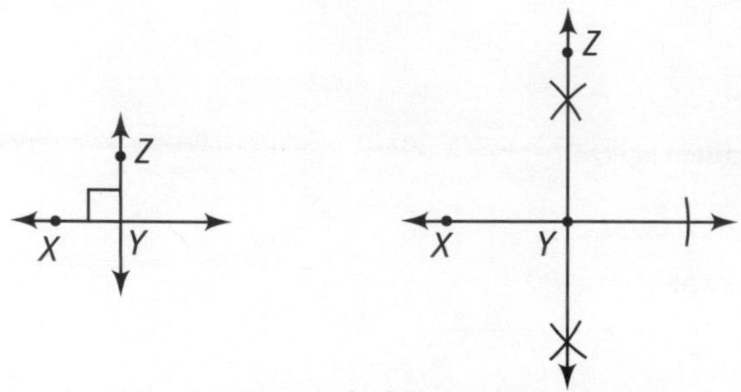

Find a segment on $\overleftrightarrow{XY}$ so that you can construct $\overleftrightarrow{YZ}$ as its perpendicular bisector.

15.

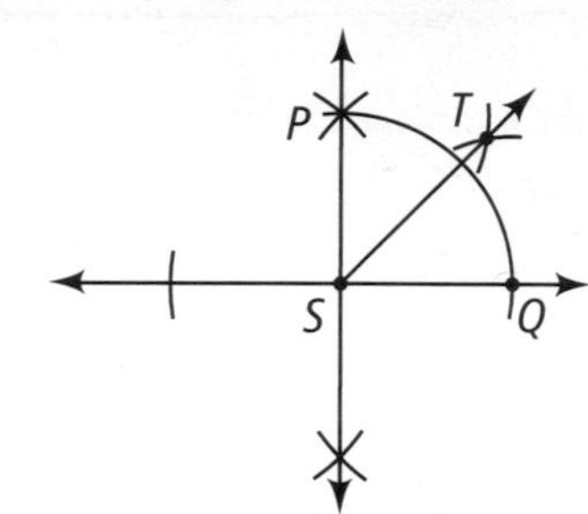

Find a segment on $\overleftrightarrow{SQ}$ so that you can construct $\overleftrightarrow{SP}$ as its perpendicular bisector. Then bisect $\angle PSQ$.

16. Answers may vary. Sample: Both constructions involve drawing arcs with the same radius from two different points, and using the point(s) of intersection of those arcs. Arcs must intersect at two points for the ⊥ bis., but only one point for the ∠ bis.

17.

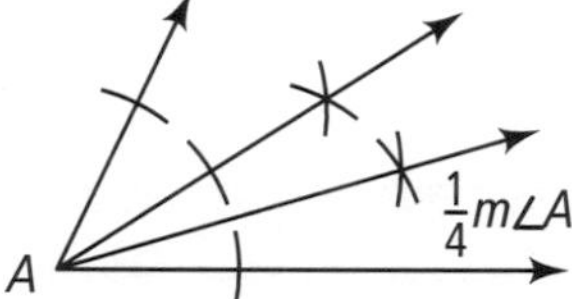

18. a. A segment has exactly one midpoint; using the Ruler Postulate (Post. 5), each point corresponds with exactly one number, and exactly one number represents half the length of a segment.

b. A segment has infinitely many bisectors because many lines can be drawn through the midpoint.

c. In the plane with the segment, there is one ⊥ bis. because only one line in that plane can be drawn through the midpoint so that it forms a right angle with the given segment.

d. Consider the plane that is ⊥ to the segment at its midpoint. Any line in that plane that contains the midpoint of the segment is a ⊥ bis. of the segment, and there are infinitely many such lines.

17. Think About a Plan Draw an $\angle A$. Construct an angle whose measure is $\frac{1}{4}m\angle A$.
- How is the angle you need to construct related to the angle bisector of $\angle A$?
- How can you use previous constructions to help you?

18. Answer the questions about a segment in a plane. Explain each answer.
a. How many midpoints does the segment have?
b. How many bisectors does it have?
c. How many lines in the plane are its perpendicular bisectors?
d. How many lines in space are its perpendicular bisectors?

For Exercises 19–21, copy $\angle 1$ and $\angle 2$. Construct each angle described.

19. $\angle B$; $m\angle B = m\angle 1 + m\angle 2$

20. $\angle C$; $m\angle C = m\angle 1 - m\angle 2$

21. $\angle D$; $m\angle D = 2m\angle 2$

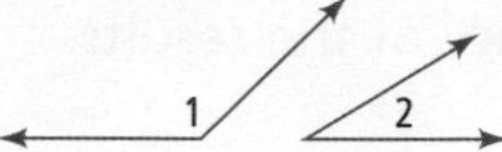

22. Writing Explain how to do each construction with a compass and straightedge.
a. Draw a segment $\overline{PQ}$. Construct the midpoint of $\overline{PQ}$.
b. Divide $\overline{PQ}$ into four congruent segments.

19.

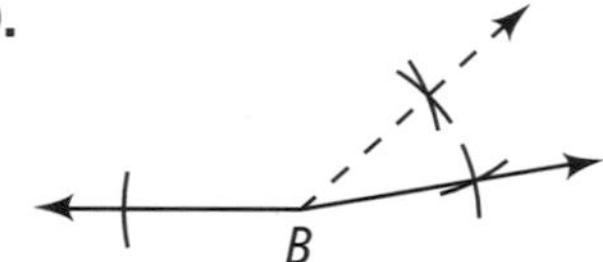

20.

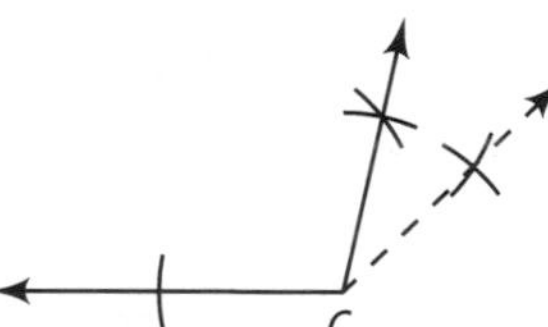

21.

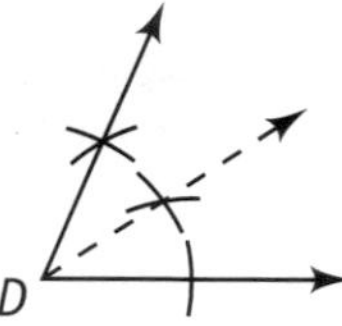

22. a. With P as center, draw an arc with radius slightly more than $\frac{1}{2}PQ$. Keeping that radius, draw an arc with Q as center. Those two arcs meet at 2 points; the line through those 2 points intersects $\overline{PQ}$ at its midpoint.

b. Follow the steps in part (a) to find the midpoint C of $\overline{PQ}$. Then repeat the process for segments $\overline{PC}$ and $\overline{CQ}$.

23. a.

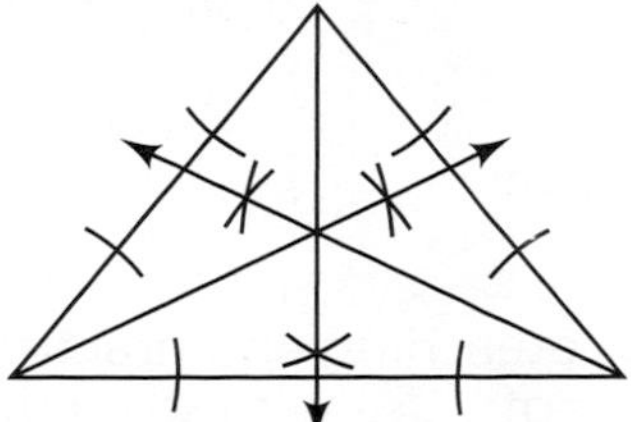

The three angle bisectors meet at a point.

b.

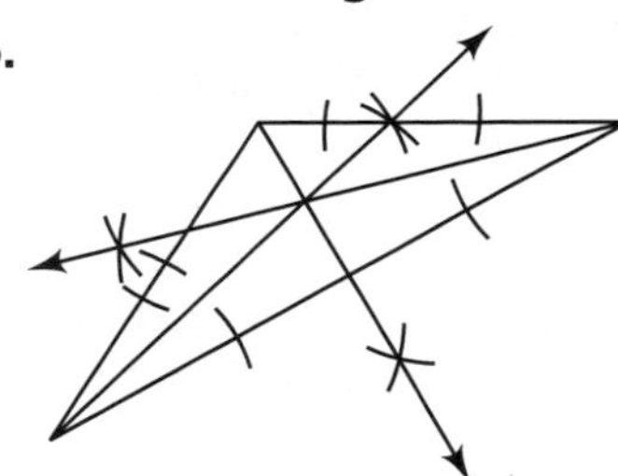

c. For any triangle, the three angle bisectors meet at a point.

24.

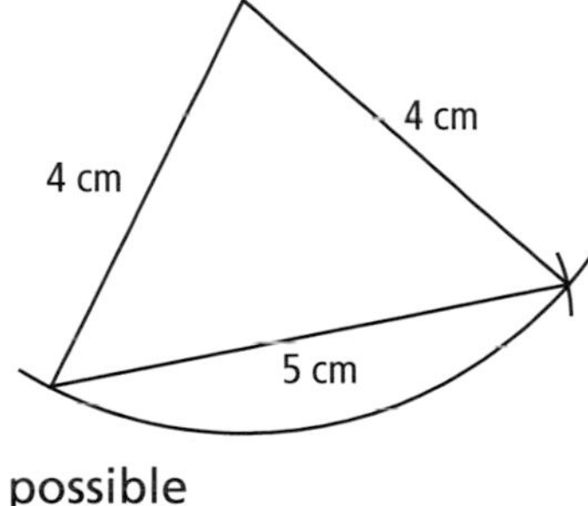

possible

25.

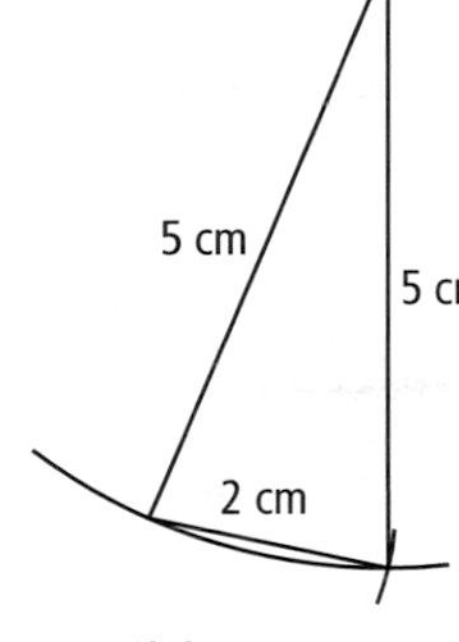

possible

26. Not possible; the two 2-cm sides do not meet.

27. Not possible; the two 2-cm sides meet on the 4-cm side, so they do not form a triangle.

28. a. X ———— Y

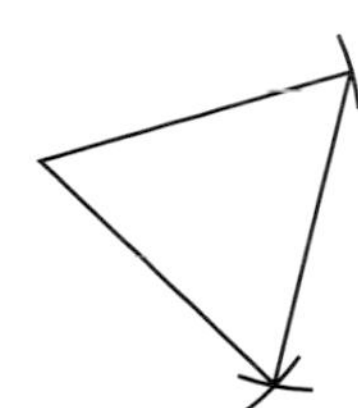

b. The measure of each angle is 60°.

c. Construct the vertices of a triangle with three congruent sides. Draw two sides of the triangle to form a 60° angle. Construct the angle bisector of that angle to form a 30° angle.

29. A

30. ⊥; contains the intersection of that line with the plane

23. a. Draw a large triangle with three acute angles. Construct the bisectors of the three angles. What appears to be true about the three angle bisectors?

b. Repeat the constructions with a triangle that has one obtuse angle.

c. Make a Conjecture What appears to be true about the three angle bisectors of any triangle?

Use a ruler to draw segments of 2 cm, 4 cm, and 5 cm. Then construct each triangle with the given side measures, if possible. If it is not possible, explain why not.

24. 4 cm, 4 cm, and 5 cm

25. 2 cm, 5 cm, and 5 cm

26. 2 cm, 2 cm, and 5 cm

27. 2 cm, 2 cm, and 4 cm

28. a. Draw a segment, $\overline{XY}$. Construct a triangle with sides congruent to $\overline{XY}$.

b. Measure the angles of the triangle.

c. Writing Describe how to construct a 60° angle using what you know. Then describe how to construct a 30° angle.

29. Which steps best describe how to construct the pattern at the right?

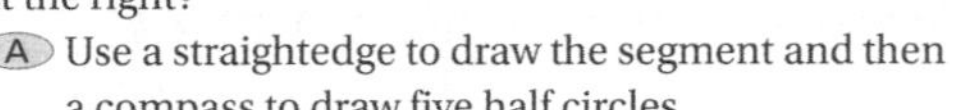

Ⓐ Use a straightedge to draw the segment and then a compass to draw five half circles.

Ⓑ Use a straightedge to draw the segment and then a compass to draw six half circles.

Ⓒ Use a compass to draw five half circles and then a straightedge to join their ends.

Ⓓ Use a compass to draw six half circles and then a straightedge to join their ends.

Challenge

30. Study the figures. Complete the definition of a line perpendicular to a plane: A line is perpendicular to a plane if it is __?__ to every line in the plane that __?__.

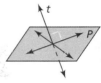

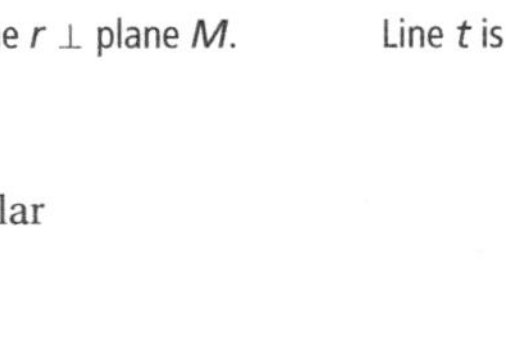

Line $r \perp$ plane M. Line t is not $\perp$ plane P.

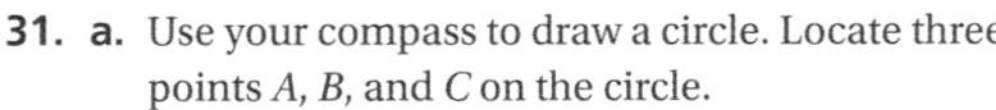

31. a. Use your compass to draw a circle. Locate three points A, B, and C on the circle.

b. Draw $\overline{AB}$ and $\overline{BC}$. Then construct the perpendicular bisectors of $\overline{AB}$ and $\overline{BC}$.

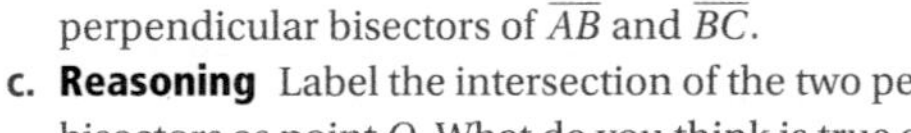

c. Reasoning Label the intersection of the two perpendicular bisectors as point O. What do you think is true about point O?

32. Two triangles are *congruent* if each side and each angle of one triangle is congruent to a side or angle of the other triangle. In Chapter 3, you will learn that if each side of one triangle is congruent to a side of the other triangle, then you can conclude that the triangles are congruent without finding the angles. Explain how you can use congruent triangles to justify the angle bisector construction.

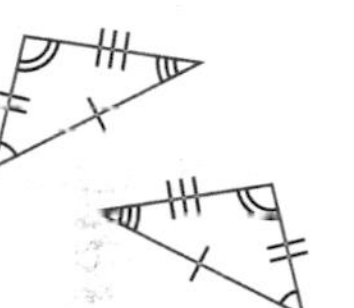

31. a–b.

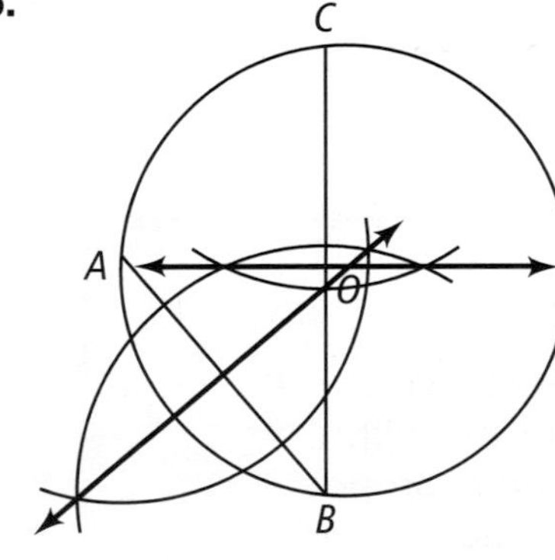

c. O is the center of the circle.

32.

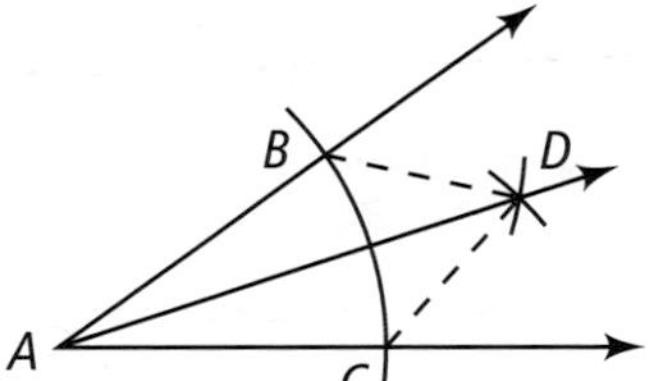

In the angle bisector construction, $\overline{AB} \cong \overline{AC}$, $\overline{BD} \cong \overline{CD}$ and $\overline{AD} \cong \overline{AD}$. Using the statement that two triangles are ≅ if three pairs of sides are ≅, then $\triangle ABD \cong \triangle ACD$. Since the △s are ≅, each ∠ of one △ is ≅ to an ∠ of the other △. So, $\angle BAD \cong \angle CAD$ and $\overrightarrow{AD}$ is the ∠ bisector of $\angle BAC$.

Assess and Remediate

Lesson Quiz

1. Construct $\angle Y$ so that $\angle Y \cong \angle Z$.

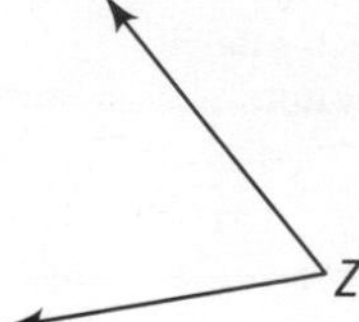

2. Construct the line $\overleftrightarrow{CD}$ so that $\overleftrightarrow{CD}$ is the perpendicular bisector of $\overline{EF}$.

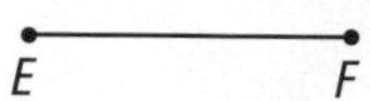

3. **Do you UNDERSTAND?** Construct $\overrightarrow{UV}$, the bisector of $\angle U$.

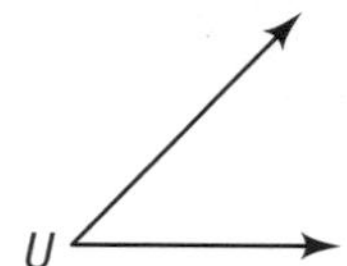

ANSWERS TO LESSON QUIZ

1.

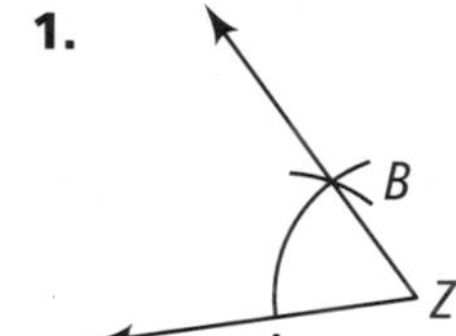

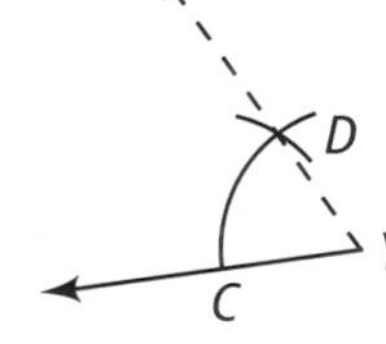

2.

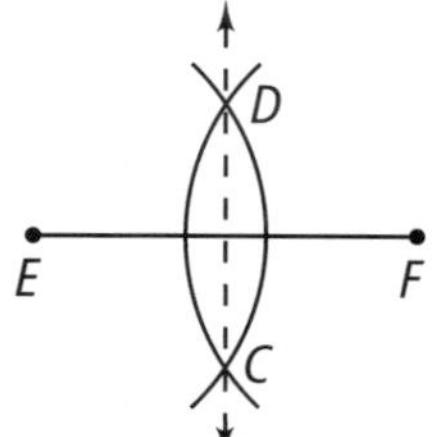

3.

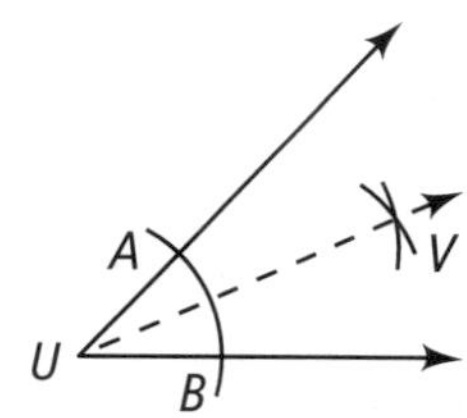

Prescription for Remediation

Use the student work on the Lesson Quiz to prescribe a differentiated assignment.

Points	Differentiated Remediation
0–1	Intervention
2	On-level
3	Extension

Online Assessment

Assign the Lesson Quiz in Success Tracker on **pearsonsuccessnet.com**. Success Tracker will automatically score the quiz and assign appropriate intervention or enrichment to each student based on the results. The compiled data appear in three different reports for instant analysis of whole class and individual student performance.

Differentiated Remediation

Intervention

- **RETEACHING** (2 pages) Provides reteaching and practice exercises for the key lesson concepts. Use with struggling students or absent students.
- **ENGLISH LANGUAGE LEARNER SUPPORT** Helps students develop and reinforce mathematical vocabulary and key concepts.

On-Level

- **PRACTICE** (2 pages) Provides extra practice for each lesson. For simpler practice exercises, use the Form K Practice pages found in the Online Teacher Resources.
- **THINK ABOUT A PLAN** Helps students develop specific problem-solving skills and strategies by providing scaffolded guiding questions.
- **STANDARDIZED TEST PREP** Focuses on all major exercises, all major question types, and helps students prepare for the high-stakes assessments.

Extension

- **ENRICHMENT** Provides students with interesting problems and activities that extend the concepts of the lesson.
- **ACTIVITIES, GAMES, AND PUZZLES** Worksheets that can be used for concept development, enrichment, and for fun!

1-2 Patterns and Inductive Reasoning

Common Core State Standards
Prepares for G.CO.9 Prove theorems about lines and angles . . . **Also prepares for G.CO.10, G.CO.11**

Preparing to Teach

BIG idea Reasoning and Proof

ESSENTIAL UNDERSTANDING

Patterns in some number sequences and some sequences of geometric figures can be used to discover relationships. Conjectures are not valid unless they are proven true. One counterexample can prove that a conjecture is false.

Math Background

Inductive reasoning is the process of identifying a pattern based on limited data. Deductive reasoning, on the other hand, is the process of concluding that a relationship is true because it is a particular case of a general principle that is known to be true. Both types of reasoning are important to mathematical thinking. Mathematicians observe particular cases and then use inductive reasoning to make conjectures. Conjectures are proved to be true by means of deductive reasoning in a mathematical proof.

ELL Support

FOCUS ON COMMUNICATION Draw several scalene triangles on the board and write *scalene*. Tell students these are scalene triangles and ask them what they can conclude about scalene triangles. You can use other examples. Then say, these are examples of *inductive reasoning*. Ask: What do you think inductive reasoning is? Guide students to conclude that inductive reasoning is based on relationships and patterns that you observe.

FOCUS ON LANGUAGE Examine the word *inductive*. What does the suffix *-ive* mean? (tending to) The root of *inductive* is *induct* or *induce*, meaning to introduce or lead to.

Lesson Vocabulary

- inductive reasoning
- conjecture
- counterexample

Mathematical Practices

LOOK FOR AND MAKE USE OF STRUCTURE. Students will discern numeric patterns in geometric figures. They will also make use of counterexamples in Problem 5.

1 Interactive Learning

Solve It!

PURPOSE To solve a problem using inductive reasoning

PROCESS Students may collect data to identify and extrapolate a pattern.

Q How many rectangles do you expect to get if you fold the paper a third time? Explain. **[Eight; the number of rectangles doubles with each fold.]**

Q How can you use your answer to the previous question to answer the Solve It? **[Test the pattern for four folds. Modify if necessary, and then use the pattern for eight folds.]**

ANSWER 256; each fold produces twice as many rectangles as the previous fold.

CONNECT THE MATH In the Solve It, students identified and extrapolated a pattern. In this lesson, students will recognize patterns in numeric and geometric sequences.

▼ DIGITAL (STUDENT WORK SPACE PAGE 11)

Getting Ready!

Fold a piece of paper in half. When you unfold it, the paper is divided into two rectangles. Refold the paper, and then fold it in half again. This time when you unfold it, there are four rectangles. How many rectangles would you get if you folded a piece of paper in half eight times? Explain.

2 Guided Instruction

Problem 1 Finding and Using a Pattern

Q Is there a way to determine the 12th term in the sequence for 1B without knowing the 11th term? Explain. **[Yes, the 12th term is a circle enclosing a polygon with 12 + 2 = 14 sides.]**

Got It?

Q How many quadrilaterals will be drawn to complete the 4th term for part (b)? **[4]**

ANSWERS

Got It? a. 25, 20 **b.** 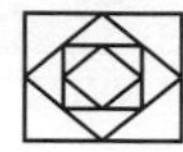 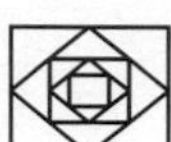

Practice

1. Multiply the previous term by $\frac{1}{2}$; $\frac{1}{16}$, $\frac{1}{32}$.
2. The colors red, orange, and blue shift clockwise to the next triangular region;

▼ STUDENT PAGE 11

In the Solve It, you may have used inductive reasoning. **Inductive reasoning** is reasoning based on patterns you observe.

Essential Understanding You can observe patterns in some number sequences and some sequences of geometric figures to discover relationships.

▼ DIGITAL

Finding and Using a Pattern

Look for a pattern. What are the next two terms in each sequence?

A 3, 9, 27, 81, . . .

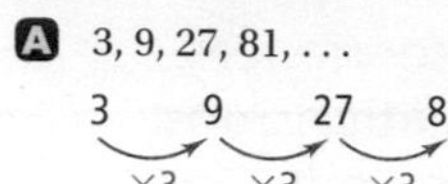

Each term is three times the previous term. The next two terms are $81 \times 3 = 243$ and $243 \times 3 = 729$.

B  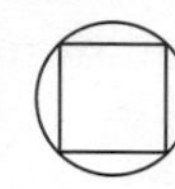 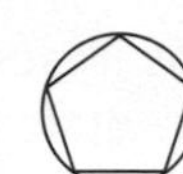

Each circle contains a polygon that has one more side than the preceding polygon. The next two circles contain a six-sided and a seven-sided polygon.

▼ STUDENT PAGES 11–12

Got It? What are the next two terms in each sequence?

a. 45, 40, 35, 30, . . .

b. 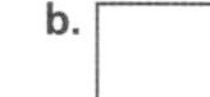 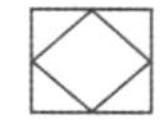 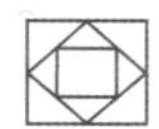

Practice Find a pattern for each sequence. Use the pattern to show the next two terms.

1. $1, \frac{1}{2}, \frac{1}{4}, \frac{1}{8}, \ldots$
2. 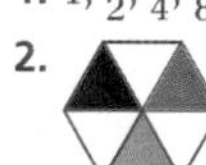  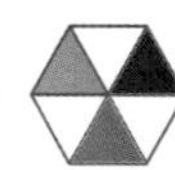

Problem 2 Using Inductive Reasoning

Q How might you test the pattern you discover in the first three circles before making a conjecture about the 20th circle? **[Use the pattern to make a conjecture about a circle with four diameters, and then draw the circle and diameters to test the conjecture.]**

Q How is the number of regions of each successive circle related to the number of regions in the previous circle? **[There are two more regions in each circle than in the previous circle.]**

▼ STUDENT PAGE 12

You may want to find the tenth or the one-hundredth term in a sequence. In this case, rather than find every previous term, you can look for a pattern and make a conjecture. A **conjecture** is a conclusion you reach using inductive reasoning.

▼ DIGITAL

Using Inductive Reasoning

Look at the circles. What conjecture can you make about the number of regions 20 diameters form?

1 diameter forms 2 regions.

2 diameters form 4 regions.

3 diameters form 6 regions.

Each circle has twice as many regions as diameters. Twenty diameters form $20 \cdot 2$, or 40 regions.

Got It?

Q How can you tell if a term will be an "R"? **[When divided by 3, the term number has a remainder of 1.]**

ANSWERS

Got It? Every 3rd term is B, so the 21st term will be B.

Practice

3. blue

4. star

▼ STUDENT PAGE 12

Got It? What conjecture can you make about the twenty-first term in R, W, B, R, W, B, . . .?

Plan Do you need to extend the sequence to 21 terms?

Practice **Use the sequence and inductive reasoning to make a conjecture.**

3. What is the color of the thirtieth figure?

4. What is the shape of the fortieth figure?

Problem 3 Collecting Information to Make a Conjecture

Q How are successive sums related to one another? **[The difference from one sum to the next increases by 2 each time.]**

Q How can you use the number of terms to determine the sum of the numbers? **[You multiply the number of terms by the number of terms plus one.]**

Got It?

Q What conjecture can you make about the sum of the first 30 natural numbers? **[The sum is $\frac{(30 \cdot 31)}{2} = 465$.]**

ANSWERS

Got It? The sum of the first 30 odd numbers is 30^2, or 900.

Practice

5. Answers may vary. Sample: The sum of the first 100 positive even numbers is $100 \cdot 101$, or 10,100.

6. Answers may vary. Sample: The product of two odd numbers is odd.

▼ STUDENT PAGE 13

It is important to gather enough data before you make a conjecture. For example, you do not have enough information about the sequence 1, 3, . . . to make a reasonable conjecture. The next term could be $3 \cdot 3 = 9$ or $3 + 2 = 5$.

▼ DIGITAL

Problem 3 **Collecting Information to Make a Conjecture**

What conjecture can you make about the sum of the first 30 even numbers?

Find the first few sums and look for a pattern.

Number of Terms	Sum
1	$2 = 2 = 1 \cdot 2$
2	$2 + 4 = 6 = 2 \cdot 3$
3	$2 + 4 + 6 = 12 = 3 \cdot 4$
4	$2 + 4 + 6 + 8 = 20 = 4 \cdot 5$

Each sum is the product of the number of terms and the number of terms plus one.

You can conclude that the sum of the first 30 even numbers is $30 \cdot 31$, or 930.

▼ STUDENT PAGE 13

Got It? What conjecture can you make about the sum of the first 30 odd numbers?

Plan What's the first step?

Practice **Make a conjecture for each scenario. Show your work.**

5. the sum of the first 100 positive even numbers

6. the product of two odd numbers

Problem 4 Making a Prediction

Q How could you use the April sales figure to estimate the May sales figure? **[Subtract 500 from the April sales figure.]**

Q How could you use the November sales figure to estimate the May sales figure? **[Subtract 500 times 6 from the November sales figure.]**

Got It?

Ask students to identify the *y*-intercept, slope, and an equation of the line. Have students estimate the June sales by using the equation of the line.

ANSWERS

Got It? a. Sales will be about 500 fewer than 8000, or 7500. **b.** No; explanations may vary. Sample: Sales may increase because students may want backpacks for school.

Practice

7. 1 mi

8. 75°F

▼ DIGITAL

Problem 4 **Making a Prediction**

Sales **Sales of backpacks at a nationwide company decreased over a period of six consecutive months. What conjecture can you make about the number of backpacks the company will sell in May?**

The points seem to fall on a line. The graph shows the number of sales decreasing by about 500 backpacks each month. By inductive reasoning, you can estimate that the company will sell approximately 8000 backpacks in May.

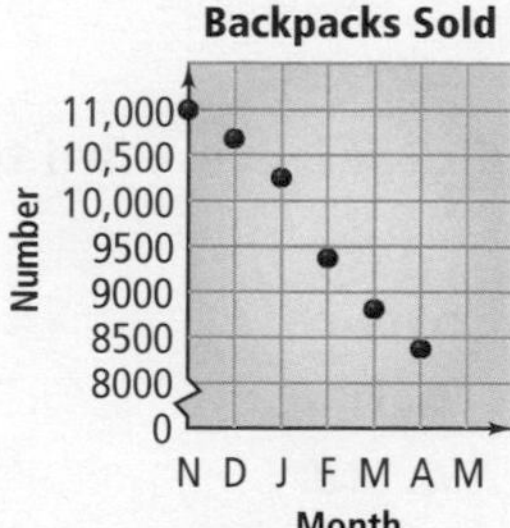

▼ STUDENT PAGES 13–14

Got It? **a.** Use the graph of the sales information from Problem 4. What conjecture can you make about backpack sales in June?

b. Reasoning Is it reasonable to use this graph to make a conjecture about sales in August? Explain.

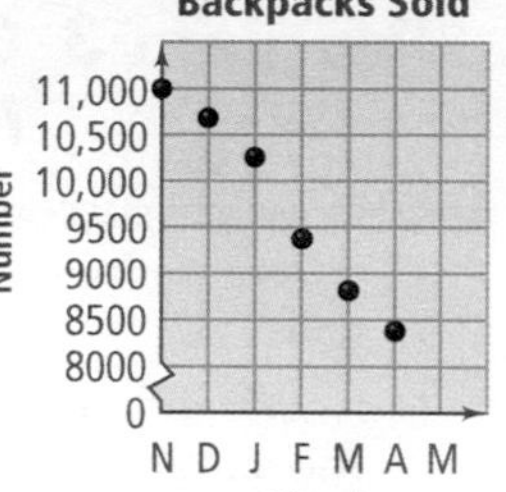

Practice **Weather** **Use inductive reasoning to make a prediction about the weather.**

STEM **7.** Lightning travels much faster than thunder, so you see lightning before you hear thunder. If you count 5 s between the lightning and thunder, how far away is the storm?

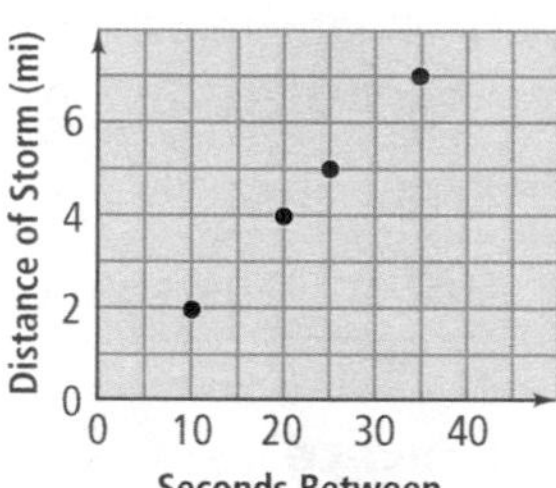

8. The speed at which a cricket chirps is affected by the temperature. If you hear 20 cricket chirps in 14 s, what is the temperature?

Number of Chirps per 14 Seconds	Temperature (°F)
5	45
10	55
15	65

Problem 5 Finding a Counterexample

Q How can you modify the statement in 5B so that there are no counterexamples? **[You can connect any three noncollinear points to form a triangle.]**

Q If you replace the word *number* in 5C with *whole number*, what number would provide the only counterexample to the statement? **[0, because $0 \cdot 2 = 0$, and 0 is not greater than 0.]**

▼ STUDENT PAGE 14

Not all conjectures turn out to be true. You should test your conjecture multiple times. You can prove that a conjecture is false by finding *one* counterexample. A **counterexample** is an example that shows that a conjecture is incorrect.

Got It?
Make sure that students understand that while one counterexample can prove a conjecture false, no number of examples can prove a conjecture true.

ANSWERS

Got It?
Answers may vary. Samples are given.
a. A carnation can be red, and it is not a rose.
b. When three points are collinear, the number of planes that can be drawn through them is infinite.
c. When you multiply 5 (or any odd number) by 3, the product is not divisible by 6.

Practice

9. Answers may vary. Sample: two right angles
10. Answers may vary. Sample: -2 and -3

▼ DIGITAL

Problem 5 **Finding a Counterexample**

What is a counterexample for each conjecture?

A **If the name of a month starts with the letter J, it is a summer month.**

Counterexample: January starts with J and it is a winter month.

B **You can connect any three points to form a triangle.**

Counterexample: If the three points lie on a line, you cannot form a triangle.

These three points support the conjecture . . .   . . . but these three points are a counterexample to the conjecture.

C **When you multiply a number by 2, the product is greater than the original number.**

The conjecture is true for positive numbers, but it is false for negative numbers and zero.

Counterexample: $-4 \cdot 2 = -8$ and $-8 \not> -4$.

▼ STUDENT PAGES 14–15

Got It? What is a counterexample for each conjecture?

a. If a flower is red, it is a rose.
b. One and only one plane exists through any three points.
c. When you multiply a number by 3, the product is divisible by 6.

Practice **Find one counterexample to show that each conjecture is false.**

9. $\angle 1$ and $\angle 2$ are supplementary, so one of the angles is acute.
10. The sum of two numbers is greater than either number.

3 Lesson Check

Do you know HOW?
If students have difficulty with Exercise 13, have them draw a figure that satisfies both conditions of the conjecture. Then have them draw a figure that satisfies the first condition, but not the second.

Do you UNDERSTAND?
If students have difficulty with Exercise 14, then ask them to explain the difference between *clockwise* and *counterclockwise* or between *productive* and *counterproductive*.

Close

Q How do you use inductive reasoning to make a conjecture? **[Analyze a limited number of cases to find a pattern, then use the pattern to make a conjecture about other cases.]**

ANSWERS

11. 31, 37

12.

O	B
LB	R

LB	O
R	B

13. Answers may vary. Sample: any nonsquare rectangle

14. One meaning of *counter* is "against," so a counterexample is an example that goes against a statement.

▼ STUDENT PAGES 15–16

Lesson Check

Do you know HOW?

What are the next two terms in each sequence?

11. 7, 13, 19, 25, . . .

12.   

13. What is a counterexample for the following conjecture?
All four-sided figures are squares.

Do you UNDERSTAND?

14. Vocabulary How does the word *counter* help you understand the term *counterexample*?

15. Compare and Contrast Clay thinks the next term in the sequence 2, 4, . . . is 6. Given the same pattern, Ott thinks the next term is 8, and Stacie thinks the next term is 7. What conjecture is each person making? Is there enough information to decide who is correct?

15. In the pattern 2, 4, . . ., the next term is 6 if the rule is "add 2"; the next term is 8 if the rule is "double the previous term"; and the next term is 7 if the rule is "add 2, then add 3, then add 4, . . . Just giving the first 2 terms does not give enough information to describe the pattern.

4 Practice

More Practice and Problem-Solving Exercises

ASSIGNMENT GUIDE
The assignments below are for the More Practice and Problem-Solving Exercises. You may also want to assign the A-Level Practice Exercises for homework if these are not used in class.
Average: 16–33
Advanced: 16–36

Mathematical Practices The exercises listed focus on the Standards for Mathematical Practices listed.

EX. 28: Make Sense of Problems (MP 1)
EX. 29, 30: Construct Arguments (MP 3)
EX. 15, 31: Critique the Reasoning of Others (MP 3)
EX. 33: Model with Mathematics (MP 4)
EX. 27: Look for Patterns (MP 7)

STEM exercises focus on science or engineering applications.

EXERCISE 32: Use the **Think About a Plan** worksheet in the Online Teacher Resources to further support students' development in becoming independent learners.

HOMEWORK QUICK CHECK
To check students' understanding of key skills and concepts, go over Exercises 18, 22, 25, 28, and 32.

ANSWERS

16. Add 2, add 4, add 6, . . .; 31, 43.
17. Add 1, then add 3; add 1, then add 3; . . .; 10, 13.
18. Divide the previous number by 10; 0.0001, 0.00001.
19. Multiply by 3, add 1; multiply by 3, add 1; . . .; 201, 202.
20. Add 2, add 4, add 8, add 16, . . .; 63, 127.
21. Add $\frac{1}{2}$, add $\frac{1}{4}$, add $\frac{1}{8}$ . . .; $\frac{31}{32}$, $\frac{63}{64}$.
22. 555,555,555
23. 123,454,321
24.
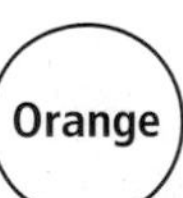

25.

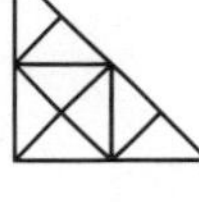

26.
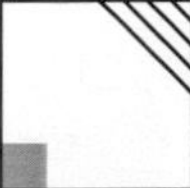

27. 102 cm
28. H; the rest of the points form the shape of a heart.

▼ STUDENT PAGES 16–17

More Practice and Problem-Solving Exercises

B Apply

Find a pattern for each sequence. Use inductive reasoning to show the next two terms.

16. 1, 3, 7, 13, 21, . . .
17. 1, 2, 5, 6, 9, . . .
18. 0.1, 0.01, 0.001, . . .
19. 2, 6, 7, 21, 22, 66, 67, . . .
20. 1, 3, 7, 15, 31, . . .
21. 0, $\frac{1}{2}$, $\frac{3}{4}$, $\frac{7}{8}$, $\frac{15}{16}$, . . .

Predict the next term in each sequence. Use your calculator to verify your answer.

22. 12345679 × 9 = 111111111
12345679 × 18 = 222222222
12345679 × 27 = 333333333
12345679 × 36 = 444444444
12345679 × 45 = ■

23. 1 × 1 = 1
11 × 11 = 121
111 × 111 = 12321
1111 × 1111 = 1234321
11111 × 11111 = ■

24. Patterns Draw the next figure in the sequence. Make sure you think about color and shape.

Draw the next figure in each sequence.

25.
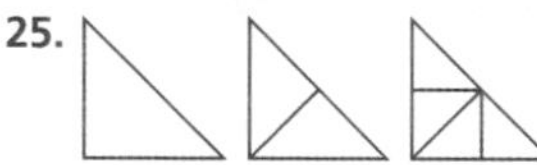

26.
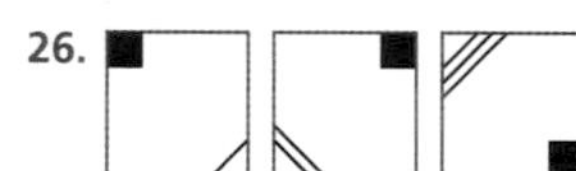

27. Reasoning Find the perimeter when 100 triangles are put together in the pattern shown. Assume that all triangle sides are 1 cm long.

28. Think About a Plan Below are 15 points. Most of the points fit a pattern. Which does not? Explain.

$A(6, -2)$ $B(6, 5)$ $C(8, 0)$ $D(8, 7)$ $E(10, 2)$ $F(10, 6)$ $G(11, 4)$ $H(12, 3)$
$I(4, 0)$ $J(7, 6)$ $K(5, 6)$ $L(4, 7)$ $M(2, 2)$ $N(1, 4)$ $O(2, 6)$

- How can you draw a diagram to help you find a pattern?
- What pattern do the majority of the points fit?

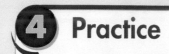

29. **a.** sì-shí-sān; lìu-shí-qī; bā-shí-sì

b. Yes; the second part of the number repeats each ten numbers.

30. Answers may vary. Sample: 1, 2, 3, 4, 5, . . . and 1, 2, 4, 8, 16, . . .

31. His conjecture is probably false because most people's growth slows by 18 until they stop growing sometime between 18 and 22 years.

32. **a.**

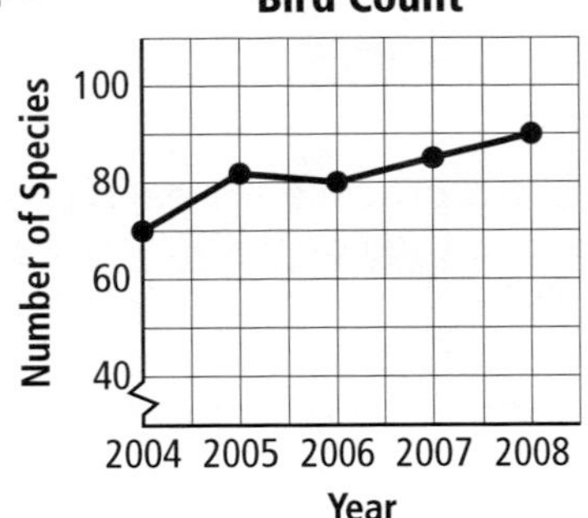

b. Answers may vary. Sample: Using just the data from 2005 to 2008, the gain is 7 species in 3 years, or between 2 and 3 species each year. The year 2015 is 7 years after 2008, so the number of new species will be between 14 and 21 more than 90; an estimate is 90 + 17, or 107 species.

33. Check students' work.

34. Answers may vary. Sample: Group the numbers in pairs that sum to 101, so the sum of the integers from 1 to 100 is $\frac{100 \cdot 101}{2} = 5050$; group the numbers in pairs that sum to $n + 1$, so the sum of the integers from 1 to n is $\frac{n(n+1)}{2}$.

35. $1 \times 1 : 64$ squares; $2 \times 2 : 49$ squares; $3 \times 3 : 36$ squares; $4 \times 4 : 25$ squares; $5 \times 5 : 16$ squares; $6 \times 6 : 9$ squares; $7 \times 7 : 4$ squares; $8 \times 8 : 1$ square; total number of squares: 204

36. **a.** 1, 3, 6, 10, 15, 21

b.

n	1	2	3	4	5	6
$\frac{n^2+n}{2}$	1	3	6	10	15	21

The values are the same.

c. $\frac{n^2+n}{2} = \frac{n(n+1)}{2}$; since the diagram represents $n(n + 1)$, half of the diagram represents $\frac{n^2+n}{2}$.

d.

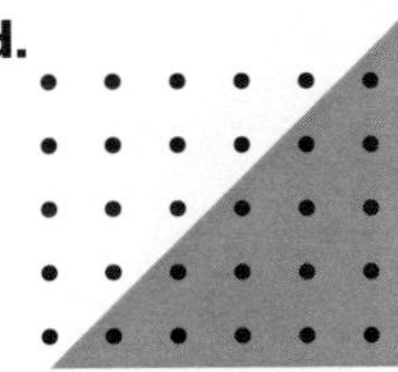

29. Language Look for a pattern in the Chinese number system.

a. What is the Chinese name for the numbers 43, 67, and 84?

b. Reasoning Do you think that the Chinese number system is base 10? Explain.

Chinese Number System

Number	Chinese Word	Number	Chinese Word
1	yī	9	jĭu
2	èr	10	shí
3	sān	11	shí-yī
4	sì	12	shí-èr
5	wŭ	⋮	⋮
6	lìu	20	èr-shí
7	qī	21	èr-shí-yī
8	bā	⋮	⋮
		30	sān-shí

30. Open-Ended Write two different number sequences that begin with the same two numbers.

31. Error Analysis For each of the past four years, Paulo has grown 2 in. every year. He is now 16 years old and is 5 ft 10 in. tall. He figures that when he is 22 years old he will be 6 ft 10 in. tall. What would you tell Paulo about his conjecture?

32. Bird Migration During bird migration, volunteers get up early on Bird Day to record the number of bird species they observe in their community during a 24-h period. Results are posted online to help scientists and students track the migration.

a. Make a graph of the data.

b. Use the graph and inductive reasoning to make a conjecture about the number of bird species the volunteers in this community will observe in 2015.

Bird Count

Year	Number of Species
2004	70
2005	83
2006	80
2007	85
2008	90

33. Writing Describe a real-life situation in which you recently used inductive reasoning.

Challenge

34. History When he was in the third grade, German mathematician Karl Gauss (1777–1855) took ten seconds to sum the integers from 1 to 100. Now it's your turn. Find a fast way to sum the integers from 1 to 100. Find a fast way to sum the integers from 1 to n. (*Hint:* Use patterns.)

35. Chess The small squares on a chessboard can be combined to form larger squares. For example, there are sixty-four 1×1 squares and one 8×8 square. Use inductive reasoning to determine how many 2×2 squares, 3×3 squares, and so on, are on a chessboard. What is the total number of squares on a chessboard?

36. **a. Algebra** Write the first six terms of the sequence that starts with 1, and for which the difference between consecutive terms is first 2, and then 3, 4, 5, and 6.

b. Evaluate $\frac{n^2+n}{2}$ for $n = 1, 2, 3, 4, 5,$ and 6. Compare the sequence you get with your answer for part (a).

c. Examine the diagram at the right and explain how it illustrates a value of $\frac{n^2+n}{2}$.

d. Draw a similar diagram to represent $\frac{n^2+n}{2}$ for $n = 5$.

$n + 1$

n ● ● ● ●
● ● ● ●
● ● ● ●

5 Assess and Remediate

Lesson Quiz

1. Look for a pattern. What are the next two terms in the sequence: 55, 44, 33, 22, . . .?
2. What conjecture can you make about the 19th term in the pattern: A, B, B, A, B, B, A, . . .?
3. **Do you UNDERSTAND?** The graph shows the level of the Little Miami River over several hours during a rainstorm. What conjecture can you make about the level of the river after 5 hours of rain? Explain.

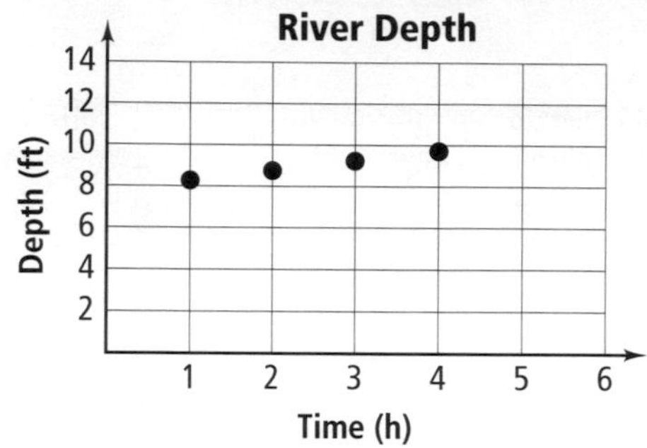

ANSWERS TO LESSON QUIZ

1. 11, 0
2. The 19th term is A.
3. The level of the river will be about 10 ft. The level is going up in a path that appears to be linear. The next point on the graph would be about (5, 10).

Prescription for Remediation

Use the student work on the Lesson Quiz to prescribe a differentiated assignment.

Points	Differentiated Remediation
0–1	Intervention
2	On-level
3	Extension

Online Assessment

Assign the Lesson Quiz in Success Tracker on **pearsonsuccessnet.com**. Success Tracker will automatically score the quiz and assign appropriate intervention or enrichment to each student based on the results. The compiled data appear in three different reports for instant analysis of whole class and individual student performance.

Differentiated Remediation

Intervention

- **RETEACHING** (2 pages) Provides reteaching and practice exercises for the key lesson concepts. Use with struggling students or absent students.
- **ENGLISH LANGUAGE LEARNER SUPPORT** Helps students develop and reinforce mathematical vocabulary and key concepts.

On-Level

- **PRACTICE** (2 pages) Provides extra practice for each lesson. For simpler practice exercises, use the Form K Practice pages found in the Online Teacher Resources.
- **THINK ABOUT A PLAN** Helps students develop specific problem-solving skills and strategies by providing scaffolded guiding questions.
- **STANDARDIZED TEST PREP** Focuses on all major exercises, all major question types, and helps students prepare for the high-stakes assessments.

Extension

- **ENRICHMENT** Provides students with interesting problems and activities that extend the concepts of the lesson.
- **ACTIVITIES, GAMES, AND PUZZLES** Worksheets that can be used for concept development, enrichment, and for fun!

1-3 Conditional Statements

Common Core State Standards
Prepares for G.CO.10 Prove theorems about triangles . . . **Also prepares for G.CO.9, G.CO.11**

Preparing to Teach

BIG idea Reasoning and Proof

ESSENTIAL UNDERSTANDING

Some mathematical relationships can be described using a variety of if-then statements. Each conditional statement has a converse, an inverse, and a contrapositive.

Math Background

Postulates and theorems in geometry are written as conditional statements, and for that reason, it is important for students to understand these types of statements. Students will encounter many geometric definitions as they progress through the textbook, and each of these definitions is a true conditional statement whose converse is also true. It is critical to stress to students that converse statements may or may not be true, regardless of the truth of the original conditional statement.

Venn diagrams provide a powerful and intuitive tool for establishing the truth of some if-then statements. Emphasize that proving a conditional statement false requires only a single counterexample, in contrast to proving a conditional statement true. No number of supporting examples is sufficient to prove a conditional statement true. Conditional statements are proved by a series of logical arguments.

ELL Support

FOCUS ON LANGUAGE Write the objectives on the board and read them aloud as you point to each word. Ask: What does it mean to *recognize* something? Ask students the meanings of key words. Have them read the text and find the definitions. After examining the objectives, ask students to rephrase them in their own words.

USE GRAPHIC ORGANIZERS Model the Venn diagram in the Key Concept box, thinking aloud as you redraw it. Model another example like: If a polygon has 3 sides, then it is a triangle. Think aloud as you draw the diagram. Ask for volunteers to contribute other conditional statements for you to model. Then have students make Venn diagrams for conditional statements.

Lesson Vocabulary

- conditional
- hypothesis
- conclusion
- truth value
- negation
- converse
- inverse
- contrapositive
- equivalent statements

Mathematical Practices

ATTEND TO PRECISION. Students will both make explicit use of conditional terms, such as *contrapositive*, and find the truth value of the different permutations of verbal conditionals.

1 Interactive Learning

Solve It!

PURPOSE To introduce students to conditional statements, their truth values, and related conditional statements

PROCESS Students may use the process of elimination and assume a statement is true unless they determine a counterexample.

Q What circumstance would show the sticker "If you are too close, then you can read this" to be a false statement? **[Answers may vary. Sample: The driver is too close, but cannot read the bumper sticker.]**

Q What circumstance would show the sticker "If you cannot read this, then you are not too close" to be a false statement? **[Answers may vary. Sample: The driver is not wearing necessary reading glasses and cannot read the bumper sticker, but is driving too close.]**

ANSWER The first two bumper stickers are false, but the third one is true. Explanations may vary.

CONNECT THE MATH The bumper stickers in the Solve It demonstrate different conditional statements that have equivalent meanings and equivalent truth values. In this lesson, students study conditional statements and related conditional statements in the context of different situations.

▼ DIGITAL (STUDENT WORK SPACE PAGE 19)

Getting Ready!

The company that prints the bumper sticker at the left below accidentally reworded the original statement and printed the sticker three different ways. Suppose the original bumper sticker is true. Are the other bumper stickers true or false? Explain.

123A547
If you can read this, THEN YOU ARE TOO CLOSE.
A If you are too close, THEN YOU CAN READ THIS.
B If you cannot read this, then you are not too close.
C If you are not too close, THEN YOU CANNOT READ THIS.

2 Guided Instruction

Problem 1 Identifying the Hypothesis and the Conclusion

Take Note VISUAL LEARNERS
Have students fill in the Venn diagram with the hypothesis and conclusion from the correct bumper sticker in the Solve It to reinforce the relationship between the parts of a conditional.

Problem 1

Q Write a variation of the conditional. What are the hypothesis and conclusion for this version? **[Answers may vary. Sample: If an animal is a bird, then it is a robin. Hypothesis: An animal is a bird; Conclusion: The animal is a robin.]**

Got It?

Q In a Venn diagram for the Got It problem, what phrase would you write in the inside circle? **[angles that measure 130 degrees]**

ANSWERS

Got It? Hypothesis: An angle measures 130. Conclusion: The angle is obtuse.

Practice

1. Hypothesis: A figure is a rectangle. Conclusion: It has four sides.
2. Hypothesis: You want to be healthy. Conclusion: You should eat vegetables.

▼ STUDENT PAGE 19

The study of *if-then* statements and their truth values is a foundation of reasoning.

Essential Understanding You can describe some mathematical relationships using a variety of *if-then* statements.

take note

Key Concept Conditional Statements

Definition	Symbols	Diagram
A **conditional** is an *if-then* statement. The **hypothesis** is the part p following *if*. The **conclusion** is the part q following *then*.	$p \rightarrow q$ Read as "if p then q" or "p implies q."	q, p

The Venn diagram above illustrates how the set of things that satisfy the hypothesis lies inside the set of things that satisfy the conclusion.

▼ DIGITAL

Problem 1 Identifying the Hypothesis and the Conclusion

What are the hypothesis and the conclusion of the conditional?
If an animal is a robin, then the animal is a bird.

Hypothesis (p): An animal is a robin.
Conclusion (q): The animal is a bird.

▼ STUDENT PAGES 19–20

Got It? What are the hypothesis and the conclusion of the conditional? If an angle measures 130, then the angle is obtuse.

Think What would a Venn diagram of the statement look like?

Practice Identify the hypothesis and conclusion of each conditional.

1. If a figure is a rectangle, then it has four sides.
2. If you want to be healthy, then you should eat vegetables.

Problem 2 Writing a Conditional

Ask students to sketch vertical angles and indicate the common vertex. Also ask students to sketch two angles that share a vertex but are not vertical angles.

Got It? VISUAL LEARNERS
Have students construct a Venn diagram to identify the hypothesis and conclusion of the conditional.

ANSWERS

Got It? If an animal is a dolphin, then it is a mammal.

Practice

3. If $3x - 7 = 14$, then $3x = 21$.
4. If something is wheat, then it is a grain.

▼ DIGITAL

Problem 2 Writing a Conditional

How can you write the following statement as a conditional?
Vertical angles share a vertex.

Step 1 Identify the hypothesis and the conclusion.

Vertical angles share a vertex.

Step 2 Write the conditional.

If two angles are vertical, then they share a vertex.

▼ STUDENT PAGE 20

Got It? How can you write "Dolphins are mammals" as a conditional?

Think Which part of the statement is the hypothesis, (p)?

Practice

3. **Algebra** Write the following sentence as a conditional.

$3x - 7 = 14$ implies that $3x = 21$.

4. Write a conditional statement that the Venn diagram illustrates.

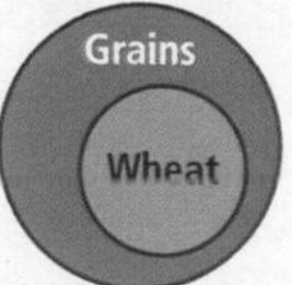

Problem 3 Finding the Truth Value of a Conditional

To help students understand the truth value of a conditional, show the following four cases and develop the truth table.
If it is your birthday, then you will have cake.

		Truth value
Case 1: It is your birthday; you have cake.		
True	True	True
Case 2: It is your birthday; you do not have cake.		
True	False	False
Case 3: It is not your birthday; you have cake.		
False	True	True
Case 4: It is not your birthday; you do not have cake.		
False	False	True

This should help students see that if the hypothesis is false, the truth value of the conditional is always true.

ANSWERS

Got It? a. False; January has 28 days, plus 3 more. **b.** True; the sum of the measures of two angles that form a linear pair is 180.

Practice

5. false; Mexico

6. true

▼ STUDENT PAGE 21

The **truth value** of a conditional is either *true* or *false*. To show that a conditional is true, show that every time the hypothesis is true, the conclusion is also true. To show that a conditional is false, find *only one* counterexample for which the hypothesis is true and the conclusion is false.

▼ DIGITAL

Problem 3 **Finding the Truth Value of a Conditional**

Is the conditional *true* or *false*? If it is false, find a counterexample.

A **If a woman is Hungarian, then she is European.**

The conditional is true. Hungary is a European nation, so Hungarians are European.

B **If a number is divisible by 3, then it is odd.**

The conditional is false. The number 12 is divisible by 3, but it is not odd.

▼ STUDENT PAGE 21

Got It? Is the conditional *true* or *false*? If it is false, find a counterexample.

a. If a month has 28 days, then it is February.

b. If two angles form a linear pair, then they are supplementary.

A Practice **Determine if the conditional is *true* or *false*. If it is false, find a counterexample.**

5. If you live in a country that borders the United States, then you live in Canada.

6. If an angle measures 80°, then it is acute.

Problem 4 Writing and Finding Truth Values of Statements

Take Note

Q What is the hypothesis, *p*, of the conditional? **[An angle measures 15°.]**

Q What is the conclusion, *q*, of the hypothesis? **[The angle is acute.]**

Use a graphic organizer to help students remember the forms of conditional statements and the relationships between the conditional statements.

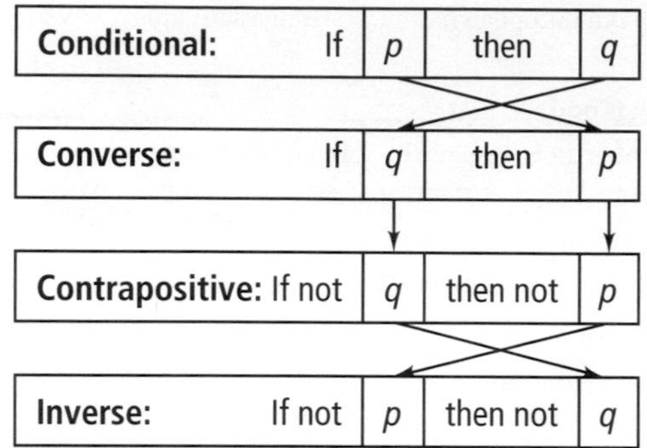

Q What is a counterexample that proves the converse false? **[Answers may vary. Sample: A 20° angle is acute, but it does not measure 15.]**

Q What is a counterexample that proves the inverse false? **[Answers may vary. Sample: A 20° angle does not measure 15, but it is acute.]**

Problem 4

Q If the conditional is true, which other statement must also be true? Explain. **[The conditional and its contrapositive are equivalent statements, so the contrapositive must be true.]**

Q How are the truth values of the inverse and the converse related? **[The truth values of the inverse and the converse must be the same, because these statements are equivalent.]**

▼ STUDENT PAGE 22

The **negation** of a statement *p* is the opposite of the statement. The symbol is $\sim p$ and is read "not *p*." The negation of the statement "The sky is blue" is "The sky is *not* blue." You can use negations to write statements related to a conditional. Every conditional has three related conditional statements.

take note

Key Concept Related Conditional Statements

Statement	How to Write It	Example	Symbols	How to Read it
Conditional	Use the given hypothesis and conclusion.	If $m\angle A = 15$, then $\angle A$ is acute.	$p \rightarrow q$	If *p*, then *q*.
Converse	Exchange the hypothesis and the conclusion.	If $\angle A$ is acute, then $m\angle A = 15$.	$q \rightarrow p$	If *q*, then *p*.
Inverse	Negate both the hypothesis and the conclusion of the conditional.	If $m\angle A \neq 15$, then $\angle A$ is not acute.	$\sim p \rightarrow \sim q$	If not *p*, then not *q*.
Contrapositive	Negate both the hypothesis and the conclusion of the converse.	If $\angle A$ is not acute, then $m\angle A \neq 15$.	$\sim q \rightarrow \sim p$	If not *q*, then not *p*.

Below are the truth values of the related statements above. **Equivalent statements** have the same truth value.

Statement	Example	Truth Value
Conditional	If $m\angle A = 15$, then $\angle A$ is acute.	True
Converse	If $\angle A$ is acute, then $m\angle A = 15$.	False
Inverse	If $m\angle A \neq 15$, then $\angle A$ is not acute.	False
Contrapositive	If $\angle A$ is not acute, then $m\angle A \neq 15$.	True

A conditional and its contrapositive are equivalent statements. They are either both true or both false. The converse and inverse of a statement are also equivalent statements.

▼ DIGITAL

ONLINE PROBLEMS **Problem 4** Writing and Finding Truth Values of Statements

What are the converse, inverse, and contrapositive of the following conditional? What are the truth values of each? If a statement is false, give a counterexample.

If the figure is a square, then the figure is a quadrilateral.

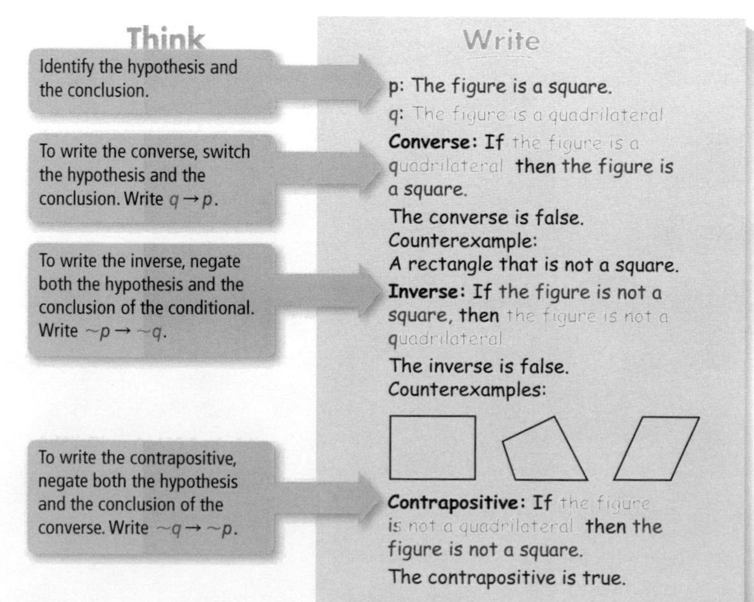

Got It?

Q What is the hypothesis of the conditional? **[The vegetable is a carrot.]**

Q What is the conclusion of the conditional? **[The vegetable contains beta carotene.]**

ANSWERS

Got It? Counterexamples may vary. Samples are given. Converse: If a vegetable contains beta carotene, then it is a carrot. Inverse: If a vegetable is not a carrot, then it does not contain beta carotene. Contrapositive: If a vegetable does not contain beta carotene, then it is not a carrot. The conditional and the contrapositive are true. The converse and inverse are false; counterexample: any vegetable, such as spinach, that contains beta carotene.

Practice

7. Converse: If $x = 5$, then $4x + 8 = 28$. Inverse: If $4x + 8 \neq 28$, then $x \neq 5$. Contrapositive: If $x \neq 5$, then $4x + 8 \neq 28$. All four statements are true.

▼ STUDENT PAGE 23

Got It? What are the converse, inverse, and contrapositive of the conditional statement below? What are the truth values of each? If a statement is false, give a counterexample.

If a vegetable is a carrot, then it contains beta carotene.

Practice **If the given statement is not in *if-then* form, rewrite it. Write the converse, inverse, and contrapositive of the given conditional statement. Determine the truth value of all four statements. If a statement is false, give a counterexample.**

7. **Algebra** If $4x + 8 = 28$, then $x = 5$.

8. Pianists are musicians.

8. Conditional: If a person is a pianist, then that person is a musician. Converse: If a person is a musician, then that person is a pianist. Inverse: If a person is not a pianist, then that person is not a musician. Contrapositive: If a person is not a musician, then that person is not a pianist. The conditional and contrapositive are true. The converse and inverse are false; counterexample: a percussionist is a musician.

3 Lesson Check

Do you know HOW?

If students have difficulty with Exercise 10, then refer students to the Take Note table on the top of page 22.

Do you UNDERSTAND?

If students have difficulty with Exercise 12, then refer students to the table at the bottom of page 22.

Close

Q How can you conclude that a conditional statement is true? **[If you determine that every time the hypothesis is true, the conclusion is also true, you can conclude that a conditional statement is true.]**

ANSWERS

9. Hypothesis: Someone is a resident of Key West. Conclusion: The person lives in Florida. Conditional: If someone is a resident of Key West, then that person lives in Florida.

10. Converse: If a figure has a perimeter of 10 cm, then it is a rectangle with sides 2 cm and 3 cm. Inverse: If a figure is not a rectangle with sides 2 cm and 3 cm, then it does not have a perimeter of 10 cm. Contrapositive: If a figure does not have a perimeter of 10 cm, then it is not a rectangle with sides 2 cm and 3 cm. The original conditional and the contrapositive are true.

▼ STUDENT PAGES 23–24

Lesson Check

Do you know HOW?

9. What are the hypothesis and the conclusion of the following statement? Write it as a conditional.

Residents of Key West live in Florida.

10. What are the converse, inverse, and contrapositive of the statement? Which statements are true?

If a figure is a rectangle with sides 2 cm and 3 cm, then it has a perimeter of 10 cm.

Do you UNDERSTAND?

11. **Error Analysis** Your classmate rewrote the statement "You jog every Sunday" as the conditional below. What is your classmate's error? Correct it.

If you jog, then it is Sunday.

12. **Reasoning** Suppose a conditional statement and its converse are both true. What are the truth values of the contrapositive and inverse? How do you know?

11. The hypothesis and conclusion were exchanged. The conditional should be "If it is Sunday, then you jog."

12. Both are true because a conditional and its contrapositive have the same truth value, and a converse and an inverse have the same truth value.

Practice

More Practice and Problem-Solving Exercises

ASSIGNMENT GUIDE

The assignments below are for the More Practice and Problem-Solving Exercises. You may also want to assign the A-Level Practice Exercises for homework if these are not used in class.

Average: 13–30
Advanced: 13–34

Mathematical Practices The exercises listed focus on the Standards for Mathematical Practices listed.

EX. 12, 17: Construct Arguments (MP 3)
EX. 11, 16, 19: Critique the Reasoning of Others (MP 3)
EX. 27: Model (MP 4)
EX. 18: Use Structure (MP 7)

EXERCISE 19: Use the **Think About a Plan** worksheet in the Online Teacher Resources to further support students' development in becoming independent learners.

HOMEWORK QUICK CHECK

To check students' understanding of key skills and concepts, go over Exercises 13, 16, 19, 25, and 30.

ANSWERS

13. If a group is half the people, then that group should make up half the Congress.

14. If you have never made a mistake, then you have never tried anything new.

15. If an event has a probability of 1, then that event is certain to occur.

16. Yes, he is correct; both are true, because a conditional and its contrapositive have the same truth value.

17. Answers may vary. Sample: If an angle is acute, its measure is less than 90; if the measure of an angle is 85, then it is acute.

18. Answers may vary. Sample: If a person is a pitcher, then that person is a baseball player. If a person is a baseball player, then that person is an athlete. If a person is a pitcher, then that person is an athlete.

19. Natalie is correct because a conditional statement and its contrapositive have the same truth value.

20.

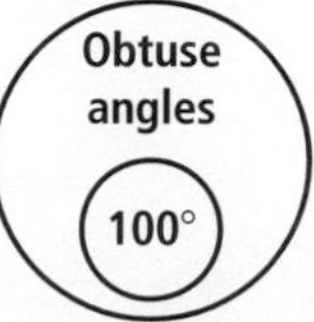

▼ STUDENT PAGES 24–25

More Practice and Problem-Solving Exercises

B Apply

Write each statement as a conditional.

13. "We're half the people; we should be half the Congress." —Jeanette Rankin, former U.S. congresswoman, calling for more women in office

14. "Anyone who has never made a mistake has never tried anything new." —Albert Einstein

15. Probability An event with probability 1 is certain to occur.

16. Think About a Plan Your classmate claims that the conditional and contrapositive of the following statement are both true. Is he correct? Explain.

If $x = 2$, then $x^2 = 4$.

- Can you find a counterexample of the conditional?
- Do you need to find a counterexample of the contrapositive to know its truth value?

17. Open-Ended Write a true conditional that has a true converse, and write a true conditional that has a false converse.

18. Multiple Representations Write three separate conditional statements that the Venn diagram illustrates.

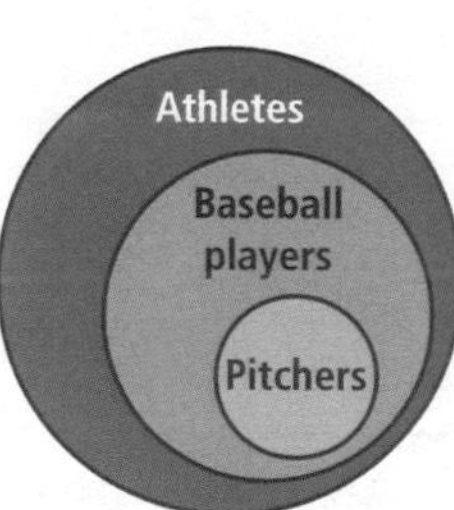

19. Error Analysis A given conditional is true. Natalie claims its contrapositive is also true. Sean claims its contrapositive is false. Who is correct and how do you know?

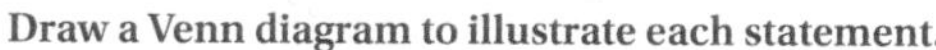

Draw a Venn diagram to illustrate each statement.

20. If an angle measures 100, then it is obtuse.

21.

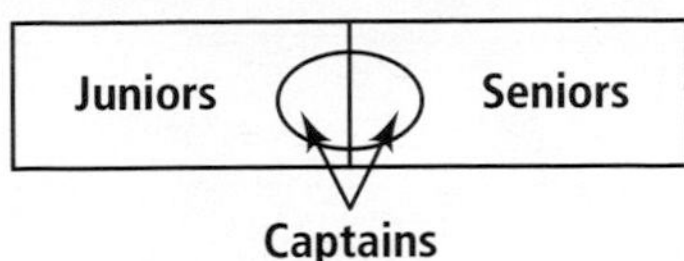

22.

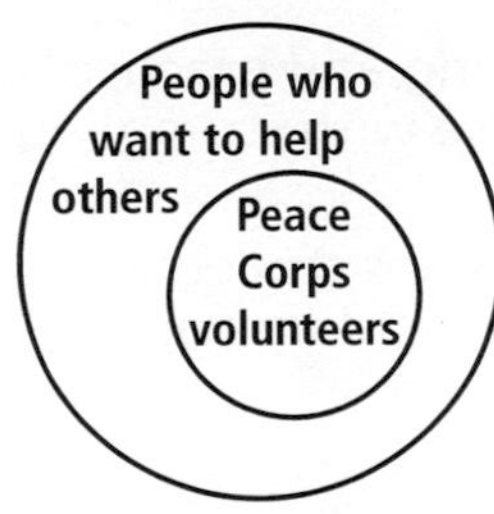

23. If $|x| = 6$, then $x = -6$; false, $x = 6$ is a counterexample.

24. If $-y$ is positive, then y is negative; true.

25. If $x^3 < 0$, then $x < 0$; true.

26. If $x^2 > 0$, then $x < 0$; false, a counterexample is $x = 1$.

27. If you wear Snazzy sneakers, then you will look cool.

28. If two lines intersect, then they meet in exactly one point.

29. If two figures are congruent, then they have equal areas.

30. If you identify any two (distinct) points, then exactly one line goes through those two points.

31. All integers divisible by 8 are divisible by 2.

32. No squares are triangles.

33. Some musicians are students or some students are musicians.

34. 25 statements

Conclusion (columns) / **Hypothesis** (rows)

→	*r*	*s*	*t*	*u*	*v*
r	T	F	T	F	T
s	F	T	T	F	T
t	F	F	T	F	T
u	T	T	T	T	T
v	F	F	T	F	T

Sample counterexamples: for $r \rightarrow s$, $r \rightarrow u$, $t \rightarrow s$, and $v \rightarrow s$: $a = 2$; for $s \rightarrow r$, $s \rightarrow u$, $t \rightarrow r$, $t \rightarrow u$, $v \rightarrow r$ and $v \rightarrow u$: $a = 1$

▼ STUDENT PAGE 25

21. If you are the captain of your team, then you are a junior or senior.

22. Peace Corps volunteers want to help other people.

Algebra **Write the converse of each statement. If the converse is true, write *true*. If it is not true, provide a counterexample.**

23. If $x = -6$, then $|x| = 6$.

24. If y is negative, then $-y$ is positive.

25. If $x < 0$, then $x^3 < 0$.

26. If $x < 0$, then $x^2 > 0$.

27. **Advertising** Advertisements often suggest conditional statements. What conditional does the ad at the right imply?

Write each postulate as a conditional statement.

28. Two intersecting lines meet in exactly one point.

29. Two congruent figures have equal areas.

30. Through any two points there is exactly one line.

Challenge

Write a statement beginning with *all*, *some*, or *no* to match each Venn diagram.

31.

32.

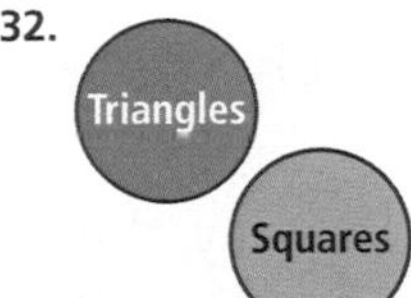

33.

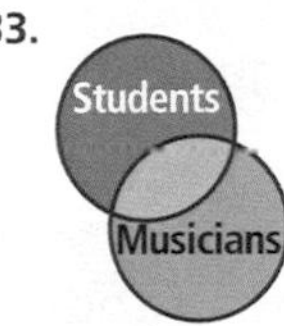

34. Let a represent an integer. Consider the five statements r, s, t, u, and v.

r: a is even. s: a is odd. t: $2a$ is even. u: $2a$ is odd. v: $2a + 1$ is odd.

How many statements of the form $p \rightarrow q$ can you make from these statements? Decide which are true, and provide a counterexample if they are false.

Assess and Remediate

Lesson Quiz

1. What are the hypothesis and the conclusion of the following conditional, "If a figure is a triangle, then it has 3 sides"?
2. How can you write the following statement as a conditional? All squares are rectangles.
3. Is the following conditional true or false? If it is false, find a counterexample. If two numbers are odd, then their sum is even.
4. **Do you UNDERSTAND?** What are the converse, inverse, and contrapositive of the following conditional statement? What are the truth values of each? "If today is Sunday, then tomorrow is Monday."

ANSWERS TO LESSON QUIZ

1. Hypothesis: A figure is a triangle. Conclusion: It has 3 sides.
2. If a figure is a square, then it is a rectangle.
3. true
4. Converse: If tomorrow is Monday, then today is Sunday. Inverse: If today is not Sunday, then tomorrow is not Monday. Contrapositive: If tomorrow is not Monday, then today is not Sunday. All three are true.

Prescription for Remediation

Use the student work on the Lesson Quiz to prescribe a differentiated assignment.

Points	Differentiated Remediation
0–2	Intervention
3	On-level
4	Extension

Online Assessment

Assign the Lesson Quiz in Success Tracker on **pearsonsuccessnet.com**. Success Tracker will automatically score the quiz and assign appropriate intervention or enrichment to each student based on the results. The compiled data appear in three different reports for instant analysis of whole class and individual student performance.

Differentiated Remediation

Intervention

- **RETEACHING** (2 pages) Provides reteaching and practice exercises for the key lesson concepts. Use with struggling students or absent students.
- **ENGLISH LANGUAGE LEARNER SUPPORT** Helps students develop and reinforce mathematical vocabulary and key concepts.

On-Level

- **PRACTICE** (2 pages) Provides extra practice for each lesson. For simpler practice exercises, use the Form K Practice pages found in the Online Teacher Resources.
- **THINK ABOUT A PLAN** Helps students develop specific problem-solving skills and strategies by providing scaffolded guiding questions.
- **STANDARDIZED TEST PREP** Focuses on all major exercises, all major question types, and helps students prepare for the high-stakes assessments.

Extension

- **ENRICHMENT** Provides students with interesting problems and activities that extend the concepts of the lesson.
- **ACTIVITIES, GAMES, AND PUZZLES** Worksheets that can be used for concept development, enrichment, and for fun!

1-4 Biconditionals and Definitions

Common Core State Standards
Prepares for G.CO.11 Prove theorems about parallelograms . . . **Also prepares for G.CO.9, G.CO.10**

Preparing to Teach

BIG idea Reasoning and Proof

ESSENTIAL UNDERSTANDING

A definition is good if it can be written as a biconditional. Every biconditional can be written as two conditionals that are converses of each other.

Math Background

Geometric knowledge can be described as a building-up process. The first terms learned in geometry must be understood and undefined; otherwise, all definitions in geometry would be circular. The terms that follow can be explained using only undefined terms or a combination of undefined terms and previously defined terms. The postulates and theorems that will be learned throughout the text follow the same progression as undefined terms and defined terms. Postulates are assumed to be true without proof, and theorems are proved using postulates and theorems.

Definitions in mathematics are biconditional statements. One way to help students learn to write mathematical definitions is to have them define everyday objects using the biconditional format. Emphasize the biconditional aspect of all definitions in geometry, because students will need to use both conditional statements in proofs.

ELL Support

ASSESS UNDERSTANDING Have students list the differences between a conditional and a biconditional statement in their own words. Ask: What is a biconditional statement? How are a conditional statement and a biconditional statement related? How are they different? How do you know a statement is biconditional and not conditional? Tell them to write an example of each.

FOCUS ON COMMUNICATION Have students work in pairs of mixed abilities. Students can share their written work orally with each other. Invite students to discuss their ideas. When they are finished talking, allow time for students to make edits to their work.

Lesson Vocabulary

- biconditional

Mathematical Practices

ATTEND TO PRECISION. By writing biconditional statements, students will clarify definitions inside or outside of mathematics. Then they will use these definitions in discussion with others and in their own reasoning.

1 Interactive Learning

Solve It!

PURPOSE To have students write a conditional statement whose converse is also true, and thus to write a definition

PROCESS Students may make observations about the sets of insects and noninsects and use deductive reasoning.

Q What characteristics do all the insects share? **[six legs and its body has three sections]**

Q Do any of the noninsects share these characteristics? Explain. **[No; none of the noninsects have six legs or bodies with three sections.]**

ANSWER "... it has 6 legs." OR "... its body has 3 sections." OR "... it has 6 legs and its body has 3 sections." All of the insects have 6 legs and bodies with 3 sections, but none of the noninsects have 6 legs or bodies with 3 sections.

CONNECT THE MATH Students will learn how to use conditional statements like those written in the Solve It to write biconditional statements and good definitions.

▼ DIGITAL (STUDENT WORK SPACE PAGE 26)

Solve It! Getting Ready!

Look at the examples of insects and noninsects below. How would you complete the following sentence: "If an animal is an insect, then . . ."? Explain your reasoning.

Insects: Ant, Fly, Beetle
Noninsects: Spider, Tick, Centipede

2 Guided Instruction

Problem 1 Writing a Biconditional

Q When writing a biconditional, is the order of the hypothesis and conclusion important? Explain. **[No, the converse and the conditional must both be true.]**

Got It?

Q Are the inverse and the contrapositive statements true? Explain. **[Yes, the contrapositive has the same truth value as the conditional, and the inverse has the same truth value as the converse.]**

ANSWERS

Got It? Converse: If two angles are congruent, then the angles have equal measure; true. Biconditional: Two angles have equal measure if and only if the angles are congruent.

Practice

1. Converse: If $|x| = 3$, then $x = 3$; false.
2. Converse: If it is Independence Day in the United States, then it is July 4; true. Biconditional: In the United States, it is July 4 if and only if it is Independence Day.

▼ STUDENT PAGE 26

In the Solve It, you used conditional statements. A **biconditional** is a single true statement that combines a true conditional and its true converse. You can write a biconditional by joining the two parts of each conditional with the phrase *if and only if.*

Essential Understanding A definition is good if it can be written as a biconditional.

▼ DIGITAL

Problem 1 **Writing a Biconditional**

What is the converse of the following true conditional? If the converse is also true, rewrite the statements as a biconditional.

If the sum of the measures of two angles is 180, then the two angles are supplementary.

Converse: If two angles are supplementary, then the sum of the measures of the two angles is 180.

The converse is true. You can form a true biconditional by joining the true conditional and the true converse with the phrase *if and only if.*

Biconditional: Two angles are supplementary if and only if the sum of the measures of the two angles is 180.

▼ STUDENT PAGES 26–27

Got It? What is the converse of the following true conditional? If the converse is also true, rewrite the statements as a biconditional.

If two angles have equal measure, then the angles are congruent.

Think
How do you form the converse of a conditional?

Practice **Each conditional statement below is true. Write its converse. If the converse is also true, combine the statements as a biconditional.**

1. **Algebra** If $x = 3$, then $|x| = 3$.
2. In the United States, if it is July 4, then it is Independence Day.

Problem 2 Identifying the Conditionals in a Biconditional

Take Note

Make sure students realize that the symbols $q \leftrightarrow p$ and the phrase "q if and only if p" are equivalent to those shown in the Key Concept box.

Problem 2

Q Why is the following Venn diagram not an accurate depiction of the biconditional? **[Because both p and q should be within the same circle.]**

rays that are angle bisectors

rays that divide an angle into two congruent angles

▼ STUDENT PAGE 27

take note

Key Concept **Biconditional Statements**

A biconditional combines $p \to q$ and $q \to p$ as $p \leftrightarrow q$.

Example	Symbols	How to Read It
A point is a midpoint if and only if it divides a segment into two congruent segments.	$p \leftrightarrow q$	"p if and only if q"

You can write a biconditional as two conditionals that are converses.

▼ DIGITAL

Problem 2 **Identifying the Conditionals in a Biconditional**

What are the two conditional statements that form this biconditional?

A ray is an angle bisector if and only if it divides an angle into two congruent angles.

Let p and q represent the following:

p: A ray is an angle bisector.

q: A ray divides an angle into two congruent angles.

$p \to q$: If a ray is an angle bisector, then it divides an angle into two congruent angles.

$q \to p$: If a ray divides an angle into two congruent angles, then it is an angle bisector.

Got It?

Q What is the relationship between the two conditional statements? **[They are converses.]**

ANSWERS

Got It? If two numbers are reciprocals, then their product is 1. If the product of two numbers is 1, then the numbers are reciprocals.

Practice

3. If you live in Washington, D.C., then you live in the capital of the United States. If you live in the capital of the United States, then you live in Washington, D.C.
4. If $x^2 = 144$, then $x = 12$ or $x = -12$. If $x = 12$ or $x = -12$, then $x^2 = 144$.

▼ STUDENT PAGE 27

Got It? What are the two conditionals that form this biconditional?

Two numbers are reciprocals if and only if their product is 1.

Practice **Write the two statements that form each biconditional.**

3. You live in Washington, D.C., if and only if you live in the capital of the United States.
4. **Algebra** $x^2 = 144$ if and only if $x = 12$ or $x = -12$.

Problem 3 Writing a Definition as a Biconditional

Ask students to consider definitions found in a science book. Ask students to determine if they have the three components necessary to classify them as *good* definitions.

Problem 3

Q Which term in the definition of a quadrilateral is assumed to be clearly understood or already defined? **[The term *polygon* is assumed to be understood or already defined.]**

Q What is a polygon? **[A polygon is a closed plane figure with at least three sides that are segments.]**

Got It?

Make sure to elicit both versions of the biconditional from students in order to emphasize that the biconditional can be written as "*p* if and only if *q*" as well as "*q* if and only if *p*."

ANSWERS

Got It? Yes, it is reversible; an angle is a straight angle if and only if its measure is 180.

Practice

5. A line, segment, or ray is a perpendicular bisector of a segment if and only if it is perpendicular to the segment at its midpoint.
6. not reversible

▼ STUDENT PAGE 28

Undefined terms such as *point*, *line*, and *plane* are the building blocks of geometry. You understand the meanings of these terms intuitively. Then you use them to define other terms such as *segment*.

A good definition is a statement that can help you identify or classify an object. A good definition has several important components.

- ✓ A good definition uses clearly understood terms. These terms should be commonly understood or already defined.
- ✓ A good definition is precise. Good definitions avoid words such as *large*, *sort of*, and *almost*.
- ✓ A good definition is reversible. That means you can write a good definition as a true biconditional.

▼ DIGITAL

Problem 3 **Writing a Definition as a Biconditional**

Is this definition of *quadrilateral* reversible? If yes, write it as a true biconditional.
Definition: A quadrilateral is a polygon with four sides.

Think	Write
Write a conditional.	**Conditional:** If a figure is a quadrilateral, then it is a polygon with four sides.
Write the converse.	**Converse:** If a figure is a polygon with four sides, then it is a quadrilateral.
The conditional and its converse are both true. The definition is reversible. Write the conditional and its converse as a true biconditional.	**Biconditional:** A figure is a quadrilateral if and only if it is a polygon with four sides.

▼ STUDENT PAGE 28

Got It? Is this definition of *straight angle* reversible? If yes, write it as a true biconditional.

A straight angle is an angle that measures 180.

Think How do you determine whether a definition is reversible?

Practice **Test each statement below to see if it is reversible. If so, write it as a true biconditional. If not, write *not reversible*.**

5. A perpendicular bisector of a segment is a line, segment, or ray that is perpendicular to a segment at its midpoint.
6. Two angles that form a linear pair are adjacent.

Problem 4 Identifying Good Definitions

Q How can you revise choice A to make it a good definition? **[Answers may vary. Sample: A fish is an animal that breathes using gills.]**

Q How can you revise choice B to make it a good definition? **[Answers may vary. Sample: Quadrilaterals have four angles.]**

Got It?

Q Can you write the definition in part (a) as a true biconditional? **[No, the conditional "If a figure has four right angles, then it is a square" is not true.]**

ANSWERS

Got It? a. No, it is not reversible; a rectangle is also a figure with four right angles. **b.** Answers may vary. Sample: Obtuse angles have measures between 90 and 180.

Practice

7. No, it is not precise; straightedges and protractors are also geometric tools.
8. yes

▼ STUDENT PAGE 29

One way to show that a statement is *not* a good definition is to find a counterexample.

▼ DIGITAL

Problem 4 Identifying Good Definitions

Multiple Choice Which of the following is a good definition?

(A) A fish is an animal that swims.
(B) Rectangles have four corners.
(C) Giraffes are animals with very long necks.
(D) A penny is a coin worth one cent.

Choice A is not reversible. A whale is a counterexample. A whale is an animal that swims, but it is a mammal, not a fish. In Choice B, *corners* is not clearly defined. All quadrilaterals have four corners. In Choice C, *very long* is not precise. Also, Choice C is not reversible because ostriches also have long necks. Choice D is a good definition. It is reversible, and all of the terms in the definition are clearly defined and precise. The answer is D.

▼ STUDENT PAGE 29

Got It? **a.** Is the following statement a good definition? Explain.

A square is a figure with four right angles.

**b. Reasoning** How can you rewrite the statement "Obtuse angles have greater measures than acute angles" so that it is a good definition?

**Practice** Is each statement below a good definition? If not, explain.

7. A compass is a geometric tool.
8. Perpendicular lines are two lines that intersect to form right angles.

3 Lesson Check

Do you know HOW?

If students have difficulty with Exercise 11, have them review Problem 3.

Do you UNDERSTAND?

If students have difficulty with Exercise 13, then refer students to the three components of a good definition listed on page 28.

Close

Q What is the definition of a biconditional? **[A statement is a biconditional if and only if both the statement and its converse are true.]**

ANSWERS

9. If points are collinear, then they lie on the same line. If points lie on the same line, then they are collinear.
10. This month is June if and only if next month is July.
11. Two angles are vertical angles if and only if their sides are opposite rays.
12. The prefix bi- means "two."
13. The word *gigantic* is not precise.
14. The second statement is a better definition. A counterexample for the first statement is any two nonadjacent right angles.

▼ STUDENT PAGES 30–31

Lesson Check

Do you know HOW?

9. How can you write the following statement as two true conditionals?

   Collinear points are points that lie on the same line.

10. How can you combine the following statements as a biconditional?

    If this month is June, then next month is July.

    If next month is July, then this month is June.

11. Write the following definition as a biconditional.

    Vertical angles are two angles whose sides are opposite rays.

Do you UNDERSTAND?

MATHEMATICAL PRACTICES

12. **Vocabulary** Explain how the term *biconditional* is fitting for a statement composed of *two* conditionals.
13. **Error Analysis** Why is the following statement a poor definition?

    Elephants are gigantic animals.

14. **Compare and Contrast** Which of the following statements is a better definition of a linear pair? Explain.

    A linear pair is a pair of supplementary angles.

    A linear pair is a pair of adjacent angles with noncommon sides that are opposite rays.

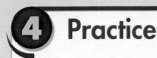

Practice

More Practice and Problem-Solving Exercises

ASSIGNMENT GUIDE

The assignments below are for the More Practice and Problem-Solving Exercises. You may also want to assign the A-Level Practice Exercises for homework if these are not used in class.

Average: 15–31

Advanced: 15–33

Mathematical Practices The exercises listed focus on the Standards for Mathematical Practices listed.

EX. 13–17, 32: Construct Arguments (MP 3)
EX. 18: Critique the Reasoning of Others (MP 3)
EX. 24–27: Model (MP 4)
EX. 33: Use Structure (MP 7)

EXERCISE 18: Use the **Think About a Plan** worksheet in the Online Teacher Resources to further support students' development in becoming independent learners.

HOMEWORK QUICK CHECK

To check students' understanding of key skills and concepts, go over Exercises 15, 16, 18, 19, and 28.

ANSWERS

15. Yes; it uses clearly understood terms, is precise, and is reversible. You can write the two statements as two true conditional statements that are converses: If a band of tough tissue connects bones or holds organs in place, then it is a ligament. If a band of tough tissue is a ligament, then it connects bones or holds organs in place.

16. No; a straight angle has a measure greater than 90, but it is not an obtuse angle.

17. Check students' work.

18. That statement, as a biconditional, is "An angle is a right angle if and only if it is greater than an acute angle." Counterexamples to that statement are obtuse angles and straight angles.

19. D

20. A point is in Quadrant III if and only if it has two negative coordinates.

21. The sum of the digits of an integer is divisible by 9 if and only if the integer is divisible by 9.

22. A number is a whole number if and only if it is a nonnegative integer.

23. A figure is a hexagon if and only if it is a six-sided polygon.

▼ STUDENT PAGES 31–32

More Practice and Problem-Solving Exercises

B Apply

15. Think About a Plan Is the following a good definition? Explain.
A ligament is a band of tough tissue connecting bones or holding organs in place.
- Can you write the statement as two true conditionals?
- Are the two true conditionals converses of each other?

16. Reasoning Is the following a good definition? Explain.
An obtuse angle is an angle with measure greater than 90.

17. Open-Ended Choose a definition from a dictionary or from a glossary. Explain what makes the statement a good definition.

18. Error Analysis Your friend defines a right angle as an angle that is greater than an acute angle. Use a biconditional to show that this is not a good definition.

19. Which conditional and its converse form a true biconditional?

A. If $x > 0$, then $|x| > 0$.

B. If $x = 3$, then $x^2 = 9$.

C. If $x^3 = 5$, then $x = 125$.

D. If $x = 19$, then $2x - 3 = 35$.

Write each statement as a biconditional.

20. Points in Quadrant III have two negative coordinates.

21. When the sum of the digits of an integer is divisible by 9, the integer is divisible by 9 and vice versa.

22. The whole numbers are the nonnegative integers.

23. A hexagon is a six-sided polygon.

More Practice and Problem-Solving Exercises *continued*

ANSWERS

24. good definition

25. No; V could fit that description.

26. good definition

27. good definition

28. If $\angle A$ and $\angle B$ are a linear pair, then $\angle A$ and $\angle B$ are supplementary.

29. If $\angle A$ and $\angle B$ are a linear pair, then $\angle A$ and $\angle B$ are adjacent angles.

30. If $\angle A$ and $\angle B$ are a linear pair, then $\angle A$ and $\angle B$ are adjacent and supplementary angles.

31. $\angle A$ and $\angle B$ are a linear pair if and only if $\angle A$ and $\angle B$ are adjacent and supplementary angles.

32. Answers may vary. Sample: A line is a circle on the sphere formed by the intersection of the sphere and a plane containing the center of the sphere.

33. a. If an integer is divisible by 10, then its last digit is 0. If the last digit of an integer is 0, then the integer is divisible by 10.

b.

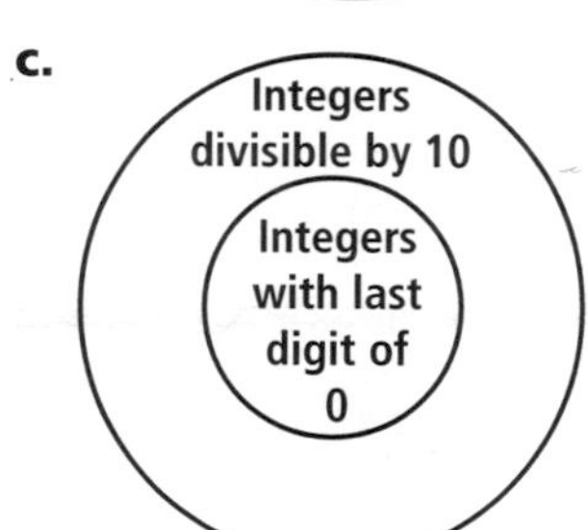

c.

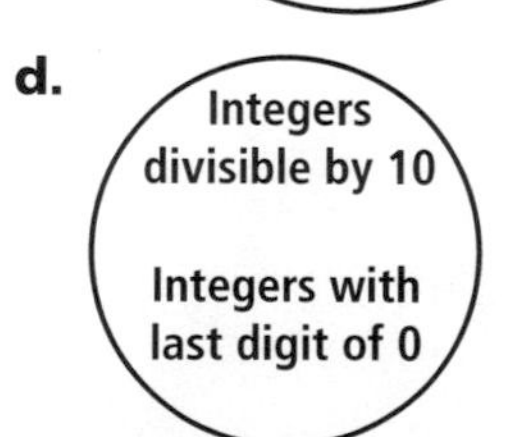

d.

Integers divisible by 10

Integers with last digit of 0

e. Answers may vary. Sample: The two circles coincide.

f. Answers may vary. Sample: A good definition can be written as a biconditional because either of the coinciding circles of its Venn diagram can be the hypothesis, and the other the conclusion.

Language For Exercises 24–27, use the chart below. Decide whether the description of each letter is a good definition. If not, provide a counterexample by giving another letter that could fit the definition.

24. The letter *D* is formed by pointing straight up with the finger beside the thumb and folding the other fingers and the thumb so that they all touch.

25. The letter *K* is formed by making a *V* with the two fingers beside the thumb.

26. You have formed the letter *I* if and only if the smallest finger is sticking up and the other fingers are folded into the palm of your hand with your thumb folded over them and your hand is held still.

27. You form the letter *B* by holding all four fingers tightly together and pointing them straight up while your thumb is folded into the palm of your hand.

Reading Math Let statements *p*, *q*, *r*, and *s* be as follows:

p: $\angle A$ and $\angle B$ are a linear pair.
q: $\angle A$ and $\angle B$ are supplementary angles.
r: $\angle A$ and $\angle B$ are adjacent angles.
s: $\angle A$ and $\angle B$ are adjacent and supplementary angles.

Substitute for *p*, *q*, *r*, and *s*, and write each statement the way you would read it.

28. $p \rightarrow q$ **29.** $p \rightarrow r$ **30.** $p \rightarrow s$ **31.** $p \leftrightarrow s$

Challenge

32. Writing Use the figures to write a good definition of a *line* in spherical geometry.

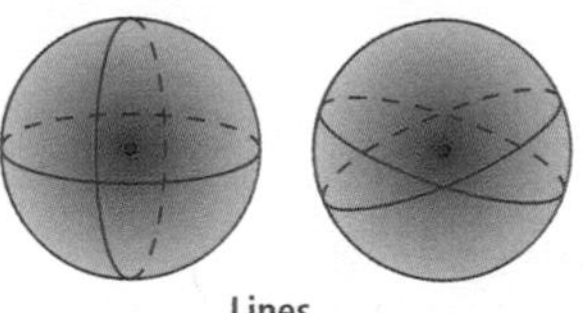
Lines

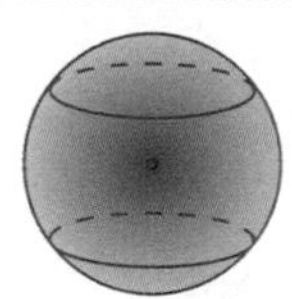
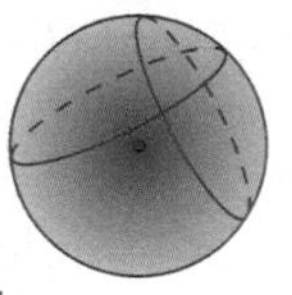
Not Lines

33. Multiple Representations You have illustrated true conditional statements with Venn diagrams. You can do the same thing with true biconditionals. Consider the following statement.

An integer is divisible by 10 if and only if its last digit is 0.

a. Write the two conditional statements that make up this biconditional.
b. Illustrate the first conditional from part (a) with a Venn diagram.
c. Illustrate the second conditional from part (a) with a Venn diagram.
d. Combine your two Venn diagrams from parts (b) and (c) to form a Venn diagram representing the biconditional statement.
e. What must be true of the Venn diagram for any true biconditional statement?
f. Reasoning How does your conclusion in part (e) help to explain why you can write a good definition as a biconditional?

Assess and Remediate

Lesson Quiz

1. What is the converse of the following true conditional? If the converse is also true, combine the statements as a biconditional.

   If a number is even, then it is divisible by 2.

2. **Do you UNDERSTAND?** What are the two conditional statements that form this biconditional?

   A quadrilateral is a trapezoid if and only if it has exactly one pair of parallel sides.

3. Is this definition of a rectangle reversible? If yes, write it as a true biconditional.

   A rectangle is a parallelogram with four right angles.

ANSWERS TO LESSON QUIZ

1. Converse: If a number is divisible by 2, then it is even. Biconditional: A number is even if and only if it is divisible by 2.
2. If a quadrilateral has exactly one pair of parallel sides, then it is a trapezoid. If a quadrilateral is a trapezoid, then it has exactly one pair of parallel sides.
3. yes; A parallelogram is a rectangle if and only if it has four right angles.

Prescription for Remediation

Use the student work on the Lesson Quiz to prescribe a differentiated assignment.

Points	Differentiated Remediation
0–1	Intervention
2	On-level
3	Extension

Online Assessment

Assign the Lesson Quiz in Success Tracker on **pearsonsuccessnet.com**. Success Tracker will automatically score the quiz and assign appropriate intervention or enrichment to each student based on the results. The compiled data appear in three different reports for instant analysis of whole class and individual student performance.

Differentiated Remediation

Intervention

- **RETEACHING** (2 pages) Provides reteaching and practice exercises for the key lesson concepts. Use with struggling students or absent students.
- **ENGLISH LANGUAGE LEARNER SUPPORT** Helps students develop and reinforce mathematical vocabulary and key concepts.

On-Level

- **PRACTICE** (2 pages) Provides extra practice for each lesson. For simpler practice exercises, use the Form K Practice pages found in the Online Teacher Resources.
- **THINK ABOUT A PLAN** Helps students develop specific problem-solving skills and strategies by providing scaffolded guiding questions.
- **STANDARDIZED TEST PREP** Focuses on all major exercises, all major question types, and helps students prepare for the high-stakes assessments.

Extension

- **ENRICHMENT** Provides students with interesting problems and activities that extend the concepts of the lesson.
- **ACTIVITIES, GAMES, AND PUZZLES** Worksheets that can be used for concept development, enrichment, and for fun!

1-5 Deductive Reasoning

Common Core State Standards
Prepares for G.CO.9 Prove theorems about lines and angles . . . **Also prepares for G.CO.10, G.CO.11**

Preparing to Teach

BIG idea Reasoning and Proof

ESSENTIAL UNDERSTANDING

Given true statements, deductive reasoning can be used to make a valid, or true, conclusion. Deductive reasoning often involves the Laws of Syllogism and Detachment.

Math Background

Students have used deduction (possibly unknowingly) when they have solved puzzles and played games. Among different types of reasoning, deductive reasoning stands out because conclusions reached are logically consistent and valid. With other forms of reasoning, such as inductive reasoning or analogy, conclusions have only the potential of holding true.

This lesson focuses on two rules of formal logic. The Law of Detachment uses a conditional statement (if p, then q) and given information "detached" from p to draw a conclusion. With a true conditional (if p, then q) and a given fact p, then the statement q may be deduced.

The Law of Syllogism is sometimes called the Law of Transitivity. A true conditional statement's conclusion becomes the hypothesis for another true conditional statement. The conclusion of the second conditional can, in turn, become the hypothesis of a third conditional statement. This process continues until the desired conclusion is reached.

ELL Support

FOCUS ON LANGUAGE Ask: What do you think *deductive* means? Have you heard the word before? Does the word *deductive* remind you of anything? The difference between the words *inductive* and *deductive* is the prefix. Because you already know *inductive* means to observe patterns to find a rule, what do you think *deductive* means?

Lesson Vocabulary

- deductive reasoning
- Law of Syllogism
- Law of Detachment

Mathematical Practices

REASON ABSTRACTLY AND QUANTITATIVELY. In their study of the Law of Syllogism and Law of Detachment, students will decontextualize verbal statements and represent them with symbols, allowing them to manipulate statements more freely. They will also contextualize, or pause and reflect on whether these manipulations are appropriate.

1 Interactive Learning

Solve It!

PURPOSE To have students use a conditional statement representing a real-world situation and the Law of Detachment to solve a problem

PROCESS Students may use trial and error, process of elimination, or logical reasoning.

Q Which three jeans would you choose to spend as little as possible? **[$24.99, $39.99, and $40.99]**

Q Of these three pairs of jeans, which will you actually pay for? **[$39.99 and $40.99]**

Q How do you find an average amount? **[Add $39.99 and $40.99 and divide by 3.]**

ANSWER $26.99; to spend as little as possible using the coupon, you should select the three lowest priced jeans. The lowest priced pair of the three is free and the average amount you spend is the sum of the two higher priced pairs divided by 3.

CONNECT THE MATH The Solve It requires that students draw conclusions based on a set of facts. They can reduce the thought process to a series of related conditionals.

- If I spend as little as possible, then I will use the coupon.

▼ DIGITAL (STUDENT WORK SPACE PAGE 34)

Getting Ready!

You want to use the coupon to buy three different pairs of jeans. You have narrowed your choices to four pairs. The costs of the different pairs are $24.99, $39.99, $40.99, and $50.00. If you spend as little as possible, what is the average amount per pair of jeans that you will pay? Explain.

BUY TWO PAIRS OF JEANS
Get a THIRD Free*
*Free jeans must be of equal or lesser value.

- If I use the coupon, then I will receive the lowest priced pair of jeans free.

Practicing these mental habits now sets the stage for problem-solving strategies and writing proofs.

2 Guided Instruction

Problem 1 Using the Law of Detachment

Take Note

The Law of Detachment can be written using symbols as $[(p \rightarrow q) \text{ and } p] \rightarrow q$. Students may voice that this law is simple common sense. This is a good opportunity to discuss that all logic is basically common sense. The Law of Detachment is also referred to by its Latin name, *Modus Ponens*.

Problem 1

Q Could you make a valid conclusion if the second statement were "Felicia passed the course?" Explain. **[No, because the statement would not match the hypothesis of the conditional.]**

Q What is the converse of the conditional statement in 1B? Is it true? **[If a ray is an angle bisector, it divides an angle into two congruent angles. It is true.]**

Q In 1C, what second statement would allow you to make a valid conclusion? **[∠1 and ∠2 are adjacent angles.]**

▼ STUDENT PAGE 34

In the Solve It, you drew a conclusion based on several facts. You used deductive reasoning. **Deductive reasoning** (sometimes called logical reasoning) is the process of reasoning logically from given statements or facts to a conclusion.

Essential Understanding Given true statements, you can use deductive reasoning to make a valid or true conclusion.

Property Law of Detachment

Law	Symbols		
If the hypothesis of a true conditional is true, then the conclusion is true.	If	$p \rightarrow q$	is true
	And	p	is true,
	Then	q	is true.

To use the Law of Detachment, identify the hypothesis of the given true conditional. If the second given statement matches the hypothesis of the conditional, then you can make a valid conclusion.

▼ DIGITAL

Problem 1 Using the Law of Detachment

What can you conclude from the given true statements?

A Given: If a student gets an A on a final exam, then the student will pass the course. Felicia got an A on her history final exam.

If a student gets an A on a final exam, then the student will pass the course.
Felicia got an A on her history final exam.

The second statement matches the hypothesis of the given conditional. By the Law of Detachment, you can make a conclusion.

You conclude: Felicia will pass her history course.

B Given: If a ray divides an angle into two congruent angles, then the ray is an angle bisector.
$\overrightarrow{RS}$ divides $\angle ARB$ so that $\angle ARS \cong \angle SRB$.

If a ray divides an angle into two congruent angles, then the ray is an angle bisector.
$\overrightarrow{RS}$ divides $\angle ARB$ so that $\angle ARS \cong \angle SRB$.

The second statement matches the hypothesis of the given conditional. By the Law of Detachment, you can make a conclusion.

You conclude: $\overrightarrow{RS}$ is an angle bisector.

C Given: If two angles are adjacent, then they share a common vertex.
$\angle 1$ and $\angle 2$ share a common vertex.

If two angles are adjacent, then they share a common vertex.
$\angle 1$ and $\angle 2$ share a common vertex.

The information in the second statement about $\angle 1$ and $\angle 2$ does not tell you if the angles are adjacent. The second statement does not match the hypothesis of the given conditional, so you cannot use the Law of Detachment. $\angle 1$ and $\angle 2$ could be vertical angles, since vertical angles also share a common vertex. You cannot make a conclusion.

Problem 1 *continued*

Got It?

ERROR PREVENTION

If students draw an invalid conclusion from part (b), first ask students to identify a counterexample for their false conclusions. Further, have them verbalize the mistake they made when employing the Law of Detachment.

ANSWERS

Got It? a. Marla is not safe out in the open. **b.** No conclusion is possible.

Practice

1. Dr. Ngemba should take an X-ray.
2. Points X, Y, and Z are collinear.

▼ STUDENT PAGE 35

Got It? What can you conclude from the given information?

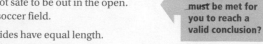

a. If there is lightning, then it is not safe to be out in the open. Marla sees lightning from the soccer field.

b. If a figure is a square, then its sides have equal length. Figure $ABCD$ has sides of equal length.

Think

What conditions must be met for you to reach a valid conclusion?

Practice **If possible, use the Law of Detachment to make a conclusion. If it is not possible to make a conclusion, tell why.**

1. If a doctor suspects her patient has a broken bone, then she should take an X-ray. Dr. Ngemba suspects Lilly has a broken arm.
2. If three points are on the same line, then they are collinear. Points X, Y, and Z are on line m.

Problem 2 Using the Law of Syllogism

Take Note

Students may recognize the Law of Syllogism as being similar to the Transitive Property introduced in a previous Algebra course.

A key difference to note between the Law of Syllogism and the Law of Detachment is that syllogism involves three statements, while detachment involves two statements.

The Law of Syllogism is also called the *Chain Rule*.

Problem 2

Q Could the statement that is concluded in 2A be written as a biconditional? Explain. **[No, the converse of the statement is not true.]**

Q How can you reword one of the statements in 2B such that the Law of Syllogism can be applied? **[Answers may vary. Sample answer: If you are flexible, then you spend time stretching your muscles.]**

▼ STUDENT PAGE 35

Another law of deductive reasoning is the Law of Syllogism. The **Law of Syllogism** allows you to state a conclusion from two true conditional statements when the conclusion of one statement is the hypothesis of the other statement.

take note **Property** Law of Syllogism

Symbols			Example
If	$p \to q$	is true	If it is July, then you are on summer vacation.
and	$q \to r$	is true,	If you are on summer vacation, then you work at a smoothie shop.
then	$p \to r$	is true.	**You conclude:** If it is July, then you work at a smoothie shop.

▼ DIGITAL

ONLINE PROBLEMS **Problem 2** **Using the Law of Syllogism**

What can you conclude from the given information?

A Given: **If a figure is a square, then the figure is a rectangle.**
If a figure is a rectangle, then the figure has four sides.

If a figure is a square, then the figure is a rectangle.
If a figure is a rectangle, then the figure has four sides.

The conclusion of the first statement is the hypothesis of the second statement, so you can use the Law of Syllogism to make a conclusion.

You conclude: If a figure is a square, then the figure has four sides.

B Given: **If you do gymnastics, then you are flexible.**
If you do ballet, then you are flexible.

If you do gymnastics, then you are flexible.
If you do ballet, then you are flexible.

The statements have the same conclusion. Neither conclusion is the hypothesis of the other statement, so you cannot use the Law of Syllogism. You cannot make a conclusion.

Got It?

Q Prior to applying the Law of Syllogism, what examination should be made of both conditional statements? **[You should make sure both conditional statements are true.]**

ANSWERS

Got It? a. If a whole number ends in 0, then it is divisible by 5; Law of Syllogism. **b.** No conclusion is possible.

Practice

3. If an animal is a Florida panther, then it is endangered.
4. If a line intersects a segment at its midpoint, then it divides the segment into two congruent segments.

▼ STUDENT PAGE 36

Got It? What can you conclude from the given information? What is your reasoning?

a. If a whole number ends in 0, then it is divisible by 10. If a whole number is divisible by 10, then it is divisible by 5.

b. If $\overrightarrow{AB}$ and $\overrightarrow{AD}$ are opposite rays, then the two rays form a straight angle. If two rays are opposite rays, then the two rays form a straight angle.

Think What conditions must be met for you to reach a valid conclusion?

Practice **If possible, use the Law of Syllogism to make a conclusion. If it is not possible to make a conclusion, tell why.**

STEM **3. Ecology** If an animal is a Florida panther, then its scientific name is *Puma concolor coryi*.

If an animal is a *Puma concolor coryi*, then it is endangered.

4. If a line intersects a segment at its midpoint, then the line bisects the segment.

If a line bisects a segment, then it divides the segment into two congruent segments.

Problem 3 Using the Laws of Syllogism and Detachment

Q To use the Law of Syllogism, what conditions must be satisfied? **[Both conditionals must be true, and the hypothesis of one of the conditionals must be equivalent to the conclusion of another conditional.]**

Q To use the Law of Detachment, what condition must be satisfied? **[The second given statement must match the hypothesis of the conditional statement.]**

▼ STUDENT PAGE 37

You can use the Law of Syllogism and the Law of Detachment together to make conclusions.

▼ DIGITAL

Problem 3 Using the Laws of Syllogism and Detachment

What can you conclude from the given information?

Given: If you live in Accra, then you live in Ghana. If you live in Ghana, then you live in Africa. Aissa lives in Accra.

If you live in Accra, then you live in Ghana.
If you live in Ghana, then you live in Africa.
Aissa lives in Accra.

You can use the first two statements and the Law of Syllogism to conclude:
If you live in Accra, then you live in Africa.

You can use this new conditional statement, the fact that Aissa lives in Accra, and the Law of Detachment to make a conclusion.

You conclude: Aissa lives in Africa.

Problem 3 *continued*

Got It?

Q What new conditional statement can you construct using the Law of Syllogism with the information given in part (a)? **[If a river is more than 4000 mi long, then it is the longest river in the world.]**

ANSWERS

Got It? a. The Nile is the longest river in the world; Law of Syllogism and Law of Detachment. **b.** Yes; if you use the Law of Detachment first, then you must use it again to reach the same conclusion. The Law of Syllogism is not used.

Practice

5. Alaska's Denali is the highest mountain in the U.S.

6. Tracy lives in the 11th state to enter the Union.

▼ STUDENT PAGE 37

Got It? **a.** What can you conclude from the given information? What is your reasoning?

If a river is more than 4000 mi long, then it is longer than the Amazon.

If a river is longer than the Amazon, then it is the longest river in the world. The Nile is 4132 mi long.

b. Reasoning In Problem 3, does it matter whether you use the Law of Syllogism or the Law of Detachment first? Explain.

**Practice** **Use the Law of Detachment and the Law of Syllogism to make conclusions from the following statements. If it is not possible to make a conclusion, tell why.**

5. If a mountain is the highest in Alaska, then it is the highest in the United States.

If an Alaskan mountain is more than 20,300 ft high, then it is the highest in Alaska.

Alaska's Denali is 20,310 ft high.

6. If you live in the Bronx, then you live in New York.

Tracy lives in the Bronx.

If you live in New York, then you live in the eleventh state to enter the Union.

3 Lesson Check

Do you know HOW?

If students have difficulty with Exercise 7, then ask students to identify the condition of the law that was not satisfied.

Do you UNDERSTAND?

If students have difficulty with Exercise 10, then first make sure that students can accurately identify the hypothesis and conclusion presented in the conditional statement, and then refer them to Problem 1C.

Close

Q If only one of the laws is to be used to reach a conclusion, how can you quickly determine which to use? **[The Law of Syllogism is used when two conditionals are provided. The Law of Detachment is used when only one conditional is provided.]**

ANSWERS

7. No conclusion is possible.

8. Figure *ABC* is a triangle; Law of Detachment.

9. If it is Saturday, then you wear sneakers; Law of Syllogism.

10. The Law of Detachment cannot be applied because the hypothesis is not satisfied.

11. Answers may vary. Sample: Deductive reasoning uses logic to reach conclusions, while inductive reasoning bases conclusions on unproved (but possibly true) conjectures.

▼ STUDENT PAGE 38

Lesson Check

Do you know HOW?

If possible, make a conclusion from the given true statements. What reasoning did you use?

7. If it is Tuesday, then you will go bowling. You go bowling.

8. If a figure is a three-sided polygon, then it is a triangle. Figure *ABC* is a three-sided polygon.

9. If it is Saturday, then you walk to work. If you walk to work, then you wear sneakers.

Do you UNDERSTAND?

10. Error Analysis What is the error in the reasoning at the right?

Birds that weigh more than 50 pounds cannot fly. A kiwi cannot fly. So, a kiwi weighs more than 50 pounds.

11. Compare and Contrast How is deductive reasoning different from inductive reasoning?

Practice

More Practice and Problem-Solving Exercises

ASSIGNMENT GUIDE
The assignments below are for the More Practice and Problem-Solving Exercises. You may also want to assign the A-Level Practice Exercises for homework if these are not used in class.
Average: 12–24
Advanced: 12–26

Mathematical Practices The exercises listed focus on the Standards for Mathematical Practices listed.

EX. 12: Persevere in Solving Problems (MP 1)
EX. 11: Construct Arguments (MP 3)
EX. 10: Critique the Reasoning of Others (MP 3)
EX. 24: Model with Mathematics (MP 4)

STEM exercises focus on science or engineering applications.

EXERCISE 24: Use the **Think About a Plan** worksheet in the Online Teacher Resources to further support students' development in becoming independent learners.

HOMEWORK QUICK CHECK
To check students' understanding of key skills and concepts, go over Exercises 12, 14, 16, 22, and 24.

ANSWERS

12. $5.99; your family goes to your favorite restaurant on the night of your weekly game, which is on Tuesday. Chicken fingers are $5.99 on Tuesday.
13. Must be true; by E and A, it is breakfast time; by D, Julio is drinking juice.
14. Must be true; by E and A, it is breakfast time; by C, Curtis is drinking water.
15. May be true; by E and A, it is breakfast time. You don't know what Kira drinks at breakfast.
16. Is not true; by E and A, it is breakfast time; by C, Curtis drinks water and nothing else.
17. May be true; by E, Maria is drinking juice. You don't know if she also drinks water.
18. Is not true; by A and E, it is breakfast time; by D, Julio is drinking juice and nothing else.
19. strange; From the table, if a quark has rest energy 540 MeV and a charge of $-\frac{1}{3}$e, then the flavor of the quark is strange; a given quark has rest energy 540 MeV and a charge of $-\frac{1}{3}$e. By the Law of Detachment, the flavor of the given quark is strange.

▼ STUDENT PAGE 39

More Practice and Problem-Solving Exercises

B Apply

12. **Think About a Plan** If it is the night of your weekly basketball game, your family eats at your favorite restaurant. When your family eats at your favorite restaurant, you always get chicken fingers. If it is Tuesday, then it is the night of your weekly basketball game. How much do you pay for chicken fingers after your game? Use the specials board at the right to decide. Explain your reasoning.
    - How can you reorder and rewrite the sentences to help you?
    - How can you use the Law of Syllogism to answer the question?

Monday
salads $4.99
Tuesday
chicken fingers $5.99
Wednesday
burgers $6.99

Beverages For Exercises 13–18, assume that the following statements are true.

A. If Maria is drinking juice, then it is breakfast time.
B. If it is lunchtime, then Kira is drinking milk and nothing else.
C. If it is mealtime, then Curtis is drinking water and nothing else.
D. If it is breakfast time, then Julio is drinking juice and nothing else.
E. Maria is drinking juice.

Use only the information given above. For each statement, write *must be true, may be true,* or *is not true.* Explain your reasoning.

13. Julio is drinking juice.
14. Curtis is drinking water.
15. Kira is drinking milk.
16. Curtis is drinking juice.
17. Maria is drinking water.
18. Julio is drinking milk.

STEM 19. **Physics** Quarks are subatomic particles identified by electric charge and rest energy. The table shows how to categorize quarks by their flavors. Show how the Law of Detachment and the table are used to identify the flavor of a quark with a charge of $-\frac{1}{3}$e and rest energy 540 MeV.

Rest Energy and Charge of Quarks

Rest Energy (MeV)	360	360	1500	540	173,000	5000
Electric Charge (e)	$+\frac{2}{3}$	$-\frac{1}{3}$	$+\frac{2}{3}$	$-\frac{1}{3}$	$+\frac{2}{3}$	$-\frac{1}{3}$
Flavor	Up	Down	Charmed	Strange	Top	Bottom

More Practice and Problem-Solving Exercises *continued*

20. If a place is a national park, then it is an interesting place; Mammoth Cave is an interesting place.
21. If a figure is a square, then it is a rectangle; *ABCD* is a rectangle.
22. If you are in Key West, Florida, then the temperature is always above 32°F; no conclusion is possible because the hypothesis is not satisfied.
23. If a person is a high school student, then the person likes art; no conclusion is possible because the hypothesis is not satisfied.
24. Check students' work.
25. a. Check students' work; the result is two more than the chosen integer.
    b. $\frac{3x+6}{3} = x + 2$
    c. The expression in part (b) is equivalent to the conjecture in part (a). In part (a) inductive reasoning was used to make a conjecture based on a pattern. In part (b) deductive reasoning was used in order to write and simplify an expression.
26. a.

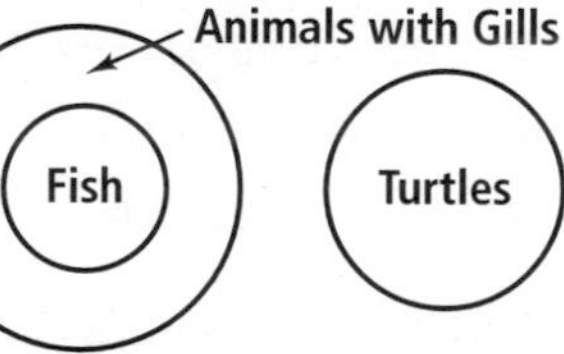

    b. Turtles are not in the circle of animals with gills, so a turtle is not a fish.

▼ STUDENT PAGE 40

Write the first statement as a conditional. If possible, use the Law of Detachment to make a conclusion. If it is not possible to make a conclusion, tell why.

20. All national parks are interesting. Mammoth Cave is a national park.
21. All squares are rectangles. *ABCD* is a square.
22. The temperature is always above 32°F in Key West, Florida. The temperature is 62°F.
23. Every high school student likes art. Ling likes art.
24. **Writing** Give an example of a rule used in your school that could be written as a conditional. Explain how the Law of Detachment is used in applying that rule.

Challenge

25. **Reasoning** Use the following algorithm: Choose an integer. Multiply the integer by 3. Add 6 to the product. Divide the sum by 3.
    a. Complete the algorithm for four different integers. Look for a pattern in the chosen integers and in the corresponding answers. Make a conjecture that relates the chosen integers to the answers.
    b. Let the variable x represent the chosen integer. Apply the algorithm to x. Simplify the resulting expression.
    c. How does your answer to part (b) confirm your conjecture in part (a)? Describe how inductive and deductive reasoning are exhibited in parts (a) and (b).

STEM 26. **Biology** Consider the following given statements and conclusion.
Given: If an animal is a fish, then it has gills.
A turtle does not have gills.

You conclude: A turtle is not a fish.
    a. Make a Venn diagram to illustrate the given information.
    b. Use the Venn diagram to help explain why the argument uses good reasoning.

Assess and Remediate

Lesson Quiz

1. What can you conclude from the given true statements?
   Given: If you want to buy the school lunch today, then you will need \$2.50. You brought \$2.50 to school today.
2. What can you conclude from the given information?
   Given: If Karl runs 1 mi, then he runs 1760 yd. If Karl runs 1760 yd, then he runs 5280 ft.
3. **Do you UNDERSTAND?** What can you conclude from the given information?
   Given: If a student is on the basketball team, then he has practice after school. If there is practice after school, then the student needs to find a ride home other than the bus. Jamal is on the basketball team.

ANSWERS TO LESSON QUIZ

1. no conclusion
2. If Karl runs 1 mile, then he runs 5280 ft.
3. Jamal needs to find a ride home other than the bus.

Prescription for Remediation

Use the student work on the Lesson Quiz to prescribe a differentiated assignment.

Points	Differentiated Remediation
0–1	Intervention
2	On-level
3	Extension

Online Assessment

Assign the Lesson Quiz in Success Tracker on **pearsonsuccessnet.com**. Success Tracker will automatically score the quiz and assign appropriate intervention or enrichment to each student based on the results. The compiled data appear in three different reports for instant analysis of whole class and individual student performance.

Differentiated Remediation

Intervention

- **RETEACHING** (2 pages) Provides reteaching and practice exercises for the key lesson concepts. Use with struggling students or absent students.
- **ENGLISH LANGUAGE LEARNER SUPPORT** Helps students develop and reinforce mathematical vocabulary and key concepts.

On-Level

- **PRACTICE** (2 pages) Provides extra practice for each lesson. For simpler practice exercises, use the Form K Practice pages found in the Online Teacher Resources.
- **THINK ABOUT A PLAN** Helps students develop specific problem-solving skills and strategies by providing scaffolded guiding questions.
- **STANDARDIZED TEST PREP** Focuses on all major exercises, all major question types, and helps students prepare for the high-stakes assessments.

Extension

- **ENRICHMENT** Provides students with interesting problems and activities that extend the concepts of the lesson.
- **ACTIVITIES, GAMES, AND PUZZLES** Worksheets that can be used for concept development, enrichment, and for fun!

1-6 Reasoning in Algebra and Geometry

Common Core State Standards
Prepares for G.CO.10 Prove theorems about triangles . . . **Also prepares for G.CO.9, G.CO.11**

Preparing to Teach

BIG idea Reasoning and Proof

ESSENTIAL UNDERSTANDING

Logical reasoning from one step to another is essential in building a proof. Reasons in a proof include given information, definitions, properties, postulates, and theorems.

Math Background

The properties of equality reviewed in the beginning of this lesson add to the students' "toolbox" for writing proofs using deductive reasoning. It is important to make a connection between the algebraic proofs that students unknowingly completed throughout all of algebra and the proofs that students will complete in geometry. Students should have a clear understanding that the process of solving an equation is an algebraic proof, although the justifications for each step are not generally written down and often not even discussed. Students should realize from this lesson that proofs are not unique to geometry.

ELL Support

USE GRAPHIC ORGANIZERS Have students fold a sheet of paper in half three times to form eight equal sections. Tell students to label each section with a Property of Equality from the Key Concept box. Discuss the meanings of the properties. Write examples of each randomly on the board and ask for volunteers to give the property and explain their reasoning. Students can write the example in the correct section of their organizers.

FOCUS ON LANGUAGE Invite students to provide a verbal example of each Property of Equality. For example, for *Transitive Property* an example might be: Tom is Jay's brother and Jay's brother is Kayla's cousin, so Tom is Kayla's cousin. Group students with similar language learners to share their work.

Lesson Vocabulary

- Reflexive Property
- Symmetric Property
- Transitive Property
- proof
- two-column proof

Mathematical Practices

CONSTRUCT VIABLE ARGUMENTS AND CRITIQUE THE REASONING OF OTHERS. In Problem 3, students will write a two-column proof that will build a logical progression of statements to establish the truth of a conjecture. They will also justify their conclusions step by step.

Interactive Learning

Solve It!

PURPOSE To analyze a series of steps which can logically lead to a consistent result

PROCESS Students may use several numbers to determine how each step of the brainteaser is affecting the original age. Students may also recognize from analyzing the steps that each operation except one is inverted.

Q Can you do the steps in any order and get the same result? Explain. **[No; changing the order results in different answers.]**

Q What is an inverse operation? Provide an example. **[An operation that is the opposite of, or undoes, another operation. Adding 6 and subtracting 6 are inverse operations.]**

ANSWER The leftmost digit(s) of the result is/are the one(s) you started with; the result is 10 times the starting age. Adding 8 and then doubling the sum is undone by subtracting 16 and then dividing by 2. So you end up with the product of the age and 10.

▼ DIGITAL (STUDENT WORK SPACE PAGE 41)

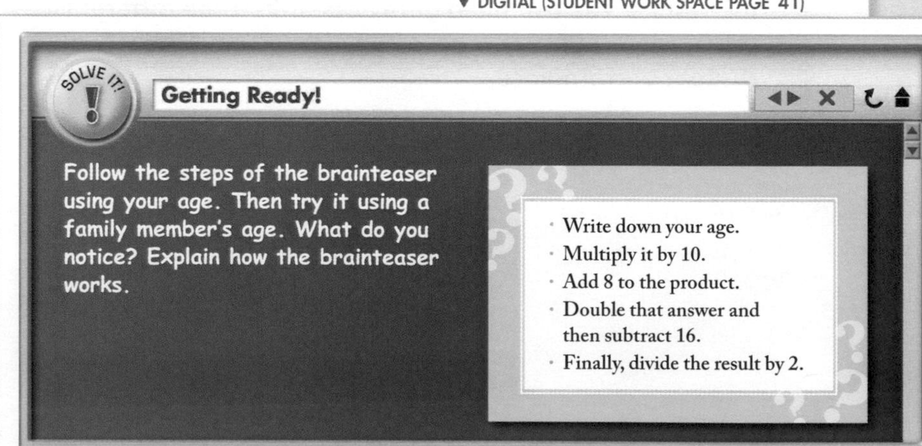

SOLVE IT!
Getting Ready!
Follow the steps of the brainteaser using your age. Then try it using a family member's age. What do you notice? Explain how the brainteaser works.
Write down your age.
Multiply it by 10.
Add 8 to the product.
Double that answer and then subtract 16.
Finally, divide the result by 2.

CONNECT THE MATH Elicit from students that while you cannot show that the brainteaser always works by trying numeric examples, you could prove that the brainteaser always works by allowing a variable to represent all real numbers. Show students that, if you begin with x as the age, the result will be $10x$ after all of the steps are applied.

2 Guided Instruction

Problem 1 Justifying Steps When Solving an Equation

Take Note

Q Could the Addition, Subtraction, Multiplication, and Division Properties all be written as biconditionals? Explain. **[Yes, the converse of each of the properties is true.]**

Take Note

Point out to students that the Distributive Property is the only property in this lesson that involves a combination of two operations. Show students that the Distributive Property can also be applied to a problem such as $a\left(\frac{1}{b} + \frac{1}{c} - \frac{1}{d}\right) = \frac{a}{b} + \frac{a}{c} - \frac{a}{d}$.

Problem 1

Q How could you use the Addition Property of Equality in place of the Subtraction Property? **[You can add (−30) to each side instead of subtracting 30 from each side.]**

Q How can you check the solution to the equation for accuracy? **[Substitute the value for x into the algebraic expressions in the diagram and check to make sure that the angles add up to 180.]**

▼ STUDENT PAGES 41–42

In the Solve It, you logically examined a series of steps. In this lesson, you will apply logical reasoning to algebraic and geometric situations.

Essential Understanding Algebraic properties of equality are used in geometry. They will help you solve problems and justify each step you take.

In geometry you accept postulates and properties as true. Some of the properties that you accept as true are the properties of equality from algebra.

take note

Key Concept Properties of Equality

Let a, b, and c be any real numbers.

Addition Property	If $a = b$, then $a + c = b + c$.
Subtraction Property	If $a = b$, then $a - c = b - c$.
Multiplication Property	If $a = b$, then $a \cdot c = b \cdot c$.
Division Property	If $a = b$ and $c \neq 0$, then $\frac{a}{c} = \frac{b}{c}$.
Reflexive Property	$a = a$
Symmetric Property	If $a = b$, then $b = a$.
Transitive Property	If $a = b$ and $b = c$, then $a = c$.
Substitution Property	If $a = b$, then b can replace a in any expression.

take note

Key Concept The Distributive Property

Use multiplication to distribute a to each term of the sum or difference within the parentheses.

Sum:
$a(b + c) = a(b + c) = ab + ac$

Difference:
$a(b - c) = a(b - c) = ab - ac$

You use deductive reasoning when you solve an equation. You can justify each step with a postulate, a property, or a definition. For example, you can use the Distributive Property to justify combining like terms. If you think of the Distributive Property as $ab + ac = a(b + c)$ or $ab + ac = (b + c)a$, then $2x + x = (2 + 1)x = 3x$.

▼ DIGITAL

Problem 1 Justifying Steps When Solving an Equation

Algebra **What is the value of x? Justify each step.**

$\angle AOM$ and $\angle MOC$ are supplementary.	∠s that form a linear pair are supplementary.
$m\angle AOM + m\angle MOC = 180$	Definition of supplementary ∠s
$(2x + 30) + x = 180$	Substitution Property
$3x + 30 = 180$	Distributive Property
$3x = 150$	Subtraction Property of Equality
$x = 50$	Division Property of Equality

Problem 1 *continued*

Got It? **ERROR PREVENTION**

Q If $\overrightarrow{AB}$ bisects $\angle RAN$, what is true about $\angle RAB$ and $\angle BAN$? Justify your answer. **[The angles have equal measure by the definition of an angle bisector.]**

ANSWERS

Got It? 75; $x = 2x - 75$ (Def. of an ∠ bis.); $x + 75 = 2x$ (Add. Prop. of Eq.); $75 = 2x - x$ (Subtr. Prop. of Eq.); $75 = x$ (Distr. Prop.)

Practice

1. a. Mult. Prop. of Eq.
   b. Distr. Prop.
   c. Add. Prop. of Eq.
2. a. Seg. Add. Post.
   b. Subst. Prop.
   c. Distr. Prop.
   d. Distr. Prop.
   e. Subtr. Prop. of Eq.
   f. Div. Prop. of Eq.

▼ STUDENT PAGES 42–43

Got It? What is the value of x? Justify each step.

Given: $\overrightarrow{AB}$ bisects $\angle RAN$.

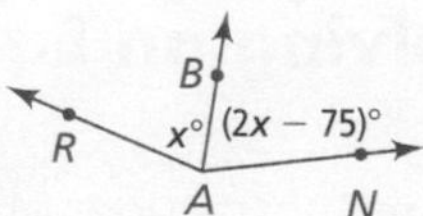

Plan How can you use the given information?

A Practice **Algebra** Fill in the reason that justifies each step.

1. $\frac{1}{2}x - 5 = 10$ Given
   $2\left(\frac{1}{2}x - 5\right) = 20$ a. ______
   $x - 10 = 20$ b. ______
   $x = 30$ c. ______

2. $XY = 42$ Given
   $XZ + ZY = XY$ a. ______
   $3(n + 4) + 3n = 42$ b. ______
   $3n + 12 + 3n = 42$ c. ______
   $6n + 12 = 42$ d. ______
   $6n = 30$ e. ______
   $n = 5$ f. ______

Problem 2 Using Properties of Equality and Congruence

Take Note

Students may not understand why the Transitive, Symmetric, and Reflexive Properties are being repeated. Make sure that students understand that the properties of equality on page 41 are true for any numbers, while the congruence properties are true for geometric figures.

Problem 2

Q To find the value of x, which properties could you apply to the equation $2x = 10$? **[Multiplication or Division Property of Equality]**

Q Why is 2C justified by the Symmetric Property of Equality rather than the Symmetric Property of Congruence? **[$\angle E$ is a geometric figure, but $m\angle E$ is a number.]**

▼ STUDENT PAGE 43

Some properties of equality have corresponding properties of congruence.

take note **Key Concept** Properties of Congruence

Reflexive Property	$\overline{AB} \cong \overline{AB}$ $\angle A \cong \angle A$
Symmetric Property	If $\overline{AB} \cong \overline{CD}$, then $\overline{CD} \cong \overline{AB}$. If $\angle A \cong \angle B$, then $\angle B \cong \angle A$.
Transitive Property	If $\overline{AB} \cong \overline{CD}$ and $\overline{CD} \cong \overline{EF}$, then $\overline{AB} \cong \overline{EF}$. If $\angle A \cong \angle B$ and $\angle B \cong \angle C$, then $\angle A \cong \angle C$. If $\angle B \cong \angle A$ and $\angle B \cong \angle C$, then $\angle A \cong \angle C$.

▼ DIGITAL

ONLINE PROBLEMS **Problem 2** Using Properties of Equality and Congruence

What is the name of the property of equality or congruence that justifies going from the first statement to the second statement?

A $2x + 9 = 19$
$2x = 10$ Subtraction Property of Equality

B $\angle O \cong \angle W$ and $\angle W \cong \angle L$
$\angle O \cong \angle L$ Transitive Property of Congruence

C $m\angle E = m\angle T$
$m\angle T = m\angle E$ Symmetric Property of Equality

Got It?

Q How could you solve the equation in part (b) for x without using the Distributive Property? **[Divide by 3 using the Division Property of Equality and subtract 5 using the Subtraction Property of Equality.]**

ANSWERS

Got It? a. Sym. Prop. of ≅ **b.** Distr. Prop. **c.** Mult. Prop. of Eq. **d.** Refl. Prop. of Eq.

Practice

3. Sym. Prop. of ≅ **4.** Add. Prop. of Eq.

▼ STUDENT PAGE 43

Got It? For parts (a)–(c), what is the name of the property of equality or congruence that justifies going from the first statement to the second statement?

a. $\overline{AR} \cong \overline{TY}$
$\overline{TY} \cong \overline{AR}$

b. $3(x + 5) = 9$
$3x + 15 = 9$

c. $\frac{1}{4}x = 7$
$x = 28$

d. Reasoning What property justifies the statement $m\angle R = m\angle R$?

Think How do you know if each justification is a property of equality or congruence?

Practice Name the property of equality or congruence that justifies going from the first statement to the second statement.

3. $\overline{ST} \cong \overline{QR}$
$\overline{QR} \cong \overline{ST}$

4. $AB - BC = 12$
$AB = 12 + BC$

Problem 3 Writing a Two-Column Proof

Students benefit from considering the path of the proof informally before they begin writing the formal proof. Ask these questions prior to beginning the formal proof process.

Q What postulate relates the measure of two smaller angles to the measure of a larger angle comprising the smaller angles? **[Angle Addition Postulate]**

Q Which two angles compose $\angle AEC$? Which two angles compose $\angle DEB$? **[$\angle 1$ and $\angle 2$; $\angle 3$ and $\angle 2$]**

▼ STUDENT PAGE 44

A **proof** is a convincing argument that uses deductive reasoning. A proof logically shows why a conjecture is true. A **two-column proof** lists each statement on the left. The justification, or the reason for each statement, is on the right. Each statement must follow logically from the steps before it. The diagram below shows the setup for a two-column proof. You will find the complete proof in Problem 3.

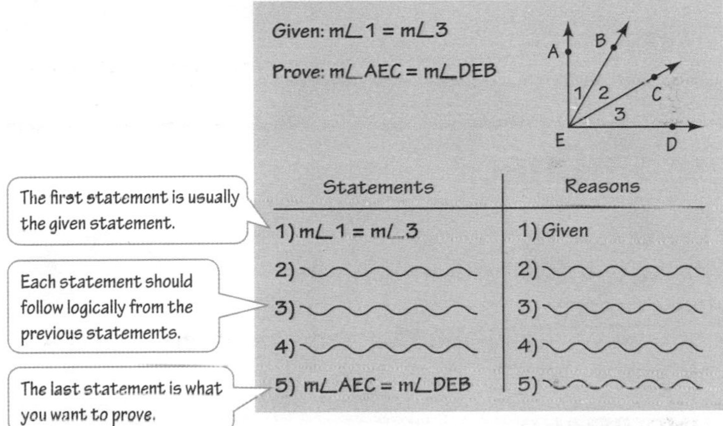

Given: m∠1 = m∠3
Prove: m∠AEC = m∠DEB
A
B
C
E
D
1
2
3
Statements
Reasons
The first statement is usually the given statement.
1) m∠1 = m∠3
1) Given
2)
3)
4)
Each statement should follow logically from the previous statements.
The last statement is what you want to prove.
5) m∠AEC = m∠DEB
5)

▼ DIGITAL

Problem 3 Writing a Two-Column Proof

Write a two-column proof.

Given: $m\angle 1 = m\angle 3$

Prove: $m\angle AEC = m\angle DEB$

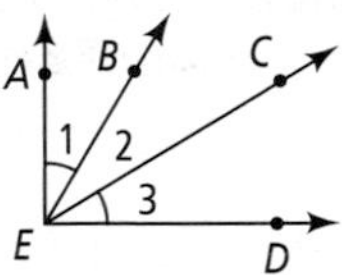

Know $m\angle 1 = m\angle 3$

Need To prove that $m\angle AEC = m\angle DEB$

Plan Add $m\angle 2$ to both $m\angle 1$ and $m\angle 3$. The resulting angles will have equal measure.

Statements	Reasons
1) $m\angle 1 = m\angle 3$	**1)** Given
2) $m\angle 2 = m\angle 2$	**2)** Reflexive Property of Equality
3) $m\angle 1 + m\angle 2 = m\angle 3 + m\angle 2$	**3)** Addition Property of Equality
4) $m\angle 1 + m\angle 2 = m\angle AEC$ $m\angle 3 + m\angle 2 = m\angle DEB$	**4)** Angle Addition Postulate
5) $m\angle AEC = m\angle DEB$	**5)** Substitution Property

Problem 3 *continued*

Got It?

Encourage students to use the proof from Problem 3 as a template for completing this proof.

ANSWERS

Got It? a. Answers may vary. Sample: $\overline{AB} \cong \overline{CD}$ (Given); $AB = CD$ (≅ segments have = length.); $BC = BC$ (Refl. Prop. of Eq.); $AB + BC = BC + CD$ (Add. Prop. of =); $AB + BC = AC$, $BC + CD = BD$ (Seg. Add. Post.); $AC = BD$ (Subst. Prop. of Eq.); $\overline{AC} \cong \overline{BD}$ (Segments with = length are ≅.) **b.** Answers may vary. Sample: You need to establish equality in order to add the same quantity ($m\angle 2$) to each side of the equation in Statement 3.

Practice

5. **a.** Given
   b. A midpt. divides a seg. into two ≅ segments.
   c. Substitution Prop.
   d. $2x = 12$
   e. Div. Prop. of Eq.

▼ STUDENT PAGES 44–45

Got It? a. Write a two-column proof.

Given: $\overline{AB} \cong \overline{CD}$

Prove: $\overline{AC} \cong \overline{BD}$

b. Reasoning In Problem 3, why is Statement 2 necessary in the proof?

Practice

5. **Developing Proof** Fill in the missing statements or reasons for the following two-column proof.

Given: C is the midpoint of $\overline{AD}$.

Prove: $x = 6$

4x, 2x + 12, A, C, D

Statements	Reasons
1) C is the midpoint of $\overline{AD}$.	1) a. ________
2) $\overline{AC} \cong \overline{CD}$	2) b. ________
3) $AC = CD$	3) ≅ segments have equal length.
4) $4x = 2x + 12$	4) c. ________
5) d. ________	5) Subtraction Property of Equality
6) $x = 6$	6) e. ________

3 Lesson Check

Do you know HOW?

If students have difficulty identifying the Distributive Property in Exercise 7, remind them that the process of combining like terms would not be possible without it.

Do you UNDERSTAND?

If students have difficulty with Exercise 9, have them show the arithmetic that is done to change one statement to the next statement. The arithmetic operation used should lead students to the property of equality that justifies it.

Close

Q What is the main difference between a Property of Equality and a Property of Congruence? **[A property of equality is used to justify equal numbers, while a property of congruence is used to justify congruent geometric figures.]**

ANSWERS

6. Trans. Prop. of Eq.
7. Distr. Prop.
8. Subtr. Prop. of Eq.
9. **a.** Given
   b. Subtr. Prop. of Eq.
   c. Div. Prop. of Eq.

▼ STUDENT PAGES 45–46

Lesson Check

Do you know HOW?

Name the property of equality or congruence that justifies going from the first statement to the second statement.

6. $m\angle A = m\angle S$ and $m\angle S = m\angle K$
   $m\angle A = m\angle K$

7. $3x + x + 7 = 23$
   $4x + 7 = 23$

8. $4x + 5 = 17$
   $4x = 12$

Do you UNDERSTAND?

9. **Developing Proof** Fill in the reasons for this algebraic proof.

Given: $5x + 1 = 21$

Prove: $x = 4$

Statements	Reasons
1) $5x + 1 = 21$	1) a. ________
2) $5x = 20$	2) b. ________
3) $x = 4$	3) c. ________

4 Practice

More Practice and Problem-Solving Exercises

ASSIGNMENT GUIDE
The assignments below are for the More Practice and Problem-Solving Exercises. You may also want to assign the A-Level Practice Exercises for homework if these are not used in class.
Average: 10–20
Advanced: 10–24

Mathematical Practices The exercises listed focus on the Standards for Mathematical Practices listed.
EX. 16: Make Sense of Problems (MP 1)
EX. 9, 18: Construct Arguments (MP 3)
EX. 17: Communicate (MP 3)
EX. 21: Critique the Reasoning of Others (MP 3)

EXERCISE 19: Use the **Think About a Plan** worksheet in the Online Teacher Resources to further support students' development in becoming independent learners.

HOMEWORK QUICK CHECK
To check students' understanding of key skills and concepts, go over Exercises 10, 12, 16, 18, and 19.

ANSWERS

10. $YU = AB$

11. $\angle K$

12. $\angle POR$

13. 3

14. $EF + 7$

15. $\angle XYZ \cong \angle WYT$

16. Samples: $\angle 1$ and $\angle 2$ are a linear pair, $m\angle 1 + m\angle 2 = 180$, $DB = EB$

17. Since $\overline{LR}$ and $\overline{RL}$ are two ways to name the same segment and $\angle CBA$ and $\angle ABC$ are two ways to name the same $\angle$, then both statements are examples of saying that something is $\cong$ to itself.

18. Domino C; Law of Syllogism

▼ STUDENT PAGES 46–47

More Practice and Problem-Solving Exercises

B Apply

Use the given property to complete each statement.

10. Symmetric Property of Equality
If $AB = YU$, then __?__.

11. Symmetric Property of Congruence
If $\angle H \cong \angle K$, then __?__ $\cong \angle H$.

12. Reflexive Property of Congruence
$\angle POR \cong$ __?__

13. Distributive Property
$3(x - 1) = 3x -$ __?__

14. Substitution Property
If $LM = 7$ and $EF + LM = NP$, then __?__ $= NP$.

15. Transitive Property of Congruence
If $\angle XYZ \cong \angle AOB$ and $\angle AOB \cong \angle WYT$, then __?__.

16. Think About a Plan A very important part in writing proofs is analyzing the diagram for key information. What true statements can you make based on the diagram at the right?
- What theorems or definitions relate to the geometric figures in the diagram?
- What types of markings show relationships between parts of geometric figures?

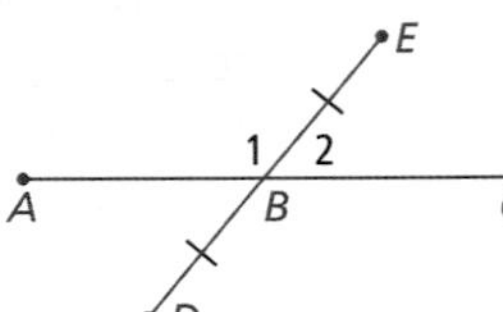

17. Writing Explain why the statements $\overline{LR} \cong \overline{RL}$ and $\angle CBA \cong \angle ABC$ are both true by the Reflexive Property of Congruence.

18. Reasoning Complete the following statement. Describe the reasoning that supports your answer.
The Transitive Property of Falling Dominoes: If Domino A causes Domino B to fall, and Domino B causes Domino C to fall, then Domino A causes Domino __?__ to fall.

More Practice and Problem-Solving Exercises *continued*

19. $KM = 35$ (Given); $KL + LM = KM$ (Seg. Add. Post.); $(2x - 5) + 2x = 35$ (Subst. Prop.); $4x - 5 = 35$ (Distr. Prop.); $4x = 40$ (Add. Prop. of Eq.); $x = 10$ (Div. Prop. of Eq.); $KL = 2x - 5$ (Given); $KL = 2(10) - 5$ (Subst. Prop.); $KL = 15$ (Simplify.)

20. $m\angle GFI = 128$ (Given); $m\angle GFE + m\angle EFI = m\angle GFI$ ($\angle$ Add. Post.); $(9x - 2) + 4x = 128$ (Subst. Prop.); $13x - 2 = 128$ (Distr. Prop.); $13x = 130$ (Add. Prop. of Eq.); $x = 10$ (Div. Prop. of Eq.); $m\angle EFI = 4x$ (Given); $m\angle EFI = 4(10)$ (Subst. Prop.); $m\angle EFI = 40$ (Simplify.)

21. The error is in the 5th step when both sides of the equation are divided by $b - a$, which is 0, and division by 0 is not defined.

22. reflexive, symmetric, and transitive; because "has the same birthday as" satisfies all three properties

23. Transitive only; A cannot be taller than A; if A is taller than B, then B is not taller than A.

24. Symmetric only; A cannot live in a different state than A, and if A lives in a different state than B and B lives in a different state than C, then it is possible that A and C live in the same state.

▼ STUDENT PAGE 47

Write a two-column proof.

Proof **19. Given:** $KM = 35$

Prove: $KL = 15$

$2x - 5$ $2x$ K L M

Proof **20. Given:** $m\angle GFI = 128$

Prove: $m\angle EFI = 40$

G $(9x - 2)°$ E $4x°$ F I

Challenge

21. Error Analysis The steps below "show" that $1 = 2$. Describe the error.

$a = b$	Given
$ab = b^2$	Multiplication Property of Equality
$ab - a^2 = b^2 - a^2$	Subtraction Property of Equality
$a(b - a) = (b + a)(b - a)$	Distributive Property
$a = b + a$	Division Property of Equality
$a = a + a$	Substitution Property
$a = 2a$	Simplify.
$1 = 2$	Division Property of Equality

Relationships **Consider the following relationships among people. Tell whether each relationship is *reflexive, symmetric, transitive,* or *none of these.* Explain.**

Sample: The relationship "is younger than" is not reflexive because Sue is not younger than herself. It is not symmetric because if Sue is younger than Fred, then Fred is not younger than Sue. It is transitive because if Sue is younger than Fred and Fred is younger than Alana, then Sue is younger than Alana.

22. has the same birthday as

23. is taller than

24. lives in a different state than

5 Assess and Remediate

Lesson Quiz

1. What is the value of x?

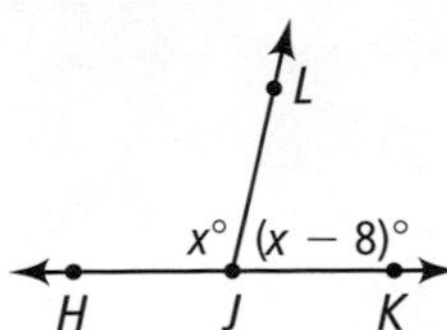

2. Do you UNDERSTAND? What is the name of the property of equality or congruence that justifies going from the first statement to the second statement?

a. $6a = 30$

$a = 5$

b. $\angle ABC \cong \angle LMN$

$\angle LMN \cong \angle ABC$

3. Write a two-column proof.

Given: $\frac{2}{3}(x - 6) = 8$

Prove: $x = 18$

ANSWERS TO LESSON QUIZ

1. $x = 94$

2. a. Division Property of Equality

b. Symmetric Property of Congruence

3. 1. $\frac{2}{3}(x - 6) = 8$, Given

2. $2(x - 6) = 24$, Multiplication Property of Equality

3. $2x - 12 = 24$, Distributive Property

4. $2x = 36$, Addition Property of Equality

5. $x = 18$, Division Property of Equality

Prescription for Remediation

Use the student work on the Lesson Quiz to prescribe a differentiated assignment.

Points	Differentiated Remediation
0–1	Intervention
2	On-level
3	Extension

Online Assessment

Assign the Lesson Quiz in Success Tracker on **pearsonsuccessnet.com**. Success Tracker will automatically score the quiz and assign appropriate intervention or enrichment to each student based on the results. The compiled data appear in three different reports for instant analysis of whole class and individual student performance.

Differentiated Remediation

Intervention

- **RETEACHING** (2 pages) Provides reteaching and practice exercises for the key lesson concepts. Use with struggling students or absent students.
- **ENGLISH LANGUAGE LEARNER SUPPORT** Helps students develop and reinforce mathematical vocabulary and key concepts.

On-Level

- **PRACTICE** (2 pages) Provides extra practice for each lesson. For simpler practice exercises, use the Form K Practice pages found in the Online Teacher Resources.
- **THINK ABOUT A PLAN** Helps students develop specific problem-solving skills and strategies by providing scaffolded guiding questions.
- **STANDARDIZED TEST PREP** Focuses on all major exercises, all major question types, and helps students prepare for the high-stakes assessments.

Extension

- **ENRICHMENT** Provides students with interesting problems and activities that extend the concepts of the lesson.
- **ACTIVITIES, GAMES, AND PUZZLES** Worksheets that can be used for concept development, enrichment, and for fun!

1-7 Proving Angles Congruent

Common Core State Standard
G.CO.9 Prove theorems about lines and angles . . . Theorems include: vertical angles are congruent . . .

Preparing to Teach

BIG idea Reasoning and Proof

ESSENTIAL UNDERSTANDING

Given information, definitions, properties, postulates, and theorems can be used as reasons in a proof.

Math Background

Students use two forms of proofs in this lesson: the two-column proof and the paragraph proof. While these proofs might look different on the written page, they are both considered direct proofs that logically progress from a given condition to the desired conclusion. Many other forms of proof are also employed in the study of mathematics.

In a sense, proofs are problems in which the answer is already known and the focus is on demonstrating how the answer is derived using principles of deductive reasoning and related definitions, postulates, and theorems.

ELL Support

FOCUS ON COMMUNICATION Arrange students into pairs of mixed abilities. Write the following statements on the board: The sum of $m\angle ABC$ and $m\angle DBC$ is 90. The sum of $m\angle RST$ and $m\angle DBC$ is 90. Prove that $m\angle ABC = m\angle RST$. Have one student write a two-column proof and the other write a paragraph proof. They can trade papers and check their work. Write another set of statements and have students switch tasks.

ASSESS UNDERSTANDING Write on the board: $\angle 1$ is one fourth the size of its complement, $\angle 2$. Draw a picture to model the measure of each angle.

Lesson Vocabulary

- theorem
- paragraph proof

Mathematical Practices

CONSTRUCT VIABLE ARGUMENTS AND CRITIQUE THE REASONING OF OTHERS. In writing proofs on the congruence of certain angles, students will communicate their reasoning clearly to others using the two-column proof as well as the paragraph proof.

1 Interactive Learning

Solve It!

PURPOSE To use inductive reasoning to make a conjecture about vertical angles

PROCESS Students may use knowledge of supplementary angles, inductive reasoning to make a conjecture, knowledge of congruent angles, or logical reasoning.

Q What is $m\angle 4$? Explain. **[$m\angle 4$ is 30; 180 − (60 + 90) = 30]**

Q If two angles are congruent, what conclusion can you make about the measures of the angles? **[If two angles are congruent, they have the same measure.]**

ANSWER $m\angle 1 = 30$; $m\angle 2 = 90$; $m\angle 3 = 60$; $m\angle 4 = 30$; $m\angle 1$ can be found by subtracting the sum of 60 and 90 from 180. The other measures can also be found by finding three angles with a sum of 180.

CONNECT THE MATH After students have completed the Solve It, ask them to state their conjecture about vertical angles. Remind students that they used inductive reasoning to make a conjecture about vertical angles, but deductive reasoning is necessary to prove that the conjecture is always true.

▼ DIGITAL (STUDENT WORK SPACE PAGE 48)

Getting Ready!

A quilter wants to duplicate this quilt but knows the measure of only two angles. What are the measures of angles 1, 2, 3, and 4? How do you know?

60° 1 2 3 4

2 Guided Instruction

Problem 1 Using the Vertical Angles Theorem

Take Note
Remind students that this theorem is a conditional statement that can be proven true. Let students know that each theorem introduced in the text will be followed with a proof using given information, postulates, definitions, properties, and theorems. Ask students to provide a description for each component of a proof.

Point out to students that the formal proof of the Vertical Angles Theorem likely resembles the logical reasoning that they used to complete the Solve It.

Problem 1

Q How can you check the solution to the equation for accuracy? **[Substitute the value for *x* into the algebraic expressions in the diagram and check to make sure that the angle measures are equal.]**

Q What are the measures of the labeled vertical angles? **[42]**

Q What are the measures of the unlabeled vertical angles? Explain. **[Using the definition of supplementary angles, the angles each measure 138.]**

▼ STUDENT PAGES 48–49

In the Solve It, you may have noticed a relationship between vertical angles. You can prove that this relationship is always true using deductive reasoning. A **theorem** is a conjecture or statement that you prove true.

Essential Understanding You can use given information, definitions, properties, postulates, and previously proven theorems as reasons in a proof.

take note **Theorem 1 Vertical Angles Theorem**

Vertical angles are congruent.

$\angle 1 \cong \angle 3$ and $\angle 2 \cong \angle 4$

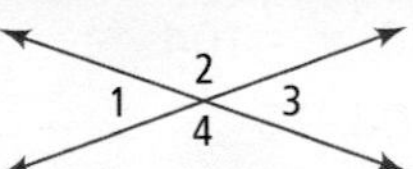

When you are writing a geometric proof, it may help to separate the theorem you want to prove into a hypothesis and conclusion. Another way to write the Vertical Angles Theorem is "If two angles are vertical, then they are congruent." The hypothesis becomes the given statement, and the conclusion becomes what you want to prove. A two-column proof of the Vertical Angles Theorem follows.

Proof Proof of Theorem 1: Vertical Angles Theorem

Given: $\angle 1$ and $\angle 3$ are vertical angles.

Prove: $\angle 1 \cong \angle 3$

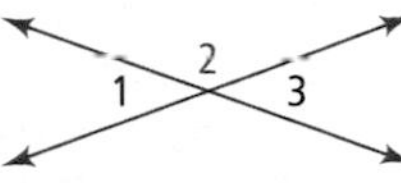

Statements	Reasons
1) $\angle 1$ and $\angle 3$ are vertical angles.	**1)** Given
2) $\angle 1$ and $\angle 2$ are supplementary. $\angle 2$ and $\angle 3$ are supplementary.	**2)** $\measuredangle$ that form a linear pair are supplementary.
3) $m\angle 1 + m\angle 2 = 180$ $m\angle 2 + m\angle 3 = 180$	**3)** The sum of the measures of supplementary $\measuredangle$ is 180.
4) $m\angle 1 + m\angle 2 = m\angle 2 + m\angle 3$	**4)** Transitive Property of Equality
5) $m\angle 1 = m\angle 3$	**5)** Subtraction Property of Equality
6) $\angle 1 \cong \angle 3$	**6)** $\measuredangle$ with the same measure are $\cong$.

▼ DIGITAL

Problem 1 Using the Vertical Angles Theorem GRIDDED RESPONSE

What is the value of *x*?

(2x + 21)° 4x°

Think

The two labeled angles are vertical angles, so set them equal.

Solve for *x* by subtracting 2x from each side and then dividing by 2.

Grid the answer as 21/2 or 10.5.

Write

$2x + 21 = 4x$

$21 = 2x$

$\frac{21}{2} = x$

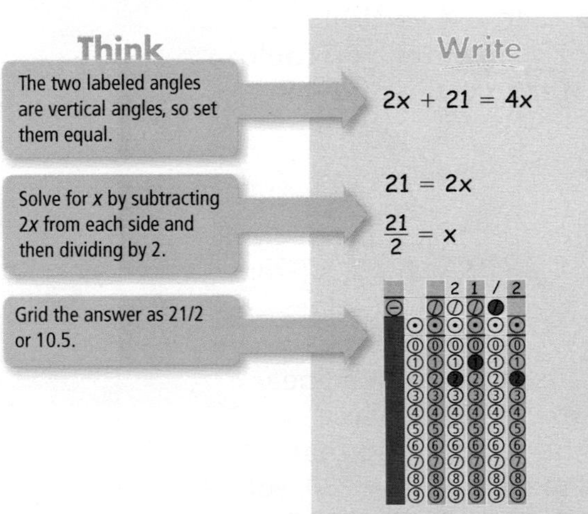

Problem 1 *continued*

Got It?

Q What is one first step for solving the equation for x? What is the justification for the step? **[Answers may vary. Sample: The Subtraction Property of Equality justifies subtracting $2x$ from both sides.]**

ANSWERS

Got It? 40

Practice

1. $x = 38$, $y = 104$

2. 76, 104, 76

▼ STUDENT PAGE 49

Got It? What is the value of x?

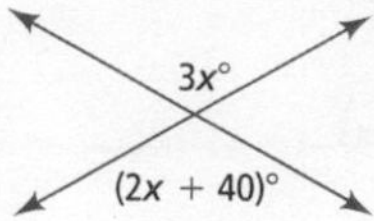

Think
How can you check that your value of x is correct?

Practice 1. Find the value of each variable.

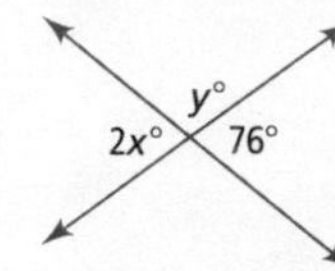

2. Find the measures of the labeled angles in Exercise 1.

Problem 2 Proof Using the Vertical Angles Theorem

Q If the given data for the proof were changed to $m\angle 1 = m\angle 4$, how would you modify the proof? **[Answers may vary. Sample: The second statement would be $\angle 1 \cong \angle 4$, justified by the definition of congruent angles.]**

Q Can you use this proof to draw a conclusion concerning the congruence of adjacent angles? Explain. **[No, the pairs in this diagram are congruent because of the given for the proof. Not all adjacent angles are congruent.]**

Got It?

Tell students to use the proof for Problem 2 as a template for the proof for part (a).

Let students know that each sentence in a paragraph proof can be worded in many ways, but the order of the sentences generally cannot change.

For example, the second sentence in the paragraph proof given could read "Because vertical angles are congruent, $\angle 4 \cong \angle 2$." However, you could not reverse the order of the second and third sentences.

ANSWERS

Got It? a. $\angle 1 \cong \angle 2$ (Given); $\angle 1 \cong \angle 3$, $\angle 2 \cong \angle 4$ (Vert. Angles are $\cong$); $\angle 1 \cong \angle 4$, $\angle 2 \cong \angle 3$ (Trans. Prop. of $\cong$); $\angle 1 \cong \angle 2 \cong \angle 3 \cong \angle 4$ (Trans. Prop. of $\cong$) **b.** Answers may vary. Sample: $m\angle 1 + m\angle 2 = 180$ because they form a linear pair. So $m\angle 1 = 90$ and $m\angle 2 = 90$ because $\angle 1 \cong \angle 2$. Then, using the relationship that $m\angle 2 + m\angle 3 = 180$ and $m\angle 1 + m\angle 4 = 180$, you can show that $m\angle 3 = m\angle 4 = 90$ by the Subtr. Prop. of Eq. Then $\angle 1 \cong \angle 2 \cong \angle 3 \cong \angle 4$ because their measures are =.

▼ DIGITAL

Problem 2 Proof Using the Vertical Angles Theorem

Given: $\angle 1 \cong \angle 4$

Prove: $\angle 2 \cong \angle 3$

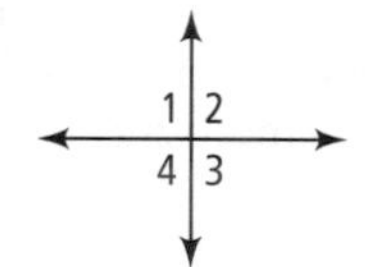

Statements	Reasons
1) $\angle 1 \cong \angle 4$	1) Given
2) $\angle 4 \cong \angle 2$	2) Vertical angles are $\cong$.
3) $\angle 1 \cong \angle 2$	3) Transitive Property of Congruence
4) $\angle 1 \cong \angle 3$	4) Vertical angles are $\cong$.
5) $\angle 2 \cong \angle 3$	5) Transitive Property of Congruence

▼ STUDENT PAGES 50–51

Proof Got It? a. Use the Vertical Angles Theorem to prove the following.

Given: $\angle 1 \cong \angle 2$

Prove: $\angle 1 \cong \angle 2 \cong \angle 3 \cong \angle 4$

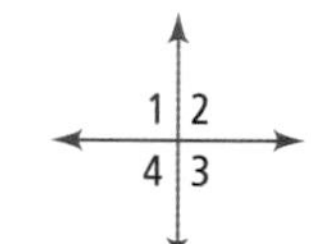

Think
How can you use the given information?

b. **Reasoning** How can you prove $\angle 1 \cong \angle 2 \cong \angle 3 \cong \angle 4$ without using the Vertical Angles Theorem?

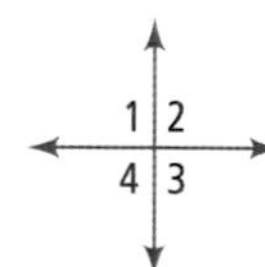

Practice 3. **Developing Proof** Complete the following proof by filling in the blanks.

Given: $\angle 1 \cong \angle 3$

Prove: $\angle 6 \cong \angle 4$

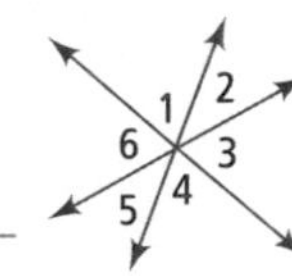

Statements	Reasons
1) $\angle 1 \cong \angle 3$	1) Given
2) $\angle 3 \cong \angle 6$	2) a. ______
3) b. ______	3) Transitive Property of Congruence
4) $\angle 1 \cong \angle 4$	4) c. ______
5) $\angle 6 \cong \angle 4$	5) d. ______

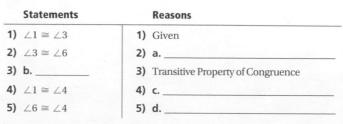

Practice

3. **a.** Vert. Angles Thm.
   b. $\angle 1 \cong \angle 6$
   c. Vert. Angles Thm.
   d. Trans. Prop. of $\cong$

▼ STUDENT PAGE 51

The proof in Problem 2 is two-column, but there are many ways to display a proof.

A **paragraph proof** is written as sentences in a paragraph. Below is the proof from Problem 2 in paragraph form. Each statement in the Problem 2 proof is red in the paragraph proof.

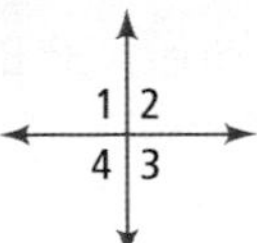

Proof **Given:** $\angle 1 \cong \angle 4$

Prove: $\angle 2 \cong \angle 3$

Proof: $\angle 1 \cong \angle 4$ is given. $\angle 4 \cong \angle 2$ because vertical angles are congruent. By the Transitive Property of Congruence, $\angle 1 \cong \angle 2$. $\angle 1 \cong \angle 3$ because vertical angles are congruent. By the Transitive Property of Congruence, $\angle 2 \cong \angle 3$.

Problem 3 Writing a Paragraph Proof

Take Note **VISUAL LEARNERS**
Ask students to make a sketch of two sets of linear angle pairs that would illustrate the Congruent Supplements Theorem. Have students label the angles with actual degree measures to make the illustrations as concrete as possible.

Problem 3
To provide students with reinforcement, ask them to write the paragraph proof for Problem 3 as a two-column proof.

Got It? **TACTILE LEARNERS**
To reinforce the necessary logical order of proofs, provide students with strips of paper that each contain one line of the proof of the Vertical Angles Theorem. Students will need to put the strips in order first before they write the steps in paragraph form.

ANSWERS

Got It? Refer to the two-column proof on Student page 49. Answers may vary. Sample: $\angle 1$ and $\angle 3$ are vert. angles because it is given. $\angle 1$ and $\angle 2$ are suppl. and $\angle 2$ and $\angle 3$ are suppl. because angles that form a linear pair are suppl. So, $m\angle 1 + m\angle 2 = 180$ and $m\angle 2 + m\angle 3 = 180$ by the def. of suppl. angles. By the Trans. Prop. of Eq., $m\angle 1 + m\angle 2 = m\angle 2 + m\angle 3$. By the Subtr. Prop. of Eq., $m\angle 1 = m\angle 3$. So, $\angle 1 \cong \angle 3$ because angles with the same measure are $\cong$.

Practice

4. **a.** 90
   b. 90
   c. $m\angle 3$
   d. $\cong$

▼ STUDENT PAGE 51

The Vertical Angles Theorem is a special case of the following theorem.

take note **Theorem 2 Congruent Supplements Theorem**

Theorem	If . . .	Then . . .
If two angles are supplements of the same angle (or of congruent angles), then the two angles are congruent.	$\angle 1$ and $\angle 3$ are supplements and $\angle 2$ and $\angle 3$ are supplements.	$\angle 1 \cong \angle 2$

You will prove Theorem 2 in Problem 3.

▼ DIGITAL

Problem 3 Writing a Paragraph Proof

Given: $\angle 1$ and $\angle 3$ are supplementary.
$\angle 2$ and $\angle 3$ are supplementary.

Prove: $\angle 1 \cong \angle 2$

Proof: $\angle 1$ and $\angle 3$ are supplementary because it is given. So $m\angle 1 + m\angle 3 = 180$ by the definition of supplementary angles. $\angle 2$ and $\angle 3$ are supplementary because it is given, so $m\angle 2 + m\angle 3 = 180$ by the same definition. By the Transitive Property of Equality, $m\angle 1 + m\angle 3 = m\angle 2 + m\angle 3$. Subtract $m\angle 3$ from each side. By the Subtraction Property of Equality, $m\angle 1 = m\angle 2$. Angles with the same measure are congruent, so $\angle 1 \cong \angle 2$.

▼ STUDENT PAGE 52

Proof **Got It?** Write a paragraph proof for the Vertical Angles Theorem.

A Practice

4. **Developing Proof** Fill in the blanks to complete this proof of the Congruent Complements Theorem (Theorem 3).

If two angles are complements of the same angle, then the two angles are congruent.

Given: $\angle 1$ and $\angle 2$ are complementary.
$\angle 3$ and $\angle 2$ are complementary.

Prove: $\angle 1 \cong \angle 3$

Proof: $\angle 1$ and $\angle 2$ are complementary and $\angle 3$ and $\angle 2$ are complementary because it is given. By the definition of complementary angles, $m\angle 1 + m\angle 2 =$ **a.** ________ and $m\angle 3 + m\angle 2 =$ **b.** ________. Then $m\angle 1 + m\angle 2 = m\angle 3 + m\angle 2$ by the Transitive Property of Equality. Subtract $m\angle 2$ from each side. By the Subtraction Property of Equality, you get $m\angle 1 =$ **c.** ________. Angles with the same measure are **d.** ________, so $\angle 1 \cong \angle 3$.

Problem 3 *continued*

Take Note

Students will be constructing proofs for these theorems in their homework. It would be beneficial to help students plan the proofs now. Elicit from students the following plans:

Theorem 3: Because both $\angle 1$ and $\angle 3$ are complementary to $\angle 2$, use their relationship with $\angle 2$ to deduce the relationship between $\angle 1$ and $\angle 3$.

Theorem 4: Use the definition of a right angle and the definition of congruent angles to conclude that $\angle 1 \cong \angle 2$.

Theorem 5: Use the definition of supplementary angles and the Substitution Property to create an equation which can be solved for either $m\angle 1$ or $m\angle 2$.

▼ STUDENT PAGE 53

The following theorems are similar to the Congruent Supplements Theorem.

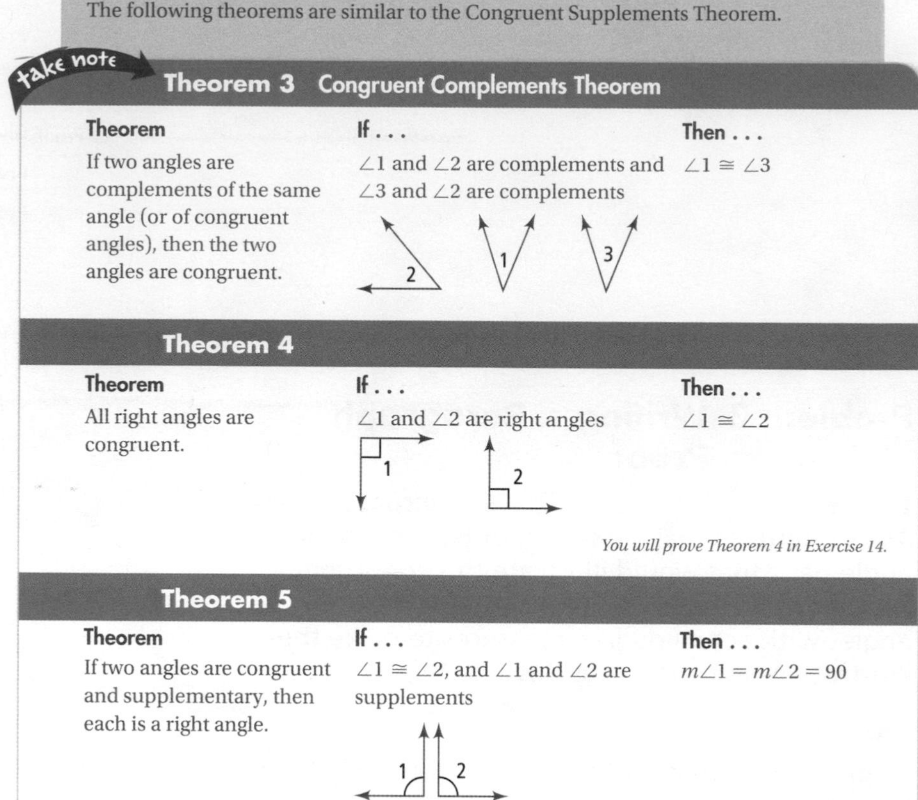

take note

Theorem 3 Congruent Complements Theorem

Theorem	If . . .	Then . . .
If two angles are complements of the same angle (or of congruent angles), then the two angles are congruent.	$\angle 1$ and $\angle 2$ are complements and $\angle 3$ and $\angle 2$ are complements	$\angle 1 \cong \angle 3$

Theorem 4

Theorem	If . . .	Then . . .
All right angles are congruent.	$\angle 1$ and $\angle 2$ are right angles	$\angle 1 \cong \angle 2$

You will prove Theorem 4 in Exercise 14.

Theorem 5

Theorem	If . . .	Then . . .
If two angles are congruent and supplementary, then each is a right angle.	$\angle 1 \cong \angle 2$, and $\angle 1$ and $\angle 2$ are supplements	$m\angle 1 = m\angle 2 = 90$

You will prove Theorem 5 in Exercise 19.

3 Lesson Check

Do you know HOW?

If students have difficulty with Exercise 5, then ask students to redraw the figure with letters for each vertex and ray. Ask them to list supplementary angles, complementary angles, and vertical angles.

Do you UNDERSTAND?

If students have difficulty understanding the relationship between a postulate and a theorem, have them compare that relationship with the notions of primary, secondary, and tertiary colors. The primary colors of red, yellow, and blue cannot be mixed from any other color and are the starting point for every other color. Secondary colors are colors made by mixing two primaries, and tertiary colors are made by mixing a primary and a secondary.

▼ STUDENT PAGE 53

Lesson Check

Do you know HOW?

5. What are the measures of $\angle 1$, $\angle 2$, and $\angle 3$?

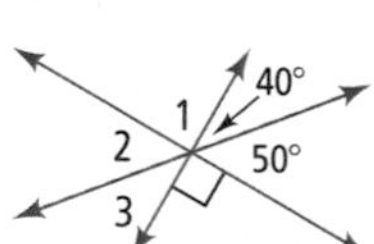

Close

Q What three equations could be used to determine the value of x in the figure below?

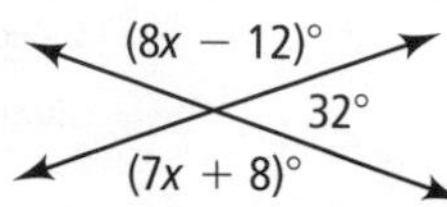

[$8x - 12 = 7x + 8$, $8x - 12 + 32 = 180$, $7x + 8 + 32 = 180$]

ANSWERS

5. $m\angle 1 = 90$, $m\angle 2 = 50$, $m\angle 3 = 40$

6. B
7. $\angle B \cong \angle C$ because both are suppl. to $\angle A$ and if two angles are suppl. to the same $\angle$, then they are $\cong$.
8. He used the Trans. Prop. of $\cong$, which does not apply here. $\angle 2$ and $\angle 3$ are $\cong$, not compl. If two angles are compl. to the same $\angle$, then they are $\cong$ to each other.
9. Answers may vary. Sample: A postulate is a statement that is assumed to be true, while a theorem is a statement that is proved to be true.

▼ STUDENT PAGE 54

6. What is the value of x?

Ⓐ 12 Ⓒ 120

Ⓑ 20 Ⓓ 136

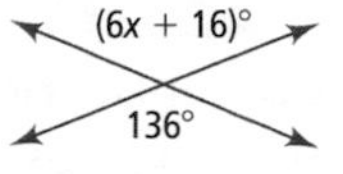

Do you UNDERSTAND?

7. **Reasoning** If $\angle A$ and $\angle B$ are supplements, and $\angle A$ and $\angle C$ are supplements, what can you conclude about $\angle B$ and $\angle C$? Explain.

8. **Error Analysis** Your friend knows that $\angle 1$ and $\angle 2$ are complementary and that $\angle 1$ and $\angle 3$ are complementary. He concludes that $\angle 2$ and $\angle 3$ must be complementary. What is his error in reasoning?

9. **Compare and Contrast** How is a theorem different from a postulate?

4 Practice

More Practice and Problem-Solving Exercises

ASSIGNMENT GUIDE
The assignments below are for the More Practice and Problem-Solving Exercises. You may also want to assign the A-Level Practice Exercises for homework if these are not used in class.
Average: 10–26
Advanced: 10–31

Mathematical Practices The exercises listed focus on the Standards for Mathematical Practices listed.

EX. 10: Make Sense of Arguments (MP 1)
EX. 7, 14, 19, 21: Construct Arguments (MP 3)
EX. 8: Critique the Reasoning of Others (MP 3)
EX. 11: Model with Mathematics (MP 4)
EX. 9: Use Clear Definitions (MP 6)

EXERCISE 21: Use the **Think About a Plan** worksheet in the Online Teacher Resources to further support students' development in becoming independent learners.

HOMEWORK QUICK CHECK
To check students' understanding of key skills and concepts, go over Exercises 10, 16, 18, 21, and 22.

ANSWERS

10. 55
11. Answers may vary. Sample: scissors
12. $x = 15$, $x + 10 = 25$, $4x - 35 = 25$
13. $x = 14$, $y = 15$; $3x + 8 = 50$, $5x - 20 = 50$, $5x + 4y = 130$
14. a. $\angle Y$
 b. right $\angle$
 c. $m\angle Y$
 d. $\angle X \cong \angle Y$
15. $x = 50$, $y = 50$

▼ STUDENT PAGE 55

More Practice and Problem-Solving Exercises

B Apply

10. **Think About a Plan** What is the measure of the angle formed by Park St. and 116th St.?
 • Can you make a connection between the angle you need to find and the labeled angle?
 • How are angles that form a right angle related?

Elm St.
116th St.
Main St.
Park St.
35°

11. **Open-Ended** Give an example of vertical angles in your home or classroom.

Algebra Find the value of each variable and the measure of each labeled angle.

12. 

13. 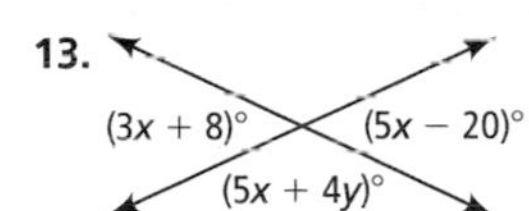

14. **Developing Proof** Fill in the blanks to complete this proof of Theorem 4. All right angles are congruent.

X Y

Given: $\angle X$ and $\angle Y$ are right angles.

Prove: $\angle X \cong \angle Y$

Proof: $\angle X$ and **a.** __?__ are right angles because it is given. By the definition of **b.** __?__, $m\angle X = 90$ and $m\angle Y = 90$. By the Transitive Property of Equality, $m\angle X =$ **c.** __?__. Because angles of equal measure are congruent, **d.** __?__.

15. **Miniature Golf** In the game of miniature golf, the ball bounces off the wall at the same angle it hit the wall. (This is the angle formed by the path of the ball and the line perpendicular to the wall at the point of contact.) In the diagram, the ball hits the wall at a 40° angle. Using Theorem 3, what are the values of x and y?

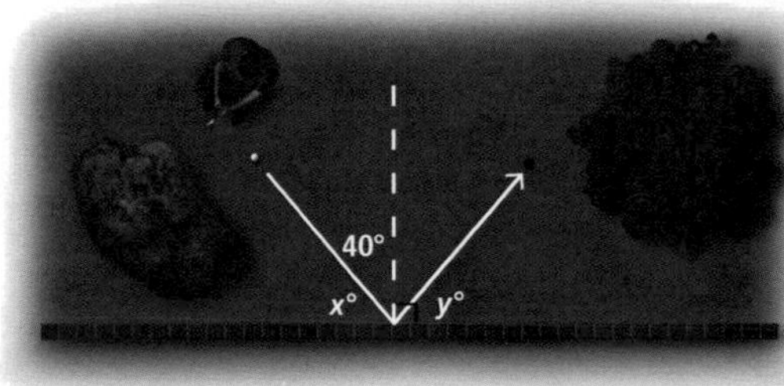

More Practice and Problem-Solving Exercises *continued*

16. $\angle AOD \cong \angle BOC$, $\angle AOB \cong \angle DOC$ because vert. angles are $\cong$. (Also, all of the straight angles are $\cong$ because each one has measure 180.)
17. $\angle EIG \cong \angle FIH$ because all rt. angles are $\cong$; $\angle EIF \cong \angle HIG$ because each one is compl. to $\angle FIG$ and compl. of the same $\angle$ are $\cong$.
18. $\angle KPJ \cong \angle MPJ$ (Given in the diagram); $\angle KPL \cong \angle MPL$ because each is suppl. to one of two $\cong$ angles. (Also, the two straight angles are $\cong$.)
19. **a.** it is given
 b. $m\angle V$
 c. 180
 d. Division
 e. right
20. If two angles are suppl. to $\cong$ angles, then the two angles are $\cong$ to each other.
21. By Theorem 5: If two angles are $\cong$ and suppl., then each is a right $\angle$.
22. $m\angle A = 60$, $m\angle B = 30$
23. $m\angle A = 30$, $m\angle B = 60$
24. $m\angle A = 120$, $m\angle B = 60$
25. $m\angle A = 90$, $m\angle B = 90$
26. $\angle 1$ and $\angle 2$ are suppl., $\angle 3$ and $\angle 4$ are suppl. (Given); $m\angle 1 + m\angle 2 = 180$, $m\angle 3 + m\angle 4 = 180$ (If two angles are suppl., then the sum of their measures is 180.); $m\angle 1 + m\angle 2 = m\angle 3 + m\angle 4$ (Subst. Prop.); $\angle 2 \cong \angle 4$ (Given); $m\angle 2 = m\angle 4$ (If two angles are $\cong$, their measures are $=$.); $m\angle 1 = m\angle 3$ (Subtr. Prop. of Eq.); $\angle 1 \cong \angle 3$ (If two angles have the same measure, then they are $\cong$.)
27. Answers may vary. Sample: $(-5, -1)$
28. **a.** B can be any point on the positive y-axis. Sample: (0, 5)
 b. Answers may vary. Sample: $(3, -1)$
29. $x = 30$, $y = 90$; 60, 120, 60
30. $x = 35$, $y = 70$; 70, 110, 70
31. $x = 50$, $y = 20$; 80, 100, 80

▼ STUDENT PAGES 56–57

Name two pairs of congruent angles in each figure. Justify your answers.

16. 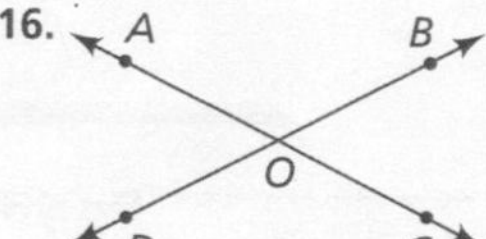

17. 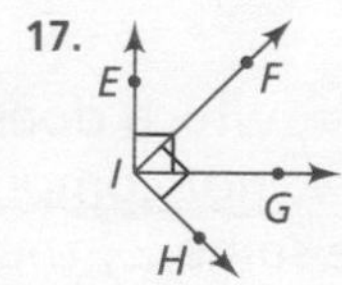

18. 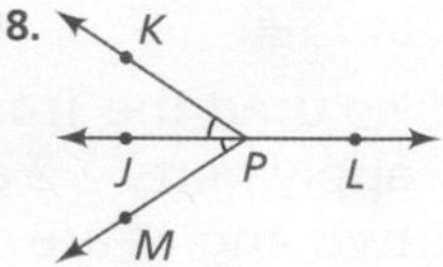

19. **Developing Proof** Fill in the blanks to complete this proof of Theorem 5. If two angles are congruent and supplementary, then each is a right angle.

Given: $\angle W$ and $\angle V$ are congruent and supplementary.

Prove: $\angle W$ and $\angle V$ are right angles.

Proof: $\angle W$ and $\angle V$ are congruent because **a.** __________. Because congruent angles have the same measure, $m\angle W =$ **b.** __________. $\angle W$ and $\angle V$ are supplementary because it is given. By the definition of supplementary angles, $m\angle W + m\angle V =$ **c.** __________. Substituting $m\angle W$ for $m\angle V$, you get $m\angle W + m\angle W = 180$, or $2m\angle W = 180$. By the **d.** __________ Property of Equality, $m\angle W = 90$. Since $m\angle W = m\angle V$, $m\angle V = 90$ by the Transitive Property of Equality. Both angles are **e.** __________ angles by the definition of right angles.

20. **Design** In the photograph, the legs of the table are constructed so that $\angle 1 \cong \angle 2$. What theorem can you use to justify the statement that $\angle 3 \cong \angle 4$?

21. **Reasoning** Explain why this statement is true: If $m\angle ABC + m\angle XYZ = 180$ and $\angle ABC \cong \angle XYZ$, then $\angle ABC$ and $\angle XYZ$ are right angles.

Algebra Find the measure of each angle.

22. $\angle A$ is twice as large as its complement, $\angle B$.
23. $\angle A$ is half as large as its complement, $\angle B$.
24. $\angle A$ is twice as large as its supplement, $\angle B$.
25. $\angle A$ is half as large as twice its supplement, $\angle B$.

Proof 26. Write a proof for this form of Theorem 2. If two angles are supplements of congruent angles, then the two angles are congruent.

Given: $\angle 1$ and $\angle 2$ are supplementary.
$\angle 3$ and $\angle 4$ are supplementary.
$\angle 2 \cong \angle 4$

Prove: $\angle 1 \cong \angle 3$

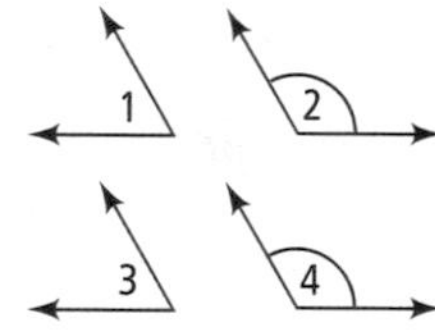

Challenge

27. **Coordinate Geometry** $\angle DOE$ contains points $D(2, 3)$, $O(0, 0)$, and $E(5, 1)$. Find the coordinates of a point F so that $\overrightarrow{OF}$ is a side of an angle that is adjacent and supplementary to $\angle DOE$.

28. **Coordinate Geometry** $\angle AOX$ contains points $A(1, 3)$, $O(0, 0)$, and $X(4, 0)$.
 a. Find the coordinates of a point B so that $\angle BOA$ and $\angle AOX$ are adjacent complementary angles.
 b. Find the coordinates of a point C so that $\overrightarrow{OC}$ is a side of a different angle that is adjacent and complementary to $\angle AOX$.

Algebra Find the value of each variable and the measure of each angle.

29. 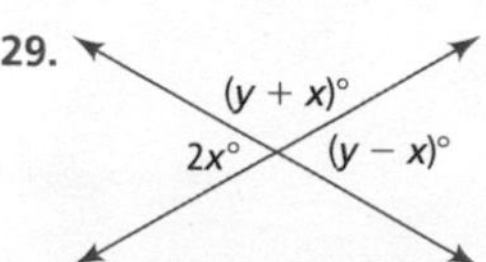

30. 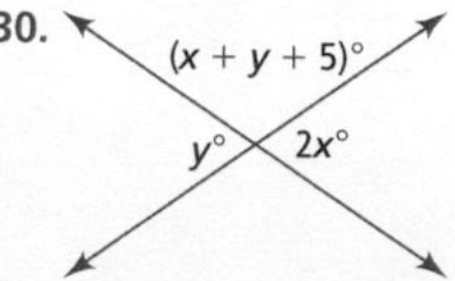

31. 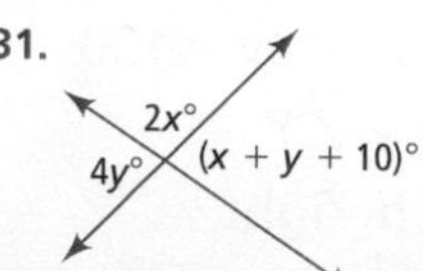

Assess and Remediate

Lesson Quiz

1. What is the value of x?

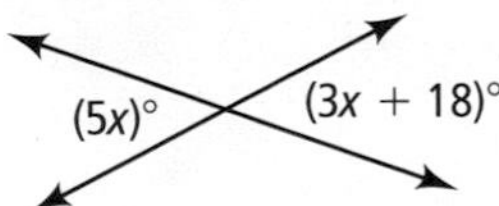

2. **Do you UNDERSTAND?** Write a paragraph proof that validates $x = 14$ as the solution in the figure below.

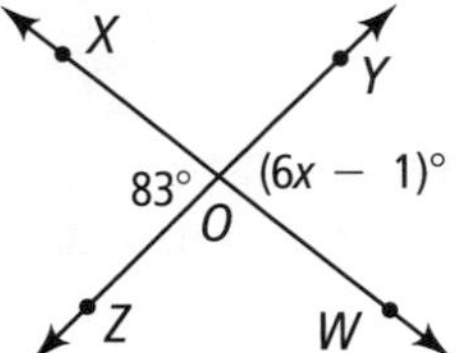

ANSWERS TO LESSON QUIZ

1. $x = 9$
2. Angles XOZ and YOW are congruent because they are vertical angles. So, their measures are equal by the definition of congruence and $83 = 6x - 1$. You can add 1 to each side of the equation by the Addition Property of Equality, which results in $84 = 6x$. Then by the Division Property of Equality $x = \frac{84}{6}$, or $x = 14$.

Prescription for Remediation

Use the student work on the Lesson Quiz to prescribe a differentiated assignment.

Points	Differentiated Remediation
0	Intervention
1	On-level
2	Extension

Online Assessment

Assign the Lesson Quiz in Success Tracker on **pearsonsuccessnet.com**. Success Tracker will automatically score the quiz and assign appropriate intervention or enrichment to each student based on the results. The compiled data appear in three different reports for instant analysis of whole class and individual student performance.

Differentiated Remediation

Intervention

- **RETEACHING** (2 pages) Provides reteaching and practice exercises for the key lesson concepts. Use with struggling students or absent students.
- **ENGLISH LANGUAGE LEARNER SUPPORT** Helps students develop and reinforce mathematical vocabulary and key concepts.

On-Level

- **PRACTICE** (2 pages) Provides extra practice for each lesson. For simpler practice exercises, use the Form K Practice pages found in the Online Teacher Resources.
- **THINK ABOUT A PLAN** Helps students develop specific problem-solving skills and strategies by providing scaffolded guiding questions.
- **STANDARDIZED TEST PREP** Focuses on all major exercises, all major question types, and helps students prepare for the high-stakes assessments.

Extension

- **ENRICHMENT** Provides students with interesting problems and activities that extend the concepts of the lesson.
- **ACTIVITIES, GAMES, AND PUZZLES** Worksheets that can be used for concept development, enrichment, and for fun!

Chapter Review

Essential Questions

BIG idea Reasoning and Proof

ESSENTIAL QUESTION How can you make a conjecture and prove that it is true?

ANSWER You can observe patterns to make a conjecture; you can prove it is true using given information, definitions, properties, postulates, and theorems.

Summative Questions

Use the following prompts as you review this chapter with your students. The prompts are designed to help you assess your students' understanding of the BIG Ideas they have studied.

- What is inductive reasoning?
- What is deductive reasoning?
- How do you write a conditional?

1-1 Basic Constructions

ANSWERS

1.

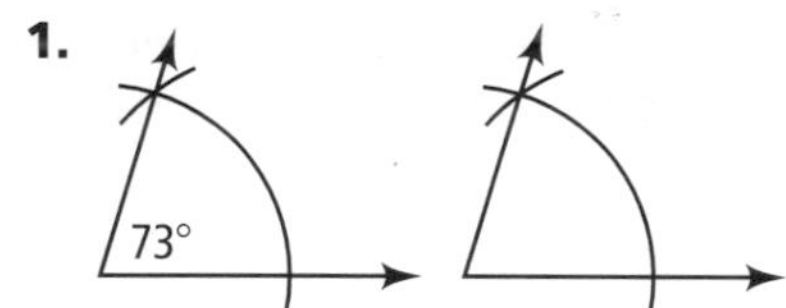

2.

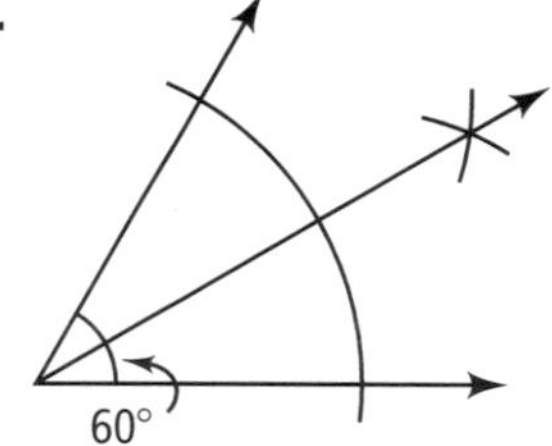

3.

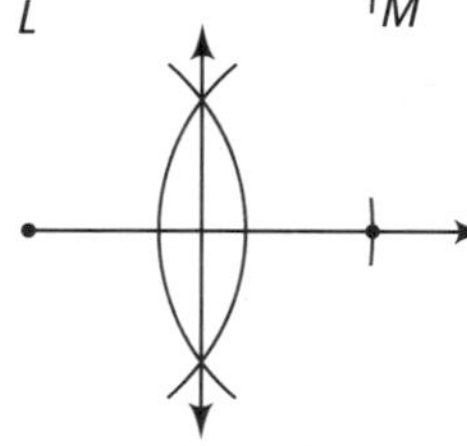

4. a-b.

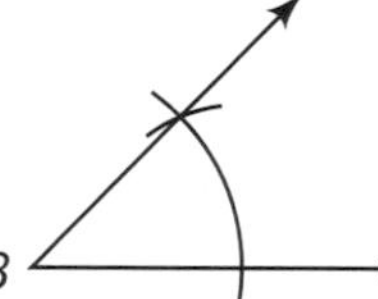

▼ STUDENT PAGE 58

1-1 Basic Constructions

Quick Review

Construction is the process of making geometric figures using a **compass** and a **straightedge**. Four basic constructions involve congruent segments, congruent angles, and bisectors of segments and angles.

Example

Construct $\overline{AB}$ congruent to $\overline{EF}$.

Step 1

Draw a ray with endpoint A.

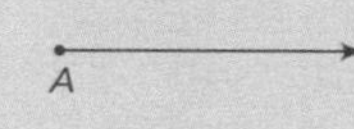

Step 2

Open the compass to the length of $\overline{EF}$. Keep that compass setting and put the compass point on point A. Draw an arc that intersects the ray. Label the point of intersection B.

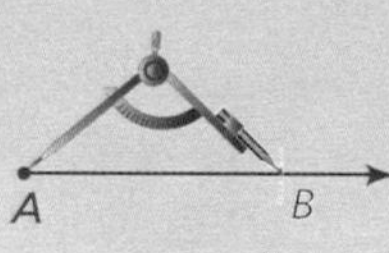

Exercises

1. Use a protractor to draw a 73° angle. Then construct an angle congruent to it.
2. Use a protractor to draw a 60° angle. Then construct the bisector of the angle.
3. Sketch $\overline{LM}$ on paper. Construct a line segment congruent to $\overline{LM}$. Then construct the perpendicular bisector of your line segment.

4. a. Sketch $\angle B$ on paper. Construct an angle congruent to $\angle B$.
   b. Construct the bisector of your angle from part (a).

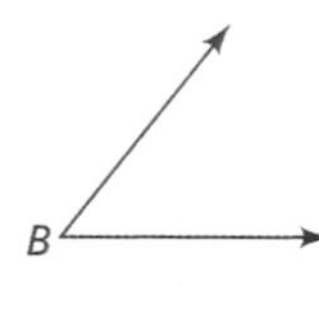

1-2 Patterns and Inductive Reasoning

ANSWERS

5. Divide the previous term by 10; 1, 0.1.
6. Multiply the previous term by −1 ; 5, −5.
7. Subtract 7 from the previous term; 6, −1.
8. Multiply the previous term by 4; 1536, 6144.
9. Answers may vary. Sample: $-1 \cdot 2 = -2$, and -2 is not greater than 2.
10. Answers may vary. Sample: Portland, Maine

▼ STUDENT PAGE 58

1-2 Patterns and Inductive Reasoning

Quick Review

You use **inductive reasoning** when you make conclusions based on patterns you observe. A **conjecture** is a conclusion you reach using inductive reasoning. A **counterexample** is an example that shows a conjecture is incorrect.

Example

Describe the pattern. What are the next two terms in the sequence?

$1, -3, 9, -27, \ldots$

Each term is −3 times the previous term. The next two terms are $-27 \times (-3) = 81$ and $81 \times (-3) = -243$.

Exercises

Find a pattern for each sequence. Describe the pattern and use it to show the next two terms.

5. 1000, 100, 10, . . .
6. 5, −5, 5, −5, . . .
7. 34, 27, 20, 13, . . .
8. 6, 24, 96, 384, . . .

Find a counterexample to show that each conjecture is false.

9. The product of any integer and 2 is greater than 2.
10. The city of Portland is in Oregon.

1-3 Conditional Statements

ANSWERS

11. If a person is a motorcyclist, then that person wears a helmet.

12. If two nonparallel lines intersect, then they intersect in one point.

13. If two angles form a linear pair, then the angles are supplementary.

14. If today is a certain holiday, then school is closed.

15. Converse: If the measure of an angle is greater than 90 and less than 180, then the angle is obtuse. Inverse: If an angle is not obtuse, then it is not true that its measure is greater than 90 and less than 180. Contrapositive: If it is not true that the measure of an angle is greater than 90 and less than 180, then the angle is not obtuse. All four statements are true.

16. Converse: If a figure has four sides, then the figure is a square. Inverse: If a figure is not a square, then it does not have four sides. Contrapositive: If a figure does not have four sides, then it is not a square. The conditional and the contrapositive are true. The converse and inverse are false.

17. Converse: If you play an instrument, then you play the tuba. Inverse: If you do not play the tuba, then you do not play an instrument. Contrapositive: If you do not play an instrument, then you do not play the tuba. The conditional and the contrapositive are true. The converse and inverse are false.

18. Converse: If you are busy on Saturday night, then you baby-sit. Inverse: If you do not baby-sit, then you are not busy on Saturday night. Contrapositive: If you are not busy on Saturday night, then you do not baby-sit. The conditional and the contrapositive are true. The converse and inverse are false.

▼ STUDENT PAGE 59

1-3 Conditional Statements

Quick Review

A **conditional** is an *if-then* statement. The symbolic form of a conditional is $p \rightarrow q$, where p is the **hypothesis** and q is the **conclusion**.

- To find the **converse**, switch the hypothesis and conclusion of the conditional ($q \rightarrow p$).
- To find the **inverse**, negate the hypothesis and the conclusion of the conditional ($\sim p \rightarrow \sim q$).
- To find the **contrapositive**, negate the hypothesis and the conclusion of the converse ($\sim q \rightarrow \sim p$).

Example

What is the converse of the conditional statement below? What is its truth value?

If you are a teenager, then you are younger than 20.

Converse: If you are younger than 20, then you are a teenager.

A 7-year-old is not a teenager. The converse is false.

Exercises

Rewrite each sentence as a conditional statement.

11. All motorcyclists wear helmets.

12. Two nonparallel lines intersect in one point.

13. Angles that form a linear pair are supplementary.

14. School is closed on certain holidays.

Write the converse, inverse, and contrapositive of the given conditional. Then determine the truth value of each statement.

15. If an angle is obtuse, then its measure is greater than 90 and less than 180.

16. If a figure is a square, then it has four sides.

17. If you play the tuba, then you play an instrument.

18. If you baby-sit, then you are busy on Saturday night.

Chapter Review *(continued)*

1-4 Biconditionals and Definitions

ANSWERS

19. No; it is not reversible; a magazine is a counterexample.

20. yes

21. No; it is not reversible; a line is a counterexample.

22. A phrase is an oxymoron if and only if it contains contradictory terms.

23. If two angles are complementary, then the sum of their measures is 90; if the sum of the measures of two angles is 90, then the angles are complementary.

▼ STUDENT PAGE 59

1-4 Biconditionals and Definitions

Quick Review

When a conditional and its converse are true, you can combine them as a true **biconditional** using the phrase *if and only if.* The symbolic form of a biconditional is $p \leftrightarrow q$. You can write a good **definition** as a true biconditional.

Example

Is the following definition reversible? If yes, write it as a true biconditional.

A hexagon is a polygon with exactly six sides.

Yes. The conditional is true: If a figure is a hexagon, then it is a polygon with exactly six sides. Its converse is also true: If a figure is a polygon with exactly six sides, then it is a hexagon.

Biconditional: A figure is a hexagon *if and only if* it is a polygon with exactly six sides.

Exercises

Determine whether each statement is a good definition. If not, explain.

19. A newspaper has articles you read.

20. A linear pair is a pair of adjacent angles whose noncommon sides are opposite rays.

21. An angle is a geometric figure.

22. Write the following definition as a biconditional. An oxymoron is a phrase that contains contradictory terms.

23. Write the following biconditional as two statements, a conditional and its converse. Two angles are complementary if and only if the sum of their measures is 90.

1-5 Deductive Reasoning

ANSWERS

24. Colin will become a better player.

25. $m\angle 1 + m\angle 2 = 180$

26. If two angles are vertical, then their measures are equal.

27. If your father buys new gardening gloves, then he will plant tomatoes.

▼ STUDENT PAGE 60

1-5 Deductive Reasoning

Quick Review

Deductive reasoning is the process of reasoning logically from given statements to a conclusion.

Law of Detachment: If $p \rightarrow q$ is true and p is true, then q is true.

Law of Syllogism: If $p \rightarrow q$ and $q \rightarrow r$ are true, then $p \rightarrow r$ is true.

Example

What can you conclude from the given information?

Given: **If you play hockey, then you are on the team. If you are on the team, then you are a varsity athlete.**

The conclusion of the first statement matches the hypothesis of the second statement. Use the Law of Syllogism to conclude: If you play hockey, then you are a varsity athlete.

Exercises

Use the Law of Detachment to make a conclusion.

24. If you practice tennis every day, then you will become a better player. Colin practices tennis every day.

25. $\angle 1$ and $\angle 2$ are supplementary. If two angles are supplementary, then the sum of their measures is 180.

Use the Law of Syllogism to make a conclusion.

26. If two angles are vertical, then they are congruent. If two angles are congruent, then their measures are equal.

27. If your father buys new gardening gloves, then he will work in his garden. If he works in his garden, then he will plant tomatoes.

1-6 Reasoning in Algebra and Geometry

ANSWERS

28. **a.** Given
b. Seg. Add. Post.
c. Subst. Prop.
d. Distr. Prop.
e. Subtr. Prop. of Eq.
f. Div. Prop. of Eq.

29. BY

30. $p - 2q$

▼ STUDENT PAGE 60

1-6 Reasoning in Algebra and Geometry

Quick Review

You use deductive reasoning and properties to solve equations and justify your reasoning.

A **proof** is a convincing argument that uses deductive reasoning. A **two-column proof** lists each statement on the left and the justification for each statement on the right.

Example

What is the name of the property that justifies going from the first line to the second line?

$\angle A \cong \angle B$ and $\angle B \cong \angle C$
$\angle A \cong \angle C$

Transitive Property of Congruence

Exercises

28. Algebra Fill in the reason that justifies each step.

Given: $QS = 42$

Prove: $x = 13$

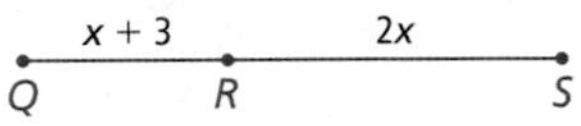

Statements	Reasons
1) $QS = 42$	1) a. ?
2) $QR + RS = QS$	2) b. ?
3) $(x + 3) + 2x = 42$	3) c. ?
4) $3x + 3 = 42$	4) d. ?
5) $3x = 39$	5) e. ?
6) $x = 13$	6) f. ?

Use the given property to complete the statement.

29. Division Property of Equality

If $2(AX) = 2(BY)$, then $AX =$? .

30. Distributive Property: $3p - 6q = 3($? $)$

1-7 Proving Angles Congruent

ANSWERS

31. 18

32. 74

33. 74

34. 106

35. $\angle 1$ is compl. to $\angle 2$, $\angle 3$ is compl. to $\angle 4$, and $\angle 2 \cong \angle 4$ are all given. So $\angle 1 \cong \angle 3$ by the Congruent Complements Theorem.

▼ STUDENT PAGE 61

1-7 Proving Angles Congruent

Quick Review

A statement that you prove true is a **theorem**. A proof written as a paragraph is a **paragraph proof**. In geometry, each statement in a proof is justified by given information, a property, postulate, definition, or theorem.

Example

Write a paragraph proof.

Given: $\angle 1 \cong \angle 4$

Prove: $\angle 2 \cong \angle 3$

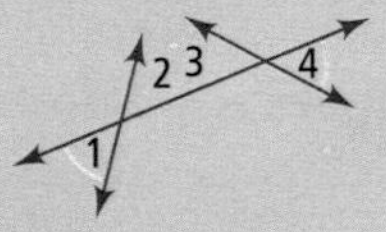

$\angle 1 \cong \angle 4$ because it is given. $\angle 1 \cong \angle 2$ because vertical angles are congruent. $\angle 4 \cong \angle 2$ by the Transitive Property of Congruence. $\angle 4 \cong \angle 3$ because vertical angles are congruent. $\angle 2 \cong \angle 3$ by the Transitive Property of Congruence.

Exercises

Use the diagram for Exercises 31–34.

31. Find the value of y.

32. Find $m\angle AEC$.

33. Find $m\angle BED$.

34. Find $m\angle AEB$.

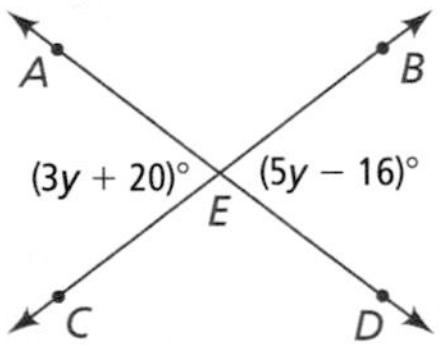

35. Given: $\angle 1$ and $\angle 2$ are complementary.
$\angle 3$ and $\angle 4$ are complementary.
$\angle 2 \cong \angle 4$

Prove: $\angle 1 \cong \angle 3$

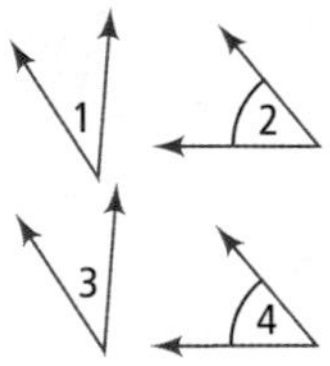

Pull It All Together

Common Core State Standard
Prepares for G.CO.9 Prove theorems . . .

Using Performance Tasks

Understanding by Design® principles support using performance tasks to assess students' progress toward mastering content standards and developing proficiency with the Mathematical Practices.

Mathematical Practices

- Make sense of problems and persevere in solving them.
- Model with mathematics.
- Construct viable arguments.

Assessing Performance

See the Implementation Guide for a holistic scoring rubric to use in assessing students' work on the performance task.

Guiding Questions

Q Can you find a counterexample that disproves your conjecture?

Q How are the numbers that lie inside any 2-by-2 square related to the number in the upper-left corner of the square?

Q Once you have represented the four numbers that lie inside any 2-by-2 square as algebraic expressions, what should you do next in order to prove your conjecture?

Solution Outline

Conjecture: If four numbers lie inside a 2-by-2 square on a calendar page, then the sums of the numbers that lie on the diagonals of the square are equal.

Proof: Let the number in the upper-left corner of the square be n. Then the other numbers in the square are $n + 1$, $n + 7$, and $n + 8$.

The numbers on one diagonal are n and $n + 8$. The sum of these numbers is $n + (n + 8) = 2n + 8$.

The numbers on the other diagonal are $n + 1$ and $n + 7$. The sum of these numbers is $(n + 1) + (n + 7) = 2n + 8$.

The sums are equal for any positive integer n. This proves that the sums of the numbers that lie on the diagonals are equal.

▼ STUDENT PAGE 62

Analyzing a Calendar Pattern

The figure shows a page from a calendar. Choose any four numbers from the calendar that lie inside a 2-by-2 square. One such set of numbers is shown below. Find the sum of the pair of numbers that lie on each diagonal of the square. What do you notice about the sums? Try this using other squares on the calendar and using calendar pages for different months.

MARCH						
SUN	MON	TUE	WED	THU	FRI	SAT
				1	2	3
4	5	6	7	8	9	10
11	12	13	14	15	16	17
18	19	20	21	22	23	24
25	26	27	28	29	30	31

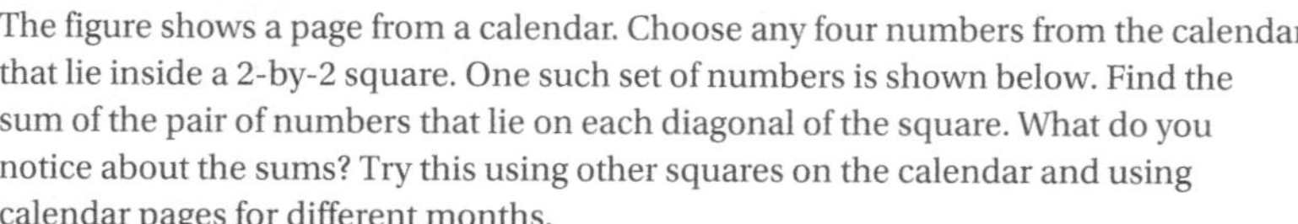

Task Description

Use inductive reasoning to make a conjecture about the calendar pattern you observed. Then use deductive reasoning to prove your conjecture.

- How can you write your conjecture as a conditional statement?
- How can you use algebraic expressions to represent the four numbers that lie inside any 2-by-2 square on any calendar page?

Get Ready!

Using This Diagnostic Assessment

Assign this diagnostic assessment to determine if students have the prerequisite skills for Chapter 2.

Lesson	Skill
Previous Course	Identifying Angle Pairs
Previous Course	Justifying Statements
Previous Course	Solving Equations

To remediate students, select from these resources (available for every lesson).

- Online Problems (pearsonsuccessnet.com)
- Reteaching (Online Teacher Resources)
- Practice (Online Teacher Resources)

Why Students Need These Skills

IDENTIFYING ANGLE PAIRS Angle relationships will be extended to parallel lines and triangles.

JUSTIFYING STATEMENTS Students will use statements to prove relationships among angles formed by parallel lines and triangles.

SOLVING EQUATIONS Equations will be used to find unknown angle measures in triangles and quadrilaterals.

Looking Ahead Vocabulary

INTERIOR AND EXTERIOR Ask students to name objects that are in the interior and exterior of the classroom.

TRANSVERSAL Have students name other words that use *trans-* as a prefix.

FLOW PROOF Show examples of flowcharts from various industries.

ANSWERS

1. $\angle 1$ and $\angle 5$, $\angle 5$ and $\angle 2$
2. $\angle 3$ and $\angle 4$
3. $\angle 1$ and $\angle 2$
4. $\angle 1$ and $\angle 5$, $\angle 5$ and $\angle 2$
5. Div. Prop. of =
6. Trans. Prop. of $\cong$
7. 4
8. 61
9. 15
10. Answers may vary. Sample: A figure divides a plane or space into three parts: the figure itself, the region inside the figure—called its interior—and the region outside the figure—called its exterior.
11. Answers may vary. Sample: *Trans-* means "cross"; a transversal crosses other lines.
12. Answers may vary. Sample: A flow proof shows the individual steps of the proof and how each step is related to the other steps.

▼ DIGITAL (STUDENT WORK SPACE PAGE 63)

Identifying Angle Pairs

Identify all pairs of each type of angles in the diagram.

1. linear pair
2. complementary angles
3. vertical angles
4. supplementary angles

1 5 2 3 4

Justifying Statements

Name the property that justifies each statement.

5. If $3x = 6$, then $x = 2$.
6. If $\angle 1 \cong \angle 2$ and $\angle 2 \cong \angle 3$, then $\angle 1 \cong \angle 3$.

Solving Equations

Algebra **Solve each equation.**

7. $3x + 11 = 7x - 5$
8. $(x - 4) + 52 = 109$
9. $(2x + 5) + (3x - 10) = 70$

Looking Ahead Vocabulary

10. The core of an apple is in the *interior* of the apple. The peel is on the *exterior*. How can the terms *interior* and *exterior* apply to geometric figures?
11. A ship sailing from the United States to Europe makes a transatlantic voyage. What does the prefix *trans-* mean in this situation? A *transversal* is a special type of line in geometry. What might a *transversal* do? Explain.
12. People in many jobs use *flow*charts to describe the logical steps of a particular process. How do you think you can use a *flow proof* in geometry?

PROVING THEOREMS ABOUT LINES AND ANGLES

Chapter 2 Overview

Log in to pearsonsuccessnet.com and click on Interactive Digital Path to access the Solve Its and animated Problems.

Chapter 2 expands on students' understandings and skills related to parallel and perpendicular lines. In this chapter, students will develop the answers to the Essential Questions posed below as they learn the bulleted concepts and skills.

BIG idea Reasoning and Proof

ESSENTIAL QUESTION How do you prove that two lines are parallel or perpendicular?

- Students will use postulates and theorems to explore lines in a plane.

BIG idea Measurement

ESSENTIAL QUESTION What is the sum of the measures of the angles of a triangle?

- Students will use the Triangle Angle-Sum Theorem.

Chapter Preview

Dynamic Activity

Use the Dynamic Activity, an interactive math tool with guided instruction, to have students explore concepts visually and support the development of the Standards for Mathematical Practice.

Content Standards

Following are the key standards covered in this chapter.

Conceptual Category Geometry

DOMAIN Congruence G.CO

CLUSTER Prove geometric theorems (Standards G.CO.9, G.CO.10)
LESSONS 2-1, 2-2, 2-3, 2-4, 2-5

CLUSTER Make geometric constructions (Standards G.CO.12, G.CO.13) **LESSON** 2-6

Vocabulary

English/Spanish Vocabulary Audio Online:

English	Spanish
alternate exterior angles, *p. 67**	ángulos alternos externos
alternate interior angles, *p. 67*	ángulos alternos internos
corresponding angles, *p. 67*	ángulos correspondientes
exterior angle of a polygon, *p. 101*	ángulo exterior de un polígono
parallel lines, *p. 65*	rectas paralelas
same-side interior angles, *p. 67*	ángulos internos del mismo lado
skew lines, *p. 65*	rectas cruzadas
transversal, *p. 67*	transversal

**All page numbers refer to the Student Edition.*

CHAPTER 2

PROVING THEOREMS ABOUT LINES AND ANGLES

Math Background

Understanding by Design® principles were central to the development of the Big Ideas and the Essential Understandings. These will help your students build a structure on which to make connections to prior learning.*

Reasoning and Proof

BIG idea Definitions establish meanings and remove possible misunderstanding. Other truths are more complex and difficult to see. It is often possible to verify complex truths by reasoning from simpler ones by using deductive reasoning.

ESSENTIAL UNDERSTANDINGS

2-1 Not all lines and not all planes intersect. When a line intersects two or more lines, the angles formed at the intersection points create special angle pairs.

2-2 The special angle pairs formed by parallel lines and a transversal are either congruent or supplementary.

2-3 Certain angle pairs can be used to decide whether two lines are parallel.

2-4 The relationships of two lines to a third line can be used to decide whether two lines are parallel or perpendicular to each other.

Measurement

BIG idea Some attributes of geometric figures, such as length, area, volume, and angle measure, are measureable. Units are used to describe these attributes.

ESSENTIAL UNDERSTANDINGS

2-5 The sum of the angle measures of a triangle is always the same.

*UNDERSTANDING BY DESIGN® and UbD™ are trademarks of ASCD, and are used under license.

Angle Relationships Given Parallel Lines

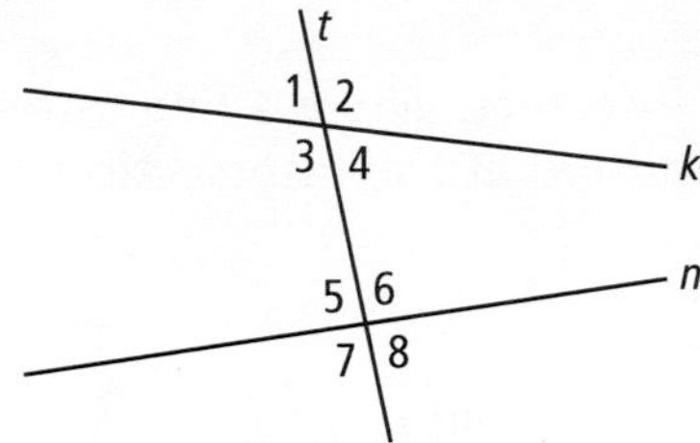

When two lines, such as *k* and *n* above, are intersected by a third line, such as *t*, the third line is called a *transversal*. There are special names for certain pairs of the eight angles that are formed. Students are likely to remember the terms and relationships better if they look closely at the reason why each term is applied.

Students need to understand that the word *linear* in linear pairs (such as $\angle 1$ and $\angle 2$ above) means "forming a line." Students should also understand that the angles between (or "inside") the two intersected lines ($\angle 3$, $\angle 4$, $\angle 5$, and $\angle 6$) are called *interior* angles. The words *interior* and *exterior* concern the relationship of an angle to the two intersected lines. The words *same-side* and *alternate* apply to two angles and their relationship to the transversal. Finally, students must understand that the word *corresponding* applies to both the intersected lines and the transversal: two corresponding angles (such as $\angle 1$ and $\angle 5$ or $\angle 4$ and $\angle 8$) are both above or both below the intersected lines and both to the left or both to the right of the transversal. The term *vertical angles* (such as $\angle 1$ and $\angle 4$) is harder to justify, but you can point out that such angles are never side by side.

Common Errors With Angle Relationships

Students may assume that the relations of corresponding angles, same-side interior angles, and alternate interior and exterior angles do not exist at all when the two intersected lines are not parallel. Students need to understand that the angle-pair relations exist when two lines are intersected by a transversal, whether the lines are parallel or not. Likewise, they need to understand that some of the angle-pair relations can be used to find angle measures only when the intersected lines are parallel.

Mathematical Practices

Attend to precision. Students use precise vocabulary and definitions to discuss angle pairs and parallel lines. Their reasoning for finding the angle-pair relationships uses previously established ideas. They continue to build their ability to prove geometric statements.

2-1 Lines and Angles

Common Core State Standards
G.CO.1 Know precise definitions of . . . perpendicular line, parallel line . . . based on the undefined notions of point, line . . . **Also prepares for G.CO.9**

Preparing to Teach

BIG idea Reasoning and Proof

ESSENTIAL UNDERSTANDING

Not all lines and not all planes intersect. When a line intersects two or more lines, the angles formed at the intersection points create special angle pairs.

Math Background

The concepts presented in this lesson will provide students with the vocabulary necessary to study the properties of parallel lines. The naming conventions for the special pairs of angles that are formed when a transversal intersects two lines are a foundation for many geometry topics. Students will need to confidently identify these relationships so that they can learn the theorems or postulates that relate to each of the four special pairs of angles. These relationships appear in problems concerning special quadrilaterals, angles of elevation and depression (triangle trigonometry), and congruent and similar triangles.

ELL Support

FOCUS ON LANGUAGE Have students make a card file with one card for each key concept and each postulate and theorem in the chapter. Have the students write in math symbols and in English using their own words. They may include illustrations for each postulate or theorem. Have students refer to the card file as they do problems throughout the chapter.

FOCUS ON COMMUNICATION Discuss the meaning of the prefixes in the words *interior* and *exterior*. [*In- means inside and ex- means outside.*] Have students identify the interior and exterior of a box, a building, and a triangle.

Lesson Vocabulary

- parallel lines
- skew lines
- parallel planes
- transversal
- alternate interior angles
- same-side interior angles
- corresponding angles
- alternate exterior angles

Mathematical Practices

ATTEND TO PRECISION. Students will consistently and appropriately use the parallel symbol in descriptions of lines and planes.

Interactive Learning

Solve It!

PURPOSE To become familiar with parallel planes using a three-dimensional object

PROCESS Students may visualize the assembled bookcase or make a paper model of the bookcase. Directions may include defined terms or descriptions of undefined terms.

Q Which pieces are the sides of the bookcase? Explain. **[A and D; They are longer than the other four pieces and have the same length.]**

Q What is the relationship of pieces B, C, E, and F to the sides of the assembled bookcase? **[Pieces B, C, E, and F form right angles with the sides of the bookcase.]**

▼ DIGITAL (STUDENT WORK SPACE PAGE 65)

Getting Ready!

You want to assemble a bookcase. You have all the pieces, but you misplaced the instructions that came with the box. How would you write the instructions?

ANSWER Pieces A and D are the sides of the bookcase. Pieces B, C, E, and F are the shelves; instructions may vary. Sample: Arrange pieces A and D so that a pair of flat faces are across from each other, and each piece stands upright with its long edges $\perp$ to the floor. Place piece B flat on the floor between A and D so that its long edge is $\perp$ to the long edges of both A and D. Attach one short edge of B to each of pieces A and D. Place piece C in between and at the top of A and D so that its long edge is $\perp$ to the long edges of both A and D. Attach one short edge of C to each of pieces A and D. Attach pieces E and F in a similar manner in between pieces B and C.

CONNECT THE MATH Discuss the relationship between the two sides of the bookcase and the relationship between the shelves and the top of the bookcase. In this lesson, students will study the concepts associated with parallel lines and planes.

2 Guided Instruction

Problem 1 Identifying Nonintersecting Lines and Planes

Take Note

Ask students to identify objects in the classroom that model parallel lines, skew lines, and parallel planes.

Problem 1

Q What planes can be constructed with the vertices shown that do not contain a face of the figure? **[*ABGH*, *CDEF*, *ADGF*, *BCHE*, *BFHD*, *AEGC*]**

Q How many planes can be constructed containing $\overline{AB}$ and at least one other segment in the diagram? **[3]**

Q Of the three planes that contain $\overline{AB}$ and at least one other segment, which does not also contain a face of the prism? **[plane *ABGH*]**

Q For a segment to be skew to $\overline{CD}$, what conditions must be true? **[The segment must not be in the same plane as $\overline{CD}$ and must not be parallel to $\overline{CD}$.]**

Q How many pairs of parallel planes are shown in the diagram? Identify each pair. **[3; top and bottom, front and back sides, left and right sides]**

Got It? TACTILE LEARNERS

Have students hold a model of a rectangular prism, such as a shoebox, to visualize the planes. Students can label the corners and edges of the box and use pieces of paper to model the different planes. The *ABGH* plane and other diagonal planes can be illustrated after removing the top of the box.

ANSWERS

Got It? a. $\overline{EH}$, $\overline{BC}$, $\overline{FG}$ **b.** Sample: They are both in plane *FEDC*, so they are coplanar. **c.** plane *BCG* ∥ plane *ADH* **d.** any two of $\overline{AB}$, $\overline{BF}$, $\overline{EF}$, and $\overline{AE}$

Practice

1. Answers may vary. Sample: $\overleftrightarrow{AB}$, $\overleftrightarrow{BH}$
2. $\overleftrightarrow{GB}$, $\overleftrightarrow{DH}$, $\overleftrightarrow{CL}$

▼ STUDENT PAGE 65

In the Solve It, you used relationships among planes in space to write the instructions. In this lesson, you will explore relationships of nonintersecting lines and planes.

Essential Understanding Not all lines and not all planes intersect.

take note

Key Concept Parallel and Skew

Definition	Symbols	Diagram
Parallel lines are coplanar lines that do not intersect. The symbol ∥ means "is parallel to."	$\overleftrightarrow{AE} \parallel \overleftrightarrow{BF}$ $\overleftrightarrow{AD} \parallel \overleftrightarrow{BC}$	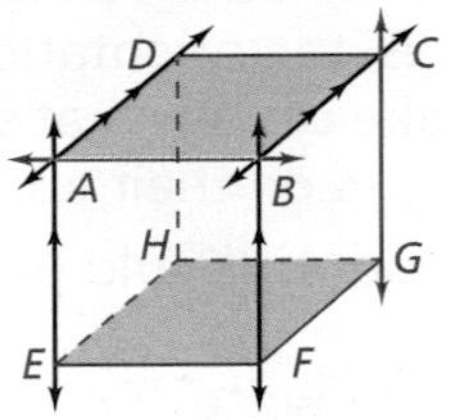
Skew lines are noncoplanar; they are not parallel and do not intersect.	$\overleftrightarrow{AB}$ and $\overleftrightarrow{CG}$ are skew.	
Parallel planes are planes that do not intersect.	plane *ABCD* ∥ plane *EFGH*	Use arrows to show $\overleftrightarrow{AE} \parallel \overleftrightarrow{BF}$ and $\overleftrightarrow{AD} \parallel \overleftrightarrow{BC}$.

A line and a plane that do not intersect are parallel. Segments and rays can also be parallel or skew. They are parallel if they lie in parallel lines and skew if they lie in skew lines.

▼ DIGITAL

Problem 1 Identifying Nonintersecting Lines and Planes

In the figure, assume that lines and planes that appear to be parallel are parallel.

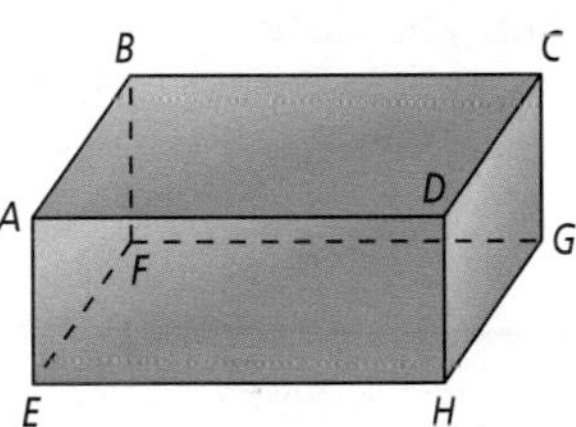

A Which segments are parallel to $\overline{AB}$?

$\overline{EF}$, $\overline{DC}$, and $\overline{HG}$

B Which segments are skew to $\overline{CD}$?

$\overline{BF}$, $\overline{AE}$, $\overline{EH}$, and $\overline{FG}$

C What are two pairs of parallel planes?

plane *ABCD* ∥ plane *EFGH*

plane *DCG* ∥ plane *ABF*

D What are two segments parallel to plane *BCGF*?

$\overline{AD}$ and $\overline{DH}$

▼ STUDENT PAGE 66

Got It? Use the figure in Problem 1, shown at the right.

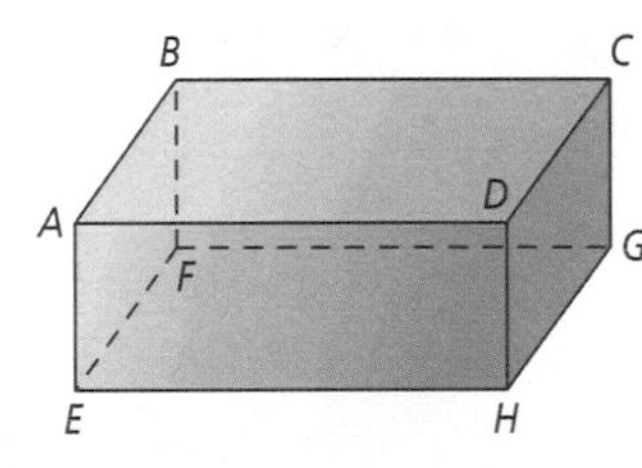

a. Which segments are parallel to $\overline{AD}$?

b. **Reasoning** Explain why $\overline{FE}$ and $\overline{CD}$ are *not* skew.

c. What is another pair of parallel planes?

d. What are two segments parallel to plane *DCGH*?

Practice Use the diagram to name each of the following. Assume that lines and planes that appear to be parallel are parallel.

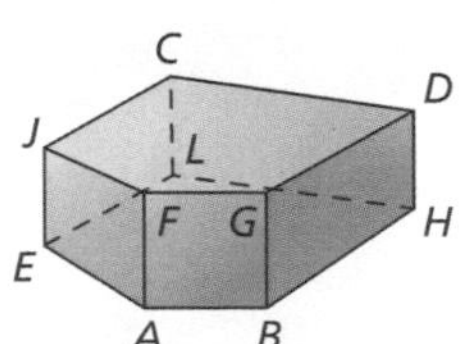

1. two lines that are skew to $\overleftrightarrow{EJ}$
2. all lines that are parallel to plane *JFAE*

Problem 2 Identifying an Angle Pair

Take Note VISUAL LEARNERS

Use the following suggestions to help students learn the names of the angles formed by two lines and a transversal.

- Students may use a colored pencil to lightly shade the four types of angles pairs.
- Students should draw several variations for each of the diagrams that are presented in the text. The variations should change the slopes of the lines, the orientation of the transversal, or both. Make certain that students label the pairs of angles on their additional diagrams.
- Students should paraphrase the definitions for each of the angle pairs. For example, a student might write "Corresponding angles: Two angles, both above a line and to the right of the transversal, etc."
- Students should note how many pairs of angles satisfy each of the four types of angle pairs.

Problem 2

Q Which line is the transversal? Explain. **[*r* is the transversal, because it intersects both line *m* and line *n*.]**

Q Why is choice B incorrect? **[∠6 and ∠7 are not on opposite sides of the transversal.]**

Got It?

Q How can you determine which angles are corresponding angles? **[The angles are on the same side of the transversal and are in exactly the same positions.]**

▼ STUDENT PAGE 67

Essential Understanding When a line intersects two or more lines, the angles formed at the intersection points create special angle pairs.

A **transversal** is a line that intersects two or more coplanar lines at distinct points. The diagram below shows the eight angles formed by a transversal *t* and two lines ℓ and *m*.

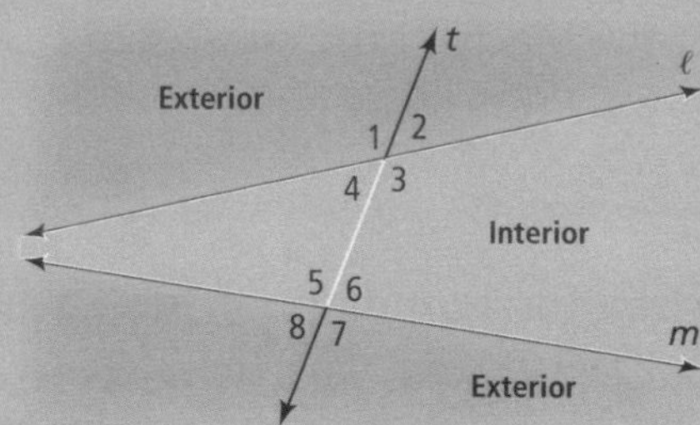

Notice that angles 3, 4, 5, and 6 lie between ℓ and *m*. They are *interior* angles. Angles 1, 2, 7, and 8 lie outside of ℓ and *m*. They are *exterior* angles.

Pairs of the eight angles have special names as suggested by their positions.

take note **Key Concept** Angle Pairs Formed by Transversals

Definition	Example
Alternate interior angles are nonadjacent interior angles that lie on opposite sides of the transversal.	∠4 and ∠6 ∠3 and ∠5
Same-side interior angles are interior angles that lie on the same side of the transversal.	∠4 and ∠5 ∠3 and ∠6
Corresponding angles lie on the same side of the transversal *t* and in corresponding positions.	∠1 and ∠5 ∠4 and ∠8 ∠2 and ∠6 ∠3 and ∠7
Alternate exterior angles are nonadjacent exterior angles that lie on opposite sides of the transversal.	∠1 and ∠7 ∠2 and ∠8

▼ DIGITAL

Problem 2 Identifying an Angle Pair

Multiple Choice Which is a pair of alternate interior angles?

Ⓐ ∠1 and ∠3 Ⓒ ∠2 and ∠6

Ⓑ ∠6 and ∠7 Ⓓ ∠4 and ∠8

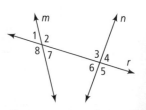

∠2 and ∠6 are alternate interior angles because they lie on opposite sides of the transversal *r* and in between *m* and *n*. The correct answer is C.

ANSWERS

Got It? any three of ∠1 and ∠3, ∠2 and ∠4, ∠8 and ∠6, ∠7 and ∠5

Practice

3. ∠5 and ∠6 (lines *d* and *e* with transversal *b*); ∠2 and ∠4 (lines *b* and *e* with transversal *c*); ∠1 and ∠7 (lines *c* and *d* with transversal *a*); ∠1 and ∠3 (lines *a* and *d* with transversal *c*)
4. ∠6 and ∠8 (lines *a* and *b* with transversal *d*)

▼ STUDENT PAGE 68

Got It? Use the figure at the right. What are three pairs of corresponding angles?

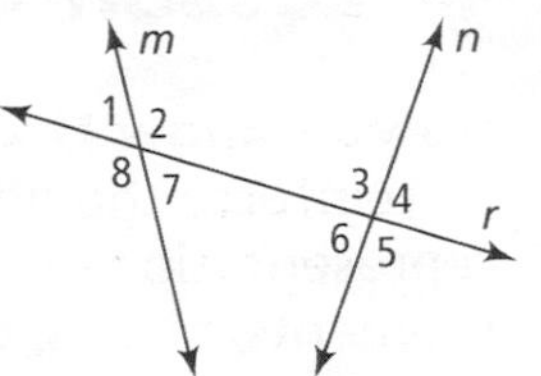

Practice Identify all pairs of each type of angles in the diagram. Name the two lines and the transversal that form each pair.

3. same-side interior angles
4. alternate exterior angles

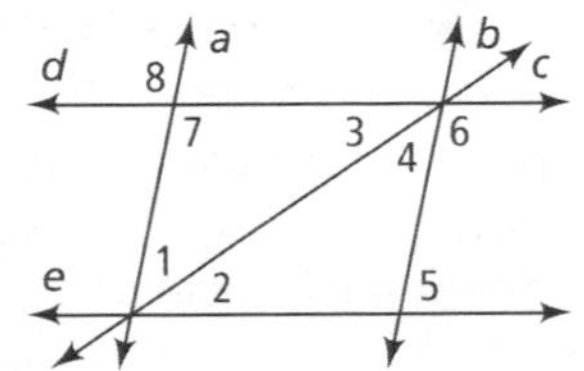

Problem 3 Classifying an Angle Pair

Q Are ∠2 and ∠4 interior or exterior angles? **[interior]**

Q Are ∠2 and ∠4 on opposite sides or the same side of the transversal? **[opposite sides]**

Got It?

Q Are ∠1 and ∠3 interior or exterior angles? **[∠1 is exterior and ∠3 is interior.]**

Q Are ∠1 and ∠3 in corresponding positions? Explain. **[Yes, both angles are above the transversal and to the left of the lines.]**

ANSWERS

Got It? corresp. ∠s

Practice

5. ∠1 and ∠2 are same-side int. ∠s; ∠3 and ∠4 are corresp. ∠s; ∠5 and ∠6 are corresp. ∠s.
6. corresp. ∠s

▼ DIGITAL

Problem 3 **Classifying an Angle Pair** STEM

Architecture The photo below shows the Royal Ontario Museum in Toronto, Canada. Are angles 2 and 4 *alternate interior angles, same-side interior angles, corresponding angles*, or *alternate exterior angles*?

Angles 2 and 4 are alternate interior angles.

▼ STUDENT PAGES 68–69

Got It? In Problem 3, are angles 1 and 3 *alternate interior angles, same-side interior angles, corresponding angles*, or *alternate exterior angles*?

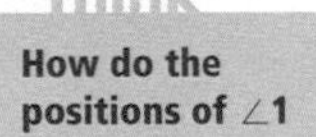
Think
How do the positions of ∠1 and ∠3 compare?

Practice

5. Are the angles labeled in the same color *alternate interior angles, same-side interior angles, corresponding angles*, or *alternate exterior angles*?

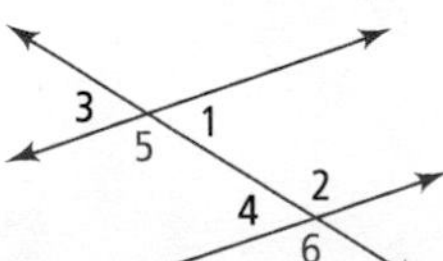

6. **Aviation** The photo shows an overhead view of airport runways. Are ∠1 and ∠2 *alternate interior angles, same-side interior angles, corresponding angles*, or *alternate exterior angles*?

3 Lesson Check

Do you know HOW?
To reinforce the definitions and their visual representations, ask students to name a pair of segments, planes, or angles that do not match the descriptions in Exercises 7–13, such as linear pairs or vertical angles.

Do you UNDERSTAND?
If students have difficulty with Exercise 15, then have them use a checklist of questions to identify what the angles have in common. They can also draw a diagram.

Close

Q Given the diagram in Problem 2 in this lesson, list a pair of same-side exterior angles **[∠1 and ∠4, or ∠5 and ∠8]**, a pair of same-side interior angles **[∠2 and ∠3, or ∠6 and ∠7]**, and pairs of corresponding angles **[∠1 and ∠3, ∠2 and ∠4, ∠5 and ∠7, ∠6 and ∠8]**.

ANSWERS

7–13. Answers may vary. Samples are given.

7. $\overline{EF}$ and $\overline{HG}$ **8.** $\overline{EF}$ and $\overline{GC}$

9. plane *ABF* ∥ plane *DCG*

10. ∠8 and ∠6 **11.** ∠3 and ∠8

12. ∠1 and ∠3 **13.** ∠1 and ∠4

14. Although lines that are not coplanar do not intersect, they are not parallel.

15. Alt. int. ∠s are ∠s between two lines on opposite, or alternate sides of a transversal.

16. Carly; the lines are coplanar since they are both in plane *ABH*, so $\overline{AB} \parallel \overline{HG}$.

▼ STUDENT PAGES 69–70

Lesson Check

Do you know HOW?

Name one pair each of the segments, planes, or angles. Lines and planes that appear to be parallel are parallel.

7. parallel segments

8. skew segments

9. parallel planes

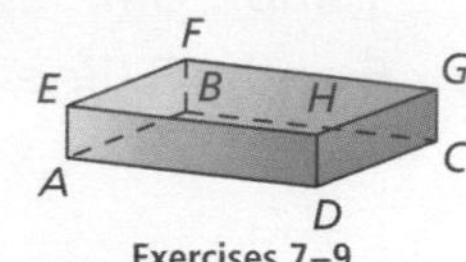

Exercises 7–9

10. alternate interior angles

11. same-side interior angles

12. corresponding angles

13. alternate exterior angles

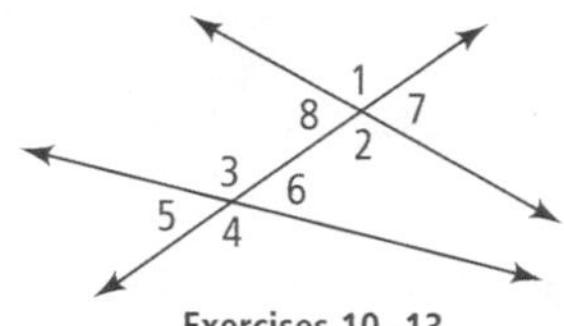

Exercises 10–13

Do you UNDERSTAND?

14. Vocabulary Why is the word *coplanar* included in the definition for parallel lines?

15. Vocabulary How does the phrase *alternate interior angles* describe the positions of the two angles?

16. Error Analysis In the figure at the right, lines and planes that appear to be parallel are parallel. Carly says $\overline{AB} \parallel \overline{HG}$. Juan says $\overline{AB}$ and $\overline{HG}$ are skew. Who is correct? Explain.

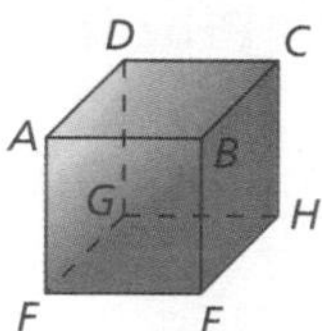

4 Practice

More Practice and Problem-Solving Exercises

ASSIGNMENT GUIDE
The assignments below are for the More Practice and Problem-Solving Exercises. You may also want to assign the A-Level Practice Exercises for homework if these are not used in class.
Average: 17–37
Advanced: 17–40

Mathematical Practices The exercises listed focus on the Standards for Mathematical Practices listed.

EX. 28, 40: Make Sense of Problems (MP 1)
EX. 36: Persevere in Solving Problems (MP 1)
EX. 37, 39: Construct Arguments (MP 3)
EX. 16: Critique the Reasoning of Others (MP 3)
EX. 35: Communicate (MP 3)
EX. 21: Model (MP 4)

EXERCISE 21: Use the **Think About a Plan** worksheet in the Online Teacher Resources to further support students' development in becoming independent learners.

HOMEWORK QUICK CHECK
To check students' understanding of key skills and concepts, go over Exercises 17, 21, 28, 32, and 36.

ANSWERS

17. 2 pairs
18. 4 pairs
19. 2 pairs
20. 4 pairs
21. Skew; answers may vary. Sample: Since the paths are not coplanar, they are skew.
22. true
23. False; $\overleftrightarrow{ED}$ and $\overleftrightarrow{HG}$ are skew.
24. true
25. False; the planes intersect.
26. true
27. False; both lines are in plane *ABC*.
28. No; the floor and the wall intersect, so figures on those planes are not parallel.
29. always
30. always
31. never
32. sometimes
33. sometimes
34. never
35. **a.** Lines may be intersecting, parallel, or skew.
b. Answers may vary. Sample: In a classroom, two adjacent edges of the floor are intersecting, two opposite edges of the floor are parallel, and one edge of the floor is skew to each of the vertical edges of the opposite wall.

▼ STUDENT PAGES 70–71

More Practice and Problem-Solving Exercises

Apply

How many pairs of each type of angles do two lines and a transversal form?

17. alternate interior angles
18. corresponding angles
19. alternate exterior angles
20. vertical angles

21. Recreation You and a friend are driving go-karts on two different tracks. As you drive on a straight section heading east, your friend passes above you on a straight section heading south. Are these sections of the two tracks *parallel, skew*, or *neither*? Explain.

In Exercises 22–27, describe the statement as *true* or *false*. If false, explain. Assume that lines and planes that appear to be parallel are parallel.

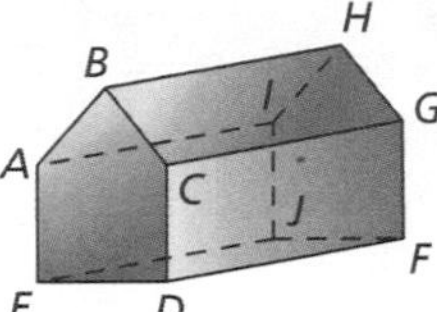

22. $\overleftrightarrow{CB} \parallel \overleftrightarrow{HG}$
23. $\overleftrightarrow{ED} \parallel \overleftrightarrow{HG}$
24. plane *AED* ∥ plane *FGH*
25. plane *ABH* ∥ plane *CDF*
26. $\overleftrightarrow{AB}$ and $\overleftrightarrow{HG}$ are skew lines.
27. $\overleftrightarrow{AE}$ and $\overleftrightarrow{BC}$ are skew lines.

28. Think About a Plan A rectangular rug covers the floor in a living room. One of the walls in the same living room is painted blue. Are the rug and the blue wall parallel? Explain.
- Can you visualize the rug and the wall as geometric figures?
- What must be true for these geometric figures to be parallel?

In Exercises 29–34, determine whether each statement is *always, sometimes*, or *never* true.

29. Two parallel lines are coplanar.
30. Two planes that do not intersect are parallel.
31. Two skew lines are coplanar.
32. Two lines that lie in parallel planes are parallel.
33. Two lines in intersecting planes are skew.
34. A line and a plane that do not intersect are skew.

35. **a. Writing** Describe the three ways in which two lines may be related.
b. Give examples from the real world to illustrate each of the relationships you described in part (a).

More Practice and Problem-Solving Exercises *continued*

36. Answers may vary. Sample: E illustrates same-side int. ∠s, and H illustrates alt. int. ∠s.

37. a. The lines of intersection are ||.

b. Sample: the lines of intersection of a wall with the ceiling and floor (or the lines of intersection of any of the 6 planes with two different, opposite faces)

38. No; if two planes intersect, then their intersection is a single line, and the intersection of planes *A* and *B* is $\overleftrightarrow{CD}$.

39. Yes;

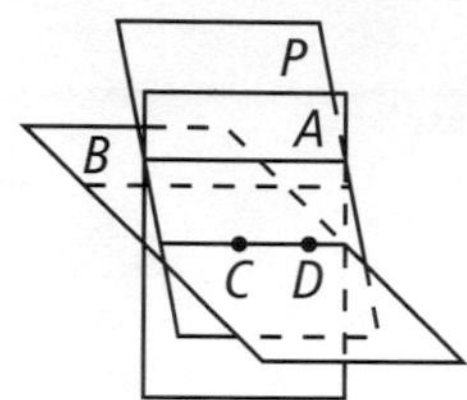

40. Answers may vary. Sample:

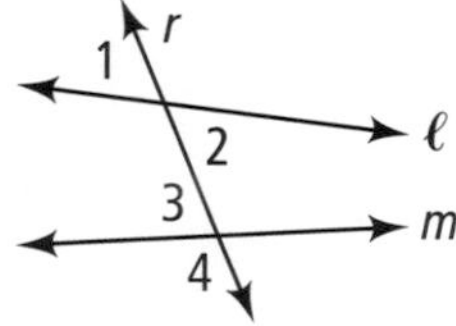

▼ STUDENT PAGE 71

36. Open-Ended The letter Z illustrates alternate interior angles. Find at least two other letters that illustrate pairs of angles presented in this lesson. Draw the letters. Then mark and describe the angles.

37. a. Reasoning Suppose two parallel planes *A* and *B* are each intersected by a third plane *C*. Make a conjecture about the intersection of planes *A* and *C* and the intersection of planes *B* and *C*.

b. Find examples in your classroom to illustrate your conjecture in part (a).

Challenge

Use the figure at the right for Exercises 38 and 39.

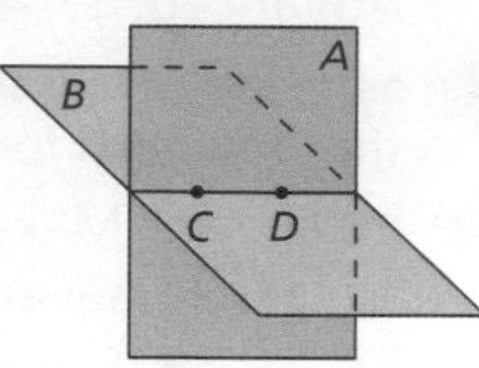

38. Do planes *A* and *B* have other lines in common that are parallel to $\overleftrightarrow{CD}$? Explain.

39. Visualization Are there planes that intersect planes *A* and *B* in lines parallel to $\overleftrightarrow{CD}$? Draw a sketch to support your answer.

40. Draw a Diagram A transversal *r* intersects lines ℓ and *m*. If ℓ and *r* form ∠1 and ∠2 and *m* and *r* form ∠3 and ∠4, sketch a diagram that meets the following conditions.

- ∠1 ≅ ∠2
- ∠3 is an interior angle.
- ∠4 is an exterior angle.
- ∠2 and ∠4 lie on opposite sides of *r*.
- ∠3 and ∠4 are supplementary.

5 Assess and Remediate

Lesson Quiz

1. Name a plane parallel to plane *ABCD*.

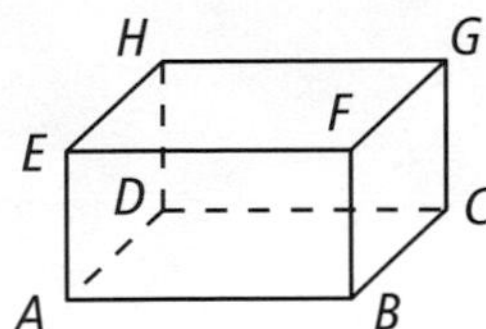

2. Name a pair of same-side interior angles in the figure below.

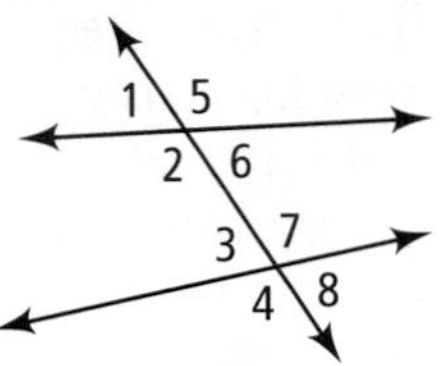

3. In the figure above, are ∠1 and ∠8 alternate interior angles, same-side interior angles, corresponding angles, or alternate exterior angles?

4. Do you UNDERSTAND? Why are alternate interior angles and alternate exterior angles both called "alternate"?

ANSWERS TO LESSON QUIZ

1. plane *EFGH*

2. ∠2 and ∠3 or ∠6 and ∠7

3. alternate exterior angles

4. Both alternate interior and alternate exterior angle pairs lie on opposite sides of the transversal.

Prescription for Remediation

Use the student work on the Lesson Quiz to prescribe a differentiated assignment.

Points	Differentiated Remediation
0–2	Intervention
3	On-level
4	Extension

Online Assessment

Assign the Lesson Quiz in Success Tracker on **pearsonsuccessnet.com**. Success Tracker will automatically score the quiz and assign appropriate intervention or enrichment to each student based on the results. The compiled data appear in three different reports for instant analysis of whole class and individual student performance.

Differentiated Remediation

Intervention

- **RETEACHING** (2 pages) Provides reteaching and practice exercises for the key lesson concepts. Use with struggling students or absent students.
- **ENGLISH LANGUAGE LEARNER SUPPORT** Helps students develop and reinforce mathematical vocabulary and key concepts.

On-Level

- **PRACTICE** (2 pages) Provides extra practice for each lesson. For simpler practice exercises, use the Form K Practice pages found in the Online Teacher Resources.
- **THINK ABOUT A PLAN** Helps students develop specific problem-solving skills and strategies by providing scaffolded guiding questions.
- **STANDARDIZED TEST PREP** Focuses on all major exercises, all major question types, and helps students prepare for the high-stakes assessments.

Extension

- **ENRICHMENT** Provides students with interesting problems and activities that extend the concepts of the lesson.
- **ACTIVITIES, GAMES, AND PUZZLES** Worksheets that can be used for concept development, enrichment, and for fun!

2-2 Properties of Parallel Lines

Common Core State Standard
G.CO.9 Prove theorems about lines and angles. Theorems include: . . . when a transversal crosses parallel lines, alternate interior angles are congruent . . .

Preparing to Teach

BIG idea Reasoning and Proof

ESSENTIAL UNDERSTANDING

The special angle pairs formed by parallel lines and a transversal are either congruent or supplementary. Geometric postulates and theorems can be combined with algebra to find some angle measures.

Math Background

The theorems in this lesson illustrate how a postulate is used as the starting point for the development of theorems. The Same-Side Interior Angles Postulate is a variation of Euclid's famous Parallel Theorem. For thousands of years, mathematicians tried to prove this postulate because they felt that it was less obviously true than Euclid's other four postulates. Mathematicians eventually realized that the Parallel Postulate is necessary for the development of Euclidean geometry and cannot be proved from the other four postulates. Other mathematicians found that systems of geometry (such as spherical geometry) exist for which the Parallel Postulate does not hold. (Students will learn the Parallel Postulate in an upcoming lesson, so you should not mention it at this point.) Note that if any of the Theorems 6, 7, or 8 had been the "postulate," the remaining theorems and Postulate 11 could be proved from that first assumed postulate.

ELL Support

CONNECT TO PRIOR KNOWLEDGE Ask: Where do you see parallel lines in our classroom? [sides of a bookshelf, opposite sides of floor tiles] Have two students hold pencils so that they model skew lines. Ask: Where do you see skew lines in our classroom? [edge of ceiling with one wall and edge of floor with an adjacent wall] Ask: Where do you see parallel planes in our classroom? [opposite walls or the floor and ceiling]

USE MANIPULATIVES Have small groups use books and pencils to model parallel and perpendicular lines and planes. (Students may use protractors to measure right angles.) Students should describe the models made by other groups. Have the students return to their groups and model skew lines. Each student should draw a picture of one of the models and write a description of it.

Mathematical Practices

ATTEND TO PRECISION. Students will use clear definitions of the included postulate and theorems relating to parallel lines to write proofs of the congruence of various angles. They will also communicate precisely, and use appropriate symbols.

Interactive Learning

Solve It!

PURPOSE To become familiar with the angles formed by a transversal and two parallel lines

PROCESS Students may use informal logical reasoning or cite previous theorems pertaining to angles.

Q Which angles form vertical pairs? **[∠1 and ∠3, ∠2 and ∠4, ∠5 and ∠7, ∠6 and ∠8, ∠9 and ∠11, ∠10 and ∠12]**

Q Which street is a transversal in the diagram? Explain. **[N. Garden Avenue is a transversal, because it intersects the streets that have numbered angles.]**

Q Does the direction of N. Garden Avenue affect the relationship that the intersections of the angles form? **[No, the angle measures change, but the relationships remain the same.]**

ANSWER ∠1 and ∠3, ∠2 and ∠4, ∠5 and ∠7, ∠6 and ∠8, ∠9 and ∠11, ∠10 and ∠12, ∠5 and ∠9, ∠8 and ∠12, ∠6 and ∠10, ∠7 and ∠11, ∠8 and ∠10, ∠7 and ∠9, ∠5 and ∠11, ∠6 and ∠12

▼ DIGITAL (STUDENT WORK SPACE PAGE 72

SOLVE IT!

Getting Ready!

Look at the map of streets in Clearwater, Florida. Nicholson Street and Cedar Street are parallel. Which pairs of angles appear to be congruent?

Palm Bluff St. 1 2 4 3 N. Garden Ave. 19 5 6 Cedar St. 8 7 9 10 Nicholson St. 12 11

CONNECT THE MATH In the Solve It, students looked for angles that appeared congruent. In this lesson, they will use measures of angles to find measures of related angles.

Guided Instruction

Problem 1 Identifying Supplementary Angles

Take Note VISUAL LEARNERS

In geometry, postulates are accepted without justification in the formal sense, although students know there is very strong evidence for them.

Problem 1

Q Which angles form a straight angle with $\angle 3$? **[$\angle 2$ and $\angle 4$]**

Q What angle forms a same-side interior angle pair with $\angle 3$? **[$\angle 8$]**

Q What angle is vertical to $\angle 8$? **[$\angle 6$]**

Got It? VISUAL LEARNERS

Have each student draw two parallel lines cut by a transversal with at least one angle measure given. Have them find the measure of each of the other angles.

ANSWERS

Got It? Yes, if you have the measure of at least one angle.

Practice

1. $\angle 7$ (vert. $\angle$s), $\angle 4$ (alt. int. $\angle$s), $\angle 5$ (corresp. $\angle$s)
2. $\angle 3$ (alt. int. $\angle$s), $\angle 1$ (corresp. $\angle$s)

▼ STUDENT PAGE 72

In the Solve It, you identified several pairs of angles that appear congruent. You already know the relationship between vertical angles. In this lesson, you will explore the relationships between the angles you learned about in Lesson 2-1 when they are formed by *parallel* lines and a transversal.

Essential Understanding The special angle pairs formed by parallel lines and a transversal are congruent, supplementary, or both.

take note

Postulate 11 Same-Side Interior Angles Postulate

Postulate	If . . .	Then . . .
If a transversal intersects two parallel lines, then same-side interior angles are supplementary.	$\ell \parallel m$	$m\angle 4 + m\angle 5 = 180$ $m\angle 3 + m\angle 6 = 180$

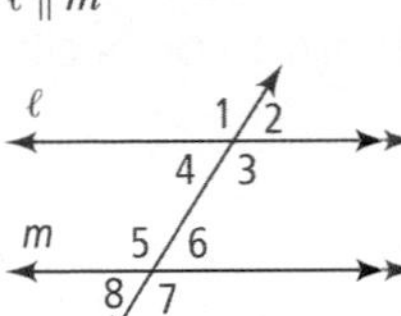

▼ DIGITAL

Problem 1 Identifying Supplementary Angles

The measure of $\angle 3$ is 55. Which angles are supplementary to $\angle 3$? How do you know?

By definition, a straight angle measures 180.

If $m\angle a + m\angle b = 180$, then $\angle a$ and $\angle b$ are supplementary by definition of supplementary angles.

$180 - 55 = 125$, so any angle x, where $m\angle x = 125$, is supplementary to $\angle 3$.

$m\angle 4 = 125$ by the definition of a straight angle.

$m\angle 8 = 125$ by the Same-Side Interior Angles Postulate.

$m\angle 6 = m\angle 8$ by the Vertical Angles Theorem, so $m\angle 6 = 125$.

$m\angle 2 = m\angle 4$ by the Vertical Angles Theorem, so $m\angle 2 = 125$.

▼ STUDENT PAGE 73

Got It? **Reasoning** If you know the measure of one of the angles, can you always find the measures of all 8 angles when two parallel lines are cut by a transversal? Explain.

Practice **Identify all the numbered angles that are congruent to the given angle. Justify your answers.**

1.

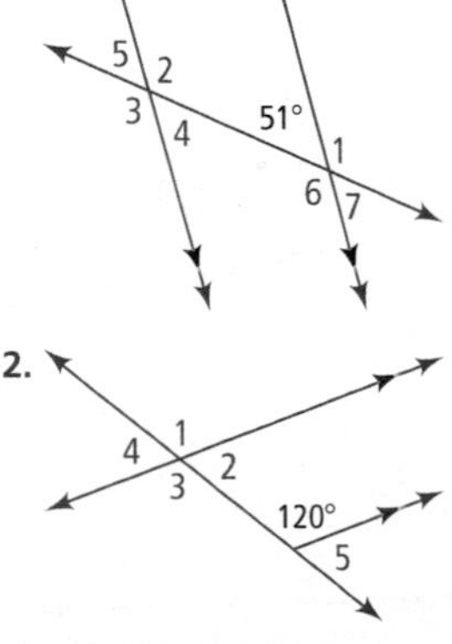

2.

Problem 2 Proving an Angle Relationship

Take Note

Ask students how the Alternate Interior Angles Theorem will lead to the Alternate Exterior Angles Theorem on p. 76. Show students that once it is known that alternate interior angles are congruent, the Vertical Angles Theorem and the Transitive Property of Congruence can be used to show that alternate exterior angles are congruent.

Students will be proving the Corresponding Angles Theorem in Exercise 22. Help students plan for the proof by using techniques from proofs of related theorems.

Proof of Theorem 6

Q What is meant by *alternate*? **[Answers may vary. Samples: to change back and forth, to take turns, one after another]**

Have students restate the proof of the Alternate Interior Angles Theorem in their own words.

Problem 2

Q What is the purpose of Statement and Reason 3 in the proof? **[The purpose is to convert a known relationship into a form that can be used for calculations.]**

Q Can Statements 4, 5, and 6 be presented in any other order? Explain. **[No; Statement 4 establishes a relationship that can be seen from the diagram. Statement 5 associates the relationship with a term that indicates a known measure. Statement 6 quantifies that relationship.]**

Q Which statements make the substitution in Statement 6 possible? **[Statements 3 and 5]**

Got It?

Q What theorem not used in the proof for Problem 2, will need to be used in this proof? Explain. **[The Vertical Angles Theorem will need to be used, because $\angle 5$ and $\angle 7$ form a vertical pair and $\angle 5$ and $\angle 1$ are corresponding angles.]**

▼ STUDENT PAGE 74

You can use the Same-Side Interior Angles Postulate to prove other angle relationships.

take note

Theorem 6 Alternate Interior Angles Theorem

Theorem	If . . .	Then . . .
If a transversal intersects two parallel lines, then alternate interior angles are congruent.	$\ell \parallel m$	$\angle 4 \cong \angle 6$ $\angle 3 \cong \angle 5$

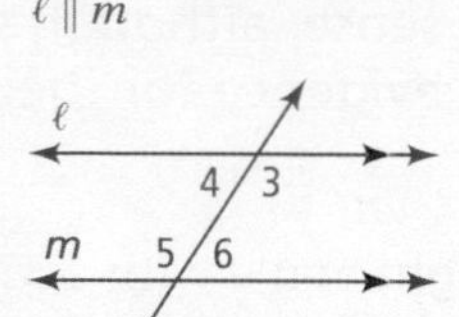

Theorem 7 Corresponding Angles Theorem

Theorem	If . . .	Then . . .
If a transversal intersects two parallel lines, then corresponding angles are congruent.	$\ell \parallel m$	$\angle 1 \cong \angle 5$ $\angle 2 \cong \angle 6$ $\angle 3 \cong \angle 7$ $\angle 4 \cong \angle 8$

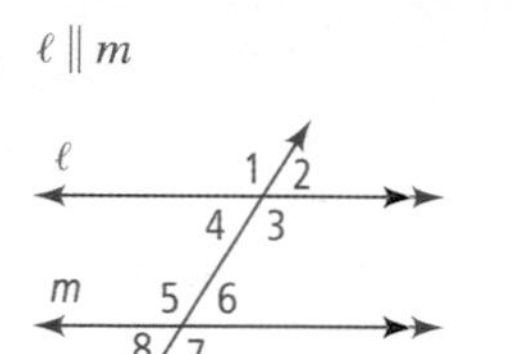

You will prove Theorem 7 in Exercise 22.

Proof Proof of Theorem 6: Alternate Interior Angles Theorem

Given: $\ell \parallel m$

Prove: $\angle 4 \cong \angle 6$

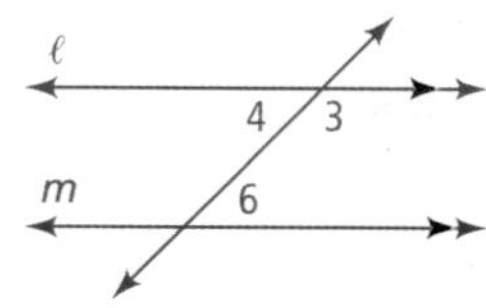

Statement	Reasons
1) $\ell \parallel m$	1) Given
2) $m\angle 3 + m\angle 4 = 180$	2) Supplementary Angles
3) $m\angle 3 + m\angle 6 = 180$	3) Same-Side Interior Angles Postulate
4) $m\angle 3 + m\angle 4 = m\angle 3 + m\angle 6$	4) Transitive Property of Equality
5) $m\angle 4 = m\angle 6$	5) Subtraction Property of Equality
6) $\angle 4 \cong \angle 6$	6) Definition of Congruence

▼ DIGITAL

ONLINE PROBLEMS **Problem 2** Proving an Angle Relationship

Given: $a \parallel b$

Prove: $\angle 1$ and $\angle 8$ are supplementary.

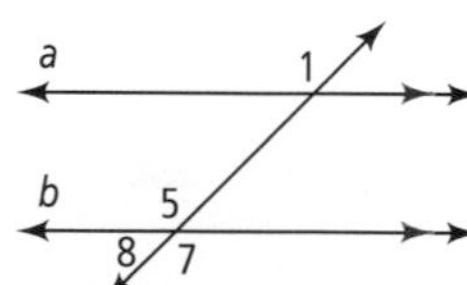

Know
- $a \parallel b$

From the diagram you know
- $\angle 1$ and $\angle 5$ are corresponding
- $\angle 5$ and $\angle 8$ form a linear pair

Need
$\angle 1$ and $\angle 8$ are supplementary, or $m\angle 1 + m\angle 8 = 180$.

Plan
Show that $\angle 1 \cong \angle 5$ and that $m\angle 5 + m\angle 8 = 180$. Then substitute $m\angle 1$ for $m\angle 5$ to prove that $\angle 1$ and $\angle 8$ are supplementary.

Statements	Reasons
1) $a \parallel b$	1) Given
2) $\angle 1 \cong \angle 5$	2) If lines are $\parallel$, then corresp. $\angle$s are $\cong$.
3) $m\angle 1 = m\angle 5$	3) Congruent $\angle$s have equal measures.
4) $\angle 5$ and $\angle 8$ are supplementary.	4) $\angle$s that form a linear pair are suppl.
5) $m\angle 5 + m\angle 8 = 180$	5) Def. of suppl. $\angle$s
6) $m\angle 1 + m\angle 8 = 180$	6) Substitution Property
7) $\angle 1$ and $\angle 8$ are supplementary.	7) Def. of suppl. $\angle$s

ANSWERS

Got It?

1. $a \parallel b$ (Given)
2. $\angle 1 \cong \angle 5$ (If lines are ∥, then corresp. ∠s are ≅.)
3. $\angle 5 \cong \angle 7$ (Vert. ∠s are ≅.)
4. $\angle 1 \cong \angle 7$ (Trans. Prop. of ≅)

Practice

3. a. If two ∥ lines are cut by a transversal, then the same-side int. ∠s are suppl.

b. If two ∥ lines are cut by a transversal, then the same-side int. ∠s are suppl.

c. If two ∠s are suppl. to the same ∠, then they are ≅.

4. 1. $a \parallel b$; $c \parallel d$ (Given)
2. $\angle 1 \cong \angle 4$ (Alt. int. ∠s are ≅.)
3. $\angle 4 \cong \angle 3$ (Corresp. ∠s are ≅.)
4. $\angle 1 \cong \angle 3$ (Trans. Prop. of ≅)

▼ STUDENT PAGES 75–76

Got It? Let $a \parallel b$. Prove that $\angle 1 \cong \angle 7$.

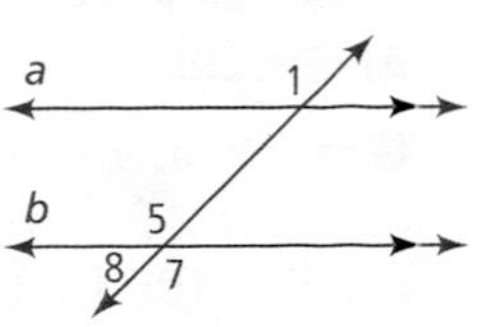

A Practice 3. **Developing Proof** Supply the missing reasons in the two-column proof.

Given: $a \parallel b$, $c \parallel d$

Prove: $\angle 1 \cong \angle 3$

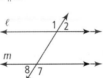

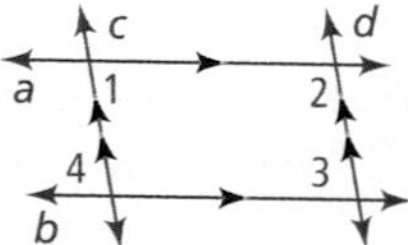

Statements	Reasons
1) $a \parallel b$	1) Given
2) ∠3 and ∠2 are supplementary.	2) a. ______
3) $c \parallel d$	3) Given
4) ∠1 and ∠2 are supplementary.	4) b. ______
5) $\angle 1 \cong \angle 3$	5) c. ______

Proof 4. Write a two-column proof for Exercise 3 that does not use ∠2.

Problem 3 Finding Measures of Angles

Take Note

Discuss with students why their work in the Got It was a proof of Theorem 8.

Problem 3

SYNTHESIZING

Q What are the angles that are congruent to ∠3? Justify each answer. **[∠5 by Vertical Angles, ∠7 and ∠8 by Corresponding Angles Theorem, ∠6 by Transitive Property of Congruence (first find ∠6 ≅ ∠7 or ∠6 ≅ ∠8 by Corresponding Angles Theorem)]**

Got It?

Q What angles do not have a measure of 105? **[∠1, ∠2, ∠4]**

Q What is the relationship of ∠1, ∠2, and ∠4 to any of the other numbered angles in the diagram? **[They are supplements.]**

EXTENSION

Q The quadrilateral formed by the two pairs of parallel lines is a parallelogram. What conjecture can you make about the measures of the four angles of the parallelogram? **[The measures of the opposite angles in a parallelogram are congruent, and the consecutive angles are supplementary.]**

▼ STUDENT PAGE 76

In the diagram for Problem 2, ∠1 and ∠7 are alternate exterior angles. In Got It 2, you proved the following theorem.

take note **Theorem 8 Alternate Exterior Angles Theorem**

Theorem	If . . .	Then . . .
If a transversal intersects two parallel lines, then alternate exterior angles are congruent.	$\ell \parallel m$	$\angle 1 \cong \angle 7$ $\angle 2 \cong \angle 8$

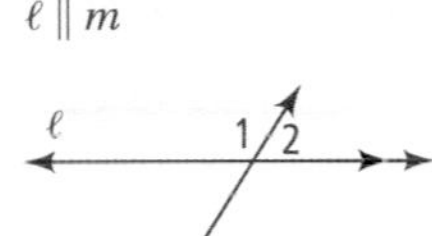

If you know the measure of one of the angles formed by two parallel lines and a transversal, you can use theorems and postulates to find the measures of the other angles.

▼ DIGITAL

Problem 3 Finding Measures of Angles

What are the measures of ∠3 and ∠4? Which theorem or postulate justifies each answer?

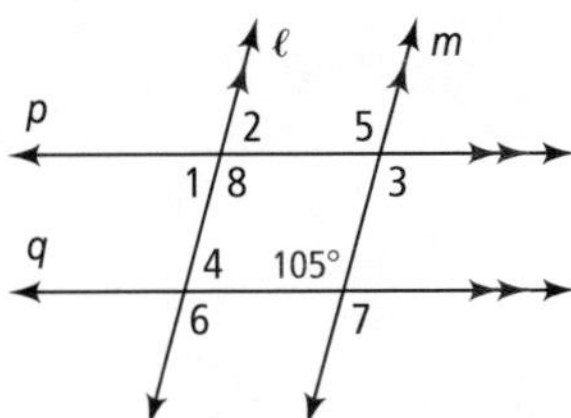

Since $p \parallel q$, $m\angle 3 = 105$ by the Alternate Interior Angles Theorem.

Since $\ell \parallel m$, $m\angle 4 + 105 = 180$ by the Same-Side Interior Angles Postulate. So, $m\angle 4 = 180 - 105 = 75$.

Problem 3 *continued*

ANSWERS

Got It? a. 75; $m\angle 1 = m\angle 4$ by the Alt. Int. ∠s Thm. **b.** 75; $m\angle 2 = m\angle 4$ by the Corresp. ∠s Thm. **c.** 105; $m\angle 5 = 105$ by the Corresp. ∠s Thm. **d.** 105; Alt. Int. ∠s Thm. **e.** 105; Vert. ∠s Thm. **f.** 105; $\angle 8 \cong \angle 6$ by the Corresp. ∠s Thm.

Practice

5. $m\angle 1 = 75$ because corresp. ∠s are ≅; $m\angle 2 = 105$ because ∠2 forms a linear pair with the given ∠.
6. $m\angle 2 = 70$ because alt. int. ∠s are ≅; $m\angle 1 = 100$ because same-side int. ∠s are suppl.

▼ STUDENT PAGE 77

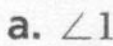

Got It? Use the diagram in Problem 3. What is the measure of each angle? Justify each answer.

a. ∠1　　b. ∠2
c. ∠5　　d. ∠6
e. ∠7　　f. ∠8

Think How does ∠4 relate to ∠1?

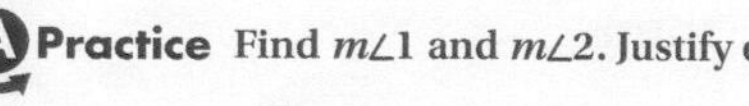

A Practice Find $m\angle 1$ and $m\angle 2$. Justify each answer.

5.
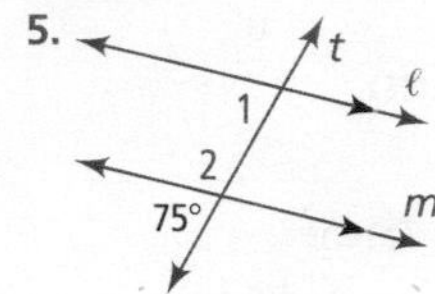

6.
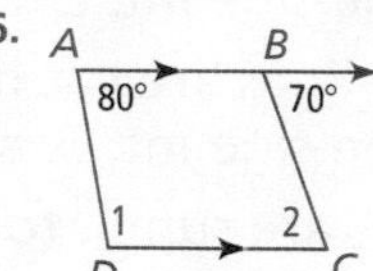

Problem 4 Finding an Angle Measure

Q How can you find the value of y using the Corresponding Angles Theorem? **[$y + 40 + 80 = 180$, using the angle to the left of the 40° angle]**

Got It? **VISUAL LEARNERS**
Students should extend the segments that form the trapezoid to identify the pair of parallel lines and the transversals. Remind students to write and solve an equation for x and an equation for y.

ANSWERS

Got It? a. $x = 64$, $y = 40$ **b.** Clockwise from the bottom left, the measures are 52, 128, 120, 60.

Practice

7. $x = 115$, $x - 50 = 65$
8. 25; $x + 40 = 65$, $3x - 10 = 65$

▼ STUDENT PAGE 78

You can combine theorems and postulates with your knowledge of algebra to find angle measures.

▼ DIGITAL

Problem 4 Finding an Angle Measure　　GRIDDED RESPONSE

Algebra What is the value of y?

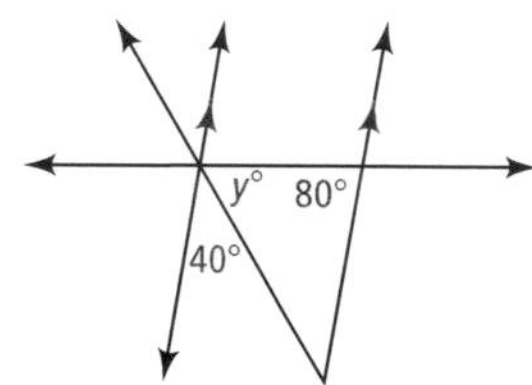

By the Angle Addition Postulate, $y + 40$ is the measure of an interior angle.

$(y + 40) + 80 = 180$	Same-side interior ∠s of ∥ lines are suppl.
$y + 120 = 180$	Simplify.
$y = 60$	Subtract 120 from each side.

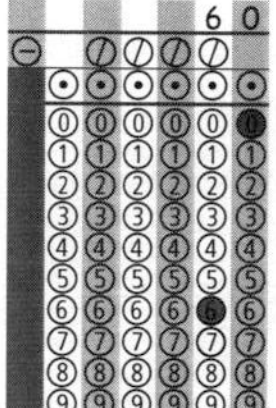

▼ STUDENT PAGE 78

Got It? a. In the figure below, what are the values of x and y?

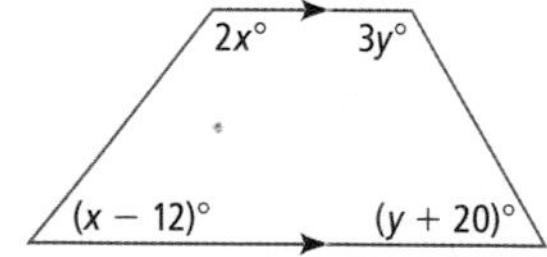

b. What are the measures of the four angles in the figure?

Think What is the relationship between the two angles on the left side of the figure?

A Practice **Algebra** Find the value of x. Then find the measure of each labeled angle.

7.
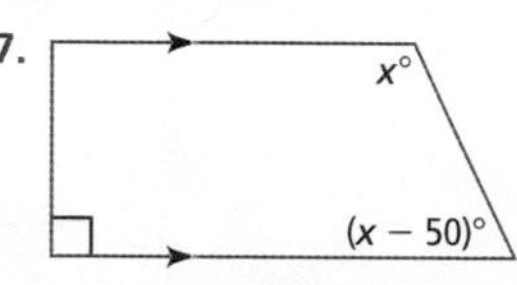

8.
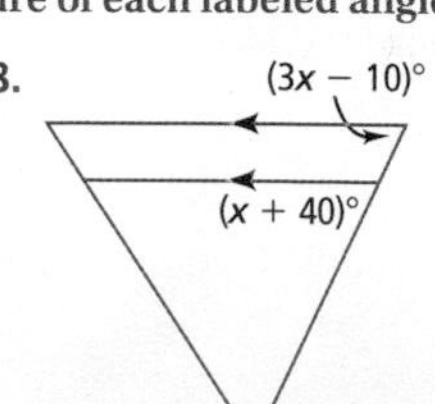

3 Lesson Check

Do you know HOW?

If students have difficulty with Exercise 11, then tell them that they can find the answer using the Alternate Exterior Angles Theorem, or by using a combination of the Vertical Angles Theorem with either the Corresponding Angles Theorem or the Alternate Interior Angles Theorem.

Do you UNDERSTAND?

If students have difficulty with Exercise 14, then ask them how this pair of angles is similar to other angle pairs for which they know the terms.

Close

Q How is a diagram of any two lines intersected by a transversal the same as a diagram of two parallel lines intersected by a transversal? How are they different? **[Both diagrams contain the special pairs of angles; the theorems apply only when the lines intersected by the transversal are parallel.]**

ANSWERS

9–10. Answers may vary. Samples are given.

9. $\angle 4$ and $\angle 5$, $\angle 2$ and $\angle 6$, $\angle 3$ and $\angle 7$, $\angle 4$ and $\angle 8$

10. $\angle 2$ and $\angle 5$, $\angle 4$ and $\angle 7$

11. 70

12. 55

13. Alike: Two parallel lines are cut by a transversal and the angles are congruent. Different: The int. ∠s are between the two parallel lines, while the ext. ∠s are not between the two parallel lines.

14. same-side ext. ∠s, because they are ext. ∠s on the same side of the transversal

▼ STUDENT PAGES 79–80

Lesson Check

Do you know HOW?

Use the diagram for Exercises 9–12.

9. Identify four pairs of congruent angles. (Exclude vertical angle pairs.)

10. Identify two pairs of supplementary angles. (Exclude linear pairs.)

11. If $m\angle 1 = 70$, what is $m\angle 8$?

12. If $m\angle 4 = 70$ and $m\angle 7 = 2x$, what is the value of x?

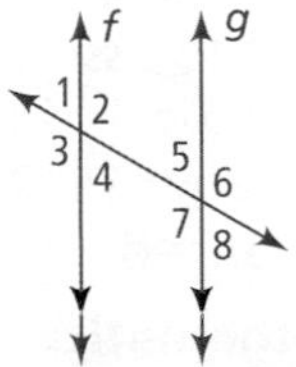

Do you UNDERSTAND?

13. Compare and Contrast How are the Alternate Interior Angles Theorem and the Alternate Exterior Angles Theorem alike? How are they different?

14. In Problem 2, you proved that $\angle 1$ and $\angle 8$, in the diagram at the right, are supplementary. What is a good name for this pair of angles? Explain.

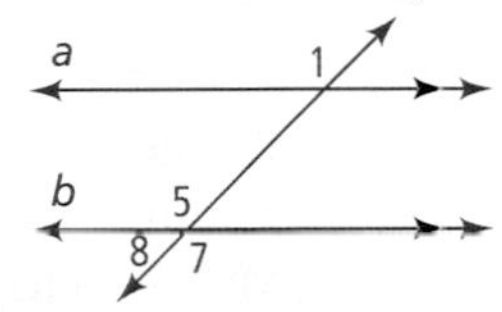

Practice

More Practice and Problem-Solving Exercises

ASSIGNMENT GUIDE
The assignments below are for the More Practice and Problem-Solving Exercises. You may also want to assign the A-Level Practice Exercises for homework if these are not used in class.
Average: 15–23
Advanced: 15–25

Mathematical Practices The exercises listed focus on the Standards for Mathematical Practices listed.
EX. 18: Persevere in Solving Problems (MP 1)
EX. 13: Construct Arguments (MP 3)
EX. 21: Communicate (MP 3)
EX. 19, 25: Critique the Reasoning of Others (MP 3)
EX. 20: Model (MP 4)

EXERCISE 20: Use the **Think About a Plan** worksheet in the Online Teacher Resources to further support students' development in becoming independent learners.

HOMEWORK QUICK CHECK
To check students' understanding of key skills and concepts, go over Exercises 16, 18, 19, 20, and 23.

ANSWERS

15. 32
16. $x = 135$, $y = 45$
17. $x = 87$, $y = 31$, $w = 20$, $v = 42$
18. 90; all the ∠s are ≅ because each pair form vert. ∠s, corresp. ∠s, or suppl. ∠s.
19. A; the marked ∠s are same-side int. ∠s, so they are suppl.
20. **a.** 117
b. same-side int. ∠s
21. Yes; same-side int. ∠s are ≅ if they are both rt. ∠s because two rt. ∠s are suppl.

More Practice and Problem-Solving Exercises

B Apply

Algebra Find the values of the variables.

15. 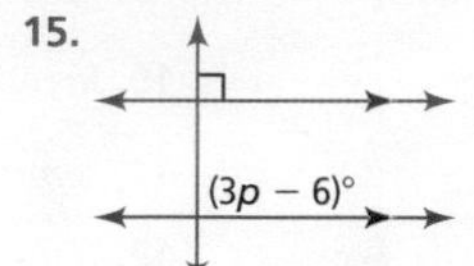

16. 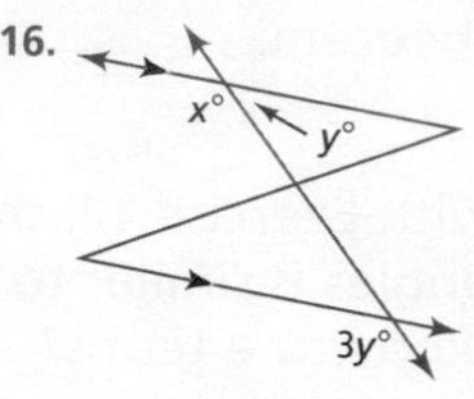

17. 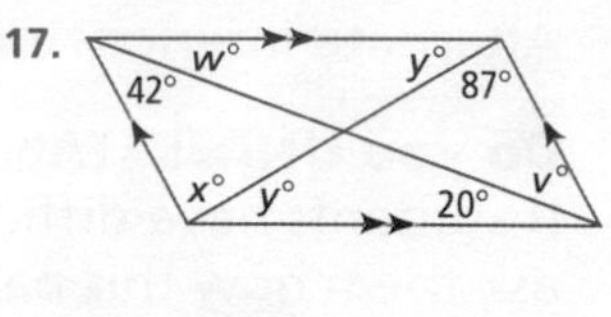

18. Think About a Plan People in ancient Rome played a game called *terni lapilli*. The exact rules of this game are not known. Etchings on floors and walls in Rome suggest that the game required a grid of two intersecting pairs of parallel lines, similar to the modern game tick-tack-toe. The measure of one of the angles formed by the intersecting lines is 90°. Find the measure of each of the other 15 angles. Justify your answers.
- How can you use a diagram to help?
- You know the measure of one angle. How does the position of that angle relate to the position of each of the other angles?
- Which angles formed by two parallel lines and a transversal are congruent? Which angles are supplementary?

19. Error Analysis Which solution for the value of x in the figure at the right is incorrect? Explain.

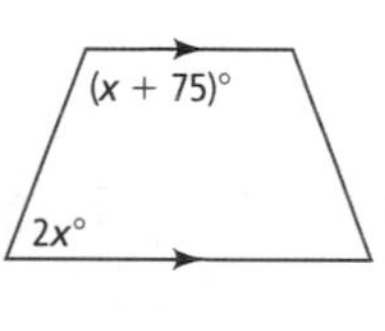

A.
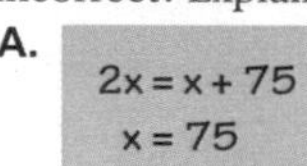
$2x = x + 75$
$x = 75$

B.
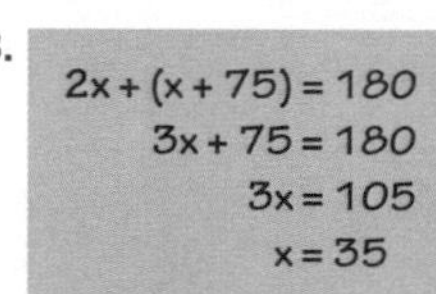
$2x + (x + 75) = 180$
$3x + 75 = 180$
$3x = 105$
$x = 35$

20. Outdoor Recreation Campers often use a "bear bag" at night to avoid attracting animals to their food supply. In the bear bag system at the right, a camper pulls or releases one end of the rope to raise or lower the food bag.
a. Suppose a camper pulls the rope taut between the two parallel trees, as shown. What is $m\angle 1$?
b. Are $\angle 1$ and the given angle *alternate interior angles, same-side interior angles,* or *corresponding angles*?

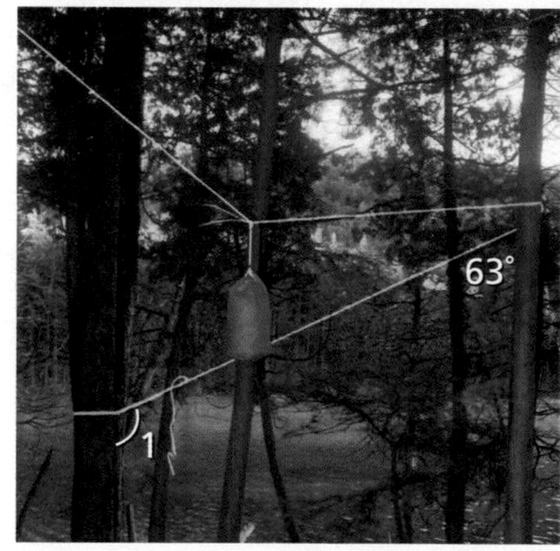

21. Writing Are same-side interior angles ever congruent? Explain.

22. 1. $\ell \parallel m$ (Given)
2. $m\angle 2 + m\angle 3 = 180$ (∠s that form a linear pair are suppl.)
3. $m\angle 3 + m\angle 6 = 180$ (Same-side interior angles are suppl.)
4. $m\angle 2 + m\angle 3 = m\angle 3 + m\angle 6$ (Substitution)
5. $m\angle 2 = m\angle 6$ (Subtraction Prop. of Eq.)
6. $\angle 2 \cong \angle 6$ (Def. of congruent angles)

23. 1. $a \parallel b$ (Given)
2. $m\angle 1 + m\angle 2 = 180$ and $m\angle 3 + m\angle 4 = 180$ (Same-side int. ∠s are suppl.)
3. $\angle 1 \cong \angle 4$ (Given)
4. $\angle 2 \cong \angle 3$ (If two ∠s are suppl. to ≅ ∠s, then the ∠s are ≅ .)

24. $m\angle 1 = 48$, $m\angle 2 = 132$

25. Sample: The labels $(60 - 2x)^\circ$ and $(2x - 60)^\circ$ contain contradictory information because those ∠s are corresp. ∠s. If $60 - 2x = 2x - 60$, then $x - 30$ and the measure of each ∠ is 0.

▼ STUDENT PAGE 81

Proof 22. Write a two-column proof to prove the Corresponding Angles Theorem (Theorem 7).

Given: $\ell \parallel m$

Prove: $\angle 2$ and $\angle 6$ are congruent.

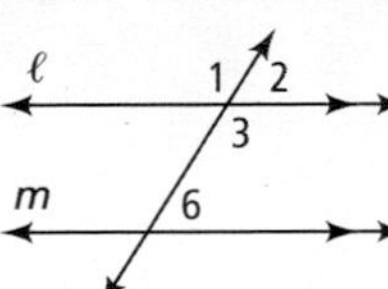

Proof 23. Write a two-column proof.

Given: $a \parallel b$, $\angle 1 \cong \angle 4$

Prove: $\angle 2 \cong \angle 3$

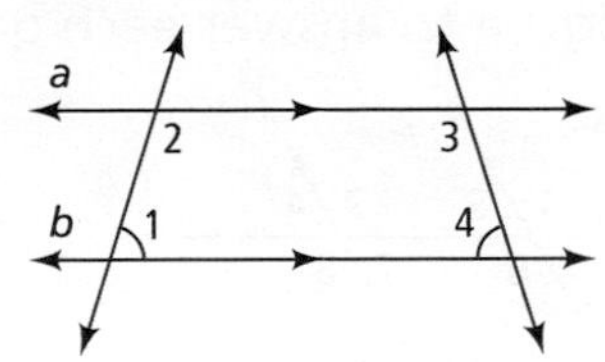

Challenge

Use the diagram at the right for Exercises 24 and 25.

24. Algebra Suppose the measures of $\angle 1$ and $\angle 2$ are in a 4 : 11 ratio. Find their measures. (Diagram is not to scale.)

25. Error Analysis The diagram at the right contains contradictory information. What is it? Why is it contradictory?

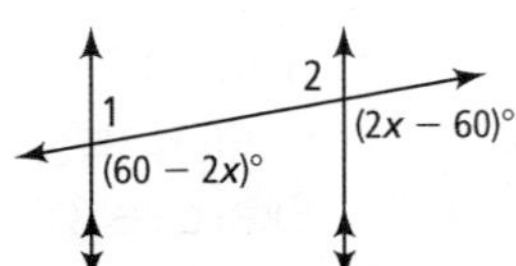

5 Assess and Remediate

Lesson Quiz

Use the figure to answer each question.

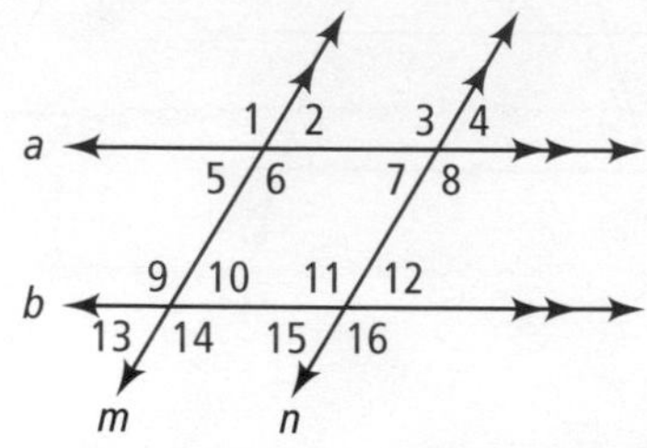

1. If $m\angle 11 = 118$, what is the measure of $\angle 8$?
2. Which theorem or postulate justifies your answer to Exercise 1?
3. If $m\angle 4 = 62$, what is the measure of $\angle 5$?
4. Which theorem or postulate justifies your answer to Exercise 3?
5. **Do you UNDERSTAND?** Which of the following does *not* prove two angles to be congruent: Vertical Angles Theorem, Corresponding Angles Theorem, Alternate Interior Angles Theorem, Same-Side Interior Angles Postulate?

ANSWERS TO LESSON QUIZ

1. 118
2. Alternate Interior Angles Theorem
3. 62
4. Alternate Exterior Angles Theorem
5. The Same-Side Interior Angles Postulate proves two angles to be supplementary, not congruent.

Prescription for Remediation

Use the student work on the Lesson Quiz to prescribe a differentiated assignment.

Points	Differentiated Remediation
0–2	Intervention
3–4	On-level
5	Extension

Online Assessment

Assign the Lesson Quiz in Success Tracker on **pearsonsuccessnet.com**. Success Tracker will automatically score the quiz and assign appropriate intervention or enrichment to each student based on the results. The compiled data appear in three different reports for instant analysis of whole class and individual student performance.

Differentiated Remediation

Intervention

- **RETEACHING** (2 pages) Provides reteaching and practice exercises for the key lesson concepts. Use with struggling students or absent students.
- **ENGLISH LANGUAGE LEARNER SUPPORT** Helps students develop and reinforce mathematical vocabulary and key concepts.

On-Level

- **PRACTICE** (2 pages) Provides extra practice for each lesson. For simpler practice exercises, use the Form K Practice pages found in the Online Teacher Resources.
- **THINK ABOUT A PLAN** Helps students develop specific problem-solving skills and strategies by providing scaffolded guiding questions.
- **STANDARDIZED TEST PREP** Focuses on all major exercises, all major question types, and helps students prepare for the high-stakes assessments.

Extension

- **ENRICHMENT** Provides students with interesting problems and activities that extend the concepts of the lesson.
- **ACTIVITIES, GAMES, AND PUZZLES** Worksheets that can be used for concept development, enrichment, and for fun!

2-3 Proving Lines Parallel

Common Core State Standard
G.CO.9 Prove theorems about lines and angles. Theorems include: . . . when a transversal crosses parallel lines, alternate interior angles are congruent and corresponding angles are congruent . . .

Preparing to Teach

BIG idea Reasoning and Proof

ESSENTIAL UNDERSTANDING

Certain angle pairs can be used to decide whether two lines are parallel. Paragraph, two-column, and flow proofs are three forms of proof.

Math Background

Teaching students to write proofs, whether two-column, paragraph, or flow proofs, is an exercise in getting students to map out a process. Students skilled in writing proofs work step by step, not assuming any relationship or taking any knowledge for granted.

Students should be encouraged to consider all the postulates, definitions, and theorems related to parallel lines when making a list of how to get from the given statement to the statement to be proved.

Proofs should be looked upon as problems where the answer is already known and the task is to demonstrate how the answer is derived. For the proofs in this lesson, students often overlook that they must prove lines parallel before using postulates and theorems involving parallel lines. They simply skip right to conditions related to the angles. Stress that although lines may appear parallel in a diagram, that fact cannot be assumed, but must be included in the logic that leads to the proof.

ELL Support

USE ROLE PLAYING Draw two parallel lines on the board. Say: Today you are detectives. Are these lines parallel? We will find out together. Each student may draw one line on the board. Each student may measure one distance or one angle. Have students take turns either drawing a line or making a measurement. Have the students record their measurements, but they should not share information with one another.

After each student has had a turn, form groups of four to five students. Have the students compare the information that they have about the two lines on the board. Ask: Does your group have enough information to prove that these lines are parallel? Have groups that do not have enough information take turns asking questions of the other students until they can prove the lines are parallel. When the group has enough information, have them write down an explanation of their proof.

Lesson Vocabulary

- flow proof

Mathematical Practices

CONSTRUCT VIABLE ARGUMENTS AND CRITIQUE THE REASONING OF OTHERS. In Problem 4, students will use stated theorems in conjunction with their background in algebra to solve for the measure of angles algebraically.

1 Interactive Learning

Solve It!

PURPOSE To visualize and investigate angle relationships when parallel lines are crossed by transversals

PROCESS Students may use visual judgment or previously learned definitions and theorems pertaining to angles.

Q How can you determine the measure of $\angle 1$? **[$\angle 1$ is supplementary to the angle that measures 60.]**

Q What are the two possible degree measures for each turn? Explain. **[60 and 120; because all the lines are parallel, all the special pairs will involve only these two measurements.]**

ANSWER Turn 1: 120°, turn 2: 120°, turn 3: 60°, turn 4: 60°, turn 5: 60°; explanations may vary. Sample: When a transversal intersects two $\parallel$ lines, the ⦞ formed are $\cong$ or suppl. If you know the measure of one of those ⦞, you can use the properties of $\parallel$ lines to find the measures of the other seven ⦞.

CONNECT THE MATH Students can identify vertical angles and supplementary angles in the maze. Students should notice the maze is made of several pairs of parallel lines. This maze demonstrates conditions used to prove two lines parallel.

▼ DIGITAL (STUDENT WORK SPACE PAGE 82)

Getting Ready!

The maze below has two intersecting sets of parallel paths. A mouse makes five turns in the maze to get to a piece of cheese. Follow the mouse's path through the maze. What are the number of degrees at each turn? Explain how you know.

2 Guided Instruction

Problem 1 Identifying Parallel Lines

Take Note

Q If one pair of corresponding angles in the diagram is given to be congruent, are all pairs of corresponding angles congruent? Explain. **[Yes, the Vertical Angles Theorem and the Congruent Supplements Theorem show that they are congruent.]**

Problem 1

Q Which lines form ∠1? Which lines form ∠2? **[lines *a* and *m*; lines *b* and *m*]**

Got It? **ERROR PREVENTION**

Recommend that students try covering up one line, so that only two parallel lines and one transversal are visible at a time.

ANSWERS

Got It? $\ell \parallel m$ by the Converse of the Corresp. ∠s Thm.

Practice

1. $\overleftrightarrow{CA} \parallel \overleftrightarrow{HR}$ by the Converse of the Corresp. ∠s Thm.
2. $\overleftrightarrow{KR} \parallel \overleftrightarrow{MT}$ by the Converse of the Corresp. ∠s Thm.

▼ STUDENT PAGE 82

In the Solve It, you used parallel lines to find congruent and supplementary relationships of special angle pairs. In this lesson you will do the converse. You will use the congruent and supplementary relationships of the special angle pairs to prove lines parallel.

Essential Understanding You can use certain angle pairs to decide whether two lines are parallel.

take note **Theorem 9 Converse of the Corresponding Angles Theorem**

Theorem	If . . .	Then . . .
If two lines and a transversal form corresponding angles that are congruent, then the lines are parallel.	∠2 ≅ ∠6	$\ell \parallel m$

You will prove Theorem 9 in Lesson 13-5.

▼ DIGITAL

Problem 1 Identifying Parallel Lines

Which lines are parallel if ∠1 ≅ ∠2? Justify your answer.

∠1 and ∠2 are corresponding angles. If ∠1 ≅ ∠2, then $a \parallel b$ by the Converse of the Corresponding Angles Theorem.

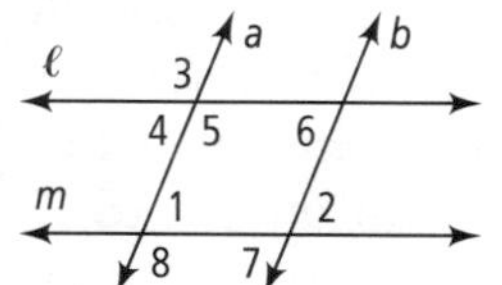

▼ STUDENT PAGE 83

Got It? Which lines are parallel if ∠6 ≅ ∠7? Justify your answer.

Think Which line is the transversal for ∠6 and ∠7?

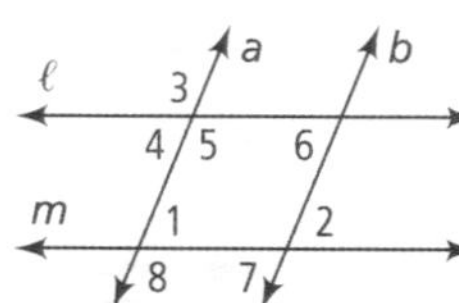

A Practice **Which lines or segments are parallel? Justify your answer.**

1. (figure: triangles CMA and HAR with 45° angles)

2. 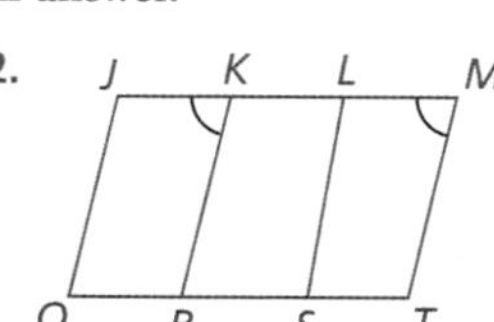

Problem 2 Writing a Flow Proof of Theorem 12

Take Note

Q How can you tell that the interior angles which form linear pairs with ∠4 and ∠6 are also congruent? **[Because they are both supplementary to congruent angles, they are also congruent by the Congruent Suppl. Thm.]**

Q What does the phrase "same-side" refer to in the diagram? **[It means the same side of the transversal, either the right side or the left side.]**

Q How many pairs of same-side interior angles are in the diagram? **[2]**

In future proofs, students may struggle to determine when to use the Alternate Exterior Angles Theorem and when to use its converse. Explain to students that the converse is used when they need to prove the lines are parallel. The theorem is used when they already know that the lines are parallel and they need to prove the alternate exterior angles are congruent.

Proof of Theorem 10

The two forms of proof students have used thus far, two-column and paragraph proofs, are deductive proofs. A third type of deductive proof is a flow proof, which is modeled after flowcharts. A flowchart, which is often used to show workflows in the business environment, is a schematic representation of a process. Flow proofs are a visual representation of a proof using statements and reasons in a logical order.

In the last lesson you proved theorems based on the Corresponding Angles Theorem. You can use the Converse of the Corresponding Angles Theorem to prove converses of the theorems and postulate you learned in the last lesson.

take note

Theorem 10 Converse of the Alternate Interior Angles Theorem

Theorem	If . . .	Then . . .
If two lines and a transversal form alternate interior angles that are congruent, then the two lines are parallel.	$\angle 4 \cong \angle 6$ 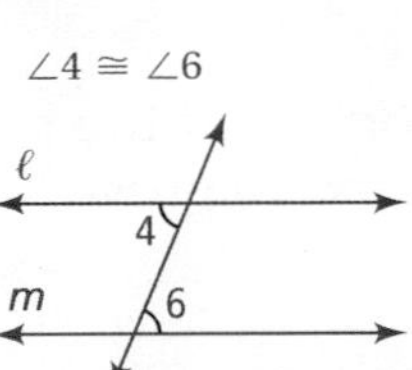	$\ell \parallel m$

take note

Theorem 11 Converse of the Same-Side Interior Angles Postulate

Theorem	If . . .	Then . . .
If two lines and a transversal form same-side interior angles that are supplementary, then the two lines are parallel.	$m\angle 3 + m\angle 6 = 180$ 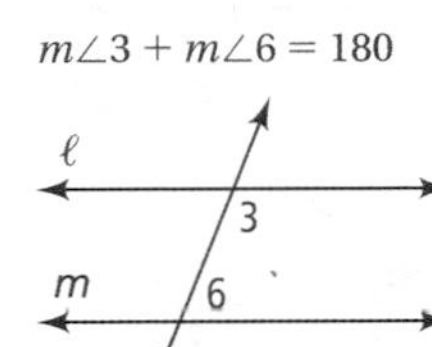	$\ell \parallel m$

Theorem 12 Converse of the Alternate Exterior Angles Theorem

Theorem	If . . .	Then . . .
If two lines and a transversal form alternate exterior angles that are congruent, then the two lines are parallel.	$\angle 1 \cong \angle 7$ 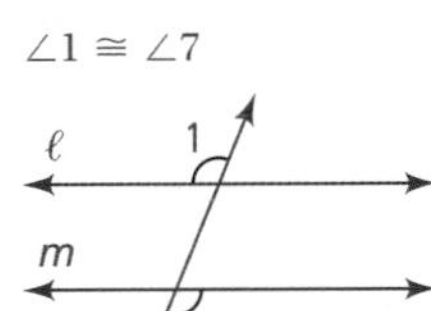	$\ell \parallel m$

The proof of the Converse of the Alternate Interior Angles Theorem below looks different than any proof you have seen so far in this course. You know two forms of proof—paragraph and two-column. In a third form, called **flow proof**, arrows show the logical connections between the statements. Reasons are written below the statements.

Proof Proof of Theorem 10: Converse of the Alternate Interior Angles Theorem

Given: $\angle 4 \cong \angle 6$

Prove: $\ell \parallel m$

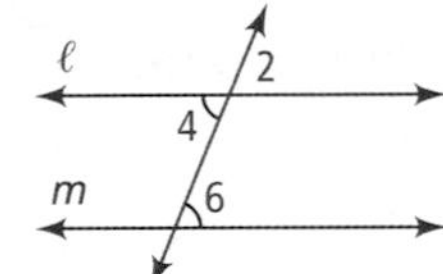

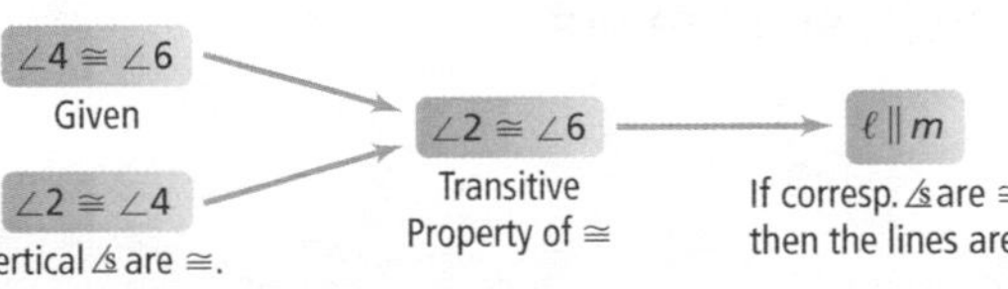

Problem 2 *continued*

Q What statements could replace the statements listed in the lower left and middle section of the proof? **[lower left: ∠5 ≅ ∠7; middle: ∠5 ≅ ∠1]**

Q How could you use this proof to prove that ∠6 and ∠3 are supplementary? **[Once you have proven the lines parallel, you can use the Same-Side Interior Angles Postulate.]**

Got It? SYNTHESIZING

Tell students that a portion of the proof written in Problem 2 can be used to prove lines ℓ and *m* parallel.

ANSWERS

Got It? Answers may vary. Sample:

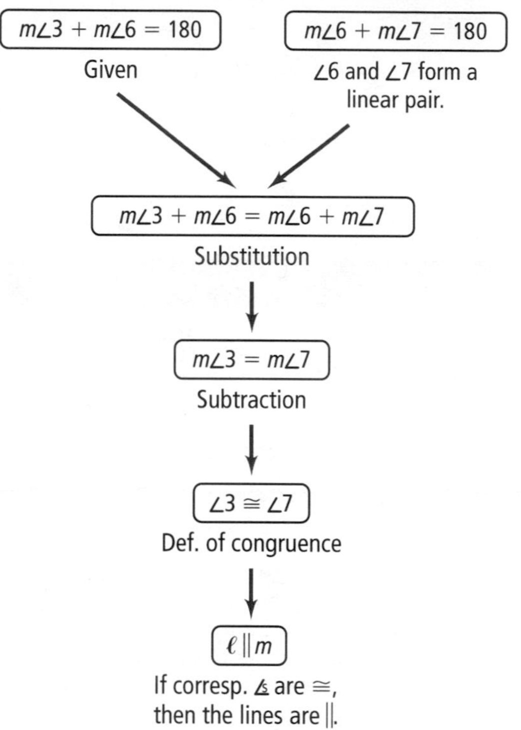

Practice

3. **a.** Given
 b. ∠1 and ∠2 form a linear pair.
 c. ∠s that form a linear pair are suppl.
 d. ∠2 ≅ ∠3
 e. If corresp. ∠s are ≅, then lines are ∥.

▼ DIGITAL

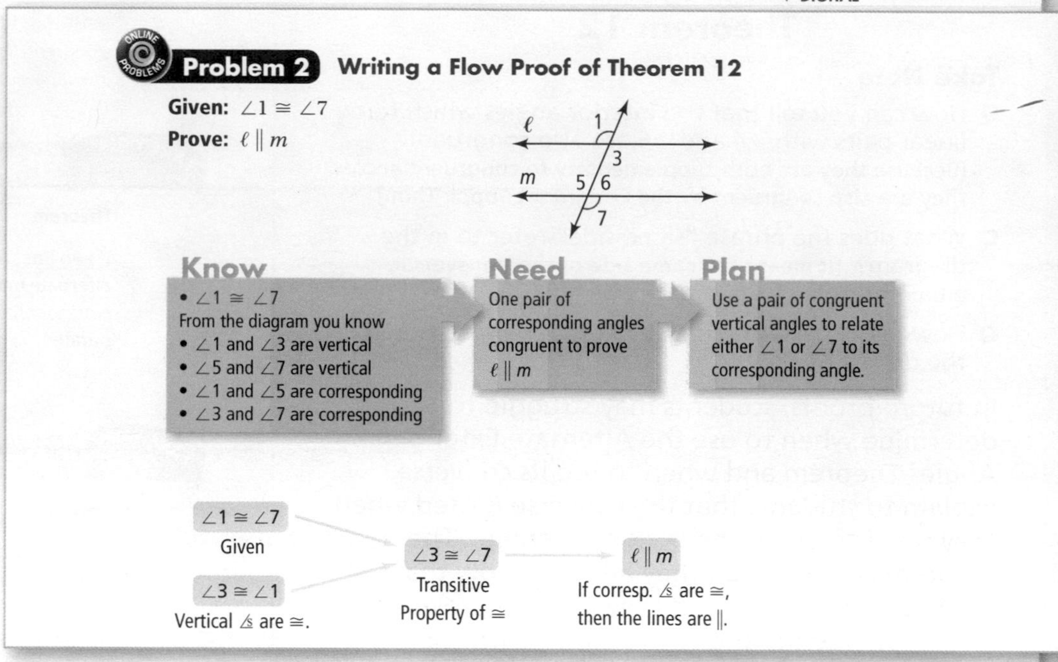

Problem 2 Writing a Flow Proof of Theorem 12
Given: ∠1 ≅ ∠7
Prove: ℓ ∥ m
ℓ
m
1
3
5 6
7
Know
• ∠1 ≅ ∠7
From the diagram you know
• ∠1 and ∠3 are vertical
• ∠5 and ∠7 are vertical
• ∠1 and ∠5 are corresponding
• ∠3 and ∠7 are corresponding
Need
One pair of corresponding angles congruent to prove ℓ ∥ m
Plan
Use a pair of congruent vertical angles to relate either ∠1 or ∠7 to its corresponding angle.
∠1 ≅ ∠7
Given
∠3 ≅ ∠1
Vertical ∠s are ≅.
∠3 ≅ ∠7
Transitive Property of ≅
ℓ ∥ m
If corresp. ∠s are ≅, then the lines are ∥.

▼ STUDENT PAGE 85

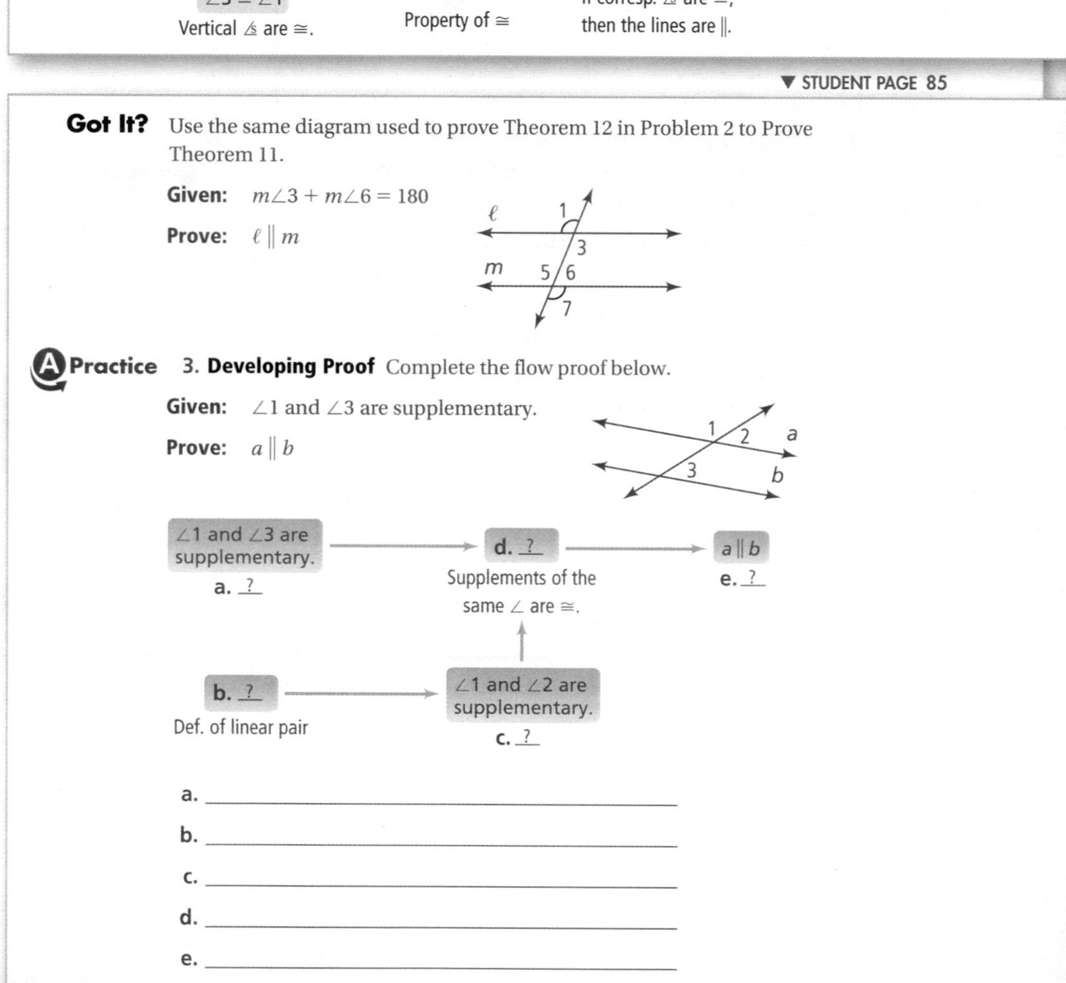

Got It? Use the same diagram used to prove Theorem 12 in Problem 2 to Prove Theorem 11.
Given: m∠3 + m∠6 = 180
Prove: ℓ ∥ m
ℓ
m
1
3
5 6
7
A Practice 3. Developing Proof Complete the flow proof below.
Given: ∠1 and ∠3 are supplementary.
Prove: a ∥ b
1 2
a
3
b
∠1 and ∠3 are supplementary.
a. ?
d. ?
Supplements of the same ∠ are ≅.
a ∥ b
e. ?
b. ?
Def. of linear pair
∠1 and ∠2 are supplementary.
c. ?
a.
b.
c.
d.
e.

Problem 3 Determining Whether Lines are Parallel

Q What piece on the gate represents the transversal in this diagram? **[the diagonal piece of wood that runs from the lower left corner of the gate to the upper right corner]**

Q Are ∠1 and ∠2 on the same side of the transversal? **[no]**

Q What labeled angle is on the same side of the transversal as ∠1? **[∠3]**

Got It?

Q What is the relationship between ∠2 and ∠3? **[They are vertical angles.]**

Q What congruence statement is a result of this relationship? **[∠2 ≅ ∠3]**

Q Using angles on the same side of the transversal, what congruence statement do you need to prove the lines parallel? **[∠1 ≅ ∠3]**

ANSWERS

Got It? ∠2 ≅ ∠3 (Vert. ∠s are ≅.), so ∠1 ≅ ∠3 (Trans. Prop. of ≅). So $r \parallel s$ by the Converse of the Corresp. ∠s Thm.

Practice

4. Yes; ∠1 and ∠2 are alt. ext. ∠s, and if alt. ext. ∠s are ≅, then the lines are ∥.

▼ STUDENT PAGE 86

The four theorems you have just learned provide you with four ways to determine if two lines are parallel.

▼ DIGITAL

Problem 3 Determining Whether Lines are Parallel

The fence gate at the right is made up of pieces of wood arranged in various directions. Suppose ∠1 ≅ ∠2. Are lines *r* and *s* parallel? Explain.

Yes, $r \parallel s$. ∠1 and ∠2 are alternate exterior angles. If two lines and a transversal form congruent alternate exterior angles, then the lines are parallel (Converse of the Alternate Exterior Angles Theorem).

▼ STUDENT PAGE 86

Got It? In Problem 3, what is another way to explain why $r \parallel s$? Justify your answer.

Practice 4. **Parking** Two workers paint lines for angled parking spaces. One worker paints a line so that $m\angle 1 = 65$. The other worker paints a line so that $m\angle 2 = 65$. Are their lines parallel? Explain.

Problem 4 Using Algebra

Q What kind of special angles are the labeled angles in the diagram? **[They are same-side interior angles.]**

Q Given what you know about same-side interior angles, what other measure is used to write the equation to solve for *x*? **[180]**

Q If $x = 60$, will lines *a* and *b* intersect to the left or to the right of the transversal? **[They will intersect to the right of the transversal.]**

Q If $x = 10$, will lines *a* and *b* intersect to the left or to the right of the transversal? **[They will intersect to the left of the transversal.]**

Got It? VISUAL LEARNERS

Q In order for *c* and *d* to be parallel, what relationship must be true for the given angles? **[The measures of corresponding angles must be equal.]**

ANSWERS

Got It? 19

Practice

5. 59

6. 31

▼ STUDENT PAGE 86

You can use algebra along with the postulates and theorems from the last lesson and this lesson to help you solve problems involving parallel lines.

▼ DIGITAL

Problem 4 Using Algebra

Algebra What is the value of *x* for which $a \parallel b$?

The two angles are same-side interior angles. By the Converse of the Same-Side Interior Angles Postulate, $a \parallel b$ if the angles are supplementary.

$(2x + 9) + 111 = 180$	Def. of supplementary angles
$2x + 120 = 180$	Simplify.
$2x = 60$	Subtract 120 from each side.
$x = 30$	Divide each side by 2.

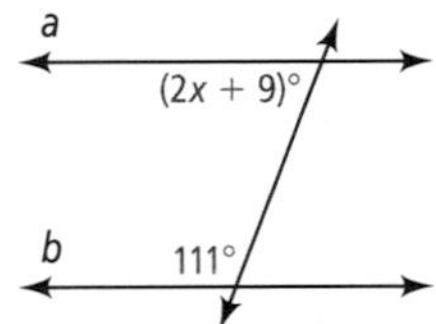

▼ STUDENT PAGES 86–87

Got It? What is the value of *w* for which $c \parallel d$?

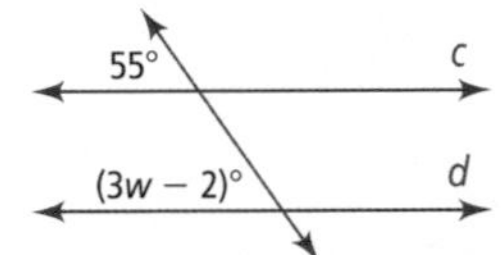

Think
What must be true of the given angles for lines *c* and *d* to be parallel?

Practice **Algebra** Find the value of *x* for which $\ell \parallel m$.

5.

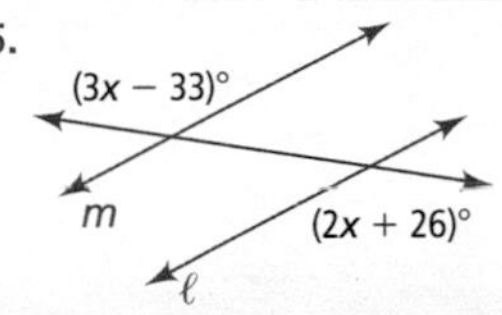

6.

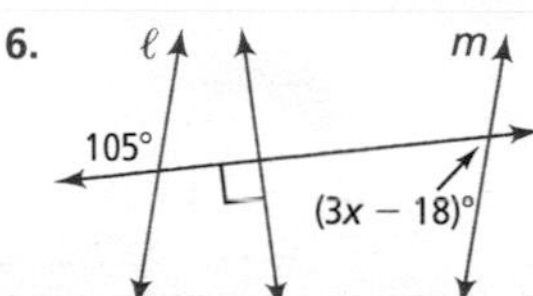

3 Lesson Check

Do you know HOW?
If students have difficulty with Exercises 7–8, then tell them to first identify the relationship of the indicated angles.

Do you UNDERSTAND?
If students have difficulty with Exercise 12, then discuss that same-side interior angles both lie along one side of the transversal, not along one of the parallel lines.

Close

Q List all the different ways that you can prove that two lines are parallel. **[Show that same-side interior angles are supplementary or show that one of the following pairs of angles is congruent: alternate interior, alternate exterior, or corresponding.]**

ANSWERS

7. Conv. of Corresp. ∠s Thm.
8. Conv. of Alt. Int. ∠s Thm.
9. 115
10. If you want to prove that alt. int. ∠s are ≅, use the Alt. Int. ∠s Thm.; if you want to prove that two lines are parallel, use the Converse of the Alt. Int. ∠s Thm.
11. Alike: Both give statements and reasons. Different: The proofs use different formats.
12. $\overleftrightarrow{DC}$ is the transversal, so the two same-side int. ∠s show that $\overleftrightarrow{AD}$ and $\overleftrightarrow{BC}$ are parallel.

▼ STUDENT PAGES 87–88

Lesson Check

Do you know HOW?

State the theorem or postulate that proves $a \parallel b$.

7. 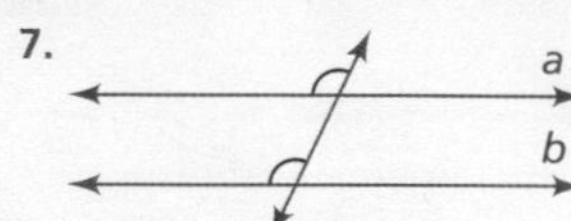

8. 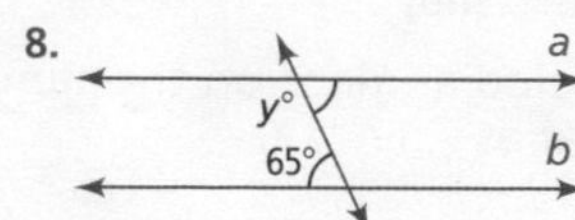

9. What is the value of y for which $a \parallel b$ in Exercise 8?

Do you UNDERSTAND?

10. Explain how you know when to use the Alternate Interior Angles Theorem and when to use the Converse of the Alternate Interior Angles Theorem.
11. **Compare and Contrast** How are flow proofs and two-column proofs alike? How are they different?
12. **Error Analysis** A classmate says that $\overleftrightarrow{AB} \parallel \overleftrightarrow{DC}$ based on the diagram at the right. Explain your classmate's error.

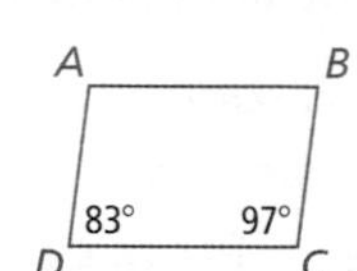

Practice

More Practice and Problem-Solving Exercises

ASSIGNMENT GUIDE
The assignments below are for the More Practice and Problem-Solving Exercises. You may also want to assign the A-Level Practice Exercises for homework if these are not used in class.
Average: 13–36
Advanced: 13–41

Mathematical Practices The exercises listed focus on the Standards for Mathematical Practices listed.
EX. 25: Make Sense of Problems (MP 1)
EX. 13–22, 30–34: Construct Arguments (MP 3)
EX. 12: Critique the Reasoning of Others (MP 3)
EX. 11: Use Structure (MP 7)

EXERCISE 29: Use the **Think About a Plan** worksheet in the Online Teacher Resources to further support students' development in becoming independent learners.

HOMEWORK QUICK CHECK
To check students' understanding of key skills and concepts, go over Exercises 13, 17, 26, 29, and 30.

ANSWERS

13. $a \parallel b$; if same-side int. ∠s are suppl., then the lines are ∥.
14. $a \parallel b$; Converse of Corresp. ∠s Thm.
15. $a \parallel b$; if same-side int. ∠s are suppl., then the lines are ∥.
16. none
17. none
18. $\ell \parallel m$ (Conv. of Corresp. ∠s Thm.)
19. $a \parallel b$ (Conv. of the Alt. Ext. ∠s Thm.)
20. $a \parallel b$ (Conv. of Corresp. ∠s Thm.)
21. none
22. $\ell \parallel m$ (Conv. of the Alt. Int. ∠s Thm.)
23. 5
24. 20
25. The corresp. ∠s are ≅, so the oars are ∥ by the Conv. of Corresp. ∠s Thm.
26. $x = 10$; $m\angle 1 = m\angle 2 = 70$
27. $x = 5$; $m\angle 1 = m\angle 2 = 50$
28. $x = 2.5$; $m\angle 1 = m\angle 2 = 30$
29. $x = 1.25$; $m\angle 1 = m\angle 2 = 10$
30. Answers may vary. Sample: If $\angle 1 \cong \angle 5$, then $\ell \parallel n$ by the Converse of Corresp. ∠s Thm.
31. Answers may vary. Sample: If $m\angle 8 = m\angle 4$, then $\ell \parallel n$ because corresp. ∠s are ≅ and $j \parallel k$ because same-side int. ∠s are suppl.
32. Answers may vary. Sample: If $\angle 5 \cong \angle 3$, then $\ell \parallel n$ by the Converse of the Alt. Int. ∠s Thm. and $j \parallel k$ by the Converse of the Corresp. ∠s Thm.
33. Answers may vary. Sample: If $\angle 11 \cong \angle 3$, then $j \parallel k$ by the Converse of the Corresp. ∠s Thm.

▼ STUDENT PAGES 89–90

More Practice and Problem-Solving Exercises

B Apply

Developing Proof Use the given information to determine which lines, if any, are parallel. Justify each conclusion with a theorem or postulate.

13. $\angle 2$ is supplementary to $\angle 3$.
14. $\angle 1 \cong \angle 3$
15. $\angle 6$ is supplementary to $\angle 7$.
16. $\angle 9 \cong \angle 12$
17. $m\angle 7 = 65$, $m\angle 9 = 115$
18. $\angle 2 \cong \angle 10$
19. $\angle 1 \cong \angle 8$
20. $\angle 8 \cong \angle 6$
21. $\angle 11 \cong \angle 7$
22. $\angle 5 \cong \angle 10$

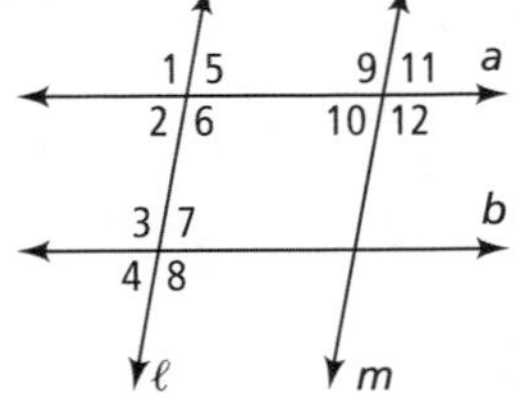

Algebra Find the value of x for which $\ell \parallel m$.

23.

24.

25. Think About a Plan If the rowing crew at the right strokes in unison, the oars sweep out angles of equal measure. Explain why the oars on each side of the shell stay parallel.
- What type of information do you need to prove lines parallel?
- How do the positions of the angles of equal measure relate?

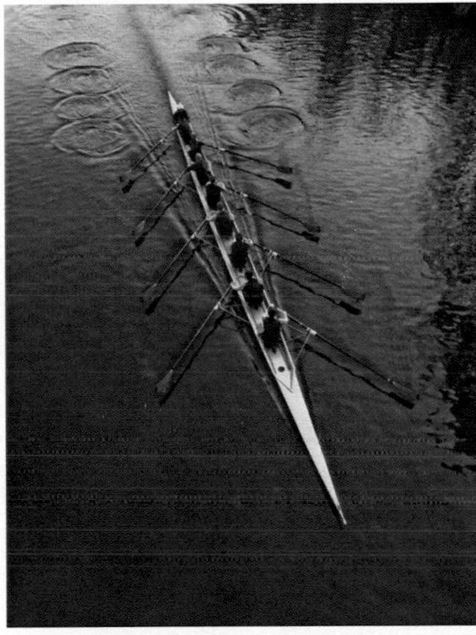

Algebra Determine the value of x for which $r \parallel s$. Then find $m\angle 1$ and $m\angle 2$.

26. $m\angle 1 = 80 - x$, $m\angle 2 = 90 - 2x$
27. $m\angle 1 = 60 - 2x$, $m\angle 2 = 70 - 4x$
28. $m\angle 1 = 40 - 4x$, $m\angle 2 = 50 - 8x$
29. $m\angle 1 = 20 - 8x$, $m\angle 2 = 30 - 16x$

Use the diagram at the right below for Exercises 30–36.

Open-Ended Use the given information. State another fact about one of the given angles that will guarantee two lines are parallel. Tell which lines will be parallel and why.

30. $\angle 1 \cong \angle 3$
31. $m\angle 8 = 110$, $m\angle 9 = 70$
32. $\angle 5 \cong \angle 11$
33. $\angle 11$ and $\angle 12$ are supplementary.

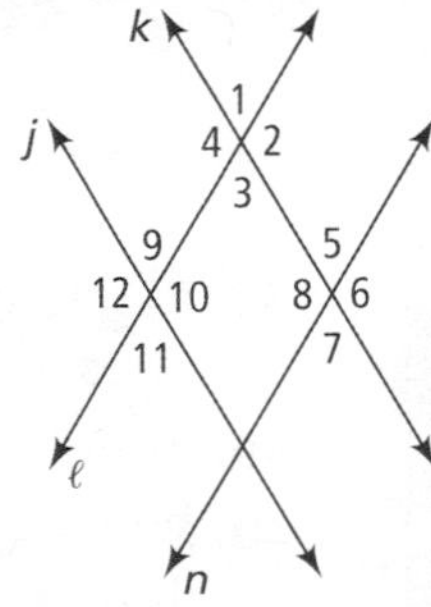

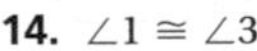

More Practice and Problem-Solving Exercises *continued*

▼ STUDENT PAGE 90

34. If alt. ext. $\angle$s are $\cong$, then the lines are $\parallel$.

35. Answers may vary. Sample:

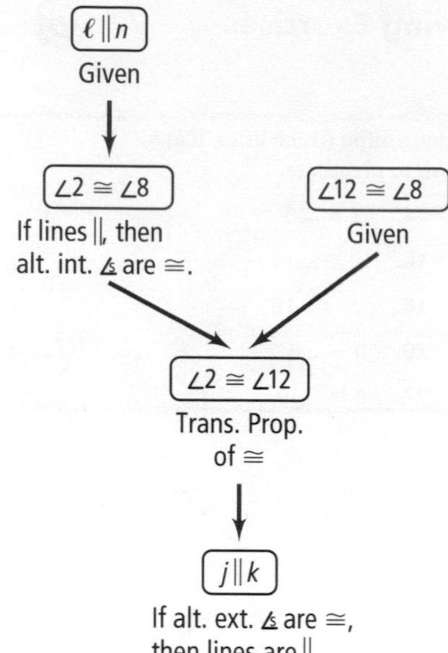

36. Answers may vary. Sample:

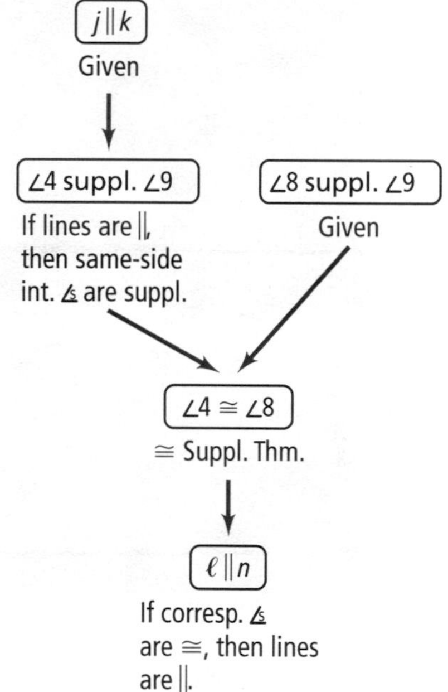

37. $\overline{PL} \parallel \overline{NA}$; $\overline{PN} \parallel \overline{LA}$; if same-side int. $\angle$s are suppl., then the lines are $\parallel$.

38. $\overline{PL} \parallel \overline{NA}$; if same-side int. $\angle$s are suppl., then the lines are $\parallel$.

39. none

40. $\overline{PN} \parallel \overline{LA}$; if same-side int. $\angle$s are suppl., then the lines are $\parallel$.

34. Reasoning If $\angle 1 \cong \angle 7$, what theorem or postulate can you use to show that $\ell \parallel n$?

Write a flow proof.

Proof 35. Given: $\ell \parallel n$, $\angle 12 \cong \angle 8$
Prove: $j \parallel k$

Proof 36. Given: $j \parallel k$, $m\angle 8 + m\angle 9 = 180$
Prove: $\ell \parallel n$

Challenge

Which sides of quadrilateral *PLAN* must be parallel? Explain.

37. $m\angle P = 72$, $m\angle L = 108$, $m\angle A = 72$, $m\angle N = 108$

38. $m\angle P = 59$, $m\angle L = 37$, $m\angle A = 143$, $m\angle N = 121$

39. $m\angle P = 67$, $m\angle L = 120$, $m\angle A = 73$, $m\angle N = 100$

40. $m\angle P = 56$, $m\angle L = 124$, $m\angle A = 124$, $m\angle N = 56$

Proof 41. Write a two-column proof to prove the following: If a transversal intersects two parallel lines, then the bisectors of two corresponding angles are parallel. (*Hint:* Start by drawing and marking a diagram.)

41. Answers may vary. Sample:

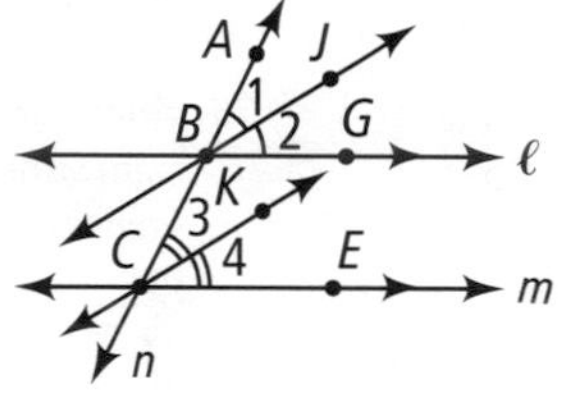

1. $\ell \parallel m$ (Given)
2. $\angle ABG \cong \angle ACE$ (If lines are $\parallel$, then corresp. $\angle$s are $\cong$.)
3. $\overline{BJ}$ bisects $\angle ABG$, $\overline{CK}$ bisects $\angle ACE$ (Given)
4. $m\angle 1 = \frac{1}{2}m\angle ABG$, $m\angle 3 = \frac{1}{2}m\angle ACE$ (A bis. divides an $\angle$ in half.)
5. $\frac{1}{2}m\angle ABG = \frac{1}{2}m\angle ACE$ (Mult. Prop. of Equality)
6. $m\angle 1 = m\angle 3$ (Substitution)
7. $\overline{CK} \parallel \overline{BJ}$ (If corresp. $\angle$s are $\cong$, then the lines are $\parallel$.)

5 Assess and Remediate

Lesson Quiz

Use the figure to answer each question.

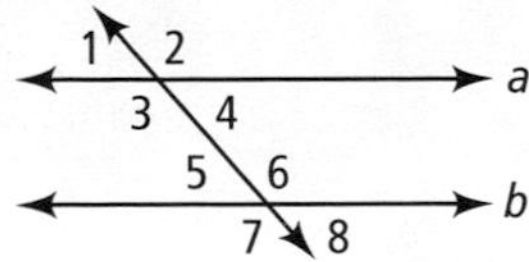

1. If $m\angle 1 = 42$, what must the measure of $\angle 7$ be in order to prove $a \parallel b$?
2. **Do you UNDERSTAND?** Suppose $m\angle 3 = 128$ and $m\angle 6 = (10x + 8)$. What value of x would result in $a \parallel b$?
3. Which theorem or postulate would you use in Question 2 to prove that $a \parallel b$?

Use the figure for Questions 4 and 5.

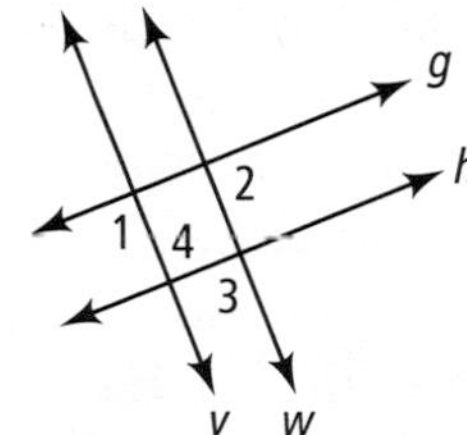

4. If $g \parallel h$ and $m\angle 2 = 88$, what is $m\angle 3$?
5. If $v \parallel w$ and $m\angle 1 = 60$, what is $m\angle 2$?

ANSWERS TO LESSON QUIZ

1. 138
2. 12
3. Converse of the Alternate Interior Angles Theorem
4. 92
5. 120

Prescription for Remediation

Use the student work on the Lesson Quiz to prescribe a differentiated assignment.

Points	Differentiated Remediation
0–2	Intervention
3–4	On-level
5	Extension

Online Assessment

Assign the Lesson Quiz in Success Tracker on **pearsonsuccessnet.com**. Success Tracker will automatically score the quiz and assign appropriate intervention or enrichment to each student based on the results. The compiled data appear in three different reports for instant analysis of whole class and individual student performance.

Differentiated Remediation

Intervention

- **RETEACHING** (2 pages) Provides reteaching and practice exercises for the key lesson concepts. Use with struggling students or absent students.
- **ENGLISH LANGUAGE LEARNER SUPPORT** Helps students develop and reinforce mathematical vocabulary and key concepts.

On-Level

- **PRACTICE** (2 pages) Provides extra practice for each lesson. For simpler practice exercises, use the Form K Practice pages found in the Online Teacher Resources.
- **THINK ABOUT A PLAN** Helps students develop specific problem-solving skills and strategies by providing scaffolded guiding questions.
- **STANDARDIZED TEST PREP** Focuses on all major exercises, all major question types, and helps students prepare for the high-stakes assessments.

Extension

- **ENRICHMENT** Provides students with interesting problems and activities that extend the concepts of the lesson.
- **ACTIVITIES, GAMES, AND PUZZLES** Worksheets that can be used for concept development, enrichment, and for fun!

2-4 Parallel and Perpendicular Lines

Common Core State Standard
G.CO.9 Prove theorems about lines and angles. Theorems include: . . . when a transversal crosses parallel lines . . .

Preparing to Teach

BIG idea Reasoning and Proof

ESSENTIAL UNDERSTANDING

The relationships of two lines to a third line can be used to decide whether two lines are parallel or perpendicular to each other.

Math Background

The theorems in this lesson provide an opportunity to continue the study and use of transitive relationships. One significant difference to highlight when presenting the theorems in this lesson is the inclusion of the phrase "in a plane" in only two of the theorems. Point out that the relationship involving all parallel lines does not include this phrase because this relationship is true in a plane and also in space.

Applications of these relationships include high-rise buildings with many floors, all of which are parallel (an illustration of the theorem in space) and the façade of buildings with rows of windows (an illustration of the theorem in a plane). The topics of parallel and perpendicular lines learned in this and other lessons in this chapter will be the basis for classifying special quadrilaterals and other polygons in subsequent chapters. Further, the theorems and postulates concerning parallel and perpendicular lines will be needed to prove the properties of special quadrilaterals.

ELL Support

USE GRAPHIC ORGANIZERS Have groups of students make a poster about parallel and perpendicular lines. Say: Show right angles and intersections on your poster. Explain what *parallel* and *perpendicular* mean. Tell how you can prove lines are parallel or perpendicular. Have students draw or collect pictures to illustrate their posters. Have them use familiar language as well as appropriate mathematical terms.

Have each group explain its poster to another group. Then allow the groups to add to their posters or change them to include what they learned from the other group. Have each student in the group copy his or her own version of the poster onto a page to be kept in his or her chapter notebook.

Mathematical Practices

CONSTRUCT VIABLE ARGUMENTS AND CRITIQUE THE REASONING OF OTHERS. Students will make conjectures about the measures or congruence of angles and build a progression of logical statements (i.e., a proof) using their knowledge of the intersections of parallel and perpendicular lines.

Interactive Learning

Solve It!

PURPOSE To provide a situation in which students can make a conjecture that relates parallel and perpendicular lines

PROCESS Students may use visual judgment or previously learned theorems about angles.

Q What is the relationship between Oak Street and Schoolhouse Road? Explain. **[They are parallel, because a pair of alternate interior angles is congruent.]**

Q How can extending the paths help to determine the relationship between Oak Street and Court Road? **[If one of the paths intersects both roads, then you might use the congruent and supplementary relationships of special angle pairs to prove lines parallel.]**

ANSWER Oak Street and Court Road are ∥. The pairs of ≅ alt. int. ∠s show that both Oak Street and Court Road are ∥ to Schoolhouse Road.

CONNECT THE MATH The relationship of Oak Street and Schoolhouse Road can be used to determine the relationship between Oak Street and Court Road. Similar patterns will be investigated in this lesson.

▼ DIGITAL (STUDENT WORK SPACE PAGE 91)

SOLVE IT! **Getting Ready!**

Jude and Jasmine leave school together to walk home. Then Jasmine cuts down a path from Schoolhouse Road to get to Oak Street and Jude cuts down another path to get to Court Road. Below is a diagram of the route each follows home. What conjecture can you make about Oak Street and Court Road? Explain.

Oak Street
School
Schoolhouse Road
Court Road

2 Guided Instruction

Problem 1 Solving a Problem With Parallel Lines

Take Note

Theorem 13

Q What are some real-life situations in which two lines are both parallel to a third line? **[Samples: school hallways, striped shirts, 25-yd lines in football]**

Take Note

Theorem 14

Remind students of the definition of perpendicular lines prior to introducing this theorem.

Problem 1

Q When the three pieces of molding are put into place, what does the diagram look like? Label the measures of any angles known.

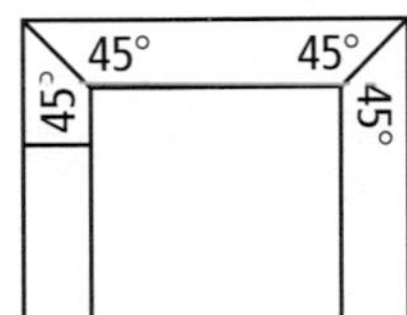

Q How can you show the angles formed on the outer sides of the doorway are right angles? **[A right angle measures 90. 45 + 45 = 90]**

▼ STUDENT PAGES 91–92

In the Solve It, you likely made your conjecture about Oak Street and Court Road based on their relationships to Schoolhouse Road. In this lesson you will use similar reasoning to prove that lines are parallel or perpendicular.

Essential Understanding You can use the relationships of two lines to a third line to decide whether the two lines are parallel or perpendicular to each other.

take note

Theorem 13

Theorem	If . . .	Then . . .
If two lines are parallel to the same line, then they are parallel to each other.	$a \parallel b$ and $b \parallel c$	$a \parallel c$

a
b
c

You will prove Theorem 13 in Exercise 2.

take note

Theorem 14

Theorem	If . . .	Then . . .
In a plane, if two lines are perpendicular to the same line, then they are parallel to each other.	$m \perp t$ and $n \perp t$	$m \parallel n$

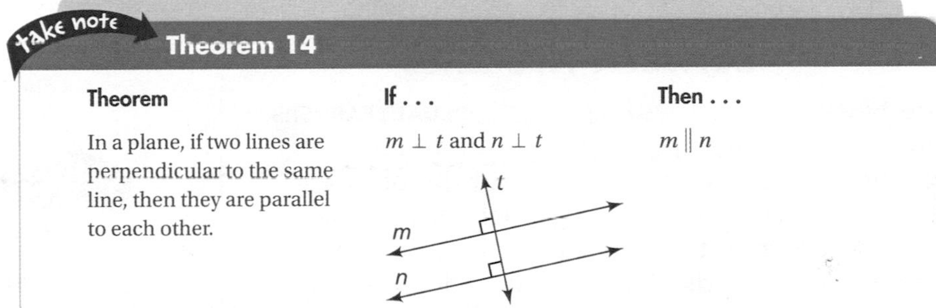

Notice that Theorem 14 includes the phrase *in a plane*. In Exercise 17, you will consider why this phrase is necessary.

Proof Proof of Theorem 14

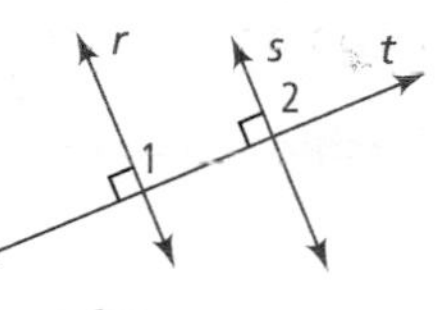

Given: In a plane, $r \perp t$ and $s \perp t$.

Prove: $r \parallel s$

Proof: $\angle 1$ and $\angle 2$ are right angles by the definition of perpendicular. So, $\angle 1 \cong \angle 2$. Since corresponding angles are congruent, $r \parallel s$.

▼ DIGITAL

Problem 1 Solving a Problem With Parallel Lines STEM

Carpentry A carpenter plans to install molding on the sides and the top of a doorway. The carpenter cuts the ends of the top piece and one end of each of the side pieces at 45° angles as shown. Will the side pieces of molding be parallel? Explain.

top
45°
45°
45°
45°
side
side

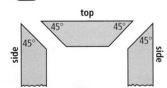

Know	Need	Plan
The angles at the connecting ends are 45°.	Determine whether the side pieces of molding are parallel.	Visualize fitting the pieces together to form new angles. Use information about the new angles to decide whether the sides are parallel.

Yes, the sides are parallel. When the pieces fit together, they form 45° + 45°, or 90°, angles. So, each side is perpendicular to the top. If two lines (the sides) are perpendicular to the same line (the top), then they are parallel to each other.

Problem 1 *continued*

Got It? **ERROR PREVENTION**

Q Will it be enough to use Theorem 14 only one time when determining if the opposite sides are parallel? Explain. **[No, you will have to prove separately that each pair of opposite sides is parallel.]**

ANSWERS

Got It? Yes; place the pieces with 60° ⦣ opposite each other and place the pieces with 30° ⦣ opposite each other. All four corners will be 90°, so opposite sides will be ∥.

Practice

1. **a.** $\angle 1 \cong \angle 2 \cong \angle 3$

   b. Sample: Attach more pieces perpendicular to piece A. Each new piece will be parallel to piece D, since the corresp. ⦣ formed are ≅ right ⦣.

▼ STUDENT PAGES 92–93

Think

How can a sketch help you visualize how to assemble the pieces?

Got It? Can you assemble the pieces below to form a picture frame with opposite sides parallel? Explain.

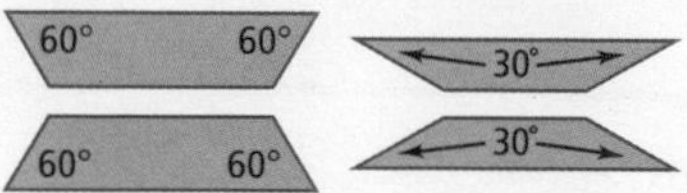

Practice 1. A carpenter is building a trellis for vines to grow on. The completed trellis will have two sets of diagonal pieces of wood that overlap each other.

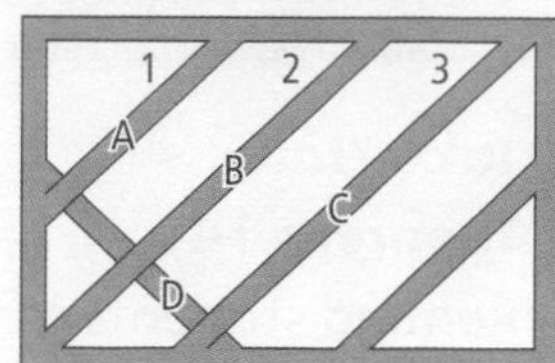

a. If pieces A, B, and C must be parallel, what must be true of $\angle 1$, $\angle 2$, and $\angle 3$?

b. The carpenter attaches piece D so that it is perpendicular to piece A. If he wants to place more pieces parallel to piece D, how can he do so? Justify your answer using theorems from this lesson.

Problem 2 Proving a Relationship Between Two Lines

Take Note **VISUAL LEARNERS**

Using a counterexample, demonstrate to students that the theorem is not true without the phrase "in a plane." Draw a pair of parallel lines on the board. At one point on one of the lines, hold a meter stick perpendicular to the board. Students should recognize that the meter stick is not perpendicular to both lines, because the three lines are not coplanar.

Problem 2

Q Is it possible to determine the measures of the other angles in the diagram prior to proving the relationship between the lines? Explain. **[Yes, you can determine the other measures by the definition of linear pairs and the Vertical Angles Theorem.]**

Q Which parallel lines must you use when planning the steps to this proof? **[lines *c* and *d*]**

Q Which line will you use as the transversal to use the Perpendicular Transversal Theorem with the lines named above? **[line *a*]**

▼ STUDENT PAGE 93

Theorems 13 and 14 give conditions that allow you to conclude that lines are parallel. The Perpendicular Transversal Theorem below provides a way for you to conclude that lines are perpendicular.

take note

Theorem 15 Perpendicular Transversal Theorem

Theorem	If . . .	Then . . .
In a plane, if a line is perpendicular to one of two parallel lines, then it is also perpendicular to the other.	$n \perp \ell$ and $\ell \parallel m$	$n \perp m$

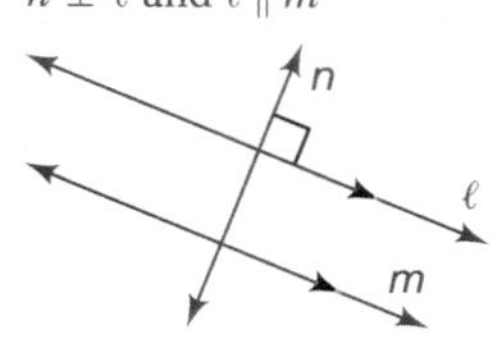

You will prove Theorem 15 in Exercise 10.

The Perpendicular Transversal Theorem states that the lines must be *in a plane*. The diagram at the right shows why. In the rectangular solid, $\overleftrightarrow{AC}$ and $\overleftrightarrow{BD}$ are parallel. $\overleftrightarrow{EC}$ is perpendicular to $\overleftrightarrow{AC}$, but it is not perpendicular to $\overleftrightarrow{BD}$. In fact, $\overleftrightarrow{EC}$ and $\overleftrightarrow{BD}$ are skew because they are not in the same plane.

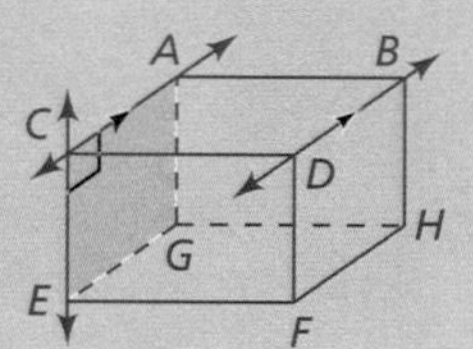

▼ DIGITAL

Problem 2 **Proving a Relationship Between Two Lines**

Given: In a plane, $c \perp b$, $b \perp d$, and $d \perp a$.

Prove: $c \perp a$

Proof: Lines c and d are both perpendicular to line b, so $c \parallel d$ because two lines perpendicular to the same line are parallel. It is given that $d \perp a$. Therefore, $c \perp a$ because a line that is perpendicular to one of two parallel lines is also perpendicular to the other (Perpendicular Transversal Theorem).

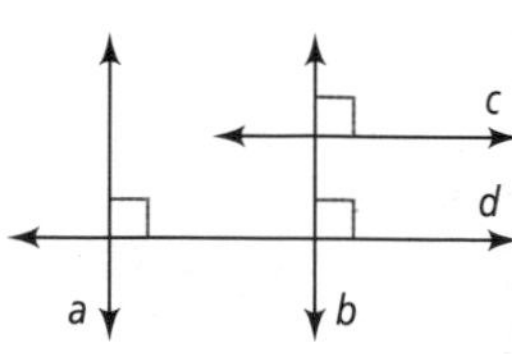

Got It? SYNTHESIZING

Point out to students that the proofs completed in Problem 2 and Got It can be used to define the characteristics of a rectangle: All four angles measure 90° and the opposite sides are parallel.

ANSWERS

Got It? Yes: $a \parallel b$ because they are both $\perp$ to d, and in a plane, two lines $\perp$ to the same line are $\parallel$.

Practice

2. a. Corresp. ⦤s
   b. $\angle 1$
   c. $\angle 3$
   d. Converse of Corresp. ⦤s Thm.
3. Since a and c are both $\perp$ to b, then $a \parallel c$ because, in a plane, if two lines are $\perp$ to the same line, they are $\parallel$. It is given that $c \parallel d$, so $a \parallel d$ because, if two lines are $\parallel$ to the same line, they are $\parallel$.

▼ STUDENT PAGE 94

Think

How do lines *a* and *b* relate to line *d*?

Got It? In Problem 2, could you also conclude $a \parallel b$? Explain.

A Practice 2. **Developing Proof** Copy and complete this paragraph proof of Theorem 13 for three coplanar lines.

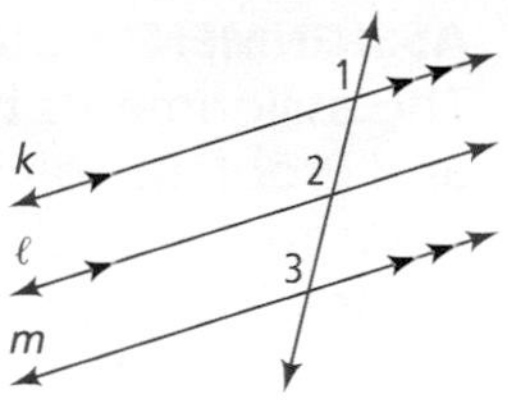

Given: $\ell \parallel k$ and $m \parallel k$

Prove: $\ell \parallel m$

Proof: Since $\ell \parallel k$, $\angle 2 \cong \angle 1$ by the **a.** __?__ Theorem. Since $m \parallel k$, **b.** __?__ $\cong$ **c.** __?__ for the same reason. By the Transitive Property of Congruence, $\angle 2 \cong \angle 3$. By the **d.** __?__ Theorem, $\ell \parallel m$.

a. ______________________

b. ______________________

c. ______________________

d. ______________________

Proof 3. Write a paragraph proof.

Given: In a plane, $a \perp b$, $b \perp c$, and $c \parallel d$.

Prove: $a \parallel d$

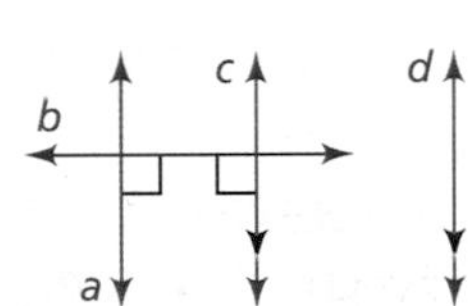

3 Lesson Check

Do you know HOW?

If students have difficulty with Exercise 4, then encourage them to make a sketch and label all given angles to represent the information provided in the question.

Do you UNDERSTAND?

If students have difficulty with Exercise 6, then have them try to find a counterexample using a line not in the same plane.

Close

Q What methods introduced in this lesson can be used to prove that two lines are parallel? **[If two lines are parallel to the same line or if two lines are perpendicular to the same line, then they are parallel to each other.]**

ANSWERS

4. They are $\perp$; using Main Street as a transversal, Avenue B $\perp$ Main Street by $\perp$ Trans. Thm.
5. $a \parallel b$; in a plane, if two lines are $\perp$ to the same line, then they are $\parallel$.
6. Sample: Even if the 3 lines are not in the same plane, each line is parallel to the other 2 lines.
7. Thm. 14 uses the Converse of the Corresp. ⦤s Thm.; the $\perp$ Trans. Thm. uses the Corresp. ⦤s Thm.
8. The diagram should show that m and r are $\perp$.

▼ STUDENT PAGES 95–96

Lesson Check

Do you know HOW?

4. Main Street intersects Avenue A and Avenue B. Avenue A is parallel to Avenue B. Avenue A is also perpendicular to Main Street. How are Avenue B and Main Street related? Explain.
5. In the diagram at the right, lines *a*, *b*, and *c* are coplanar. What conclusion can you make about lines *a* and *b*? Explain.

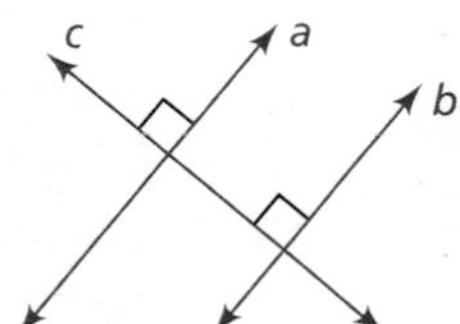

Do you UNDERSTAND? MATHEMATICAL PRACTICES

6. Explain why the phrase *in a plane* is not necessary in Theorem 13.
7. Which theorem or postulate from earlier in the chapter supports the conclusion in Theorem 14? In the Perpendicular Transversal Theorem? Explain.
8. **Error Analysis** Shiro sketched coplanar lines *m*, *n*, and *r* on his homework paper. He claims that it shows that lines *m* and *n* are parallel. What other information do you need about line *r* in order for Shiro's claim to be true? Explain.

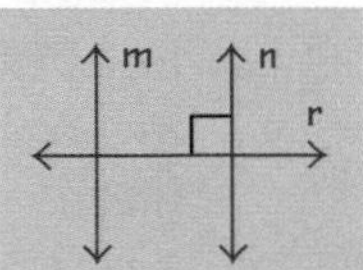

Practice

More Practice and Problem-Solving Exercises

ASSIGNMENT GUIDE

The assignments below are for the More Practice and Problem-Solving Exercises. You may also want to assign the A-Level Practice Exercises for homework if these are not used in class.

Average: 9–18
Advanced: 9–26

Mathematical Practices The exercises listed focus on the Standards for Mathematical Practices listed.

EX. 9: Make Sense of Problems (MP 1)
EX. 17, 25, 26: Construct Arguments (MP 3)
EX. 8: Critique the Reasoning of Others (MP 3)
EX. 18: Model (MP 4)

EXERCISE 18: Use the **Think About a Plan** worksheet in the Online Teacher Resources to further support students' development in becoming independent learners.

HOMEWORK QUICK CHECK

To check students' understanding of key skills and concepts, go over Exercises 9, 12, 14, 17, and 18.

ANSWERS

9. Measure any three int. ∠s to be rt. ∠s and opp. walls will be ∥ because two walls ⊥ to the same wall are ∥.
10. In the diagram, $a \perp b$ means the marked ∠ is a right ∠. $b \parallel c$ means that the corresp. ∠ formed by a and c is a right ∠, so $a \perp c$.
11. The rungs are ∥ to each other because they are all ⊥ to the same side.
12. All of the rungs are ⊥ to one side. The side is ⊥ to the top rung, and because all of the rungs are ∥ to each other, the side is ⊥ to all of the rungs.
13. The rungs are ⊥ to both sides. The rungs are ⊥ to one of two ∥ sides, so they are ⊥ to both sides.
14. The sides are ∥ because they are both ⊥ to one rung.
15. The rungs are ∥ because they are all ⊥ to one side.
16. They are ⊥; answers may vary. Sample: The light blue and black lines are ∥ because they are both ⊥ to the red line. Since the orange line is ⊥ to one of those two ∥ lines, it must also be ⊥ to the other.

▼ STUDENT PAGE 96

More Practice and Problem-Solving Exercises

9. **Think About a Plan** One traditional type of log cabin is a single rectangular room. Suppose you begin building a log cabin by placing four logs in the shape of a rectangle. What should you measure to guarantee that the logs on opposite walls are parallel? Explain.
   - What type of information do you need to prove lines parallel?
   - How can you use a diagram to help you?
   - What do you know about the angles of the geometric shape?

Proof 10. Prove the Perpendicular Transversal Theorem (Theorem 15): In a plane, if a line is perpendicular to one of two parallel lines, then it is also perpendicular to the other.

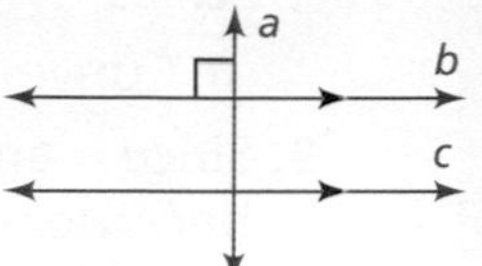

Given: In a plane, $a \perp b$ and $b \parallel c$.

Prove: $a \perp c$

The following statements describe a ladder. Based only on the statement, make a conclusion about the rungs, one side, or both sides of the ladder. Explain.

11. The rungs are each perpendicular to one side.
12. The rungs are parallel and the top rung is perpendicular to one side.
13. The sides are parallel. The rungs are perpendicular to one side.
14. Each side is perpendicular to the top rung.
15. The rungs are perpendicular to one side. The sides are not parallel.
16. **Public Transportation** The map at the right is a section of a subway map. The light blue line is perpendicular to the red line, the red line is perpendicular to the black line, and the black line is perpendicular to the orange line. What conclusion can you make about the light blue line and the orange line? Explain.

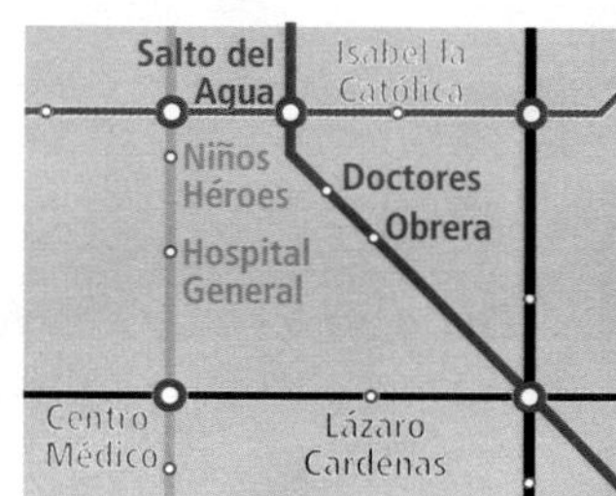

17. Sample: Using the diagram underneath Thm. 15, $\overleftrightarrow{EC}$ and $\overleftrightarrow{AB}$ are both $\perp$ to $\overleftrightarrow{AC}$, but $\overleftrightarrow{EC}$ and $\overleftrightarrow{AB}$ are skew, so they cannot be $\parallel$.
18. The rt. triangles must have acute ⦞ that measure 45.
19. $a \parallel d$ by Thm. 13
20. $a \perp d$ by Thms. 13 and 15
21. $a \perp d$ by Thm. 15
22. $a \perp d$ by Thm. 15
23. $a \parallel d$ by Thms. 13 and 14
24. $a \parallel d$ by Thms. 14 and 15
25. Reflexive: $a \parallel a$; false; every line intersects itself. Symmetric: If $a \parallel b$, then $b \parallel a$; true; lines a and b are coplanar and do not meet. Transitive: If $a \parallel b$ and $b \parallel c$, then $a \parallel c$; true; that is Thm. 13.
26. Reflexive: $a \perp a$; false; a line does not intersect itself at a rt. $\angle$. Symmetric: If $a \perp b$, then $b \perp a$; true; lines a and b form rt. ⦞. Transitive: If $a \perp b$ and $b \perp c$, then $a \perp c$; false; if a and c are both $\perp$ to b, then $a \parallel c$ or a and c are skew.

▼ STUDENT PAGE 97

17. **Writing** Theorem 14 states that in a plane, two lines perpendicular to the same line are parallel. Explain why the phrase *in a plane* is needed. (*Hint:* Refer to a rectangular solid to help you visualize the situation.)

18. **Quilting** You plan to sew two triangles of fabric together to make a square for a quilting project. The triangles are both right triangles and have the same side and angle measures. What must also be true about the triangles in order to guarantee that the opposite sides of the fabric square are parallel? Explain.

Challenge

For Exercises 19–24, *a, b, c,* and *d* are distinct lines in the same plane. For each combination of relationships, tell how *a* and *d* relate. Justify your answer.

19. $a \parallel b, b \parallel c, c \parallel d$
20. $a \parallel b, b \parallel c, c \perp d$
21. $a \parallel b, b \perp c, c \parallel d$
22. $a \perp b, b \parallel c, c \parallel d$
23. $a \parallel b, b \perp c, c \perp d$
24. $a \perp b, b \parallel c, c \perp d$

25. **Reasoning** Review the reflexive, symmetric, and transitive properties for congruence in Lesson 10-6. Write reflexive, symmetric, and transitive statements for "is parallel to" ($\parallel$). Tell whether each statement is *true* or *false*. Justify your answer.

26. **Reasoning** Repeat Exercise 25 for "is perpendicular to" ($\perp$).

5 Assess and Remediate

Lesson Quiz

1. What value of x results in $\overline{AB} \parallel \overline{CD}$?

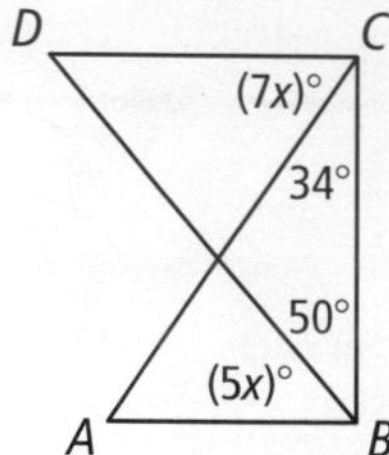

2. In a plane, if $\ell \perp n$ and $\ell \parallel m$, prove that $m \perp n$.

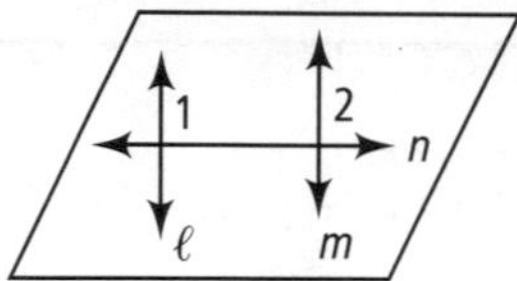

3. **Do you UNDERSTAND?** A fly and an ant are sitting in the middle of a floor. If the fly starts moving along a straight path of his choice, will the ant be able to move along a parallel path?

ANSWERS TO LESSON QUIZ

1. 8
2. Since $\ell \parallel m$, $\angle 1 \cong \angle 2$ because they are corresponding angles. $m\angle 1 = m\angle 2$ by definition of congruent angles. Because $\angle 1$ is a right angle, $m\angle 1 = 90$. By substitution, $m\angle 2 = 90$. By definition of right angles, $\angle 2$ is a right angle. So, by the definition of perpendicular lines, $m \perp n$.
3. Not necessarily; if the fly's path goes straight up, for instance, the ant cannot move in a parallel path.

Prescription for Remediation

Use the student work on the Lesson Quiz to prescribe a differentiated assignment.

Points	Differentiated Remediation
0–1	Intervention
2	On-level
3	Extension

Online Assessment

Assign the Lesson Quiz in Success Tracker on **pearsonsuccessnet.com**. Success Tracker will automatically score the quiz and assign appropriate intervention or enrichment to each student based on the results. The compiled data appear in three different reports for instant analysis of whole class and individual student performance.

Differentiated Remediation

Intervention

- **RETEACHING** (2 pages) Provides reteaching and practice exercises for the key lesson concepts. Use with struggling students or absent students.
- **ENGLISH LANGUAGE LEARNER SUPPORT** Helps students develop and reinforce mathematical vocabulary and key concepts.

On-Level

- **PRACTICE** (2 pages) Provides extra practice for each lesson. For simpler practice exercises, use the Form K Practice pages found in the Online Teacher Resources.
- **THINK ABOUT A PLAN** Helps students develop specific problem-solving skills and strategies by providing scaffolded guiding questions.
- **STANDARDIZED TEST PREP** Focuses on all major exercises, all major question types, and helps students prepare for the high-stakes assessments.

Extension

- **ENRICHMENT** Provides students with interesting problems and activities that extend the concepts of the lesson.
- **ACTIVITIES, GAMES, AND PUZZLES** Worksheets that can be used for concept development, enrichment, and for fun!

2-5 Parallel Lines and Triangles

Common Core State Standards
G.CO.10 Prove theorems about triangles . . . measures of interior angles of a triangle sum to 180°. **Also G.CO.9**

Preparing to Teach

BIG idea Measurement

ESSENTIAL UNDERSTANDING

The sum of the angle measures of a triangle is always the same. Any exterior angle of a triangle has a special relationship with the two remote interior angles of a triangle.

Math Background

It is important that students know that the geometry studied in the course is Euclidean geometry and that its formulation depends on the Parallel Postulate put forth by Euclid. The conjecture (through a point not on a line, there is one and only one line parallel to a given line) put forth in the postulate is assumed to be true, and provides a framework for all of the other theorems and postulates in Euclidean geometry. Mathematicians have developed other geometries by modifying the assumption of the parallel postulate. For example, hyperbolic geometry was developed by assuming that for a point not on a line, there are an infinite number of lines though the point that are parallel to the given line. Projective geometry was developed by assuming that for a point not on a line there are no lines through the point that are parallel to the given line. Many students find the introduction of other geometries interesting, but more importantly, the study of such geometries often helps to solidify an understanding of Euclidean geometry.

ELL Support

USE MANIPULATIVES Have the students form mixed-ability groups of three or four students each. Ask students to show examples of right, acute, obtuse, isosceles, and equilateral triangles. Have each group draw different kinds of triangles. Say: Label each of your triangles. Have each group measure the interior angles of its triangles. Say: Write the sum of the interior angles of each triangle next to the triangle. Ask: Is each of your sums 180°? Have groups that answer *No* check their triangles again more carefully.

Have the groups exchange triangles with another group and measure the exterior angles of the other group's triangles, with one angle at each vertex. Ask: What is the sum of the angle measures?

Lesson Vocabulary

- auxiliary line
- exterior angle of a polygon
- remote interior angles

Mathematical Practices

ATTEND TO PRECISION. Students will explicitly define, use, and calculate exterior and interior angles of triangles.

1 Interactive Learning

Solve It!

PURPOSE To discover that the angles of any triangle can form a straight angle

PROCESS Students use visual judgment and knowledge of straight angles.

Q Does the measure of the angle formed by the corner of the triangle depend on where you make the tear in the paper? Explain. **[No, the place you tear the paper only affects the lengths of the sides of the angle.]**

Q If you cut out a right triangle, what is true about the measures of the two acute angles? **[The measures of the two acute angles add to 90. They form a right angle when they are adjacent.]**

ANSWER 180; the corners of the triangle fit together to make a straight angle. The measure of a straight angle is 180.

▼ DIGITAL (STUDENT WORK SPACE PAGE 98)

Getting Ready!

Draw and cut out a large triangle. What is the sum of the angle measures of the triangle? Explain. Do not use a protractor. (Hint: Tear off and rearrange the three corners of the triangle.)

CONNECT THE MATH The angles of any triangle can be cut apart and rearranged to form a straight angle. There is no way to draw all possible triangles to test this conjecture. Students must prove the Triangle Angle-Sum Theorem deductively, thus the need to introduce the Parallel Postulate at this time.

Guided Instruction

Problem 1 Using the Triangle Angle-Sum Theorem

Take Note

Parallel Postulate

Demonstrate to students that there are an infinite number of lines through P, but that only one of those lines is parallel to ℓ.

Take Note

Triangle Angle-Sum Theorem

Q Is this theorem true for all sizes and classifications of triangles? Explain. **[Yes, when the angles of any triangle are placed so that they share a common vertex and adjacent sides, but not interior points, they form a straight angle.]**

Q Does the order in which you add the measures of the angles affect the sum? Explain. **[No, addition is commutative, even when the addends are degrees.]**

Make sure that students understand that the auxiliary line in the diagram can be drawn through any of the vertices of the triangle. Draw two additional diagrams to illustrate this statement; one for each of the vertices not used in the Take Note diagram.

It may help students to visualize the use of the Alternate Interior Angles Theorem if the segment AC is extended to show the rest of the line containing it.

In the Solve It, you may have discovered that you can rearrange the corners of the triangle to form a straight angle. You can do this for any triangle.

Essential Understanding The sum of the angle measures of a triangle is always the same.

The Solve It suggests an important theorem about triangles. To prove this theorem, you will need to use parallel lines.

take note

Postulate 12 Parallel Postulate

Through a point not on a line, there is one and only one line parallel to the given line.

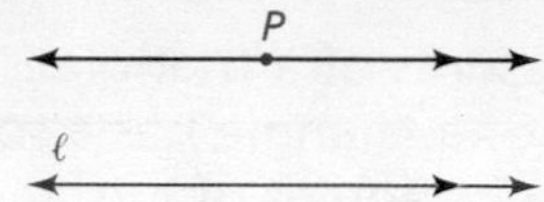

There is exactly one line through P parallel to ℓ.

take note

Theorem 16 Triangle Angle-Sum Theorem

The sum of the measures of the angles of a triangle is 180.

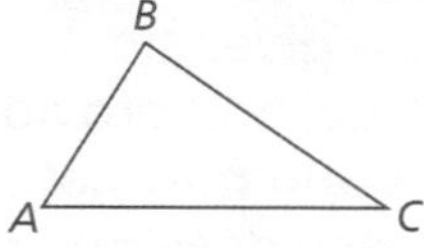

$m\angle A + m\angle B + m\angle C = 180$

The proof of the Triangle Angle-Sum Theorem requires an *auxiliary line*. An **auxiliary line** is a line that you add to a diagram to help explain relationships in proofs. The red line in the diagram below is an auxiliary line.

Proof Proof of Theorem 16: Triangle Angle-Sum Theorem

Given: $\triangle ABC$

Prove: $m\angle A + m\angle 2 + m\angle C = 180$

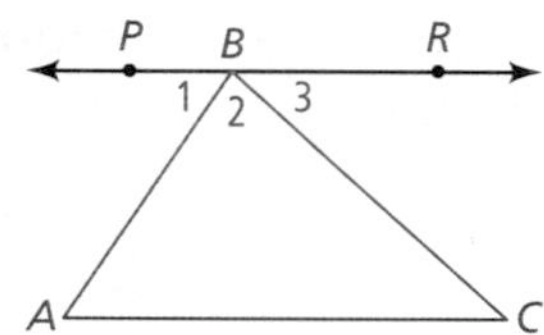

Statements	Reasons
1) Draw $\overleftrightarrow{PR}$ through B, parallel to $\overleftrightarrow{AC}$.	**1)** Parallel Postulate
2) $\angle PBC$ and $\angle 3$ are supplementary.	**2)** ∠s that form a linear pair are suppl.
3) $m\angle PBC + m\angle 3 = 180$	**3)** Definition of suppl. ∠s
4) $m\angle PBC = m\angle 1 + m\angle 2$	**4)** Angle Addition Postulate
5) $m\angle 1 + m\angle 2 + m\angle 3 = 180$	**5)** Substitution Property
6) $\angle 1 \cong \angle A$ and $\angle 3 \cong \angle C$	**6)** If lines are $\parallel$, then alternate interior ∠s are $\cong$.
7) $m\angle 1 = m\angle A$ and $m\angle 3 = m\angle C$	**7)** Congruent ∠s have equal measure.
8) $m\angle A + m\angle 2 + m\angle C = 180$	**8)** Substitution Property

When you know the measures of two angles of a triangle, you can use the Triangle Angle-Sum Theorem to find the measure of the third angle.

Problem 1

Q How many distinct triangles are represented in the diagram? Name each triangle. **[3; △ABC, △ABD, and △BDC]**

Q How is the measure of ∠BDC related to the measures of ∠BAC and ∠ABD? **[m∠BAC + m∠ABD = m∠BDC]**

Got It? **ERROR PREVENTION**

Q What two equations can you use to determine the value of z? **[49 + 102 + z = 180 or 59 + 92 + z = 180]**

ANSWERS

Got It? 29

Practice

1. 30 **2.** $x = y = 80$

▼ DIGITAL

Problem 1 Using the Triangle Angle-Sum Theorem

Algebra What are the values of x and y in the diagram at the right?

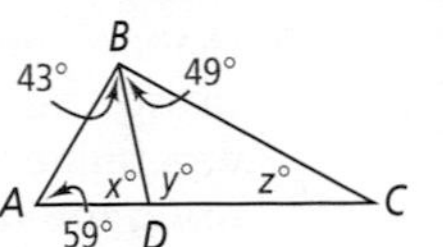

Think	Write
Use the Triangle Angle-Sum Theorem to write an equation involving x.	59 + 43 + x = 180
Solve for x by simplifying and then subtracting 102 from each side.	102 + x = 180 x = 78
∠ADB and ∠CDB form a linear pair, so they are supplementary.	m∠ADB + m∠CDB = 180
Substitute 78 for m∠ADB and y for m∠CDB in the above equation.	x + y = 180 78 + y = 180
Solve for y by subtracting 78 from each side.	y = 102

▼ STUDENT PAGE 100

Got It? Use the diagram below. What is the value of z?

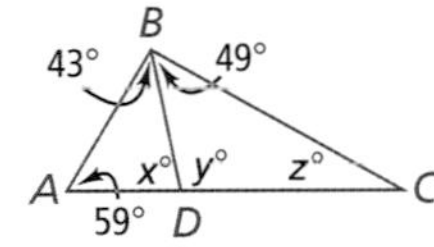

Plan

Which triangle will you use to find the value of z?

A Practice **1.** Find $m\angle 1$.

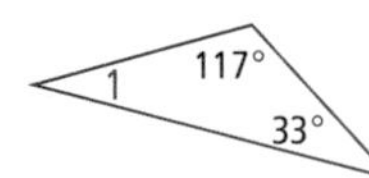

2. Algebra Find the value of each variable.

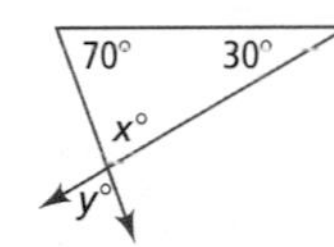

Problem 2 Using the Triangle Exterior Angle Theorem

Take Note **TACTILE LEARNERS**

Complete an activity similar to the Solve It activity to explore this theorem. Make two copies of a triangle, numbering all interior angles with 1a, 2a, 3a, and all exterior angles with 1b, 2b, and 3b. On the first triangle, extend the segments beyond the vertices. Cut out the second triangle and tear off the corners. Compare the torn-off corners with the exterior angles created in the first triangle.

▼ STUDENT PAGE 101

An **exterior angle of a polygon** is an angle formed by a side and an extension of an adjacent side. For each exterior angle of a triangle, the two nonadjacent interior angles are its **remote interior angles**. In each triangle below, ∠1 is an exterior angle and ∠2 and ∠3 are its remote interior angles.

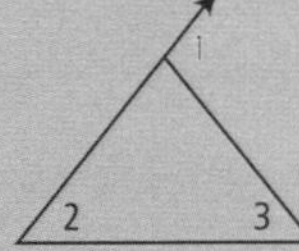

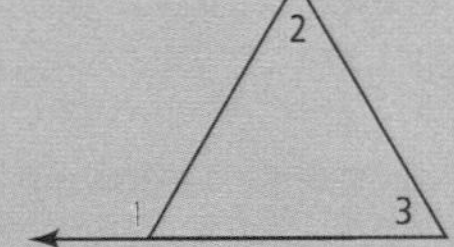

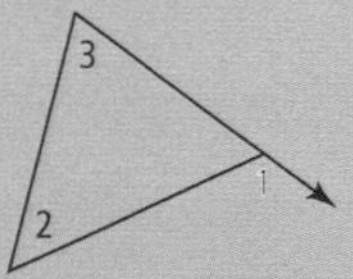

The theorem below states the relationship between an exterior angle and its two remote interior angles.

take note **Theorem 17** Triangle Exterior Angle Theorem

The measure of each exterior angle of a triangle equals the sum of the measures of its two remote interior angles.

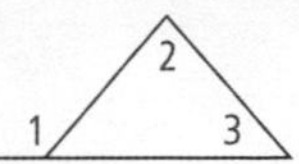

$$m\angle 1 = m\angle 2 + m\angle 3$$

You will prove Theorem 17 in Exercise 26.

You can use the Triangle Exterior Angle Theorem to find angle measures.

Problem 2 *continued*

Q How could you determine the measure of ∠1 without using the Triangle Exterior Angles Theorem? **[You first determine the measure of the third angle of the triangle using the Triangle Angle-Sum Theorem. Then use the definitions of linear and supplementary angles.]**

Q How could you determine the measure of ∠2 without using the Exterior Angles Theorem? **[You first determine the measure of the angle adjacent to the exterior angle through the definitions of linear and supplementary angles. Then use the Triangle Angle-Sum Theorem.]**

Got It? **VISUAL LEARNERS**

Have students make a sketch of the triangle prior to beginning the problem. Students should realize that an exterior angle can be formed at a vertex by extending either of the sides of the triangle at that vertex; which side is chosen will not affect the measure of the exterior angle.

ANSWERS

Got It? 127, 127, 106

Practice

3. **a.** ∠5, ∠6, ∠8
   b. For ∠5: ∠1 and ∠3; for ∠6: ∠1 and ∠2; for ∠8: ∠1 and ∠2
   c. ∠6 ≅ ∠8
4. 115.5

▼ DIGITAL

Problem 2 **Using the Triangle Exterior Angle Theorem**

A **What is the measure of ∠1?**

$m\angle 1 = 80 + 18$ Triangle Exterior Angle Theorem

$m\angle 1 = 98$ Simplify.

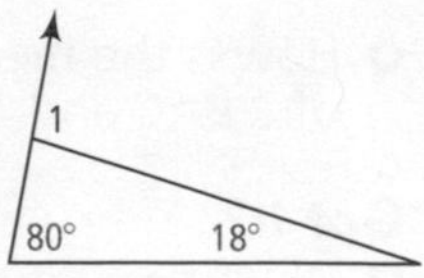

B **What is the measure of ∠2?**

$124 = 59 + m\angle 2$ Triangle Exterior Angle Theorem

$65 = m\angle 2$ Subtract 59 from each side.

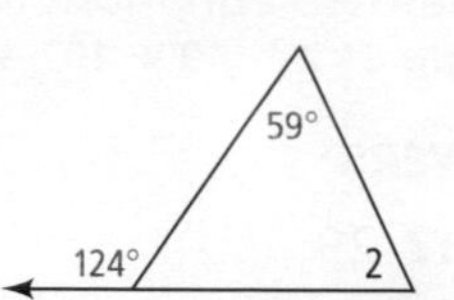

▼ STUDENT PAGES 101–102

Got It? Two angles of a triangle measure 53. What is the measure of an exterior angle at each vertex of the triangle?

Think
How can you draw a diagram to represent the given information?

Practice 3. **a.** Which of the numbered angles are exterior angles?

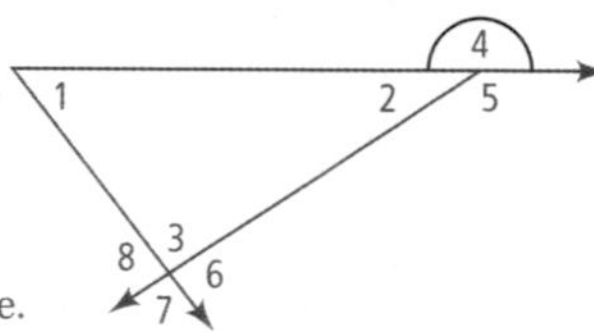

b. Name the remote interior angles for each exterior angle.

c. How are exterior angles 6 and 8 related?

4. **Algebra** Find the measure of ∠2.

Problem 3 Applying the Triangle Theorems

Q What equation containing x can be justified by the Triangle Exterior Angle Theorem? **[$x + 30 = 80$]**

Q What is the measure of the third angle of the triangle? Explain. **[The third angle measures 100, because $180 - 30 - 50 = 100$]**

▼ DIGITAL

Problem 3 **Applying the Triangle Theorems**

Multiple Choice When radar tracks an object, the reflection of signals off the ground can result in clutter. Clutter causes the receiver to confuse the real object with its reflection, called a ghost. At the right, there is a radar receiver at A, an airplane at B, and the airplane's ghost at D. What is the value of x?

Ⓐ 30 Ⓒ 70

Ⓑ 50 Ⓓ 80

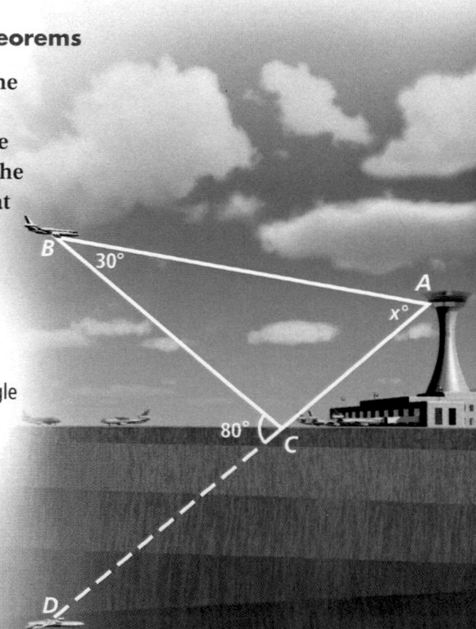

$m\angle A + m\angle B = m\angle BCD$ Triangle Exterior Angle Theorem

$x + 30 = 80$ Substitute.

$x = 50$ Subtract 30 from each side.

The value of x is 50. The correct answer is B.

Got It? VISUAL LEARNERS

Q Which angle forms a linear pair with the exterior angle that measures 80? What is its measure? **[∠ACB; 100]**

ANSWERS

Got It? Yes; answers may vary. Sample: $m\angle ACB$ must $= 100$, so by the Triangle Angle-Sum Thm., $m\angle A + 30 + 100 = 180$, and $m\angle A = 50$.

Practice

5. $a = 162$, $b = 18$

6. 114

▼ STUDENT PAGE 102

Got It? **Reasoning** In Problem 3, can you find $m\angle A$ without using the Triangle Exterior Angle Theorem? Explain.

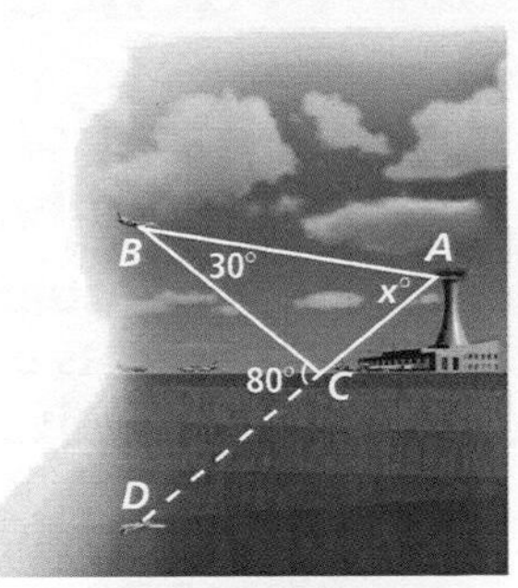

Practice **5.** A ramp forms the angles shown at the right. What are the values of a and b?

a°
b°
72°

6. A lounge chair has different settings that change the angles formed by its parts. Suppose $m\angle 2 = 71$ and $m\angle 3 = 43$. Find $m\angle 1$.

3 Lesson Check

Do you know HOW?

If students have difficulty with Exercises 11–12, then have them review Problem 2.

Do you UNDERSTAND?

If students have difficulty with Exercise 14, then ask them to try to justify each step for the correct solution method.

Close

Q What is always true about the interior angles of any triangle? **[The sum of the measures of the angles equals 180.]**

ANSWERS

7. 58 **8.** 45

9. 68 **10.** $130 - x$

11. $m\angle 1 = 130$ **12.** $m\angle 3 = 38$

13. Answers may vary. Sample: Consider the int. $\angle A$ of $\triangle ABC$. By the $\triangle$ $\angle$-Sum Thm., the sum of the measures of angles A, B, and C is 180°. $\angle A$ is suppl. to its ext. $\angle$. So the sum of the measures of angles B and C is equal to the measure of the ext. $\angle$ of $\angle A$.

14. A; all 3 $\angle$s are int. $\angle$s, so the solution should use the Triangle Angle-Sum Thm.

▼ STUDENT PAGES 103–104

Lesson Check

Do you know HOW?

Find the measure of the third angle of a triangle given the measures of two angles.

7. 34 and 88 **8.** 45 and 90

9. 10 and 102 **10.** x and 50

In a triangle, ∠1 is an exterior angle and ∠2 and ∠3 are its remote interior angles. Find the missing angle measure.

11. $m\angle 2 = 24$ and $m\angle 3 = 106$ **12.** $m\angle 1 = 70$ and $m\angle 2 = 32$

Do you UNDERSTAND?

13. Explain how the Triangle Exterior Angle Theorem makes sense based on the Triangle Angle-Sum Theorem.

14. Error Analysis The measures of the interior angles of a triangle are 30, x, and $3x$. Which of the following methods for solving for x is incorrect? Explain.

A.
$x + 3x = 30$
$4x = 30$
$x = 7.5$

B.
$x + 3x + 30 = 180$
$4x + 30 = 180$
$4x = 150$
$x = 37.5$

Practice

More Practice and Problem-Solving Exercises

ASSIGNMENT GUIDE

The assignments below are for the More Practice and Problem-Solving Exercises. You may also want to assign the A-Level Practice Exercises for homework if these are not used in class.
Average: 15–28
Advanced: 15–35

Mathematical Practices The exercises listed focus on the Standards for Mathematical Practices listed.

EX. 18, 21: Make Sense of Problems (MP 1)
EX. 20, 27: Construct Arguments (MP 3)
EX. 14: Critique the Reasoning of Others (MP 3)

EXERCISE 28: Use the **Think About a Plan** worksheet in the Online Teacher Resources to further support students' development in becoming independent learners.

HOMEWORK QUICK CHECK

To check students' understanding of key skills and concepts, go over Exercises 15, 18, 20, 27, and 28.

ANSWERS

15. 30, 60
16. 60, 80
17. 12, 60
18. 102, 65, 13
19. Answers may vary. Sample: $m\angle A + m\angle B + m\angle C = 180$ by the Triangle Angle-Sum Thm. It is given that $m\angle C = 90$, so $m\angle A + m\angle B + 90 = 180$. By the Subtr. Prop. of Equality, $m\angle A + m\angle B = 90$. Thus $\angle A$ and $\angle B$ are compl. by the def. of compl. ∠s.
20. 60; answers may vary. Sample: $180 \div 3 = 60$, so each ∠ is 60.
21. III; I does not have any ext. ∠s at *A*. II has only one ext. ∠ at *A* and only one side of the △ extended.
22. $x = 37$; $m\angle P = 65$, $m\angle Q = 78$, $m\angle R = 37$
23. $x = 7$; $m\angle A = 35$, $m\angle B = 55$, $m\angle C = 90$
24. $a = 67$, $b = 58$, $c = 125$, $d = 23$, $e = 90$
25. $x = 38$; $y = 36$, $z = 90$, $m\angle ABC = 74$
26. ∠1 is an ext. ∠ of the △. (Given); ∠1 and ∠4 are suppl. (∠s that form a straight ∠ are suppl.); $m\angle 1 + m\angle 4 = 180$ (Def. of suppl.); $m\angle 2 + m\angle 3 + m\angle 4 = 180$ (△ ∠-Sum Thm.); $m\angle 1 + m\angle 4 = m\angle 2 + m\angle 3 + m\angle 4$ (Subst. Prop.); $m\angle 1 = m\angle 2 + m\angle 3$ (Subtr. Prop. of =)
27. 132; the smallest interior ∠ is adjacent to the largest ext. ∠, so the largest ext. ∠ has measure $180 - 48 = 132$.

▼ STUDENT PAGES 104–105

More Practice and Problem-Solving Exercises

B Apply

Algebra Use the given information to find the unknown angle measures in the triangle.

15. The ratio of the angle measures of the acute angles in a right triangle is 1 : 2.

16. The measure of one angle of a triangle is 40. The measures of the other two angles are in a ratio of 3 : 4.

17. The measure of one angle of a triangle is 108. The measures of the other two angles are in a ratio of 1 : 5.

18. Think About a Plan The angle measures of $\triangle RST$ are represented by $2x$, $x + 14$, and $x - 38$. What are the angle measures of $\triangle RST$?
- How can you use the Triangle Angle-Sum Theorem to write an equation?
- How can you check your answer?

Proof 19. Prove the following theorem: The acute angles of a right triangle are complementary.

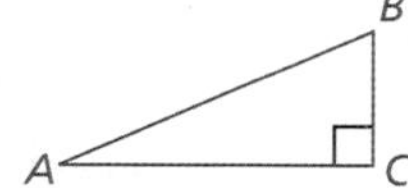

Given: $\triangle ABC$ with right angle *C*

Prove: $\angle A$ and $\angle B$ are complementary.

20. Reasoning What is the measure of each angle of an equiangular triangle? Explain.

21. Draw a Diagram Which diagram below correctly represents the following description? Explain your reasoning.

Draw any triangle. Label it $\triangle ABC$. Extend two sides of the triangle to form two exterior angles at vertex *A*.

I.
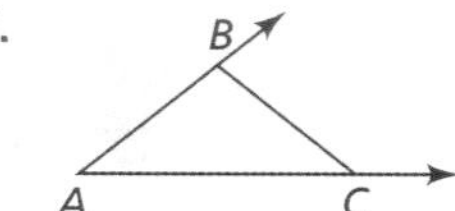

II.
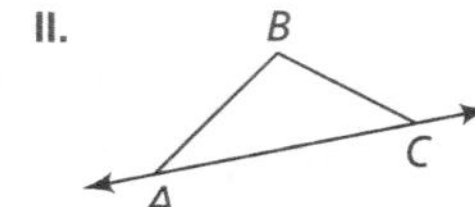

III.
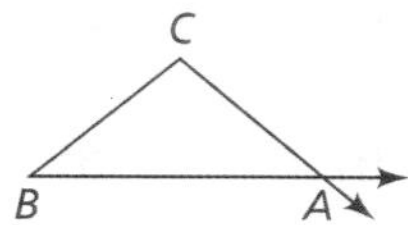

Find the values of the variables and the measures of the angles.

22.
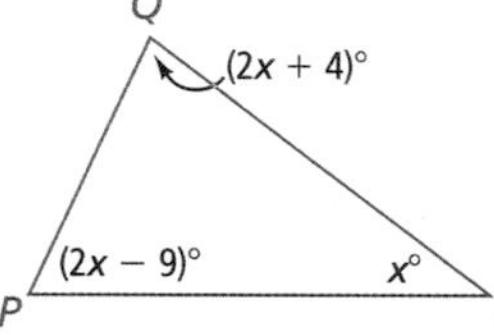

23.
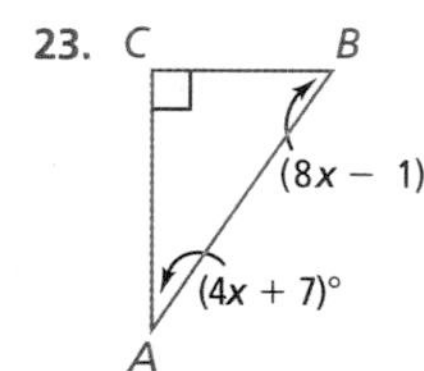

24.
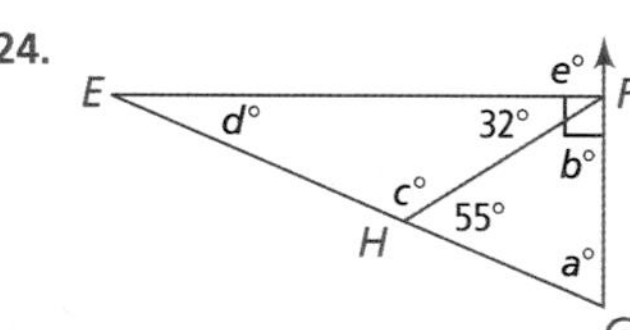

25.
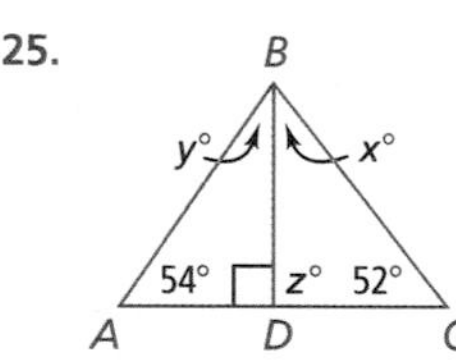

Proof 26. Prove the Triangle Exterior Angle Theorem (Theorem 17). The measure of each exterior angle of a triangle equals the sum of the measures of its two remote interior angles.

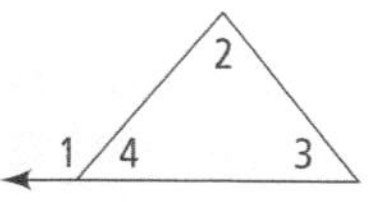

Given: $\angle 1$ is an exterior angle of the triangle.

Prove: $m\angle 1 = m\angle 2 + m\angle 3$

27. Reasoning Two angles of a triangle measure 64 and 48. What is the measure of the largest exterior angle of the triangle? Explain.

28. 40, 50

29. $\frac{1}{3}$

30. $\frac{1}{7}$

31. 1

32. $\frac{1}{19}$

33. 0

34. 115

35. The bisector is ∥ to the side common to the ≅ ⦣s. If the measure of each ≅ ∠ is *x*, then the measure of the ext. ∠ is 2*x* so the bisector forms 2 ⦣s of measure *x*. Alt. int. ⦣s are ≅ , so the bisector is ∥ to the side common to the ≅ int. ⦣s.

28. Algebra A right triangle has exterior angles at each of its acute angles with measures in the ratio 13 : 14. Find the measures of the two acute angles of the right triangle.

Challenge

Probability In Exercises 29–33, you know only the given information about the measures of the angles of a triangle. Find the probability that the triangle is equiangular.

29. Each is a multiple of 30.

30. Each is a multiple of 20.

31. Each is a multiple of 60.

32. Each is a multiple of 12.

33. One angle is obtuse.

34. In the figure at the right, $\overline{CD} \perp \overline{AB}$ and $\overline{CD}$ bisects $\angle ACB$. Find $m\angle DBF$.

35. If the remote interior angles of an exterior angle of a triangle are congruent, what can you conclude about the bisector of the exterior angle? Justify your answer.

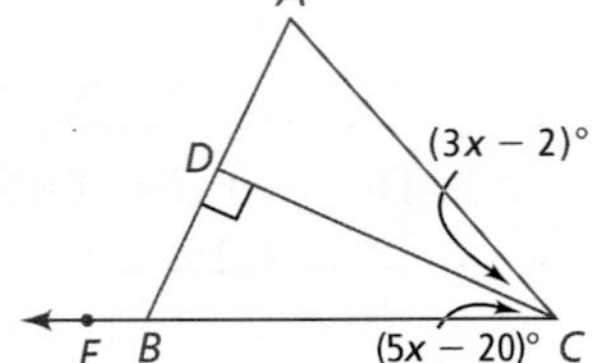

5 Assess and Remediate

Lesson Quiz

1. Solve for *x*, *y*, and *z* in the figure below.

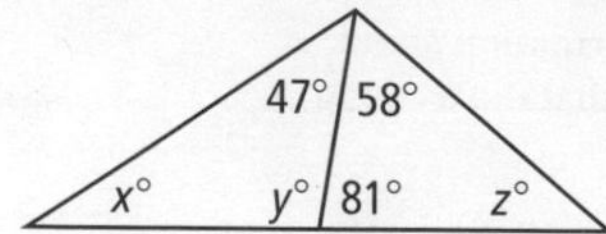

2. What are the measures of ∠1 and ∠2?

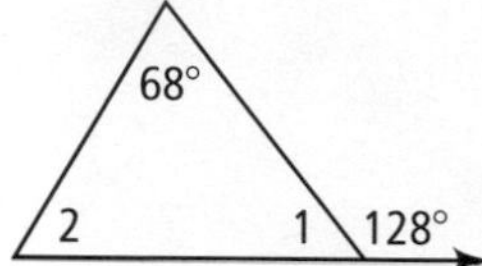

3. **Do you UNDERSTAND?** Neko made the triangular flag shown below. He wanted to attach it to the stick and then trim off the extra fabric so the flag would form an isosceles triangle. By how many degrees was he off when he attached the triangle to the stick?

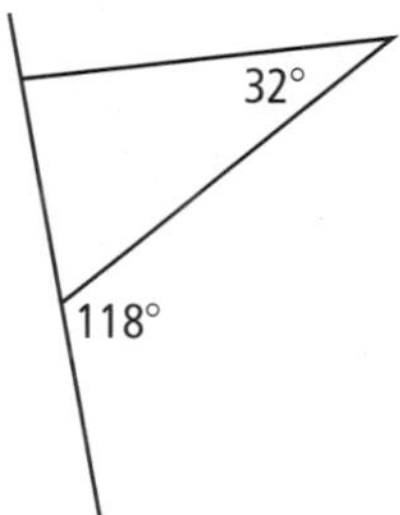

ANSWERS TO LESSON QUIZ

1. $x = 34$, $y = 99$, $z = 41$
2. $m\angle 1 = 52$, $m\angle 2 = 60$
3. Neko's flag ended up with base angles of 86° and 62°, so his stick was 12° out of alignment from the correct position (both angles 74°).

Prescription for Remediation

Use the student work on the Lesson Quiz to prescribe a differentiated assignment.

Points	Differentiated Remediation
0–1	Intervention
2	On-level
3	Extension

Online Assessment

Assign the Lesson Quiz in Success Tracker on **pearsonsuccessnet.com**. Success Tracker will automatically score the quiz and assign appropriate intervention or enrichment to each student based on the results. The compiled data appear in three different reports for instant analysis of whole class and individual student performance.

Differentiated Remediation

Intervention

- **RETEACHING** (2 pages) Provides reteaching and practice exercises for the key lesson concepts. Use with struggling students or absent students.
- **ENGLISH LANGUAGE LEARNER SUPPORT** Helps students develop and reinforce mathematical vocabulary and key concepts.

On-Level

- **PRACTICE** (2 pages) Provides extra practice for each lesson. For simpler practice exercises, use the Form K Practice pages found in the Online Teacher Resources.
- **THINK ABOUT A PLAN** Helps students develop specific problem-solving skills and strategies by providing scaffolded guiding questions.
- **STANDARDIZED TEST PREP** Focuses on all major exercises, all major question types, and helps students prepare for the high-stakes assessments.

Extension

- **ENRICHMENT** Provides students with interesting problems and activities that extend the concepts of the lesson.
- **ACTIVITIES, GAMES, AND PUZZLES** Worksheets that can be used for concept development, enrichment, and for fun!

Constructing Parallel and Perpendicular Lines

Common Core State Standards
G.CO.12 Make formal geometric constructions with a variety of tools and methods . . . constructing perpendicular lines . . . and constructing a line parallel to a given line through a point not on the line. **Also G.CO.13**

Preparing to Teach

ESSENTIAL UNDERSTANDING

Parallel and perpendicular lines can be constructed with a straightedge and compass. Special quadrilaterals can be constructed with a straightedge and compass.

Math Background

Constructions are often a difficult topic for students to understand. They fail to grasp that drawings can be made more precisely when they do not rely on marked measuring devices. You can demonstrate the discrepancies introduced when a ruler or protractor is used by creating two of the same diagram, one using a finely sharpened pencil and one using a pencil that needs to be sharpened. Once students see the precision achieved through constructions, it is important to offer different methods for performing constructions, including paper folding, straightedge and compass, and geometric software. Students should also realize that there are different steps and different theorems to use. Just as lines can be proven parallel through the use of multiple theorems, parallel lines can be constructed using multiple methods. The paper-folding activity at the beginning of the lesson is based on the theorem "In a plane, if two lines are perpendicular to the same line, then they are parallel to each other." The straightedge-and-compass construction shown in the lesson is based on the Converse of the Corresponding Angles Theorem. Another method for constructing parallel lines could be based on the Converse of the Alternate Interior Angles Theorem.

ELL Support

FOCUS ON COMMUNICATION Model using a straightedge and compass to construct parallel lines. Use sentences like the following: Draw a line with the straightedge; use the compass to draw an arc; use the straightedge to draw a line through the two points; the lines are parallel. Have the students repeat each sentence and imitate each action after you demonstrate it.

Now arrange students into pairs of mixed abilities. Have one student in each pair read the directions for constructing perpendicular lines while the other student uses a compass and straightedge to construct the lines. Have each pair of students compare their construction with another pair's. Help the students decide which constructions are more accurate. Have the students switch roles so that students who were reading now do the construction. The students who did the construction should now read the directions. Display the better example from each pair on a bulletin board.

Mathematical Practices

USE APPROPRIATE TOOLS STRATEGICALLY. Students will use a compass to construct lines parallel or perpendicular to a given line.

1 Interactive Learning

Solve It!

PURPOSE To put together a paper-folding construction for parallel and perpendicular lines

PROCESS Students use paper folding and spatial reasoning using known definitions and theorems.

Q What is true about two lines that are perpendicular to the same line in a plane? **[They are the same line or they are parallel to each other.]**

ANSWER $m \parallel p$; both m and p are perpendicular to n.

CONNECT THE MATH Guide students to see the difference between a drawing and a construction. A drawing is a sketch used as an aid for understanding. A construction is a method of accurately creating a figure using specified tools.

▼ DIGITAL (STUDENT WORK SPACE PAGE 107)

SOLVE IT! **Getting Ready!**

Draw a line m on a sheet of paper. Fold your paper so that line m falls on itself. Label your fold line n. Fold your paper again so that n falls on itself. Label your new fold line p. How are m and p related? How do you know?

2 Guided Instruction

Problem 1 Constructing Parallel Lines

Q What is the first step necessary to construct ∠1? **[Put the compass point on vertex *H*, and draw an arc that intersects the sides of ∠*NHJ*.]**

Q What do you do next, keeping the compass open to the same width? **[Put the compass point on vertex *N* and draw an arc that intersects $\overleftrightarrow{HN}$.]**

Got It? **ERROR PREVENTION**
Students should use the Converse of the Corresponding Angles Theorem rather than the Corresponding Angles Theorem.

ANSWERS

Got It? ∠1 and ∠*NHJ* are corresp. ∠s for lines *m* and ℓ. Since ∠1 ≅ ∠*NHJ*, then *m* ∥ ℓ by the Converse of the Corresp. ∠s Thm.

Practice

1.

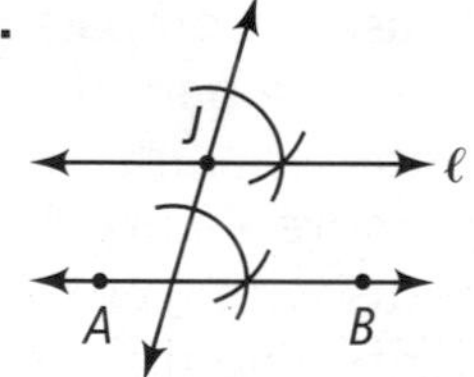

2.

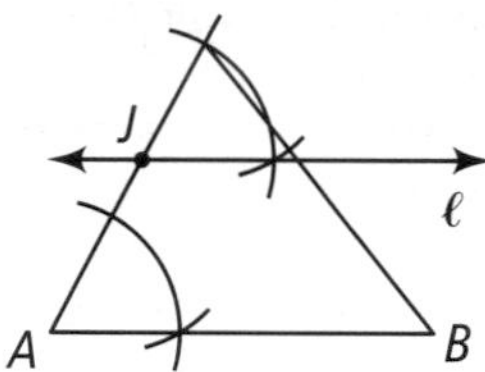

▼ STUDENT PAGE 107

In the Solve It, you used paper-folding to construct lines.

Essential Understanding You can also use a straightedge and a compass to construct parallel and perpendicular lines.

In Lesson 2-5, you learned that through a point not on a line, there is a unique line parallel to the given line. Problem 1 shows the construction of this line.

▼ DIGITAL

Problem 1 **Constructing Parallel Lines**

Construct the line parallel to a given line and through a given point that is not on the line.

Given: line ℓ and point *N* not on ℓ

Construct: line *m* through *N* with *m* ∥ ℓ

Step 1 Label two points *H* and *J* on ℓ. Draw $\overleftrightarrow{HN}$.

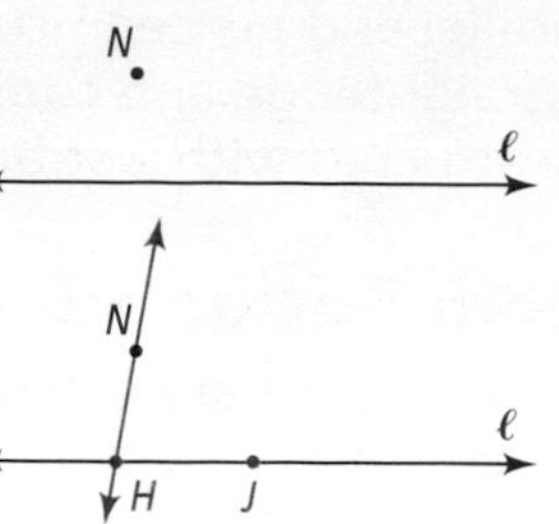

Step 2 At *N*, construct ∠1 congruent to ∠*NHJ*. Label the new line *m*.

m ∥ ℓ

▼ STUDENT PAGES 107–108

Got It? **Reasoning** In Problem 1, why must lines ℓ and *m* be parallel?

Practice Construct the line through point *J* that is parallel to $\overleftrightarrow{AB}$.

1.

2.

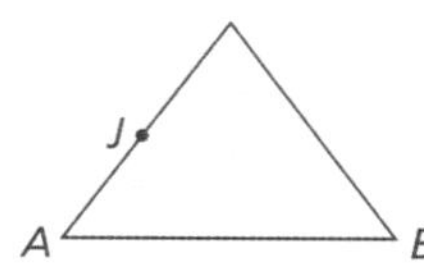

Problem 2 Constructing a Special Quadrilateral

Q What biconditional serves as a definition for congruent segments? **[Answers may vary. Sample: Two segments are congruent if and only if the two segments have the same length.]**

Q Why is a compass used to construct congruent segments rather than a ruler? **[Using a compass to construct congruent segments is more accurate than using a ruler, because the compass can match the length exactly, while the ruler can only match it to the nearest mark.]**

Q Will the lines that contain $\overline{AB}$ and $\overline{YZ}$ intersect? Explain. **[Yes, the lines will intersect because they are not parallel.]**

Got It? **VISUAL LEARNERS**

Q Will every quadrilateral *ABCD* that meets the requirements have the same size and shape? Explain. **[No; the length of $\overline{AB}$ and the measure of $\angle A$ can vary.]**

ANSWERS

Got It? a. Answers may vary. Sample:

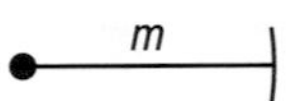

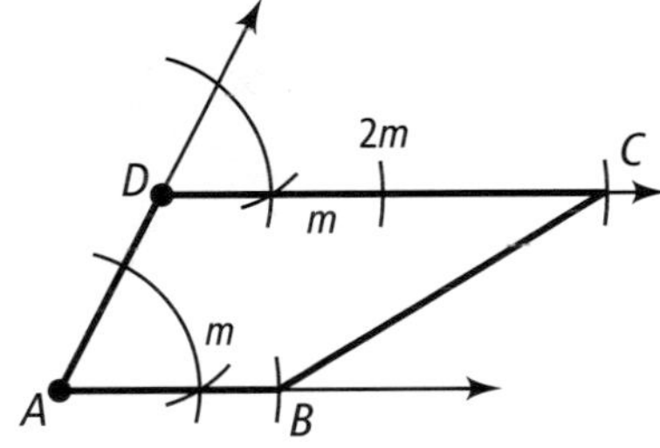

b. No; the length of $\overline{AB}$ and $m\angle A$ are not determined.

Practice

3–4. Constructions may vary. Samples using the following segments are given.

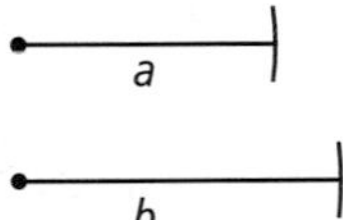

3.

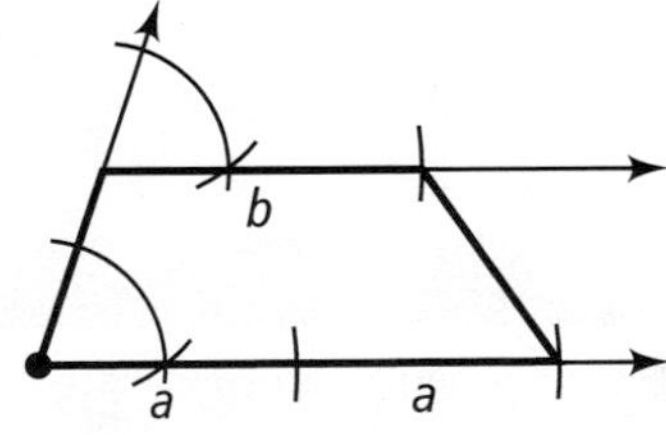

4.

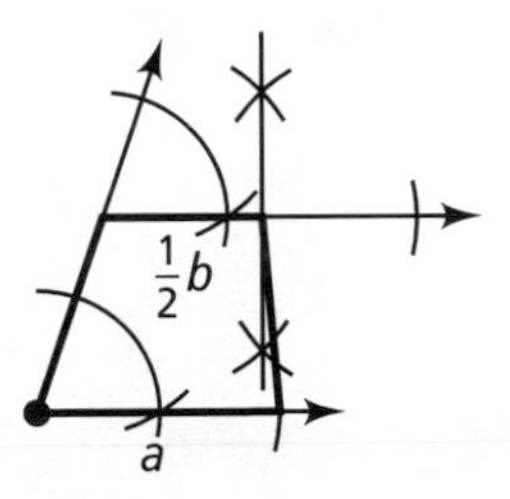

▼ DIGITAL

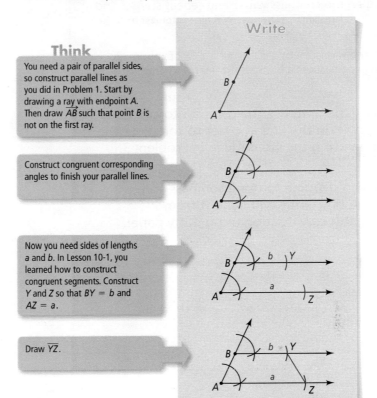

Problem 2 Constructing a Special Quadrilateral

Construct a quadrilateral with one pair of parallel sides of lengths *a* and *b*.

Given: segments of lengths *a* and *b*

Construct: quadrilateral *ABYZ* with $AZ = a$, $BY = b$, and $\overleftrightarrow{AZ} \parallel \overleftrightarrow{BY}$

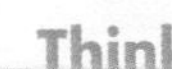

Think | **Write**

You need a pair of parallel sides, so construct parallel lines as you did in Problem 1. Start by drawing a ray with endpoint *A*. Then draw $\overrightarrow{AB}$ such that point *B* is not on the first ray.

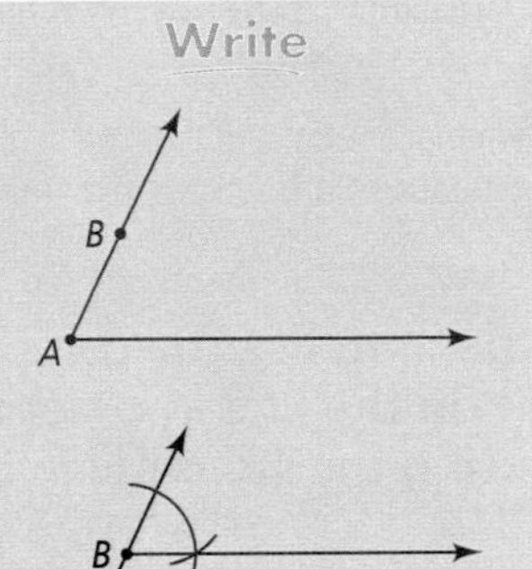

Construct congruent corresponding angles to finish your parallel lines.

Now you need sides of lengths *a* and *b*. In Lesson 10-1, you learned how to construct congruent segments. Construct *Y* and *Z* so that $BY = b$ and $AZ = a$.

Draw $\overline{YZ}$.

ABYZ is a quadrilateral with parallel sides of lengths *a* and *b*.

▼ STUDENT PAGES 108–109

Got It? **a.** Draw a segment. Label its length *m*. Construct quadrilateral *ABCD* with $\overleftrightarrow{AB} \parallel \overleftrightarrow{CD}$, so that $AB = m$ and $CD = 2m$.

b. Reasoning Suppose you and a friend both use the steps in Problem 2 to construct *ABYZ* independently. Will your quadrilaterals necessarily have the same angle measures and side lengths? Explain.

Think How can you test whether your answer to part (b) is correct?

A Practice **Draw two segments. Label their lengths *a* and *b*. Construct a quadrilateral with one pair of parallel sides as described.**

3. The sides have length $2a$ and b.

4. The sides have length a and $\frac{1}{2}b$.

Problem 3 Perpendicular at a Point on a Line

Q How could this construction be completed using paper folding? **[Fold line ℓ onto itself creating a new line (crease) that contains point *P*.]**

Q What segment measures exactly $\frac{1}{2}AB$? **[$\overline{AP}$ or $\overline{PB}$]**

Q If you open the compass wider and repeat steps 2 and 3, what will happen? **[The arcs will also intersect at a point on $\overleftrightarrow{CP}$.]**

Q What is the measure of $\angle CPA$? of $\angle CPB$? Explain. **[Both angles measure 90 because the lines are perpendicular.]**

Got It? VISUAL LEARNERS

Students will need to use the compass to add an auxiliary point on the line in order to complete the construction using the steps given in Problem 3.

TACTILE LEARNERS

Students who struggle to use a compass and straightedge efficiently will benefit from performing this construction using patty paper.

ANSWERS

Got It?

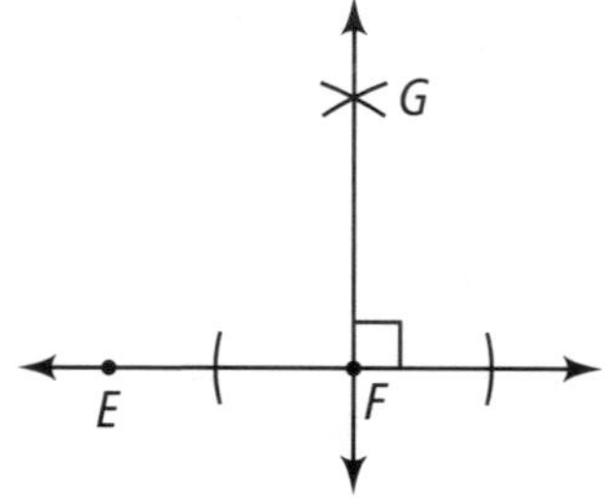

Practice

5.

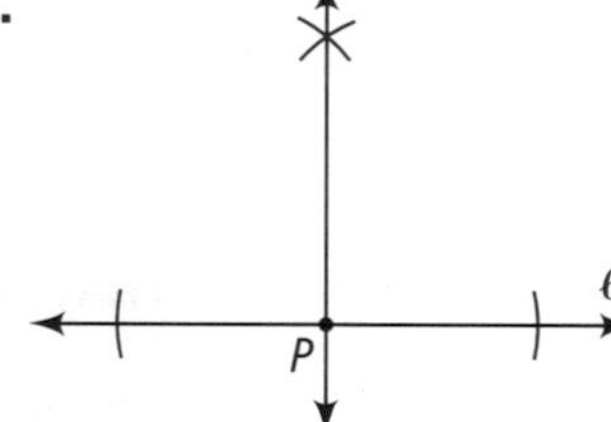

6.

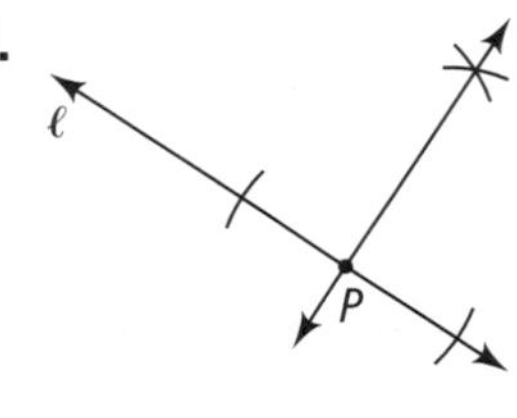

▼ DIGITAL

Problem 3 Perpendicular at a Point on a Line

Construct the perpendicular to a given line at a given point on the line.

Given: point *P* on line ℓ

Construct: $\overleftrightarrow{CP}$ with $\overleftrightarrow{CP} \perp \ell$

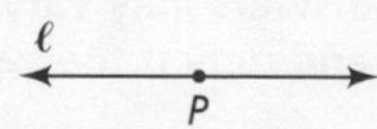

Step 1 Construct two points on ℓ that are equidistant from *P*. Label the points *A* and *B*.

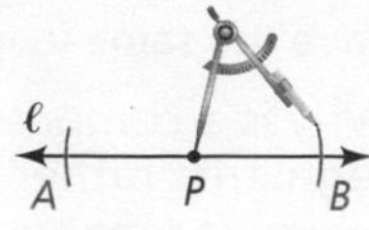

Step 2 Open the compass wider so the opening is greater than $\frac{1}{2}AB$. With the compass tip on *A*, draw an arc above point *P*.

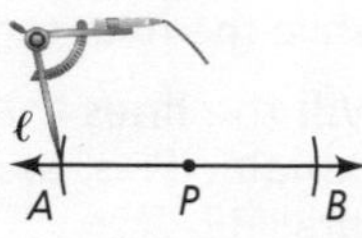

Step 3 Without changing the compass setting, place the compass point on point *B*. Draw an arc that intersects the arc from Step 2. Label the point of intersection *C*.

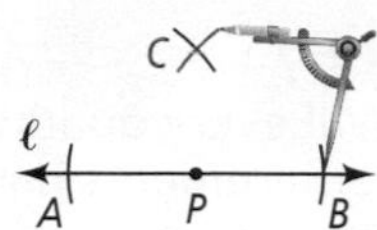

Step 4 Draw $\overleftrightarrow{CP}$.

$\overleftrightarrow{CP} \perp \ell$

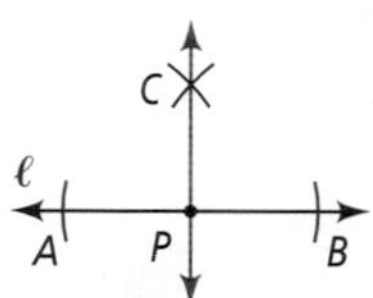

▼ STUDENT PAGES 109–110

Got It? Use a straightedge to draw $\overleftrightarrow{EF}$. Construct $\overleftrightarrow{FG}$ so that $\overleftrightarrow{FG} \perp \overleftrightarrow{EF}$ at point *F*.

Think Can you use any compass setting when locating point *G*?

A Practice Construct the line that is perpendicular to ℓ at point *P*.

5.

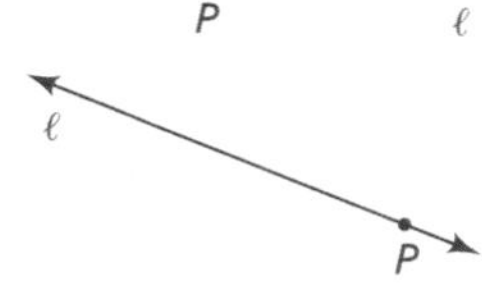

6. ℓ P

Problem 4 Perpendicular From a Point to a Line

Take Note SYNTHESIZING

Ask students to compare and contrast the Parallel Postulate with the Perpendicular Postulate.

▼ STUDENT PAGE 110

You can also construct a perpendicular line from a point to a line. This perpendicular line is unique according to the Perpendicular Postulate. You will prove in Chapter 4 that the shortest path from any point to a line is along this unique perpendicular line.

take note

Postulate 13 Perpendicular Postulate

Through a point not on a line, there is one and only one line perpendicular to the given line.

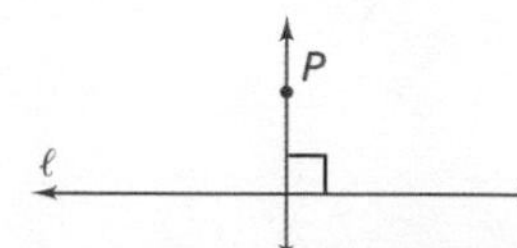

There is exactly one line through *P* perpendicular to ℓ.

Problem 4

Q Is every point on line ℓ equidistant from point R? Explain. **[No, segments connecting point R to various points on line ℓ are not congruent.]**

Q If you do not change the width of the compass setting from Step 1 to Step 2, where will the two new arcs intersect? **[They will intersect at point R and at a point below the arc drawn in Step 1.]**

Q If a point, H, is created on the opposite side of line ℓ by repeating Step 3, what is the relationship of H to $\overleftrightarrow{RG}$? Explain. **[The point lies on $\overleftrightarrow{RG}$.]**

Got It? **ERROR PREVENTION**

Many students are whole-part learners, which means they do not learn in step-by-step sequence. For these students, seeing a sketch of the final product before beginning the construction process can be crucial in helping them to understand the construction and the geometry being demonstrated.

ANSWERS

Got It?

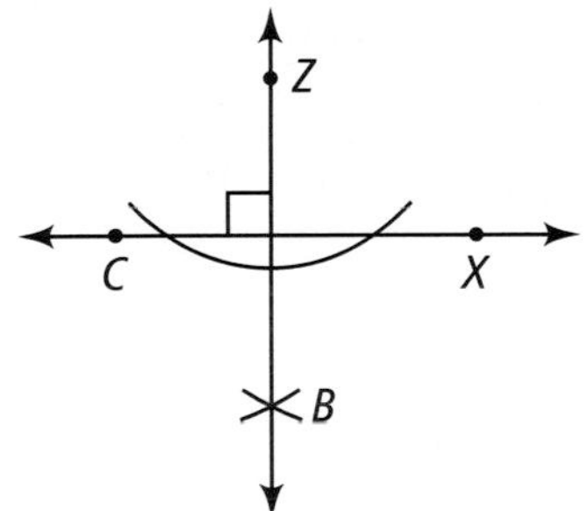

Practice

7.

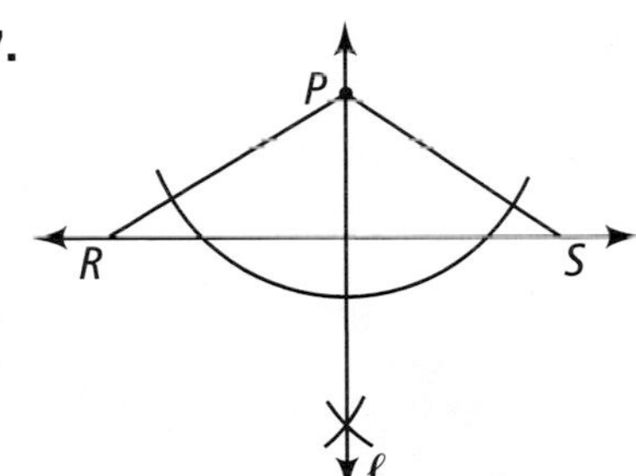

8.

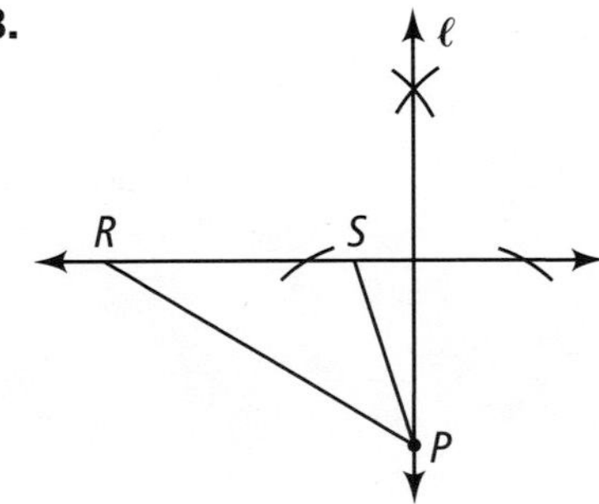

▼ DIGITAL

Problem 4 Perpendicular From a Point to a Line

Construct the perpendicular to a given line through a given point not on the line.

Given: line ℓ and point R not on ℓ

Construct: $\overleftrightarrow{RG}$ with $\overleftrightarrow{RG} \perp \ell$

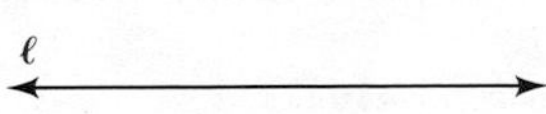

Step 1 Open your compass to a size greater than the distance from R to ℓ. With the compass on point R, draw an arc that intersects ℓ at two points. Label the points E and F.

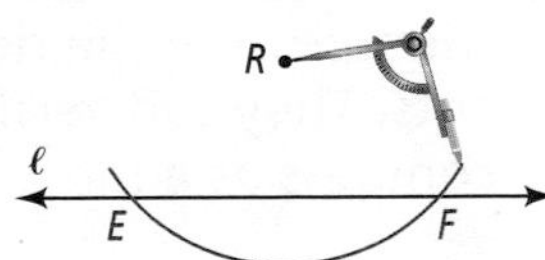

Step 2 Place the compass point on E and make an arc.

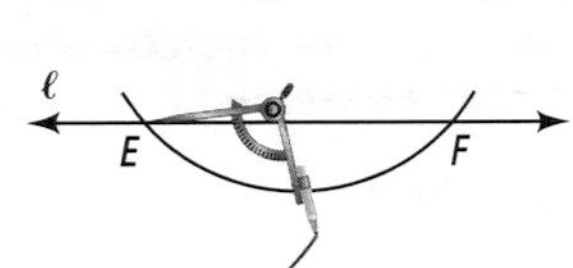

Step 3 Keep the same compass setting. With the compass tip on F, draw an arc that intersects the arc from Step 2. Label the point of intersection G.

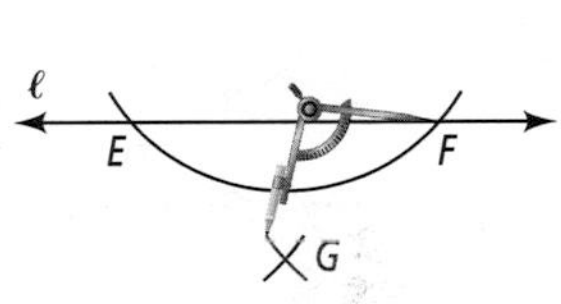

Step 4 Draw $\overleftrightarrow{RG}$.

$\overleftrightarrow{RG} \perp \ell$

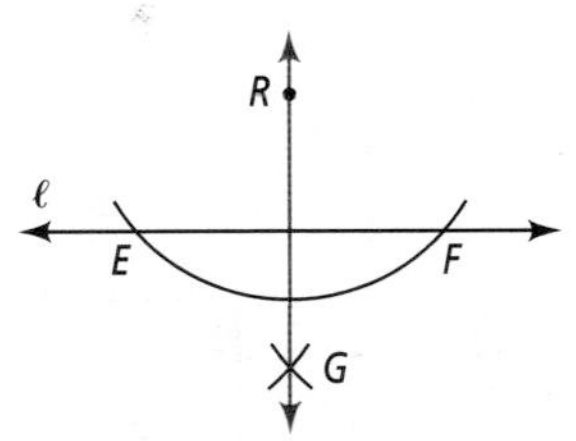

▼ STUDENT PAGE 111

Got It? Draw $\overleftrightarrow{CX}$ and a point Z not on $\overleftrightarrow{CX}$. Construct $\overleftrightarrow{ZB}$ so that $\overleftrightarrow{ZB} \perp \overleftrightarrow{CX}$.

Practice Construct the line through point P that is perpendicular to $\overleftrightarrow{RS}$.

7.

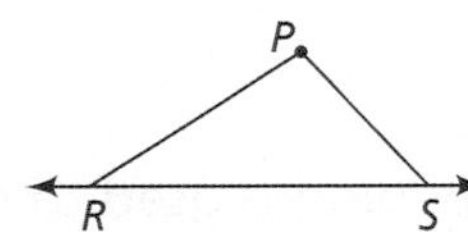

8.

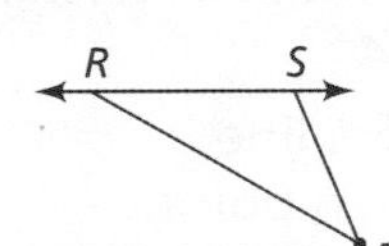

Lesson Check

Do you know HOW?
If students have difficulty with Exercise 10, then have them review the steps shown in Problem 3.

Do you UNDERSTAND?
If students have difficulty with Exercise 12, then have them review the definition of congruent segments. They can verify their answer by using their compass as a measuring tool.

Close

Q How could you use the construction of two perpendicular lines to construct a line parallel to a given line? Explain. **[Construct a line perpendicular to the given line; then construct another line perpendicular to the line created.]**

ANSWERS

9.

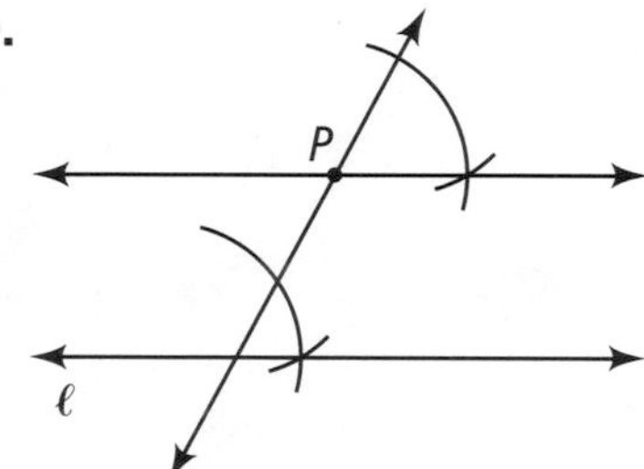

10.

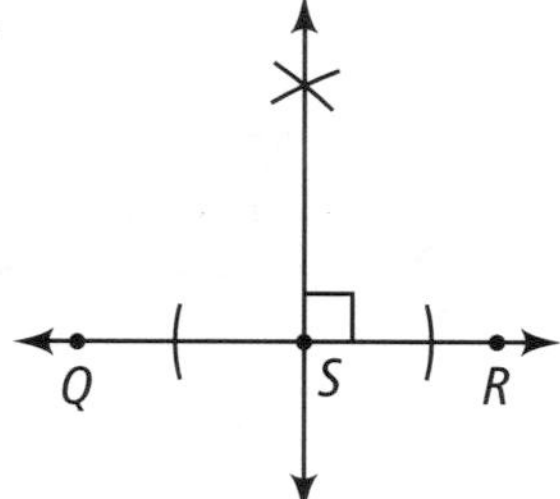

11.

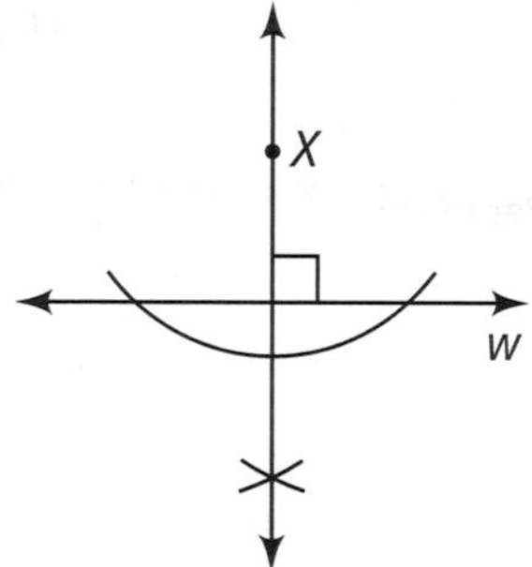

12. Yes; the same compass opening is used to draw the arcs at *C*.

13. No; points *E* and *F* would have been further apart, but the new point *G* would determine the same line $\overleftrightarrow{RG}$ as in Step 4.

14. Similar: You are constructing a line ⊥ to a given line through a given point. Different: The given point is on the given line in Problem 3 and is not on the given line in Problem 4.

▼ STUDENT PAGES 112–113

Lesson Check

Do you know HOW?

9. Draw a line ℓ and a point P not on the line. Construct the line through P parallel to line ℓ.

10. Draw $\overleftrightarrow{QR}$ and a point S on the line. Construct the line perpendicular to $\overleftrightarrow{QR}$ at point S.

11. Draw a line w and a point X not on the line. Construct the line perpendicular to line w at point X.

Do you UNDERSTAND?

12. In Problem 3, is $\overline{AC}$ congruent to $\overline{BC}$? Explain.

13. Suppose you use a wider compass setting in Step 1 of Problem 4. Will you construct a different perpendicular line? Explain.

14. Compare and Contrast How are the constructions in Problems 3 and 4 similar? How are they different?

4 Practice

More Practice and Problem-Solving Exercises

ASSIGNMENT GUIDE

The assignments below are for the More Practice and Problem-Solving Exercises. You may also want to assign the A-Level Practice Exercises for homework if these are not used in class.

Average: 15–25

Advanced: 15–35

Mathematical Practices The exercises listed focus on the Standards for Mathematical Practices listed.

EX. 14, 15: Make Sense of Problems (MP 1)

EX. 22, 24: Construct Arguments (MP 3)

EX. 17: Communicate (MP 3)

EXERCISE 23: Use the **Think About a Plan** worksheet in the Online Teacher Resources to further support students' development in becoming independent learners.

HOMEWORK QUICK CHECK

To check students' understanding of key skills and concepts, go over Exercises 15, 17, 21, 23, and 25.

ANSWERS

15. 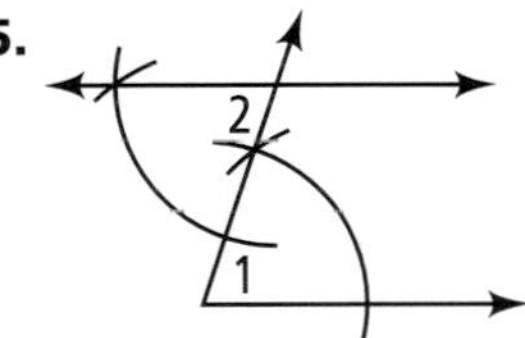

16. 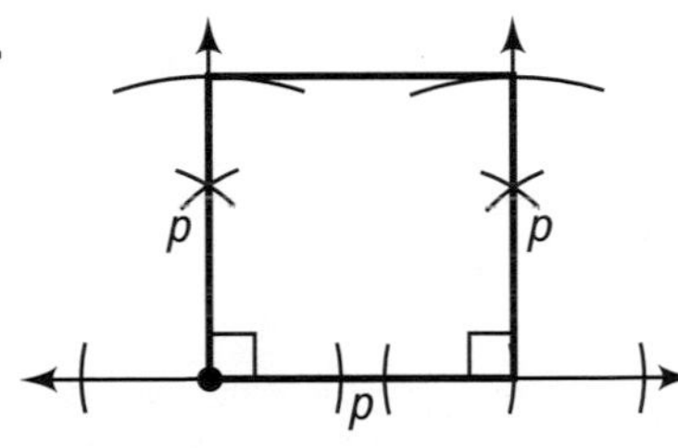

17. Construct a ≅ alt. int. ∠, then draw the ∥ line.

18. 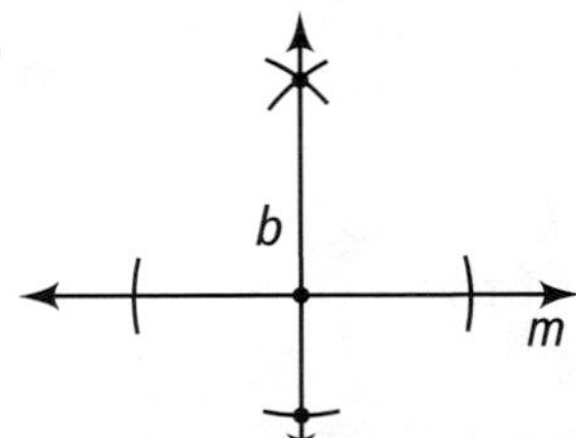

19. 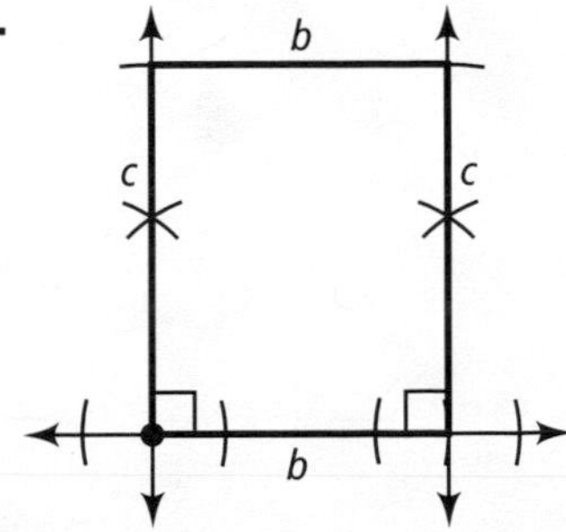

▼ STUDENT PAGES 113–114

More Practice and Problem-Solving Exercises

B Apply

15. **Think About a Plan** Draw an acute angle. Construct an angle congruent to your angle so that the two angles are alternate interior angles.
    - What does a sketch of the angle look like?
    - Which construction(s) should you use?

16. **Constructions** Construct a square with side length p.

17. **Writing** Explain how to use the Converse of the Alternate Interior Angles Theorem to construct a line parallel to the given line through a point not on the line. (*Hint:* See Exercise 15.)

For Exercises 18–24, use the segments at the right.

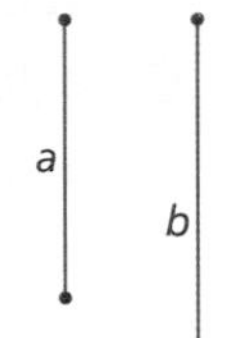

18. Draw a line m. Construct a segment of length b that is perpendicular to line m.

19. Construct a rectangle with base b and height c.

20. Construct a square with sides of length a.

21. Construct a rectangle with one side of length a and a diagonal of length b.

22. a. Construct a quadrilateral with a pair of parallel sides of length c.
    b. **Make a Conjecture** What appears to be true about the other pair of sides in the quadrilateral you constructed?
    c. Use a protractor, a ruler, or both to check the conjecture you made in part (b).

23. Construct a right triangle with legs of lengths a and b.

20. 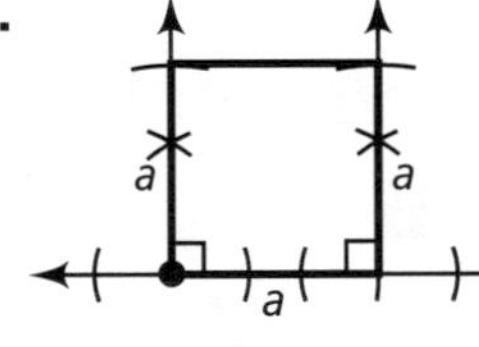

21. 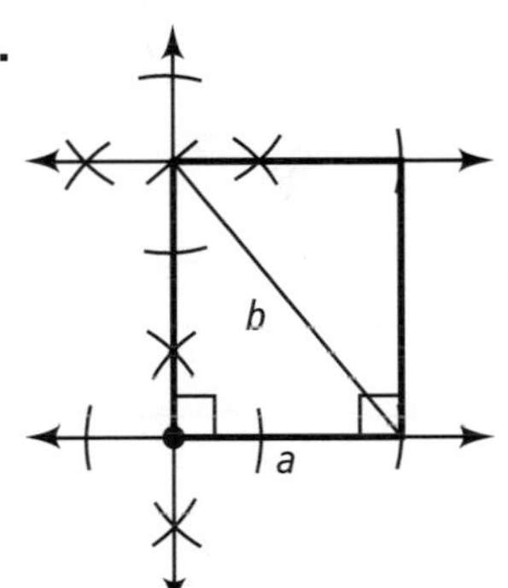

22. a. Answers may vary. Sample:

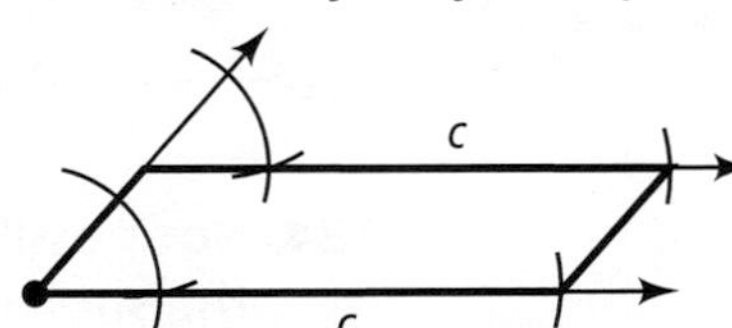

b. Sample: The sides are ∥ and ≅.

c. Check students' work.

23. 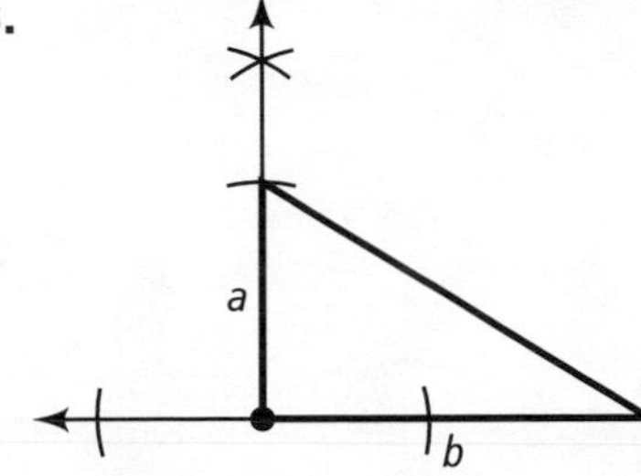

More Practice and Problem-Solving Exercises *continued*

24. a.–c.

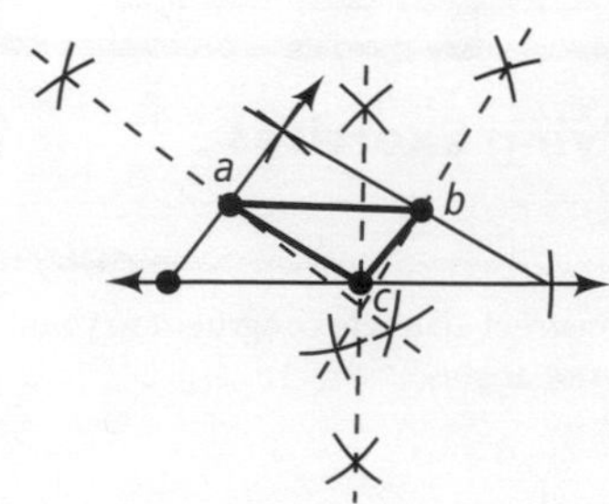

d. Sample: The sides of the smaller triangle are half the lengths and ∥ to the sides of the larger triangle.

e. Check students' work.

25. a. II, IV, III, I

b. III: points C and G; I: the intersection of $\overleftrightarrow{GC}$ with the arcs from Step III

26–35. Constructions may vary. Samples are given.

26.

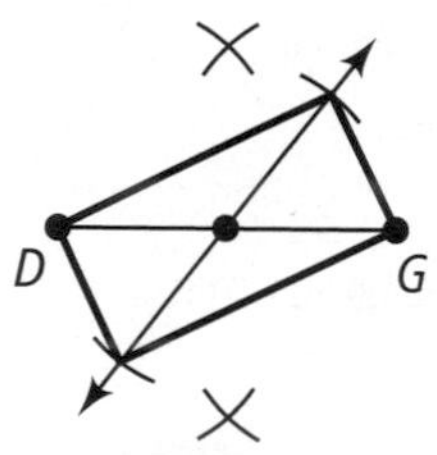

rectangle

27.

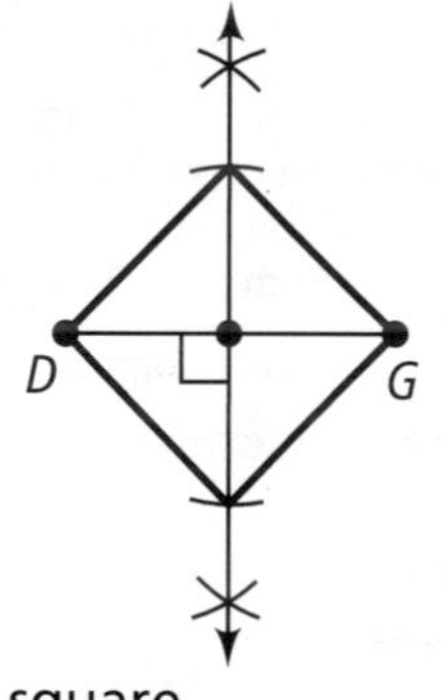

square

▼ STUDENT PAGE 114

24. a. Construct a triangle with sides of lengths a, b, and c.
b. Construct the midpoint of each side of the triangle.
c. Form a new triangle by connecting the midpoints.
d. Make a Conjecture How do the sides of the smaller triangle and the sides of the larger triangle appear to be related?
e. Use a protractor, ruler, or both to check the conjecture you made in part (d).

25. Constructions The diagrams below show steps for a parallel line construction.

I. G C ℓ

II.

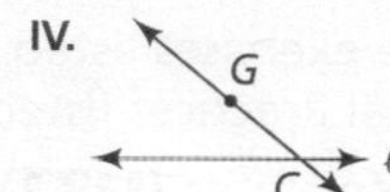

III. G C ℓ

IV. G C ℓ

a. List the construction steps in the correct order.
b. For the steps that use a compass, describe the location(s) of the compass point.

Challenge

Draw $\overline{DG}$. Construct a quadrilateral with diagonals that are congruent to $\overline{DG}$, bisect each other, and meet the given conditions. Describe the figure.

26. The diagonals are not perpendicular. **27.** The diagonals are perpendicular.

Construct a rectangle with side lengths a and b that meets the given condition.

28. $b = 2a$ **29.** $b = \frac{1}{2}a$ **30.** $b = \frac{1}{3}a$ **31.** $b = \frac{2}{3}a$

Construct a triangle with side lengths a, b, and c that meets the given conditions. If such a triangle is not possible, explain.

32. $a = b = c$ **33.** $a = b = 2c$ **34.** $a = 2b = 2c$ **35.** $a = b + c$

28.

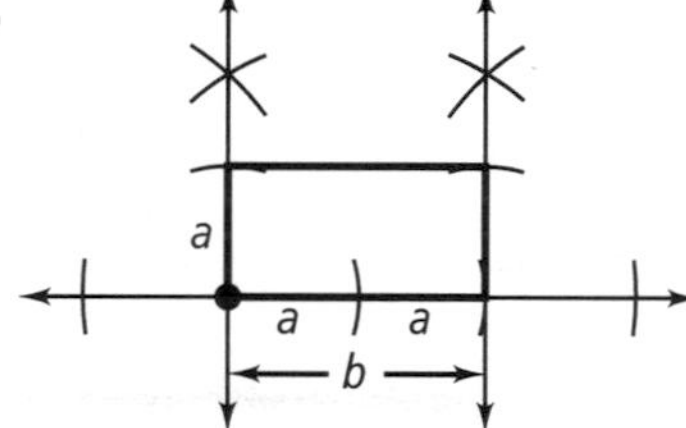

29.

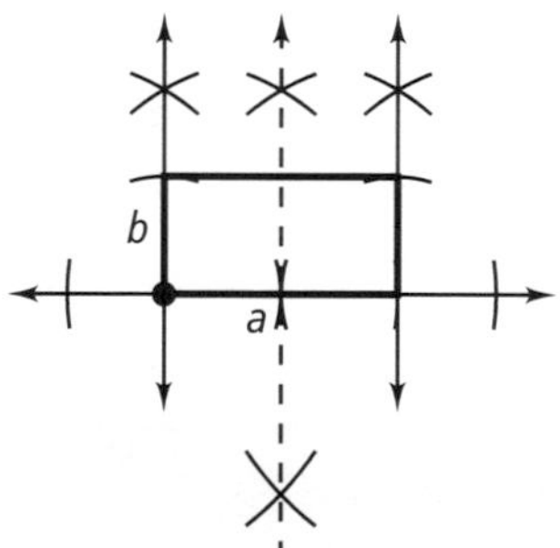

30.

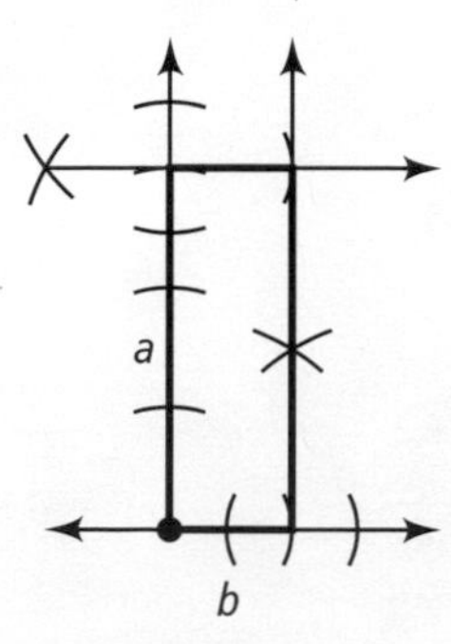

31.

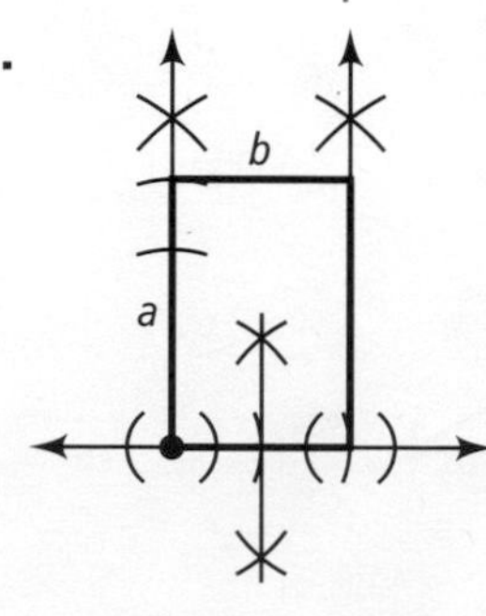

32.

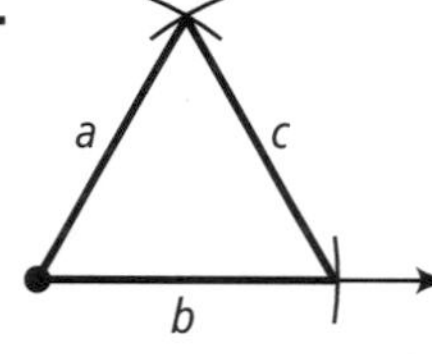

33.

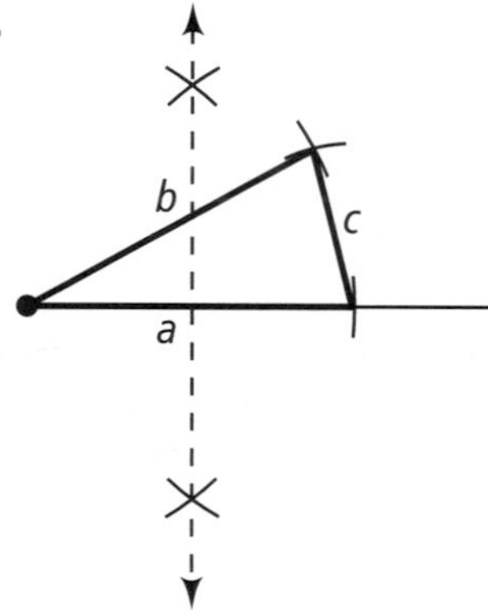

34. Not possible; if $a = 2b = 2c$, then $b = c$ and $a = b + c$. So the shorter sides would meet at the midpoint of the longer side, forming a segment.

35. Not possible; the shorter sides would meet at a point on the longer side, forming a segment.

Assess and Remediate

Lesson Quiz

1. Construct line k through D with $k \parallel \ell$.

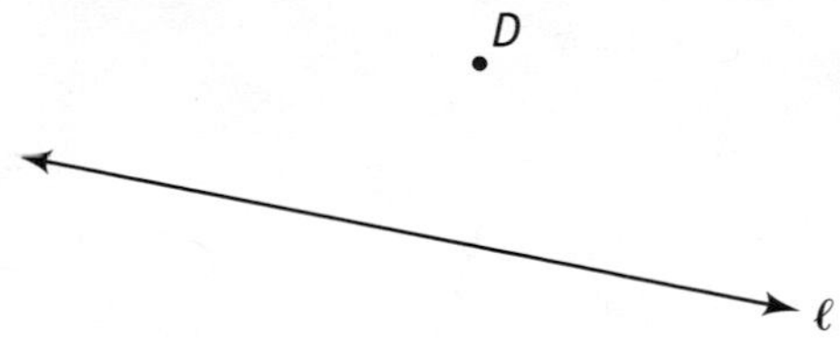

2. Construct $\overline{FG}$ with $\overline{FG} \perp h$.

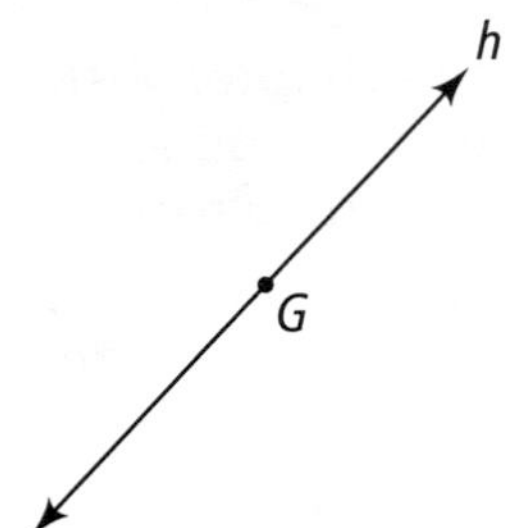

ANSWERS TO LESSON QUIZ

1.

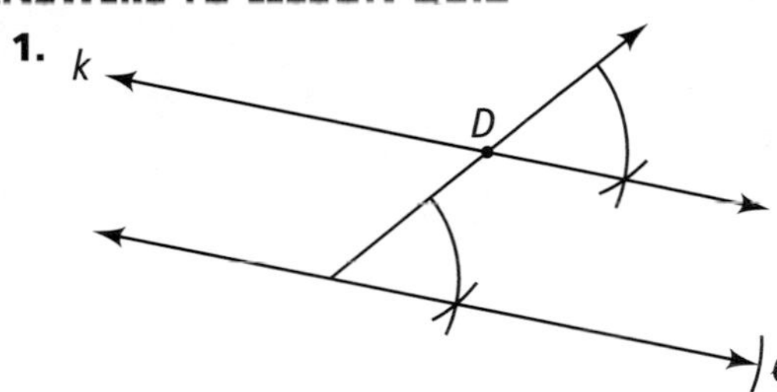

2.

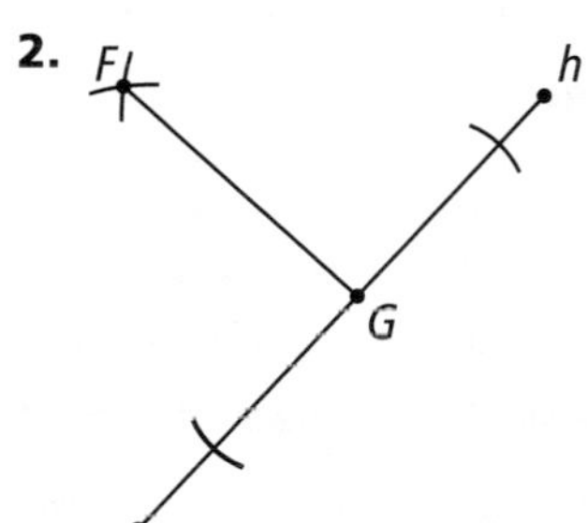

Prescription for Remediation

Use the student work on the Lesson Quiz to prescribe a differentiated assignment.

Points	Differentiated Remediation
0	Intervention
1	On-level
2	Extension

Online Assessment

Assign the Lesson Quiz in Success Tracker on **pearsonsuccessnet.com**. Success Tracker will automatically score the quiz and assign appropriate intervention or enrichment to each student based on the results. The compiled data appear in three different reports for instant analysis of whole class and individual student performance.

Differentiated Remediation

Intervention

- **RETEACHING** (2 pages) Provides reteaching and practice exercises for the key lesson concepts. Use with struggling students or absent students.
- **ENGLISH LANGUAGE LEARNER SUPPORT** Helps students develop and reinforce mathematical vocabulary and key concepts.

On-Level

- **PRACTICE** (2 pages) Provides extra practice for each lesson. For simpler practice exercises, use the Form K Practice pages found in the Online Teacher Resources.
- **THINK ABOUT A PLAN** Helps students develop specific problem-solving skills and strategies by providing scaffolded guiding questions.
- **STANDARDIZED TEST PREP** Focuses on all major exercises, all major question types, and helps students prepare for the high-stakes assessments.

Extension

- **ENRICHMENT** Provides students with interesting problems and activities that extend the concepts of the lesson.
- **ACTIVITIES, GAMES, AND PUZZLES** Worksheets that can be used for concept development, enrichment, and for fun!

Chapter Review

Essential Questions

BIG idea Reasoning and Proof

ESSENTIAL QUESTION How do you prove that two lines are parallel or perpendicular?

ANSWER You can prove that two lines are parallel or perpendicular by using special angle relationships and the relationships of two lines to a third line.

BIG idea Measurement

ESSENTIAL QUESTION What is the sum of the measures of the angles of a triangle?

ANSWER The sum of the measures of the angles of a triangle is 180.

Summative Questions

Use the following prompts as you review this chapter with your students. The prompts are designed to help you assess your students' understanding of the BIG Ideas they have studied.

- What are the names for the relationships of angles formed by two lines and a transversal?
- What does it mean for two lines to be parallel?
- What does it mean for two lines to be perpendicular?

2-1 Lines and Angles

ANSWERS

1. $\angle 2$ and $\angle 7$, *a* and *b*, transversal *d*; $\angle 3$ and $\angle 6$, *c* and *d*, transversal *e*; $\angle 3$ and $\angle 8$, *b* and *e*, transversal *c*
2. $\angle 5$ and $\angle 8$, lines *a* and *b*, transversal *c*; $\angle 2$ and $\angle 6$, *a* and *e*, transversal *d*
3. $\angle 1$ and $\angle 4$, lines *c* and *d*, transversal *b*; $\angle 2$ and $\angle 4$, lines *a* and *b*, transversal *d*; $\angle 2$ and $\angle 5$, lines *c* and *d*, transversal *a*; $\angle 1$ and $\angle 5$, lines *a* and *b*, transversal *c*; $\angle 3$ and $\angle 4$, *b* and *c*, transversal *e*
4. $\angle 1$ and $\angle 7$, lines *c* and *d*, transversal *b*
5. corresp. ∠s
6. alt. int. ∠s

▼ STUDENT PAGE 115

2-1 Lines and Angles

Quick Review

A **transversal** is a line that intersects two or more coplanar lines at distinct points.

$\angle 1$ and $\angle 3$ are **corresponding angles.**

$\angle 2$ and $\angle 6$ are **alternate interior angles.**

$\angle 2$ and $\angle 3$ are **same-side interior angles.**

$\angle 4$ and $\angle 8$ are **alternate exterior angles.**

Example

Name two other pairs of corresponding angles in the diagram above.

$\angle 5$ and $\angle 7$

$\angle 2$ and $\angle 4$

Exercises

Identify all numbered angle pairs that form the given type of angle pair. Then name the two lines and transversal that form each pair.

1. alternate interior angles
2. same-side interior angles
3. corresponding angles
4. alternate exterior angles

Classify the angle pair formed by $\angle 1$ and $\angle 2$.

5.

6.

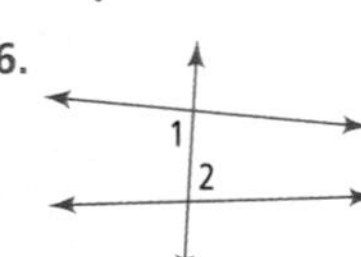

2-2 Properties of Parallel Lines

ANSWERS

7. $m\angle 1 = 120$ because corresp. $\angle$s are $\cong$; $m\angle 2 = 120$ because $\angle 1$ and $\angle 2$ are vert. $\angle$s.

8. $m\angle 1 = 75$ because same-side int. $\angle$s are suppl.; $m\angle 2 = 105$ because alt. int. $\angle$s are $\cong$.

9. $x = 118$, $y = 37$

▼ STUDENT PAGE 115

2-2 Properties of Parallel Lines

Quick Review

If two parallel lines are cut by a transversal, then

- corresponding angles, alternate interior angles, and alternate exterior angles are congruent
- same-side interior angles are supplementary

Example

Which other angles measure 110?

$\angle 6$ (corresponding angles)

$\angle 3$ (alternate interior angles)

$\angle 8$ (vertical angles)

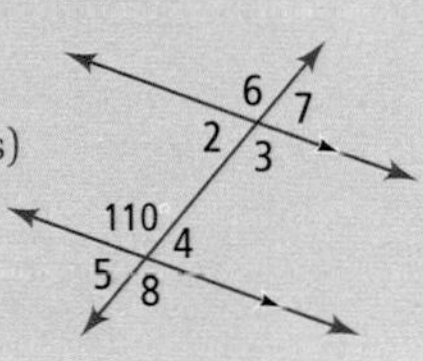

Exercises

Find $m\angle 1$ and $m\angle 2$. Justify your answers.

7. **8.**

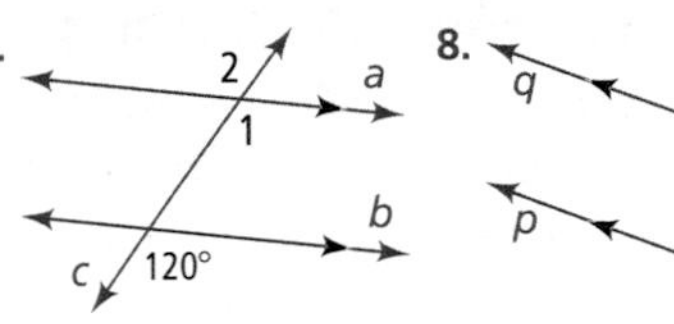

9. Find the values of x and y in the diagram below.

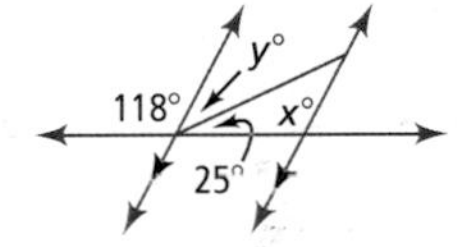

2-3 Proving Lines Parallel

ANSWERS

10. 20

11. 20

12. $n \parallel p$; if corresp. $\angle$s are $\cong$, then the lines are $\parallel$.

13. none; $\angle 3$ and $\angle 6$ form a linear pair.

14. $\ell \parallel m$; if same-side int. $\angle$s are suppl., then the lines are $\parallel$.

15. $n \parallel p$; if alt. int. $\angle$s are $\cong$, then the lines are $\parallel$.

▼ STUDENT PAGE 116

2-3 Proving Lines Parallel

Quick Review

If two lines and a transversal form

- congruent corresponding angles,
- congruent alternate interior angles,
- congruent alternate exterior angles, or
- supplementary same-side interior angles,

then the two lines are parallel.

Example

What is the value of x for which $\ell \parallel m$?

The given angles are alternate interior angles. So, $\ell \parallel m$ if the given angles are congruent.

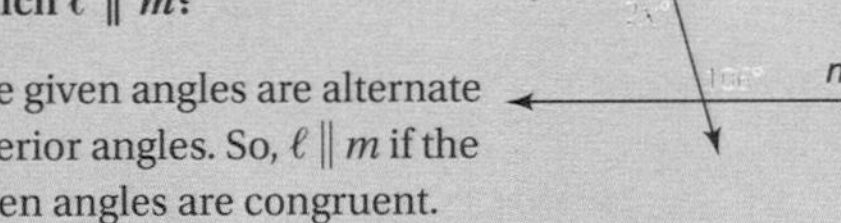

$2x = 106$ Congruent $\angle$s have equal measures.

$x = 53$ Divide each side by 2.

Exercises

Find the value of x for which $\ell \parallel m$.

10. **11.**

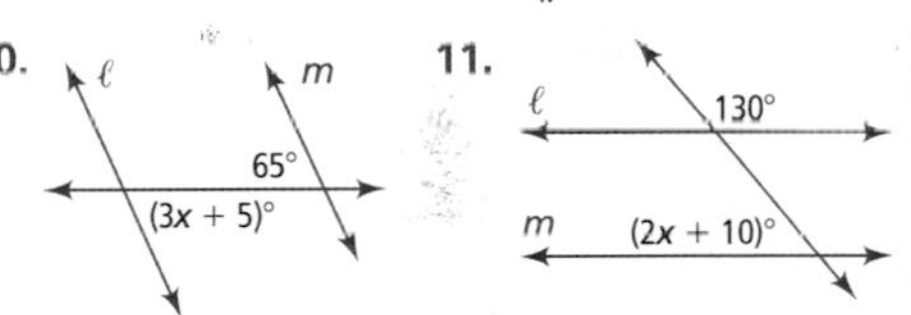

Use the given information to decide which lines, if any, are parallel. Justify your conclusion.

12. $\angle 1 \cong \angle 9$

13. $m\angle 3 + m\angle 6 = 180$

14. $m\angle 2 + m\angle 3 = 180$

15. $\angle 5 \cong \angle 11$

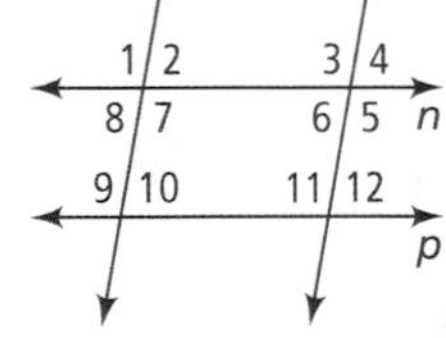

Chapter Review *(continued)*

2-4 Parallel and Perpendicular Lines

ANSWERS

16. $\parallel$

17. *a*

18. 1st Street and 3rd Street are $\parallel$ because they are both $\perp$ to Morris Avenue. Since 1st Street and 5th street are both $\parallel$ to 3rd Street, 1st Street and 5th Street are $\parallel$ to each other.

▼ STUDENT PAGE 116

2-4 Parallel and Perpendicular Lines

Quick Review

- Two lines $\parallel$ to the same line are $\parallel$ to each other.
- In a plane, two lines $\perp$ to the same line are $\parallel$.
- In a plane, if one line is $\perp$ to one of two $\parallel$ lines, then it is $\perp$ to both $\parallel$ lines.

Example

What are the pairs of parallel and perpendicular lines in the diagram?

$\ell \parallel n$, $\ell \parallel m$, and $m \parallel n$.

$a \perp \ell$, $a \perp m$, and $a \perp n$.

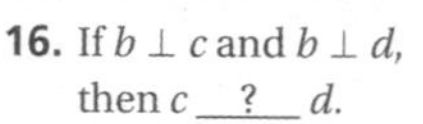

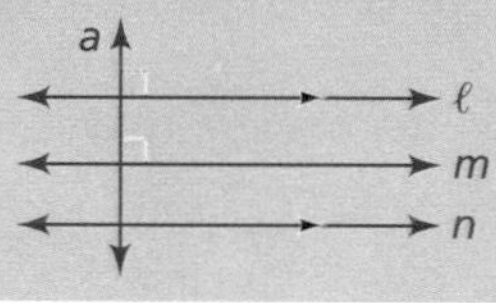

Exercises

Use the diagram at the right to complete each statement.

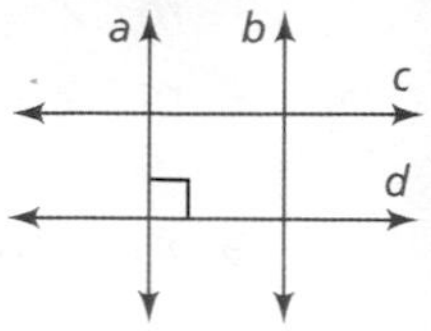

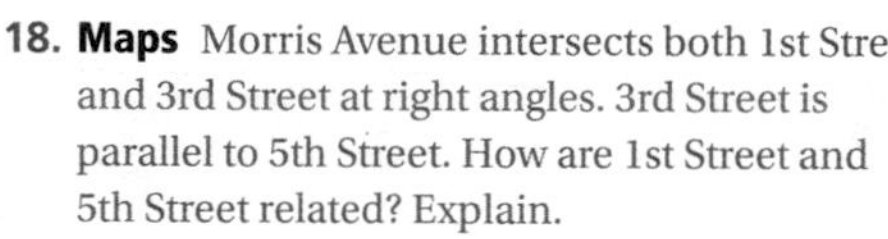

16. If $b \perp c$ and $b \perp d$, then c __?__ d.

17. If $c \parallel d$, then __?__ $\perp c$.

18. Maps Morris Avenue intersects both 1st Street and 3rd Street at right angles. 3rd Street is parallel to 5th Street. How are 1st Street and 5th Street related? Explain.

2-5 Parallel Lines and Triangles

ANSWERS

19. $x = 60$, $y = 60$

20. $x = 45$, $y = 45$

21. 30

22. 55

23. 3

▼ STUDENT PAGE 117

2-5 Parallel Lines and Triangles

Quick Review

The sum of the measures of the angles of a triangle is 180.

The measure of each **exterior angle** of a triangle equals the sum of the measures of its two **remote interior angles.**

Example

What are the values of x and y?

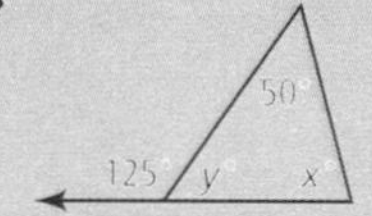

$x + 50 = 125$	Exterior Angle Theorem
$x = 75$	Simplify.
$x + y + 50 = 180$	Triangle Angle-Sum Theorem
$75 + y + 50 = 180$	Substitute 75 for x.
$y = 55$	Simplify.

Exercises

Find the values of the variables.

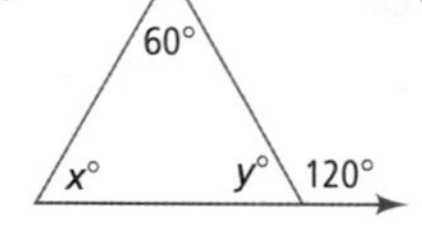

19. **20.**

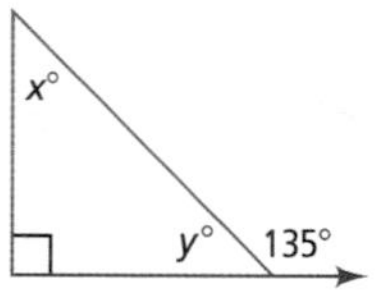

The measures of the three angles of a triangle are given. Find the value of x.

21. $x, 2x, 3x$

22. $x + 10, x - 20, x + 25$

23. $20x + 10, 30x - 2, 7x + 1$

2-6 Constructing Parallel and Perpendicular Lines

ANSWERS

24. 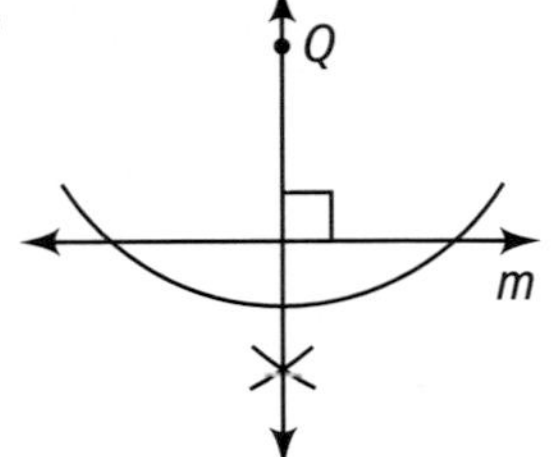

25. 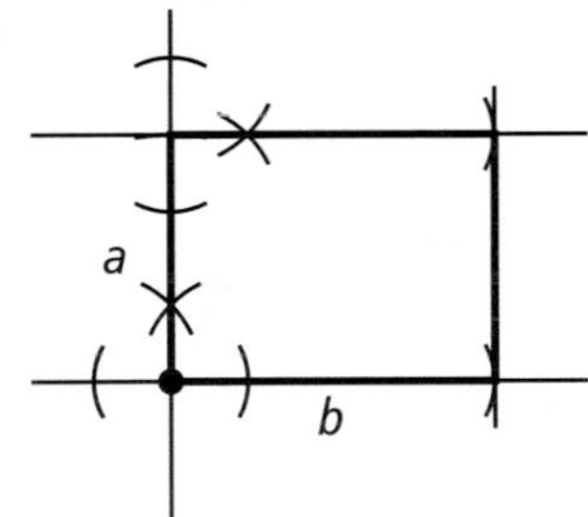

26. 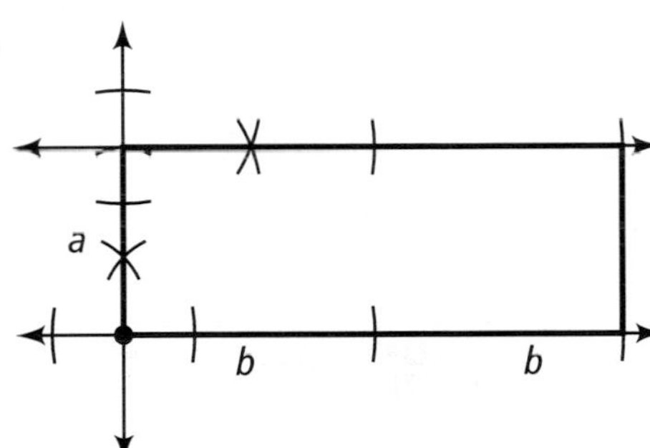

27. 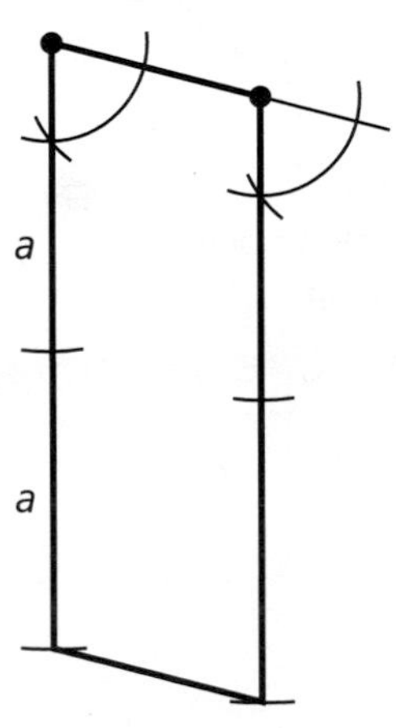

▼ STUDENT PAGE 117

2-6 Constructing Parallel and Perpendicular Lines

Quick Review

You can use a compass and a straightedge to construct

- a line parallel to a given line through a point not on the line
- a line perpendicular to a given line through a point on the line, or through a point not on the line

Example

Which step of the parallel lines construction guarantees the lines are parallel?

The parallel lines construction involves constructing a pair of congruent angles. Since the congruent angles are corresponding angles, the lines are parallel.

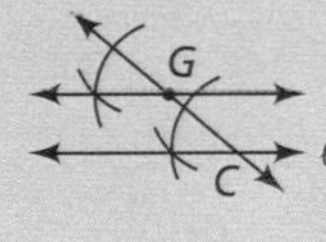

Exercises

24. Draw a line m and point Q not on m. Construct a line perpendicular to m through Q.

Use the segments below.

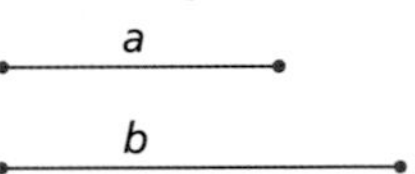

25. Construct a rectangle with side lengths a and b.

26. Construct a rectangle with side lengths a and $2b$.

27. Construct a quadrilateral with one pair of parallel opposite sides, each side of length $2a$.

Pull It All Together

Common Core State Standards
G.CO.9 Prove theorems about lines and angles. Also G.CO.10

Using Performance Tasks

Understanding by Design® principles support using performance tasks to assess students' progress toward mastering content standards and developing proficiency with the Mathematical Practices.

Mathematical Practices

- Make sense of problems and persevere in solving them.
- Model with mathematics.
- Attend to precision.

Assessing Performance

See the Implementation Guide for a holistic scoring rubric to use in assessing students' work on the performance task.

Guiding Questions

Q Which lines in the figure are transversals that intersect parallel lines?

Q Which angles are corresponding angles with the 121° angle? Which angles are alternate-interior angles with the 121° angle?

Q Which angle measures can you find immediately and which ones require that you first find other angle measures?

ANSWERS

$m\angle 1 = 59$, $m\angle 2 = 121$, $m\angle 3 = 59$,
$m\angle 4 = 31$, $m\angle 5 = 121$, $m\angle 6 = 59$,
$m\angle 7 = 121$, $m\angle 8 = 59$, $m\angle 9 = 90$,
$m\angle 10 = 59$, $m\angle 11 = 26$, $m\angle 12 = 17$,
$m\angle 13 = 42$, $m\angle 14 = 121$,
$m\angle 15 = 43$, $m\angle 16 = 137$,
$m\angle 17 = 43$, $m\angle 18 = 137$,
$m\angle 19 = 121$, $m\angle 20 = 42$,
$m\angle 21 = 26$, $m\angle 22 = 95$,
$m\angle 23 = 59$, $m\angle 24 = 90$,
$m\angle 25 = 59$, $m\angle 26 = 121$,
$m\angle 27 = 59$, $m\angle 28 = 31$,
$m\angle 29 = 59$, $m\angle 30 = 121$,
$m\angle 31 = 59$

▼ STUDENT PAGE 118

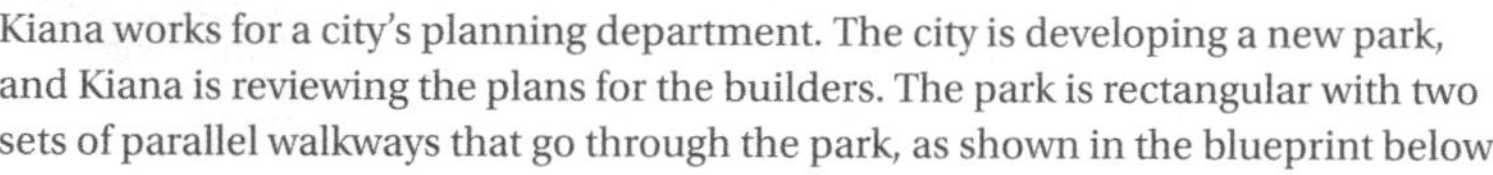

Planning the Paths for a Park

ASSESSMENT

Kiana works for a city's planning department. The city is developing a new park, and Kiana is reviewing the plans for the builders. The park is rectangular with two sets of parallel walkways that go through the park, as shown in the blueprint below.

Kiana notices that only a few angle measures are provided in the blueprint. She would like to add additional angle measures to make it easier for the builders to create the correct paths.

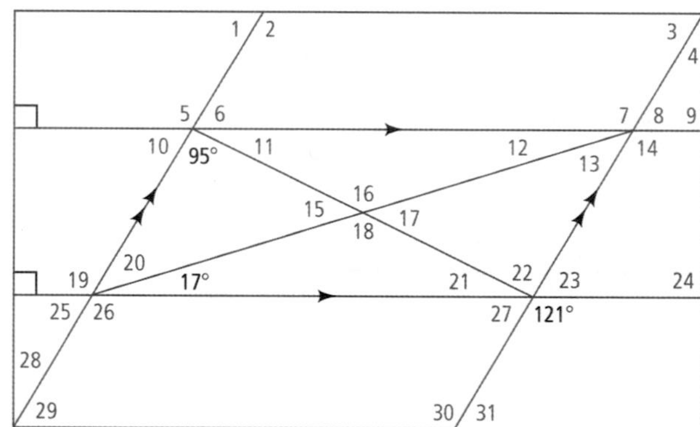

Task Description

Determine the measure of each numbered angle in the blueprint.

- Which postulates theorems can you use to help you find the angle measures?
- Which angles in the blueprint must be congruent to the 121° angle?

Get Ready!

Using This Diagnostic Assessment

Assign this diagnostic assessment to determine if students have the prerequisite skills for Chapter 3.

Lesson	Skill
Previous Course	The Distance Formula
1-7	Proving Angles Congruent
2-2 and 2-5	Parallel Lines and the Triangle Angle-Sum Theorem

To remediate students, select from these resources (available for every lesson).

- Online Problems (pearsonsuccessnet.com)
- Reteaching (Online Teacher Resources)
- Practice (Online Teacher Resources)

Why Students Need These Skills

THE DISTANCE FORMULA Students will use the distance formula to show that sides of triangles on the coordinate plane are congruent.

PROVING ANGLES CONGRUENT Congruent angles will be used to prove triangles congruent.

PARALLEL LINES AND THE TRIANGLE ANGLE-SUM THEOREM Students will use deductive reasoning to show that angles are congruent and to find missing measures of angles to prove triangles congruent.

Looking Ahead Vocabulary

BASE OF AN ISOSCELES TRIANGLE Show examples of isosceles triangles in different orientations and have students identify the base.

LEGS OF AN ISOSCELES TRIANGLE Have students describe how their own legs may help them remember the definition.

CORRESPONDING PARTS Have students examine other uses of the word *corresponding*.

ANSWERS

1. $AB = 4$, $BC = 3$, $AC = 5$
2. $AB = 8$, $BC = \sqrt{265}$, $AC = \sqrt{137}$
3. $AB = \sqrt{58}$, $BC = \sqrt{32}$, $AC = \sqrt{58}$
4. $\angle J \cong \angle L$
5. $m\angle M = m\angle N = 90$
6. $\angle B$ is a rt. $\angle$.
7. $\angle AFB \cong \angle CFD$
8. $\angle B \cong \angle C$, $\angle A \cong \angle D$, $\angle AEB \cong \angle CED$
9. $\angle DAC \cong \angle BCA$, $\angle DCA \cong \angle BAC$, $\angle DAB \cong \angle BCD$, $\angle B \cong \angle D$
   Consecutive angles in quad. ABCD are supplementary.
10. $m\angle A = 21$, $m\angle B = 71$, $m\angle C = 88$
11. Answers may vary. Sample: The base is the side that meets each of the two $\cong$ sides of the $\triangle$.
12. Answers may vary. Sample: The legs are the $\cong$ sides of an isosc. $\triangle$.
13. Answers may vary. Sample: Corresp. parts are the sides or ⦤s that are in the same relative position in each figure.

▼ STUDENT PAGE 119

The Distance Formula

Find the side lengths of $\triangle ABC$.

1. $A(3, 1)$, $B(-1, 1)$, $C(-1, -2)$
2. $A(-3, 2)$, $B(-3, -6)$, $C(8, 6)$
3. $A(-1, -2)$, $B(6, 1)$, $C(2, 5)$

Proving Angles Congruent

Draw a conclusion based on the information given.

4. $\angle J$ is supplementary to $\angle K$; $\angle L$ is supplementary to $\angle K$.
5. $\angle M$ is supplementary to $\angle N$; $\angle M \cong \angle N$.
6. $\angle 1$ is complementary to $\angle 2$.

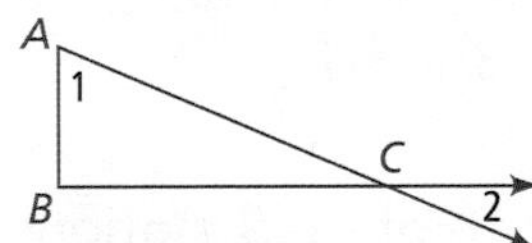

7. $\overrightarrow{FA} \perp \overrightarrow{FC}$, $\overrightarrow{FB} \perp \overrightarrow{FD}$

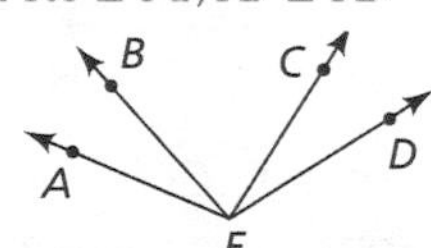

Parallel Lines and the Triangle Angle-Sum Theorem

What can you conclude about the angles in each diagram?

8.

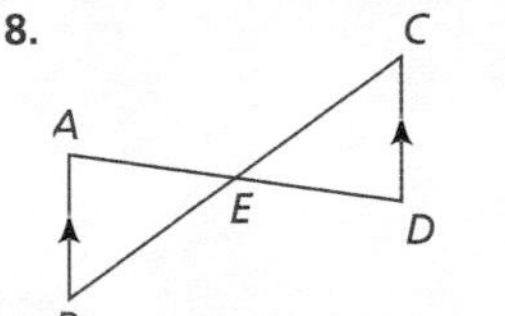

9.

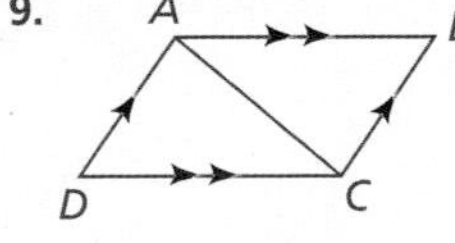

10.

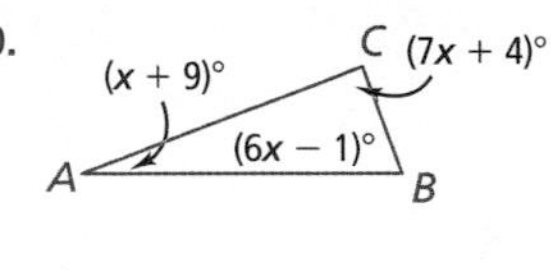

Looking Ahead Vocabulary

11. The foundation of a building is the *base* of the building. How would you describe the *base of an isosceles triangle* in geometry?
12. The *legs* of a table support the tabletop and are equal in length. How might they be similar to the *legs of an isosceles triangle*?
13. A postal worker delivers each piece of mail to the mailbox that *corresponds* to the address on the envelope. What might the term *corresponding parts* of geometric figures mean?

CHAPTER
3

CONGRUENT TRIANGLES

Chapter 3 Overview

Chapter 3 builds on students' understanding and skills related to angles and triangles. In this chapter, students will develop the answers to the Essential Questions posed below as they learn the bulleted concepts and skills.

BIG idea Visualization

ESSENTIAL QUESTION How do you identify corresponding parts of congruent triangles?

- Students will visualize the triangles placed on top of each other.
- Students will use tick marks and angle marks to label corresponding sides and corresponding angles.

BIG idea Reasoning and Proof

ESSENTIAL QUESTION How do you show that two triangles are congruent?

- Students will use the Side-Side-Side Postulate, the Side-Angle-Side Postulate, the Angle-Side-Angle Postulate, the Angle-Angle-Side Theorem, and the Hypotenuse-Leg Theorem.

Interactive Digital Path
Log in to pearsonsuccessnet.com and click on Interactive Digital Path to access the Solve Its and animated Problems.

BIG idea Reasoning and Proof

ESSENTIAL QUESTION How can you tell whether a triangle is isosceles or equilateral?

- Students will use the definitions and look at the number of congruent sides and angles.

Chapter Preview

3-1 Congruent Figures
3-2 Triangle Congruence by SSS and SAS
3-3 Triangle Congruence by ASA and AAS
3-4 Using Corresponding Parts of Congruent Triangles
3-5 Isosceles and Equilateral Triangles
3-6 Congruence in Right Triangles
3-7 Congruence in Overlapping Triangles
3-8 Congruence Transformations

DYNAMIC ACTIVITIES

Dynamic Activity

Use the Dynamic Activity, a virtual manipulative with guided instruction, to have students explore concepts visually and support the development of the Standards for Mathematical Practice.

Content Standards

Following are the key standards covered in this chapter.

Conceptual Category Geometry

DOMAIN Similarity, Right Triangles, and Trigonometry G.SRT
CLUSTER Prove theorems involving similarity (Standard G.SRT.5) **LESSONS** 3-1, 3-2, 3-3, 3-4, 3-5, 3-6, 3-7

DOMAIN Congruence G.CO
CLUSTER Understand congruence in terms of rigid motions (Standards G.CO.6, G.CO.7, G.CO.8) **LESSONS** LL 3-8, 3-8

VOCABULARY

Vocabulary

English/Spanish Vocabulary Audio Online:

English	Spanish
base angles of an isosceles triangle, *p. 156**	ángulos de base de un triángulo isósceles
base of an isosceles triangle *p. 156*	base de un triángulo isósceles
congruence transformation, *p. 186*	transformación de congruencia
congruent polygons, *p. 121*	polígonos congruentes
corollary, *p. 159*	corolario
hypotenuse, *p. 165*	hipotenusa
legs of an isosceles triangle, *p. 156*	catetos de un triángulo isósceles
legs of a right triangle, *p. 165*	catetos de un triángulo rectángulo
vertex angle of an isosceles triangle, *p. 156*	ángulo en vértice de un triángulo isósceles

**All page numbers refer to the Student Edition.*

CONGRUENT TRIANGLES

Math Background

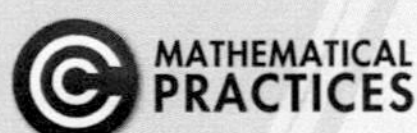

Understanding by Design® principles were central to the development of the Big Ideas and the Essential Understandings. These will help your students build a structure on which to make connections to prior learning.*

Visualization

BIG idea Visualization can help you connect properties of real objects with two-dimensional drawings of these objects.

ESSENTIAL UNDERSTANDINGS

3-1 Comparing the corresponding parts of two figures can show whether the figures are congruent.

3-8 If two figures can be mapped to each other by a sequence of rigid motions, then the figures are congruent.

Reasoning and Proof

BIG idea Definitions establish meanings and remove possible misunderstanding. Other truths are more complex and difficult to see. It is often possible to verify complex truths by reasoning from simpler ones by using deductive reasoning.

ESSENTIAL UNDERSTANDINGS

3-2, 3-3, & 3-6 Two triangles can be proven to be congruent without having to show that all corresponding parts are congruent. Triangles can be proven to be congruent by using (1) three pairs of corresponding sides, (2) two pairs of corresponding sides and one pair of corresponding angles, (3) one pair of corresponding sides and two pairs of corresponding angles, or (4) one pair of right angles, a pair of hypotenuses, and a pair of legs.

3-4 If two triangles are congruent, then every pair of their corresponding parts is also congruent.

3-5 The angles and sides of isosceles and equilateral triangles have special relationships.

3-7 Congruent corresponding parts of one pair of congruent triangles can sometimes be used to prove another pair of triangles congruent. This often involves overlapping triangles.

*UNDERSTANDING BY DESIGN® and UbD™ are trademarks of ASCD, and are used under license.

Proving Triangles Congruent

Congruent triangles are the same shape and the same size. Geometrically, congruent triangles have all corresponding parts congruent.

Congruent triangles have six pairs of congruent parts, three pairs of angles and three pairs of sides.

$\triangle ABC \cong \triangle DEF$

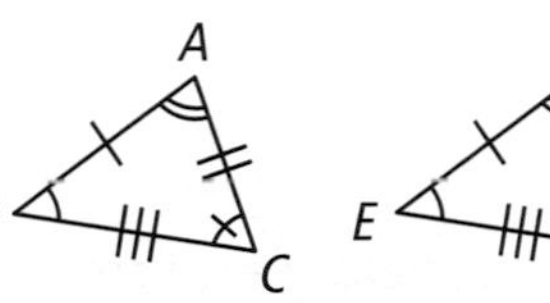

$\angle A \cong \angle D$, $\angle B \cong \angle E$, $\angle C \cong \angle F$
$\overline{AB} \cong \overline{DE}$, $\overline{BC} \cong \overline{EF}$, $\overline{AC} \cong \overline{DF}$

You can also prove that two triangles are congruent by using one of the following:

Side-Side-Side (SSS) Postulate

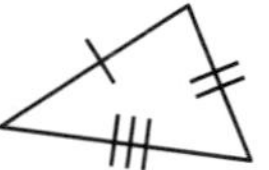

Side-Angle-Side (SAS) Postulate

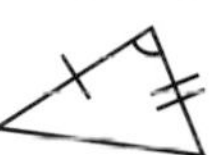

Angle-Side-Angle (ASA) Postulate

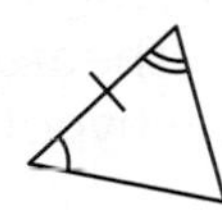

Angle-Angle-Side (AAS) Theorem

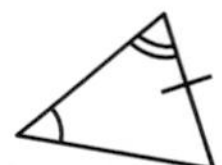
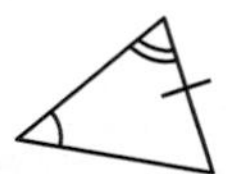

(See p. 126 for a way to prove right triangles congruent.)

Common Errors With Proving Triangles Congruent

Students will often try to use Side-Side-Angle and Angle-Angle-Angle corresponding parts to prove that two triangles are congruent. These are not valid methods.

Mathematical Practices

Reason abstractly and quantitatively Students combine visual and deductive skills to determine triangle congruence. They can see inductively how SSS works, using dynamic geometry software. They build their deductive arguments to prove consequences of congruent triangles, such as two congruent triangles having congruent third sides or altitudes.

Math Background *(continued)*

Proving Right Triangles Congruent

There is a special theorem that can be used to prove right triangles congruent. In order to understand this theorem, look at the following proof.

Two triangles cannot be proven congruent by Side-Side-Angle (SSA). This can be demonstrated by giving a counterexample.

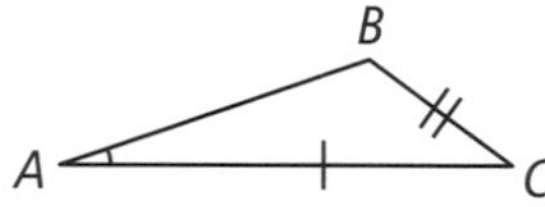

Start with $\triangle ABC$ above. Draw $\overrightarrow{AB}$ as shown below and rotate $\overline{BC}$—without changing its length—until point B touches a point B' on $\overrightarrow{AB}$.

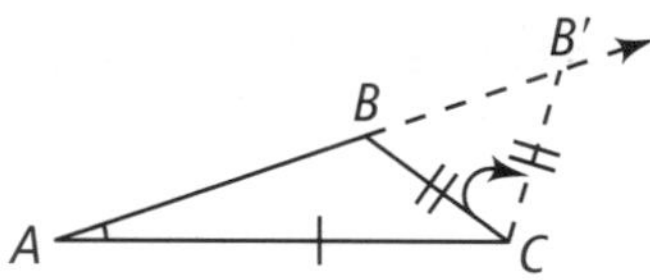

$\angle A \cong \angle A'$, $\overline{AC} \cong \overline{A'C'}$, and $\overline{CB} \cong \overline{C'B'}$, but $\triangle ABC$ is not congruent to $\triangle A'B'C'$.

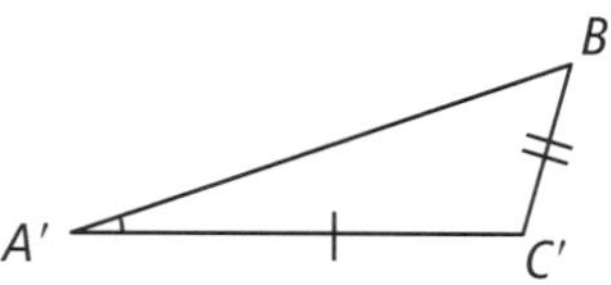

However, you can prove two right triangles congruent by Side-Side-Angle. This is the Hypotenuse-Leg Theorem (HL). The angle is the right angle and the sides are the hypotenuse and one of the legs.

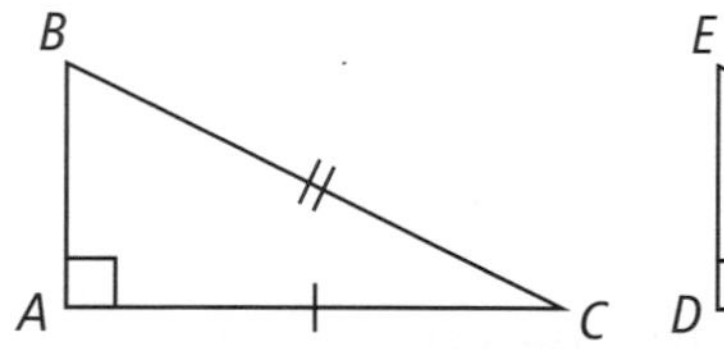

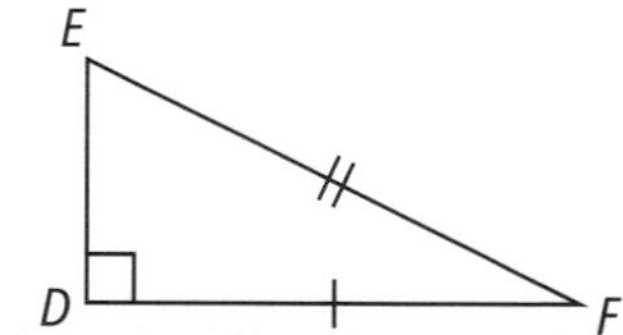

Common Errors With Proving Right Triangles Congruent

Students cannot use the Hypotenuse-Leg (HL) Theorem if they know only that the legs are congruent. In this case they can still prove that the triangles are congruent by Side-Angle-Side (SAS).

Mathematical Practices

Look for and make use of structure In proving right triangles congruent, students not only use deductive reasoning but also follow a more advanced argument involving three triangles, bringing back a more intricate use of the transitive property, and using an auxiliary line.

Overlapping Triangles

Sometimes triangles share one or more parts. In this case, it may be helpful to redraw the triangles separately to see which parts are corresponding.

Triangles That Share an Angle

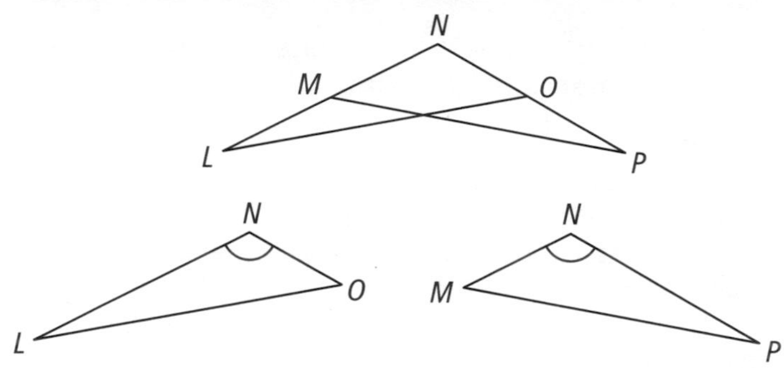

Triangles That Share a Side

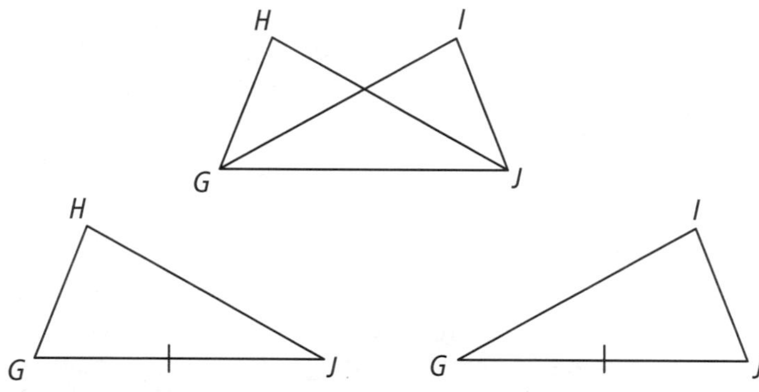

Common Errors With Overlapping Triangles

Students may struggle to distinguish the triangles in the diagram. Have students use their fingers to trace the triangle they are trying to draw, then cover the segments and points that they do not need.

Mathematical Practices

Look for and make use of structure Students look for patterns in overlapping triangles to structure their understanding. They use early examples of overlapping triangles as guides to examine more complex diagrams.

Congruent Figures

Common Core State Standards
Prepares for G.CO.7 . . . Show that two triangles are congruent if and only if corresponding pairs of sides and corresponding pairs of angles are congruent. **Also prepares for G.SRT.5**

Preparing to Teach

BIG ideas Visualization
Reasoning and Proof

ESSENTIAL UNDERSTANDING

Comparing the corresponding parts of two figures can show whether the figures are congruent.

Math Background

Congruent figures are found in nature and in structures made by humans. Architects, surveyors, and doctors are among the many professionals who rely on properties of congruent figures to perform their jobs.

For figures to be congruent, corresponding parts must be congruent. For n-gons with n sides and n angles, $2n$ congruence statements can be written to show two of the figures are congruent.

To shorten the number of steps needed to prove figures are congruent, the Third Angles Theorem (presented in this lesson), and more theorems and postulates presented in upcoming lessons make it possible to write proofs without proving $2n$ congruence statements.

ELL Support

ASSESS UNDERSTANDING Pair more proficient students with less proficient students. Then draw the following diagram on the board.

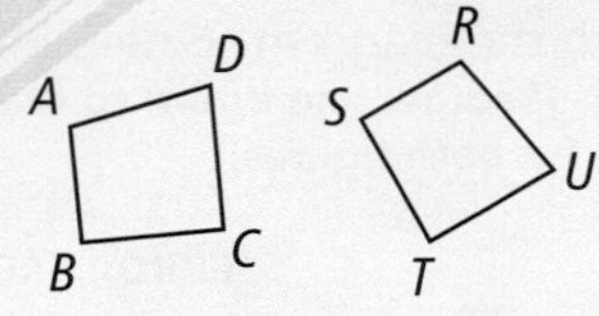

$ABCD \cong RSTU$

Touch the congruency symbol and ask: What does this symbol mean? Working in pairs, students will write congruency statements for the corresponding parts. Give another example without a diagram.

Lesson Vocabulary

- congruent polygons

Mathematical Practices

LOOK FOR AND MAKE USE OF STRUCTURE. In the discussion of congruent figures and transposing them, students will shift their perspective of geometric figures.

1 Interactive Learning

▼ DIGITAL (STUDENT WORK SPACE PAGE 121)

Solve It!

PURPOSE To recognize the characteristics of congruent figures

PROCESS Students can

- visually compare the remaining pieces with the spaces in the diagram.
- copy the page and cut out the pieces to determine which piece fits each space.

Q How would you describe the piece that goes into space A? **[It should have three indentations on three sides, and one protrusion.]**

Q What characteristics are the same between the space and the piece that fits it? **[The size and shape should be the same.]**

ANSWER Piece 1 fits in A, piece 2 in B, and piece 3 in C; explanations may vary. Sample: You can match up the parts that stick out with the parts that "go in" based on their size and location.

CONNECT THE MATH The Solve It introduces the concept of congruent figures. In this lesson, students learn to identify congruent polygons.

SOLVE IT!

Getting Ready!

You are working on a puzzle. You've almost finished, except for a few pieces of the sky. Place the remaining pieces in the puzzle. How did you figure out where to place the pieces?

A B C 1 2 3

2 Guided Instruction

Problem 1 Finding Congruent Parts

Take Note

Have students redraw quadrilateral *EFGH* so that it is oriented the same way as *ABCD*. Students should be able to identify corresponding vertices.

Problem 1

Q How can you use the order of the congruence statement to identify corresponding sides? **[The vertices are listed in corresponding order, so the sides can be listed in the order they appear in the congruence statement.]**

Q What can you do with the diagram to help identify corresponding parts? **[Redraw one figure so that the orientation is the same for both figures.]**

Got It? ERROR PREVENTION

Have students draw the triangles and label the vertices in the same order in which they appear in the congruence statement.

ANSWERS

Got It? $\overline{WY} \cong \overline{MK}$, $\overline{YS} \cong \overline{KV}$, $\overline{WS} \cong \overline{MV}$, $\angle W \cong \angle M$, $\angle Y \cong \angle K$, $\angle S \cong \angle V$

Practice

1. $\overline{AB} \cong \overline{AB}$, $\overline{BC} \cong \overline{BD}$, $\overline{AC} \cong \overline{AD}$, $\angle CAB \cong \angle DAB$, $\angle C \cong \angle D$, $\angle ABC \cong \angle ABD$
2. $\overline{EF} \cong \overline{HI}$, $\overline{FG} \cong \overline{IJ}$, $\overline{EG} \cong \overline{HJ}$, $\angle EFG \cong \angle HIJ$, $\angle FGE \cong \angle IJH$, $\angle FEG \cong \angle IHJ$

▼ STUDENT PAGE 121

Congruent figures have the same size and shape. When two figures are congruent, you can slide, flip, or turn one so that it fits exactly on the other one, as shown below. In this lesson, you will learn how to determine if geometric figures are congruent.

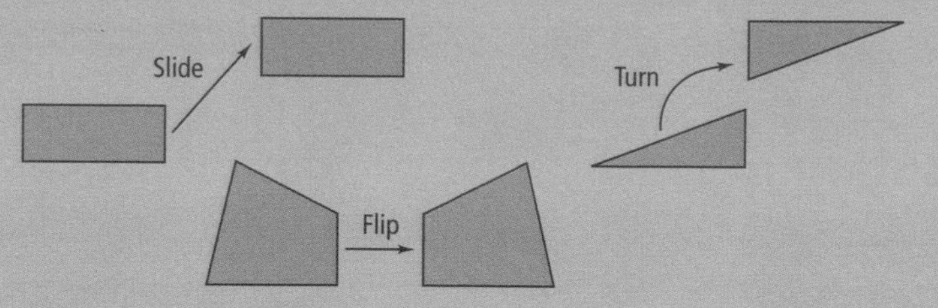

Essential Understanding You can determine whether two figures are congruent by comparing their corresponding parts.

take note

Key Concept Congruent Figures

Definition	Example	
Congruent polygons have congruent corresponding parts—their matching sides and angles. When you name congruent polygons, you must list corresponding vertices in the same order.	 $ABCD \cong EFGH$	$\overline{AB} \cong \overline{EF}$ $\overline{BC} \cong \overline{FG}$ $\overline{CD} \cong \overline{GH}$ $\overline{DA} \cong \overline{HE}$ $\angle A \cong \angle E$ $\angle B \cong \angle F$ $\angle C \cong \angle G$ $\angle D \cong \angle H$

▼ DIGITAL

ONLINE PROBLEMS

Problem 1 Finding Congruent Parts

If *HIJK* ≅ *LMNO*, what are the congruent corresponding parts?

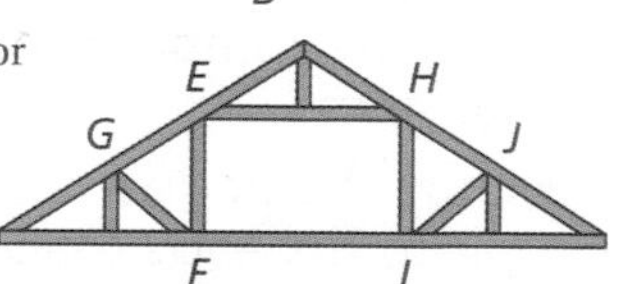

Sides: $\overline{HI} \cong \overline{LM}$ $\overline{IJ} \cong \overline{MN}$ $\overline{JK} \cong \overline{NO}$ $\overline{KH} \cong \overline{OL}$

Angles: $\angle H \cong \angle L$ $\angle I \cong \angle M$ $\angle J \cong \angle N$ $\angle K \cong \angle O$

▼ STUDENT PAGE 122

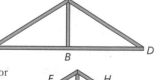

Got It? If $\triangle WYS \cong \triangle MKV$, what are the congruent corresponding parts?

A Practice

1. **Construction** Builders use the king post truss for the top of a simple structure. In this truss, $\triangle ABC \cong \triangle ABD$. List the congruent corresponding parts.

2. The attic frame truss provides open space in the center for storage. In this truss, $\triangle EFG \cong \triangle HIJ$. List the congruent corresponding parts.

Problem 2 Using Congruent Parts

Q How can you find the missing angle measure in $\triangle ABC$? **[Use the Triangle Angle-Sum Theorem. Subtract the known angle measures from 180°.]**

Q Which angle is congruent to $\angle D$? **[$\angle A$]**

Got It? **VISUAL LEARNERS**

Students should draw congruent triangles and label them according to the congruence statement.

ANSWERS

Got It? $m\angle V = 83$; $\angle W \cong \angle M$ and $\angle Y \cong \angle K$ because they are corresp. parts of $\cong$ ⚠s. By the Triangle Angle-Sum Theorem, $m\angle M + m\angle K + m\angle V = 180$. By substitution, $62 + 35 + m\angle V = 180$. So by subtraction, $m\angle V = 83$.

Practice

3. 335 ft **4.** 128

▼ DIGITAL

Problem 2 **Using Congruent Parts**

Multiple Choice The wings of an SR-71 Blackbird aircraft suggest congruent triangles. What is $m\angle D$?

(A) 30 (B) 75 (C) 105 (D) 150

Think	Write
Use the Triangle Angle-Sum Theorem to write an equation involving $m\angle A$.	$m\angle A + 30 + 75 = 180$
Solve for $m\angle A$.	$m\angle A + 105 = 180$ $m\angle A = 75$
$\angle A$ and $\angle D$ are corresponding parts of congruent triangles, so $\angle A \cong \angle D$.	$m\angle A = m\angle D = 75$ The correct answer is B.

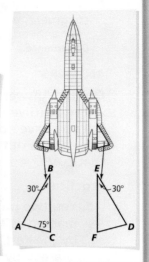

▼ STUDENT PAGES 122–123

Got It? Suppose that $\triangle WYS \cong \triangle MKV$. If $m\angle W = 62$ and $m\angle Y = 35$, what is $m\angle V$? Explain.

Plan

How do you know which sides and angles correspond?

Practice At an archaeological site, the remains of two ancient step pyramids are congruent. If $ABCD \cong EFGH$, find each of the following. (Diagrams are not to scale.)

3. AD **4.** $m\angle DCB$

Problem 3 Finding Congruent Triangles

Q How many conditions must be proved to show that two triangles are congruent? **[The definition states that the figures must have congruent sides and angles. There are 3 pairs of angles and 3 pairs of sides that must be shown to be congruent.]**

Q There is one pair of unmarked angles in the diagram. What special name and relationship describes these angles? **[They are vertical angles and they are congruent.]**

Q What do the marks on the sides of the triangles mean? **[The sides with the matching marks are congruent.]**

Q How are congruent segments defined? **[Congruent segments have the same length.]**

▼ DIGITAL

Finding Congruent Triangles

Are the triangles congruent? Justify your answer.

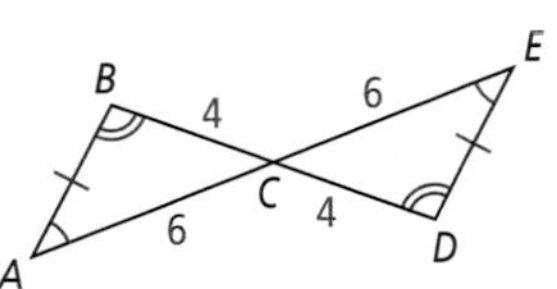

$\overline{AB} \cong \overline{ED}$	Given
$\overline{BC} \cong \overline{DC}$	$BC = 4 = DC$
$\overline{AC} \cong \overline{EC}$	$AC = 6 = EC$
$\angle A \cong \angle E, \angle B \cong \angle D$	Given
$\angle BCA \cong \angle DCE$	Vertical angles are congruent.

$\triangle ABC \cong \triangle EDC$ by the definition of congruent triangles.

Problem 3 *continued*

Got It?

Q Other than the pair of sides that are marked congruent, which pair of sides is congruent? Justify your answer. **[$\overline{DB} \cong \overline{DB}$ by the Reflexive Property of Congruence.]**

ANSWERS

Got It? Answers may vary. Sample: You know that $\overline{AD} \cong \overline{CD}$ (Given) and $\overline{BD} \cong \overline{BD}$ (Reflexive Prop. of ≅), but you have no other information about the sides and ∠s of the △, so you cannot conclude that $\triangle ABD \cong \triangle CBD$.

Practice

5. Yes; two pairs of sides and two pairs of ∠s are marked as ≅; the third pair of sides are ≅ by the Refl. Prop. of ≅, and the third pair of ∠s are ≅ by the Third ∠s Theorem. The third pair of angles are ≅ because each has measure $180 - m\angle R - m\angle RTK$.
6. No; there are not three pairs of ≅ corresp. sides.

▼ STUDENT PAGES 123–124

Got It? Is $\triangle ABD \cong \triangle CBD$? Justify your answer.

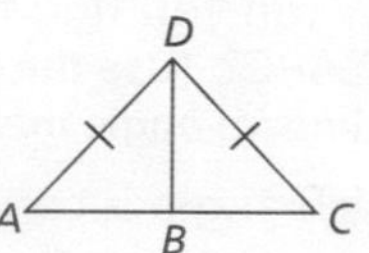

Practice For Exercises 5 and 6, can you conclude that the triangles are congruent? Justify your answers.

5. $\triangle TRK$ and $\triangle TUK$

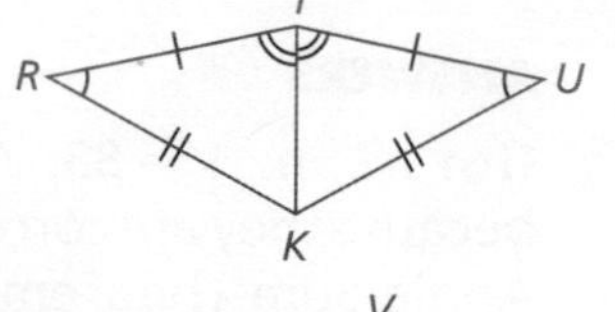

6. $\triangle SPQ$ and $\triangle TUV$

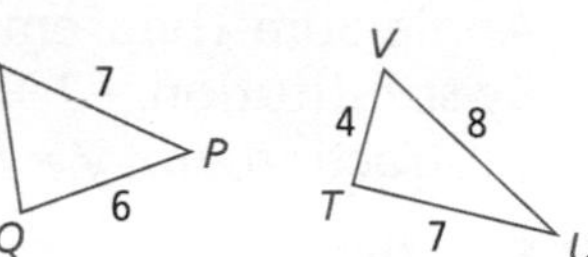

Problem 4 Proving Triangles Congruent

Take Note

When completing a proof, many students benefit from thinking through the problem backwards. Have them begin with the desired conclusion and work backward to identify the information given and needed.

Q You can find equations involving $m\angle C$ and $m\angle F$ using which theorem? **[Triangle Angle-Sum Theorem]**

Q What is true about those equations? **[They both include other angle measures that are equal.]**

▼ STUDENT PAGE 124

Recall the Triangle Angle-Sum Theorem: The sum of the measures of the angles in a triangle is 180. The next theorem follows from the Triangle Angle-Sum Theorem.

take note

Theorem 18 Third Angles Theorem

Theorem	If . . .	Then . . .
If two angles of one triangle are congruent to two angles of another triangle, then the third angles are congruent.	$\angle A \cong \angle D$ and $\angle B \cong \angle E$	$\angle C \cong \angle F$

Proof of Theorem 18: Third Angles Theorem

Given: $\angle A \cong \angle D$, $\angle B \cong \angle E$
Prove: $\angle C \cong \angle F$

Statements	Reasons
1) $\angle A \cong \angle D$, $\angle B \cong \angle E$	1) Given
2) $m\angle A = m\angle D$, $m\angle B = m\angle E$	2) Def. of ≅ ∠s
3) $m\angle A + m\angle B + m\angle C = 180$, $m\angle D + m\angle E + m\angle F = 180$	3) △ Angle-Sum Thm.
4) $m\angle A + m\angle B + m\angle C = m\angle D + m\angle E + m\angle F$	4) Subst. Prop.
5) $m\angle D + m\angle E + m\angle C = m\angle D + m\angle E + m\angle F$	5) Subst. Prop.
6) $m\angle C = m\angle F$	6) Subtraction Prop. of =
7) $\angle C \cong \angle F$	7) Def. of ≅ ∠s

Problem 4

Q What property of congruence verifies that $\overline{LN} \cong \overline{LN}$? **[Reflexive Property of Congruence]**

Q How many pairs of angles are marked congruent? **[2]**

Q Is there a theorem that allows you to state that the third angles are congruent? If so, what is it? **[Yes, the Third Angles Theorem]**

Got It?

Ask students to list the pairs of congruent corresponding parts. Then have students identify the missing congruence statement that leads to the proof.

ANSWERS

Got It? $\angle A \cong \angle D$ (Given), and $\angle ABE \cong \angle DBC$ because vertical ⦣ are ≅. Also, $\angle AEB \cong \angle DCB$ (Third ⦣ Theorem). The three pairs of sides are ≅ (Given), so $\triangle AEB \cong \triangle DCB$ by the def. of ≅ ⧍.

Practice

7. $\angle B \cong \angle D$ (Given); it is also given that $\overline{AB} \parallel \overline{DC}$, so $\angle BAC \cong \angle DCA$ because they are alt. int. ⦣. $\angle BCA \cong \angle DAC$ by the Third ⦣ Thm. $\overline{BC} \cong \overline{AD}$ and $\overline{AB} \cong \overline{DC}$ (Given), and $\overline{AC} \cong \overline{AC}$ by the Refl. Prop. of ≅. So $\triangle ABC \cong \triangle CDA$ by the def. of ≅ ⧍.

▼ DIGITAL

Problem 4 Proving Triangles Congruent

Given: $\overline{LM} \cong \overline{LO}$, $\overline{MN} \cong \overline{ON}$, $\angle M \cong \angle O$, $\angle MLN \cong \angle OLN$

Prove: $\triangle LMN \cong \triangle LON$

Statements	Reasons
1) $\overline{LM} \cong \overline{LO}$, $\overline{MN} \cong \overline{ON}$	1) Given
2) $\overline{LN} \cong \overline{LN}$	2) Reflexive Property of ≅
3) $\angle M \cong \angle O$, $\angle MLN \cong \angle OLN$	3) Given
4) $\angle MNL \cong \angle ONL$	4) Third Angles Theorem
5) $\triangle LMN \cong \triangle LON$	5) Definition of ≅ triangles

▼ STUDENT PAGE 125

Got It? **Given:** $\angle A \cong \angle D$, $\overline{AE} \cong \overline{DC}$, $\overline{EB} \cong \overline{CB}$, $\overline{BA} \cong \overline{BD}$

Prove: $\triangle AEB \cong \triangle DCB$

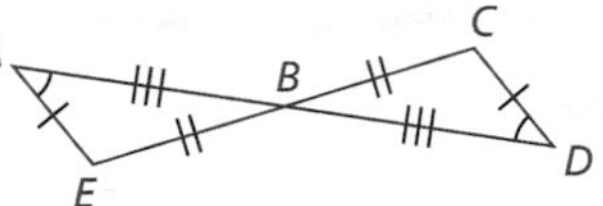

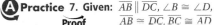

Plan

What else do you need to prove that the triangles are congruent?

Practice 7. **Given:** $\overline{AB} \parallel \overline{DC}$, $\angle B \cong \angle D$, $\overline{AB} \cong \overline{DC}$, $\overline{BC} \cong \overline{AD}$

Proof

Prove: $\triangle ABC \cong \triangle CDA$

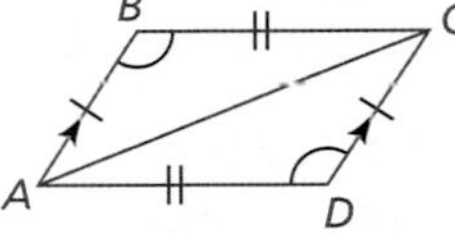

3 Lesson Check

Do you know HOW?

If students have difficulty with Exercises 8-10, then have them review Problem 1.

Do you UNDERSTAND?

If students have difficulty with Exercise 13, then have them try to draw a counterexample.

Close

Q How many statements must be proved to show that two *n*-gons are congruent? **[2*n*]**

Q Based on the definition of congruent triangles, how many pairs of angles must be shown to be congruent when proving two triangles congruent? **[3]**

Q Based on the Third Angles Theorem, how many pairs of angles must be shown to be congruent when proving two triangles congruent? **[2]**

ANSWERS

8. a. $\overline{NY}$
   b. $\angle X$
9. a. $\overline{RO}$
   b. $\angle T$
10. a. $\angle A$
    b. $\overline{KL}$
    c. *CKLU*
11. a. $\angle M \cong \angle T$
    b. 92

▼ STUDENT PAGE 126

Lesson Check

Do you know HOW?

Complete the following statements.

8. **Given:** $\triangle QXR \cong \triangle NYC$
   a. $\overline{QX} \cong$ ______
   b. $\angle Y \cong$ ______

9. **Given:** $\triangle BAT \cong \triangle FOR$
   a. $\overline{TA} \cong$ ______
   b. $\angle R \cong$ ______

10. **Given:** $BAND \cong LUCK$
    a. $\angle U \cong$ ______
    b. $\overline{DB} \cong$ ______
    c. $NDBA \cong$ ______

11. In $\triangle MAP$ and $\triangle TIE$, $\angle A \cong \angle I$ and $\angle P \cong \angle E$.
    a. What is the relationship between $\angle M$ and $\angle T$?
    b. If $m\angle A = 52$ and $m\angle P = 36$, what is $m\angle T$?

Lesson Check *continued*

ANSWERS

12. Answers may vary. Sample: finding the correct top for a food container.

13. No; the △s could be the same shape but not necessarily the same size.

14. He has not shown that corresp. angles are ≅.

Do you UNDERSTAND?

12. Open-Ended When do you think you might need to know that things are congruent in your everyday life?

13. If each angle in one triangle is congruent to its corresponding angle in another triangle, are the two triangles congruent? Explain.

14. Error Analysis Walter sketched the diagram at the right. He claims it shows that the two polygons are congruent. What information is missing to support his claim?

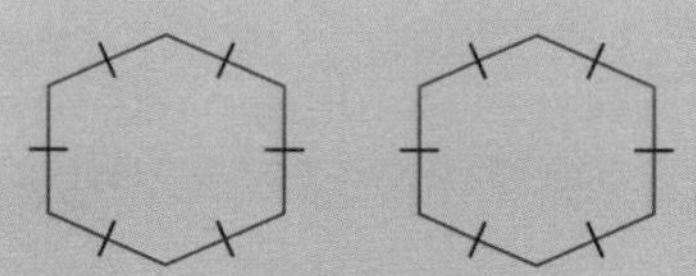

Practice

More Practice and Problem-Solving Exercises

ASSIGNMENT GUIDE

The assignments below are for the More Practice and Problem-Solving Exercises. You may also want to assign the A-Level Practice Exercises for homework if these are not used in class.

Average: 15–28

Advanced: 15–31

Mathematical Practices The exercises listed focus on the Standards for Mathematical Practices listed.

EX. 21: Make Sense of Problems (MP 1)
EX. 28: Communicate (MP 3)
EX. 14, 16: Critique the Reasoning of Others (MP 3)
EX. 12: Model with Mathematics (MP 4)
EX. 25: Use Clear Definitions (MP 6)

EXERCISE 22: Use the **Think About a Plan** worksheet in the Online Teacher Resources to further support students' development in becoming independent learners.

HOMEWORK QUICK CHECK

To check students' understanding of key skills and concepts, go over Exercises 16, 18, 21, 22, and 25.

ANSWERS

15. C

16. Yes. The diagram shows that $\angle CBD \cong \angle ADB$ and $\angle CDB \cong \angle ABD$. By the Third △s Theorem, $\angle C \cong \angle A$. The diagram shows that $\overline{CD} \cong \overline{AB}$ and $\overline{CB} \cong \overline{AD}$. $\overline{BD} \cong \overline{BD}$ by the Relf. Prop. of ≅. So $\triangle BCD \cong \triangle DAB$ by the def. of ≅ △s.

17. $m\angle A = m\angle D = 20$

18. $m\angle B = m\angle E = 12$

19. $BC = EF = 8$

20. $AC = DF = 19$

21. 43

22. $x = 15$, $t = 2$

23. 5

24. $\triangle NRZ$, $\triangle ZRN$ (also $\triangle MLJ$)

More Practice and Problem-Solving Exercises

B Apply

15. If $\triangle DEF \cong \triangle LMN$, which of the following must be a correct congruence statement?

Ⓐ $\overline{DE} \cong \overline{LN}$

Ⓑ $\overline{FE} \cong \overline{NL}$

Ⓒ $\angle N \cong \angle F$

Ⓓ $\angle M \cong \angle F$

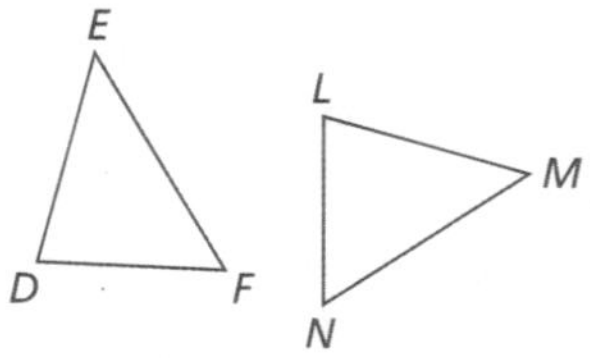

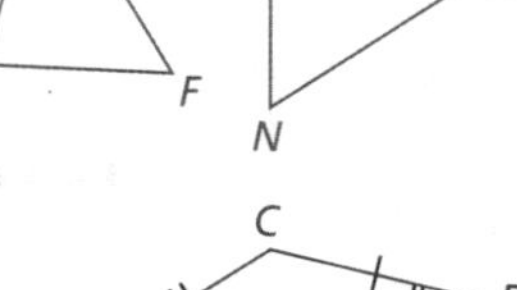

16. Reasoning Randall says he can use the information in the figure to prove $\triangle BCD \cong \triangle DAB$. Is he correct? Explain.

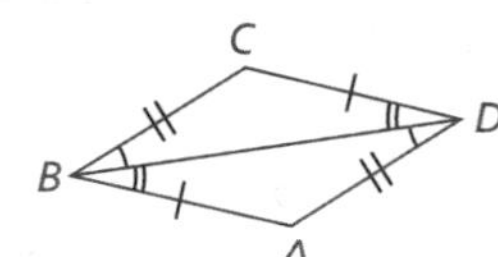

Algebra $\triangle ABC \cong \triangle DEF$. **Find the measures of the given angles or the lengths of the given sides.**

17. $m\angle A = x + 10$, $m\angle D = 2x$

18. $m\angle B = 3y$, $m\angle E = 6y - 12$

19. $BC = 3z + 2$, $EF = z + 6$

20. $AC = 7a + 5$, $DF = 5a + 9$

21. Think About a Plan $\triangle ABC \cong \triangle DBE$. Find the value of x.

- What does it mean for two triangles to be congruent?
- Which angle measures do you already know?
- How can you find the missing angle measure in a triangle?

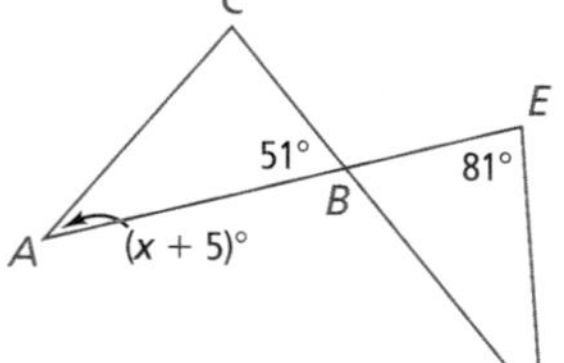

Algebra Find the values of the variables.

22.

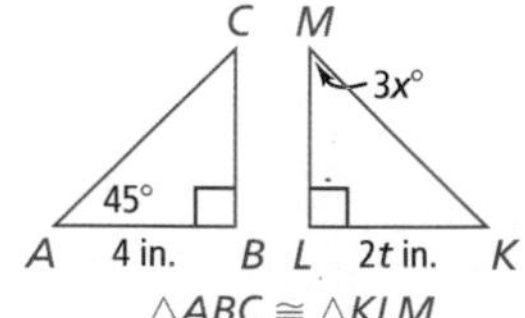

23.

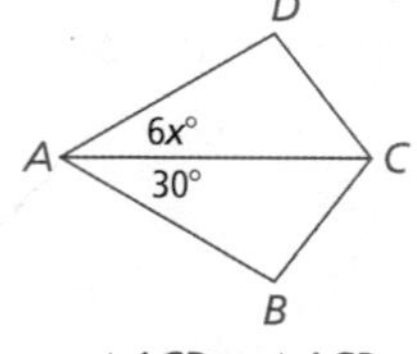

24. Complete in two different ways: $\triangle JLM \cong$ ___?___.

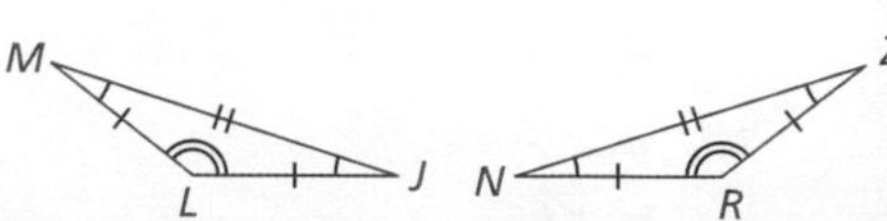

25. Answers may vary. Sample: If $\triangle PQR \cong \triangle XYZ$, then $\overline{PQ} \cong \overline{XY}$, $\overline{QR} \cong \overline{YZ}$, $\overline{PR} \cong \overline{XZ}$, $\angle P \cong \angle X$, $\angle Q \cong \angle Y$, and $\angle R \cong \angle Z$.

26. Two pairs of sides are given as $\cong$, and the third pair of sides are $\cong$ by the Refl. Prop. of $\cong$. $\angle A \cong \angle C$ because $\perp$ lines form rt. ∠s, and all rt. ∠s are $\cong$. $\angle ABD \cong \angle CDB$ by the Alt. Int. ∠s Thm., and $\angle ADB \cong \angle CBD$ by the Third ∠s Thm. So $\triangle ABD \cong \triangle CDB$ by the def. of $\cong$ △s.

27. Two pairs of $\cong$ sides are given, and the third pair of sides are $\cong$ because $\overline{PQ}$ bisects $\overline{RT}$, so $\overline{TS} \cong \overline{RS}$. $\overline{PR} \parallel \overline{TQ}$, so $\angle P \cong \angle Q$ and $\angle R \cong \angle T$ because they are alt. int. ∠s; the third pair of ∠s are vertical ∠s, so they are $\cong$. Thus $\triangle PRS \cong \triangle QTS$ by the def. of $\cong$ △s.

28. Answers may vary. Sample: Sort $\cong$ cards into three piles.

29. $KL = 4$, $LM = 3$, $KM = 5$

30. two; (3,1) or (3,−7)

31. **a.** 16 quadrilaterals

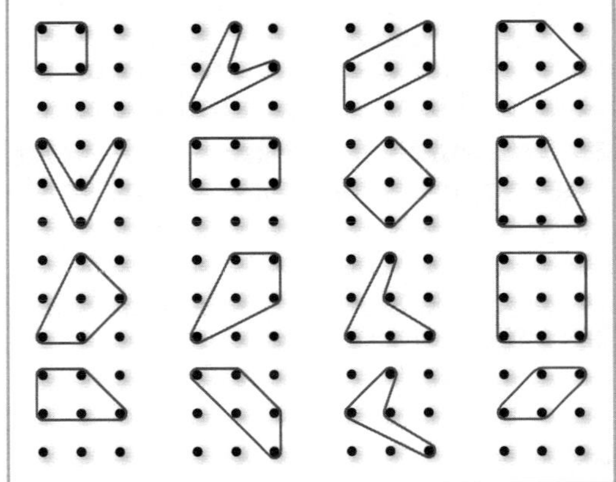

b. 12 convex, 4 concave

25. Open-Ended Write a congruence statement for two triangles. List the congruent sides and angles.

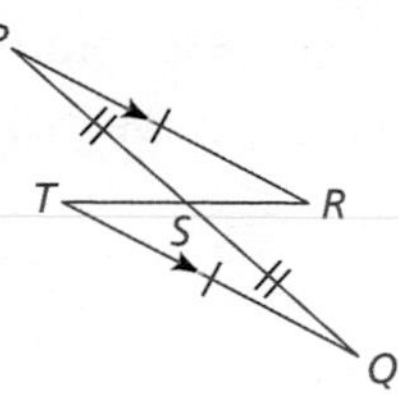

Proof **26. Given:** $\overline{AB} \perp \overline{AD}$, $\overline{BC} \perp \overline{CD}$, $\overline{AB} \cong \overline{CD}$
$\overline{AD} \cong \overline{CB}$, $\overline{AB} \parallel \overline{CD}$
Prove: $\triangle ABD \cong \triangle CDB$

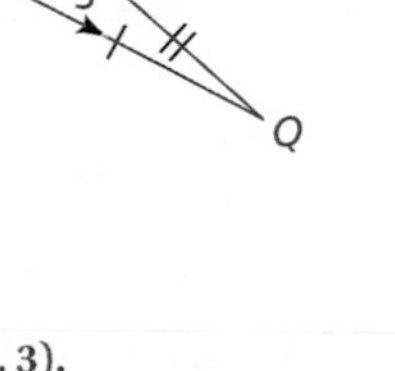

Proof **27. Given:** $\overline{PR} \parallel \overline{TQ}$, $\overline{PR} \cong \overline{TQ}$, $\overline{PS} \cong \overline{QS}$, $\overline{PQ}$ bisects $\overline{RT}$
Prove: $\triangle PRS \cong \triangle QTS$

28. Writing The 225 cards in Tracy's sports card collection are rectangles of three different sizes. How could Tracy quickly sort the cards?

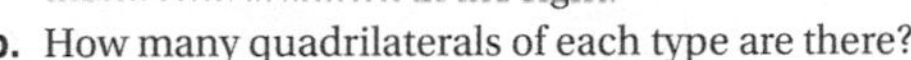

Challenge

Coordinate Geometry The vertices of $\triangle GHJ$ are $G(-2, -1)$, $H(-2, 3)$, and $J(1, 3)$.

29. $\triangle KLM \cong \triangle GHJ$. Find KL, LM, and KM.

30. If L and M have coordinates $L(3, -3)$ and $M(6, -3)$, how many pairs of coordinates are possible for K? Find one such pair.

31. **a.** A polygon is called *convex* if it has no diagonals with points outside the polygon. A polygon is called *concave* if it has at least one diagonal with points outside the polygon. How many quadrilaterals (convex and concave) with different shapes or sizes can you make on a three-by-three geoboard? Sketch them. One is shown at the right.

b. How many quadrilaterals of each type are there?

5 Assess and Remediate

Lesson Quiz

1. If $CDEF \cong KLMN$, what are the congruent corresponding parts?
2. If $\triangle UVW \cong \triangle EFC$, what is the measure of $\angle FEC$?

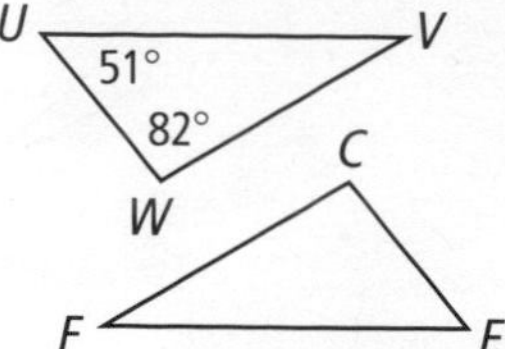

3. **Do you UNDERSTAND?** Suppose it is given that $\angle C \cong \angle B$, $\angle D \cong \angle A$, $\overline{AE} \cong \overline{BE}$, and $\overline{CE} \cong \overline{DE}$. Does that prove that the triangles are congruent? Justify your answer.

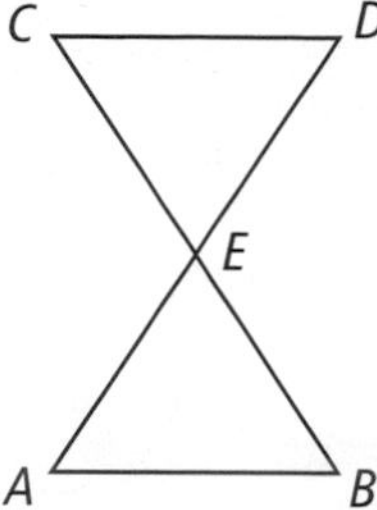

ANSWERS TO LESSON QUIZ

1. Sides: $\overline{CD} \cong \overline{KL}$, $\overline{DE} \cong \overline{LM}$, $\overline{FE} \cong \overline{MN}$, $\overline{CF} \cong \overline{KN}$; Angles: $\angle C \cong \angle K$, $\angle D \cong \angle L$, $\angle E \cong \angle M$, $\angle F \cong \angle N$
2. 51
3. No, the two triangles have congruent angles but not necessarily congruent sides.

Prescription for Remediation

Use the student work on the Lesson Quiz to prescribe a differentiated assignment.

Points	Differentiated Remediation
0–1	Intervention
2	On-level
3	Extension

Online Assessment

Assign the Lesson Quiz in Success Tracker on **pearsonsuccessnet.com**. Success Tracker will automatically score the quiz and assign appropriate intervention or enrichment to each student based on the results. The compiled data appear in three different reports for instant analysis of whole class and individual student performance.

Differentiated Remediation

Intervention

- **RETEACHING** (2 pages) Provides reteaching and practice exercises for the key lesson concepts. Use with struggling students or absent students.
- **ENGLISH LANGUAGE LEARNER SUPPORT** Helps students develop and reinforce mathematical vocabulary and key concepts.

On-Level

- **PRACTICE** (2 pages) Provides extra practice for each lesson. For simpler practice exercises, use the Form K Practice pages found in the Online Teacher Resources.
- **THINK ABOUT A PLAN** Helps students develop specific problem-solving skills and strategies by providing scaffolded guiding questions.
- **STANDARDIZED TEST PREP** Focuses on all major exercises, all major question types, and helps students prepare for the high-stakes assessments.

Extension

- **ENRICHMENT** Provides students with interesting problems and activities that extend the concepts of the lesson.
- **ACTIVITIES, GAMES, AND PUZZLES** Worksheets that can be used for concept development, enrichment, and for fun!

3-2 Triangle Congruence by SSS and SAS

Common Core State Standards
G.SRT.5 Use congruence . . . criteria for triangles to solve problems and to prove relationships in geometric figures. **Also prepares for G.CO.8**

Preparing to Teach

BIG idea Reasoning and Proof

ESSENTIAL UNDERSTANDING

Two triangles can be proven to be congruent without having to show that all corresponding parts are congruent. Two ways triangles can be proven to be congruent are by using three pairs of corresponding sides or by using two pairs of corresponding sides and one pair of corresponding angles.

Math Background

To prove triangles congruent using the definition, you must prove that three pairs of sides are congruent and three pairs of angles are congruent. However, there are postulates and theorems that shorten this process. The SSS and SAS Postulates allow you to prove two triangles are congruent by showing only three conditions are true.

Students quickly learn that S stands for side and A stands for angle in the triangle congruence postulates. Stress to students that the names of these postulates and theorems are reminders, in and of themselves, of the relative positions of the sides and angles. The A in the SAS Postulate is between the two letters S, which indicates that the congruent angles must be between the corresponding congruent sides. Students should specify that SSS and SAS are postulates and not theorems to differentiate them from results that follow in later sections (AAS, HL).

ELL Support

USE MANIPULATIVES Divide students into small groups. Hand out premeasured wooden sticks of three different lengths. Students can use markers or pencils to color the sticks so each size is a different color. Ask students to form two triangles using one of each color for each side. Ask students if their triangles are congruent. Discuss reasons.

Mathematical Practices

LOOK FOR AND MAKE USE OF STRUCTURE. Students will recognize the significance of elements in a triangle, such as the congruences of sides and angles, and will determine the congruence (or lack thereof) between two triangles using SSS and SAS.

1 Interactive Learning

Solve It!

PURPOSE To prove that two triangles are congruent using the definition of congruence

PROCESS Students can

- use the Third Angles Theorem to show that the remaining angles of two triangles are congruent.
- use the Distance Formula to find the lengths of the sides of the triangles.

Q What theorem will allow you to conclude that the last pair of angles is congruent? **[Third Angles Theorem]**

Q To prove the triangles congruent, what must you know about the sides of the triangles? **[Their lengths are equal.]**

Q What formula can you use to find the lengths of segments that are neither horizontal nor vertical? Write the formula. **[Distance Formula; $d = \sqrt{(x_1 - x_2)^2 + (y_1 - y_2)^2}$]**

ANSWER Answers may vary. Sample: Yes, $\triangle ABC \cong \triangle DEF$. $\angle B \cong \angle E$ (Given) and $\angle C \cong \angle F$ (All rt. ∠s are ≅.). By the Third Angles Theorem, $\angle A \cong \angle D$. By the Distance Formula, $AB = DE = \sqrt{50}$, $BC = EF = 5$, and $AC = DF = 5$. So the two △s are ≅ by def. of ≅ △s.

▼ DIGITAL (STUDENT WORK SPACE PAGE 129)

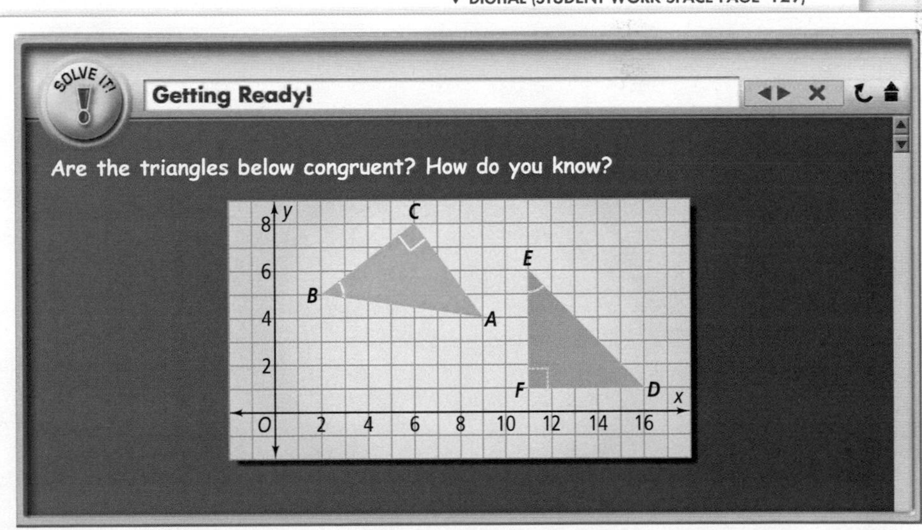

CONNECT THE MATH Two congruent triangles have corresponding angles that are congruent and corresponding sides that are congruent. But it is not necessary to know all six pairs are congruent. In this lesson, students will use the Side-Side-Side and Side-Angle-Side Postulates to prove that triangles are congruent without knowing that all six corresponding pairs are congruent.

Guided Instruction

Problem 1 Using SSS

Take Note

Ask students to identify the minimum number of congruence statements needed to prove two triangles are congruent. Have them draw a set of congruent triangles with vertices labeled and congruent parts marked. Identify the statements necessary to prove them congruent using this postulate.

Problem 1

Q Which side of each triangle is not named in the given statement? **[$\overline{LN}$ of $\triangle LMN$ and $\overline{LN}$ of $\triangle NLP$]**

Q What three pairs of congruent sides are needed to use the SSS Postulate? **[$\overline{LP}$ and $\overline{NM}$, $\overline{NP}$ and $\overline{LM}$, $\overline{LN}$ and $\overline{NL}$]**

Q What property of congruence confirms the third pair of sides to be congruent? **[Reflexive Property of Congruence]**

Got It? **ERROR PREVENTION**

Have students name the two sides they need to show are congruent to prove that the triangles are congruent. Ask them to describe the similarities between this diagram and the one in Problem 1. **[$\overline{BD} \cong \overline{BD}$. The triangles in each diagram share a side. In both proofs, the Reflexive Property of Congruence is used.]**

▼ STUDENT PAGES 129–130

In the Solve It, you looked for relationships between corresponding sides and angles. In Lesson 3-1, you learned that if two triangles have three pairs of congruent corresponding angles and three pairs of congruent corresponding sides, then the triangles are congruent.

If you know . . .

$\angle F \cong \angle J$ $\quad \overline{FG} \cong \overline{JK}$

$\angle G \cong \angle K$ $\quad \overline{GH} \cong \overline{KL}$

$\angle H \cong \angle L$ $\quad \overline{FH} \cong \overline{JL}$

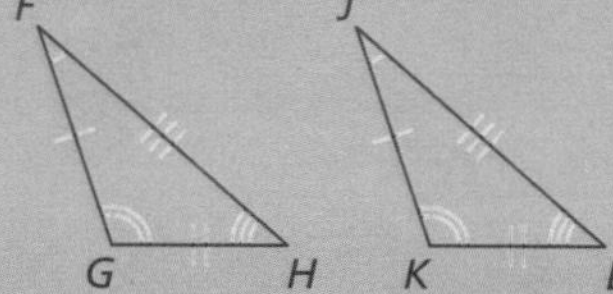

. . . then you know $\triangle FGH \cong \triangle JKL$.

However, this is more information about the corresponding parts than you need to prove triangles congruent.

Essential Understanding You can prove that two triangles are congruent without having to show that *all* corresponding parts are congruent. In this lesson, you will prove triangles congruent by using (1) three pairs of corresponding sides and (2) two pairs of corresponding sides and one pair of corresponding angles.

take note

Postulate 14 Side-Side-Side (SSS) Postulate

Postulate	If . . .	Then . . .
If the three sides of one triangle are congruent to the three sides of another triangle, then the two triangles are congruent.	$\overline{AB} \cong \overline{DE}$, $\overline{BC} \cong \overline{EF}$, $\overline{AC} \cong \overline{DF}$	$\triangle ABC \cong \triangle DEF$

A postulate is an accepted statement of fact. The Side-Side-Side Postulate is perhaps the most logical fact about triangles. It agrees with the notion that triangles are rigid figures; their shape does not change until pressure on their sides forces them to break. This rigidity property is important to architects and engineers when they build things such as bicycle frames and steel bridges.

▼ DIGITAL

Problem 1 Using SSS

Given: $\overline{LM} \cong \overline{NP}$, $\overline{LP} \cong \overline{NM}$

Prove: $\triangle LMN \cong \triangle NPL$

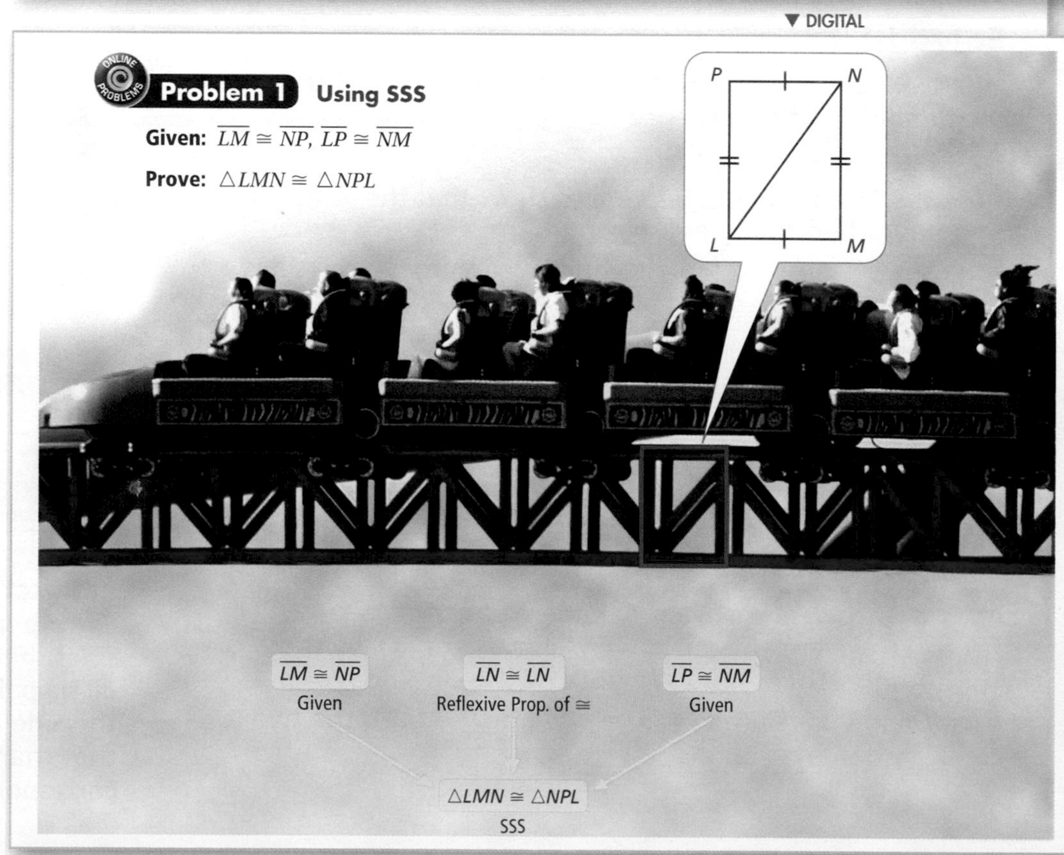

ANSWERS

Got It? Two pairs of sides are given as ≅, and $\overline{BD} \cong \overline{BD}$ by the Refl. Prop. of ≅. So $\triangle BCD \cong \triangle BFD$ by SSS.

Practice

1. **a.** Given
   b. Refl. Prop. of ≅
   c. $\triangle JKM$
   d. $\triangle LMK$
2. F is the midpt. of $\overline{GI}$ (Given), so $\overline{IF} \cong \overline{GF}$ because a midpt. divides a segment into two ≅ segments. The other two pairs of sides are given as ≅, so $\triangle EFI \cong \triangle HFG$ by SSS.

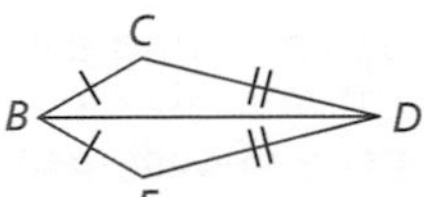

Got It? **Given:** $\overline{BC} \cong \overline{BF}$, $\overline{CD} \cong \overline{FD}$

Prove: $\triangle BCD \cong \triangle BFD$

A Practice 1. **Developing Proof** Complete the flow proof.

Given: $\overline{JK} \cong \overline{LM}$, $\overline{JM} \cong \overline{LK}$

Prove: $\triangle JKM \cong \triangle LMK$

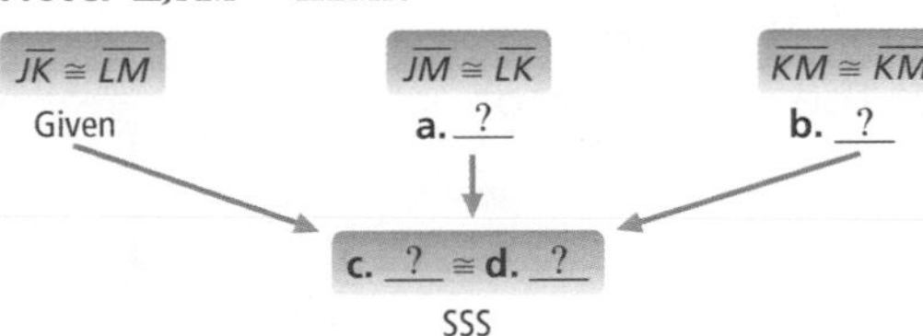

a. ______________

b. ______________

c. ______________

d. ______________

Proof 2. **Given:** $\overline{IE} \cong \overline{GH}$, $\overline{EF} \cong \overline{HF}$, F is the midpoint of $\overline{GI}$

Prove: $\triangle EFI \cong \triangle HFG$

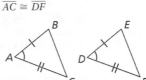

Problem 2 Using SAS

Take Note

Have students practice identifying included angles given two sides. When drawing a diagram of the SAS Postulate, have students mark the sides and angles that are congruent. Students should understand that congruent sides are marked with one, two, or three very short segments made perpendicular to the sides of the triangle. The corresponding sides will have matching congruence markings. Congruent angles are marked using one, two, or three arcs inside the angle. Again, the corresponding angles will have matching congruence markings. Note that there is no relationship between the sides with one mark and sides with two marks; they are intended only to signify different lengths.

Ask students to identify the congruent sides and angles in the example at the bottom of the page. The arms represent congruent sides and the angles between them are the included congruent angles.

You can also show relationships between a pair of corresponding sides and an *included* angle.

The word *included* refers to the angles and the sides of a triangle, as shown at the right.

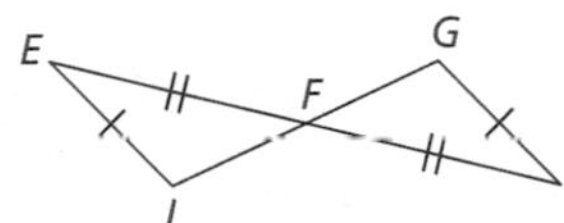

take note **Postulate 15 Side-Angle-Side (SAS) Postulate**

Postulate	If . . .	Then . . .
If two sides and the included angle of one triangle are congruent to two sides and the included angle of another triangle, then the two triangles are congruent.	$\overline{AB} \cong \overline{DE}$, $\angle A \cong \angle D$, $\overline{AC} \cong \overline{DF}$	$\triangle ABC \cong \triangle DEF$

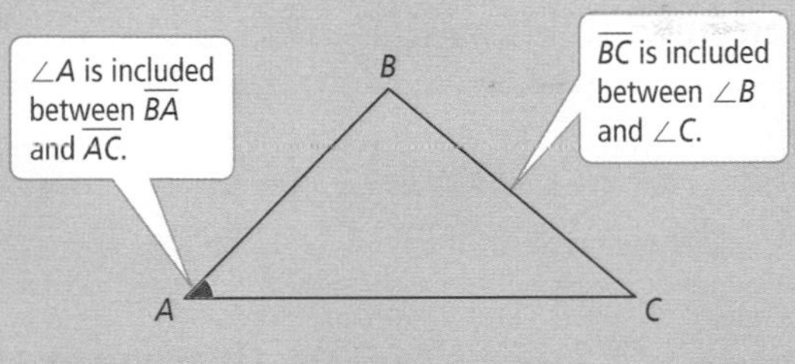

You likely have used the properties of the Side-Angle-Side Postulate before. For example, SAS can help you determine whether a box will fit through a doorway.

Suppose you keep your arms at a fixed angle as you move from the box to the doorway. The triangle you form with the box is congruent to the triangle you form with the doorway. The two triangles are congruent because two sides and the included angle of one triangle are congruent to the two sides and the included angle of the other triangle.

Problem 2 *continued*

Q Which sides are marked congruent? **[$\overline{EF} \cong \overline{DG}$]**

Q For what other sides of the triangle can you write a congruence statement and give a justification? **[$\overline{DF} \cong \overline{DF}$; Reflexive Property of Congruence]**

Q Which angle in each triangle is the included angle between the two sides? **[$\angle GDF$ in $\triangle FGD$ and $\angle EFD$ in $\triangle DEF$]**

Got It?

Have students list the sides that form the marked angles. Remind them of the definition of an included angle.

ANSWERS

Got It? $\overline{LE} \cong \overline{BN}$

Practice

3. You need to know $\overline{LG} \cong \overline{MN}$; the diagram shows that $\overline{LT} \cong \overline{MQ}$ and $\angle L \cong \angle M$. $\angle L$ is included between $\overline{LG}$ and $\overline{LT}$, and $\angle M$ is included between $\overline{MN}$ and $\overline{MQ}$.
4. You need to know $\overline{RS} \cong \overline{WU}$; the diagram shows that $\angle R \cong \angle W$ and $\overline{RT} \cong \overline{WV}$. $\angle R$ is included between $\overline{RT}$ and $\overline{RS}$, and $\angle W$ is included between $\overline{WV}$ and $\overline{WU}$. Alternatively, you need to know that $\angle T \cong \angle V$.

▼ DIGITAL

Problem 2 **Using SAS**

What other information do you need to prove $\triangle DEF \cong \triangle FGD$ by SAS? Explain.

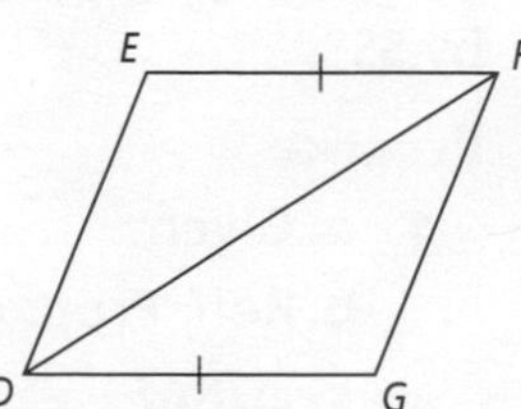

The diagram shows that $\overline{EF} \cong \overline{GD}$. Also, $\overline{DF} \cong \overline{DF}$ by the Reflexive Property of Congruence. To prove that $\triangle DEF \cong \triangle FGD$ by SAS, you must have congruent included angles. You need to know that $\angle EFD \cong \angle GDF$.

▼ STUDENT PAGE 132

Got It? What other information do you need to prove $\triangle LEB \cong \triangle BNL$ by SAS?

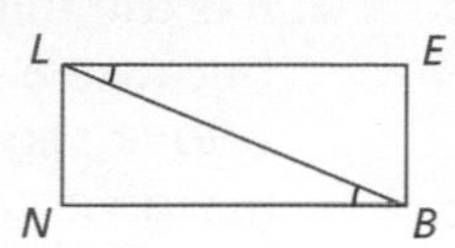

Practice **What other information, if any, do you need to prove the two triangles congruent by SAS? Explain.**

3.

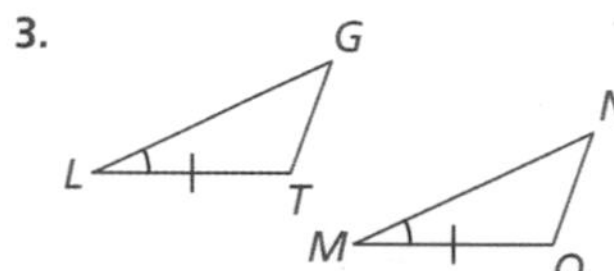

4.

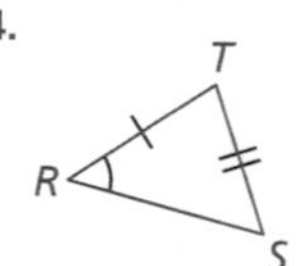

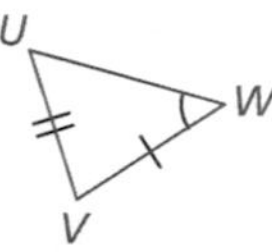

▼ STUDENT PAGE 133

Recall that, in Lesson 1-1, you learned to construct segments using a compass open to a fixed angle. Now you can show that it works. Similar to the situation with the box and the doorway, the Side-Angle-Side Postulate tells you that the triangles outlined at the right are congruent. So, $\overline{AB} \cong \overline{CD}$.

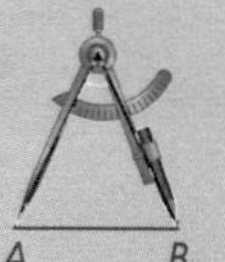

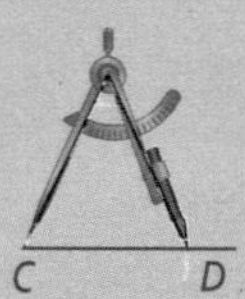

Problem 3 Identifying Congruent Triangles

Q What corresponding parts are labeled congruent in 3A? **[There are two pairs of sides and the included angle.]**

Q In 3B, what is the relationship between the sides and angles that are marked congruent? **[In the first triangle, the angle is included between the marked sides. In the second triangle, the angle is not included between the marked sides.]**

Q What corresponding parts are labeled congruent in 3C? **[There are three pairs of congruent sides.]**

Q How can you prove at least one pair of angles congruent in 3D? **[The angles that share a vertex are congruent because they are vertical angles.]**

▼ DIGITAL

Problem 3 **Identifying Congruent Triangles**

Would you use SSS or SAS to prove the triangles congruent? If there is not enough information to prove the triangles congruent by SSS or SAS, write *not enough information*. Explain your answer.

A

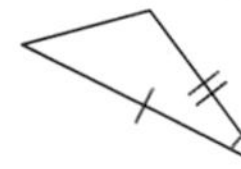

Use SAS because two pairs of corresponding sides and their included angles are congruent.

B

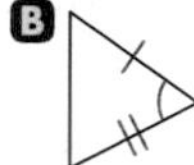

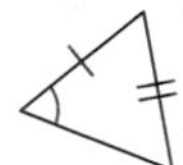

There is not enough information; two pairs of corresponding sides are congruent, but one of the angles is not the included angle.

C

Use SSS because three pairs of corresponding sides are congruent.

D

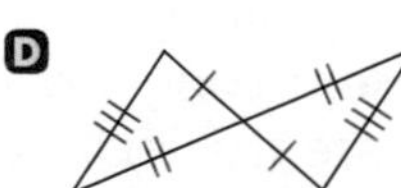

Use SSS or SAS because all three pairs of corresponding sides and a pair of included angles (the vertical angles) are congruent.

Got It? AUDITORY LEARNERS

The triangles are congruent by SSS only. SAS cannot be used because the sides marked on either side of the angle are not congruent. Have students explain this aloud to the class.

ANSWERS

Got It? SSS; three pairs of corresp. sides are ≅.

Practice

5. Not enough information; the congruent vertical angles *TQP* and *RQS* are not included by the pairs of ≅ sides.
6. SAS; the ≅ angles *BAC* and *DCA* are included by the pairs of sides $\overline{AB} \cong \overline{CD}$ (Given) and $\overline{AC} \cong \overline{AC}$ (Refl. Prop. of ≅).

▼ STUDENT PAGE 133

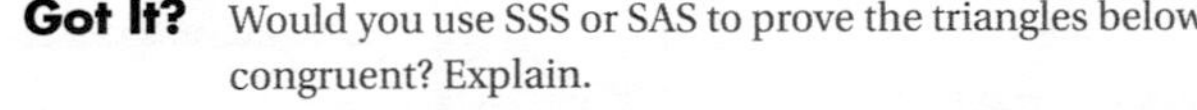

Plan

What should you look for first, congruent sides or congruent angles?

Got It? Would you use SSS or SAS to prove the triangles below congruent? Explain.

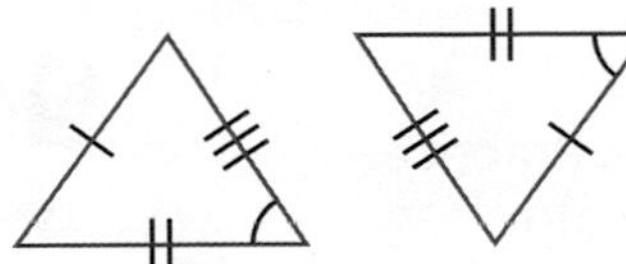

Practice Would you use SSS or SAS to prove the triangles congruent? If there is not enough information to prove the triangles congruent by SSS or SAS, write *not enough information*. Explain your answer.

5.

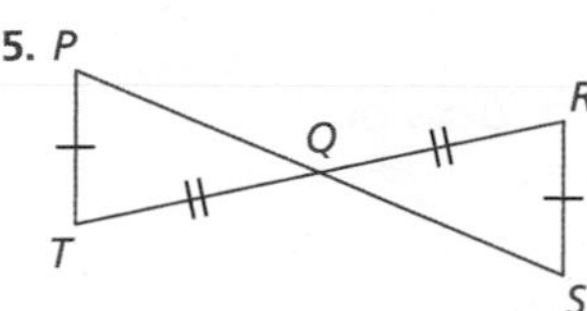

6.

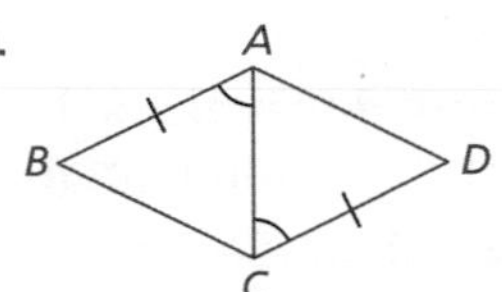

3 Lesson Check

Do you know HOW?

If students have difficulty with Exercises 7–8, then have them draw each triangle and label the vertices in order.

Do you UNDERSTAND?

If students have difficulty with Exercise 12, then have them review Problem 3B.

Close

Q What is the minimum number of conditions necessary to prove that two triangles are congruent? **[Three conditions must be proved.]**

Q Name two postulates that can be used to show that two triangles are congruent. **[SSS Postulate and SAS Postulate]**

ANSWERS

7. **a.** ∠*PEN* (or ∠*E*)
   b. ∠*NPE* (or ∠*P*)
8. **a.** $\overline{HA}$ and $\overline{HT}$
   b. $\overline{TH}$ and $\overline{TA}$
9. SAS
10. SSS
11. Answers may vary. Sample: Alike: Both use three pairs of ≅ parts to prove △ ≅. Different: SSS uses three pairs of ≅ sides, while SAS uses two pairs of ≅ sides and their ≅ included ∠s.
12. No; the ≅ ∠s are not included between the pairs of ≅ sides.
13. No; the △s have the same perimeter, but the three side lengths of one △ are not necessarily = to the three side lengths of the other △, so you cannot use SSS. There is no information about the ∠s of the △s, so you cannot use SAS.

▼ STUDENT PAGES 134–135

Lesson Check

Do you know HOW?

7. In △*PEN*, name the angle that is included between the given sides.
   a. $\overline{PE}$ and $\overline{EN}$ **b.** $\overline{NP}$ and $\overline{PE}$
8. In △*HAT*, between which sides is the given angle included?
   a. ∠*H* **b.** ∠*T*

Name the postulate you would use to prove the triangles congruent.

9.

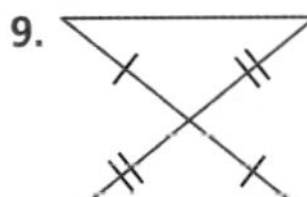

10.

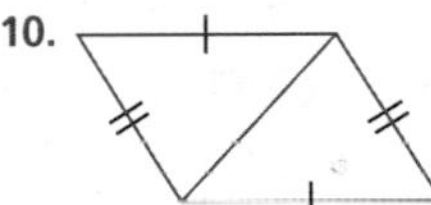

Do you UNDERSTAND? MATHEMATICAL PRACTICES

11. **Compare and Contrast** How are the SSS Postulate and the SAS Postulate alike? How are they different?
12. **Error Analysis** Your friend thinks that the triangles shown at the right are congruent by SAS. Is your friend correct? Explain.

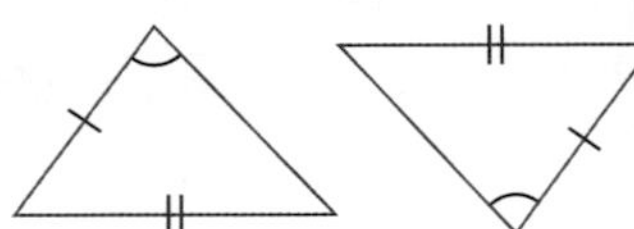

13. **Reasoning** A carpenter trims a triangular peak of a house with three 7-ft pieces of molding. The carpenter uses 21 ft of molding to trim a second triangular peak. Are the two triangles formed congruent? Explain.

Practice

More Practice and Problem-Solving Exercises

ASSIGNMENT GUIDE

The assignments below are for the More Practice and Problem-Solving Exercises. You may also want to assign the A-Level Practice Exercises for homework if these are not used in class.

Average: 14–30

Advanced: 14–33

Mathematical Practices The exercises listed focus on the Standards for Mathematical Practices listed.

EX. 11, 14: Make Sense of Problems (MP 1)
EX. 13, 26, 33: Construct Arguments (MP 3)
EX. 12: Critique the Reasoning of Others (MP 3)
EX. 20: Model with Mathematics (MP 4)

EXERCISE 17: Use the **Think About a Plan** worksheet in the Online Teacher Resources to further support students' development in becoming independent learners.

HOMEWORK QUICK CHECK

To check students' understanding of key skills and concepts, go over Exercises 14, 16, 17, 20, and 27.

ANSWERS

14. If the 40° ∠ is *always* included between the two 5-in. sides, then all the triangles will be congruent by SAS. In other cases, the triangles may or may not be congruent.

15. $\overline{BC} \cong \overline{DA}$ and $\angle CBD \cong \angle ADB$ (Given). $\overline{BD} \cong \overline{BD}$ (Refl. Prop. of ≅), so $\triangle BCD \cong \triangle DAB$ by SAS.

16. X is the midpt. of $\overline{AG}$ and $\overline{NR}$ (Given), so $\overline{AX} \cong \overline{GX}$ and $\overline{NX} \cong \overline{RX}$ by the def. of midpt. Also, $\angle AXN \cong \angle GXR$ because they are vertical ∠s, so $\triangle ANX \cong \triangle GRX$ by SAS.

17. $AB = \sqrt{16+1} = \sqrt{17}$ and $DE = \sqrt{16+1} = \sqrt{17}$; $BC = \sqrt{9+9} = \sqrt{18}$ and $EF = \sqrt{9+9} = \sqrt{18}$; $AC = \sqrt{1+4} = \sqrt{5}$ and $DF = \sqrt{1+4} = \sqrt{5}$; so $\triangle ABC \cong \triangle DEF$ by SSS.

18. $AB = \sqrt{25+16} = \sqrt{41}$. No side of $\triangle DEF$ has this length, so the triangles are not congruent.

19. $AB = 5$, $BC = 3$, $AC = \sqrt{9+25} = \sqrt{34}$; $DE = 5$, $EF = 3$, $DF = \sqrt{9+25} = \sqrt{34}$; $\triangle ABC \cong \triangle DEF$ by SSS.

20. Answers may vary. Sample: roof trusses for a house, sections of a Ferris wheel, sawhorses used by a carpenter; explanations will vary.

▼ STUDENT PAGES 135–136

More Practice and Problem-Solving Exercises

Apply

14. Think About a Plan You and a friend are cutting triangles out of felt for an art project. You want all the triangles to be congruent. Your friend tells you that each triangle should have two 5-in. sides and a 40° angle. If you follow this rule, will all your felt triangles be congruent? Explain.
- How can you use diagrams to help you?
- Which postulate, SSS or SAS, are you likely to apply to the given situation?

Proof **15. Given:** $\overline{BC} \cong \overline{DA}$, $\angle CBD \cong \angle ADB$

Prove: $\triangle BCD \cong \triangle DAB$

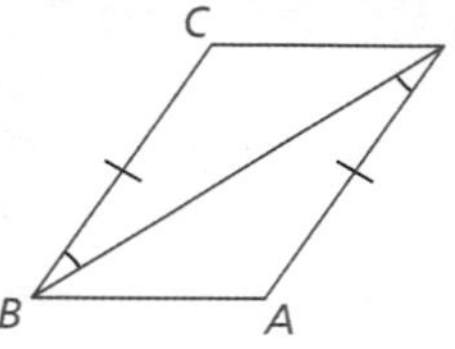

Proof **16. Given:** X is the midpoint of $\overline{AG}$ and $\overline{NR}$.

Prove: $\triangle ANX \cong \triangle GRX$

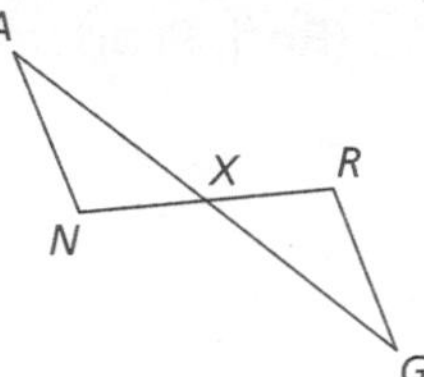

Use the Distance Formula to determine whether $\triangle ABC$ and $\triangle DEF$ are congruent. Justify your answer.

17. $A(1, 4)$, $B(5, 5)$, $C(2, 2)$;
$D(-5, 1)$, $E(-1, 0)$, $F(-4, 3)$

18. $A(3, 8)$, $B(8, 12)$, $C(10, 5)$;
$D(3, -1)$, $E(7, -7)$, $F(12, -2)$

19. $A(2, 9)$, $B(2, 4)$, $C(5, 4)$;
$D(1, -3)$, $E(1, 2)$, $F(-2, 2)$

20. Writing List three real-life uses of congruent triangles. For each real-life use, describe why you think congruence is necessary.

21. Yes; two sides of the original △ are ≅, and finding successive midpts. of ≅ segments results in pairs of (smaller) ≅ segments. The bottom sides of the triangles are congruent because the length of each segment is half the length of the original triangle. The base ∠s of the original isosc. △ are ≅, so the △s outlined in red are ≅ by SAS.

22. **a.** Answers may vary. Sample:

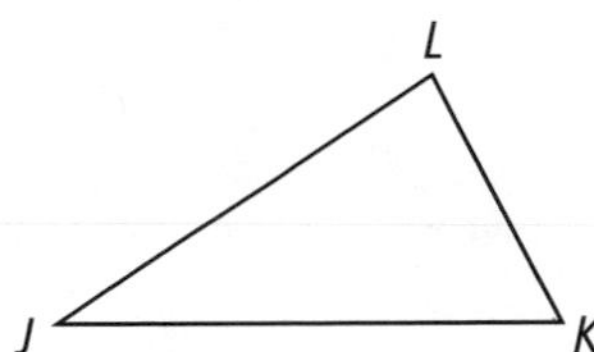

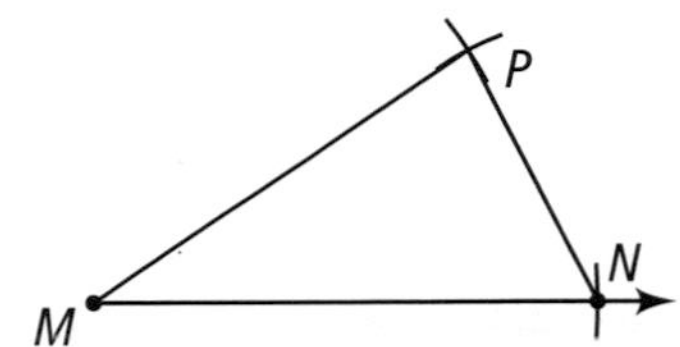

b. Answers may vary. Sample:

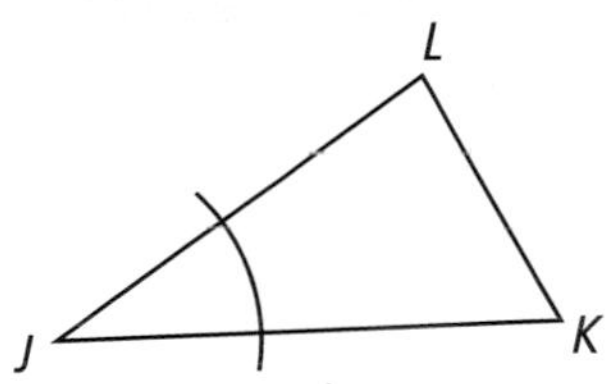

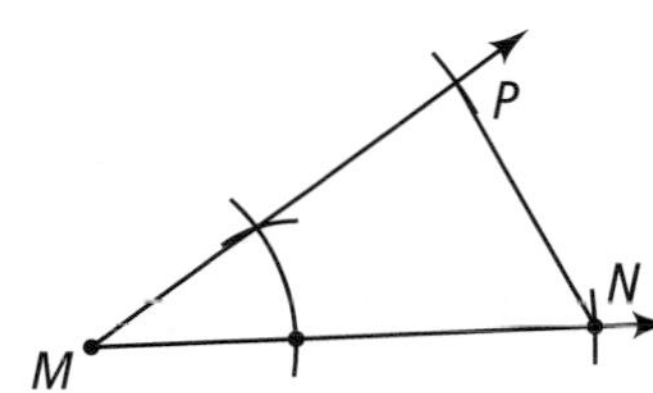

23. △*ANG* ≅ △*RWT* by SAS.

24. Not enough information; you need $\overline{DY} \cong \overline{TK}$ to show the △s are ≅ by SSS, or you need ∠*H* ≅ ∠*P* to show the △s are ≅ by SAS.

25. △*JEF* ≅ △*SFV* (or △*JEF* ≅ △*SVF*) by SSS

26. Not necessarily; the ≅ ∠s are not included between the pairs of ≅ sides.

27. $\overline{GK}$ bisects ∠*JGM* (Given), so ∠*JGK* ≅ ∠*MGK* (Def. of ∠ bisector). $\overline{GJ} \cong \overline{GM}$ (Given) and $\overline{GK} \cong \overline{GK}$ (Refl. Prop. of ≅), so △*GJK* ≅ △*GMK* by SAS.

28. $\overline{AE}$ and $\overline{BD}$ bisect each other (Given), so $\overline{AC} \cong \overline{EC}$ and $\overline{DC} \cong \overline{BC}$ (Def. of seg. bisector). ∠*ACB* ≅ ∠*ECD* (Vert. ∠s are ≅.), so △*ACB* ≅ △*ECD* by SAS.

▼ STUDENT PAGE 136

21. Sierpinski's Triangle Sierpinski's triangle is a famous geometric pattern. To draw Sierpinski's triangle, start with a single triangle and connect the midpoints of the sides to draw a smaller triangle. If you repeat this pattern over and over, you will form a figure like the one shown. This particular figure started with an isosceles triangle. Are the triangles outlined in red congruent? Explain.

22. Constructions Use a straightedge to draw any triangle *JKL*. Then construct △*MNP* ≅ △*JKL* using the given postulate.

a. SSS

b. SAS

Can you prove the triangles congruent? If so, write the congruence statement and name the postulate you would use. If not, write *not enough information* and tell what other information you would need.

23.

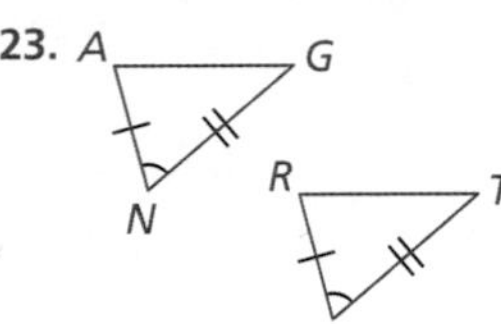

24.

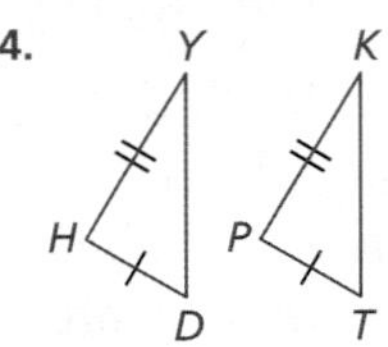

25.

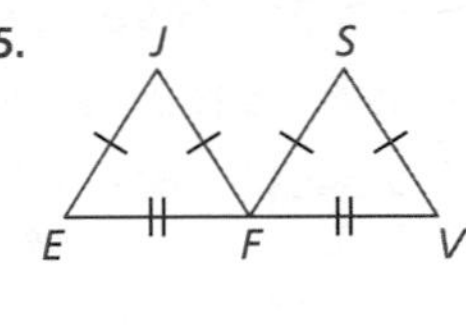

26. Reasoning Suppose $\overline{GH} \cong \overline{JK}$, $\overline{HI} \cong \overline{KL}$, and ∠*I* ≅ ∠*L*. Is △*GHI* congruent to △*JKL*? Explain.

Proof **27. Given:** $\overline{GK}$ bisects ∠*JGM*, $\overline{GJ} \cong \overline{GM}$

Prove: △*GJK* ≅ △*GMK*

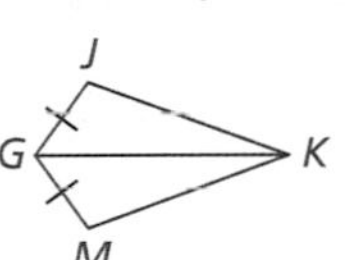

Proof **28. Given:** $\overline{AE}$ and $\overline{BD}$ bisect each other.

Prove: △*ACB* ≅ △*ECD*

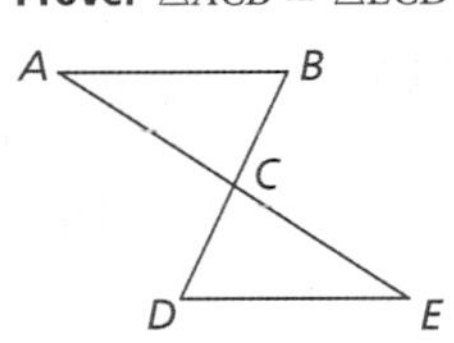

More Practice and Problem-Solving Exercises *continued*

29. $\overline{FG} \parallel \overline{KL}$ (Given), so $\angle GFK \cong \angle LKF$ because they are alt. int. $\angle$s. $\overline{FG} \cong \overline{KL}$ (Given) and $\overline{KF} \cong \overline{KF}$ (Refl. Prop. of $\cong$), so $\triangle FGK \cong \triangle KLF$ by SAS.

30. Given the $\perp$ segments, $\angle B \cong \angle CMA$ because all rt. $\angle$s are $\cong$. M is the midpt. of $\overline{AB}$ (Given), so $\overline{AM} \cong \overline{MB}$ by the def. of midpt. Since $\overline{DB} \cong \overline{CM}$ (Given), then $\triangle AMC \cong \triangle MBD$ by SAS.

31. $\overline{KG} \cong \overline{KG}$ by the Refl. Prop. of $\cong$. Since $\overline{HK} \cong \overline{LG}$ (Given), $HK + KG = LG + KG$ by the Seg. Add. Post. So, $\overline{HG} \cong \overline{LK}$. $\overline{HF} \cong \overline{LJ}$ and $\overline{FG} \cong \overline{JK}$ (Given), so $\triangle FGH \cong \triangle JKL$ by SSS.

32. Answers may vary. Sample: $\angle N \cong \angle L$, $\overline{MN} \cong \overline{OL}$, and $\overline{NO} \cong \overline{LM}$ (Given), so $\triangle MNO \cong \triangle OLM$ by SAS. $\angle NMO \cong \angle LOM$ (Def. of $\cong$ $\triangle$s). So $\overline{MN} \parallel \overline{OL}$ because if alt. int. $\angle$s are $\cong$, then the lines are $\parallel$.

33. Answers may vary. Sample: Given 4 pairs of $\cong$ sides, the two quadrilaterals do not have to be $\cong$ because the $\angle$s of the quadrilaterals may be different. To make the quadrilaterals rigid, add a diagonal to each figure. If corresponding diagonals are $\cong$, then the quadrilaterals form two pairs of $\cong$ $\triangle$s (each by SSS), and so the quadrilaterals will be $\cong$.

▼ STUDENT PAGE 137

29. Given: $\overline{FG} \parallel \overline{KL}$, $\overline{FG} \cong \overline{KL}$
Proof
Prove: $\triangle FGK \cong \triangle KLF$

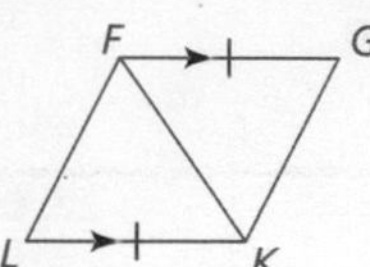

30. Given: $\overline{AB} \perp \overline{CM}$, $\overline{AB} \perp \overline{DB}$, $\overline{CM} \cong \overline{DB}$,
Proof *M* is the midpoint of $\overline{AB}$.
Prove: $\triangle AMC \cong \triangle MBD$

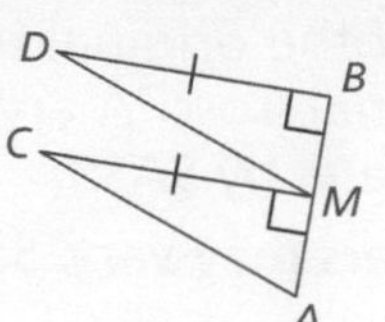

Challenge

31. Given: $\overline{HK} \cong \overline{LG}$, $\overline{HF} \cong \overline{LJ}$, $\overline{FG} \cong \overline{JK}$
Proof
Prove: $\triangle FGH \cong \triangle JKL$

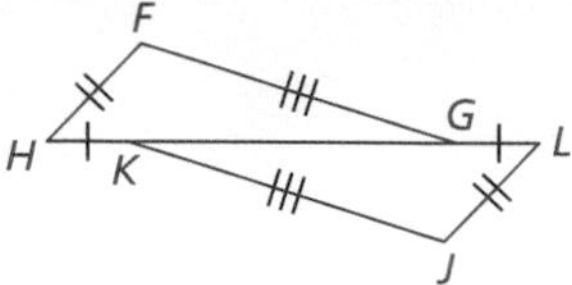

32. Given: $\angle N \cong \angle L$, $\overline{MN} \cong \overline{OL}$, $\overline{NO} \cong \overline{LM}$
Proof
Prove: $\overline{MN} \parallel \overline{OL}$

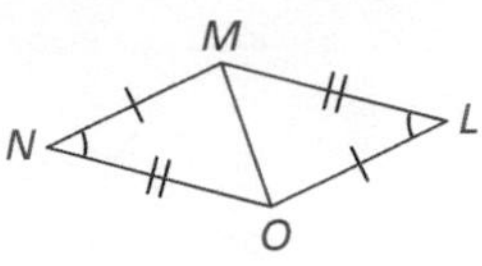

33. Reasoning Four sides of polygon *ABCD* are congruent, respectively, to the four sides of polygon *EFGH*. Are *ABCD* and *EFGH* congruent? Is a quadrilateral a rigid figure? If not, what could you add to make it a rigid figure? Explain.

Assess and Remediate

Lesson Quiz

1. What other information do you need to prove $\triangle GHK \cong \triangle KLG$ by SAS? Explain.

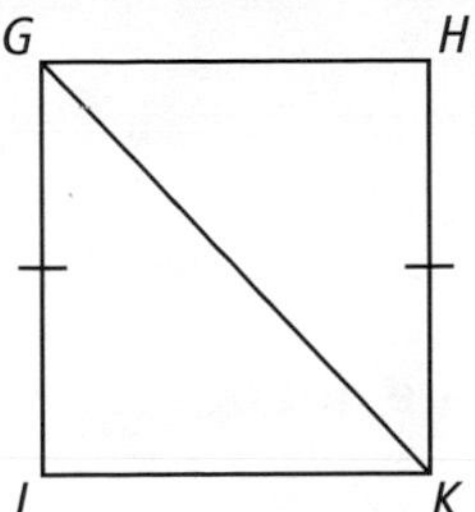

2. **Do you UNDERSTAND?** Would you use SSS or SAS to prove the triangles congruent? If there is not enough information to prove the triangles congruent by SSS or SAS, write *not enough information.* Explain your answer.

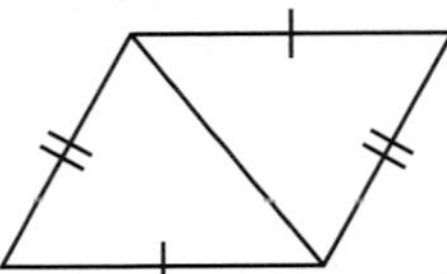

ANSWERS TO LESSON QUIZ

1. $\angle HKG \cong \angle LGK$. These are the angles included by the corresponding congruent sides.
2. SSS; 2 pairs of congruent sides are given and the third pair is congruent by the Reflexive Prop. of Congruence.

Prescription for Remediation

Use the student work on the Lesson Quiz to prescribe a differentiated assignment.

Points	Differentiated Remediation
0	Intervention
1	On-level
2	Extension

Online Assessment

Assign the Lesson Quiz in Success Tracker on **pearsonsuccessnet.com**. Success Tracker will automatically score the quiz and assign appropriate intervention or enrichment to each student based on the results. The compiled data appear in three different reports for instant analysis of whole class and individual student performance.

Differentiated Remediation

Intervention

- **RETEACHING** (2 pages) Provides reteaching and practice exercises for the key lesson concepts. Use with struggling students or absent students.
- **ENGLISH LANGUAGE LEARNER SUPPORT** Helps students develop and reinforce mathematical vocabulary and key concepts.

On-Level

- **PRACTICE** (2 pages) Provides extra practice for each lesson. For simpler practice exercises, use the Form K Practice pages found in the Online Teacher Resources.
- **THINK ABOUT A PLAN** Helps students develop specific problem-solving skills and strategies by providing scaffolded guiding questions.
- **STANDARDIZED TEST PREP** Focuses on all major exercises, all major question types, and helps students prepare for the high-stakes assessments.

Extension

- **ENRICHMENT** Provides students with interesting problems and activities that extend the concepts of the lesson.
- **ACTIVITIES, GAMES, AND PUZZLES** Worksheets that can be used for concept development, enrichment, and for fun!

3-3 Triangle Congruence by ASA and AAS

Common Core State Standards
G.SRT.5 Use congruence . . . criteria for triangles to solve problems and to prove relationships in geometric figures. **Also prepares for G.CO.8**

Preparing to Teach

BIG idea Reasoning and Proof

ESSENTIAL UNDERSTANDING

Two triangles can be proven to be congruent without having to show that all corresponding parts are congruent. Another way triangles can be proven to be congruent is by using one pair of corresponding sides and two pairs of corresponding angles.

Math Background

The postulate and theorem in this lesson allow students to prove that two triangles are congruent based on two pairs of congruent angles and one pair of congruent sides. This adds to the collection of methods students have to prove triangles congruent. These postulates and theorem represent the minimum number of conditions necessary to prove triangle congruence. In the next lesson, students will have the opportunity to use the postulates and theorem from this and previous lessons to determine whether triangles are congruent.

As in other lessons, the names of congruence postulates and theorems are reminders about the position of the congruent corresponding parts. The S in the ASA Postulate is between the two letters A, which indicates that the congruent sides must be between the corresponding congruent angles. The S in the AAS Theorem is **not** between the two letters A, which indicates that the congruent sides are **not** between the corresponding congruent angles.

ELL Support

FOCUS ON LANGUAGE Project or write the ASA Postulate on the board. Read the postulate, pointing to each word as you read. Discuss its meaning. Do the same for the AAS Theorem. Ask how these two methods are different and how they are the same.

FOCUS ON COMMUNICATION Turn off the projector or erase the board and have students write the ASA Postulate and AAS Theorem in their own words. Pair students and ask them to read their sentences to each other. Encourage questions, clarification (What do you mean?), and peer assistance in learning.

Mathematical Practices

LOOK FOR AND MAKE USE OF STRUCTURE. Students will recognize the significance of elements in a triangle, such as the congruences of sides and angles, and will determine the congruence (or lack thereof) between two triangles using ASA and AAS.

1 Interactive Learning

Solve It!

PURPOSE To prove that two triangles are congruent using methods learned in previous lessons

PROCESS Students may draw diagrams of the triangles by combining the information on both copies, use the Third Angles Theorem to identify a third pair of congruent angles, or use the SAS Postulate to prove that two triangles are congruent.

Q Can you draw a complete diagram of each triangle? Explain. **[Yes, by combining the information in both copies.]**

Q Do any of the triangles have enough information to indicate congruence by SSS or SAS? **[No]**

Q What theorem will allow you to determine that all three pairs of angles in a triangle are congruent when two congruent pairs are known? **[Third Angles Theorem]**

ANSWER The markings indicate that $\angle L \cong \angle A \cong \angle E$, $\angle C \cong \angle T \cong \angle N$, $\angle B \cong \angle M$ by Third Angles Theorem, $\overline{BC} \cong \overline{DE} \cong \overline{VT} \cong \overline{MN}$, and $\overline{LM} \cong \overline{AB} \cong \overline{EF}$. So $\triangle ABC \cong \triangle LMN$ by SAS.

▼ DIGITAL (STUDENT WORK SPACE PAGE 138)

SOLVE IT! Getting Ready!

Oh no! The school's photocopier is not working correctly. The copies all have some ink missing. Below are two photocopies of the same geometry worksheet. Which triangles are congruent? How do you know?

Copy 1 Copy 2

CONNECT THE MATH Students should see that the SAS and SSS Postulates are not always enough to prove two triangles congruent. In this lesson they will learn two more options for proving congruence.

Guided Instruction

Problem 1 Using ASA

Take Note
Have students use the ASA Postulate to show that △*ABC* and △*LMN* in the Solve It are congruent.

Problem 1

Q In each pair of triangles, how many pairs of congruent angles are shown? **[There are two pairs of angles that are congruent in each pair of triangles.]**

Q Which sides are included between the pairs of congruent angles? **[$\overline{UV}$, $\overline{EO}$, and $\overline{WT}$]**

Q Of the three triangles, which have two pairs of congruent angles and one pair of congruent included sides? **[△*SUV* and △*NEO*]**

Got It? **VISUAL LEARNERS**
Students can reproduce the three triangles complete with the congruence markings on their own papers. Have them use two different colored highlighter markers to mark one congruent angle pair in each triangle. Draw over the side in each triangle that is congruent with a third color. Students can identify the congruent triangles because both will have the same color pattern marking the included side between two colored angles.

ANSWERS

Got It? △*HGO* ≅ △*ACT* because $\overline{HG} \cong \overline{AC}$ and the ≅ segments are included between two pairs of ≅ ∠s.

Practice

1. △*PRQ* ≅ △*VWX*
2. △*ABC* ≅ △*EDF*

▼ STUDENT PAGE 138

You already know that triangles are congruent if two pairs of sides and the included angles are congruent (SAS). You can also prove triangles congruent using other groupings of angles and sides.

Essential Understanding You can prove that two triangles are congruent without having to show that *all* corresponding parts are congruent. In this lesson, you will prove triangles congruent by using one pair of corresponding sides and two pairs of corresponding angles.

take note

Postulate 16 Angle-Side-Angle (ASA) Postulate

Postulate	If . . .	Then . . .
If two angles and the included side of one triangle are congruent to two angles and the included side of another triangle, then the two triangles are congruent.	$\angle A \cong \angle D$, $\overline{AC} \cong \overline{DF}$, $\angle C \cong \angle F$ 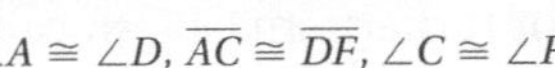 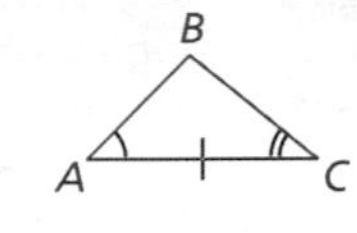 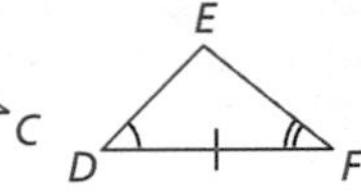	$\triangle ABC \cong \triangle DEF$

▼ DIGITAL

Problem 1 Using ASA

Which two triangles are congruent by ASA? Explain.

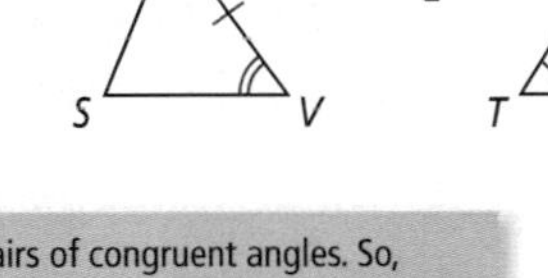

Know
From the diagram you know
- $\angle U \cong \angle E \cong \angle T$
- $\angle V \cong \angle O \cong \angle W$
- $\overline{UV} \cong \overline{EO} \cong \overline{AW}$

Need
To use ASA, you need two pairs of congruent angles and a pair of included congruent sides.

Plan
You already have pairs of congruent angles. So, identify the included side for each triangle and see whether it has a congruence marking.

In △*SUV*, $\overline{UV}$ is included between ∠*U* and ∠*V* and has a congruence marking. In △*NEO*, $\overline{EO}$ is included between ∠*E* and ∠*O* and has a congruence marking. In △*ATW*, $\overline{TW}$ is included between ∠*T* and ∠*W* but does *not* have a congruence marking.

Since $\angle U \cong \angle E$, $\overline{UV} \cong \overline{EO}$, and $\angle V \cong \angle O$, $\triangle SUV \cong \triangle NEO$.

▼ STUDENT PAGE 139

Got It? Which two triangles are congruent by ASA? Explain.

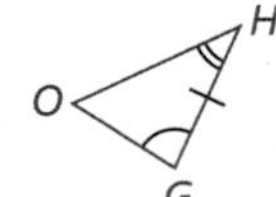
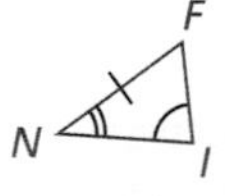
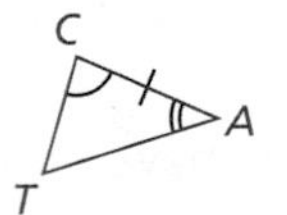

Think
When you use ASA, what must be true about the corresponding sides?

Practice Name two triangles that are congruent by ASA.

1.
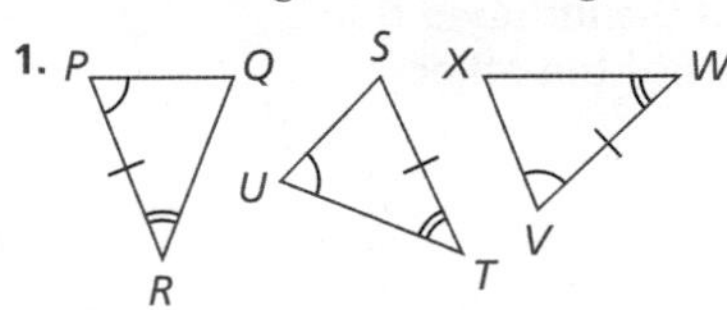

2.
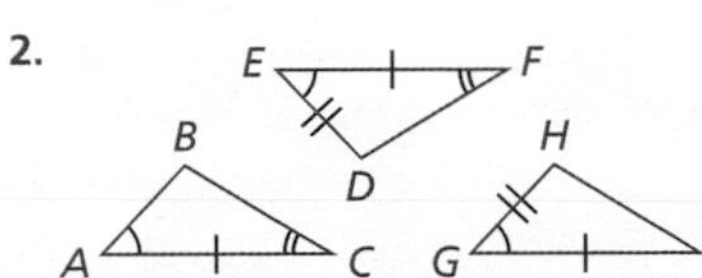

Problem 2 Writing a Proof Using ASA

To complete the proof have students work backward. Ask them to identify information they need and then identify theorems or postulates that will support the statements.

Q Which two pairs of angles are congruent? Justify your answer. **[It is given that $\angle A \cong \angle D$. $\angle B \cong \angle E$ because they are both right angles.]**

Q Which sides are included between these two angles? **[$\overline{AB}$ and $\overline{DE}$]**

Got It?

Q What are the similarities between the diagram for Problem 2 and the Got It diagram? **[Both pairs of triangles contain right angles, which are congruent. Both diagrams contain two pairs of congruent angles, one given and one implied. Both diagrams show the congruence of the given included sides.]**

ANSWERS

Got It? $\angle B \cong \angle E$ because all rt. ∠s are ≅. $\overline{AB} \cong \overline{AE}$ and $\angle CAB \cong \angle DAE$ (Given), so $\triangle ABC \cong \triangle AED$ by ASA.

Practice

3. **a.** Reflexive
   b. ASA
4. It is given that $\overline{QR} \cong \overline{TS}$ and $\overline{QR} \parallel \overline{TS}$. Then $\angle RQT \cong \angle STQ$ because alt. int. ∠s are ≅. Also, $\overline{QT} \cong \overline{QT}$ by the Refl. Prop. of ≅. So $\triangle QRT \cong \triangle TSQ$ by SAS.

▼ DIGITAL

Proof  **Problem 2** Writing a Proof Using ASA

Recreation Members of a teen organization are building a miniature golf course at your town's youth center. The design plan calls for the first hole to have two congruent triangular bumpers. Prove that the bumpers on the first hole, shown at the right, meet the conditions of the plan.

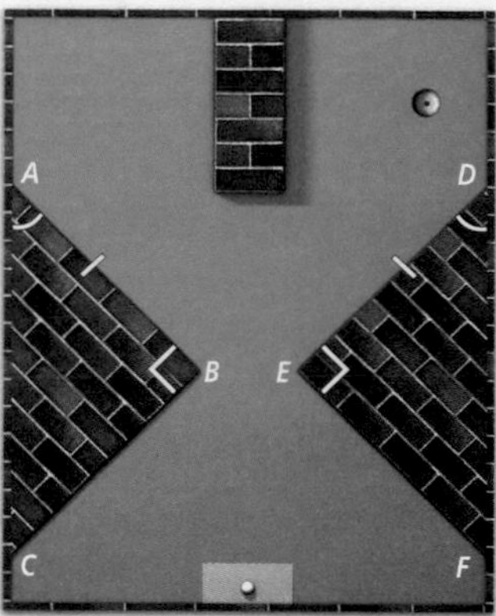

Given: $\overline{AB} \cong \overline{DE}$, $\angle A \cong \angle D$, $\angle B$ and $\angle E$ are right angles

Prove: $\triangle ABC \cong \triangle DEF$

Proof: $\angle B \cong \angle E$ because all right angles are congruent, and you are given that $\angle A \cong \angle D$. $\overline{AB}$ and $\overline{DE}$ are included sides between the two pairs of congruent angles. You are given that $\overline{AB} \cong \overline{DE}$. Thus, $\triangle ABC \cong \triangle DEF$ by ASA.

▼ STUDENT PAGE 140

Got It? **Given:** $\angle CAB \cong \angle DAE$, $\overline{BA} \cong \overline{EA}$, $\angle B$ and $\angle E$ are right angles

Prove: $\triangle ABC \cong \triangle AED$

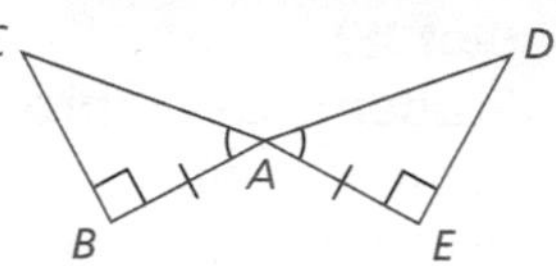

3. Developing Proof Complete the paragraph proof by filling in the blanks.

Given: $\angle LKM \cong \angle JKM$, $\angle LMK \cong \angle JMK$

Prove: $\triangle LKM \cong \triangle JKM$

Proof: $\angle LKM \cong \angle JKM$ and $\angle LMK \cong \angle JMK$ are given.

$\overline{KM} \cong \overline{KM}$ by the **a.** ______________ Property of Congruence.

So, $\triangle LKM \cong \triangle JKM$ by **b.** ______________.

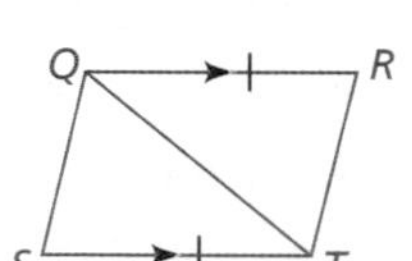

Proof **4. Given:** $\overline{QR} \cong \overline{TS}$, $\overline{QR} \parallel \overline{TS}$

Prove: $\triangle QRT \cong \triangle TSQ$

Q R S T

Problem 3 Writing a Proof Using AAS

Take Note

Discuss the similarities and differences between the ASA Postulate and the AAS Theorem. Have students discuss the location of the side needed for each statement.

Q Can you draw two triangles that have two pairs of congruent angles and one pair of congruent sides, but cannot be proved congruent using ASA or AAS? Explain. **[Yes; one triangle would need the included side marked congruent to a nonincluded side of the other triangle.]**

▼ STUDENT PAGE 141

You can also prove triangles congruent by using two angles and a nonincluded side, as stated in the theorem below.

take note **Theorem 19 Angle-Angle-Side (AAS) Theorem**

Theorem	If . . .	Then . . .
If two angles and a nonincluded side of one triangle are congruent to two angles and the corresponding nonincluded side of another triangle, then the triangles are congruent.	$\angle A \cong \angle D$, $\angle B \cong \angle E$, $\overline{AC} \cong \overline{DF}$ 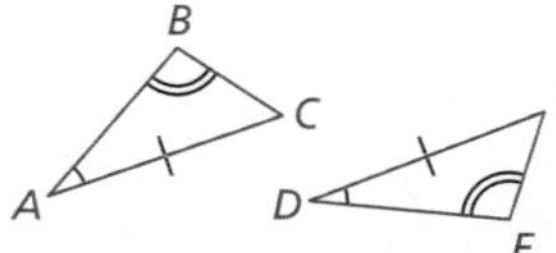	$\triangle ABC \cong \triangle DEF$

Proof of Theorem 19

This proof uses the ASA Postulate to prove the theorem. Discuss the ramifications of using a postulate (which can be assumed true) to prove a theorem. If students have difficulty understanding the flow proof, have them transfer the proof into a two-column format.

Problem 3

Once students understand this proof, challenge them to prove the triangles congruent using the ASA Postulate.

Q In order to use the AAS Theorem, what information do you need that is not directly given? **[one pair of congruent angles and one pair of congruent sides that is not included]**

Q What property of congruence can you use to prove that two of the triangles' sides are congruent? Write the congruence statement. **[Reflexive Property of Congruence; $\overline{WR} \cong \overline{WR}$]**

Q Which pair of angles do you need to use the AAS Theorem? **[$\angle KRW$ and $\angle MWR$ or $\angle KWR$ and $\angle MRW$]**

Got It? ELL SUPPORT

Review the word *bisect* and its meaning. Remind students of the meaning of the prefix *bi-*. Discuss the significance of the statement that $\overline{RP}$ bisects $\angle SRQ$ and the congruence statement that follows from this fact.

ANSWERS

Got It?

a. $\overline{RP}$ bisects $\angle SRQ$ (Given), so $\angle SRP \cong \angle QRP$ by the def. of $\angle$ bisector. $\angle S \cong \angle Q$ (Given) and $\overline{RP} \cong \overline{RP}$ (Refl. Prop. of $\cong$), so $\triangle SRP \cong \triangle QRP$ by AAS.

b. After Step 3 in the proof, state that $\angle MRW \cong \angle KWR$ by the Third $\angle$s Theorem and write Step 4, so $\triangle WMR \cong \triangle RKW$ by ASA.

Practice

5. a. Vert. $\angle$s are $\cong$.
   b. Given
   c. $\overline{TQ} \cong \overline{RQ}$
   d. AAS

6. Given the $\perp$ segments, $\angle Q \cong \angle S$ because $\perp$ lines form rt. $\angle$s, and all rt. $\angle$s are $\cong$. It is given that T is the midpt. of $\overline{PR}$, so $\overline{PT} \cong \overline{RT}$ by the def. of midpt. $\angle PTQ \cong \angle RTS$ because vert. $\angle$s are $\cong$, so $\triangle PQT \cong \triangle RST$ by AAS.

▼ STUDENT PAGE 141

Proof **Proof of Theorem 19: Angle-Angle-Side Theorem**

Given: $\angle A \cong \angle D$, $\angle B \cong \angle E$, $\overline{AC} \cong \overline{DF}$

Prove: $\triangle ABC \cong \triangle DEF$

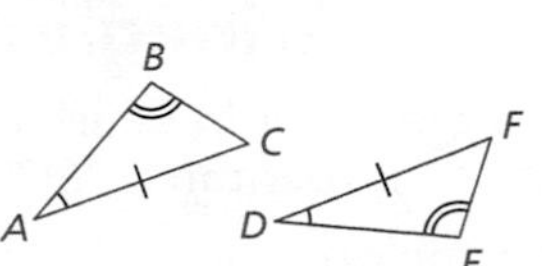

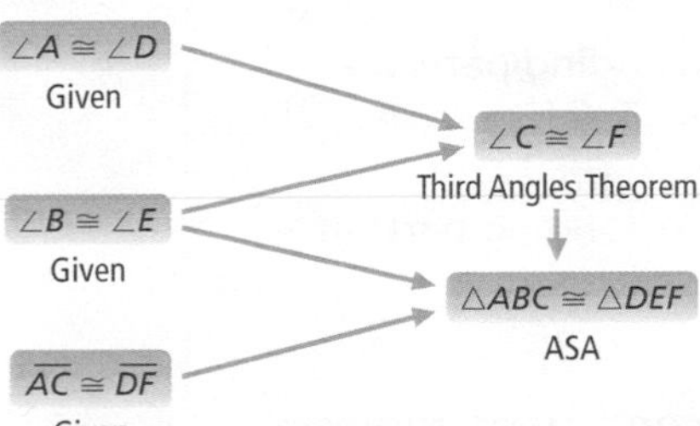

You have seen and used three methods of proof in this book—two-column, paragraph, and flow proof. Each method is equally as valid as the others. Unless told otherwise, you can choose any of the three methods to write a proof. Just be sure your proof always presents logical reasoning with justification.

▼ DIGITAL

Proof  **Problem 3** **Writing a Proof Using AAS**

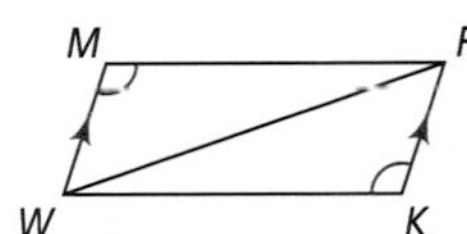

Given: $\angle M \cong \angle K$, $\overline{WM} \parallel \overline{RK}$

Prove: $\triangle WMR \cong \triangle RKW$

Statements	Reasons
1) $\angle M \cong \angle K$	1) Given
2) $\overline{WM} \parallel \overline{RK}$	2) Given
3) $\angle MWR \cong \angle KRW$	3) If lines are $\parallel$, then alternate interior $\angle$s are $\cong$.
4) $\overline{WR} \cong \overline{WR}$	4) Reflexive Property of Congruence
5) $\triangle WMR \cong \triangle RKW$	5) AAS

▼ STUDENT PAGES 142–143

Got It? a. **Given:** $\angle S \cong \angle Q$, $\overline{RP}$ bisects $\angle SRQ$

Prove: $\triangle SRP \cong \triangle QRP$

Think
How can you show on a diagram that $\overline{RP}$ bisects $\angle SRQ$?

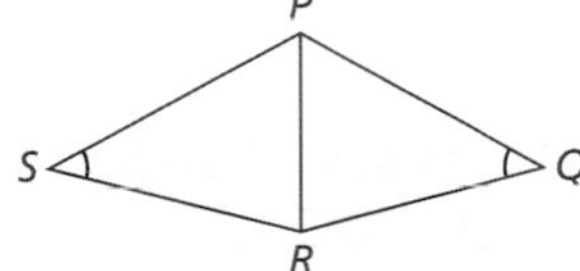

b. **Reasoning** In Problem 3, how could you prove that $\triangle WMR \cong \triangle RKW$ by ASA? Explain.

A Practice 5. **Developing Proof** Complete the two-column proof by filling in the blanks.

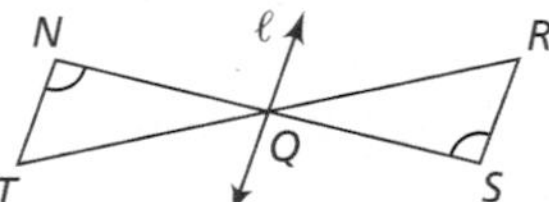

Given: $\angle N \cong \angle S$, line ℓ bisects $\overline{TR}$ at Q

Prove: $\triangle NQT \cong \triangle SQR$

Statements	Reasons
1) $\angle N \cong \angle S$	1) Given
2) $\angle NQT \cong \angle SQR$	2) a. ______
3) Line ℓ bisects $\overline{TR}$ at Q.	3) b. ______
4) c. ______	4) Definition of bisect
5) $\triangle NQT \cong \triangle SQR$	5) d. ______

Proof 6. **Given:** $\overline{PQ} \perp \overline{QS}$, $\overline{RS} \perp \overline{SQ}$, T is the midpoint of $\overline{PR}$

Prove: $\triangle PQT \cong \triangle RST$

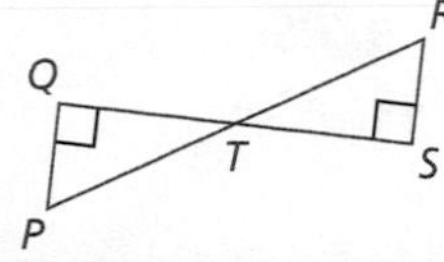

Problem 4 Determining Whether Triangles Are Congruent

Q What is the order in which corresponding parts are marked congruent in $\triangle FBI$? **[$\overline{FB}$, $\angle B$, $\angle I$]**

Q What is the order in which corresponding parts are marked congruent in $\triangle OUT$? **[$\angle U$, $\angle T$, $\overline{OT}$]**

Q Is there a postulate or theorem that proves the triangles congruent with the corresponding parts in this order? **[No.]**

Got It?

Have students identify a pair of congruent angles which are not marked in the diagram. Then ask students to list the sides and angles that are congruent in the order that they are marked.

ANSWERS

Got It? Yes; $\overline{PR} \cong \overline{SR}$ and $\angle A \cong \angle I$ (Given). $\angle ARP \cong \angle IRS$ (Vert. ∠s are ≅.), so $\triangle PAR \cong \triangle SIR$ by AAS.

Practice

7. $\triangle PMO \cong \triangle NMO$ by ASA.

8 $\triangle UST \cong \triangle RTS$ by AAS.

▼ DIGITAL

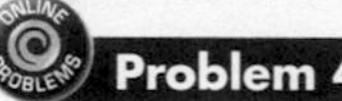

Problem 4 Determining Whether Triangles Are Congruent

Multiple Choice Use the diagram at the right. Which of the following statements best represents the answer and justification to the question, "Is $\triangle BIF \cong \triangle UTO$?"

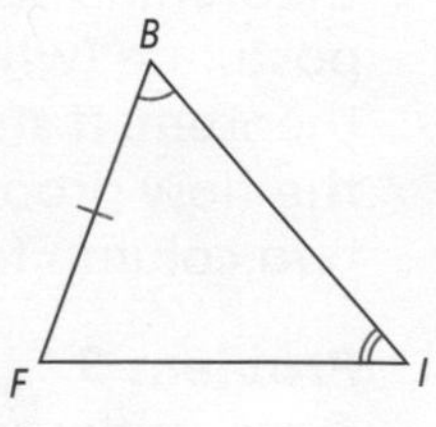

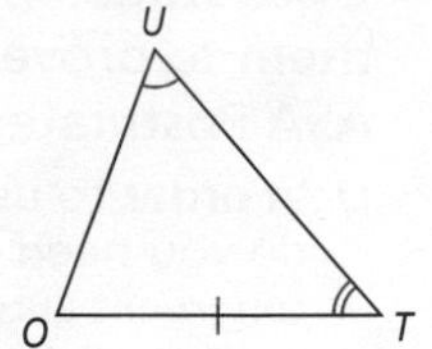

(A) Yes, the triangles are congruent by ASA.

(B) No, $\overline{FB}$ and $\overline{OT}$ are not corresponding sides.

(C) Yes, the triangles are congruent by AAS.

(D) No, $\angle B$ and $\angle U$ are not corresponding angles.

The diagram shows that two pairs of angles and one pair of sides are congruent. The third pair of angles is congruent by the Third Angles Theorem. To prove these triangles congruent, you need to satisfy ASA or AAS.

ASA and AAS both fail because $\overline{FB}$ and $\overline{TO}$ are not included between the same pair of congruent corresponding angles, so they are not corresponding sides. The triangles are not necessarily congruent. The correct answer is B.

▼ STUDENT PAGES 143–144

Got It? Are $\triangle PAR$ and $\triangle SIR$ congruent? Explain.

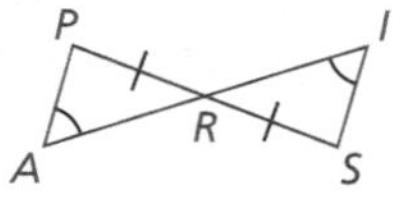

Practice Determine whether the triangles must be congruent. If so, name the postulate or theorem that justifies your answer. If not, explain.

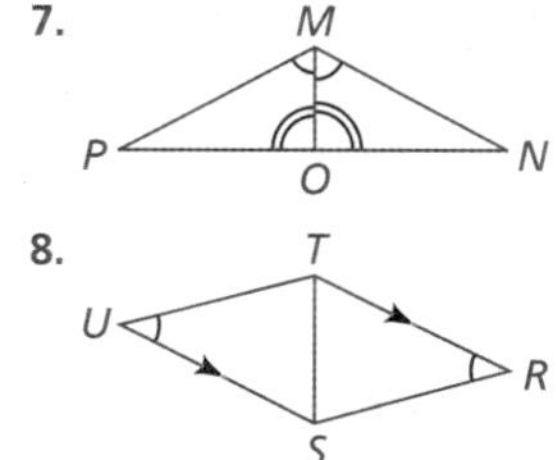

Lesson Check

Do you know HOW?

If students have difficulty with Exercises 11 and 12, then have them review Problems 2 and 3.

Do you UNDERSTAND?

If students have difficulty with Exercise 14, then have them redraw the triangles so that they have the same orientation.

Close

Q The theorem and the postulate in this lesson allow you to prove triangles are congruent based on what conditions? **[two pairs of congruent corresponding angles and one pair of congruent corresponding sides]**

Q How do these two methods of proving congruence differ? **[In one case, the congruent sides are included between the congruent angles; in the other case, they are not.]**

ANSWERS

9. $\overline{RS}$

10. $\angle N$, $\angle O$

11. ASA

12. AAS

▼ STUDENT PAGES 144–145

Lesson Check

Do you know HOW?

9. In $\triangle RST$, which side is included between $\angle R$ and $\angle S$?

10. In $\triangle NOM$, $\overline{NO}$ is included between which angles?

Which postulate or theorem could you use to prove $\triangle ABC \cong \triangle DEF$?

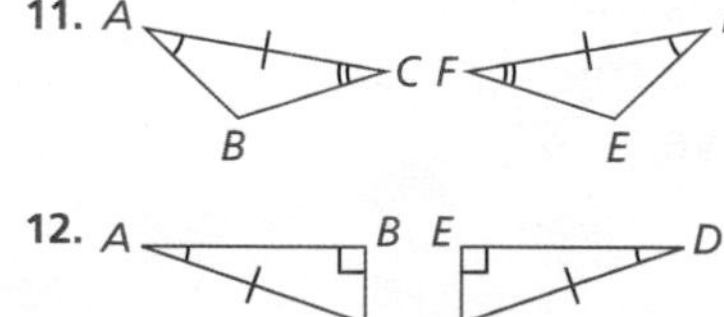

13. Answers may vary. Sample: Alike: Both postulates use three pairs of ≅ corresp. parts. Different: To use the ASA Postulate, the sides must be included between the pairs of corresp. angles, while to use the SAS Postulate, the angles must be included between the pairs of corresp. sides.

14. $\overline{LM}$ is not included between the pairs of ≅ corresp. angles.

15. $\angle F \cong \angle G$, $\angle D \cong \angle H$

Do you UNDERSTAND?

13. **Compare and Contrast** How are the ASA Postulate and the SAS Postulate alike? How are they different?

14. **Error Analysis** Your friend asks you for help on a geometry exercise. To the right is your friend's paper. What error did your friend make? Explain.

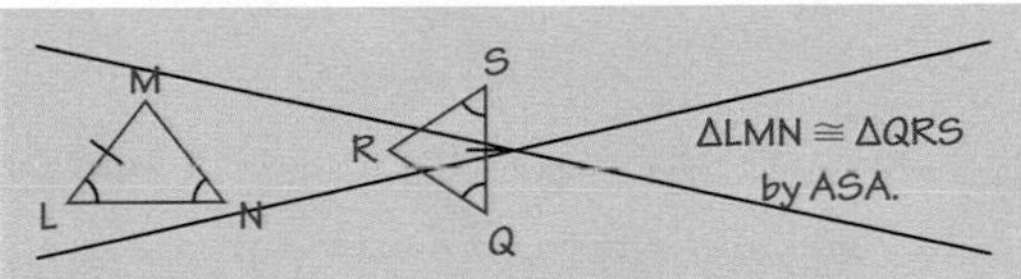

15. **Reasoning** Suppose $\angle E \cong \angle I$ and $\overline{FE} \cong \overline{GI}$. What else must you know in order to prove $\triangle FDE \cong \triangle GHI$ by ASA? By AAS?

4 Practice

More Practice and Problem-Solving Exercises

ASSIGNMENT GUIDE

The assignments below are for the More Practice and Problem-Solving Exercises. You may also want to assign the A-Level Practice Exercises for homework if these are not used in class.

Average: 16–25

Advanced: 16–28

Mathematical Practices The exercises listed focus on the Standards for Mathematical Practices listed.

EX. 13, 18, 24: Make Sense of Problems (MP 1)

EX. 15, 20: Construct Arguments (MP 3)

EX. 14, 21: Critique the Reasoning of Others (MP 3)

EXERCISE 25: Use the **Think About a Plan** worksheet in the Online Teacher Resources to further support students' development in becoming independent learners.

HOMEWORK QUICK CHECK

To check students' understanding of key skills and concepts, go over Exercises 16, 18, 19, 21, and 25.

ANSWERS

16. It is given that $\angle N \cong \angle P$ and $\overline{MO} \cong \overline{QO}$. Also, $\angle MON \cong \angle QOP$ because vert. ∡s are ≅. So $\triangle MON \cong \triangle QOP$ by AAS.

17. It is given that $\angle FJG \cong \angle HGJ$ and $\overline{FG} \parallel \overline{JH}$. Then $\angle FGJ \cong \angle HJG$ because alt. int. ∡s are ≅. Since $\overline{GJ} \cong \overline{GJ}$ by the Refl. Prop. of ≅, then $\triangle FGJ \cong \triangle HJG$ by ASA.

18. Answers may vary. Sample: Yes; ASA guarantees a unique triangle with vertices at the oak tree, the maple tree, and the time capsule.

More Practice and Problem-Solving Exercises

B Apply

Proof 16. **Given:** $\angle N \cong \angle P$, $\overline{MO} \cong \overline{QO}$

Prove: $\triangle MON \cong \triangle QOP$

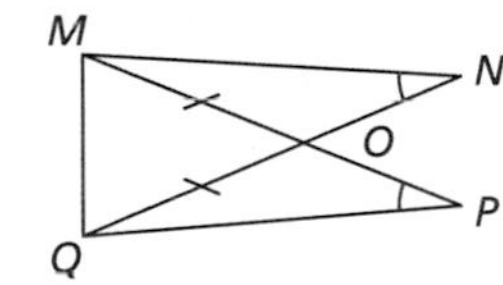

Proof 17. **Given:** $\angle FJG \cong \angle HGJ$, $\overline{FG} \parallel \overline{JH}$

Prove: $\triangle FGJ \cong \triangle HJG$

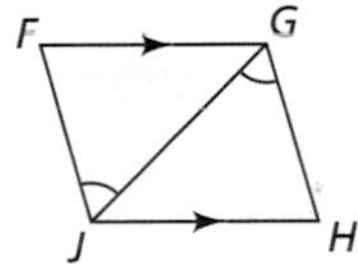

18. **Think About a Plan** While helping your family clean out the attic, you find the piece of paper shown at the right. The paper contains clues to locate a time capsule buried in your backyard. The maple tree is due east of the oak tree in your backyard. Will the clues always lead you to the correct spot? Explain.
- How can you use a diagram to help you?
- What type of geometric figure do the paths and the marked line form?
- How does the position of the marked line relate to the positions of the angles?

> Mark a line on the ground from the oak tree to the maple tree. From the oak tree, walk along a path that forms a 70° angle with the marked line, keeping the maple tree to your right. From the maple tree, walk along a path that forms a 40° angle with the marked line. The time capsule is buried where the paths meet.

19.

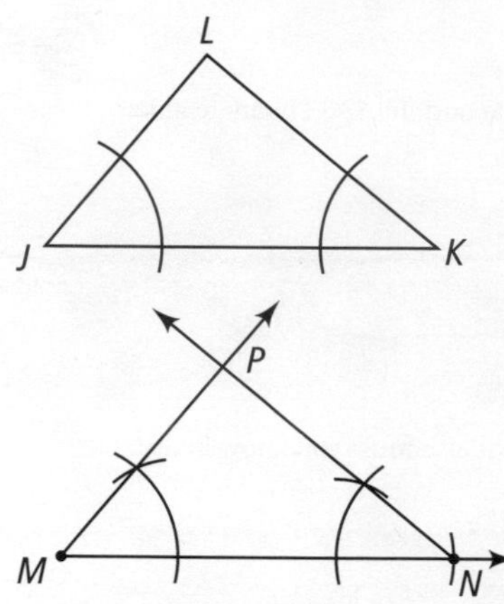

20. No; the common side is included between the two ≅ ∠s in one △, but it is not included between the ≅ ∠s in the other △.

21. Yes; use the Third ∠s Thm. Then you have three pairs of ≅ ∠s and one pair of ≅ sides, so you can use the ASA Postulate.

22. $\overline{AE} \parallel \overline{BD}$ (Given), so $\angle A \cong \angle DBC$ (If ∥ lines, corresp. ∠s are ≅.). Since $\angle E \cong \angle D$ and $\overline{AE} \cong \overline{BD}$ (Given), then $\triangle AEB \cong \triangle BDC$ by ASA.

23. $\overline{DH}$ bisects $\angle BDF$ (Given), so $\angle BDH \cong \angle FDH$ by the def. of ∠ bisector. $\angle 1 \cong \angle 2$ (Given) and $\overline{DH} \cong \overline{DH}$ (Refl. Prop. of ≅), so $\triangle BDH \cong \triangle FDH$ by ASA.

24. Answers may vary. Sample:

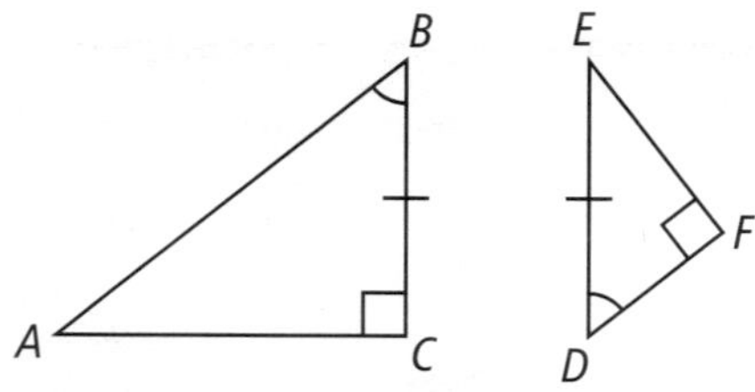

25. Given the parallel lines, $\angle BAC \cong \angle DCA$ and $\angle DAC \cong \angle BCA$ because alt. int. ∠s are ≅. Also, $\overline{AC} \cong \overline{AC}$ by the Refl. Prop. of ≅. So $\triangle ABC \cong \triangle CDA$ by ASA.

26. $\triangle ABD \cong \triangle CDB$, $\triangle ABC \cong CDA$

27.

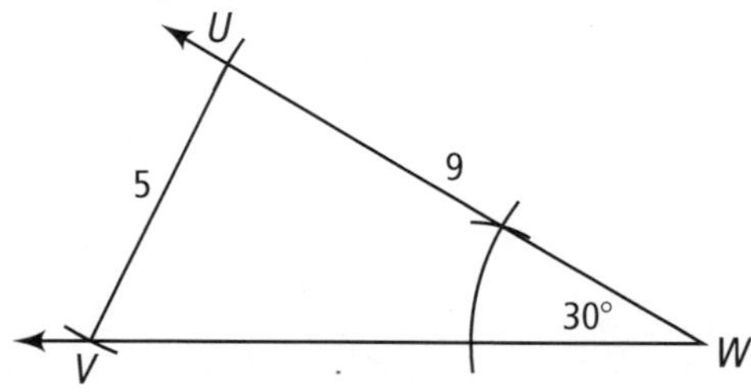

28. $\frac{13}{20}$

▼ STUDENT PAGES 146–147

19. Constructions Use a straightedge to draw a triangle. Label it $\triangle JKL$. Construct $\triangle MNP$ so that $\triangle MNP \cong \triangle JKL$ by ASA.

20. Reasoning Can you prove that the triangles at the right are congruent? Justify your answer.

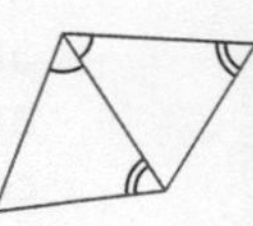

21. Writing Anita says that you can rewrite any proof that uses the AAS Theorem as a proof that uses the ASA Postulate. Do you agree with Anita? Explain.

Proof **22. Given:** $\overline{AE} \parallel \overline{BD}$, $\overline{AE} \cong \overline{BD}$, $\angle E \cong \angle D$

Prove: $\triangle AEB \cong \triangle BDC$

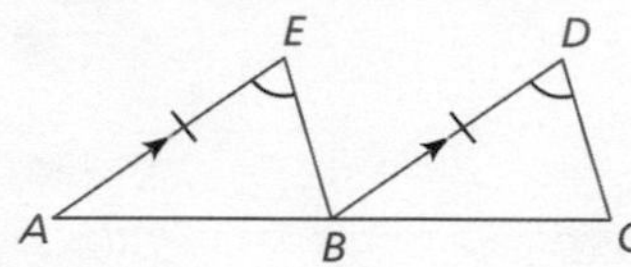

Proof **23. Given:** $\angle 1 \cong \angle 2$, and $\overline{DH}$ bisects $\angle BDF$.

Prove: $\triangle BDH \cong \triangle FDH$

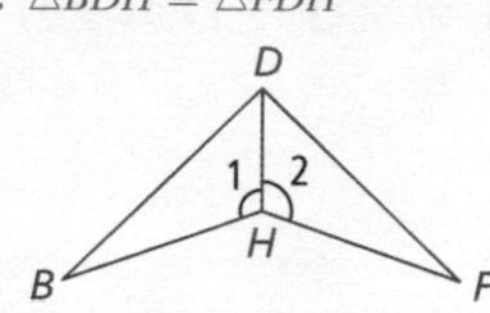

24. Draw a Diagram Draw two noncongruent triangles that have two pairs of congruent angles and one pair of congruent sides.

Proof **25. Given:** $\overline{AB} \parallel \overline{DC}$, $\overline{DA} \parallel \overline{BC}$

Prove: $\triangle ABC \cong \triangle CDA$

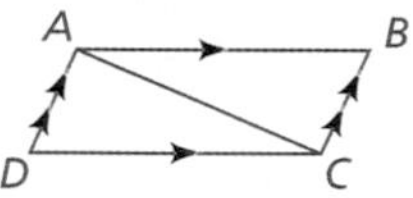

Challenge

26. Given $\overline{AD} \parallel \overline{BC}$ and $\overline{AB} \parallel \overline{DC}$, name as many pairs of congruent triangles as you can.

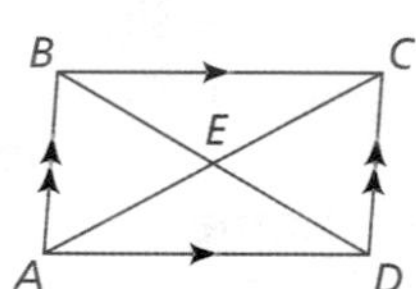

27. Constructions In $\triangle RST$ at the right, $RS = 5$, $RT = 9$, and $m\angle T = 30$. Show that there is no SSA congruence rule by constructing $\triangle UVW$ with $UV = RS$, $UW = RT$, and $m\angle W = m\angle T$, but with $\triangle UVW \not\cong \triangle RST$.

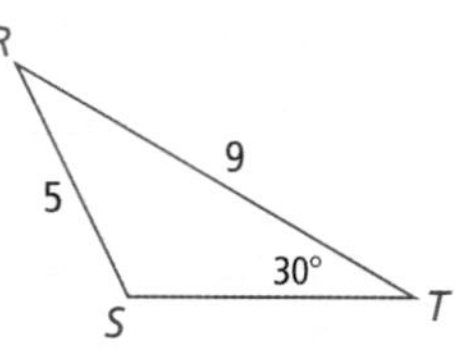

28. Probability Below are six statements about the triangles.

$\angle A \cong \angle X$	$\angle B \cong \angle Y$	$\angle C \cong \angle Z$
$\overline{AB} \cong \overline{XY}$	$\overline{AC} \cong \overline{XZ}$	$\overline{BC} \cong \overline{YZ}$

There are 20 ways to choose a group of three statements from these six. What is the probability that three statements chosen at random from the six will guarantee that the triangles are congruent?

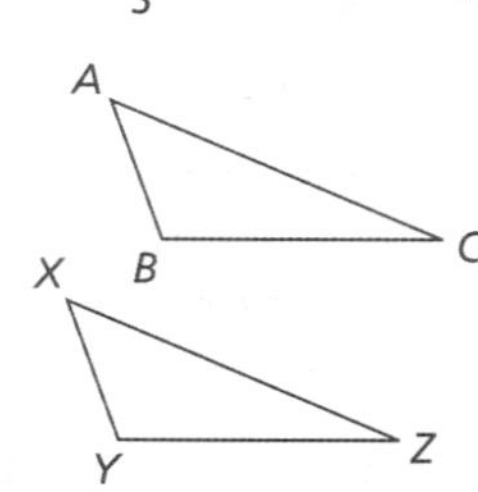

Assess and Remediate

Lesson Quiz

1. **Given:** $\angle XWY \cong \angle ZYW$, $\angle X$ and $\angle Z$ are both right angles.
   Prove: $\triangle YXW \cong \triangle WZY$

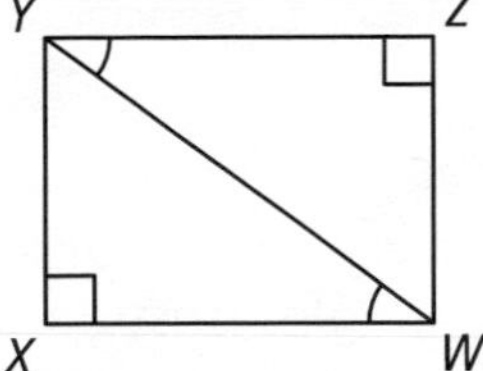

2. In Exercise 1, how could you prove the triangles congruent using ASA?
3. **Do you UNDERSTAND?** Which of the following best represents the answer and justification to the question: "Are the triangles congruent?"
   A. Yes, by ASA.
   B. Yes, by AAS.
   C. Yes, by SSA.
   D. No, there is not enough information to prove congruence.

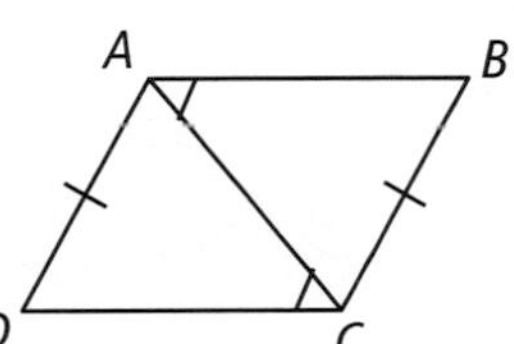

ANSWERS TO LESSON QUIZ

1. It is given that $\angle XWY \cong \angle ZYW$, and $\angle X$ and $\angle Z$ are both right angles. So, $\angle X \cong \angle Z$ because all rt. $\angle$s are $\cong$. $\overline{WY} \cong \overline{WY}$ by the Reflexive Property of Congruence. So, $\triangle YXW \cong \triangle WZY$ by AAS.
2. Get $\angle XYW \cong \angle ZWY$ by the Third Angles Thm.
3. D

Prescription for Remediation

Use the student work on the Lesson Quiz to prescribe a differentiated assignment.

Points	Differentiated Remediation
0–1	Intervention
2	On-level
3	Extension

Online Assessment

Assign the Lesson Quiz in Success Tracker on **pearsonsuccessnet.com**. Success Tracker will automatically score the quiz and assign appropriate intervention or enrichment to each student based on the results. The compiled data appear in three different reports for instant analysis of whole class and individual student performance.

Differentiated Remediation

Intervention

- **RETEACHING** (2 pages) Provides reteaching and practice exercises for the key lesson concepts. Use with struggling students or absent students.
- **ENGLISH LANGUAGE LEARNER SUPPORT** Helps students develop and reinforce mathematical vocabulary and key concepts.

On-Level

- **PRACTICE** (2 pages) Provides extra practice for each lesson. For simpler practice exercises, use the Form K Practice pages found in the Online Teacher Resources.
- **THINK ABOUT A PLAN** Helps students develop specific problem-solving skills and strategies by providing scaffolded guiding questions.
- **STANDARDIZED TEST PREP** Focuses on all major exercises, all major question types, and helps students prepare for the high-stakes assessments.

Extension

- **ENRICHMENT** Provides students with interesting problems and activities that extend the concepts of the lesson.
- **ACTIVITIES, GAMES, AND PUZZLES** Worksheets that can be used for concept development, enrichment, and for fun!

3-4 Using Corresponding Parts of Congruent Triangles

Common Core State Standards
G.SRT.5 Use congruence . . . criteria for triangles to solve problems and to prove relationships in geometric figures. **Also G.CO.12, prepares for G.CO.7**

Preparing to Teach

BIG idea Reasoning and Proof

ESSENTIAL UNDERSTANDING

If two triangles are congruent, then every pair of their corresponding parts is also congruent.

Math Background

The statement *corresponding parts of congruent triangles are congruent* can be thought of as one half of the biconditional definition of congruent triangles. Two triangles are congruent if and only if their corresponding parts are congruent. In Lesson 3-1 students used the " ← " direction: If two triangles' corresponding parts are congruent, then the triangles are congruent. Here they are using the " → " direction: If two triangles are congruent, then their corresponding parts are congruent. The SSS, SAS, ASA Postulates and AAS Theorem offer shortcuts to the " ← " direction. Now the " → " direction leads to individual congruence statements about the parts.

The statement *corresponding parts of congruent triangles are congruent* is often abbreviated CPCTC. When teaching proofs that culminate in using the CPCTC statement, guide students to think of stages within the proof. One common line of logic is to use congruent parts to prove triangles congruent and then use the congruent triangles to prove other corresponding parts are congruent. Students will develop a skill set that allows them to determine characteristics of figures based on only a few given statements. Building proofs like these is essential to many career fields. Logical reasoning and drawing conclusions are skills needed in any area of study.

ELL Support

USE GRAPHIC ORGANIZERS Have students draw a concept wheel. Label a middle circle: Congruent triangles postulates/theorems. Add five spokes off the wheel that lead to five more circles. Label four of the circles with the concepts SSS, SAS, ASA, and AAS. Have students write each postulate or theorem in its respective circle, along with an example. Point out that there is another congruence concept to come. Have students discuss what it could be.

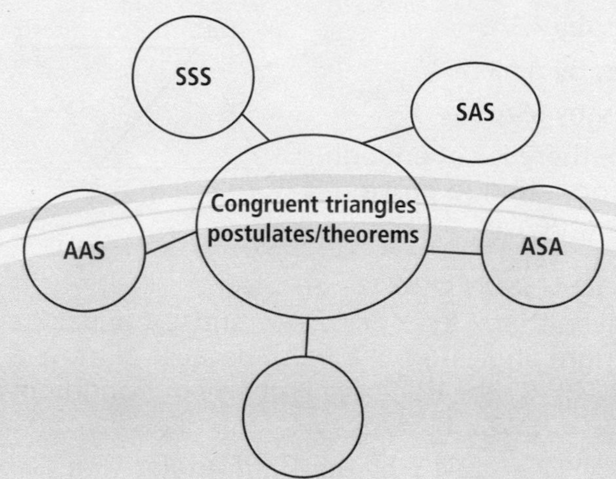

Mathematical Practices

CONSTRUCT VIABLE ARGUMENTS AND CRITIQUE THE REASONING OF OTHERS. Using the stated definition of congruence, students will show corresponding parts of triangles to be congruent.

Interactive Learning

Solve It!

PURPOSE To draw conclusions about triangles based on congruence statements

PROCESS Students must prove $\triangle ABC \cong \triangle DEF$ by SAS or prove $\triangle DEF \cong \triangle GHI$ by AAS or ASA.

Q What is the measure of $\angle E$? **[80]**

Q Which angle in each triangle measures 62? **[$\angle A$, $\angle D$, $\angle G$]**

Q What theorems can prove $\triangle DEF \cong \triangle GHI$? **[Third Angles Theorem and AAS or ASA.]**

ANSWER $m\angle E = 80$ and $m\angle G = 62$ by the Triangle Angle-Sum Theorem. So $\triangle ABC \cong \triangle DEF$ by SAS and $\triangle DEF \cong \triangle GHI$ by AAS or ASA. Since both $\triangle ABC$ and $\triangle GHI$ are $\cong$ to $\triangle DEF$, they are $\cong$ to each other by the Transitive Prop. of $\cong$.

▼ DIGITAL (STUDENT WORK SPACE PAGE 148)

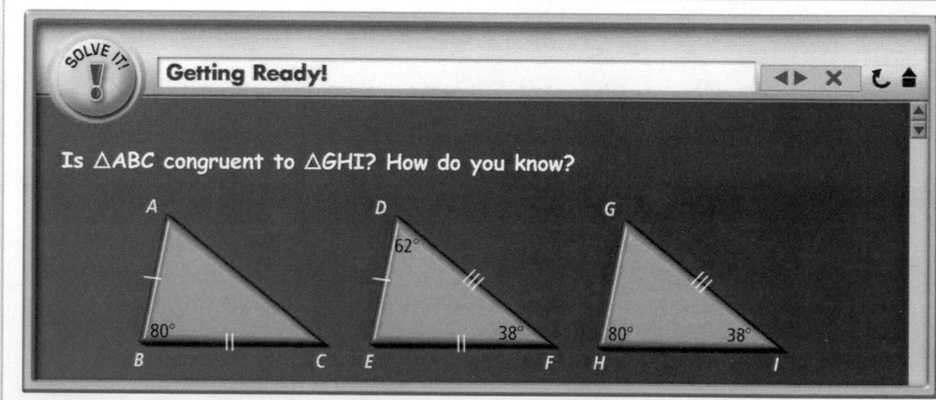

CONNECT THE MATH Students have learned how to use congruent parts to prove triangles are congruent. In this lesson they will use congruent triangles to prove that parts are congruent.

2 Guided Instruction

Problem 1 Proving Parts of Triangles Congruent

Q What is the relationship between the two triangles in the diagram? Explain. **[They are congruent by AAS.]**

Got It?

Q Which angles in the diagram do you know to be congruent? Explain your answer. **[$\angle CAB \cong \angle EAD$; vertical angles are $\cong$.]**

ANSWERS

Got It? $\overline{BA} \cong \overline{DA}$ and $\overline{CA} \cong \overline{EA}$ (Given). $\angle CAB \cong \angle EAD$ (Vert. ∠s are $\cong$.) So $\triangle ABC \cong \triangle ADE$ by SAS and $\angle C \cong \angle E$ because corresp. parts of $\cong$ △s are $\cong$.

Practice

1. $\triangle KLJ \cong \triangle OMN$ by SAS; $\overline{KJ} \cong \overline{ON}$, $\angle K \cong \angle O$, $\angle J \cong \angle N$.

▼ STUDENT PAGE 148

With SSS, SAS, ASA, and AAS, you know how to use three congruent parts of two triangles to show that the triangles are congruent. Once you know that two triangles are congruent, you can make conclusions about their other corresponding parts because, by definition, corresponding parts of congruent triangles are congruent.

Essential Understanding If you know two triangles are congruent, then you know that every pair of their corresponding parts is also congruent.

▼ DIGITAL

Proof **Problem 1** **Proving Parts of Triangles Congruent**

Given: $\angle KBC \cong \angle ACB$, $\angle K \cong \angle A$

Prove: $\overline{KB} \cong \overline{AC}$

Statement	Reason
$\angle KBC \cong \angle ACB$	Given
$\overline{BC} \cong \overline{BC}$	Reflexive Property of $\cong$
$\angle K \cong \angle A$	Given
$\triangle KBC \cong \triangle ACB$	AAS Theorem
$\overline{KB} \cong \overline{AC}$	Corresp. parts of $\cong$ △s are $\cong$.

▼ STUDENT PAGES 148–149

Got It? **Given:** $\overline{BA} \cong \overline{DA}$, $\overline{CA} \cong \overline{EA}$

Prove: $\angle C \cong \angle E$

Think

In the diagram, which congruent pair is not marked?

A Practice 1. **Developing Proof** Tell why the two triangles are congruent. Give the congruence statement. Then list all the other corresponding parts of the triangles that are congruent.

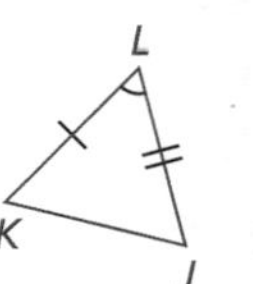

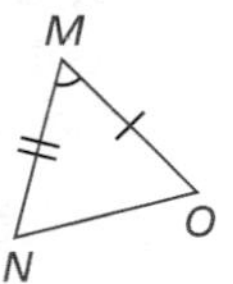

Problem 2 Proving Triangle Parts Congruent to Measure Distance

Students may benefit from working backward through this proof. Have students begin with the conclusion and identify information that is needed to reach the desired congruence statement. Then ask students to find a justification of each claim.

Q What congruence statement must be proved before you can state $\overline{RS} \cong \overline{RL}$? **[$\triangle TRS \cong \triangle TRL$]**

Q The compass setting is the same toward the ship as it is toward the landmark. What can you conclude about the triangles? **[The angles *STR* and *LTR* are congruent.]**

Q Which side is shared by the triangles? **[$\overline{TR}$ is shared by both triangles.]**

Q What postulate or theorem proves that the triangles are congruent? **[ASA]**

Got It?

ERROR PREVENTION

Caution students to use only congruence statements that can be justified by postulates, theorems, definitions, properties, and given information. They should not allow themselves to be misled by appearances in a diagram. Point out to students that although $\angle BMA$ and $\angle CMA$ appear to be right angles, it cannot be assumed that they are. Likewise, although $\overline{AM}$ appears to bisect angle $\angle BAC$, that cannot be assumed from the diagram.

ANSWERS

Got It? a. *M* is the midpt. of $\overline{BC}$, so $\overline{BM} \cong \overline{CM}$ by the def. of midpt. $\overline{AB} \cong \overline{AC}$ (Given) and $\overline{AM} \cong \overline{AM}$ (Refl. Prop of $\cong$), so $\triangle AMB \cong \triangle AMC$ by SSS. Thus $\angle AMB \cong \angle AMC$ because corresp. parts of $\cong$ ⚠ are $\cong$. **b.** No; while $\overline{TR} \perp \overline{RS}$, if point *L* is not at sea level, then $\overline{TR}$ would not be $\perp$ to $\overline{RL}$.

Practice

2. $\overline{OM} \cong \overline{ER}$ and $\overline{ME} \cong \overline{RO}$ (Given). $\overline{OE} \cong \overline{OE}$ by the Refl. Prop. of $\cong$. $\triangle MOE \cong \triangle REO$ by SSS, so $\angle M \cong \angle R$ because corresp. parts of $\cong$ ⚠ are $\cong$.
3. **a.** $\triangle KRA$
   b. ASA
   c. Corresp. parts of $\cong$ ⚠ are $\cong$.

▼ DIGITAL

Proof  **Problem 2** Proving Triangle Parts Congruent to Measure Distance 

Measurement Thales, a Greek philosopher, is said to have developed a method to measure the distance to a ship at sea. He made a compass by nailing two sticks together. Standing on top of a tower, he would hold one stick vertical and tilt the other until he could see the ship *S* along the line of the tilted stick. With this compass setting, he would find a landmark *L* on the shore along the line of the tilted stick. How far would the ship be from the base of the tower?

Given: $\angle TRS$ and $\angle TRL$ are right angles, $\angle RTS \cong \angle RTL$

Prove: $\overline{RS} \cong \overline{RL}$

Statements	Reasons
1) $\angle RTS \cong \angle RTL$	1) Given
2) $\overline{TR} \cong \overline{TR}$	2) Reflexive Property of Congruence
3) $\angle TRS$ and $\angle TRL$ are right angles.	3) Given
4) $\angle TRS \cong \angle TRL$	4) All right angles are congruent.
5) $\triangle TRS \cong \triangle TRL$	5) ASA Postulate
6) $\overline{RS} \cong \overline{RL}$	6) Corresponding parts of $\cong$ ⚠ are $\cong$.

The distance between the ship and the base of the tower would be the same as the distance between the base of the tower and the landmark.

▼ STUDENT PAGES 149–150

Plan Which congruency rule can you use?

Got It? a. **Given:** $\overline{AB} \cong \overline{AC}$, *M* is the midpoint of $\overline{BC}$

Prove: $\angle AMB \cong \angle AMC$

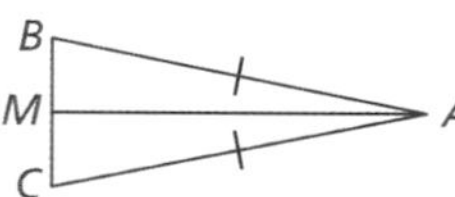

 b. **Reasoning** If the landmark in Problem 2 were not at sea level, would the method in Problem 2 work? Explain.

Practice 2. **Given:** $\overline{OM} \cong \overline{ER}$, $\overline{ME} \cong \overline{RO}$

Proof **Prove:** $\angle M \cong \angle R$

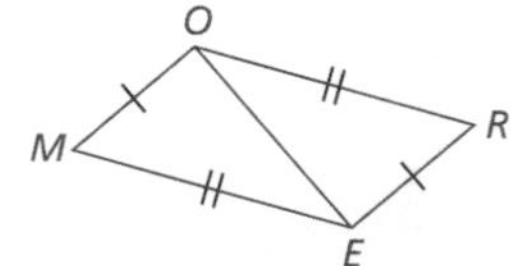

3. **Developing Proof** A balalaika is a stringed instrument. Prove that the bases of the balalaikas are congruent.

Given: $\overline{RA} \cong \overline{NY}$, $\angle KRA \cong \angle JNY$, $\angle KAR \cong \angle JYN$

Prove: $\overline{KA} \cong \overline{JY}$

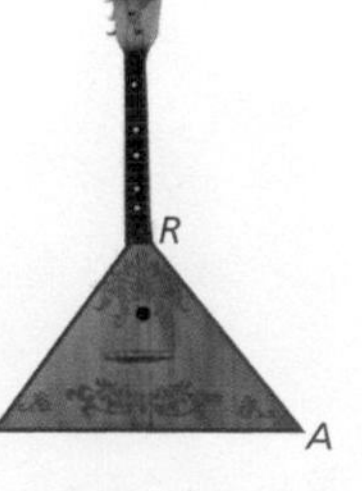

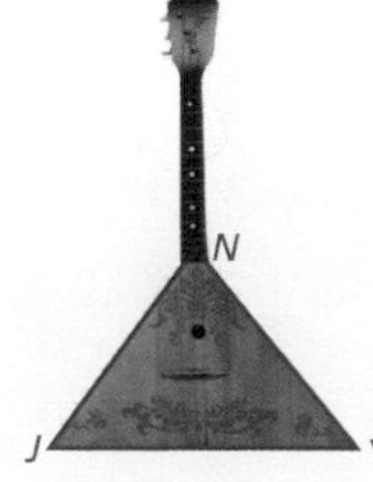

Proof: It is given that two angles and the included side of one triangle are congruent to two angles and the included side of the other.

So, **a.** ________ $\cong \triangle JNY$ by **b.** ________.

$\overline{KA} \cong \overline{JY}$ because **c.** ________.

Lesson Check

▼ STUDENT PAGES 151–152

Do you know HOW?
If students have difficulty with Exercise 5, then have them review Problem 2.

Do you UNDERSTAND?
If students have difficulty with Exercise 7, then have them review Problem 1.

Close

Q What postulates or theorems can be used to show that two triangles are congruent? **[AAS, SAS, SSS, ASA]**

Q How can you use congruent triangles to make statements about their parts? **[Once you know triangles are congruent, you can state that any corresponding parts of the triangles are congruent.]**

ANSWERS

4. SAS; so $\overline{EA} \cong \overline{MA}$ because corresp. parts of ≅ ▵ are ≅.
5. SSS; so $\angle U \cong \angle E$ because corresp. parts of ≅ ▵ are ≅.
6. "Corresp. parts of ≅ ▵ are ≅" is a short version of the def. of ≅ ▵.
7. $\triangle KHL \cong \triangle NHM$ by AAS Thm.

Lesson Check

Do you know HOW?

Name the postulate or theorem that you can use to show the triangles are congruent. Then explain why the statement is true.

4. $\overline{EA} \cong \overline{MA}$

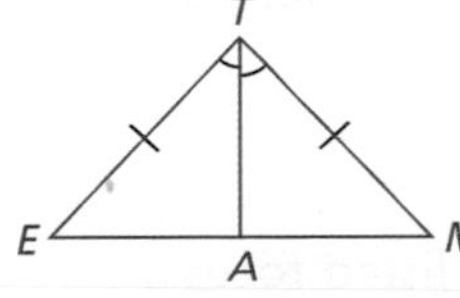

5. $\angle U \cong \angle E$

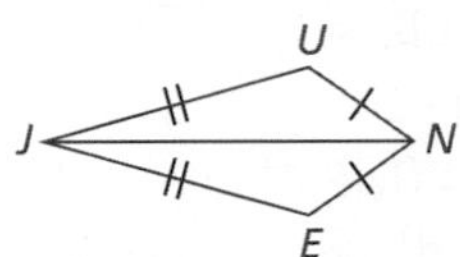

Do you UNDERSTAND?

6. Reasoning How does the fact that corresponding parts of congruent triangles are congruent relate to the definition of congruent triangles?

7. Error Analysis Find and correct the error(s) in the proof.

Given: $\overline{KH} \cong \overline{NH}$, $\angle L \cong \angle M$

Prove: H is the midpoint of $\overline{LM}$.

Proof: $\overline{KH} \cong \overline{NH}$ because it is given. $\angle L \cong \angle M$ because it is given. $\angle KHL \cong \angle NHM$ because vertical angles are congruent. So, $\triangle KHL \cong \triangle MHN$ by ASA Postulate. Since corresponding parts of congruent triangles are congruent, $\overline{LH} \cong \overline{MH}$. By the definition of midpoint, H is the midpoint of LM.

Practice

More Practice and Problem-Solving Exercises

ASSIGNMENT GUIDE

The assignments below are for the More Practice and Problem-Solving Exercises. You may also want to assign the A-Level Practice Exercises for homework if these are not used in class.
Average: 8–19
Advanced: 8–21

Mathematical Practices The exercises listed focus on the Standards for Mathematical Practices listed.

EX. 6: Make Sense of Problems (MP 1)
EX. 13: Persevere in Solving Problems (MP 1)
EX. 10–12: Construct Arguments (MP 3)
EX. 7: Critique the Reasoning of Others (MP 3)
EX. 19: Model with Mathematics (MP 4)

EXERCISE 16: Use the **Think About a Plan** worksheet in the Online Teacher Resources to further support students' development in becoming independent learners.

HOMEWORK QUICK CHECK

To check students' understanding of key skills and concepts, go over Exercises 8, 11, 13, 16, and 19.

▼ STUDENT PAGES 152–153

More Practice and Problem-Solving Exercises

B Apply

8. Given: $\angle SPT \cong \angle OPT$, $\overline{SP} \cong \overline{OP}$

Prove: $\angle S \cong \angle O$

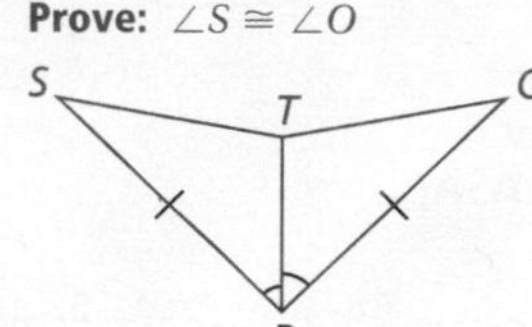

Proof 9. Given: $\overline{YT} \cong \overline{YP}$, $\angle C \cong \angle R$, $\angle T \cong \angle P$

Prove: $\overline{CT} \cong \overline{RP}$

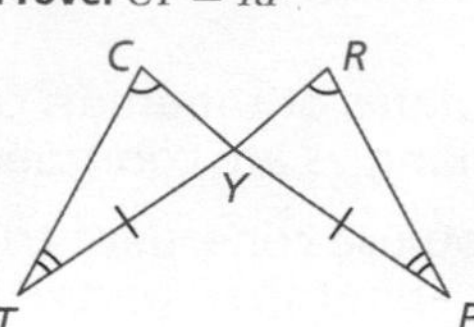

Reasoning Copy and mark the figure to show the given information. Explain how you would prove $\angle P \cong \angle Q$.

10. Given: $\overline{PK} \cong \overline{QK}$, $\overline{KL}$ bisects $\angle PKQ$

11. Given: $\overline{KL}$ is the perpendicular bisector of $\overline{PQ}$.

12. Given: $\overline{KL} \perp \overline{PQ}$, $\overline{KL}$ bisects $\angle PKQ$

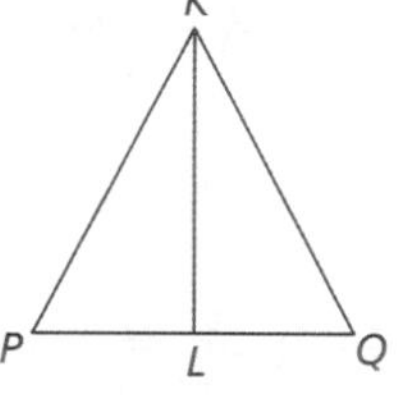

13. Think About a Plan The construction of a line perpendicular to line ℓ through point P on line ℓ is shown. Explain why you can conclude that $\overleftrightarrow{CP}$ is perpendicular to ℓ.

- How can you use congruent triangles to justify the construction?
- Which lengths or distances are equal by construction?

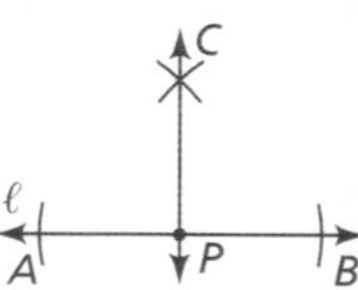

ANSWERS

8. A pair of $\cong$ sides and a pair of $\cong$ $\angle$s are given. Since $\overline{PT} \cong \overline{PT}$ (Refl. Prop. of $\cong$), then $\triangle STP \cong \triangle OTP$ by SAS. $\angle S \cong \angle O$ because corresp. parts of $\cong$ $\triangle$s are $\cong$.

9. From the given information, $\triangle YCT \cong \triangle YRP$ by AAS. So $\overline{CT} \cong \overline{RP}$ because corresp. parts of $\cong$ $\triangle$s are $\cong$.

10–12. Check students' diagrams.

10. $\overline{KL}$ bisects $\angle PKQ$, so $\angle PKL \cong \angle QKL$. $\overline{KL} \cong \overline{KL}$ by Refl. Prop. of $\cong$. $\triangle PKL \cong \triangle QKL$ by SAS, so $\angle P \cong \angle Q$ because corresp. parts of $\cong$ $\triangle$s are $\cong$.

11. From the def. of $\perp$ bisector, $\overline{PL} \cong \overline{QL}$ and $\angle PLK \cong \angle QLK$ because all rt. $\angle$s are $\cong$. Since $\overline{KL} \cong \overline{KL}$, by Refl. Prop. of $\cong$ then $\triangle PKL \cong \triangle QKL$ by SAS, and $\angle P \cong \angle Q$ because corresp. parts of $\cong$ $\triangle$s are $\cong$.

12. $\angle PLK \cong \angle QLK$ because $\perp$ lines form rt. $\angle$s, and all rt. $\angle$s are $\cong$. From the $\angle$ bisector, $\angle PKL \cong \angle QKL$. So with $\overline{KL} \cong \overline{KL}$ by the Refl. Prop. of $\cong$, $\triangle PKL \cong \triangle QKL$ by ASA and $\angle P \cong \angle Q$ because corresp. parts of $\cong$ $\triangle$s are $\cong$.

13. The arcs with center P make $\overline{PA} \cong \overline{PB}$, and the arcs with centers at A and B make $\overline{CA} \cong \overline{CB}$. Since $\overline{CP} \cong \overline{CP}$, $\triangle APC \cong \triangle BPC$ by SSS. $\angle APC \cong \angle BPC$ because corresp. parts of $\cong$ $\triangle$s are $\cong$. $\angle APC$ and $\angle BPC$ are suppl. because they form a linear pair. So $\angle APC$ is a rt. $\angle$, which means its sides are $\perp$.

14. $\overline{BA} \cong \overline{BC}$ (Given) and $\overline{BD}$ bisects $\angle ABC$ (Given). $\angle ABD \cong \angle CBD$ (Def. of $\angle$ bisector). $\overline{BD} \cong \overline{BD}$ (Refl. Prop. of $\cong$), so $\triangle ABD \cong \triangle CBD$ by SAS. $\angle ADB \cong \angle CDB$ (Corresp. parts of $\cong$ ⚠ are $\cong$.) and $\angle ADB$ and $\angle CDB$ are suppl. so they must be rt. $\angle$s. By def. of $\perp$ lines, $\overline{BD} \perp \overline{AC}$. $\overline{AD} \cong \overline{CD}$ (Corresp. parts of $\cong$ $\triangle$s are $\cong$.), so $\overline{BD}$ bisects $\overline{AC}$ (Def. of seg. bisector).

15. $\ell \perp \overline{AB}$ (Given), so $\angle ACP$ and $\angle BCP$ are rt. $\angle$s (Def. of $\perp$ lines). $\angle ACP \cong \angle BCP$ (All rt. $\angle$s are $\cong$.). ℓ bisects $\overline{AB}$ at C (Given), so $\overline{AC} \cong \overline{BC}$ (Def. of seg. bisector). P is on ℓ (Given), and $\overline{PC} \cong \overline{PC}$ (Refl. Prop. of $\cong$), so $\triangle PAC \cong \triangle PBC$ by SAS. $\overline{PA} \cong \overline{PB}$ because corresp. parts of $\cong$ $\triangle$s are $\cong$. So $PA = PB$ by def. of $\cong$ segments.

16. The construction makes $\overline{AC} \cong \overline{BE}$, $\overline{AD} \cong \overline{BF}$, and $\overline{CD} \cong \overline{EF}$. So $\triangle ACD \cong \triangle BEF$ by SSS. Thus $\angle A \cong \angle B$ because corresp. parts of $\cong$ $\triangle$s are $\cong$.

17. $\overline{BE} \perp \overline{AC}$ (Given) and $\overline{DF} \perp \overline{AC}$ (Given). $\angle AEB$ and $\angle CFD$ are rt. $\angle$s (Def. of $\perp$ lines). $\angle AEB \cong \angle CFD$ (All rt. $\angle$s are $\cong$.). $\overline{BE} \cong \overline{DF}$ (Given) and $\overline{AF} \cong \overline{CE}$ (Given), so $AF = CE$, $AE + EF = CF + FE$ (Segment Addition Post.), $AE = CF$ (Subtraction Prop. of $=$) and $\overline{AE} \cong \overline{CF}$. $\triangle AEB \cong \triangle CFD$ by SAS, so $\overline{AB} \cong \overline{CD}$ because corresp. parts of $\cong$ $\triangle$s are $\cong$.

18. It is given that $\overline{JK} \parallel \overline{QP}$, so $\angle K \cong \angle Q$ and $\angle J \cong \angle P$ because they are alt. int. $\angle$s. With $\overline{JK} \cong \overline{PQ}$ (Given), $\triangle KJM \cong \triangle QPM$ by ASA and then $\overline{JM} \cong \overline{PM}$ because corresp. parts of $\cong$ $\triangle$s are $\cong$. Thus M is the midpt. of $\overline{JP}$ by def. of midpt. So $\overline{KQ}$, which contains point M, bisects $\overline{JP}$ by the def. of segment bisector.

19. 36

20–21. Using the given information and $\overline{AE} \cong \overline{AE}$ (Refl. Prop. of $\cong$), $\triangle AKE \cong \triangle ABE$ by SSS. Thus $\angle KAS \cong \angle BAS$ because corresp. parts of $\cong$ $\triangle$s are $\cong$. In $\triangle KAS$ and $\triangle BAS$, $\overline{AK} \cong \overline{AB}$ (Given) and $\overline{AS} \cong \overline{AS}$ (Refl. Prop. of $\cong$), so $\triangle KAS \cong \triangle BAS$ by SAS. Thus $\overline{KS} \cong \overline{BS}$ because corresp. parts of $\cong$ $\triangle$s are $\cong$, and S is the midpt. of $\overline{BK}$ by the def. of midpt. $\angle KSA \cong \angle BSA$ because corresp. parts of $\cong$ $\triangle$s are $\cong$; the angles are also suppl., so the measure of each is 90. Thus $\overline{BK} \perp \overline{AE}$ by the def. of $\perp$ lines.

▼ STUDENT PAGE 153

Proof **14. Given:** $\overline{BA} \cong \overline{BC}$, $\overline{BD}$ bisects $\angle ABC$

Prove: $\overline{BD} \perp \overline{AC}$, $\overline{BD}$ bisects $\overline{AC}$

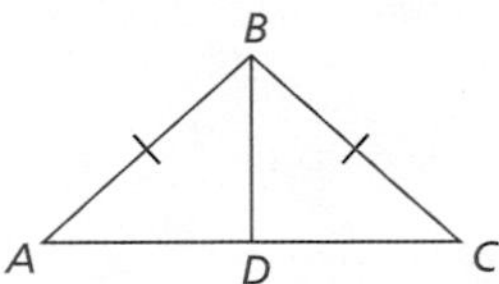

Proof **15. Given:** $\ell \perp \overline{AB}$, ℓ bisects $\overline{AB}$ at C, P is on ℓ

Prove: $PA = PB$

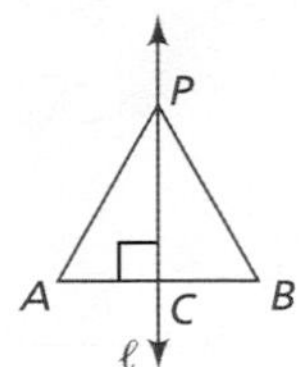

16. Constructions The construction of $\angle B$ congruent to given $\angle A$ is shown. $\overline{AD} \cong \overline{BF}$ because they are congruent radii. $\overline{DC} \cong \overline{FE}$ because both arcs have the same compass settings. Explain why you can conclude that $\angle A \cong \angle B$.

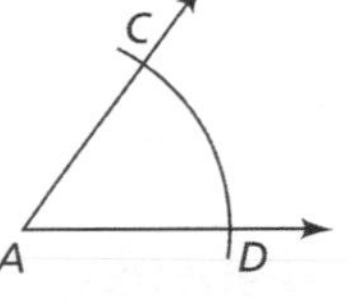

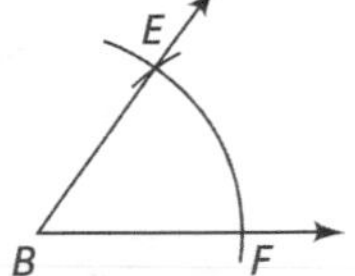

Proof **17. Given:** $\overline{BE} \perp \overline{AC}$, $\overline{DF} \perp \overline{AC}$

$\overline{BE} \cong \overline{DF}$, $\overline{AF} \cong \overline{CE}$

Prove: $\overline{AB} \cong \overline{CD}$

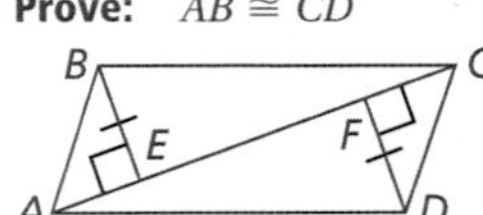

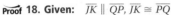

Proof **18. Given:** $\overline{JK} \parallel \overline{QP}$, $\overline{JK} \cong \overline{PQ}$

Prove: $\overline{KQ}$ bisects $\overline{JP}$.

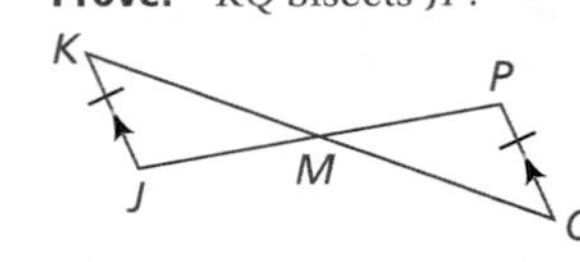

19. Designs Rangoli is a colorful design pattern drawn outside houses in India, especially during festivals. Vina plans to use the pattern at the right as the base of her design. In this pattern, $\overline{RU}$, $\overline{SV}$, and $\overline{QT}$ bisect each other at O. $RS = 6$, $RU = 12$, $\overline{RU} \cong \overline{SV}$, $\overline{ST} \parallel \overline{RU}$, and $\overline{RS} \parallel \overline{QT}$. What is the perimeter of the hexagon?

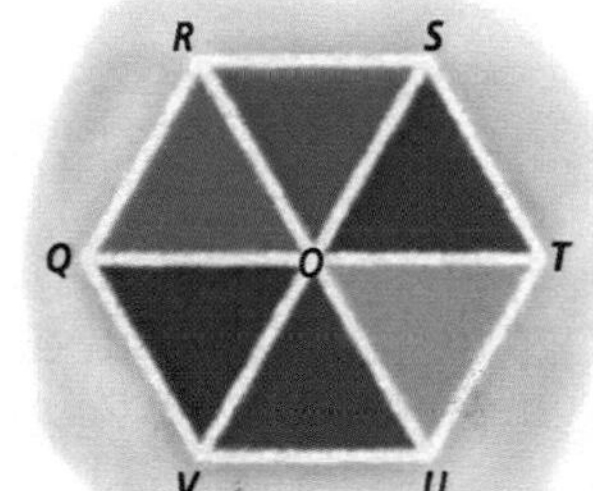

Challenge

In the diagram below, $\overline{BA} \cong \overline{KA}$ and $\overline{BE} \cong \overline{KE}$.

Proof **20. Prove:** S is the midpoint of $\overline{BK}$.

Proof **21. Prove:** $\overline{BK} \perp \overline{AE}$

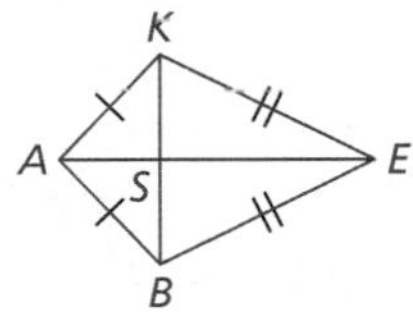

5 Assess and Remediate

Lesson Quiz

1. **Given:** $\overline{WX} \cong \overline{ZY}$, $\overline{WY} \cong \overline{ZX}$

   Prove: $\angle W \cong \angle Z$

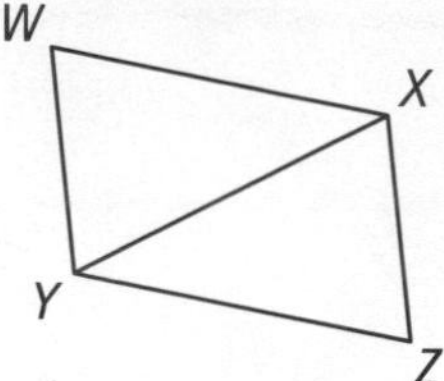

2. **Do you UNDERSTAND?**

   Given: $\angle ONL \cong \angle MLN$, $\angle O$ and $\angle M$ are right angles.

   Prove: $\overline{LM} \cong \overline{NO}$

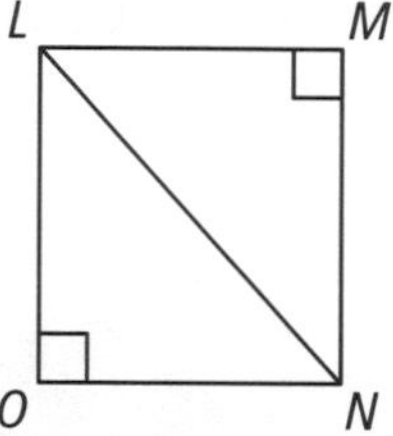

ANSWERS TO LESSON QUIZ

1. It is given that $\overline{WX} \cong \overline{ZY}$ and $\overline{WY} \cong \overline{ZX}$. $\overline{XY} \cong \overline{XY}$ by the Reflexive Property of Congruence. So, $\triangle WXY \cong \triangle ZYX$ by the SSS Postulate. So, $\angle W \cong \angle Z$ because they are corresponding parts of congruent triangles.
2. It is given that $\angle ONL \cong \angle MLN$ and $\angle O$ and $\angle M$ are right angles. So, $\angle O \cong \angle M$ because all right angles are congruent. So, $\triangle ONL \cong \triangle MLN$ by AAS. $\overline{LM} \cong \overline{NO}$ because they are corresponding parts of congruent triangles.

Prescription for Remediation

Use the student work on the Lesson Quiz to prescribe a differentiated assignment.

Points	Differentiated Remediation
0	Intervention
1	On-level
2	Extension

Online Assessment

Assign the Lesson Quiz in Success Tracker on **pearsonsuccessnet.com.** Success Tracker will automatically score the quiz and assign appropriate intervention or enrichment to each student based on the results. The compiled data appear in three different reports for instant analysis of whole class and individual student performance.

Differentiated Remediation

Intervention

- **RETEACHING** (2 pages) Provides reteaching and practice exercises for the key lesson concepts. Use with struggling students or absent students.
- **ENGLISH LANGUAGE LEARNER SUPPORT** Helps students develop and reinforce mathematical vocabulary and key concepts.

On-Level

- **PRACTICE** (2 pages) Provides extra practice for each lesson. For simpler practice exercises, use the Form K Practice pages found in the Online Teacher Resources.
- **THINK ABOUT A PLAN** Helps students develop specific problem-solving skills and strategies by providing scaffolded guiding questions.
- **STANDARDIZED TEST PREP** Focuses on all major exercises, all major question types, and helps students prepare for the high-stakes assessments.

Extension

- **ENRICHMENT** Provides students with interesting problems and activities that extend the concepts of the lesson.
- **ACTIVITIES, GAMES, AND PUZZLES** Worksheets that can be used for concept development, enrichment, and for fun!

ACTIVITY LAB

Use With Lesson 3-5

Paper-Folding Conjectures

Common Core State Standards
G.CO.12 Make formal geometric constructions with a variety of tools and methods (. . . paper folding . . .). **Also prepares for G.CO.10**

Mathematical Practices

This Activity Lab supports students in becoming proficient in constructing arguments, Mathematical Practice 3.

Guided Instruction

PURPOSE To use paper-folding activities to reveal important properties of isosceles triangles

PROCESS Students will

- construct an isosceles triangle and make conjectures about this triangle and its parts.
- draw an acute angle and one segment as a side of a triangle, then construct a second angle (as shown) that is congruent to the first acute angle and make conjectures about this triangle and its parts.

DISCUSS These activities focus primarily on isosceles triangles and some unique properties they have.

Q Are there any other kinds of triangles for which you could use this paper-folding technique and end up with similar results? **[equilateral triangles]**

Activity 1

In this Activity students construct an isosceles triangle, perform some paper-folding with their isosceles triangle, and make conjectures with regards to the base angles of their triangle, the fold line, the angles the fold line makes with the triangle's base, and the two segments into which the fold line divides the base.

Q If you use the "fold line" created, what postulate allows you to prove $\triangle CDA$ and $\triangle CDB$ congruent? **[SAS]**

ANSWERS

1. $\angle A \cong \angle B$; in an isosc. △, the ⦣ opposite the ≅ sides are ≅ to each other.
2. **a.** Rt. ⦣; they are ≅. **b.** ⊥ bisector

Activity 2

In this Activity students use the paper-folding technique to study whether the converse of what they discovered in Activity 1 is true.

Q Side 1 intersects the fold line in a point H_1. Side 2 intersects the fold line in a point H_2. How do you show that $H_1 = H_2 = H$? **[If the fold line and $\overline{FG}$ intersect in point L, show $\triangle FLH_1 \cong \triangle FLH_2$ by ASA.]**

ANSWERS

3. Answers may vary. Sample: The fold line is the ⊥ bisector of $\overline{FG}$. The two parts of $\overline{FG}$ formed by the fold line are ≅, and the ⦣ formed by the fold line and $\overline{FG}$ are ≅ rt. ⦣. Since $\angle F \cong \angle G$, the two △ are ≅ by ASA. Thus the side the two △ share is ≅ to itself, so sides 1 and 2 meet at the fold line. Conjecture: If two ⦣ of a △ are ≅, then the sides opposite those ⦣ are ≅.
4. Two sides of a △ are ≅ if and only if the ⦣ opposite those sides are ≅.

▼ STUDENT PAGES 154–155

Isosceles triangles have two congruent sides. Folding one of the sides onto the other will suggest another important property of isosceles triangles.

Activity 1

Step 1 Construct an isosceles $\triangle ABC$ on tracing paper, with $\overline{AC} \cong \overline{BC}$.

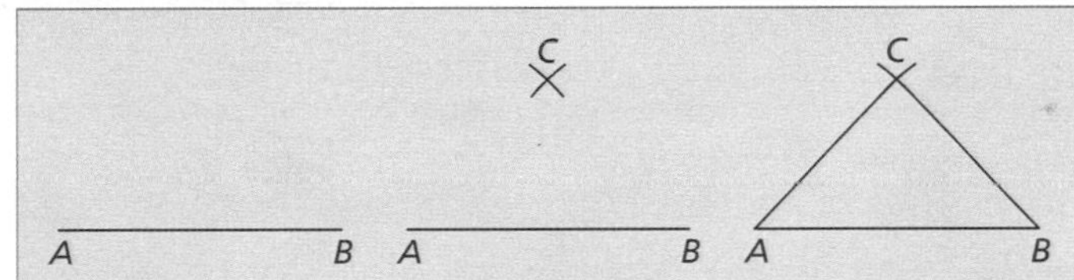

Step 2 Fold the paper so the two congruent sides fit exactly one on top of the other. Crease the paper. Label the intersection of the fold line and $\overline{AB}$ as point D.

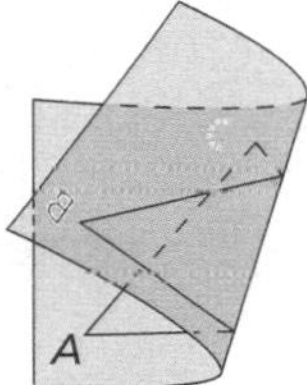

1. What do you notice about $\angle A$ and $\angle B$? Compare your results with others. Make a conjecture about the angles opposite the congruent sides in an isosceles triangle.
2. **a.** Study the fold line $\overline{CD}$ and the base $\overline{AB}$. What type of angles are $\angle CDA$ and $\angle CDB$? How do $\overline{AD}$ and $\overline{BD}$ seem to be related?
   b. Use your answers to part (a) to complete the conjecture: The fold line $\overline{CD}$ is the ______________ of the base $\overline{AB}$ of isosceles $\triangle ABC$.

Activity 2

In Activity 1, you made a conjecture about angles opposite the congruent sides of a triangle. You can also fold paper to study whether the converse is true.

Step 1 On tracing paper, draw acute angle F and one side $\overline{FG}$. Construct $\angle G$ as shown, so that $\angle G \cong \angle F$.

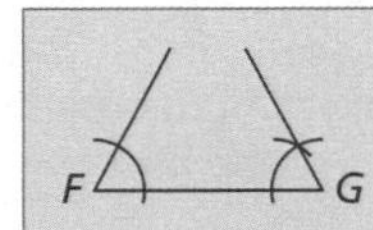

Step 2 Fold the paper so $\angle F$ and $\angle G$ fit exactly one on top of the other.

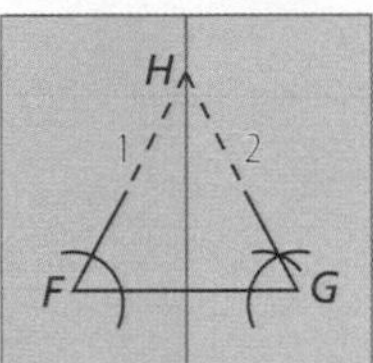

3. Why do sides 1 and 2 meet at point H on the fold line? Make a conjecture about sides $\overline{FH}$ and $\overline{GH}$ opposite congruent angles in a triangle.
4. Write your conjectures from Questions 1 and 3 as a biconditional.

Isosceles and Equilateral Triangles

Common Core State Standards
G.CO.10 Prove theorems about triangles . . . base angles of isosceles triangles are congruent . . . **Also G.CO.13, G.SRT.5**

Preparing to Teach

BIG idea Reasoning and Proof

ESSENTIAL UNDERSTANDING

The angles and sides of isosceles and equilateral triangles have special relationships.

Math Background

The Venn diagram on the left illustrates how quadrilaterals, rectangles, and squares are related. All squares are rectangles. All rectangles are quadrilaterals, which means all squares are also quadrilaterals.

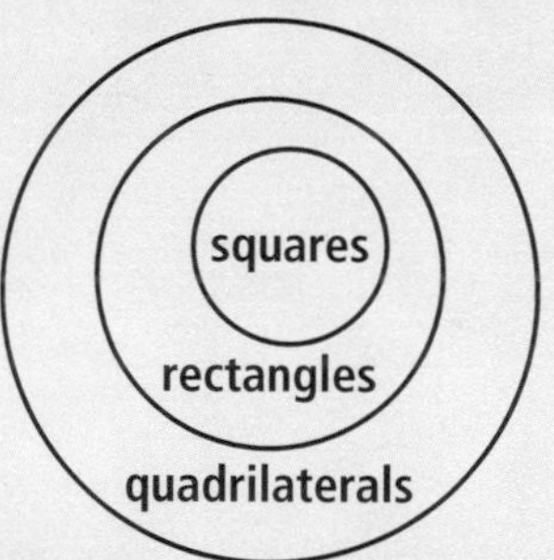

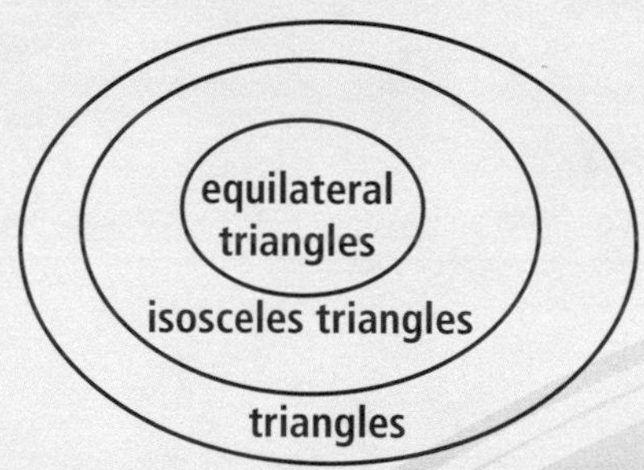

The relationship between triangles is shown in the Venn diagram on the right. From the diagram, you can state the following relationships: All equilateral triangles are isosceles triangles and some isosceles triangles are not equilateral triangles. Also, some triangles are not isosceles triangles.

ELL Support

FOCUS ON LANGUAGE Draw an isosceles triangle on the board. Ask: What type of triangle is this? Trace the base of the triangle. Ask: What is this side of the triangle called? Trace the congruent sides and ask: What are these sides called? Trace the vertex angle and ask: What is this angle called? How would you define it? What are the other two angles called?

FOCUS ON COMMUNICATION Place the "Think and Write" presentation from Problem 3 on the overhead projector. Point to each word as you read. Ask students to come up with their own examples in the "Write" column for each row. Place students in mixed pairs and have them share their four examples with their partner.

Lesson Vocabulary

- legs of an isosceles triangle
- base of an isosceles triangle
- vertex angle of an isosceles triangle
- base angles of an isosceles triangle
- corollary

Mathematical Practices

CONSTRUCT VIABLE ARGUMENTS AND CRITIQUE THE REASONING OF OTHERS. Drawing on the definition of the congruence of triangles, students will construct algebraic equations in Problem 2.

Interactive Learning

Solve It!

PURPOSE To discover that an isosceles triangle has two congruent base angles

PROCESS Students use their knowledge of congruent triangles to complete the puzzle.

Q Which triangles have sides that could be adjacent sides in the large triangle? **[Any of the congruent triangles could be adjacent at corresponding sides. The orange triangles have a side that could be adjacent to a side of the blue triangles.]**

Q Which triangles have sides that could combine together to equal the side length of another triangle? **[The green triangles have side lengths of 3, which together add up to the blue triangle's side length of 6.]**

ANSWER

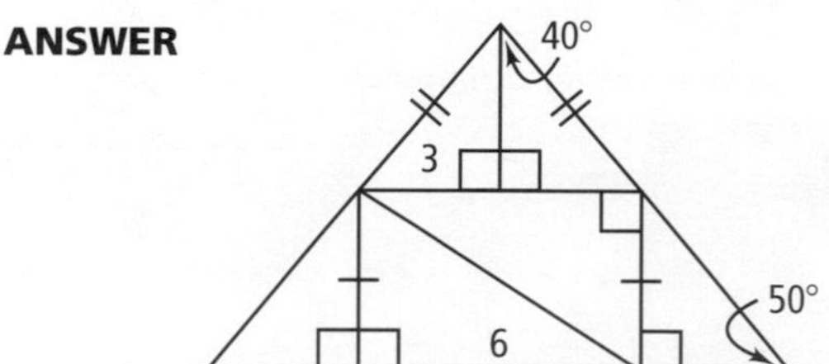

isosc.; 50, 50, 80

▼ DIGITAL (STUDENT WORK SPACE PAGE 156)

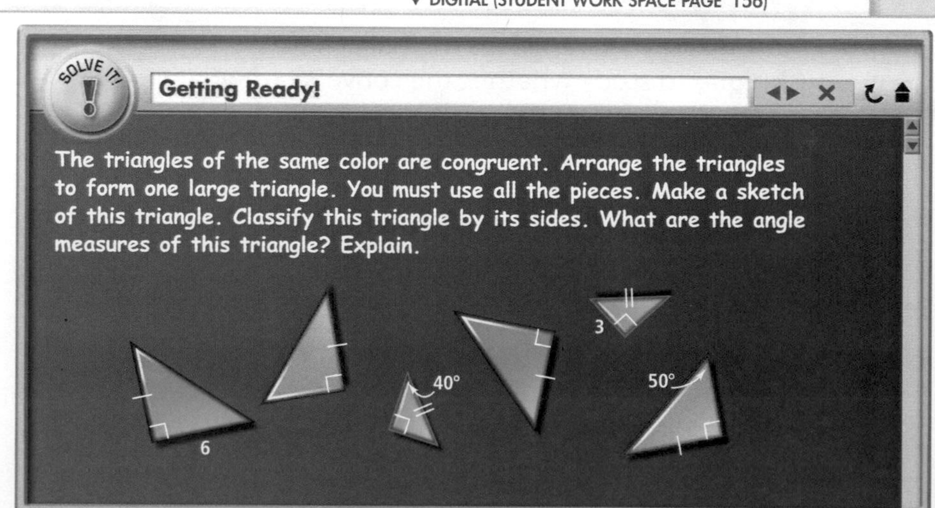

SOLVE IT!
Getting Ready!
The triangles of the same color are congruent. Arrange the triangles to form one large triangle. You must use all the pieces. Make a sketch of this triangle. Classify this triangle by its sides. What are the angle measures of this triangle? Explain.
6
40°
3
50°

CONNECT THE MATH Students will make several conjectures about the properties of isosceles triangles as they manipulate the pieces of this puzzle. The lesson investigates these conjectures and other special relationships in isosceles triangles.

Guided Instruction

Problem 1 Using the Isosceles Triangle Theorem

Take Note

Isosceles Triangle Theorem

Discuss the definition of *isosceles triangle*. Ask what is true about the two triangles that you get if you consider, from the vertex, the angle bisector. Be certain students understand what is meant by an angle being "opposite" a side.

Remind students of the definition of an auxiliary line. Ask them to identify the type of line that is used as the auxiliary line in this proof.

Take Note

Converse of the Isosceles Triangle Theorem

Ask students to identify the relationship between this theorem and the previous one. Have them identify the hypothesis and conclusion of each theorem. Then, have students write the two theorems as one biconditional statement.

Problem 1

Have students draw the triangles separately for both parts.

Q In 1A, what are the base angles of the large triangle? **[$\angle BAC$ and $\angle BCA$]**

Q What conclusion can you draw about $\triangle ABC$ using a congruence statement about the base angles? **[Congruent base angles imply that the opposite sides are congruent, and therefore $\triangle ABC$ is an isosceles triangle.]**

Q In 1B, what is true about the small triangle with the marked sides? **[It is isosceles.]**

▼ STUDENT PAGES 156–157

In the Solve It, you classified a triangle based on the lengths of its sides. You can also identify certain triangles based on information about their angles. In this lesson, you will learn how to use and apply properties of isosceles and equilateral triangles.

Essential Understanding The angles and sides of isosceles and equilateral triangles have special relationships.

Isosceles triangles are common in the real world. You can frequently see them in structures such as bridges and buildings, as well as in art and design. The congruent sides of an isosceles triangle are its **legs.** The third side is the **base.** The two congruent legs form the **vertex angle.** The other two angles are the **base angles.**

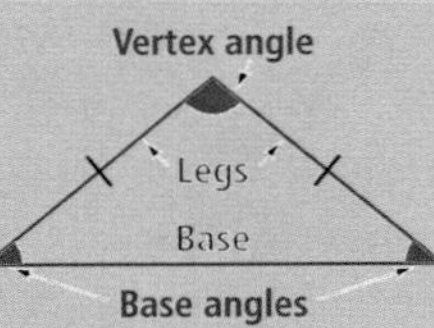

Take note — Theorem 20 Isosceles Triangle Theorem

Theorem	If . . .	Then . . .
If two sides of a triangle are congruent, then the angles opposite those sides are congruent.	$\overline{AC} \cong \overline{BC}$  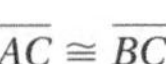 	$\angle A \cong \angle B$ 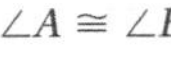 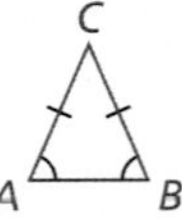

The proof of the Isosceles Triangle Theorem requires an auxiliary line.

Proof Proof of Theorem 20: Isosceles Triangle Theorem

Begin with isosceles $\triangle XYZ$ with $\overline{XY} \cong \overline{XZ}$. Draw $\overline{XB}$, the bisector of the vertex angle $\angle YXZ$.

X, 1, 2, Y, B, Z

Given: $\overline{XY} \cong \overline{XZ}$, $\overline{XB}$ bisects $\angle YXZ$

Prove: $\angle Y \cong \angle Z$

Proof: $\overline{XY} \cong \overline{XZ}$ is given. By the definition of angle bisector, $\angle 1 \cong \angle 2$. By the Reflexive Property of Congruence, $\overline{XB} \cong \overline{XB}$. So by the SAS Postulate, $\triangle XYB \cong \triangle XZB$. $\angle Y \cong \angle Z$ since corresponding parts of congruent triangles are congruent.

Take note — Theorem 21 Converse of the Isosceles Triangle Theorem

Theorem	If . . .	Then . . .
If two angles of a triangle are congruent, then the sides opposite those angles are congruent.	$\angle A \cong \angle B$ 	$\overline{AC} \cong \overline{BC}$ 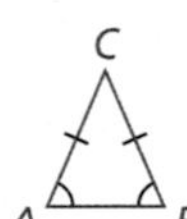

You will prove Theorem 21 in Exercise 22.

▼ DIGITAL

Problem 1 Using the Isosceles Triangle Theorems

A **Is $\overline{AB}$ congruent to $\overline{CB}$? Explain.**

Yes. Since $\angle C \cong \angle A$, $\overline{AB} \cong \overline{CB}$ by the Converse of the Isosceles Triangle Theorem.

B **Is $\angle A$ congruent to $\angle DEA$? Explain.**

Yes. Since $\overline{AD} \cong \overline{ED}$, $\angle A \cong \angle DEA$ by the Isosceles Triangle Theorem.

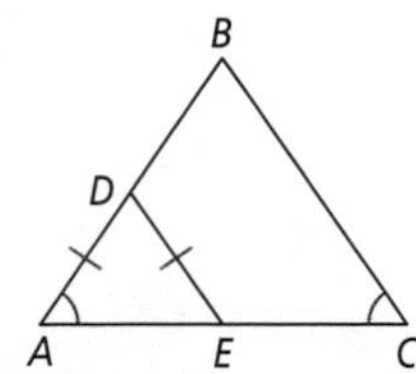

Problem 1 *continued*

Got It? **ERROR PREVENTION**

To answer part (b), students should draw on their answer to part (a). The reasoning that leads to the conclusion involves several steps.

ANSWERS

Got It? a. Yes; since $\overline{WV} \cong \overline{WS}$, $\angle WVS \cong \angle S$ by the Isosc. △ Thm. Yes; since $\angle WVS \cong \angle S$, and $\angle R \cong \angle WVS$ (Given), $\angle R \cong \angle S$ (Trans. Prop. of $\cong$). Therefore, $\overline{TR} \cong \overline{TS}$ by the Converse of the Isosc. △ Thm. **b.** No; there is not enough information about the sides or ⦞ of △RUV.

Practice

1. $\overline{VX}$; Converse of Isosc. △ Thm.
2. $\overline{UW}$; Converse of Isosc. △ Thm.
3. $\overline{VY}$; Converse of Isosc. △ Thm. and Segment Addition Postulate
4. Answers may vary. Sample: $\angle VUY$; Isosc. △ Thm.

▼ STUDENT PAGES 157–158

Got It? a. Is $\angle WVS$ congruent to $\angle S$? Is $\overline{TR}$ congruent to $\overline{TS}$? Explain.

Think

What are you looking for in the diagram?

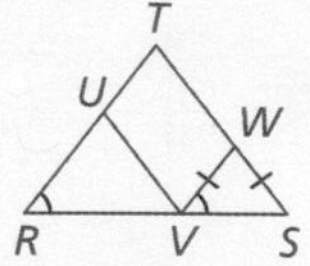

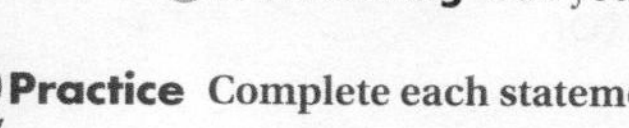

b. Reasoning Can you conclude that △RUV is isosceles? Explain.

Practice Complete each statement. Explain why it is true.

1. $\overline{VT} \cong$ ________
2. $\overline{UT} \cong$ ________ $\cong \overline{YX}$
3. $\overline{VU} \cong$ ________
4. $\angle VYU \cong$ ________

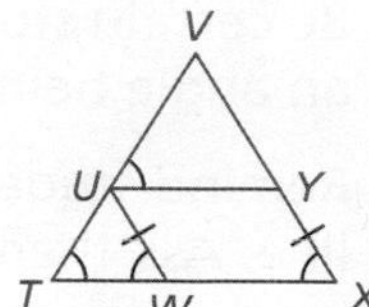

Problem 2 Using Algebra

Take Note

Emphasize to students that Theorem 22 can be proven only by using congruent triangles.

Problem 2

Q What type of triangle is in the diagram? **[an isosceles triangle]**

Q Can you determine the measure of $\angle C$? Justify your answer. **[$m\angle C = 54$ because the base angles in an isosceles triangle are congruent.]**

Q The fact that $\angle ABD \cong \angle CBD$ implies that $\overline{BD}$ is what type of segment? **[an angle bisector]**

Q Because $\overline{BD}$ is an angle bisector, what is $m\angle BDC$? Justify your answer. **[$m\angle BDC = 90$ by Theorem 22.]**

▼ STUDENT PAGE 158

An isosceles triangle has a certain type of symmetry about a line through its vertex angle.

take note

Theorem 22

Theorem	If . . .	Then . . .
If a line bisects the vertex angle of an isosceles triangle, then the line is also the perpendicular bisector of the base.	$\overline{AC} \cong \overline{BC}$ and $\angle ACD \cong \angle BCD$	$\overline{CD} \perp \overline{AB}$ and $\overline{AD} \cong \overline{BD}$

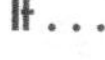

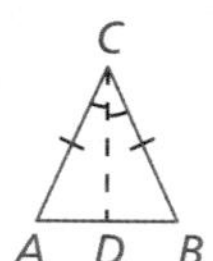

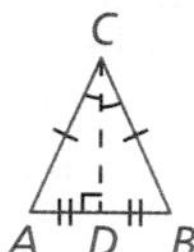

You will prove Theorem 22 in Exercise 25.

▼ DIGITAL

Problem 2 Using Algebra

GRIDDED RESPONSE

What is the value of *x*?

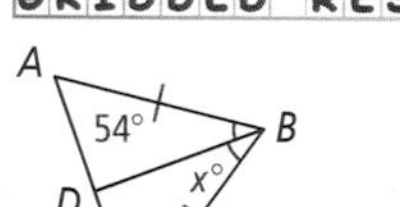

Since $\overline{AB} \cong \overline{CB}$, by the Isosceles Triangle Theorem, $\angle A \cong \angle C$. So $m\angle C = 54$.

Since $\overline{BD}$ bisects $\angle ABC$, you know by Theorem 22 that $\overline{BD} \perp \overline{AC}$. So $m\angle BDC = 90$.

$m\angle C + m\angle BDC + m\angle DBC = 180$	Triangle Angle-Sum Theorem
$54 + 90 + x = 180$	Substitute.
$x = 36$	Subtract 144 from each side.

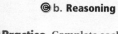

Got It? VISUAL LEARNERS

Students should redraw the triangle with the new angle measure. Students could also use an equation based on the Triangle Angle-Sum Theorem and substitute the new value for $m\angle C$.

ANSWERS

Got It? 63

Practice

5. $x = 80$, $y = 40$

6. $x = 40$, $y = 70$

▼ STUDENT PAGE 159

Got It? Suppose $m\angle A = 27$. What is the value of x?

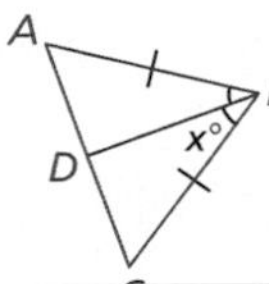

Think How can you determine the measure of $\angle C$?

Practice **Algebra** Find the values of x and y.

5.

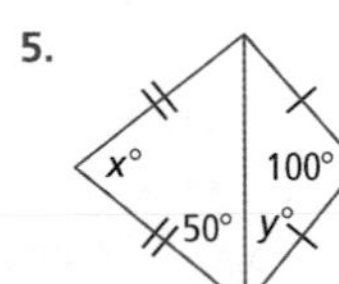

6.

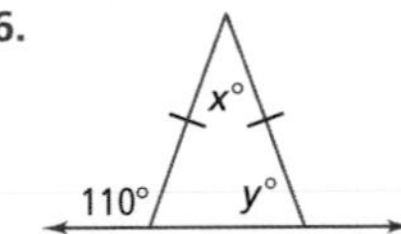

Problem 3 Finding Angle Measures

Take Note

Ask students to describe the relationship between the two corollaries presented. They should identify the corollaries as converses of each other. Have students combine the two to form one biconditional statement.

Problem 3

Q What types of triangles are shown in the stained glass window? **[equilateral triangles]**

Q What is the relationship between the angles in an equilateral triangle? **[They are all congruent.]**

Q How can you find the measure of one angle in the equilateral triangle? What theorem will you use? **[Use the Triangle Angle-Sum Theorem to write an equation. Let x = the measure of an angle in the equilateral triangle. $3x = 180$]**

Q Can you write $m\angle ADC$ as the sum of two angle measures? **[Yes; $m\angle ADC = m\angle ADE + m\angle EDC$]**

▼ STUDENT PAGE 159

A **corollary** is a theorem that can be proved easily using another theorem. Since a corollary is a theorem, you can use it as a reason in a proof.

take note

Corollary to Theorem 20

Corollary	If . . .	Then . . .
If a triangle is equilateral, then the triangle is equiangular.	$\overline{XY} \cong \overline{YZ} \cong \overline{ZX}$	$\angle X \cong \angle Y \cong \angle Z$

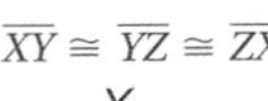

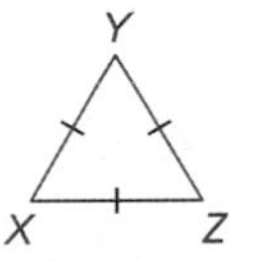

Corollary to Theorem 21

Corollary	If . . .	Then . . .
If a triangle is equiangular, then the triangle is equilateral.	$\angle X \cong \angle Y \cong \angle Z$	$\overline{XY} \cong \overline{YZ} \cong \overline{ZX}$

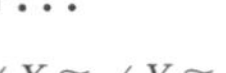

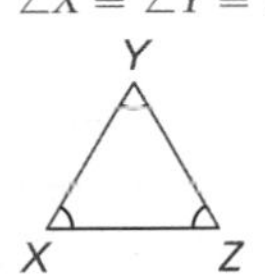

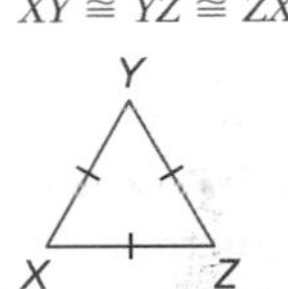

▼ DIGITAL

Problem 3 **Finding Angle Measures**

Design What are the measures of $\angle A$, $\angle B$, and $\angle ADC$ in the photo at the right?

Think	Write
The triangles are equilateral, so they are also equiangular. Find the measure of each angle of an equilateral triangle.	Let a = measure of one angle. $3a = 180$ $a = 60$
$\angle A$ and $\angle B$ are both angles in an equilateral triangle.	$m\angle A = m\angle B = 60$
Use the Angle Addition Postulate to find the measure of $\angle ADC$.	$m\angle ADC = m\angle ADE + m\angle CDE$
Both $\angle ADE$ and $\angle CDE$ are angles in an equilateral triangle. So $m\angle ADE = 60$ and $m\angle CDE = 60$. Substitute into the above equation and simplify.	$m\angle ADC = 60 + 60$ $m\angle ADC = 120$

Problem 3 *continued*

Got It? **VISUAL LEARNERS**

Have students draw the isosceles triangles in the problem and label the given measures.

ANSWERS

Got It? $m\angle A = 61$, $m\angle BCD = 119$

Practice

7. 108

▼ STUDENT PAGE 160

Got It? Suppose the triangles in Problem 3 are isosceles triangles, where $\angle ADE$, $\angle DEC$, and $\angle ECB$ are vertex angles. If the vertex angles each have a measure of 58, what are $m\angle A$ and $m\angle BCD$?

A Practice **7.** The equilateral triangle and the isosceles triangle shown here share a common side. What is the measure of $\angle ABC$?

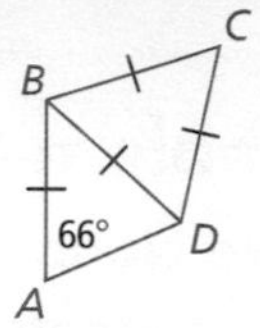

3 Lesson Check

Do you know HOW?
If students have difficulty with Exercise 8, then have them review Problem 2.

Do you UNDERSTAND?
If students have difficulty with Exercise 12, then have them review the Isosceles Triangle Theorem.

Close

Q What properties are specific to isosceles triangles? **[The triangles have two congruent sides and two congruent base angles, and the vertex angle bisector is perpendicular to and bisects the opposite side.]**

Q How are the angles of an equilateral triangle related? **[All angles are congruent.]**

ANSWERS

8. a. 70
b. 53

9. a. 75
b. 48

10. 23, 134

11. a. The ⦻ opposite the ≅ sides are ≅.
b. All three ⦻ have measure 60, and all three sides are ≅.

12. The ≅ ⦻ should be opposite the ≅ sides.

▼ STUDENT PAGES 160–161

Lesson Check

Do you know HOW?

8. What is $m\angle A$?

a. 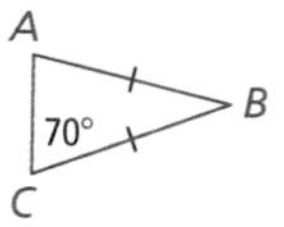

b. 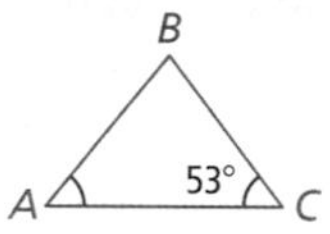

9. What is the value of x?

a. 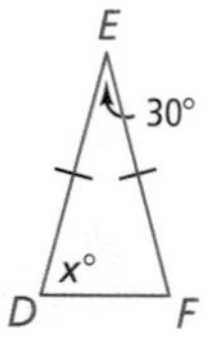

b. 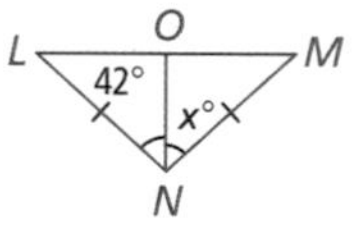

10. The measure of one base angle of an isosceles triangle is 23. What are the measures of the other two angles?

Do you UNDERSTAND? MATHEMATICAL PRACTICES

11. What is the relationship between sides and angles for each type of triangle?

a. isosceles **b.** equilateral

12. Error Analysis Claudia drew an isosceles triangle. She asked Sue to mark it. Explain why the marking of the diagram is incorrect.

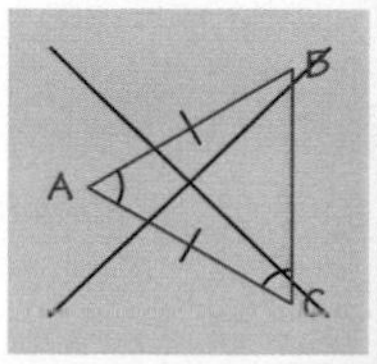

Practice

More Practice and Problem-Solving Exercises

ASSIGNMENT GUIDE

The assignments below are for the More Practice and Problem-Solving Exercises. You may also want to assign the A-Level Practice Exercises for homework if these are not used in class.

Average: 13–33
Advanced: 13–37

Mathematical Practices The exercises listed focus on the Standards for Mathematical Practices listed.

EX. 19: Make Sense of Problems (MP 1)
EX. 20: Persevere in Solving Problems (MP 1)
EX. 14, 21, 23, 37: Construct Arguments (MP 3)
EX. 12: Critique the Reasoning of Others (MP 3)
EX. 13, 26: Model (MP 4)

STEM exercises focus on science or engineering applications.

EXERCISE 27: Use the **Think About a Plan** worksheet in the Online Teacher Resources to further support students' development in becoming independent learners.

HOMEWORK QUICK CHECK

To check students' understanding of key skills and concepts, go over Exercises 14, 17, 19, 23, and 27.

ANSWERS

13. 52, 52

14. 45 and 45; the sum of the measures of the acute △ must be 90, so the measure of each acute ∠ must be half of 90.

15. 64 **16.** 2.5

17. 42 **18.** 35

19. The △ is an obtuse isosc. △; $(x + 15) + (3x - 35) + 4x = 180$, so the ∠ measures are 40, 40, and 100.

20. 20, 80, 80 or 50, 50, 80

21. **a.** $\overline{KM}$
b. $\overline{KM}$
c. Given
d. Def. of bisector
e. Refl. Prop. of ≅
f. SSS
g. Corresp. parts of ≅ △ are ≅.

22. **a.** $\overline{RS}$
b. $\overline{RS}$
$\overline{RS} \cong \overline{RS}$ (Refl. Prop. of ≅) and $\angle PRS \cong \angle QRS$ (def. of ∠ bisector). Also, $\angle P \cong \angle Q$ (Given). So $\triangle PRS \cong \triangle QRS$ by AAS. $\overline{PR} \cong \overline{QR}$ because corresp. parts of ≅ △ are ≅.

▼ STUDENT PAGES 162–163

More Practice and Problem-Solving Exercises

B Apply

STEM **13. Architecture** Each face of the Great Pyramid at Giza is an isosceles triangle with a 76° vertex angle. What are the measures of the base angles?

14. Reasoning What are the measures of the base angles of a right isosceles triangle? Explain.

Given isosceles $\triangle JKL$ with base $\overline{JL}$, find each value.

15. If $m\angle L = 58$, then $m\angle LKJ =$? .

16. If $JL = 5$, then $ML =$? .

17. If $m\angle JKM = 48$, then $m\angle J =$? .

18. If $m\angle J = 55$, then $m\angle JKM =$? .

19. Think About a Plan A triangle has angle measures $x + 15$, $3x - 35$, and $4x$. What type of triangle is it? Be as specific as possible. Justify your answer.
- What do you know about the sum of the angle measures of a triangle?
- What do you need to know to classify a triangle?
- What type of triangle has no congruent angles? Two congruent angles? Three congruent angles?

20. Reasoning An exterior angle of an isosceles triangle has measure 100. Find two possible sets of measures for the angles of the triangle.

21. Developing Proof Here is another way to prove the Isosceles Triangle Theorem. Supply the missing information.

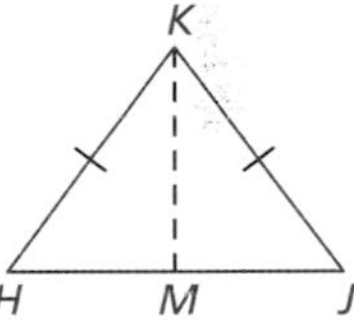

Begin with isosceles $\triangle HKJ$ with $\overline{KH} \cong \overline{KJ}$.

Draw **a.** ? , a bisector of the base $\overline{HJ}$.

Given: $\overline{KH} \cong \overline{KJ}$, **b.** ? bisects HJ

Prove: $\angle H \cong \angle J$

Statements	Reasons
1) $\overline{KM}$ bisects $\overline{HJ}$.	1) **c.** ?
2) $\overline{HM} \cong \overline{JM}$	2) **d.** ?
3) $\overline{KH} \cong \overline{KJ}$	3) Given
4) $\overline{KM} \cong \overline{KM}$	4) **e.** ?
5) $\triangle KHM \cong \triangle KJM$	5) **f.** ?
6) $\angle H \cong \angle J$	6) **g.** ?

Proof **22.** Supply the missing information in this statement of the Converse of the Isosceles Triangle Theorem. Then write a proof.

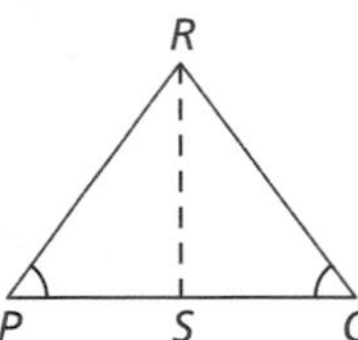

Begin with $\triangle PRQ$ with $\angle P \cong \angle Q$.

Draw **a.** ? , a bisector of $\angle PRQ$.

Given: $\angle P \cong \angle Q$, **b.** ? bisects $\angle PRQ$

Prove: $\overline{PR} \cong \overline{QR}$

More Practice and Problem-Solving Exercises *continued*

23. Answers may vary. Sample: Apply the Isosc. △ Thm. (or the Converse of the Isosc. △ Thm.) two times to show that each angle (or side) is ≅ to each of the other two ⊿s (or sides), so that all three ⊿s (or sides) are ≅.

24. $\overline{AE} \cong \overline{DE}$ (Given), so $\angle A \cong \angle D$ by the Isosc. △ Thm. Since $\overline{AB} \cong \overline{DC}$ (Given), then $\triangle ABE \cong \triangle DCE$ by SAS.

25. $\overline{AC} \cong \overline{BC}$ and $\angle ACD \cong \angle BCD$ (Given). Also, $\overline{CD} \cong \overline{CD}$ by the Refl. Prop. of ≅. So $\triangle CAD \cong \triangle CBD$ by SAS. Therefore $\overline{AD} \cong \overline{BD}$ and $\angle ADC \cong \angle BDC$ because corresp. parts of ≅ ⊿s are ≅. Since $\angle ADC$ and $\angle BDC$ are suppl., each must have measure 90. So $\overline{CD} \perp \overline{AB}$ (Def. of ⊥).

26. **a.** isosc. ⊿

b. 900 ft; 1100 ft

c. The tower is the ⊥ bisector of each base.

27. 6

28.

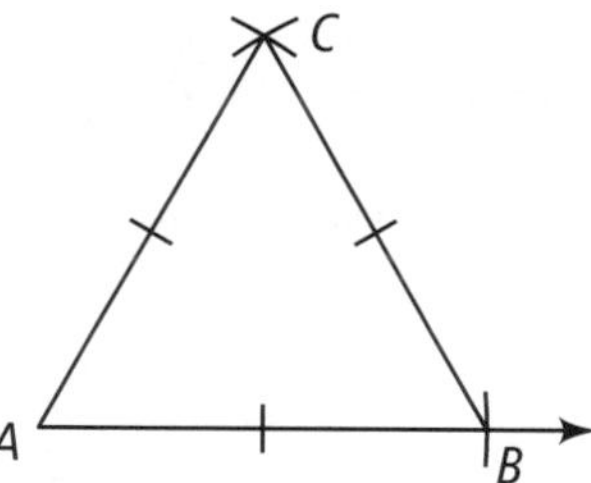

Draw $\overline{AB}$. Using AB as a radius, draw arcs with centers A and B. The intersection of these arcs is C. $\triangle ABC$ is equilateral, so it is also equiangular.

29. $m = 20$, $n = 45$

30. $m = 36$, $n = 27$

31. $m = 60$, $n = 30$

32.

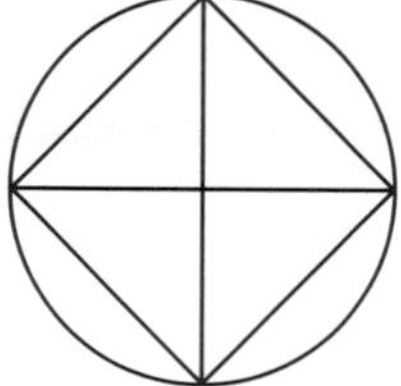

Draw a diameter of the circle, then construct another diameter perpendicular to the first. Connect the points where the diameters intersect the circle. Since all radii of the circle are congruent, the four triangles formed are isosceles. By the Isosceles Triangle Theorem, the angles opposite the congruent sides in each triangle are congruent. Since the angles formed by the intersection of the diameters are all right angles and are included by sides that are radii of the circle, the four triangles are all congruent to each other. Moreover, each base angle of the isosceles triangles have measure 45°, by the Triangle Angle-Sum Theorem. So the measure of each angle of the inscribed quadrilateral is $45° + 45° = 90°$. And since the four right triangles are all congruent, their hypotenuses are all congruent. So the inscribed quadrilateral has four right angles and four congruent sides and is a square.

---

23. Writing Explain how the corollaries to the Isosceles Triangle Theorem and its converse follow from the theorems.

Proof **24. Given:** $\overline{AE} \cong \overline{DE}$, $\overline{AB} \cong \overline{DC}$

Prove: $\triangle ABE \cong \triangle DCE$

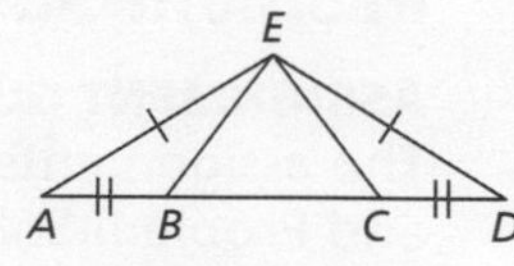

Proof **25.** Prove Theorem 22. Use the diagram given in the statement of the theorem.

STEM **26. a. Communications** In the diagram at the right, what type of triangle is formed by the cables of the same height and the ground?

b. What are the two different base lengths of the triangles?

c. How is the tower related to each of the triangles?

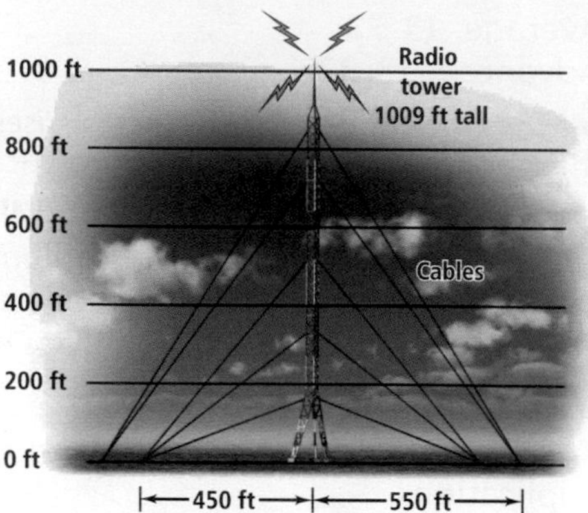

27. Algebra The length of the base of an isosceles triangle is x. The length of a leg is $2x - 5$. The perimeter of the triangle is 20. Find x.

28. Constructions Construct equiangular triangle ABC. Justify your method.

Algebra Find the values of m and n.

29.

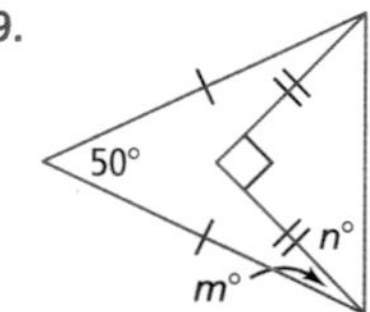

30.

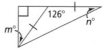

31.

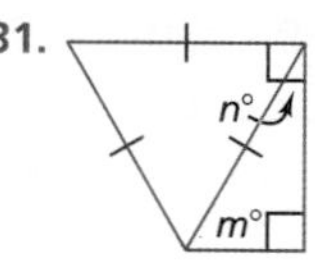

32. Constructions A polygon is *inscribed in* a circle if the vertices of the polygon are on the circle. Given a circle and its center, construct a square inscribed in the circle. Justify your method by showing that the figure you inscribed is a quadrilateral with four right angles and four congruent sides.

33. a–c.

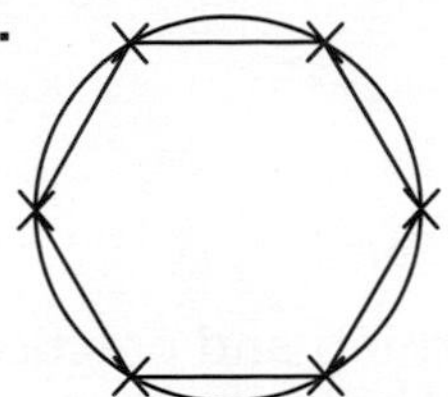

regular hexagon; Each side is the radius of a circle with radius equal to the radius of the original circle, so the sides of the hexagon are all congruent. Drawing segments connecting the vertices of the hexagon with the center of the original circle gives six congruent equilateral triangles. The angles of the hexagon each have measure $60° + 60° = 120°$. So the angles of the hexagon are all congruent, and the figure is a regular hexagon.

d.

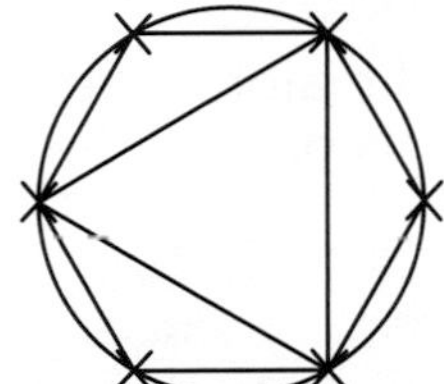

Connect alternating vertices of the inscribed hexagon. The sides of the resulting inscribed triangle are the bases of congruent isosceles triangles. Therefore the inscribed triangle is equilateral.

34. (−4, 0), (0, 0), (0, −4), (4, 4), (4, 8), (8, 4)

35. (−5, 5), (0, 5), (0, 10), (5, 0), (5, −5), (10, 0)

36. (−1, 6), (2, 6), (2, 9), (5, 0), (5, 3), (8, 3)

37. any real number greater than 45 and less than 90

33. Constructions Use a compass to draw a circle.

- **a.** Using the same compass setting, place the point of the compass on the circle and draw two arcs that intersect the circle.
- **b.** Again using the same compass setting, place the point of the compass on one of the two points of intersection from part (a) and draw two more arcs that intersect the original circle. Continue in this way until you have gone entirely around the original circle.
- **c.** Connect points of intersection of the arcs and the original circle. What regular polygon have you constructed? Explain.
- **d.** Use the construction from parts (a)–(c) to construct an equilateral triangle inscribed in a circle. Justify your construction.

Challenge

Coordinate Geometry For each pair of points, there are six points that could be the third vertex of an isosceles right triangle. Find the coordinates of each point.

34. (4, 0) and (0, 4) **35.** (0, 0) and (5, 5) **36.** (2, 3) and (5, 6)

37. Reasoning What measures are possible for the base angles of an acute isosceles triangle?

5 Assess and Remediate

Lesson Quiz

1. Is $\overline{DE} \cong \overline{DF}$? Explain.

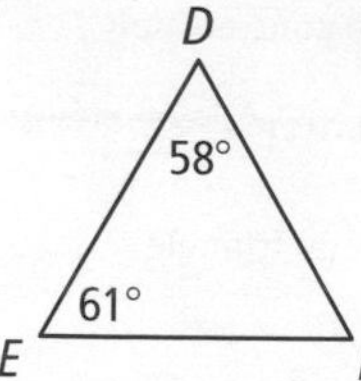

2. Do you UNDERSTAND? What is the value of x?

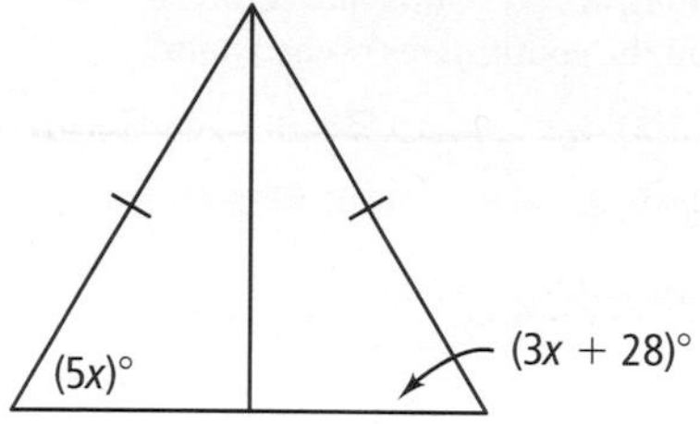

3. Isosceles triangle XYZ has base $\overline{XY}$ and $m\angle Y = 34$. What is $m\angle Z$?

ANSWERS TO LESSON QUIZ

1. yes; $m\angle F = 61$, so $\overline{DE} \cong \overline{DF}$ by the Converse of the Isosceles Triangle Theorem.

2. 14

3. 112

Prescription for Remediation

Use the student work on the Lesson Quiz to prescribe a differentiated assignment.

Points	Differentiated Remediation
0–1	Intervention
2	On-level
3	Extension

Online Assessment

Assign the Lesson Quiz in Success Tracker on **pearsonsuccessnet.com**. Success Tracker will automatically score the quiz and assign appropriate intervention or enrichment to each student based on the results. The compiled data appear in three different reports for instant analysis of whole class and individual student performance.

Differentiated Remediation

Intervention

- **RETEACHING** (2 pages) Provides reteaching and practice exercises for the key lesson concepts. Use with struggling students or absent students.
- **ENGLISH LANGUAGE LEARNER SUPPORT** Helps students develop and reinforce mathematical vocabulary and key concepts.

On-Level

- **PRACTICE** (2 pages) Provides extra practice for each lesson. For simpler practice exercises, use the Form K Practice pages found in the Online Teacher Resources.
- **THINK ABOUT A PLAN** Helps students develop specific problem-solving skills and strategies by providing scaffolded guiding questions.
- **STANDARDIZED TEST PREP** Focuses on all major exercises, all major question types, and helps students prepare for the high-stakes assessments.

Extension

- **ENRICHMENT** Provides students with interesting problems and activities that extend the concepts of the lesson.
- **ACTIVITIES, GAMES, AND PUZZLES** Worksheets that can be used for concept development, enrichment, and for fun!

3-6 Congruence in Right Triangles

Common Core State Standards
G.SRT.5 Use congruence . . . criteria . . . to solve problems and to prove relationships in geometric figures. **Also G.CO.10**

Preparing to Teach

BIG idea Reasoning and Proof

ESSENTIAL UNDERSTANDING

Two triangles can be proven to be congruent without having to show that all corresponding parts are congruent. Another way triangles can be proven to be congruent is by using one pair of right angles, a pair of hypotenuses, and a pair of legs.

Math Background

Student can use the Pythagorean Theorem to find information to prove right triangles congruent. If you are given two right triangles with congruent hypotenuses and congruent legs, you can show that the remaining legs are congruent.

In Triangle$_1$, let c = length of the hypotenuse. Because the hypotenuses are congruent, c = length of the hypotenuse in Triangle$_2$.

Let b be the length of the congruent legs of each triangle.

In Triangle$_1$, the length of the other leg $a_1 = \sqrt{c^2 - b^2}$.

In Triangle$_2$, the length of the other leg $a_2 = \sqrt{c^2 - b^2}$.

Therefore, $a_1 = a_2$. The triangles are congruent by SSS.

This line of reasoning leads to the HL Theorem presented in this lesson. With the introduction of the HL Theorem, students can use this shortcut in their proofs.

ELL Support

FOCUS ON LANGUAGE Consider the word *hypotenuse*. The hypotenuse is the side of a right triangle that is opposite the right angle. Possible origins are in 1571, Late Latin, *hypotenusa*, from the Greek *hypoteinousa* "stretching under" (the right angle), formed from *hypo-* "under" + *teinein* "to stretch." The derivation is more understandable if you visualize an inverted right triangle with its base at the top, as shown below.

FOCUS ON LANGUAGE Place students in groups of mixed proficiency. Have them each make a set of flash cards with a vocabulary word on one side. Then students can discuss the meaning of the term before writing its definition, including sketches, on the other side. Students can quiz one another on the topics learned in this chapter and keep the cards for later individual review.

Lesson Vocabulary

- hypotenuse
- legs of a right triangle

Mathematical Practices

CONSTRUCT VIABLE ARGUMENTS AND CRITIQUE THE REASONING OF OTHERS. Students will use SSA to prove right triangles congruent and will use counterexamples of nonright triangles to find why SSA is not a universal rule.

Interactive Learning

Solve It!

PURPOSE To use properties of isosceles triangles to show that right triangles are congruent

PROCESS Students must conclude that $\triangle ABC$ is an isosceles triangle and show that $\triangle ABD \cong \triangle CBD$ using the Isosc. △ Thm. and AAS.

Q What type of triangle is $\triangle ABC$? **[isosceles]**

Q Knowing that the triangle is isosceles leads you to conclude which angles are congruent? **[$\angle A$ and $\angle C$]**

Q What is the relationship between $\angle ADB$ and $\angle CDB$? **[They are congruent.]**

ANSWER Yes; $\overline{AB} \cong \overline{CB}$ (Given). By the Isosc. △ Thm., $\angle A \cong \angle C$ and $\angle BDC \cong \angle BDA$ (All rt. ∠s are ≅.), so $\triangle ABD \cong \triangle CBD$ by AAS.

CONNECT THE MATH Once students realize that the right triangles in the diagram are congruent, they will see a new set of conditions to prove that the two right triangles are congruent.

▼ DIGITAL (STUDENT WORK SPACE PAGE 165)

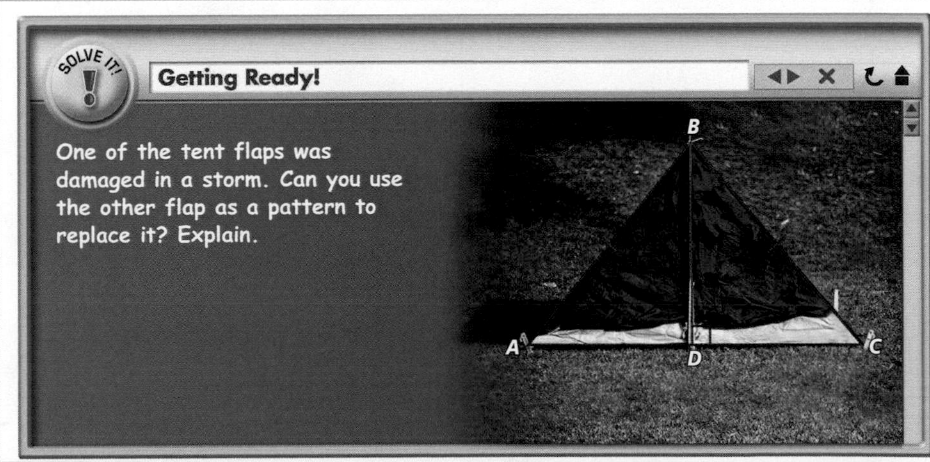

SOLVE IT!
Getting Ready!
One of the tent flaps was damaged in a storm. Can you use the other flap as a pattern to replace it? Explain.
B
A
D
C

Guided Instruction

Problem 1 Using the HL Theorem

Take Note

Hypotenuse-Leg (HL) Theorem

Have students compare and contrast the triangle congruence postulates and theorem with this right triangle congruence theorem. They should notice that though only two conditions are specified in the HL Theorem, there are three conditions met by the theorem: 1) the triangles are right triangles, 2) the hypotenuses are congruent, and 3) one pair of legs is congruent. This theorem is a specific case of SSA.

Challenge students to prove the Hypotenuse-Leg Theorem using the Pythagorean Theorem. Students should be able to write *QR* and *YZ* in terms of the lengths of the other two sides. Then they can show that the two quantities are equal by the Substitution Property of Equality.

Take Note

Conditions for HL Theorem

Ask students to draw diagrams that show the three conditions listed for the HL Theorem in Take Note.

▼ STUDENT PAGES 165–166

In the diagram below, two sides and a nonincluded angle of one triangle are congruent to two sides and the nonincluded angle of another triangle.

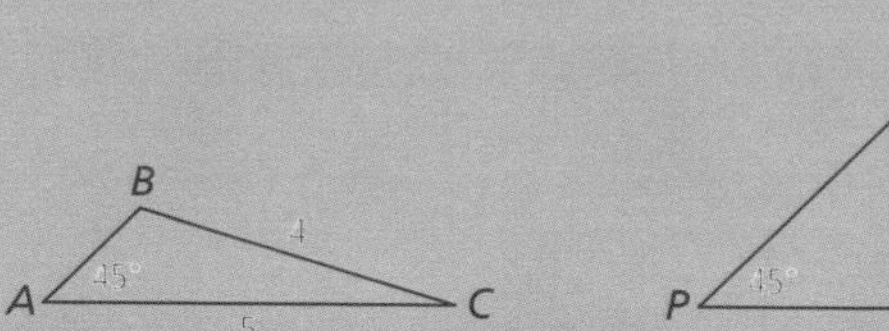

Notice that the triangles are not congruent. So, you can conclude that Side-Side-Angle is *not* a valid method for proving two triangles congruent. This method, however, works in the special case of right triangles, where the right angles are the nonincluded angles.

In a right triangle, the side opposite the right angle is called the **hypotenuse.** It is the longest side in the triangle. The other two sides are called **legs.**

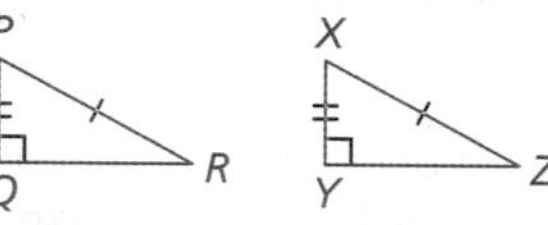

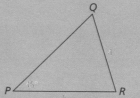

Essential Understanding You can prove that two triangles are congruent without having to show that *all* corresponding parts are congruent. In this lesson, you will prove right triangles congruent by using one pair of right angles, a pair of hypotenuses, and a pair of legs.

take note **Theorem 23 Hypotenuse-Leg (HL) Theorem**

Theorem	If . . .	Then . . .
If the hypotenuse and a leg of one right triangle are congruent to the hypotenuse and a leg of another right triangle, then the triangles are congruent.	$\triangle PQR$ and $\triangle XYZ$ are right $\triangle$s, $\overline{PR} \cong \overline{XZ}$, and $\overline{PQ} \cong \overline{XY}$	$\triangle PQR \cong \triangle XYZ$

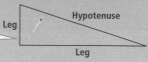

To prove the HL Theorem you will need to draw auxiliary lines to make a third triangle.

Proof of Theorem 23: Hypotenuse-Leg Theorem

Given: $\triangle PQR$ and $\triangle XYZ$ are right triangles, with right angles Q and Y. $\overline{PR} \cong \overline{XZ}$ and $\overline{PQ} \cong \overline{XY}$.

Prove: $\triangle PQR \cong \triangle XYZ$

Proof: On $\triangle XYZ$, draw $\overrightarrow{ZY}$.

Mark point S so that $YS = QR$. Then, $\triangle PQR \cong \triangle XYS$ by SAS.

Since corresponding parts of congruent triangles are congruent, $\overline{PR} \cong \overline{XS}$. It is given that $\overline{PR} \cong \overline{XZ}$, so $\overline{XS} \cong \overline{XZ}$ by the Transitive Property of Congruence. By the Isosceles Triangle Theorem, $\angle S \cong \angle Z$, so $\triangle XYS \cong \triangle XYZ$ by AAS. Therefore, $\triangle PQR \cong \triangle XYZ$ by the Transitive Property of Congruence.

take note **Key Concept Conditions for HL Theorem**

To use the HL Theorem, the triangles must meet three conditions.

Conditions

- There are two right triangles.
- The triangles have congruent hypotenuses.
- There is one pair of congruent legs.

Problem 1

Q Which angles can be marked as right angles in the diagram? **[$\angle ADC$ and $\angle BDC$]**

Q Which segments are legs of $\triangle ACD$? **[$\overline{AD}$ and $\overline{CD}$]**

Q Which segments are legs of $\triangle BCD$? **[$\overline{BD}$ and $\overline{CD}$]**

Q Is there another pair of congruent sides in the triangles? Explain. **[Yes, side $\overline{CD}$ is shared by both triangles; therefore it is congruent to itself by the Reflexive Property of Congruence.]**

Got It? ERROR PREVENTION

For part (a), have students list the given information and identify what other information they need to prove the triangles are congruent. For part (b), your friend is right! By the Pythagorean Theorem, the other two legs are automatically congruent. The only issue is one of correspondence.

ANSWERS

Got It? a. $\triangle PRS$ and $\triangle RPQ$ are rt. $\triangle$s with $\cong$ hypotenuses ($\overline{SP} \cong \overline{QR}$) and $\cong$ legs ($\overline{PR} \cong \overline{PR}$). So $\triangle PRS \cong \triangle RPQ$ by HL. **b.** Yes; the two $\triangle$s satisfy the three conditions of the HL Thm., so they are $\cong$.

▼ DIGITAL

Proof **Problem 1** **Using the HL Theorem**

On the basketball backboard brackets shown below, $\angle ADC$ and $\angle BDC$ are right angles and $\overline{AC} \cong \overline{BC}$. Are $\triangle ADC$ and $\triangle BDC$ congruent? Explain.

- You are given that $\angle ADC$ and $\angle BDC$ are right angles. So, $\triangle ADC$ and $\triangle BDC$ are right triangles.
- The hypotenuses of the two right triangles are $\overline{AC}$ and $\overline{BC}$. You are given that $\overline{AC} \cong \overline{BC}$.
- $\overline{DC}$ is a common leg of both $\triangle ADC$ and $\triangle BDC$. $\overline{DC} \cong \overline{DC}$ by the Reflexive Property of Congruence.

Yes, $\triangle ADC \cong \triangle BDC$ by the HL Theorem.

▼ STUDENT PAGE 167

Got It? **a. Given:** $\angle PRS$ and $\angle RPQ$ are right angles, $\overline{SP} \cong \overline{QR}$

Prove: $\triangle PRS \cong \triangle RPQ$

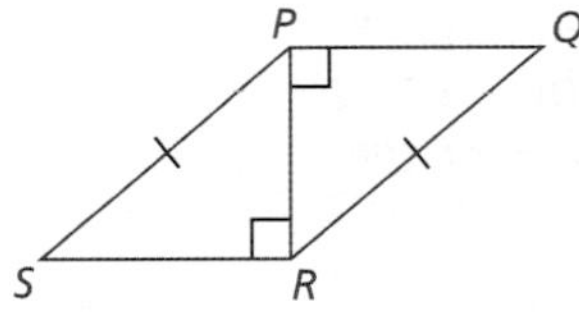

b. Reasoning Your friend says, "Suppose you have two right triangles with congruent hypotenuses and one pair of congruent legs. It does not matter which leg in the first triangle is congruent to which leg in the second triangle. The triangles will be congruent." Is your friend correct? Explain.

Think
What do you need to know if you want to use the HL Theorem?

Problem 1 *continued*

Practice

1. **a** If two ∡ are ≅ and suppl., they are rt. ∡.
   b. def. of a rt. △
   c. Given
   d. Refl. Prop. of ≅
   e. HL
2. **a.** △*ABE* and △*DEB* are rt. ⨺.
   b. $\overline{BE} \cong \overline{EB}$
   c. $\overline{AB} \cong \overline{DE}$
   d. HL

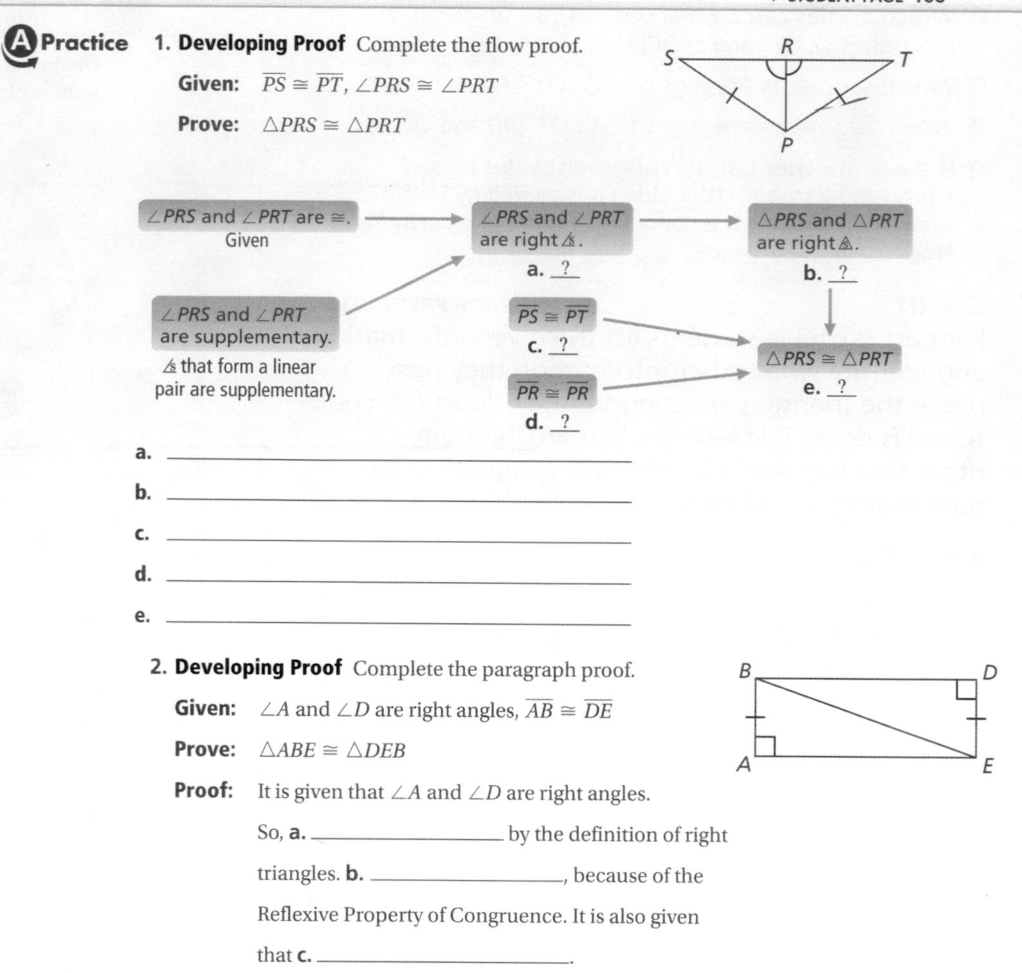

▼ STUDENT PAGE 168
A Practice
1. Developing Proof Complete the flow proof.
Given: PS ≅ PT, ∠PRS ≅ ∠PRT
Prove: △PRS ≅ △PRT
∠PRS and ∠PRT are ≅.
Given
∠PRS and ∠PRT are right ∡.
a. ?
△PRS and △PRT are right ⨺.
b. ?
∠PRS and ∠PRT are supplementary.
∡ that form a linear pair are supplementary.
PS ≅ PT
c. ?
PR ≅ PR
d. ?
△PRS ≅ △PRT
e. ?
a.
b.
c.
d.
e.
2. Developing Proof Complete the paragraph proof.
Given: ∠A and ∠D are right angles, AB ≅ DE
Prove: △ABE ≅ △DEB
Proof: It is given that ∠A and ∠D are right angles.
So, a. ________ by the definition of right
triangles. b. ________, because of the
Reflexive Property of Congruence. It is also given
that c. ________.
So, △ABE ≅ △DEB by d. ________.

Problem 2 Writing a Proof Using the HL Theorem

Q What statement results from knowing that $\overline{BE}$ bisects $\overline{AD}$? **[$\overline{AC} \cong \overline{CD}$]**

Q What types of triangles are shown in the diagram? Justify your answer. **[Because $\overline{AB} \perp \overline{BC}$ and $\overline{DE} \perp \overline{EC}$, ∠*B* and ∠*E* are right angles. Therefore the triangles are right triangles.]**

Q What information do you need to prove right triangles are congruent? **[The hypotenuses and one pair of legs must be congruent.]**

Got It?

Have students review the definition of *perpendicular bisector*. Ask them to draw the diagram and mark the properties of this line. Students should be able to use the HL Theorem to prove the triangles congruent.

ANSWERS

Got It? It is given that $\overline{AD}$ is the ⊥ bisector of $\overline{CE}$, so △*CBD* and △*EBA* are rt. ⨺ and $\overline{CB} \cong \overline{EB}$ by the def. of ⊥ bisector. Also, $\overline{CD} \cong \overline{EA}$ (Given), so △*CBD* ≅ △*EBA* by HL.

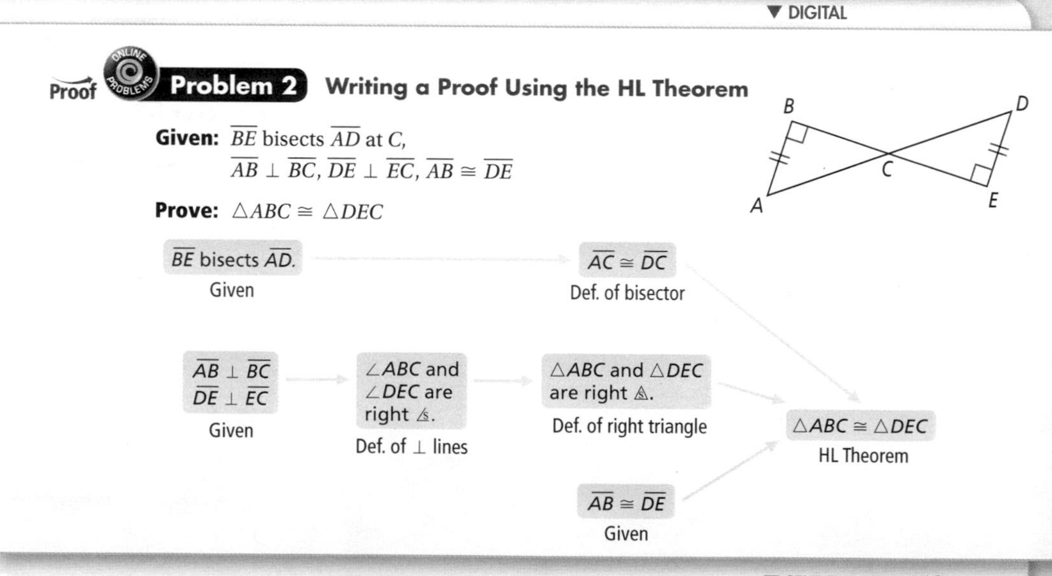

▼ STUDENT PAGE 168

Got It? Given: $\overline{CD} \cong \overline{EA}$, $\overline{AD}$ is the perpendicular bisector of $\overline{CE}$

Prove: △*CBD* ≅ △*EBA*

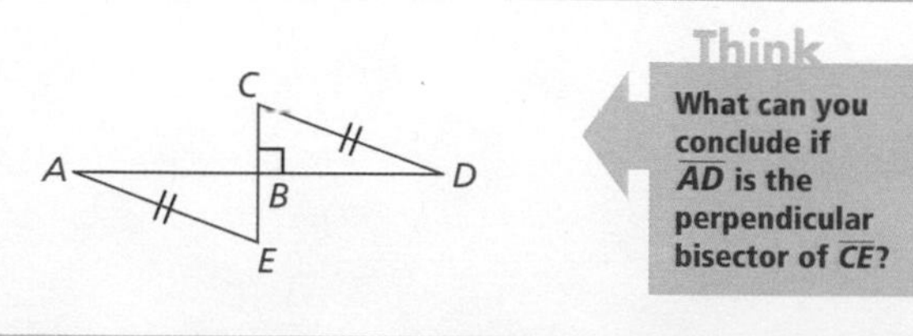

Think
What can you conclude if AD is the perpendicular bisector of CE?

Practice

3. Since $\overline{HV} \perp \overline{GT}$ (Given), $\triangle IGH$ and $\triangle ITV$ are rt. ⚠. It is given that $\overline{GH} \cong \overline{TV}$, and it is also given that point I is the midpt. of $\overline{HV}$, so $\overline{HI} \cong \overline{VI}$ by the def. of midpt. So $\triangle IGH \cong \triangle ITV$ by HL.
4. From the given information about $\perp$ segments, $\triangle PTM$ and $\triangle RMJ$ are rt. ⚠. $\overline{PM} \cong \overline{RJ}$ (Given), and since M is the midpt. of $\overline{TJ}$, $\overline{TM} \cong \overline{JM}$. Thus $\triangle PTM \cong \triangle RMJ$ by HL.

▼ STUDENT PAGE 169

A Practice Proof 3. **Given:** $\overline{HV} \perp \overline{GT}$, $\overline{GH} \cong \overline{TV}$, I is the midpoint of $\overline{HV}$

Prove: $\triangle IGH \cong \triangle ITV$

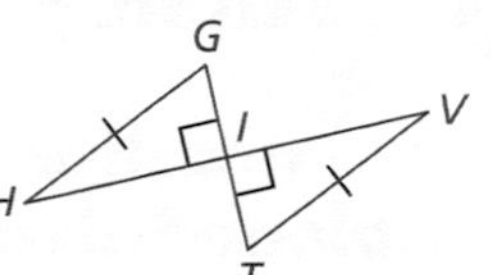

Proof 4. **Given:** $\overline{PM} \cong \overline{RJ}$, $\overline{PT} \perp \overline{TJ}$, $\overline{RM} \perp \overline{TJ}$, M is the midpoint of $\overline{TJ}$.

Prove: $\triangle PTM \cong \triangle RMJ$

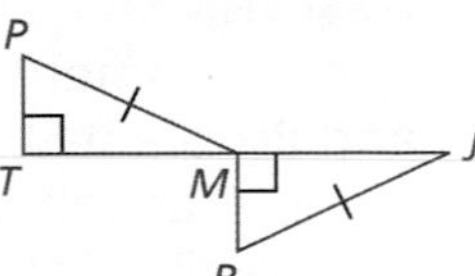

3 Lesson Check

Do you know HOW?
If students have difficulty with Exercise 7, then have them refer to the Take Note at the bottom of page 166.

Do you UNDERSTAND?
If students have difficulty with Exercise 11, then have them review Problem 1.

Close

Q What two conditions are necessary to prove two right triangles are congruent? **[The hypotenuses and one pair of sides are congruent.]**

ANSWERS

5. yes; $\triangle BCA \cong \triangle EFD$
6. yes; $\triangle MPL \cong \triangle MNO$
7. no
8. yes; $\triangle XVR \cong \triangle TVR$
9. 13 cm; the hypotenuse is the longest side of a rt. $\triangle$.
10. Answers may vary. Sample: Alike: They both require information on two pairs of sides and one pair of angles. Different: For HL, the rt. angles are NOT included between the two pairs of $\cong$ sides, while for SAS the angles ARE included between the two pairs of $\cong$ sides.
11. No; $\triangle LMJ$ and $\triangle JKL$ are rt. ⚠ with $\cong$ hypotenuses ($\overline{MJ} \cong \overline{KL}$) and $\cong$ legs ($\overline{LJ} \cong \overline{LJ}$), so $\triangle LMJ \cong \triangle JKL$ by HL.

▼ STUDENT PAGES 169–170

Lesson Check

Do you know HOW?

For Exercises 5–8, determine whether the two triangles are congruent. If so, write the congruence statement.

5.

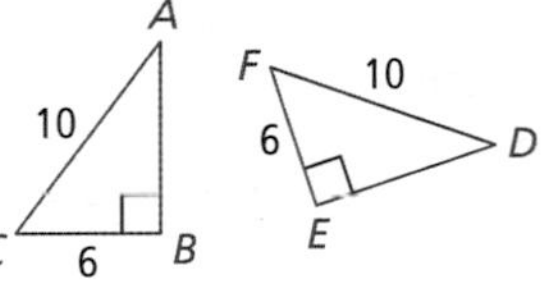

6.

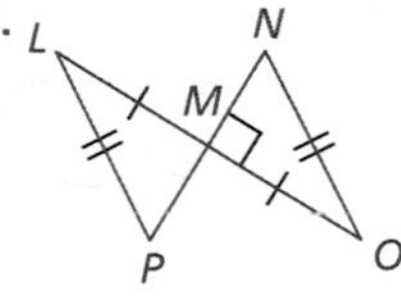

7.

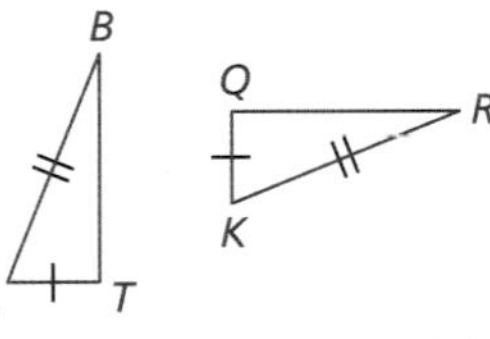

8.

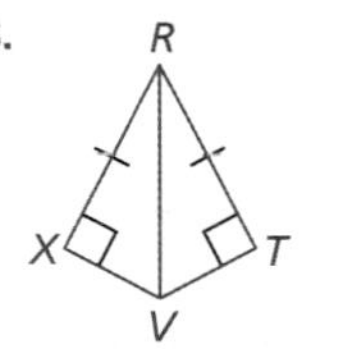

Do you UNDERSTAND?

9. **Vocabulary** A right triangle has side lengths of 5 cm, 12 cm, and 13 cm. What is the length of the hypotenuse? How do you know?
10. **Compare and Contrast** How do the HL Theorem and the SAS Postulate compare? How are they different? Explain.
11. **Error Analysis** Your classmate says that there is not enough information to determine whether the two triangles at the right are congruent. Is your classmate correct? Explain.

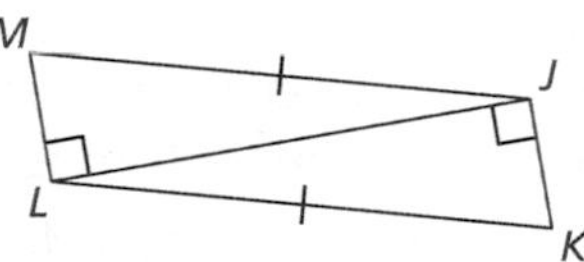

4 Practice

More Practice and Problem-Solving Exercises

ASSIGNMENT GUIDE

The assignments below are for the More Practice and Problem-Solving Exercises. You may also want to assign the A-Level Practice Exercises for homework if these are not used in class.

Average: 12–26

Advanced: 12–28

Mathematical Practices The exercises listed focus on the Standards for Mathematical Practices listed.

EX. 10, 15: Make Sense of Problems (MP 1)

EX. 25: Construct Arguments (MP 3)

EX. 11, 16: Critique the Reasoning of Others (MP 3)

EXERCISE 13: Use the **Think About a Plan** worksheet in the Online Teacher Resources to further support students' development in becoming independent learners.

HOMEWORK QUICK CHECK

To check students' understanding of key skills and concepts, go over Exercises 13, 15, 18, 20, and 25.

ANSWERS

12. $x = 3$, $y = 2$

13. $x = -1$, $y = 3$

14. Answers may vary. Sample: $\angle S \cong \angle T$ by the Isosc. $\triangle$ Thm., so $\triangle PRS \cong \triangle PRT$ by AAS.

15. Yes; the two ⚠ are rt. ⚠ with $\cong$ hypotenuses and $\cong$ legs, so the two ⚠ are $\cong$ by HL. Then $\overline{RQ} \cong \overline{CB}$ because corresp. parts of $\cong$ ⚠ are $\cong$.

16. Yes; two rt. ⚠ with $\cong$ hypotenuses and a pair of $\cong$ acute ∠s also have a pair of $\cong$ rt. ∠s. So the two rt. ⚠ are $\cong$ by AAS.

17. Using the information about $\perp$ segments, $\triangle RST$ and $\triangle TUV$ are rt. ⚠. $\overline{RS} \cong \overline{TU}$ (Given), and T is the midpt. of $\overline{RV}$ (Given), so $\overline{RT} \cong \overline{TV}$ (Def. of midpt.). Thus $\triangle RST \cong \triangle TUV$ by HL.

18. From the information about $\perp$ segments, $\triangle MNL$ and $\triangle QPL$ are rt. ⚠. It is given that $\overline{ML} \cong \overline{QL}$, and since $\overline{NP}$ is the base of isosc. $\triangle LNP$ (Given), then $\overline{LN} \cong \overline{LP}$ (Def. of isosc. $\triangle$). So $\triangle MNL \cong \triangle QPL$ by HL.

▼ STUDENT PAGES 171–172

More Practice and Problem-Solving Exercises

B Apply

Algebra For what values of x and y are the triangles congruent by HL?

12. x, $x + 3$; $3y$, $y + 1$

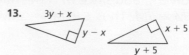

13. $3y + x$, $y - x$; $x + 5$, $y + 5$

14. Study Exercise 1. Can you prove that $\triangle PRS \cong \triangle PRT$ without using the HL Theorem? Explain.

15. Think About a Plan $\triangle ABC$ and $\triangle PQR$ are right triangular sections of a fire escape, as shown. Is each story of the building the same height? Explain.

- What can you tell from the diagram?
- How can you use congruent triangles here?

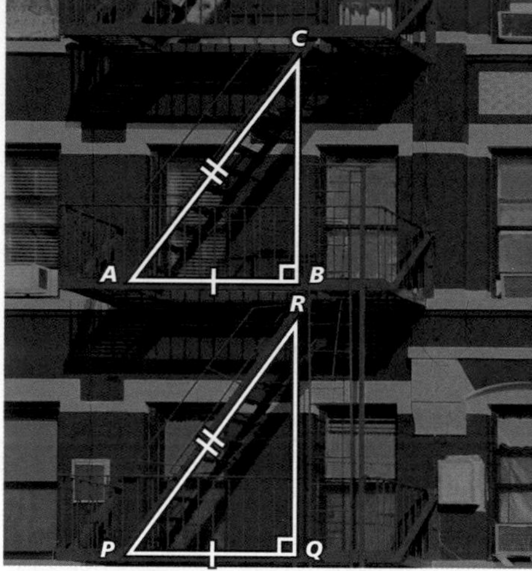

16. Writing "A HA!" exclaims your classmate. "There must be an HA Theorem, sort of like the HL Theorem!" Is your classmate correct? Explain.

Proof 17. Given: $\overline{RS} \cong \overline{TU}$, $\overline{RS} \perp \overline{ST}$, $\overline{TU} \perp \overline{UV}$, T is the midpoint of $\overline{RV}$

Prove: $\triangle RST \cong \triangle TUV$

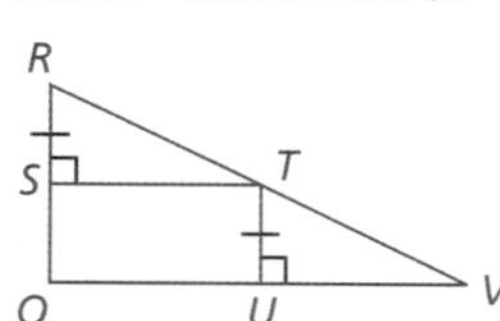

Proof 18. Given: $\triangle LNP$ is isosceles with base $\overline{NP}$, $\overline{MN} \perp \overline{NL}$, $\overline{QP} \perp \overline{PL}$, $\overline{ML} \cong \overline{QL}$

Prove: $\triangle MNL \cong \triangle QPL$

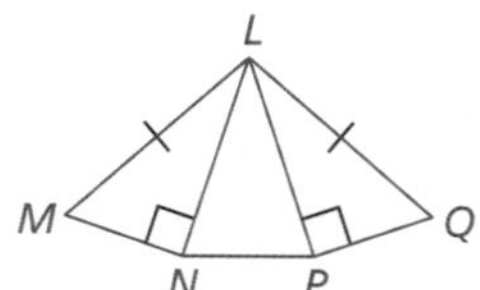

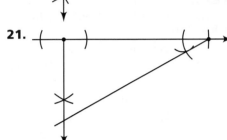

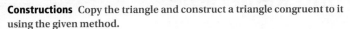

Constructions Copy the triangle and construct a triangle congruent to it using the given method.

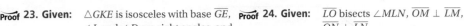

19. SAS **20.** HL

21. ASA **22.** SSS

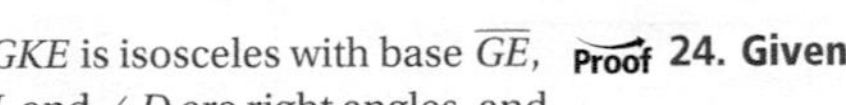

Proof **23. Given:** $\triangle GKE$ is isosceles with base $\overline{GE}$, $\angle L$ and $\angle D$ are right angles, and K is the midpoint of $\overline{LD}$.

Prove: $\overline{LG} \cong \overline{DE}$

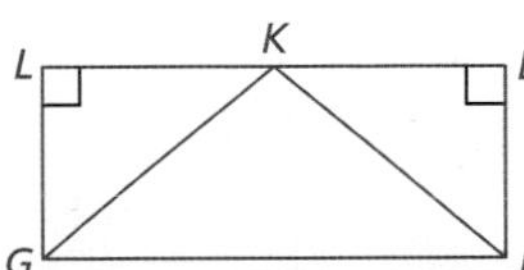

Proof **24. Given:** $\overline{LO}$ bisects $\angle MLN$, $\overline{OM} \perp \overline{LM}$, $\overline{ON} \perp \overline{LN}$

Prove: $\triangle LMO \cong \triangle LNO$

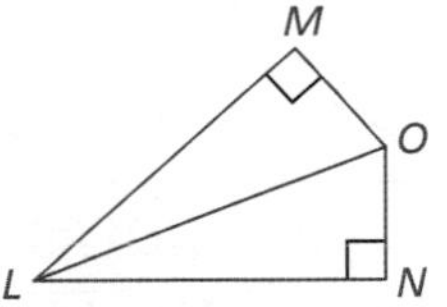

25. Reasoning Are the triangles to the right congruent? Explain.

26. a. Coordinate Geometry Graph the points $A(-5, 6)$, $B(1, 3)$, $D(-8, 0)$, and $E(-2, -3)$. Draw $\overline{AB}$, $\overline{AE}$, $\overline{BD}$, and $\overline{DE}$. Label point C, the intersection of $\overline{AE}$ and $\overline{BD}$.

b. Find the slopes of $\overline{AE}$ and $\overline{BD}$. How would you describe $\angle ACB$ and $\angle ECD$?

c. Algebra Write equations for $\overleftrightarrow{AE}$ and $\overleftrightarrow{BD}$. What are the coordinates of C?

d. Use the Distance Formula to find AB, BC, DC, and DE.

e. Write a paragraph to prove that $\triangle ABC \cong \triangle EDC$.

Challenge

Geometry in 3 Dimensions For Exercises 27 and 28, use the figure at the right.

Proof **27. Given:** $\overline{BE} \perp \overline{EA}$, $\overline{BE} \perp \overline{EC}$, $\triangle ABC$ is equilateral

Prove: $\triangle AEB \cong \triangle CEB$

28. Given: $\triangle AEB \cong \triangle CEB$, $\overline{BE} \perp \overline{EA}$, $\overline{BE} \perp \overline{EC}$
Can you prove that $\triangle ABC$ is equilateral? Explain.

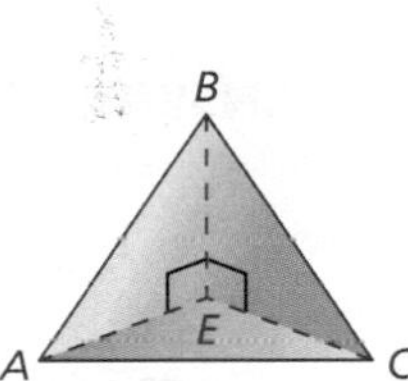

19.

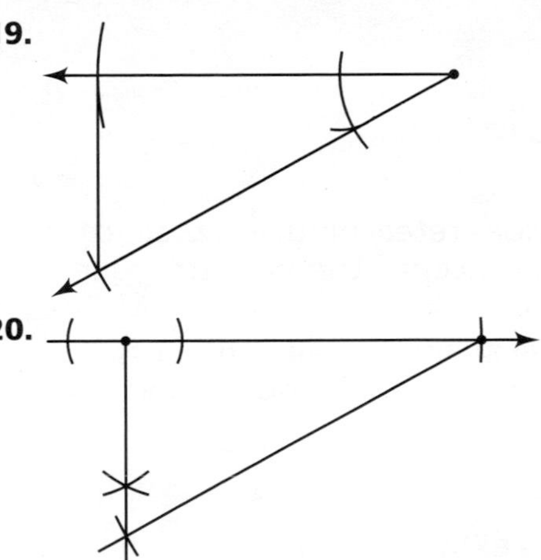

20.

21.

22.

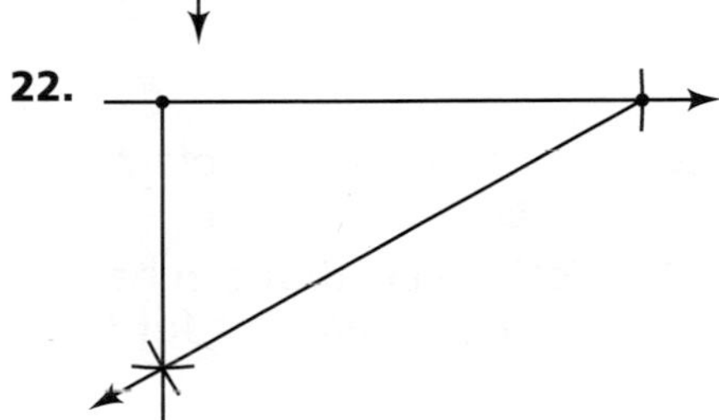

23. From the given information about an isosc. △, rt. ⦣s, and midpt., you can conclude that $\overline{KG} \cong \overline{KE}$ (Def. of isosc. △), $\triangle LKG$ and $\triangle DKE$ are rt. △s (Def. of rt. △), and $\overline{LK} \cong \overline{DK}$ (Def. of midpt.). So $\triangle LKG \cong \triangle DKE$ by HL, and $\overline{LG} \cong \overline{DE}$ because corresp. parts of ≅ △s are ≅.

24. From the given ⊥ segments, $\angle M \cong \angle N$ because ⊥ lines form rt. ⦣s, which are ≅. $\overline{LO}$ bisects $\angle MLN$ (Given), so $\angle MLO \cong \angle NLO$ by the def. of ∠ bisector. The Refl. Prop. of ≅ gives $\overline{LO} \cong \overline{LO}$, so $\triangle LMO \cong \triangle LNO$ by AAS.

25. No, the triangles are not ≅. Explanations may vary. Sample: $\overline{DF}$ is the hypotenuse of $\triangle DEF$, so it is the longest side of the triangle. Therefore, it is greater than 5 and greater than 13 because it is longer than either of the legs. So $\overline{DF}$ cannot be congruent to $\overline{AC}$, which is the hypotenuse of $\triangle ABC$ and has length 13.

26. a.

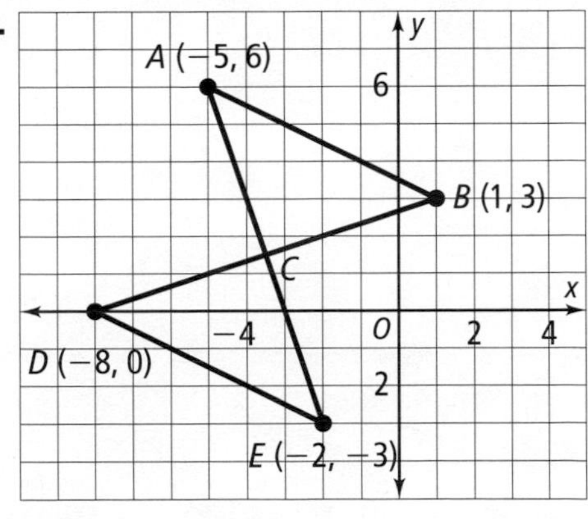

b. Slope of $AE = -3$, slope of $\overline{BD} = \frac{1}{3}$; they are rt. ⦣s.

c. $\overleftrightarrow{AE}$: $y - 6 = -3(x + 5)$
$\overleftrightarrow{BD}$: $y - 3 = \frac{1}{3}(x - 1)$; $C\left(-\frac{7}{2}, \frac{3}{2}\right)$

d. $AB = \sqrt{45}$, $BC = \sqrt{\frac{45}{2}}$, $DC = \sqrt{\frac{45}{2}}$, $DE = \sqrt{45}$

e. Answers may vary. Sample: $\angle ACB$ and $\angle ECD$ are rt. ⦣s so $\triangle ABC$ and $\triangle EDC$ are rt. △s. $AB = DE = \sqrt{45}$, so the hypotenuses of the two △s are ≅. $BC = DC = \sqrt{\frac{45}{2}}$, so a pair of legs are congruent. So $\triangle ABC \cong \triangle EDC$ by HL.

27. $\triangle AEB$ and $\triangle CEB$ are rt. △s because the given information includes $\overline{BE} \perp \overline{EA}$ and $\overline{BE} \perp \overline{EC}$. $\triangle ABC$ is equilateral (Given), so $\overline{AB} \cong \overline{CB}$ by the def. of equilateral. Also, $\overline{BE} \cong \overline{BE}$ by the Refl. Prop. of ≅. So $\triangle AEB \cong \triangle CEB$ by HL.

28. No; visualize "squeezing" at points A and C. That would change the distance AC but would not change any of the given information. Since you can change the length of $\overline{AC}$, you cannot prove $\triangle ABC$ to be equilateral.

5 Assess and Remediate

Lesson Quiz

1. Are the triangles shown below congruent? Explain.

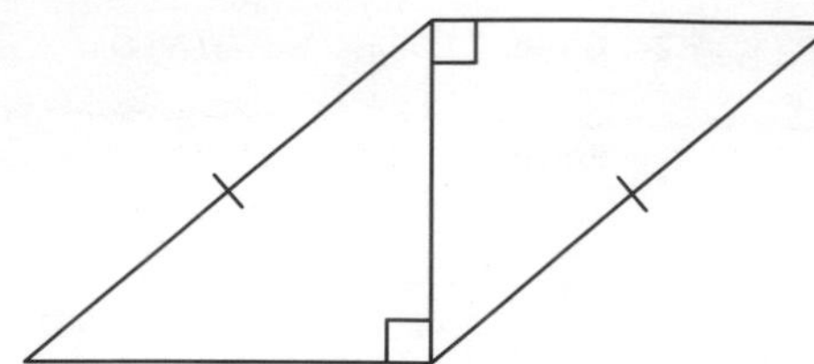

2. Do you UNDERSTAND?

Given: $\overline{ON} \cong \overline{ML}$, $\overline{LP} \cong \overline{PN}$, $\angle OPN$ is a right angle.

Prove: $\triangle OPN \cong \triangle MPL$

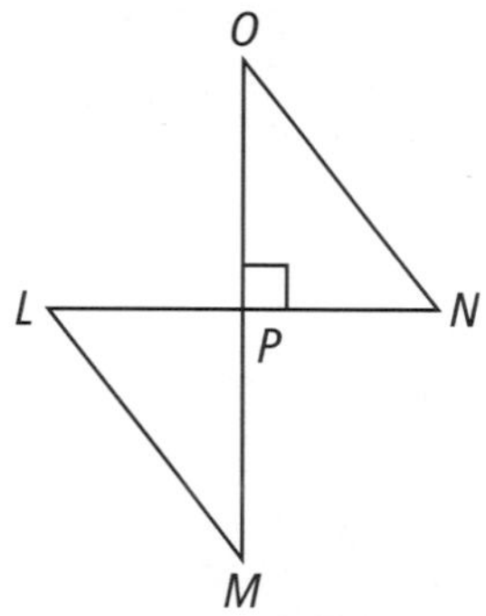

ANSWERS TO LESSON QUIZ

1. yes, by the HL Theorem

2. It is given that $\overline{ON} \cong \overline{ML}$, $\overline{LP} \cong \overline{PN}$, and $\angle OPN$ is a right angle. $\angle OPN \cong \angle LPM$ by Vertical Angles Theorem. $m\angle OPN = m\angle LPM$ by the def. of cong. angles. $m\angle OPN = 90$ by the def. of right angles. $m\angle LPM = 90$ by subst. $\angle LPM$ is a right angle by the def. of right angles. $\triangle OPN$ and $\triangle MPL$ are right triangles. So, $\triangle OPN \cong \triangle MPL$ by HL.

Prescription for Remediation

Use the student work on the Lesson Quiz to prescribe a differentiated assignment.

Points	Differentiated Remediation
0	Intervention
1	On-level
2	Extension

Online Assessment

Assign the Lesson Quiz in Success Tracker on **pearsonsuccessnet.com**. Success Tracker will automatically score the quiz and assign appropriate intervention or enrichment to each student based on the results. The compiled data appear in three different reports for instant analysis of whole class and individual student performance.

Differentiated Remediation

Intervention

- **RETEACHING** (2 pages) Provides reteaching and practice exercises for the key lesson concepts. Use with struggling students or absent students.
- **ENGLISH LANGUAGE LEARNER SUPPORT** Helps students develop and reinforce mathematical vocabulary and key concepts.

On-Level

- **PRACTICE** (2 pages) Provides extra practice for each lesson. For simpler practice exercises, use the Form K Practice pages found in the Online Teacher Resources.
- **THINK ABOUT A PLAN** Helps students develop specific problem-solving skills and strategies by providing scaffolded guiding questions.
- **STANDARDIZED TEST PREP** Focuses on all major exercises, all major question types, and helps students prepare for the high-stakes assessments.

Extension

- **ENRICHMENT** Provides students with interesting problems and activities that extend the concepts of the lesson.
- **ACTIVITIES, GAMES, AND PUZZLES** Worksheets that can be used for concept development, enrichment, and for fun!

Congruence in Overlapping Triangles

Common Core State Standards
G.SRT.5 Use congruence . . . criteria . . . to solve problems and to prove relationships in geometric figures. **Also G.CO.10**

Preparing to Teach

BIG ideas Reasoning and Proof
Visualization

ESSENTIAL UNDERSTANDING

Congruent corresponding parts of one pair of congruent triangles can sometimes be used to prove another pair of triangles congruent. This often involves overlapping triangles.

Math Background

The topic of overlapping triangles is a topic rich in both spatial reasoning and logical reasoning. Activities and proofs with overlapping triangles provide opportunities to use definitions, properties, postulates, and theorems.

Overlapping triangles may share angles, sides, or portions of angles or sides.

Visualizing the triangles and their parts is a challenge for many students. Using color can help distinguish the triangles and make their corresponding parts easier to track. Being able to see the separate triangles when they share sides and angles is a skill that students will use throughout geometry. The visual skills students develop, together with the skills of logic and proof, are invaluable in this course and in other studies.

ELL Support

USE GRAPHIC ORGANIZERS Set up a "word wall" where you post vocabulary words and their definitions from each lesson. Have students draw diagrams and models to represent each concept. Ask students for words that share the same word base (cognates) or use the Internet or a dictionary. These roots can be placed on the word wall in a separate section on different colored paper to differentiate them.

USE MANIPULATIVES Have students draw a pair of congruent, overlapping triangles. Then they can trade with a partner and separate and redraw the triangles.

Mathematical Practices

MAKE SENSE OF PROBLEMS AND PERSEVERE IN SOLVING THEM. Students will consider analogous situations in their study of congruent overlapping triangles by separating the figures and creating a simpler form of the original situation.

Interactive Learning

Solve It!

PURPOSE To discover ways to identify triangles when they overlap

PROCESS Students may redraw the triangles separately or systematically count the number of triangles in the diagram.

Q Does the diagram have a line of symmetry? If yes, describe the location of that line. **[yes, a vertical line that can be drawn in the middle of the diagram]**

Q Using the line of symmetry, how many triangles do you count on the left side of the design? **[10]**

Q Can you double that number to find the number of triangles in the entire design? Explain. **[No; there are triangles that include sections on both sides of the line of symmetry.]**

ANSWER 23; Explanations may vary. Sample: Count individual △. Then count overlapping △ and look for symmetry.

CONNECT THE MATH Students can see that there are many ways two triangles can overlap. In designs such as the one in the Solve It, students need to be able to count triangles systematically to ensure an accurate count.

▼ DIGITAL (STUDENT WORK SPACE PAGE 173)

Getting Ready!

An assignment for your graphic design class is to make a colorful design using triangles. How many triangles are in your design? Explain how you count them.

2 Guided Instruction

Problem 1 Identifying Common Parts

Q What segments (or parts of segments) are shared by the two triangles? **[$\overline{BC}$ and $\overline{CD}$]**

Got It? **ERROR PREVENTION**
Have students redraw the triangles. Have them use their hand or a piece of paper to cover up parts that are not included as they work.

ANSWERS

Got It? a. $\overline{AD}$ **b.** $\overline{AB}$

Practice

1. $\overline{DF}$
2. 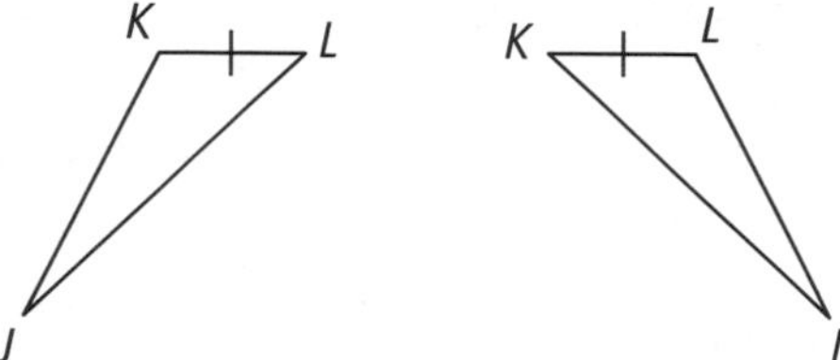

$\overline{KL}$ is a common side.

▼ STUDENT PAGE 173

In the Solve It, you located individual triangles among a jumble of triangles. Some triangle relationships are difficult to see because the triangles overlap.

Essential Understanding You can sometimes use the congruent corresponding parts of one pair of congruent triangles to prove another pair of triangles congruent. This often involves overlapping triangles.

Overlapping triangles may have a common side or angle. You can simplify your work with overlapping triangles by separating and redrawing the triangles.

▼ DIGITAL

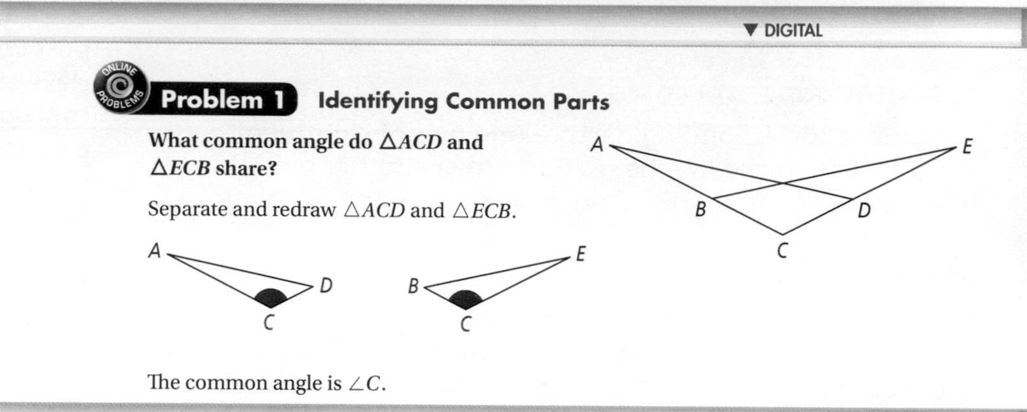

Problem 1 **Identifying Common Parts**

What common angle do $\triangle ACD$ and $\triangle ECB$ share?

Separate and redraw $\triangle ACD$ and $\triangle ECB$.

The common angle is $\angle C$.

▼ STUDENT PAGES 173–174

Got It? **a.** What is the common side in $\triangle ABD$ and $\triangle DCA$?

b. What is the common side in $\triangle ABD$ and $\triangle BAC$?

A Practice

1. In the diagram, the red and blue triangles are congruent. Identify the common side or angle.

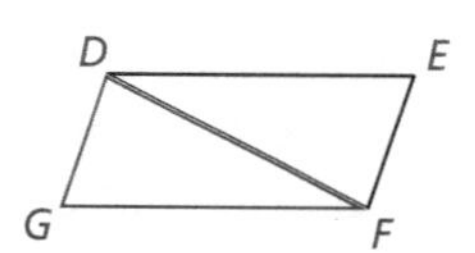

2. Separate and redraw $\triangle JKL$ and $\triangle MLK$. Identify any common angles or sides.

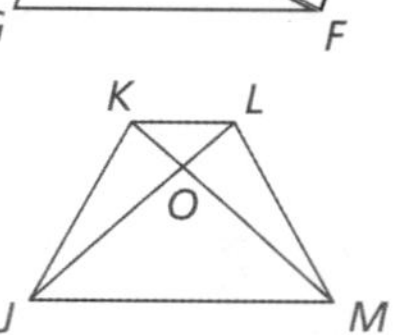

Problem 2 Using Common Parts

Q Which part of the triangles is common to both? **[$\overline{WX}$]**

Q What theorem or postulate can you use to prove that the two triangles are congruent? **[ASA Postulate]**

Q Once the two triangles are proved congruent, how can you show that $\overline{ZW} \cong \overline{YX}$? Explain. **[They are corresponding sides of congruent triangles. Thus, they are congruent.]**

▼ DIGITAL

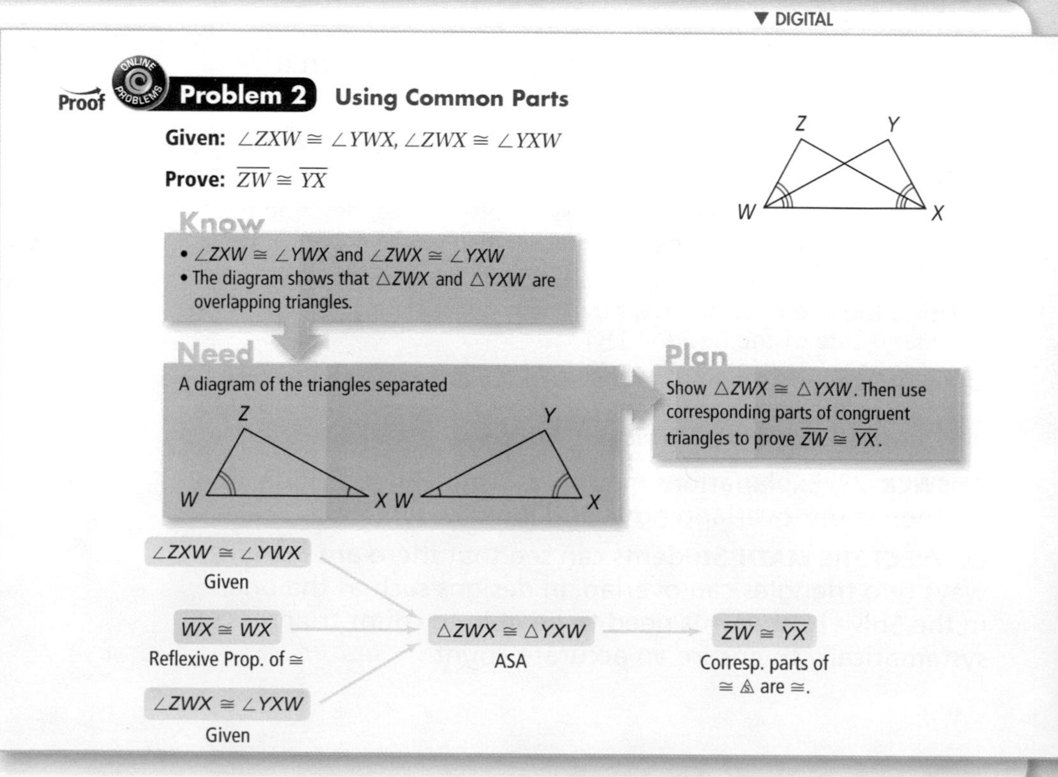

Proof **Problem 2** **Using Common Parts**

Given: $\angle ZXW \cong \angle YWX$, $\angle ZWX \cong \angle YXW$

Prove: $\overline{ZW} \cong \overline{YX}$

Got It?

Students can show that $\angle ACD \cong \angle DBC$ since they are corresponding parts of congruent triangles. Then $\overline{CE} \cong \overline{BE}$ by the converse of the Isosceles Triangle Theorem.

ANSWERS

Got It? It is given that $\triangle CAB \cong \triangle BDC$, so $\angle ACB \cong \angle DBC$ because corresp. parts of ≅ △ are ≅. Therefore, $\overline{CE} \cong \overline{BE}$ by the Converse of the Isosc. △ Thm.

Practice

3. **a.** Given
   b. Refl. Prop. of ≅
   c. Given
   d. AAS
   e. Corresp. parts of ≅ triangles are ≅.
4. $\overline{QD} \cong \overline{UA}$ and $\angle QDA \cong \angle UAD$ (Given), and $\overline{DA} \cong \overline{DA}$ (Refl. Prop. of ≅). So $\triangle QDA \cong \triangle UAD$ by SAS.

▼ STUDENT PAGES 174–175

Got It? **Given:** $\triangle CAB \cong \triangle BDC$

Prove: $\overline{CE} \cong \overline{BE}$

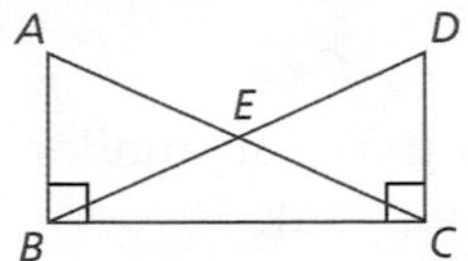

Practice **3. Developing Proof** Complete the flow proof.

Given: $\angle T \cong \angle R$, $\overline{PQ} \cong \overline{PV}$

Prove: $\angle PQT \cong \angle PVR$

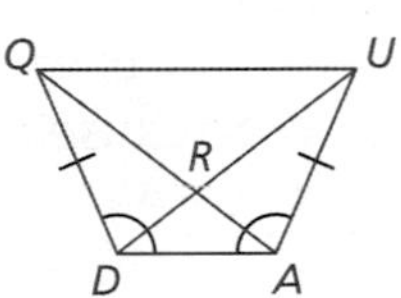

$\angle T \cong \angle R$ — a. ?

$\angle TPQ \cong \angle RPV$ — b. ?

$\overline{PQ} \cong \overline{PV}$ — c. ?

→ $\triangle TPQ \cong \triangle RPV$ — d. ?

→ $\angle PQT \cong \angle PVR$ — e. ?

a. ______________________

b. ______________________

c. ______________________

d. ______________________

e. ______________________

Proof 4. Given: $\overline{QD} \cong \overline{UA}$, $\angle QDA \cong \angle UAD$

Prove: $\triangle QDA \cong \triangle UAD$

Q U R D A

Problem 3 Using Two Pairs of Triangles

Q Are there any special pairs of angles present in the diagram? Explain. **[Yes, there are three pairs of congruent vertical angles.]**

Q For which pair of triangles can you use this information? **[$\triangle AED$ and $\triangle CEB$]**

Q How can you use these triangles to show that two other triangles are congruent? **[Because corresponding parts of congruent triangles are congruent, $\angle D \cong \angle B$. This is the last piece of information you need to conclude that $\triangle GED \cong \triangle JEB$.]**

▼ DIGITAL

Proof **Problem 3** **Using Two Pairs of Triangles**

Given: In the origami design, E is the midpoint of $\overline{AC}$ and $\overline{DB}$.

Prove: $\triangle GED \cong \triangle JEB$

Proof: E is the midpoint of $\overline{AC}$ and $\overline{DB}$, so $\overline{AE} \cong \overline{CE}$ and $\overline{DE} \cong \overline{BE}$. $\angle AED \cong \angle CEB$ because vertical angles are congruent. Therefore, $\triangle AED \cong \triangle CEB$ by SAS. $\angle D \cong \angle B$ because corresponding parts of congruent triangles are congruent. $\angle GED \cong \angle JEB$ because vertical angles are congruent. Therefore, $\triangle GED \cong \triangle JEB$ by ASA.

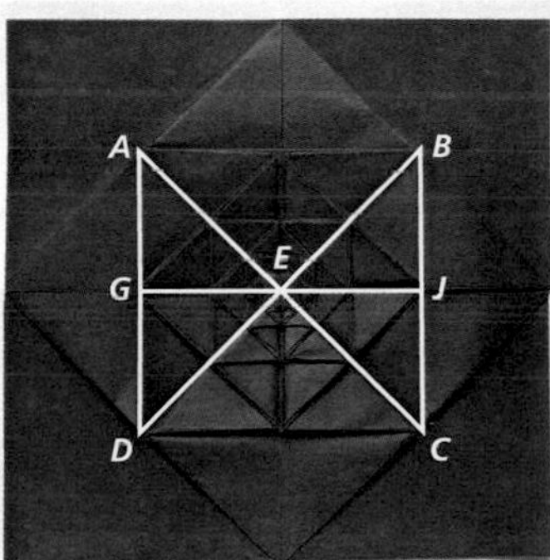

Problem 3 *continued*

Got It? **SYNTHESIZING**

Instruct students to think of smaller proofs within the complete proof. Students must first prove that $\triangle PSQ \cong \triangle RSQ$ by the SAS Postulate. Then, $\overline{PQ} \cong \overline{QR}$ and $\angle PQT \cong \angle RQT$ because they are corresponding parts of congruent triangles. Because $\overline{QT} \cong \overline{QT}$ (Refl. Prop. of $\cong$), $\triangle QPT \cong \triangle QRT$ by the SAS Postulate.

ANSWERS

Got It? $\triangle PSQ \cong \triangle RSQ$ by SAS becuse $\overline{PS} \cong \overline{RS}$ (Given), $\angle PSQ \cong \angle RSQ$ (Given), and $\overline{SQ} \cong \overline{SQ}$ (Refl. Prop. of $\cong$). So $\overline{PQ} \cong \overline{RQ}$ and $\angle PQT \cong \angle RQT$ (Corresp. parts of $\cong$ △ are $\cong$.). Also, $\overline{QT} \cong \overline{QT}$ (Refl. Prop. of $\cong$), so $\triangle QPT \cong \triangle QRT$ by SAS.

Practice

5. Answers may vary. Sample: $\overline{AD} \cong \overline{ED}$ and D is the midpt. of $\overline{BF}$ (Given). $\overline{BD} \cong \overline{FD}$ (Def. of midpt.) and $\angle ADB \cong \angle EDF$ (Vert. ∠ are $\cong$.). So $\triangle ADB \cong \triangle EDF$ by SAS, and $\angle A \cong \angle E$ because corresp. parts of $\cong$ △ are $\cong$. $\angle ADC \cong \angle EDG$ because vert. ∠ are $\cong$, so $\triangle ADC \cong \triangle EDG$ by ASA.

▼ STUDENT PAGE 176

Got It? **Given:** $\overline{PS} \cong \overline{RS}$, $\angle PSQ \cong \angle RSQ$

Prove: $\triangle QPT \cong \triangle QRT$

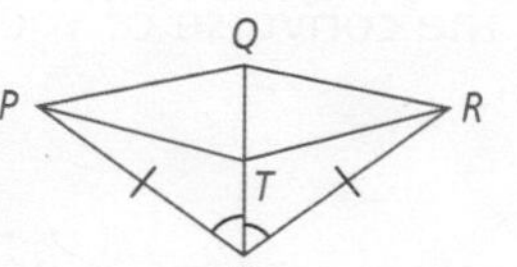

Plan

How do you choose another pair of triangles to help in your proof?

Practice **Proof** 5. **Given:** $\overline{AD} \cong \overline{ED}$, D is the midpoint of $\overline{BF}$

Prove: $\triangle ADC \cong \triangle EDG$

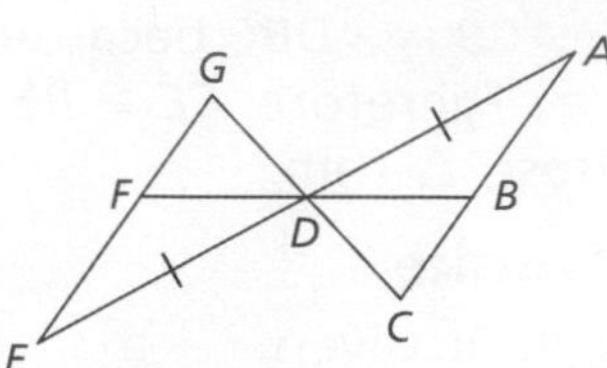

Problem 4 Separating Overlapping Triangles

Q What type of triangle is $\triangle CAE$? **[isosceles]**

Q Which triangles have the sides $\overline{BX}$ and $\overline{DX}$? **[$\triangle BXA$ and $\triangle DXE$]**

Q What parts of these triangles are congruent? **[$\overline{BA} \cong \overline{DE}$ and $\angle BXA \cong \angle DXE$]**

Q What other information do you need to prove $\triangle BXA$ and $\triangle DXE$ are congruent? **[$\angle ABE \cong \angle EDA$]**

Got It?

Students should dissect the diagram similarly to the way the diagram was dissected in Problem 4. They should model the proof to match the proof in Problem 4.

Students will need to prove $\triangle AED \cong \triangle ACD$. Then they should be able to use corresponding parts to prove that $\triangle FED \cong \triangle BCD$ by the ASA Postulate.

▼ STUDENT PAGE 177

When several triangles overlap and you need to use one pair of congruent triangles to prove another pair congruent, you may find it helpful to draw a diagram of each pair of triangles.

▼ DIGITAL

Proof **Problem 4** **Separating Overlapping Triangles**

Given: $\overline{CA} \cong \overline{CE}$, $\overline{BA} \cong \overline{DE}$

Prove: $\overline{BX} \cong \overline{DX}$

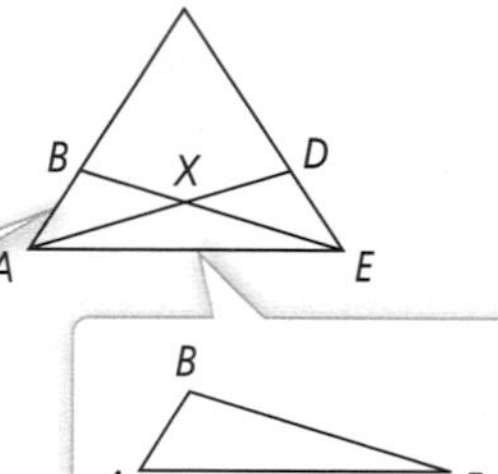

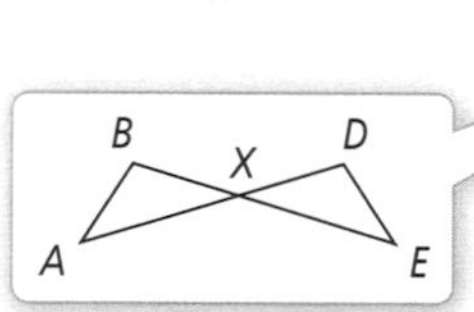

Statements	Reasons
1) $\overline{BA} \cong \overline{DE}$	1) Given
2) $\overline{CA} \cong \overline{CE}$	2) Given
3) $\angle CAE \cong \angle CEA$	3) Base ∠ of an isosceles △ are $\cong$.
4) $\overline{AE} \cong \overline{AE}$	4) Reflexive Property of $\cong$
5) $\triangle BAE \cong \triangle DEA$	5) SAS
6) $\angle ABE \cong \angle EDA$	6) Corresp. parts of $\cong$ △ are $\cong$.
7) $\angle BXA \cong \angle DXE$	7) Vertical angles are $\cong$.
8) $\triangle BXA \cong \triangle DXE$	8) AAS
9) $\overline{BX} \cong \overline{DX}$	9) Corresp. parts of $\cong$ △ are $\cong$.

ANSWERS

Got It? Using $\overline{AD} \cong \overline{AD}$ (Refl. Prop. of $\cong$) and the two given pairs of $\cong$ ∠s, $\triangle ACD \cong \triangle AED$ by AAS. Then $\overline{CD} \cong \overline{ED}$ (Corresp. parts of $\cong$ △s are $\cong$.) and $\angle BDC \cong \angle FDE$ (Vert. ∠s are $\cong$.). Therefore, $\triangle BDC \cong \triangle FDE$ by ASA, and $\overline{BD} \cong \overline{FD}$ because corresp. parts of $\cong$ △s are $\cong$.

Practice

6. $\angle 1 \cong \angle 2$ and $\angle 3 \cong \angle 4$ (Given), and $\overline{QB} \cong \overline{QB}$ by the Refl. Prop. of $\cong$. So $\triangle QTB \cong \triangle QUB$ by ASA. Thus $\overline{QT} \cong \overline{QU}$ (Corresp. parts of $\cong$ △s are $\cong$.). $\overline{QE} \cong \overline{QE}$ (Refl. Prop. of $\cong$), so $\triangle QET \cong \triangle QEU$ by SAS.

▼ STUDENT PAGE 177

Got It? **Given:** $\angle CAD \cong \angle EAD$, $\angle C \cong \angle E$

Prove: $\overline{BD} \cong \overline{FD}$

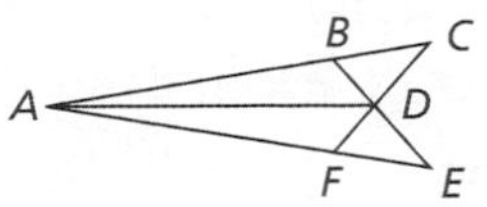

Plan

Which triangles are useful here?

Practice 6. **Given:** $\angle 1 \cong \angle 2$, $\angle 3 \cong \angle 4$

Proof **Prove:** $\triangle QET \cong \triangle QEU$

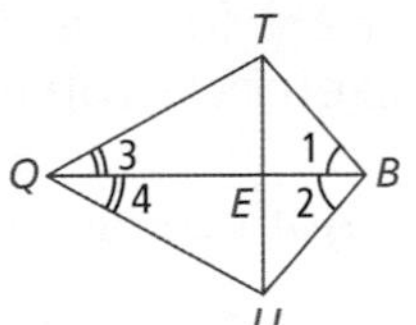

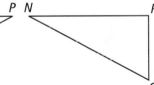

3 Lesson Check

Do you know HOW?

If students have difficulty with Exercise 7, then have them review Problem 1.

Do you UNDERSTAND?

If students have difficulty with Exercise 12, then have them review Problem 2.

Close

Q When triangles overlap, what parts can you use to show that the triangles are congruent? **[Any parts that are shared in their entirety may be used as congruent parts.]**

ANSWERS

7. $\overline{JK}$

8. $\angle D$

9.

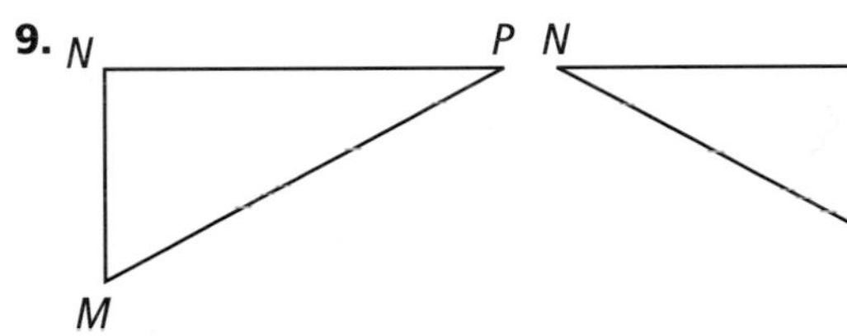

10.

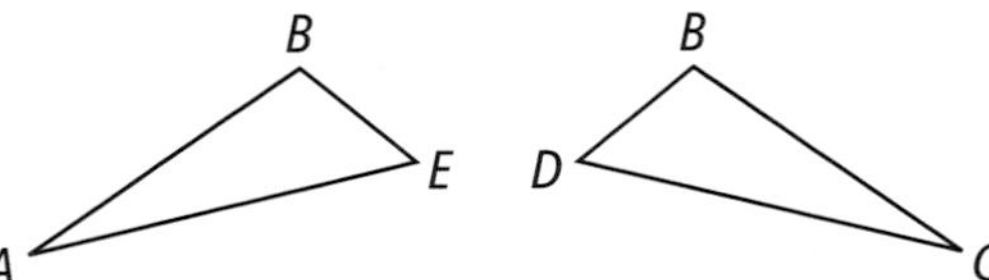

11. No; there are several △s with vertex J and several △s with vertex K, and a different ∠ at each vertex is in each △.

12. Answers may vary. Sample: Based on the given statement that $\triangle PSY \cong \triangle SPL$, $\overline{PL} \cong \overline{SY}$, and $\angle L \cong \angle Y$ because corresp. parts of $\cong$ △s are $\cong$. $\angle PRL \cong \angle SRY$ because vert. ∠s are $\cong$. So $\triangle PRL \cong \triangle SRY$ by AAS.

13. Answers may vary. Sample: Prove $\triangle AEB \cong \triangle CED$ (by SAS) to get $\overline{AB} \cong \overline{CD}$ and $\angle BAE \cong \angle DCE$. Use those $\cong$ segments and $\cong$ angles, along with rt. △s ADC and ABC, to show $\triangle ACD \cong \triangle CAB$ by ASA.

▼ STUDENT PAGES 178–179

Lesson Check

Do you know HOW?

Identify any common angles or sides.

7. $\triangle MKJ$ and $\triangle LJK$

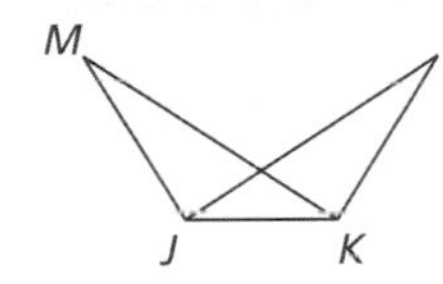

8. $\triangle DEH$ and $\triangle DFG$

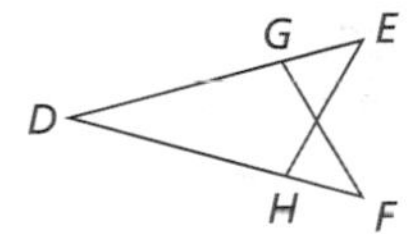

Separate and redraw the overlapping triangles. Label the vertices.

9.

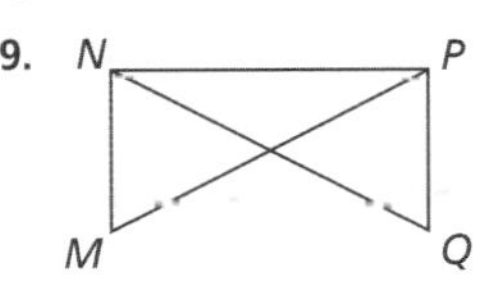

10.

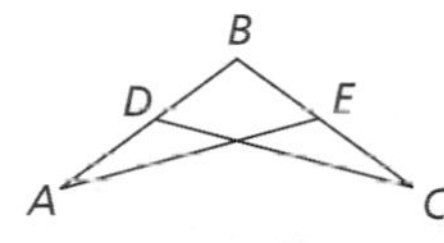

Do you UNDERSTAND? MATHEMATICAL PRACTICES

11. **Reasoning** In Exercise 7, both triangles have vertices J and K. Are $\angle J$ and $\angle K$ common angles for $\triangle MKJ$ and $\triangle LJK$? Explain.

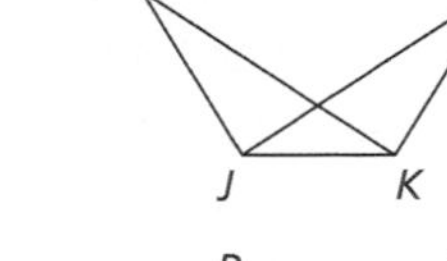

12. **Error Analysis** In the diagram, $\triangle PSY \cong \triangle SPL$. Based on that fact, your friend claims that $\triangle PRL$ is not congruent to $\triangle SRY$. Explain why your friend is incorrect.

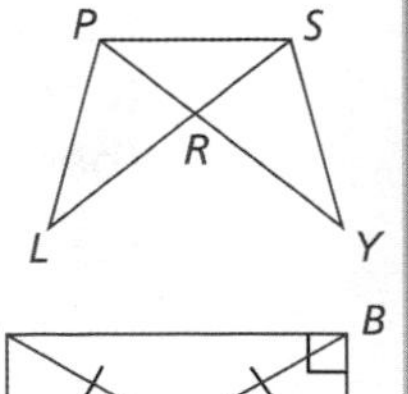

13. In the figure at the right, which pair of triangles could you prove congruent first in order to prove that $\triangle ACD \cong \triangle CAB$? Explain.

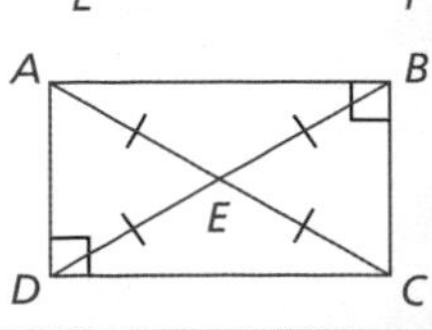

Practice

More Practice and Problem-Solving Exercises

ASSIGNMENT GUIDE
The assignments below are for the More Practice and Problem-Solving Exercises. You may also want to assign the A-Level Practice Exercises for homework if these are not used in class.
Average: 14–21
Advanced: 14–23

Mathematical Practices The exercises listed focus on the Standards for Mathematical Practices listed.

EX. 11, 14, 18, 19: Make Sense of Problems (MP 1)
EX. 23: Construct Arguments (MP 3)
EX. 12: Critique the Reasoning of Others (MP 3)
EX. 15: Model (MP 4)

STEM exercises focus on science or engineering applications.

EXERCISE 17: Use the **Think About a Plan** worksheet in the Online Teacher Resources to further support students' development in becoming independent learners.

HOMEWORK QUICK CHECK
To check students' understanding of key skills and concepts, go over Exercises 14, 15, 17, 19, and 21.

ANSWERS

14. Since $VT = VU + UT = UT + TS = US$, $\overline{VT} \cong \overline{US}$. Therefore, $\triangle QVT \cong \triangle PSU$ by SAS.

15. **a.** $m\angle 1 = 50$, $m\angle 2 = 50$, $m\angle 3 = 40$, $m\angle 4 = 90$, $m\angle 5 = 10$, $m\angle 6 = 40$, $m\angle 7 = 40$, $m\angle 8 = 80$, $m\angle 9 = 100$

b. $\triangle ABC \cong \triangle FCG$ by ASA because $\angle B \cong \angle FCG$ (All rt. ∠s are ≅.), $\overline{AB} \cong \overline{FC}$ (Given), and $\angle A \cong \angle GFC$ (Their measures are =.).

16. It is given that $\overline{AC} \cong \overline{EC}$ and $\overline{CD} \cong \overline{CB}$, and $\angle C \cong \angle C$ by the Refl. Prop. of ≅. So $\triangle ACD \cong \triangle ECB$ by SAS, and $\angle A \cong \angle E$ because corresp. parts of ≅ △s are ≅.

17. $\triangle PQT \cong \triangle RQT$ by SAS because $\overline{QT} \cong \overline{QT}$ (Refl. Prop. of ≅), $\angle PQT \cong \angle RQT$ (⊥ lines form rt. ∠s, which are ≅.), and $\overline{PQ} \cong \overline{RQ}$ (because $\overline{QT}$ bisects $\overline{PR}$). Then $\angle QTP \cong \angle QTR$ (because corresp. parts of ≅ △s are ≅. Also, $\angle VQT \cong \angle SQT$ (because $\overline{QT}$ bisects $\angle VQS$), so $\triangle VQT \cong \triangle SQT$ by ASA. So $\overline{VQ} \cong \overline{SQ}$ because corresp. parts of ≅ △s are ≅.

▼ STUDENT PAGES 179–180

More Practice and Problem-Solving Exercises

B Apply

14. Think About a Plan In the diagram at the right, $\angle V \cong \angle S$, $\overline{VU} \cong \overline{ST}$, and $\overline{PS} \cong \overline{QV}$. Which two triangles are congruent by SAS? Explain.
- How can you use a new diagram to help you identify the triangles?
- What do you need to prove triangles congruent by SAS?

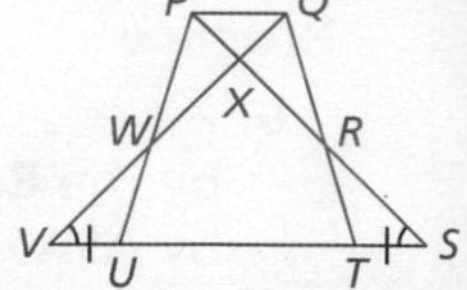

STEM 15. Clothing Design The figure at the right is part of a clothing design pattern, and it has the following relationships.
- $\overline{GC} \perp \overline{AC}$
- $\overline{AB} \perp \overline{BC}$
- $\overline{AB} \parallel \overline{DE} \parallel \overline{FG}$
- $m\angle A = 50$
- $\triangle DEC$ is isosceles with base $\overline{DC}$.

a. Find the measures of all the numbered angles in the figure.
b. Suppose $\overline{AB} \cong \overline{FC}$. Name two congruent triangles and explain how you can prove them congruent.

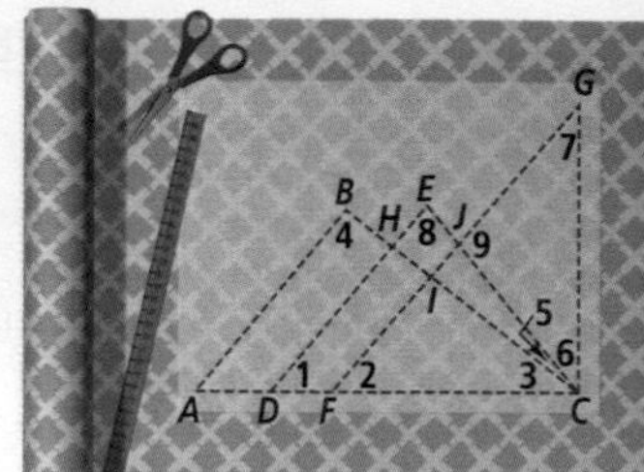

Proof 16. Given: $\overline{AC} \cong \overline{EC}$, $\overline{CB} \cong \overline{CD}$
Prove: $\angle A \cong \angle E$

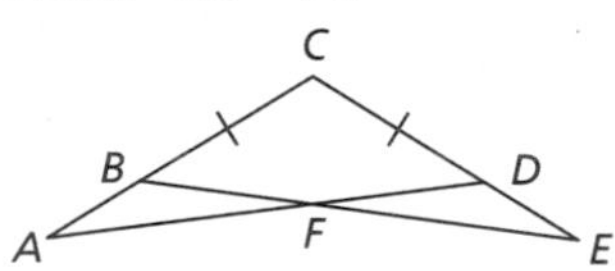

Proof 17. Given: $\overline{QT} \perp \overline{PR}$, $\overline{QT}$ bisects $\overline{PR}$, $\overline{QT}$ bisects $\angle VQS$
Prove: $\overline{VQ} \cong \overline{SQ}$

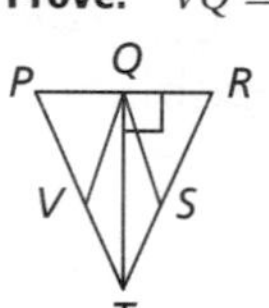

18. Answers may vary. Sample:

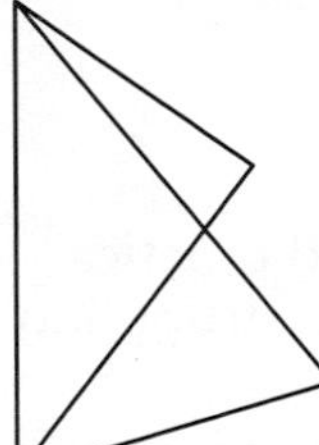

19. Answers may vary. Sample:

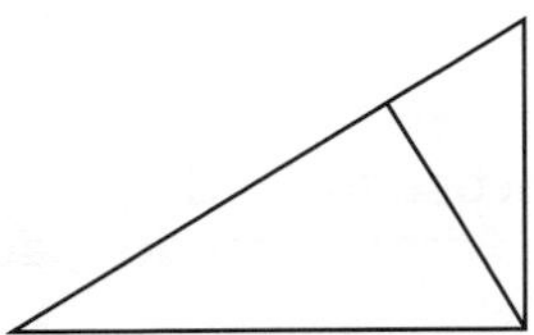

20. $\overline{TE} \cong \overline{RI}$ and $\overline{TI} \cong \overline{RE}$ (Given) and $\overline{EI} \cong \overline{EI}$ (Refl. Prop. of $\cong$), so $\triangle TEI \cong \triangle RIE$ by SSS. Thus $\angle TIE \cong \angle REI$ because corresp. parts of $\cong$ ▵s are $\cong$. Also, $\angle TDI \cong \angle ROE$ because $\angle TDI$ and $\angle ROE$ are rt. ∠s (Given) and all rt. ∠s are $\cong$. So $\triangle TDI \cong \triangle ROE$ by AAS and $\overline{TD} \cong \overline{RO}$ because corresp. parts of $\cong$ ▵s are $\cong$.

21. The given $\perp$ segments indicate that $\triangle ABC$ and $\triangle DCB$ are rt. ▵s. Since $\overline{AC} \cong \overline{DB}$ (Given) and $\overline{BC} \cong \overline{BC}$ (Refl. Prop. of $\cong$), then $\triangle ABC \cong \triangle DCB$ by HL. $\overline{AB} \cong \overline{DC}$, and $\angle A \cong \angle D$ because corresp. parts of $\cong$ ▵s are $\cong$. $\angle AEB \cong \angle DEC$ because vert. ∠s are $\cong$, so $\triangle AEB \cong \triangle DEC$ by AAS, and $\overline{AE} \cong \overline{DE}$ because corresp. parts $\cong$ ▵s are $\cong$.

22. The overlapping ▵s are $\triangle CAE$ and $\triangle CBD$. It is given that $\overline{AC} \cong \overline{BC}$ and $\angle A \cong \angle B$. Also, $\angle C \cong \angle C$ by the Refl. Prop. of $\cong$. So $\triangle CAE \cong \triangle CBD$ by ASA.

23.

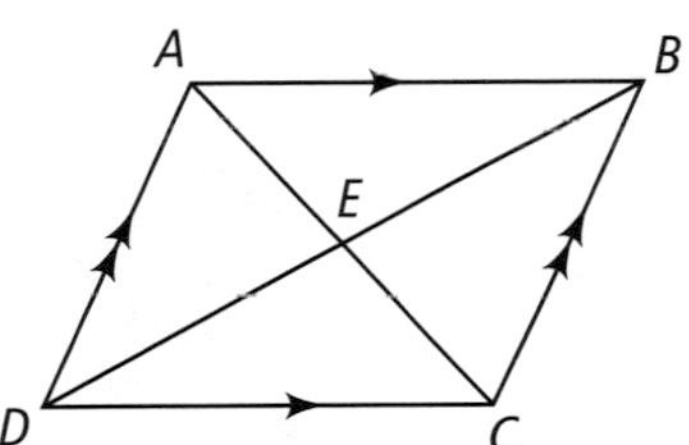

a. $\overline{AB} \cong \overline{DC}$, $\overline{AD} \cong \overline{BC}$, $\overline{AE} \cong \overline{EC}$, $\overline{DE} \cong \overline{EB}$

b. By showing that $\triangle ABC \cong \triangle CDA$ (by ASA), you can then prove that $\triangle AEB \cong \triangle CED$ and $\triangle AED \cong \triangle CEB$ (by ASA or AAS). The segments are $\cong$ because corresp. parts of $\cong$ ▵s are $\cong$.

▼ STUDENT PAGE 180

Open-Ended Draw the diagram described.

18. Draw a vertical segment on your paper. On the right side of the segment draw two triangles that share the vertical segment as a common side.

19. Draw two triangles that have a common angle.

Proof 20. **Given:** $\overline{TE} \cong \overline{RI}$, $\overline{TI} \cong \overline{RE}$, $\angle TDI$ and $\angle ROE$ are right ∠s

Prove: $\overline{TD} \cong \overline{RO}$

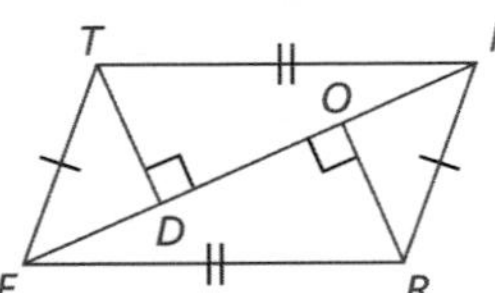

Proof 21. **Given:** $\overline{AB} \perp \overline{BC}$, $\overline{DC} \perp \overline{BC}$, $\overline{AC} \cong \overline{DB}$

Prove: $\overline{AE} \cong \overline{DE}$

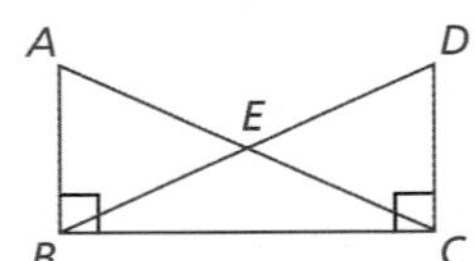

Challenge

22. Identify a pair of overlapping congruent triangles in the diagram at the right. Then use the given information to write a proof to show that the triangles are congruent.

Given: $\overline{AC} \cong \overline{BC}$, $\angle A \cong \angle B$

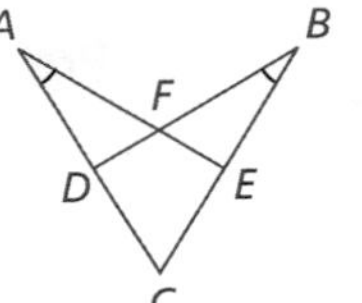

23. **Reasoning** Draw a quadrilateral $ABCD$ with $\overline{AB} \parallel \overline{DC}$, $\overline{AD} \parallel \overline{BC}$, and diagonals $\overline{AC}$ and $\overline{DB}$ intersecting at E. Label your diagram to indicate the parallel sides.

a. List all the pairs of congruent segments in your diagram.

b. **Writing** Explain how you know that the segments you listed are congruent.

5 Assess and Remediate

Lesson Quiz

1. **Do you UNDERSTAND?** What is the common angle in $\triangle LMP$ and $\triangle LNO$?

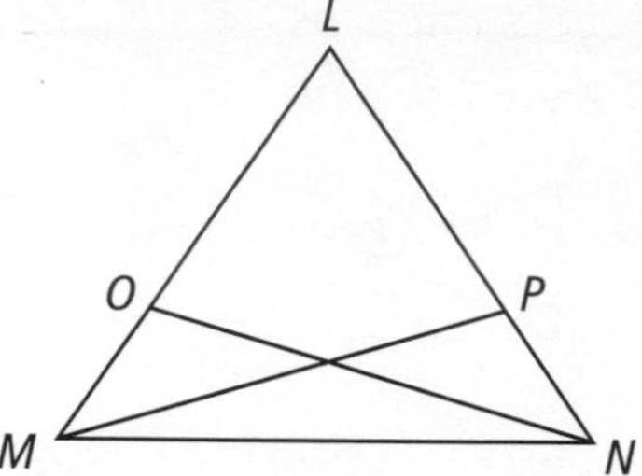

2. **Given:** $\overline{RU} \cong \overline{TS}$, V is the midpoint of $\overline{RT}$ and $\overline{US}$.

   Prove: $\angle RUV \cong \angle TSV$

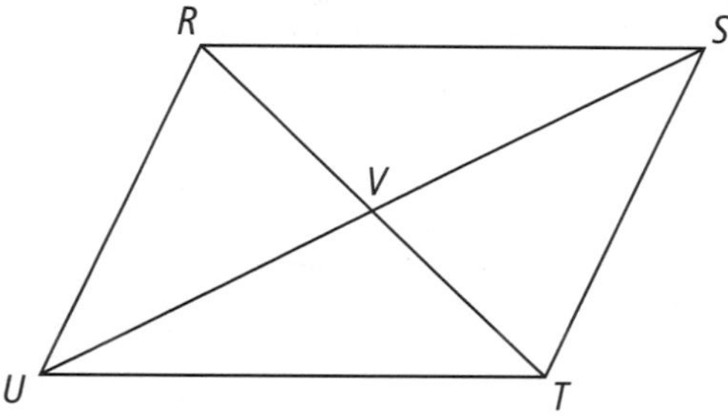

ANSWERS TO LESSON QUIZ

1. $\angle L$
2. It is given that $\overline{RU} \cong \overline{TS}$ and V is the midpoint of $\overline{RT}$ and $\overline{US}$. So, $RV = VT$ and $UV = VS$ by the definition of midpoint. So, $\overline{RV} \cong \overline{VT}$ and $\overline{UV} \cong \overline{VS}$ by the definition of congruent segments. So, $\triangle RVU \cong \triangle TVS$ by SSS. $\angle RUV \cong \angle TSV$ because they are corresponding parts of congruent triangles.

Prescription for Remediation

Use the student work on the Lesson Quiz to prescribe a differentiated assignment.

Points	Differentiated Remediation
0	Intervention
1	On-level
2	Extension

Online Assessment

Assign the Lesson Quiz in Success Tracker on **pearsonsuccessnet.com**. Success Tracker will automatically score the quiz and assign appropriate intervention or enrichment to each student based on the results. The compiled data appear in three different reports for instant analysis of whole class and individual student performance.

Differentiated Remediation

Intervention

- **RETEACHING** (2 pages) Provides reteaching and practice exercises for the key lesson concepts. Use with struggling students or absent students.
- **ENGLISH LANGUAGE LEARNER SUPPORT** Helps students develop and reinforce mathematical vocabulary and key concepts.

On-Level

- **PRACTICE** (2 pages) Provides extra practice for each lesson. For simpler practice exercises, use the Form K Practice pages found in the Online Teacher Resources.
- **THINK ABOUT A PLAN** Helps students develop specific problem-solving skills and strategies by providing scaffolded guiding questions.
- **STANDARDIZED TEST PREP** Focuses on all major exercises, all major question types, and helps students prepare for the high-stakes assessments.

Extension

- **ENRICHMENT** Provides students with interesting problems and activities that extend the concepts of the lesson.
- **ACTIVITIES, GAMES, AND PUZZLES** Worksheets that can be used for concept development, enrichment, and for fun!

LESSON LAB

Use With Lesson 3-8

Review of Transformations

Common Core State Standard
G.CO.6 Use geometric descriptions of rigid motions to transform figures . . .

Mathematical Practices

This Lesson Lab supports students in becoming proficient in making sense of problems and persevering in solving them, Mathematical Practice 1.

Guided Instruction

PURPOSE To review translations, reflections, and rotations and use function notation to describe transformations

PROCESS Students will

- identify transformations of geometric figures shown on a coordinate grid.
- use function notation to describe transformations of geometric figures.

DISCUSS Discuss with students what they have already learned about translations, reflections, and rotations in previous courses

Example 1

In this Example, students describe the translation of a triangle on a coordinate grid and write a function rule for this translation.

Q A translation is also referred to as a *slide* or *glide*. Explain why this term is an appropriate description of a translation. **[Sample answer: When a figure is translated, it *slides* or *glides* across the coordinate plane without being flipped or turned.]**

Q What transformation would describe the mapping from $\triangle A'B'C'$ back onto triangle $\triangle ABC$? What is the function rule for this transformation? **[A translation 8 units to the left and 2 units up. $T_{<-8,2>}(\triangle A'B'C')$]**

Example 2

In this Example, students describe the reflection of a trapezoid on a coordinate grid and write a function rule for this reflection.

Q A reflection is also referred to as a *flip*. Explain why this term is an appropriate description of a reflection. **[Sample answer: When a figure is reflected, it is *flipped* over the line of reflection to create a mirror image.]**

Q Are angle measures preserved by the reflection? How do you know? **[Sample answer: Yes, angle measures are preserved because reflections are rigid motions, and all rigid motions preserve distance and angle measure.]**

Q What can you say about the distance between points in the preimage and corresponding points in the image? **[Sample answer: The distance between two points in the preimage is the same as the distance between the corresponding points in the image because reflections preserve distance.]**

Q What transformation maps $R'S'T'U'$ to $RSTU$? **[a reflection back over the x-axis]**

▼ STUDENT PAGE 181

Recall that a transformation of a geometric figure is a function, or *mapping*, that results in a change in the position, shape, or size of the figure. The original figure is called the *preimage* and the result of the transformation is the *image*. A special kind of transformation that preserves distance is a *rigid motion*, or *isometry*. Translations, reflections, and rotations are examples of rigid motions.

Example 1

What is a rule that describes the transformation that maps $\triangle ABC$ onto $\triangle A'B'C'$?

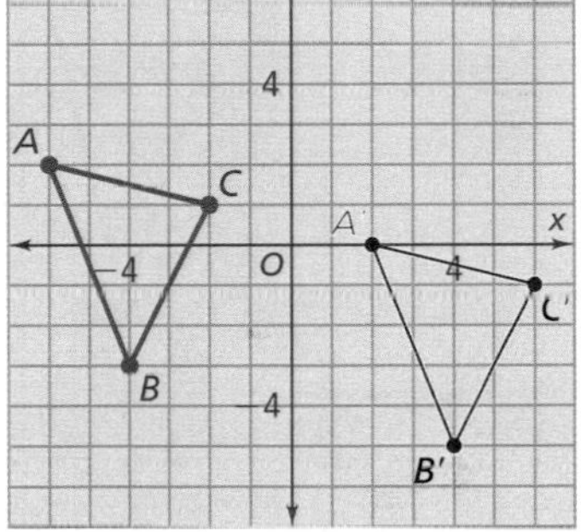

Find the vertices of the preimage $\triangle ABC$ and the image $\triangle A'B'C'$.

Preimage:	$A(-6, 2)$	Image:	$A'(2, 0)$
	$B(-4, -3)$		$B'(4, -5)$
	$C(-2, 1)$		$C'(6, -1)$

If you add 8 to each x-coordinate of the preimage and subtract 2 from each y-coordinate, the results are of the vertices of the image. This is an example of a translation. A translation is a transformation that maps all points of a figure the same distance in the same direction.

This translation is written using the function notation $T_{<8,-2>}(\triangle ABC) = \triangle A'B'C'$.

Example 2

What is a rule that describes the transformation that maps trapezoid $STUV$ onto trapezoid $S'T'U'V'$?

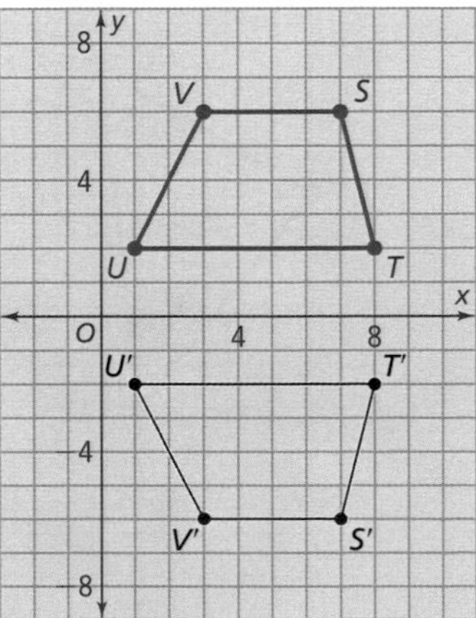

Find the vertices of the preimage $STUV$ and the image $S'T'U'V'$.

Preimage:	$S(7, 6)$	Image:	$S'(7, -6)$
	$T(8, 2)$		$T'(8, -2)$
	$U(1, 2)$		$U'(1, -2)$
	$V(3, 6)$		$V'(3, -6)$

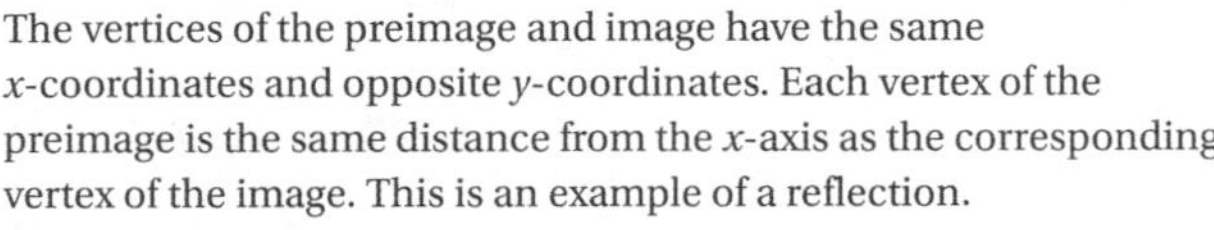
The vertices of the preimage and image have the same x-coordinates and opposite y-coordinates. Each vertex of the preimage is the same distance from the x-axis as the corresponding vertex of the image. This is an example of a reflection.

This reflection is written using function notation as $R_{x\text{-axis}}(STUV) = S'T'U'V'$.

Example 3

In this Example, students describe the rotation of a triangle on a coordinate grid and write a function rule for this rotation.

Q A rotation is also referred to as a *turn*. Explain why this term is an appropriate description of a rotation. **[Answers may vary. Sample: When a figure is rotated, it is *turned* about the center of rotation.]**

Q What is the center of rotation? What is the angle of rotation? **[The origin is the center of rotation. The angle of rotation is 90° counterclockwise.]**

Q What rotation maps the image to the preimage? What is the function rule? **[Answers may vary Sample: A 270° counterclockwise rotation about the origin; $r_{(270°,\ O)}(\triangle M'N'P')$.]**

Q A 90° counterclockwise rotation about the origin maps (x, y) onto $(-y, x)$. Describe how 180°, 270°, and 360° rotations about the origin map (x, y). **[A 180° rotation maps (x, y) onto $(-x, -y)$. A 270° rotation maps (x, y) onto $(y, -x)$. A 360° rotation maps (x, y) onto (x, y).]**

Exercises

ANSWERS

1. $r_{(90°,\ O)}(\triangle HIJ)$
2. $T_{<-6,\ -4>}(\triangle DEF)$
3. 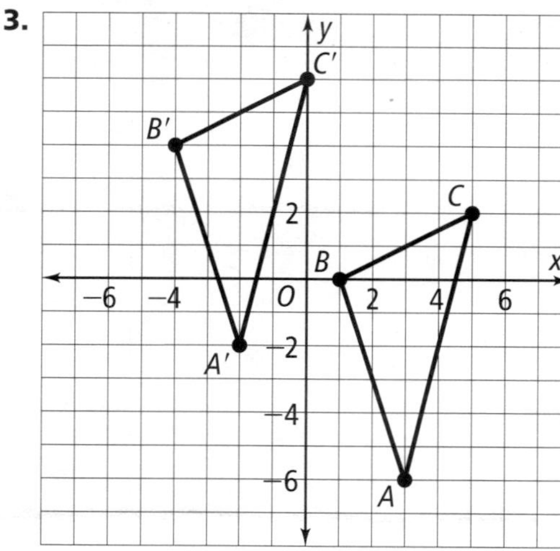

4. 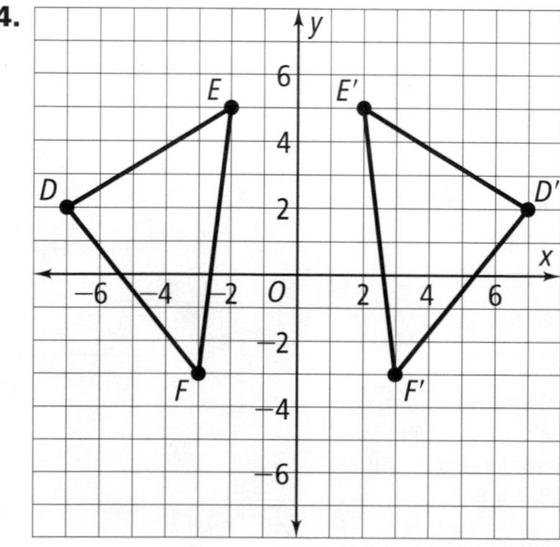

5. 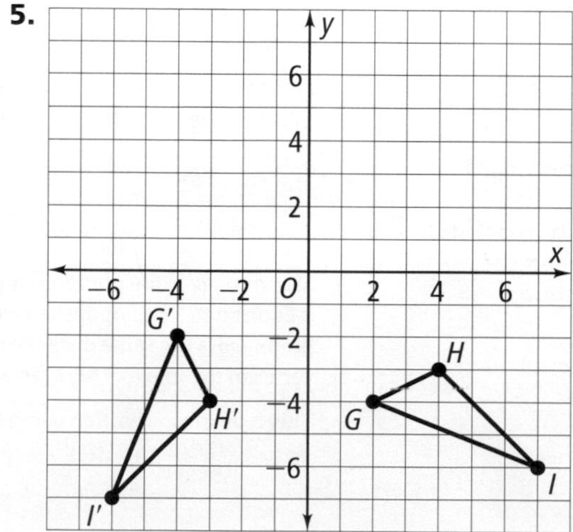

6. 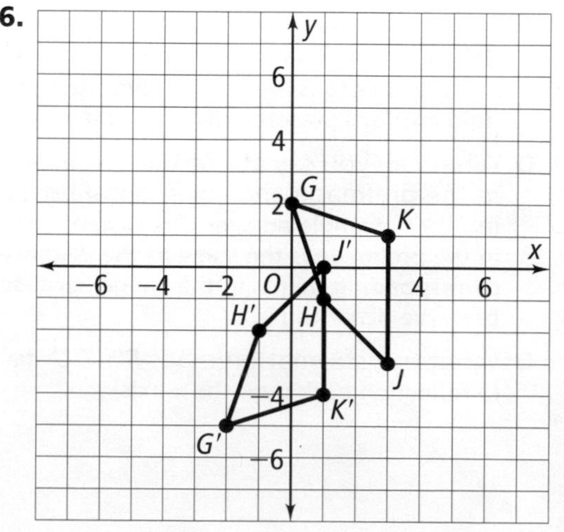

Example 3

What is a rule that describes the transformation that maps $\triangle MNP$ onto $\triangle M'N'P'$?

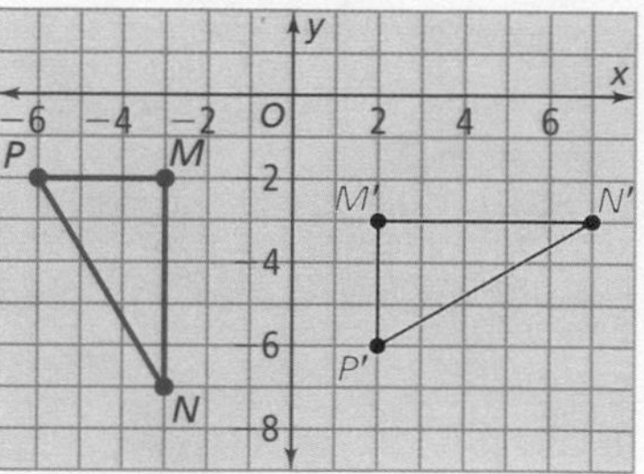

Find the vertices of the preimage $\triangle MNP$ and the image $\triangle M'N'P'$.

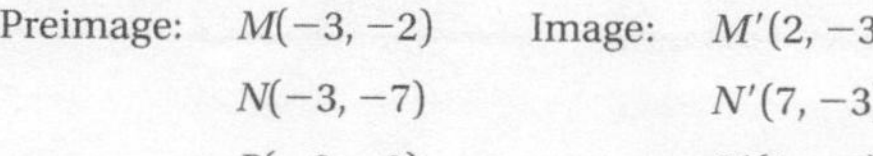

Preimage:	$M(-3, -2)$	Image:	$M'(2, -3)$
	$N(-3, -7)$		$N'(7, -3)$
	$P(-6, -2)$		$P'(2, -6)$

Each vertex (x, y) of the preimage is mapped to $(-y, x)$. Notice that the distance from the origin to each vertex of the preimage and each corresponding vertex of the image is the same. $\triangle MNP$ has been *turned* about the origin to form $\triangle M'N'P'$. A rotation is a transformation that turns the preimage about a fixed point, called the center of rotation, to form the image.

In this Example, $\triangle MNP$ has been rotated 90° counterclockwise about the origin to form $\triangle M'N'P'$. This rotation is written using function notation as $r_{(90°, O)}(\triangle MNP) = \triangle M'N'P'$.

Exercises

What is a rule that describes the transformation from each preimage onto each image?

1. 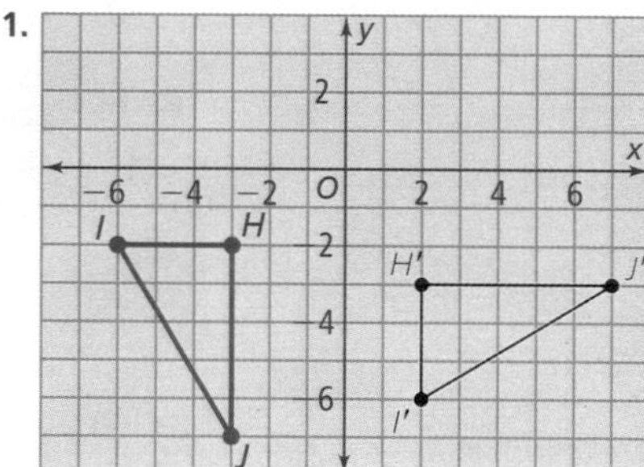

2. 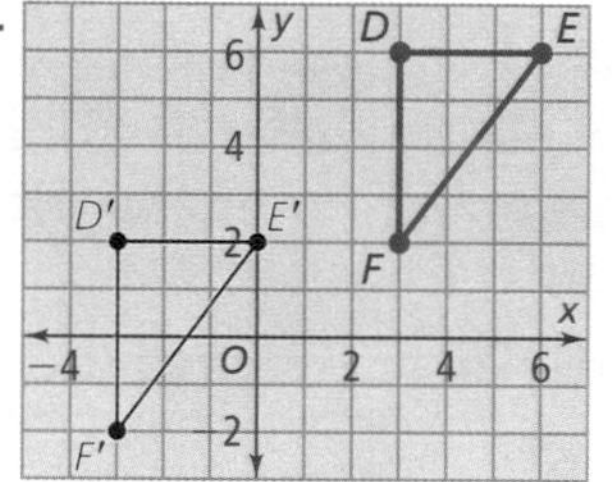

Sketch each preimage and image.

3. $\triangle ABC$ has vertices $A(3, -6)$, $B(1, 0)$, $C(5, 2)$; $T_{<-5,\ 4>}(\triangle ABC)$
4. $\triangle DEF$ has vertices $D(-7, 2)$, $E(-2, 5)$, $F(-3, -3)$; $R_{y\text{-axis}}(\triangle DEF)$
5. $\triangle GHI$ has vertices $G(2, -4)$, $H(4, -3)$, $I(7, -6)$; $r_{(270°,\ O)}(\triangle GHI)$
6. Recall that you can write the composition of rigid motions that describes a translation of quadrilateral $GHJK$ 2 units left and 3 units up, followed by a reflection across the x-axis as $(R_{x\text{-axis}} \circ T_{<-2,3>})(GHJK)$. $GHJK$ has vertices $G(0, 2)$, $H(1, -1)$, $J(3, -3)$, and $K(3, 1)$. Sketch $GHJK$ and $(R_{x\text{-axis}} \circ T_{<-2,3>})(GHJK)$.

3-8 Congruence Transformations

Common Core State Standards
G.CO.7 Use the definition of congruence in terms of rigid motions to show that two triangles are congruent . . .
Also G.CO.6, G.CO.8

Preparing to Teach

BIG ideas Transformations
Visualization

ESSENTIAL UNDERSTANDING

If two figures can be mapped to each other by a sequence of rigid motions, then the figures are congruent.

Math Background

In previous lessons, students have learned that two figures are congruent if and only if corresponding sides have the same length and corresponding angles have the same measure. In this lesson, students explore the concept of congruence transformations. Two figures are congruent if and only if there is a rigid motion or composition of rigid motions that maps one figure to the other.

This new approach to determining congruence can be used to verify postulates such as the SAS Postulate or the SSS Postulate. Students will learn that if there is a way to map one figure onto another through a series of rigid motions, then the figures are congruent.

ELL Support

CONNECT TO PRIOR KNOWLEDGE OF MATH Review with students the Reflexive, Symmetric, and Transitive Properties of Congruence. Discuss with students how you can use congruence transformations to justify these properties.

- Reflexive Property – The identity mapping from a figure onto itself can be used to demonstrate the Reflexive Property of Congruence.
- Symmetric Property – If an isometry is performed on a figure, then the inverse isometry can be performed to map the image back onto the preimage.
- Transitive Property – In a composition of two isometries, the intermediate image (Figure A') is congruent to the preimage (Figure A) and the final image (Figure A'') is congruent to the intermediate image (Figure A'). Because there is a congruence transformation that maps Figure A onto Figure A'', all three figures are congruent.

Lesson Vocabulary

- congruent
- congruence transformation

Mathematical Practices

CONSTRUCT VIABLE ARGUMENTS AND CRITIQUE THE REASONING OF OTHERS. Students will use the properties of rigid motions to construct arguments for the validity of the SAS and SSS congruence postulates.

1 Interactive Learning

Solve It!

PURPOSE To develop an intuitive sense of congruence when working with rigid motions

PROCESS Students may determine that the two wings are identical because one was formed by tracing the other so they overlap exactly.

Q Which angles do you think have the same measures in the two figures? Explain. **[Corresponding angles; the figures are congruent.]**

Q Which sides do you think have the same lengths in the two figures? Explain. **[Corresponding sides; the figures are congruent.]**

ANSWER There is a rigid motion (reflection) from one wing onto the other. When you fold one side of the paper onto the other, the two wings coincide exactly.

CONNECT THE MATH In the Solve It, students connect their knowledge of rigid motions with congruence. They learn that if a transformation preserves angles and lengths, then the preimage and image are congruent figures.

▼ DIGITAL (STUDENT WORK SPACE PAGE 184)

Getting Ready!

Suppose that you want to create two identical wings for a model airplane. You draw one wing on a large sheet of tracing paper, fold it along the dashed line, and then trace the first wing. How do you know that the two wings are identical?

2 Guided Instruction

Problem 1 Identifying Equal Measures

In this problem, students will identify corresponding angles and side lengths after a composition of rigid motions.

Q Would the answer change if trapezoid *LMNO* were reflected first and then rotated to create trapezoid *GHJK*? Explain. **[No, the corresponding angles and sides would still be the same.]**

Got It?

Q How can you use the order of the vertices of the preimage and image to solve the problem? **[The corresponding vertices are listed in order in the composition statement.]**

ANSWERS

Got It? $m\angle A = m\angle X$, $m\angle B = m\angle Y$, $m\angle C = m\angle Z$; $AB = XY$, $BC = YZ$, $AC = XZ$

Practice

1. $m\angle H = m\angle P$, $m\angle J = m\angle R$, $m\angle K = m\angle S$, $HJ = PR$, $JK = RS$, $HK = PS$

▼ STUDENT PAGE 184

In the Solve It, you may have used the properties of rigid motions to describe why the wings are identical.

Essential Understanding You can use compositions of rigid motions to understand congruence.

▼ DIGITAL

Problem 1 Identifying Equal Measures

The composition $(R_n \circ r_{(90°, P)})(LMNO) = GHJK$ is shown at the right.

A Which angle pairs have equal measures?

Because compositions of isometries preserve angle measure, corresponding angles have equal measures.

$m\angle L = m\angle G$, $m\angle M = m\angle H$, $m\angle N = m\angle J$, and $m\angle O = m\angle K$.

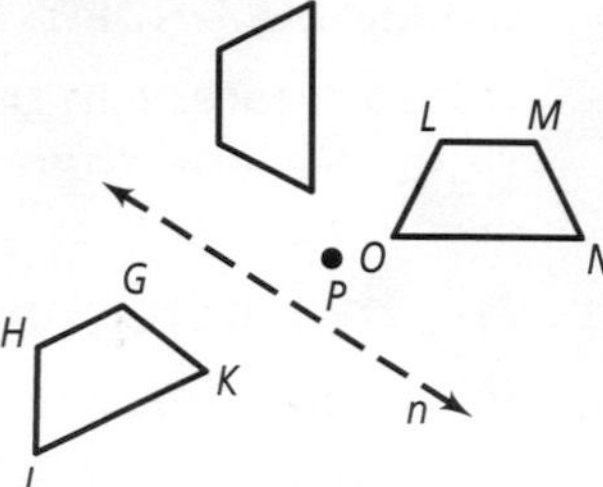

B Which sides have equal lengths?

By definition, isometries preserve distance. So, corresponding side lengths have equal measures.

$LM = GH$, $MN = HJ$, $NO = JK$, and $LO = GK$.

▼ STUDENT PAGE 184

Got It? The composition $(R_t \circ T_{<2, 3>})(\triangle ABC) = \triangle XYZ$. List all of the pairs of angles and sides with equal measures.

Practice 1. The composition $(r_{(180°, O)} \circ T_{<-4, -6>})(\triangle HJK) = \triangle PRS$. List all of the pairs of angles and sides with equal measures.

Problem 2 Identifying Congruent Figures

Take Note EXTENSION

Discuss with students the differences between this definition and the previously learned definition of congruent figures.

Problem 2 VISUAL LEARNERS

Point out to students that the first step should always be to look for two figures that appear to have the same size and shape. Then to verify congruence, they must identify a rigid motion or composition of rigid motions that map one figure to the other.

Q Is there another composition of rigid motions that you could have used to determine the congruence of $\triangle DEF$ and $\triangle LMN$? Explain. **[Yes. For example, a composition of reflections across both axes.]**

▼ STUDENT PAGE 185

In Problem 1 you saw that compositions of rigid motions preserve corresponding side lengths and angle measures. This suggests another way to define congruence.

take note

Key Concept Congruent Figures

Two figures are **congruent** if and only if there is a sequence of one or more rigid motions that maps one figure onto the other.

▼ DIGITAL

Problem 2 Identifying Congruent Figures

Which pairs of figures in the grid are congruent? For each pair, what is a sequence of rigid motions that maps one figure to the other?

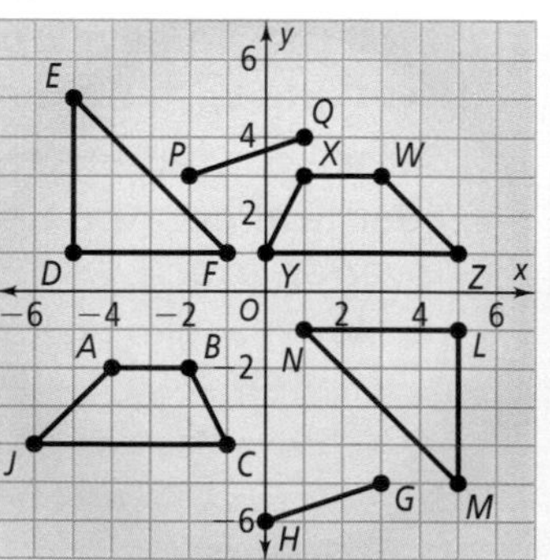

Figures are congruent if and only if there is a sequence of rigid motions that maps one figure to the other. So, to find congruent figures, look for sequences of translations, rotations, and reflections that map one figure to another.

Because $r_{(180°, O)}(\triangle DEF) = \triangle LMN$, the triangles are congruent.

Because $(T_{<-1, 5>} \circ R_{y\text{-axis}})(ABCJ) = WXYZ$, the trapezoids are congruent.

Because $T_{<-2, 9>}(\overline{HG}) = \overline{PQ}$, the line segments are congruent.

Got It?

Q How might you have verified the congruence of $\triangle UVW$ and $\triangle MNQ$ prior to learning the methods of this lesson? Explain. **[Sample answer: Use the Distance Formula to show that the sides have the same lengths and then apply the SSS Postulate.]**

ANSWERS

Got It?

Because $(R_{x\text{-axis}} \circ T_{<-6,\ 0>})(\triangle UVW) = \triangle QNM$, the triangles are congruent. Because $T_{<6,\ -5>}(ABCD) = HIJK$, the parallelograms are congruent.

Practice

2. $\overline{GC} \cong \overline{FD}$; Sample answer: Reflect segment GC over the y-axis; then translate 1 unit right and 2 units down.
3. $FAKE \cong CMDI$; Sample answer: Rotate $FAKE$ 180° about the origin.

▼ STUDENT PAGE 185

Got It? Which pairs of figures in the grid are congruent? For each pair, what is a sequence of rigid motions that maps one figure to the other?

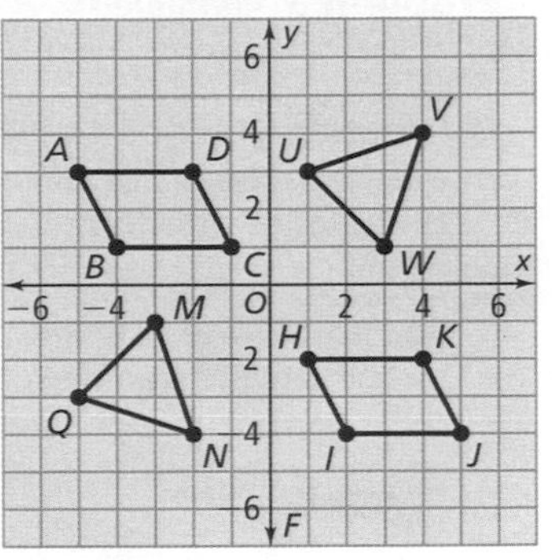

Practice For each coordinate grid, identify a pair of congruent figures. Then determine a congruence transformation that maps the preimage to the congruent image.

2.

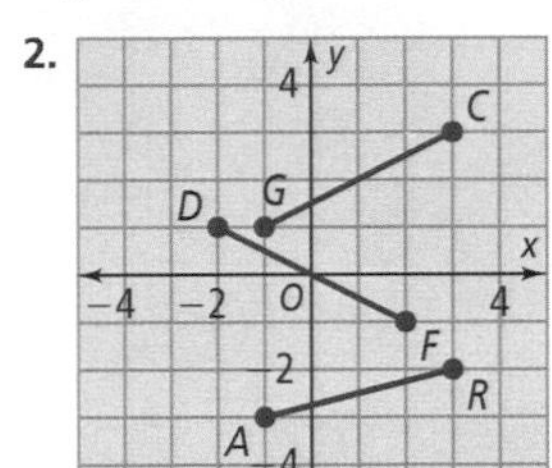

3.

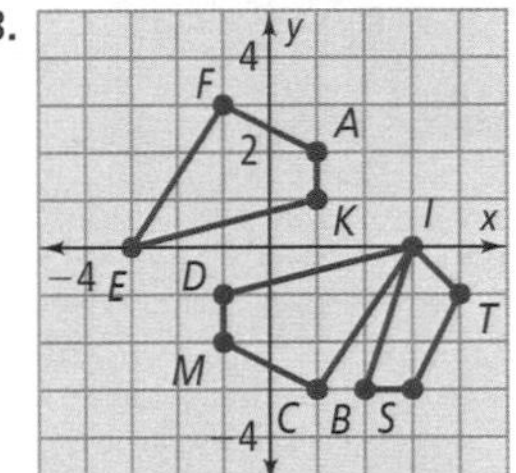

Problem 3 Identifying Congruence Transformations

In this problem, students will identify a congruence transformation that maps one triangle onto another.

Q Is there a single rigid motion that can be used to map $\triangle JQV$ onto $\triangle EWT$? Explain. **[No, $\triangle JQV$ cannot be reflected, translated, or rotated to overlap $\triangle EWT$. A composition of rigid motions is necessary.]**

▼ STUDENT PAGE 186

Because compositions of rigid motions take figures to congruent figures, they are also called **congruence transformations.**

▼ DIGITAL

Problem 3 Identifying Congruence Transformations

In the diagram at the right, $\triangle JQV \cong \triangle EWT$. What is a congruence transformation that maps $\triangle JQV$ onto $\triangle EWT$?

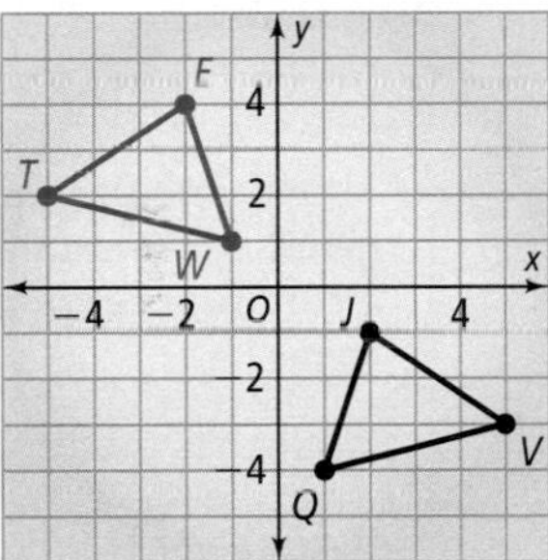

Know
The coordinates of the vertices of the triangles

Need
A sequence of rigid motions that maps $\triangle JQV$ onto $\triangle EWT$

Plan
Identify the corresponding parts and find a congruence transformation that maps the preimage to the image. Then use the vertices to verify the congruence transformation.

Because $\triangle EWT$ lies above $\triangle JQV$ on the plane, a translation can map $\triangle JQV$ up on the plane. Also, notice that $\triangle EWT$ is on the opposite side of the y-axis and has the opposite orientation of $\triangle JQV$. This suggests that the triangle is reflected across the y-axis.

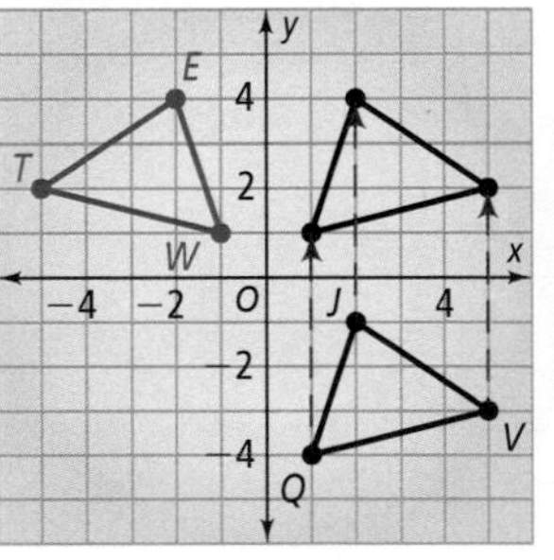

It appears that a translation of $\triangle JQV$ up 5 units, followed by a reflection across the y-axis maps $\triangle JQV$ to $\triangle EWT$. Verify by using the coordinates of the vertices.

$$T_{<5,\ 0>}(x, y) = (x + 5, y)$$
$$T_{<5,\ 0>}(J) = (2, 4)$$
$$R_{y\text{-axis}}(2, 4) = (-2, 4) = E$$

Next, verify that the sequence maps Q to W and V to T.

$$T_{<5,\ 0>}(Q) = (1, 1) \qquad T_{<5,\ 0>}(V) = (5, 2)$$
$$R_{y\text{-axis}}(1, 1) = (-1, 1) = W \qquad R_{y\text{-axis}}(5, 2) = (-5, 2) = T$$

So, the congruence transformation $R_{y\text{-axis}} \circ T_{<5,\ 0>}$ maps $\triangle JQV$ onto $\triangle EWT$. Note that there are other possible congruence transformations that map $\triangle JQV$ onto $\triangle EWT$.

Problem 3 *continued*

Got It?

Q What do you need to show to prove that the triangles are congruent? **[You need to show that there is a congruence transformation that maps △*NAV* onto △*BCY*.]**

Q Looking at the orientation of the triangles, how do you think one triangle can be transformed to map it to the other triangle? **[Sample answer: translation and reflection]**

ANSWERS

Got It? Answers may vary. Sample: $R_{x\text{-axis}} \circ T_{<-5,\ 0>}$

Practice

4. Sample: $T_{<-2,\ 0>} \circ R_{x\text{-axis}}$
5. Sample: $r_{(180°,\ O)}$

▼ STUDENT PAGE 186

Got It? What is a congruence transformation that maps △*NAV* to △*BCY*?

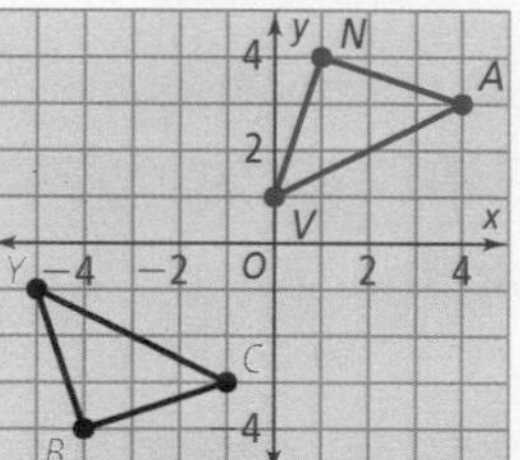

Think What does the orientation of the triangles tell you?

A Practice In Exercises 4 and 5, find a congruence transformation that maps △*LMN* to △*RST*.

4. 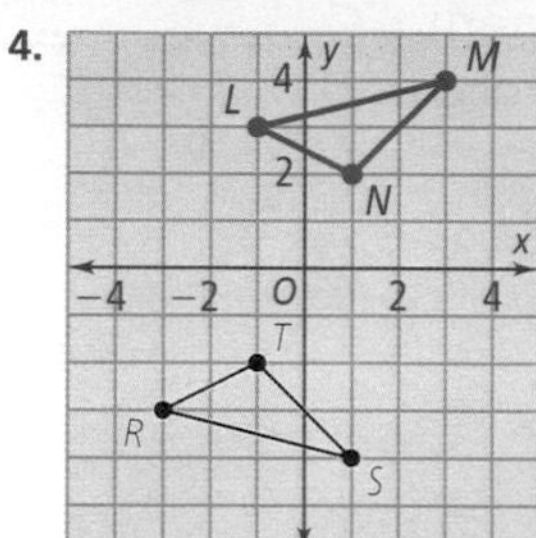

5. 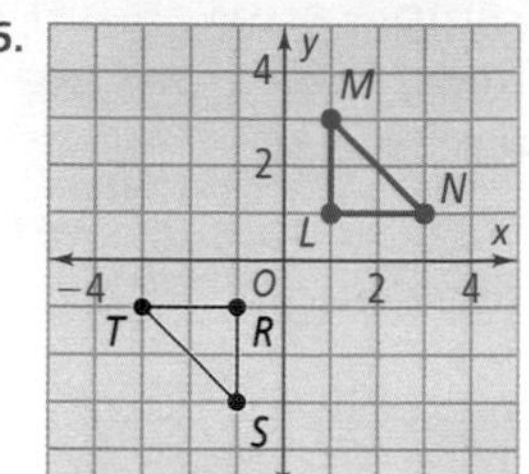

Problem 4 Verifying the SAS Postulate

EXTENSION

In this problem, students will verify the SAS Postulate for proving triangle congruence by finding a congruence transformation that maps one triangle onto the other.

Q Do you think you could use similar methods to verify the SSS Postulate, the ASA Postulate, and the AAS Theorem? Explain. **[Yes, the only difference would be the given information. In all cases, you would simply identify a congruence transformation that maps one triangle to the other.]**

Got It?

Q If a friend is having difficulty seeing the congruence transformation in this problem, how might you help him or her? **[Sample answer: Suggest tracing the triangles on tracing paper and cutting them out. Then slide, flip, and turn the cutouts until they overlap.]**

▼ STUDENT PAGE 187

Earlier in this chapter, you studied triangle congruence postulates and theorems. You can use congruence transformations to justify criteria for determining triangle congruence.

▼ DIGITAL

Problem 4 Verifying the SAS Postulate

Given: $\angle J \cong \angle P$, $\overline{PA} \cong \overline{JO}$, $\overline{FP} \cong \overline{SJ}$

Prove: $\triangle JOS \cong \triangle PAF$

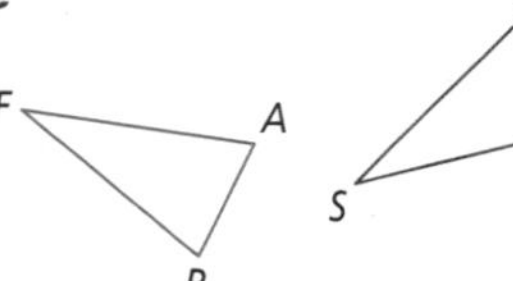

Step 1 Translate △*PAF* so that points *A* and *O* coincide.

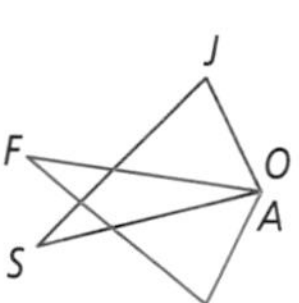

Step 2 Because $\overline{PA} \cong \overline{JO}$, you can rotate △*PAF* about point *A* so that $\overline{PA}$ and $\overline{JO}$ coincide.

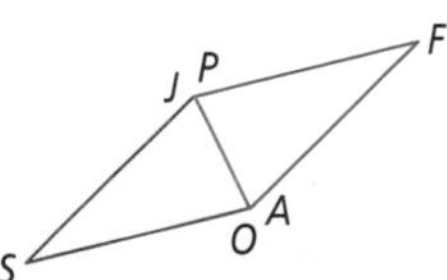

Step 3 Reflect △*PAF* across $\overline{PA}$. Because reflections preserve angle measure and distance, and because $\angle J \cong \angle P$ and $\overline{FP} \cong \overline{SJ}$, you know that the reflection maps $\angle P$ to $\angle J$ and $\overline{FP}$ to $\overline{SJ}$. Since points *S* and *F* coincide, △*PAF* coincides with △*JOS*.

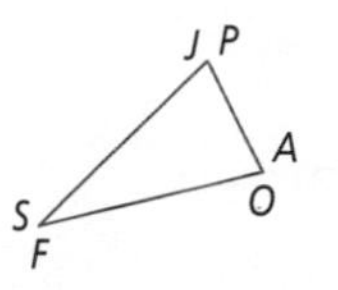

There is a congruence transformation that maps △*PAF* onto △*JOS*, so △*PAF* ≅ △*JOS*.

ANSWERS

Got It? Answers may vary. Sample: Translate $\triangle YDT$ so that point D and point N coincide. Since $\overline{TD} \cong \overline{EN}$, you can rotate $\triangle YDT$ so that $\overline{TD}$ and $\overline{EN}$ coincide. Since rotations preserve angle measure and distance, the other two pairs of sides will also coincide. Therefore, this composition of a translation followed by a rotation maps $\triangle YDT$ to $\triangle SNE$, and $\triangle YDT \cong \triangle SNE$.

Practice

6. Answers will vary. Sample answer: Rotate $\triangle LAH$ so that side HA is parallel to side ES. Translate $\triangle LAH$ so that points E and H coincide. $\triangle EKS \cong \triangle HLA$
7. Answers will vary. Sample answer: Translate $\triangle CIQ$ so that points Q and Z coincide. Rotate $\triangle CIQ$ so that sides QC and NZ coincide. Reflect $\triangle CIQ$ across side NZ so that the triangles overlap. $\triangle NVZ \cong \triangle CIQ$

▼ STUDENT PAGES 187–188

Got It? Verify the SSS postulate.

Given: $TD = EN$, $YT = SE$, $YD = SN$
Prove: $\triangle YDT \cong \triangle SNE$

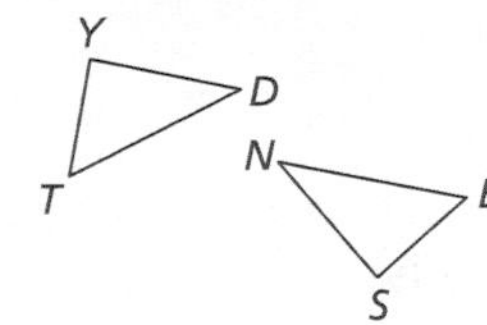

Think

How do you show that the two triangles are congruent?

Practice 6. Verify the ASA Postulate for triangle congruence by using congruence **Proof** transformations.

Given: $\overline{EK} \cong \overline{LH}$, $\angle E \cong \angle H$, $\angle K \cong \angle L$ **Prove:** $\triangle EKS \cong \triangle HLA$

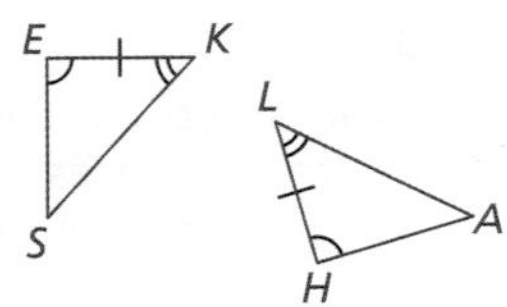

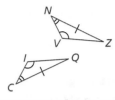

Proof 7. Verify the AAS Postulate for triangle congruence by using congruence transformations.

Given: $\angle I \cong \angle V$, $\angle C \cong \angle N$, $\overline{QC} \cong \overline{NZ}$ **Prove:** $\triangle NVZ \cong \triangle CIQ$

N, V, Z, I, Q, C

Problem 5 Determining Congruence

In this problem, students will determine the congruence of two plane figures.

Challenge students to see how many different ways they can show that figures A and B are congruent.

Got It?

Q How can you show that two figures are not congruent? **[If corresponding distances are not equal, figures are not congruent.]**

ANSWERS

Got It? No, there is no congruence transformation from one figure onto the other because the image is not congruent to the preimage.

Practice

8. yes, reflection
9. No, there is no congruence transformation because the image is not congruent to the preimage.

▼ STUDENT PAGE 188

In Problem 4, you used the transformational approach to prove triangle congruence. Because this approach is more general, you can use what you know about congruence transformations to determine whether any two figures are congruent.

▼ DIGITAL

Problem 5 Determining Congruence

Is Figure A congruent to Figure B? Explain how you know.

Figure A can be mapped to Figure B by a sequence of reflections or a simple translation. So, Figure A is congruent to Figure B because there is a congruence transformation that maps one to the other.

Figure A

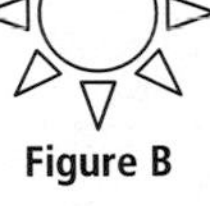

Figure B

▼ STUDENT PAGES 188–189

Got It? Are the figures shown at the right congruent? Explain.

Practice In Exercises 8 and 9, determine whether the figures are congruent. If so, describe a congruence transformation that maps one to the other. If not, explain.

8.

9.

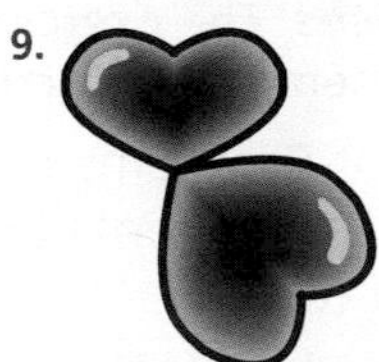

3 Lesson Check

Do you know HOW?

ERROR INTERVENTION

If students have trouble solving Exercise 10, then ask them which triangles could be placed on top of each other so that they coincide.

Do you UNDERSTAND?

Have students share their responses to Exercise 14 with the rest of the class so that everyone is exposed to different real-world examples of congruence transformations.

Close

Q What do you know about corresponding sides and angles of figures that are mapped using a composition of rigid motions? **[They have equal measures.]**

Q How can you show that two figures are congruent? **[Show that there is a sequence of rigid motions that maps one figure onto the other.]**

Q Suppose two figures are congruent. What do you know about how the figures are related in the plane? **[There is a congruence transformation that maps one figure onto the other.]**

ANSWERS

10. $\triangle RAV \cong \triangle QSI$
11. Answers may vary. Sample: $R_{x\text{-axis}} \circ T_{<5,\,-1>}$
12. Answers may vary. Sample answer: Using transformations, you can define congruence of figures other than polygons.
13. Yes. Rotations, translations, and reflections are rigid motions, and a glide reflection is a composition of a translation and a reflection. Compositions of rigid motions are rigid motions, so a rotation followed by a glide reflection is a congruence transformation.
14. Sample answer: The game of chess requires that the chess pieces move on the board by using congruence transformations.

▼ STUDENT PAGES 189–190

Lesson Check

Do you know HOW?

Use the graph for Exercises 10 and 11.

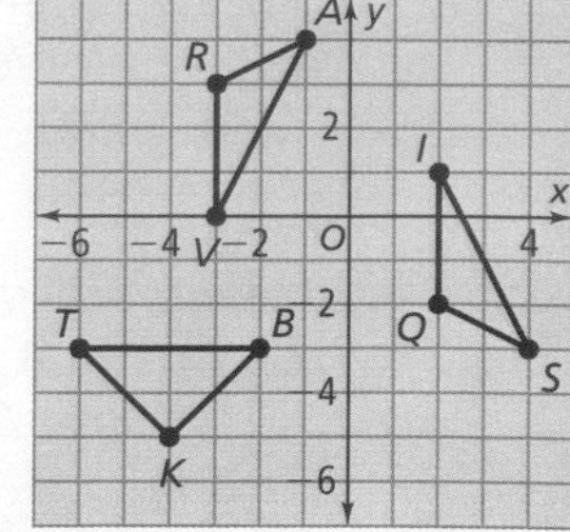

10. Identify a pair of congruent figures and write a congruence statement.
11. What is a congruence transformation that relates two congruent figures?

Do you UNDERSTAND?

12. How can the definition of congruence in terms of rigid motions be more useful than a definition of congruence that relies on corresponding angles and sides?
13. **Reasoning** Is a composition of a rotation followed by a glide reflection a congruence transformation? Explain.
14. **Open-Ended** What is an example of a board game in which a game piece is moved by using a congruence transformation?

4 Practice

More Practice and Problem-Solving Exercises

ASSIGNMENT GUIDE

The assignments below are for the More Practice and Problem-Solving Exercises. You may also want to assign the A-Level Practice Exercises for homework if these are not used in class.

Average: 15–25
Advanced: 15–26

Mathematical Practices The exercises listed focus on the Standards for Mathematical Practices listed.

EX. 19: Make Sense of Problems (MP 1)
EX. 13, 26: Construct Arguments (MP 3)
EX. 14, 20, 21: Model (MP 4)

EXERCISE 25: Use the **Think About a Plan** worksheet in the Online Teacher Resources to further support students' development in becoming independent learners.

▼ STUDENT PAGE 190

More Practice and Problem-Solving Exercises

B Apply

Construction The figure at the right shows a roof truss of a new building. Identify an isometry or composition of isometries to justify each of the following statements.

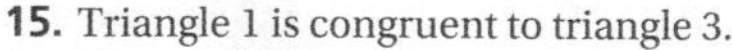
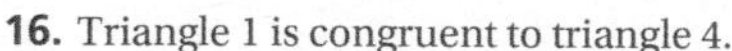

15. Triangle 1 is congruent to triangle 3.
16. Triangle 1 is congruent to triangle 4.
17. Triangle 2 is congruent to triangle 5.
18. **Vocabulary** If two figures are __?__, then there is an isometry that maps one figure onto the other.
19. **Think About a Plan** The figure at the right shows two congruent, isosceles triangles. What are four different isometries that map the top triangle onto the bottom triangle?
    - How can you use the three basic rigid motions to map the top triangle onto the bottom triangle?
    - What other isometries can you use?

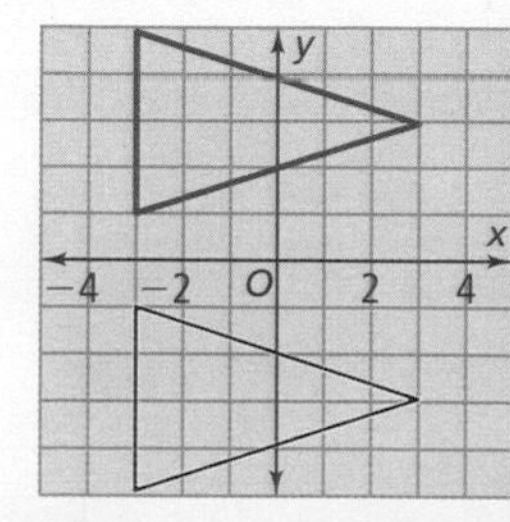

HOMEWORK QUICK CHECK

To check students' understanding of key skills and concepts, go over Exercises 16, 18, 19, 23, and 25.

ANSWERS

15. translation

16. translation and reflection

17. reflection

18. congruent

19. Answers may vary. Sample: Translate the top triangle down 6 units; reflect across the x-axis; rotate the bottom triangle 180° about the point $(-3, 0)$, then reflect across the line $x = -3$; reflect the bottom triangle across the line $x = -4$, then rotate 180° about the point $(-4, 0)$.

20. reflection or rotation

21. **a.** rotations and translations

b. translations and glide reflections

22. glide reflection

23. **a.** Congruence transformations preserve distances and angle measures.

b. Answers may vary. Sample: Use SAS, proven in Problem 4.

24. Sample answer: reflections, translations, rotations, glide reflections

25. Sample answer: Draw and label the midpoint of $\overline{GH}$ as point M. Draw $\overline{FM}$. Using the identity mapping, $\overline{FM} \cong \overline{FM}$. It is given that $\overline{FG} \cong \overline{FH}$, and $\overline{GM} \cong \overline{MH}$ by the definition of midpoint. Therefore, if triangle FHM is reflected across $\overline{FM}$, it will overlap triangle FGM. Because there is an isometry mapping triangle FHM onto triangle FGM, $\triangle FHM \cong \triangle FGM$. Therefore, $\angle G \cong \angle H$ because corresp. parts of $\cong$ △ are $\cong$.

26. Sample answer: No, the image is likely enlarged to be seen more easily, so it is not congruent to the preimage.

▼ STUDENT PAGE 191

20. Graphic Design Most companies have a logo that is used on company letterhead and signs. A graphic designer sketched the logo at the right. What congruence transformations might she have used to draw this logo?

21. Art Artists frequently use congruence transformations in their work. The artworks shown below are called *tessellations*. What types of congruence transformations can you identify in the tessellations?

a.

b.

22. In the footprints shown below, what congruence transformations can you use to extend the footsteps?

Proof **23.** Prove the statements in parts (a) and (b) to show congruence in terms of transformations is equivalent to the criteria for triangle congruence you learned earlier in this chapter.

a. If there is a congruence transformation that maps $\triangle ABC$ to $\triangle DEF$ then corresponding pairs of sides and corresponding pairs of angles are congruent.

b. In $\triangle ABC$ and $\triangle DEF$, if corresponding pairs of sides and corresponding pairs of angles are congruent, then there is a congruence transformation that maps $\triangle ABC$ to $\triangle DEF$.

24. Baking Cookie makers often use a cookie press so that the cookies all look the same. The baker fills a cookie sheet for baking in the pattern shown. What types of congruence transformations are being used to set each cookie on the sheet?

Proof **25.** Use congruence transformations to prove the Isosceles Triangle Theorem.

Given: $\overline{FG} \cong \overline{FH}$

Prove: $\angle G \cong \angle H$

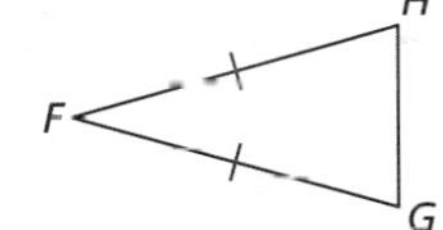

Challenge

26. Reasoning You project an image for viewing in a large classroom. Is the projection of the image an example of a congruence transformation? Explain your reasoning.

5 Assess and Remediate

Lesson Quiz

1. What is a congruence transformation that maps $\triangle KNO$ to $\triangle AWN$?

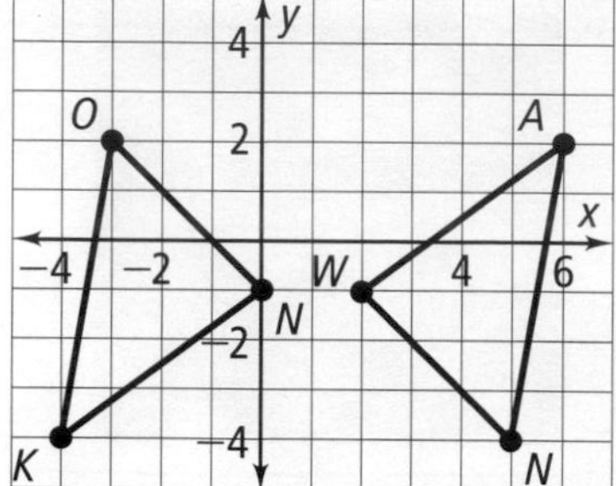

2. **Do you UNDERSTAND?** Is there only one congruence transformation that maps one figure to another figure? Explain.
3. Are the figures below congruent? Explain.

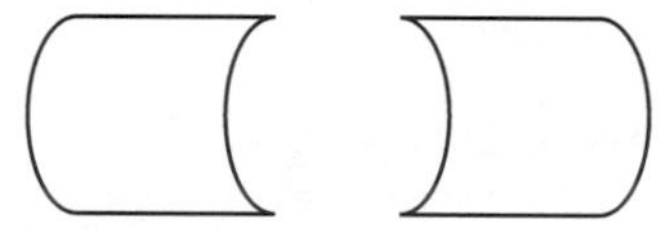

ANSWERS TO LESSON QUIZ

1. Sample answer: $(T_{<2, -2>} \circ r_{(180°, O)})(\triangle KNO) = \triangle AWN$.
2. Sample answer: No, there are typically other congruence transformations that map one figure to another. For example, any translation or rotation can be described as a composition of reflections.
3. Yes, there is a congruence transformation (reflection) from one figure to the other.

Prescription for Remediation

Use the student work on the Lesson Quiz to prescribe a differentiated assignment.

Points	Differentiated Remediation
0–1	Intervention
2	On-level
3	Extension

Online Assessment

Assign the Lesson Quiz in Success Tracker on **pearsonsuccessnet.com**. Success Tracker will automatically score the quiz and assign appropriate intervention or enrichment to each student based on the results. The compiled data appear in three different reports for instant analysis of whole class and individual student performance.

Differentiated Remediation

Intervention

- **RETEACHING** (2 pages) Provides reteaching and practice exercises for the key lesson concepts. Use with struggling students or absent students.
- **ENGLISH LANGUAGE LEARNER SUPPORT** Helps students develop and reinforce mathematical vocabulary and key concepts.

On-Level

- **PRACTICE** (2 pages) Provides extra practice for each lesson. For simpler practice exercises, use the Form K Practice pages found in the Online Teacher Resources.
- **THINK ABOUT A PLAN** Helps students develop specific problem-solving skills and strategies by providing scaffolded guiding questions.
- **STANDARDIZED TEST PREP** Focuses on all major exercises, all major question types, and helps students prepare for the high-stakes assessments.

Extension

- **ENRICHMENT** Provides students with interesting problems and activities that extend the concepts of the lesson.
- **ACTIVITIES, GAMES, AND PUZZLES** Worksheets that can be used for concept development, enrichment, and for fun!

3 Chapter Review

Essential Questions

BIG idea Visualization

ESSENTIAL QUESTION How do you identify corresponding parts of congruent triangles?

ANSWER You can identify corresponding parts of congruent triangles by visualizing the figures placed on top of each other.

BIG idea Reasoning and Proof

ESSENTIAL QUESTION How do you show that two triangles are congruent?

ANSWER You can show two triangles are congruent by proving that certain relationships exist between three pairs of corresponding parts.

BIG idea Reasoning and Proof

ESSENTIAL QUESTION How can you tell whether a triangle is isosceles or equilateral?

ANSWER You can tell whether a triangle is isosceles or equilateral by looking at the number of congruent angles or sides.

Summative Questions

Use the following prompts as you review this chapter with your students. The prompts are designed to help you assess your students' understanding of the BIG Ideas they have studied.

- What are the postulates and theorems used to prove triangles congruent?
- What conditions exist in isosceles triangles?
- Is every equilateral triangle isosceles?

3-1 Congruent Figures

ANSWERS

1. $\overline{ML}$
2. $\angle U$
3. $\overline{ST}$
4. *ONMLK*
5. 80
6. 3
7. 5
8. 35
9. 100
10. 145

▼ STUDENT PAGE 192

3-1 Congruent Figures

Quick Review

Congruent polygons have congruent corresponding parts. When you name congruent polygons, always list corresponding vertices in the same order.

Example

$HIJK \cong PQRS$. Write all possible congruence statements.

The order of the parts in the congruence statement tells you which parts correspond.

Sides: $\overline{HI} \cong \overline{PQ}$, $\overline{IJ} \cong \overline{QR}$, $\overline{JK} \cong \overline{RS}$, $\overline{KH} \cong \overline{SP}$

Angles: $\angle H \cong \angle P$, $\angle I \cong \angle Q$, $\angle J \cong \angle R$, $\angle K \cong \angle S$

Exercises

$RSTUV \cong KLMNO$. Complete the congruence statements.

1. $\overline{TS} \cong$ __?__
2. $\angle N \cong$ __?__
3. $\overline{LM} \cong$ __?__
4. $VUTSR \cong$ __?__

$WXYZ \cong PQRS$. Find each measure or length.

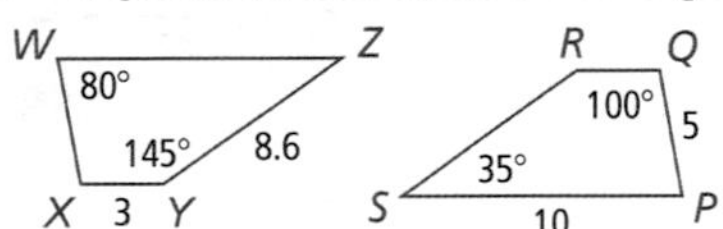

5. $m\angle P$
6. QR
7. WX
8. $m\angle Z$
9. $m\angle X$
10. $m\angle R$

Chapter Review *(continued)*

3-2 and 3-3 Triangle Congruence by SSS, SAS, ASA, and AAS

ANSWERS

11. $\angle D$

12. $\overline{MR}$

13. not enough information

14. not enough information

15. SAS

16. AAS or ASA

▼ STUDENT PAGE 192

3-2 and 3-3 Triangle Congruence by SSS, SAS, ASA, and AAS

Quick Review

You can prove triangles congruent with limited information about their congruent sides and angles.

Postulate or Theorem	You Need
Side-Side-Side (SSS)	three sides
Side-Angle-Side (SAS)	two sides and an included angle
Angle-Side-Angle (ASA)	two angles and an included side
Angle-Angle-Side (AAS)	two angles and a nonincluded side

Example

What postulate would you use to prove the triangles congruent?

You know that three pairs of sides are congruent. Use SSS.

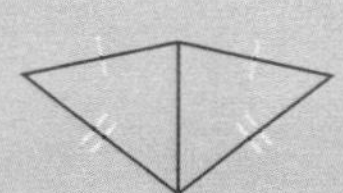

Exercises

11. In $\triangle HFD$, what angle is included between $\overline{DH}$ and $\overline{DF}$?

12. In $\triangle OMR$, what side is included between $\angle M$ and $\angle R$?

Which postulate or theorem, if any, could you use to prove the two triangles congruent? If there is not enough information to prove the triangles congruent, write *not enough information.*

13. 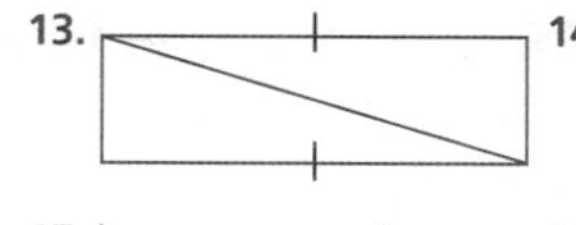

14. 

15.

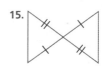

16. 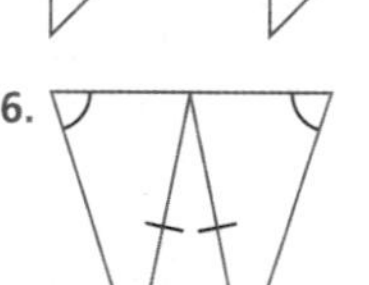

3-4 Using Corresponding Parts of Congruent Triangles

ANSWERS

17. $\triangle TVY \cong \triangle YWX$ by AAS, so $\overline{TV} \cong \overline{YW}$ because corresp. parts of $\cong$ ⚠ are $\cong$.

18. $\triangle BEC \cong \triangle DEC$ by ASA, so $\overline{BE} \cong \overline{DE}$ because corresp. parts of $\cong$ ⚠ are $\cong$.

19. $\triangle BEC \cong \triangle DEC$ by SSS, so $\angle B \cong \angle D$ because corresp. parts of $\cong$ ⚠ are $\cong$.

20. If lines are $\parallel$, then alt. int. ∠s are $\cong$, so $\angle LKM \cong \angle NMK$. Then $\triangle LKM \cong \triangle NMK$ by SAS, and $\overline{KN} \cong \overline{ML}$ because corresp. parts of $\cong$ ⚠ are $\cong$.

▼ STUDENT PAGE 193

3-4 Using Corresponding Parts of Congruent Triangles

Quick Review

Once you know that triangles are congruent, you can make conclusions about corresponding sides and angles because, by definition, corresponding parts of congruent triangles are congruent. You can use congruent triangles in the proofs of many theorems.

Example

How can you use congruent triangles to prove $\angle Q \cong \angle D$?

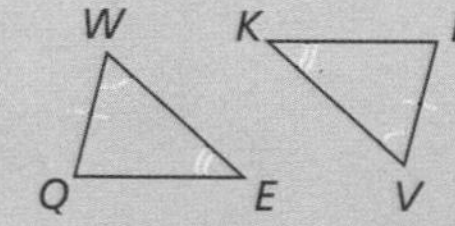

Since $\triangle QWE \cong \triangle DVK$ by AAS, you know that $\angle Q \cong \angle D$ because corresponding parts of congruent triangles are congruent.

Exercises

How can you use congruent triangles to prove the statement true?

17. $\overline{TV} \cong \overline{YW}$

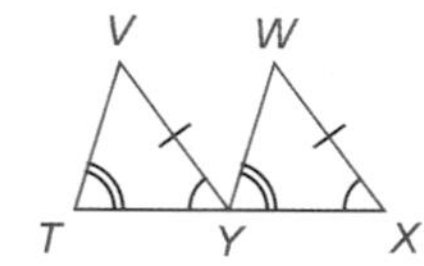

18. $\overline{BE} \cong \overline{DE}$

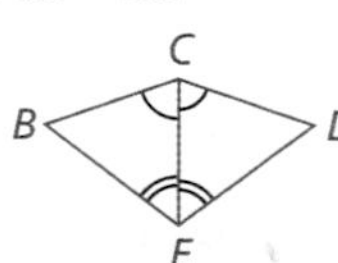

19. $\angle B \cong \angle D$

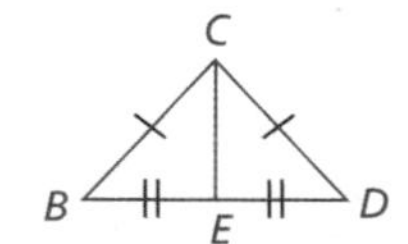

20. $\overline{KN} \cong \overline{ML}$

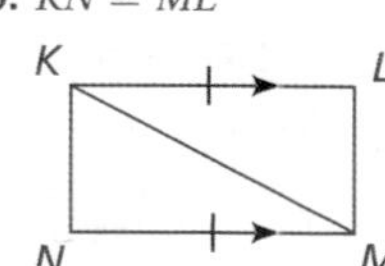

3-5 Isosceles and Equilateral Triangles

ANSWERS

21. $x = 4$, $y = 65$

22. $x = 55$, $y = 62.5$

23. $x = 65$, $y = 90$

24. $x = 7$, $y = 60$

▼ STUDENT PAGE 193

3-5 Isosceles and Equilateral Triangles

Quick Review

If two sides of a triangle are congruent, then the angles opposite those sides are also congruent by the **Isosceles Triangle Theorem.** If two angles of a triangle are congruent, then the sides opposite the angle are congruent by the **Converse of the Isosceles Triangle Theorem.**

Equilateral triangles are also equiangular.

Example

What is $m\angle G$?

Since $\overline{EF} \cong \overline{EG}$, $\angle F \cong \angle G$ by the Isosceles Triangle Theorem. So $m\angle G = 30$.

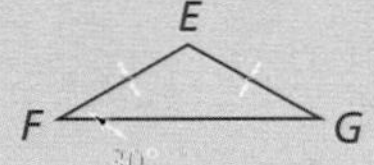

Exercises

Algebra Find the values of x and y.

21.

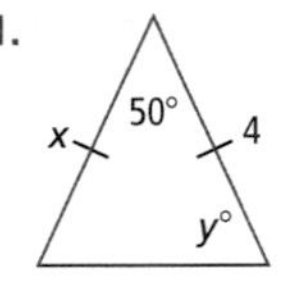

22.

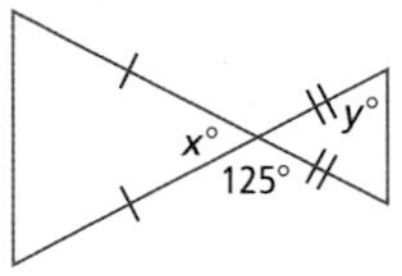

23.

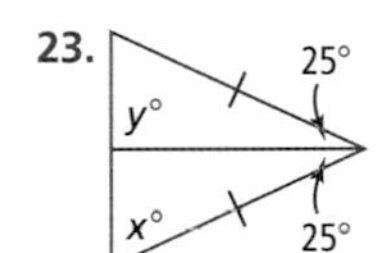

24.

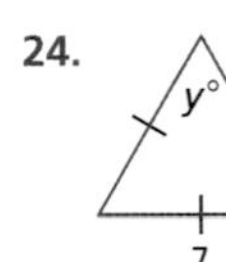

3-6 Congruence in Right Triangles

ANSWERS

25. $\overline{LN} \perp \overline{KM}$ (Given), so $\triangle KLN$ and $\triangle MLN$ are rt. $\triangle$s. $\overline{KL} \cong \overline{ML}$ (Given) and $\overline{LN} \cong \overline{LN}$ (Refl. Prop. of $\cong$), so $\triangle KLN \cong \triangle MLN$ by HL.

26. The given information on $\perp$ segments means $\triangle PSQ$ and $\triangle RQS$ are rt. $\triangle$s. You know $\overline{PQ} \cong \overline{RS}$ (Given) and $\overline{QS} \cong \overline{QS}$ (Refl. Prop. of $\cong$). So $\triangle PSQ \cong \triangle RQS$ by HL.

▼ STUDENT PAGE 194

3-6 Congruence in Right Triangles

Quick Review

If the hypotenuse and a leg of one right triangle are congruent to the hypotenuse and a leg of another right triangle, then the triangles are congruent by the **Hypotenuse-Leg (HL) Theorem.**

Example

Which two triangles are congruent? Explain.

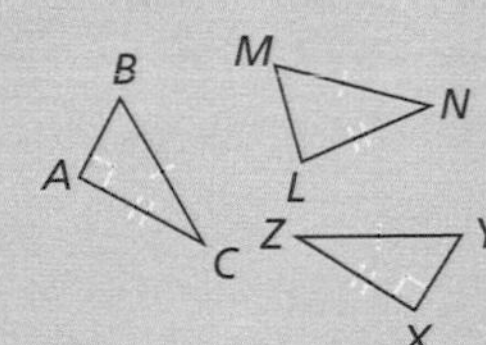

Since $\triangle ABC$ and $\triangle XYZ$ are right triangles with congruent legs, and $\overline{BC} \cong \overline{YZ}$, $\triangle ABC \cong \triangle XYZ$ by HL.

Exercises

Write a proof for each of the following.

25. Given: $\overline{LN} \perp \overline{KM}$, $\overline{KL} \cong \overline{ML}$

Prove: $\triangle KLN \cong \triangle MLN$

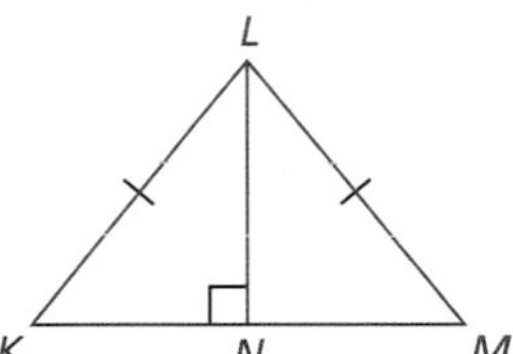

26. Given: $\overline{PS} \perp \overline{SQ}$, $\overline{RQ} \perp \overline{QS}$, $\overline{PQ} \cong \overline{RS}$

Prove: $\triangle PSQ \cong \triangle RQS$

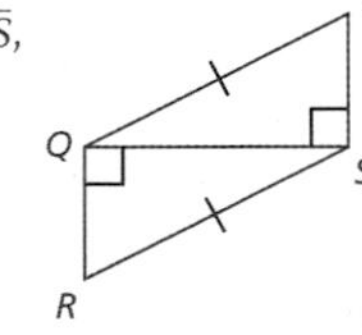

Chapter Review *(continued)*

3-7 Congruence in Overlapping Triangles

ANSWERS

27. $\triangle AEC \cong \triangle ABD$ by SAS, ASA, or AAS.

28. $\triangle FIH \cong \triangle GHI$ by SAS.

29. $\triangle TAR \cong \triangle TSP$ by ASA.

▼ STUDENT PAGE 194

3-7 Congruence in Overlapping Triangles

Quick Review

To prove overlapping triangles congruent, you look for the common or shared sides and angles.

Example

Separate and redraw the overlapping triangles. Label the vertices.

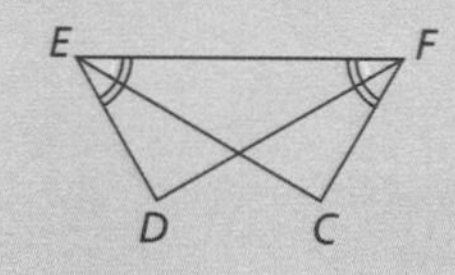

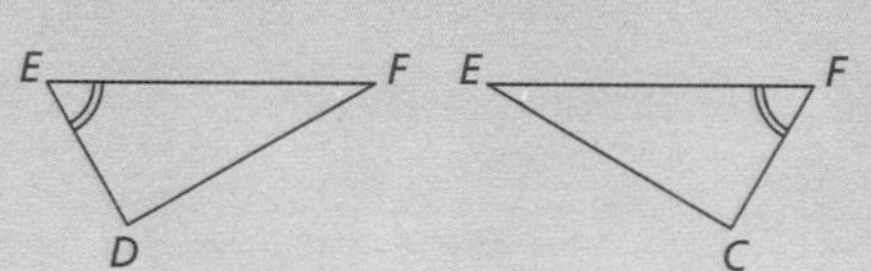

Exercises

Name a pair of overlapping congruent triangles in each diagram. State whether the triangles are congruent by SSS, SAS, ASA, AAS, or HL.

27.

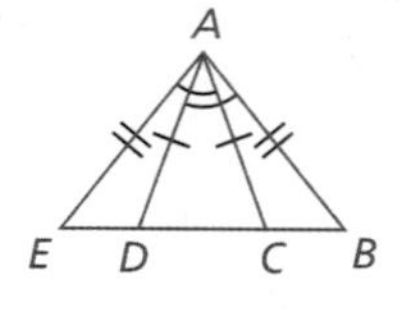

28.

29.

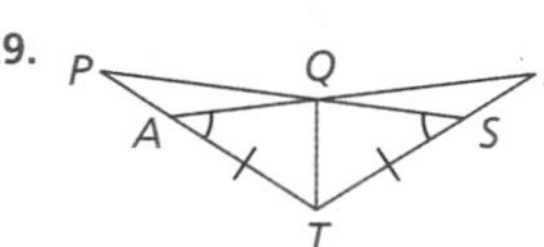

3-8 Congruence Transformations

ANSWERS

30. Answers may vary. Sample: $(r_{(90°, O)} \circ R_{x\text{-axis}})(\triangle XYZ)$

31. Answers may vary. Sample: Yes, the letters are congruent. The *p* can be mapped to the *d* with a composition of a translation followed by a rotation.

▼ STUDENT PAGE 195

3-8 Congruence Transformations

Quick Review

Two figures are congruent if and only if there is a sequence of rigid motions that maps one figure onto the other.

Example

$R_{y\text{-axis}}(TGMB) = KWAV$. What are all of the congruent angles and all of the congruent sides?

A reflection is a congruence transformation, so $TGMB \cong KWAV$, and corresponding angles and corresponding sides are congruent.

$\angle T \cong \angle K$, $\angle G \cong \angle W$, $\angle M \cong \angle A$, and $\angle B \cong \angle V$
$TG = KW$, $GM = WA$, $MB = AV$, and $TB = KV$

Exercises

30. In the diagram below, $\triangle LMN \cong \triangle XYZ$. Identify a congruence transformation that maps $\triangle LMN$ onto $\triangle XYZ$.

31. Fonts Graphic designers use some fonts because they have pleasing proportions or are easy to read from far away. The letters p and d above are used on a sign using a special font. Are the letters congruent? If so, describe a congruence transformation that maps one onto the other. If not, explain why not.

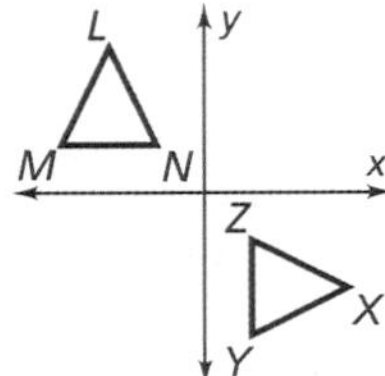

Pull It All Together

Common Core State Standards
G.SRT.5 Use congruence . . . criteria for triangles to solve problems and to prove relationships in geometric figures.
Also G.CO.10

Using Performance Tasks

Understanding by Design® principles support using performance tasks to assess students' progress toward mastering content standards and developing proficiency with the Mathematical Practices.

Mathematical Practices

- Make sense of problems and persevere in solving them.
- Model with mathematics.
- Construct viable arguments.

Assessing Performance

See the Implementation Guide for a holistic scoring rubric to use in assessing students' work on the performance task.

Guiding Questions

Q Which angles in the diagram are right angles? Which are vertical angles?

Q Is it possible to prove that triangles *ABC* and *AYX* are congruent? How?

Solution Outline

The diagram can be labeled as shown.

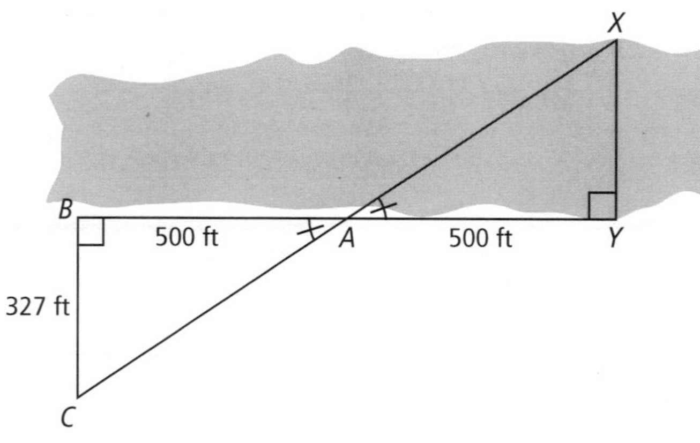

The distances are measured by Jamal. The right angles indicate that $\overline{BC}$ and $\overline{XY}$ are perpendicular to the canyon. $\angle BAC$ and $\angle YAX$ are congruent vertical angles.

XY represents the required distance across the canyon. $\triangle ABC$ and $\triangle AYX$ are congruent by ASA. Because corresponding parts of congruent triangles are congruent, $\overline{BC}$ and $\overline{XY}$ are congruent. Therefore $XY = BC$ and the approximate distance across the canyon is 327 feet.

▼ STUDENT PAGE 196

ASSESSMENT

Applying Indirect Measurement

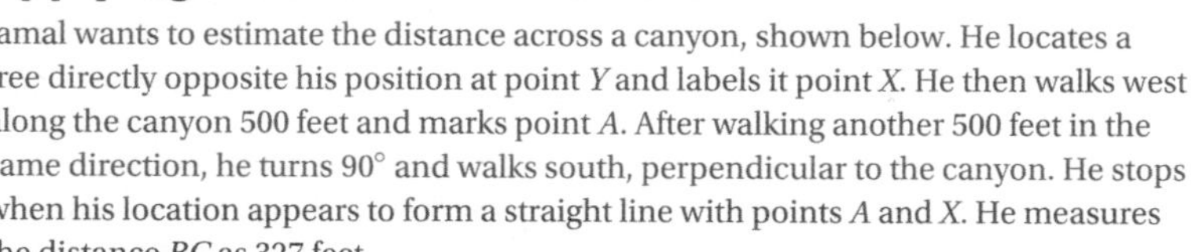
Jamal wants to estimate the distance across a canyon, shown below. He locates a tree directly opposite his position at point *Y* and labels it point *X*. He then walks west along the canyon 500 feet and marks point *A*. After walking another 500 feet in the same direction, he turns 90° and walks south, perpendicular to the canyon. He stops when his location appears to form a straight line with points *A* and *X*. He measures the distance *BC* as 327 feet.

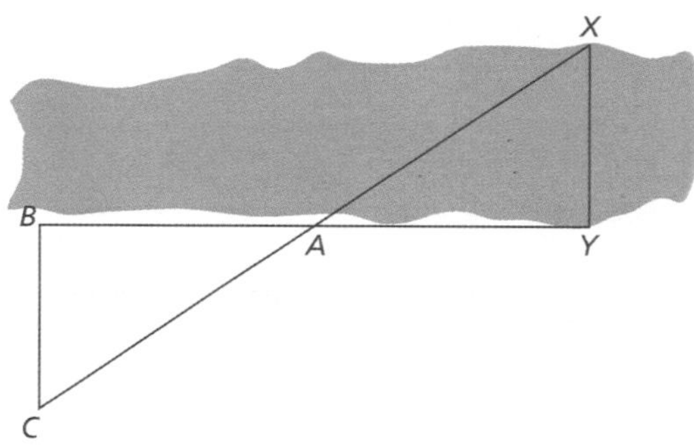

Task Description

Label the diagram above using the information given. Then estimate the distance across the canyon. Justify your answer.

- What part of the diagram represents the distance across the canyon?
- How are triangles *ABC* and *AYX* related?

Get Ready!

Using This Diagnostic Assessment

Assign this diagnostic assessment to determine if students have the prerequisite skills for Chapter 4.

Lesson	Skill
1-1	Basic Constructions
Previous Course	The Midpoint Formula and Distance Formula
1-3	Finding the Negation
Previous Course	Slope

To remediate students, select from these resources (available for every lesson).

- Online Problems (pearsonsuccessnet.com)
- Reteaching (Online Teacher Resources)
- Practice (Online Teacher Resources)

Why Students Need These Skills

BASIC CONSTRUCTIONS Students will use construction techniques for generating perpendicular and angle bisectors.

THE MIDPOINT FORMULA AND DISTANCE FORMULA For triangles on the coordinate plane, these formulas are used to identify special segments in triangles.

FINDING THE NEGATION Negations are used to begin indirect proofs.

SLOPE Students will use slope to find relationships within triangles on the coordinate plane.

Looking Ahead Vocabulary

DISTANCE BETWEEN A POINT AND A LINE Have students identify the shortest path between their location and a wall in the classroom.

MIDSEGMENT Have students identify other words that use the prefix *mid-*.

CONCURRENT Have students name events that may occur concurrently.

ANSWERS

1.

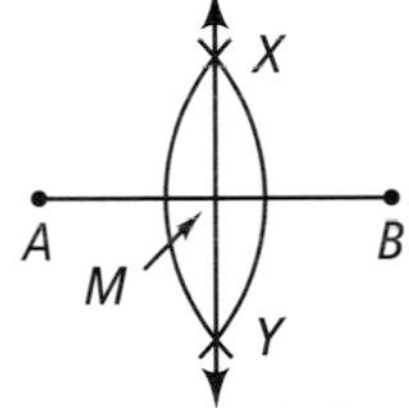

2.

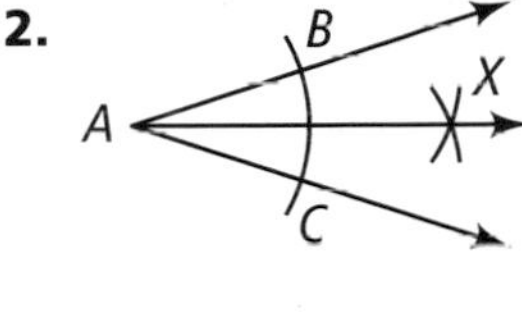

3. midpt. of $\overline{AB}$: (1, 2); midpt. of $\overline{BC}$: (−1, −2); midpt. of $\overline{AC}$: (3, −3); $AB = 2\sqrt{17}$; $BC = 2\sqrt{29}$; $AC = 4\sqrt{5}$

4. midpt. of $\overline{AB}$: (4, 2); midpt. of $\overline{BC}$: (4, 5); midpt. of $\overline{AC}$: (−1, 5); $AB = 10$; $BC = 2\sqrt{34}$; $AC = 6$

5. midpt. of $\overline{AB}$: (0, −3); midpt. of $\overline{BC}$: (1, 0); midpt. of $\overline{AC}$: (−1, 0); $AB = 4$; $BC = 2\sqrt{10}$; $AC = 2\sqrt{10}$

6. The team did not win.

7. It is too late. **8.** $m\angle R \leq 60$

9. −6 **10.** $-\frac{8}{3}$ **11.** undefined

12. the length of a ⊥ segment from the point to the line

13. a segment that connects the midpts. of 2 sides of the triangle

14. The lines intersect at one point, or the lines have exactly one point in common.

▼ STUDENT PAGE 197

Basic Constructions

Use a compass and straightedge for each construction.

1. Construct the perpendicular bisector of a segment.

2. Construct the bisector of an angle.

The Midpoint Formula and Distance Formula

Find the coordinates of the midpoints of the sides of $\triangle ABC$. Then find the lengths of the three sides of the triangle.

3. $A(5, 1)$, $B(-3, 3)$, $C(1, -7)$

4. $A(-1, 2)$, $B(9, 2)$, $C(-1, 8)$

5. $A(-2, -3)$, $B(2, -3)$, $C(0, 3)$

Finding the Negation

Write the negation of each statement.

6. The team won. **7.** It is not too late. **8.** $m\angle R > 60$

Slope

Find the slope of the line passing through the given points.

9. $A(9, 6)$, $B(8, 12)$ **10.** $C(3, -2)$, $D(0, 6)$ **11.** $E(-3, 7)$, $F(-3, 12)$

Looking Ahead Vocabulary

12. The *distance* between your home and your school is the length of the shortest path connecting them. How might you define the *distance between a point and a line* in geometry?

13. Consider the *midpoint* of a segment. What do you think a *midsegment* of a triangle is?

14. If two parties are happening at the same time, they are *concurrent*. What would it mean for three lines to be *concurrent*?

CHAPTER
4

PROVING THEOREMS ABOUT TRIANGLES

Chapter 4 Overview

Interactive Digital Path
Log in to pearsonsuccessnet.com and click on Interactive Digital Path to access the Solve Its and animated Problems.

In Chapter 4 students expand on the skills learned in the previous chapter. In this chapter, students will develop the answers to the Essential Questions posed below as they learn the bulleted concepts and skills.

BIG idea Coordinate Geometry

ESSENTIAL QUESTION How do you use coordinate geometry to find relationships within triangles?

- Students will use the Midpoint Formula to find midsegments of triangles.
- Students will use the Distance and Slope Formulas to examine relationships in triangles.

BIG idea Measurement

ESSENTIAL QUESTION How do you solve problems that involve measurements of triangles?

- Students will examine inequalities in one triangle.
- Students will examine inequalities in two triangles.

BIG idea Reasoning and Proof

ESSENTIAL QUESTION How do you write indirect proofs?

- Students will begin with the negation of the statement to be proved and will show a counterexample.

Chapter Preview

4-1 Midsegments of Triangles
4-2 Perpendicular and Angle Bisectors
4-3 Bisectors in Triangles
4-4 Medians and Altitudes
4-5 Indirect Proof
4-6 Inequalities in One Triangle
4-7 Inequalities in Two Triangles

Dynamic Activity

Use the Dynamic Activity, an interactive math tool with guided instruction, to have students explore concepts visually and support the development of the Standards for Mathematical Practice.

Content Standards

Following are the key standards covered in this chapter.

Conceptual Category Geometry

DOMAIN Congruence G.CO
CLUSTER Prove geometric theorems (Standards G.CO.9, G.CO.10) **LESSONS** 4-1, 4-2, 4-3, 4-4, 4-5, 4-6, 4-7
CLUSTER Make geometric constructions (Standard G.CO.12) **LESSON** 4-2

DOMAIN Similarity, Right Triangles, and Trigonometry G.SRT
CLUSTER Prove theorems involving similarity (Standard G.SRT.5) **LESSONS** 4-1, 4-2, 4-4

DOMAIN Circles G.C
CLUSTER Understand and apply theorems about circles (Standard G.C.3) **LESSON** 4-3

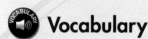

Vocabulary

English/Spanish Vocabulary Audio Online:

English	Spanish
altitude of a triangle *p. 225**	altura de un triángulo
centroid *p. 223*	centroid
circumcenter *p. 215*	circuncentro
concurrent *p. 215*	concurrente
equidistant *p. 207*	equidistante
incenter *p. 218*	incentro
indirect proof *p. 232*	prueba indirecta
median *p. 223*	mediana
midsegment of a triangle *p. 199*	segmento medio de un triángulo
orthocenter *p. 226*	ortocentro

**All page numbers refer to the Student Edition.*

Proving Theorems About Triangles

Math Background

Understanding by Design® principles were central to the development of the Big Ideas and the Essential Understandings. These will help your students build a structure on which to make connections to prior learning.*

Coordinate Geometry

BIG idea A coordinate system in a plane is formed by two perpendicular number lines, called the *x*- and *y*-axes, and the quadrants they form. It is possible to verify some complex truths using deductive reasoning in combination with Distance, Midpoint, and Slope formulas.

ESSENTIAL UNDERSTANDINGS

4-1 The midsegment of a triangle can be used to uncover relationships within a triangle.

Reasoning and Proof

BIG idea Definitions establish meanings and remove possible misunderstanding. Other truths are more complex and difficult to see. It is often possible to verify complex truths by reasoning from simpler ones by using deductive reasoning.

ESSENTIAL UNDERSTANDINGS

4-2 Triangles play a key role in relationships involving perpendicular bisectors and angle bisectors.

4-3 to 4-4 There are special parts of a triangle that are always concurrent. A triangle's three perpendicular bisectors are always concurrent, as are a triangle's three angle bisectors, its three medians, and its three altitudes.

4-5 In indirect reasoning, all possibilities are considered and then all but one are proved false. The remaining possibility must be true.

4-6 The measures of the angles of a triangle are related to the lengths of the opposite sides.

4-7 In triangles that have two pairs of congruent sides, there is a relationship between the included angles and the third pair of sides.

Measurement

BIG idea Some attributes of geometric figures, such as length, area, volume, and angle measure, are measurable. Units are used to describe these attributes.

ESSENTIAL UNDERSTANDINGS

4-2 Geometric figures such as angle bisectors and perpendicular bisectors can be used to cut the measure of an angle or segment in half.

4-3 Angle bisectors and segment bisectors can be used in triangles to determine various angle and segment measures.

4-4 The length of medians and altitudes in a triangle can be determined given the measures of other triangle segments.

*UNDERSTANDING BY DESIGN® and UbD™ are trademarks of ASCD, and are used under license.

Special Segments in Triangles

Five special segments are defined in this chapter.

Midsegment is a segment that connects the midpoints of two sides.

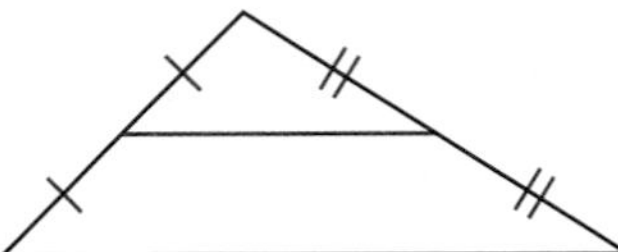

Perpendicular Bisector is a segment that bisects a side and is perpendicular to that side.

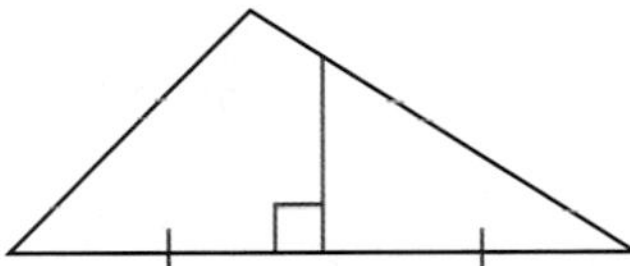

Angle Bisector is a segment that bisects an angle.

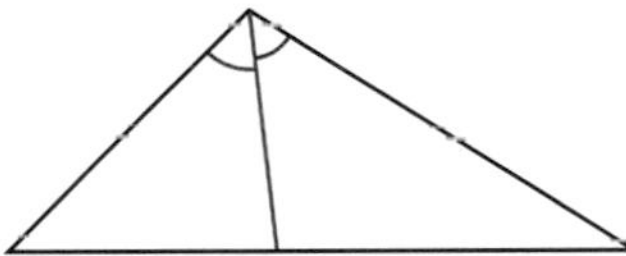

Median is a segment that connects a vertex to the midpoint of the opposite side.

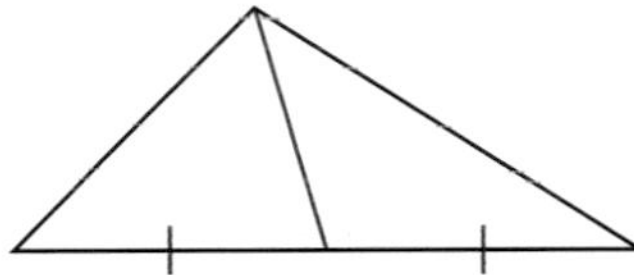

Altitude is a segment from a vertex, perpendicular to the line that contains the opposite side.

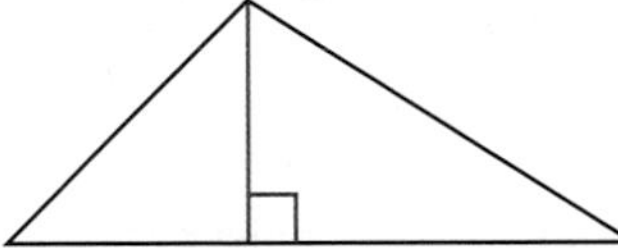

Common Errors With Special Segments in Triangles

Special segments can often be difficult to distinguish from each other. Students should use angle and segment congruency marks and right angle marks (as above) to help make clear the purpose of a given segment.

Mathematical Practices

Use appropriate tools strategically Students explore special segments and their intersections using a mix of coordinate geometry and deductive reasoning. They can see how different mathematical tools are useful in different situations. The dynamic geometry software inductively shows numerous examples of the midsegment theorem and the theorems on concurrency of perpendicular bisectors and angle bisectors.

Math Background *(continued)*

Indirect Proof

Indirect proof involves assuming the opposite of a statement you wish to prove, then showing a contradiction of the given information. Indirect proof is usually used in situations where there are only two possibilities: the given is true or the given is false. If there are more possibilities, each must be contradicted in order to use an indirect proof.

For example:

Given: Two distinct lines in a plane do not intersect.

Prove: The two lines are parallel.

Two distinct lines in a plane are either parallel, or they are not parallel. Since only two possibilities exist, an indirect proof can be used.

1. Assume the opposite of what you want to prove:
   The two lines are *not* parallel.
2. Show that this assumption leads to a contradiction:
   If they are *not* parallel, then they intersect.
   This contradicts the given information that they do not intersect.
3. Conclude the assumption is false.
   It is false that the two lines are not parallel.
   There is only one other possibility: the lines are parallel.

Common Errors With Indirect Proof

Sometimes it is not safe to assume that there are only two possibilities. To demonstrate this, consider the example above. Notice that it was given that the two lines were in a plane. If the two lines were in three-dimensional space, there would be a third possibility: the two lines might be skew. In this case, to prove that the two lines are parallel by indirect proof, students would also need to have sufficient given information to show that the lines being skew leads to a contradiction. Otherwise they could not prove the lines parallel from the given information.

Mathematical Practices

Reason abstractly and quantitatively Students learn an important method of reasoning: indirect proof, or proof by contradiction. In practicing this thinking, they find structure in building their arguments. Their reasoning ranges from decontextualizing an abstract approach using indirect proof methods to contextualizing by relating the method to the specific instance.

The Triangle Inequality Theorem

It is possible to have three line segments but not be able to use those segments to form a triangle. Consider the following three segments:

One segment is longer than the other two combined and therefore cannot be used to form a triangle. The Triangle Inequality Theorem states: the sum of the lengths of any two sides of a triangle must be greater than the length of the third side.

The best way to check this is to see if the sum of the shorter two segments is greater than the longest segment.

Can the side lengths 6, 8, and 9 form a triangle?
Check that the sum of the lengths of the two shorter sides is greater than the length of the longest side.

$6 + 8 > 9$

The side lengths 6, 8, and 9 can form a triangle.

Can the side lengths 12, 15, and 32 form a triangle?

Check that the sum of the lengths of the two shorter sides is greater than the length of the longest side.

$12 + 15 < 32$

Because the sum of the lengths of the two shorter sides is not greater than the length of the longest side, the side lengths 12, 15, and 32 cannot form a triangle.

Common Errors With The Triangle Inequality Theorem

Sometimes students have trouble accepting the fact that any three given sides may not form a triangle. Giving them experiences in trying to form triangles using pieces of spaghetti before studying the inequality theorems will help them go from the concrete to the abstract.

When checking to see if three segments can be combined to form a triangle, students must make sure they are comparing the sum of the lengths of the two shorter sides to the length of the longest side.

Mathematical Practices

Reason abstractly and quantitatively Students can reason concretely about the Triangle Inequality Theorem using physical models and then more abstractly as they move to the inequality $a + b > c$. In using the abstract principle they keep their quantitative experience in mind.

Midsegments of Triangles

Common Core State Standards
G.CO.10 Prove theorems about triangles . . . the segment joining midpoints of two sides of a triangle is parallel to the third side and half the length . . . **Also G.SRT.5**

Preparing to Teach

BIG idea Coordinate Geometry

ESSENTIAL UNDERSTANDING

To draw a midsegment, students must find the midpoint of two sides of a triangle and draw the segment joining the midpoints. The midsegment of a triangle is related to the third side in two ways.

Math Background

The midsegment is one of a number of special segments in a triangle. Because of the relationship to the side lengths of the triangle, midsegments create a second triangle within the original triangle that is similar to the original triangle. Midsegments are used to create a type of fractal because they represent an iterative process of shortening side lengths. The Midsegment Theorem is proved using coordinate geometry. There are different proofs of this theorem, and a few appear later in the book. Later in this text, a midsegment is also presented in the discussion of trapezoids.

ELL Support

USE MANIPULATIVES Pair a more proficient student with a less proficient student. Have one student give the directions and the other student implement them with a compass and straightedge.

The students should:

- draw a triangle with a straightedge.
- label the vertices.
- bisect each side of the triangle.
- label the midpoints.
- connect the midpoints to form an inscribed triangle.
- measure and list the length of each side of the triangles.
- discuss what they have learned through the activity.

Encourage students to use full sentences and proper mathematical language in their conversation as they complete this project.

Lesson Vocabulary

- midsegment of a triangle

Mathematical Practices

MAKE SENSE OF PROBLEMS AND PERSEVERE IN SOLVING THEM. Students will draw diagrams of midpoints on triangles and note the relationship between a line segment created by midpoints on two sides (a midsegment) and the third side.

Interactive Learning

Solve It!

PURPOSE To identify characteristics of midsegments

PROCESS Students may cut out and fold the triangle as instructed or use properties of isosceles triangles using $\triangle ALD$ and $\triangle BND$ to discover the relationship of LN and AB.

Q What kind of triangles are $\triangle ALD$ and $\triangle BND$? **[Isosceles; $\overline{AL} \cong \overline{LD}$ and $\overline{BN} \cong \overline{ND}$]**

Q After both A and B are folded to D, what is the relationship between MP and AB? **[$MP = \frac{1}{2}AD + \frac{1}{2}BD = \frac{1}{2}AB$]**

Q What is the apparent relationship between $\overline{LN}$ and $\overline{AB}$? **[$LN = \frac{1}{2}AB$]**

ANSWER

$MP = \frac{1}{2}AB$; answers may vary. Sample: From the folding process you know that $AM = MD$ and $DP = PB$. $AB = AM + MD + DP + PB$, so $AB = MD + MD + DP + DP$ or $AB = 2(MD + DP) = 2MP$. Then $\frac{1}{2}AB = \frac{1}{2}(2MP) = MP$. Conjecture: LN is the same length as MP, so $LN = \frac{1}{2}AB$.

CONNECT THE MATH Students should begin to see that the midsegment is related to the third side of the triangle. In the lesson, students learn that the midsegment is half the length of the third side and is parallel to the third side.

▼ DIGITAL (STUDENT WORK SPACE PAGE 199)

SOLVE IT! **Getting Ready!**

Cut out a triangle of any shape. Label its largest angle C, and the other angles A and B. Fold A onto C to find the midpoint of $\overline{AC}$. Do the same for $\overline{BC}$. Label the midpoints L and N, and then draw $\overline{LN}$.

Fold the triangle on $\overline{LN}$ as shown.

Fold A to D and fold B to D.

Label the vertices M and P as shown.

What is the relationship between MP and AB? How do you know?

What conjecture can you make about the relationship between LN and AB?

C L N A D B L N A D B L N M D P B

Guided Instruction

Problem 1 Identifying Parallel Segments

Take Note

Have students draw the other two midsegments of the triangle. Then they can use the Triangle Midsegment Theorem to practice writing statements about the relationships between the midsegments they drew and the sides of the triangle.

Here's Why It Works

The problem given in the Here's Why It Works is a specific problem that demonstrates the Triangle Midsegment Theorem. Students can be challenged by having them draw a triangle in a coordinate plane with general coordinates *A*(0, 0), *B*(*a*, *b*), and *C*(*c*, 0). Students will be able to re-create the proof of the Triangle Midsegment Theorem using these general coordinates. They will be able to show that the same two properties are always true. This proof is in Chapter 5.

Q What will having the coordinates of the points *D* and *E* allow you to verify? **[Sample: I will be able to find the length of $\overline{DE}$, which I will need to compare to the length of $\overline{AB}$.]**

Q What will having the slopes of $\overline{DE}$ and $\overline{AB}$ allow you to verify? **[Sample: I can verify that the lines are parallel because I will know if their slopes are the same.]**

Problem 1

Q The midsegment $\overline{RS}$ is parallel to which side of $\triangle DEF$? **[$\overline{DF}$]**

Q The midsegment $\overline{TS}$ is parallel to which side of $\triangle DEF$? **[$\overline{DE}$]**

▼ STUDENT PAGES 199–200

In the Solve It, $\overline{LN}$ is a midsegment of $\triangle ABC$. A **midsegment of a triangle** is a segment connecting the midpoints of two sides of the triangle.

Essential Understanding There are two special relationships between a midsegment of a triangle and the third side of the triangle.

take note **Theorem 24 Triangle Midsegment Theorem**

Theorem	If . . .	Then . . .
If a segment joins the midpoints of two sides of a triangle, then the segment is parallel to the third side and is half as long.	*D* is the midpoint of $\overline{CA}$ and *E* is the midpoint of $\overline{CB}$	$\overline{DE} \parallel \overline{AB}$ and $DE = \frac{1}{2}AB$

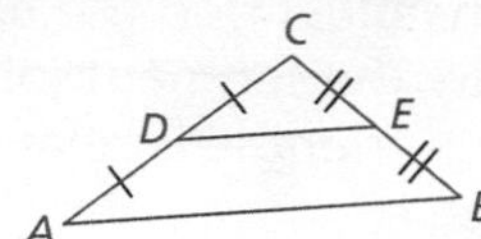

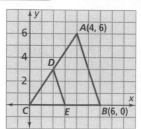

You will prove Theorem 24 in Lesson 5-8.

Here's Why It Works You can verify that the Triangle Midsegment Theorem works for a particular triangle. Use the following steps to show that $\overline{DE} \parallel \overline{AB}$ and that $DE = \frac{1}{2}AB$ for a triangle with vertices at *A*(4, 6), *B*(6, 0), and *C*(0, 0), where *D* and *E* are the midpoints of $\overline{CA}$ and $\overline{CB}$.

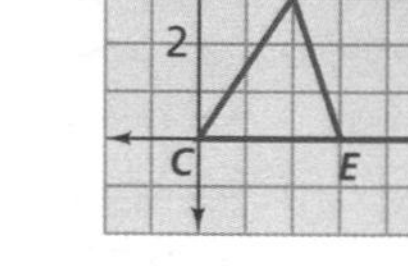

Step 1 Use the Midpoint Formula, $M = \left(\frac{x_1 + x_2}{2}, \frac{y_1 + y_2}{2}\right)$, to find the coordinates of *D* and *E*.

The midpoint of $\overline{CA}$ is $D\left(\frac{0+4}{2}, \frac{0+6}{2}\right) = D(2, 3)$.

The midpoint of $\overline{CB}$ is $E\left(\frac{0+6}{2}, \frac{0+0}{2}\right) = E(3, 0)$.

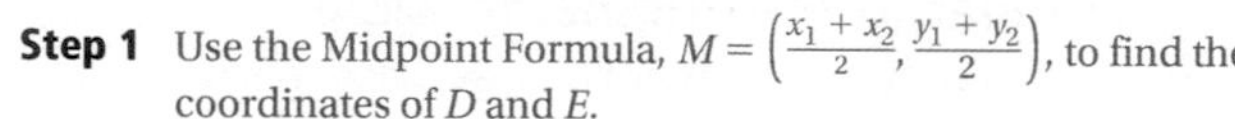

Step 2 To show that the midsegment $\overline{DE}$ is parallel to the side $\overline{AB}$, find the slope, $m = \frac{y_2 - y_1}{x_2 - x_1}$, of each segment.

slope of $\overline{DE} = \frac{0-3}{3-2} = \frac{-3}{1} = -3$

slope of $\overline{AB} = \frac{0-6}{6-4} = \frac{-6}{2} = -3$

The slopes of $\overline{DE}$ and $\overline{AB}$ are equal, so $\overline{DE}$ and $\overline{AB}$ are parallel.

Step 3 To show $DE = \frac{1}{2}AB$, use the Distance Formula, $d = \sqrt{(x_2 - x_1)^2 + (y_2 - y_1)^2}$, to find *DE* and *AB*.

$DE = \sqrt{(3-2)^2 + (0-3)^2} = \sqrt{1+9} = \sqrt{10}$

$AB = \sqrt{(6-4)^2 + (0-6)^2} = \sqrt{4+36} = \sqrt{40} = 2\sqrt{10}$

Since $\sqrt{10} = \frac{1}{2}(2\sqrt{10})$, you know that $DE = \frac{1}{2}AB$.

▼ DIGITAL

Problem 1 **Identifying Parallel Segments**

What are the three pairs of parallel segments in $\triangle DEF$?

$\overline{RS}$, $\overline{ST}$, and $\overline{TR}$ are the midsegments of $\triangle DEF$. By the Triangle Midsegment Theorem, $\overline{RS} \parallel \overline{DF}$, $\overline{ST} \parallel \overline{ED}$, and $\overline{TR} \parallel \overline{FE}$.

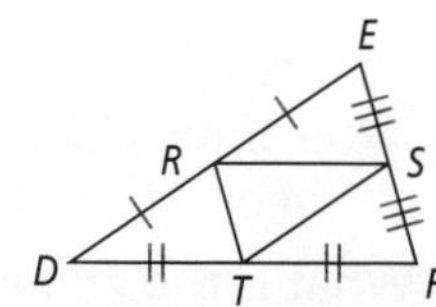

Got It? **ERROR PREVENTION**

In part (a), have students draw the triangle and label each point as given in the instructions. Have them look for the side not connected to the midsegment.

ANSWERS

Got It? a. $\overline{AC} \parallel \overline{YZ}$, $\overline{CB} \parallel \overline{XY}$, $\overline{AB} \parallel \overline{XZ}$ **b.** 65; $\overline{UV}$ is a midsegment of $\triangle NOM$, so by the Triangle Midseg. Thm., $\overline{UV} \parallel \overline{NM}$. Then $m\angle VUO = m\angle N = 65$ because corresp. angles of $\parallel$ lines are $\cong$.

Practice

1. $\overline{GJ} \parallel \overline{FK}$, $\overline{JL} \parallel \overline{FH}$, $\overline{GL} \parallel \overline{HK}$

2. $\overline{AC}$

▼ STUDENT PAGES 200–201

Got It? **a.** In $\triangle XYZ$, A is the midpoint of $\overline{XY}$, B is the midpoint of $\overline{YZ}$, and C is the midpoint of $\overline{ZX}$. What are the three pairs of parallel segments?

b. Reasoning What is $m\angle VUO$ in the figure below? Explain your reasoning.

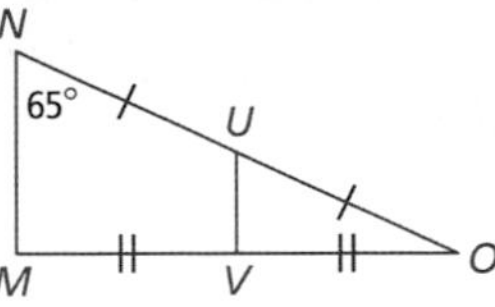

Think
What is the relationship between the 65° angle and $\angle VUO$?

A Practice **1.** Identify three pairs of parallel segments in the diagram.

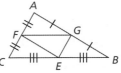

2. Name the segment that is parallel to $\overline{GE}$.

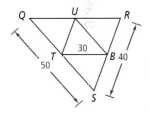

Problem 2 Finding Lengths

Q What is the relationship between the length of a midsegment and the length of the side to which it is parallel? **[The midsegment is half the length of the third side.]**

Q How can you find the length of a side given the length of the midsegment parallel to it? **[Multiply the length of the midsegment by 2.]**

Got It?

Have students describe the relationship between each of the segments in the question and the segment with the given length.

ANSWERS

Got It? $DC = 6$; $AC = 12$; $EF = 6$; $AB = 15$

Practice

3. 4.5

4. 12.5

▼ DIGITAL

Problem 2 **Finding Lengths**

In $\triangle QRS$, T, U, and B are midpoints. What are the lengths of $\overline{TU}$, $\overline{UB}$, and $\overline{QR}$?

Use the relationship
length of a midsegment $= \frac{1}{2}$(length of the third side)
to write an equation about the length of each midsegment.

$TU = \frac{1}{2}SR$	$UB = \frac{1}{2}QS$	$TB = \frac{1}{2}QR$
$= \frac{1}{2}(40)$	$= \frac{1}{2}(50)$	$30 = \frac{1}{2}QR$
$= 20$	$= 25$	$60 = QR$

▼ STUDENT PAGE 202

Got It? In the figure at the right, $AD = 6$ and $DE = 7.5$. What are the lengths of $\overline{DC}$, $\overline{AC}$, $\overline{EF}$, and $\overline{AB}$?

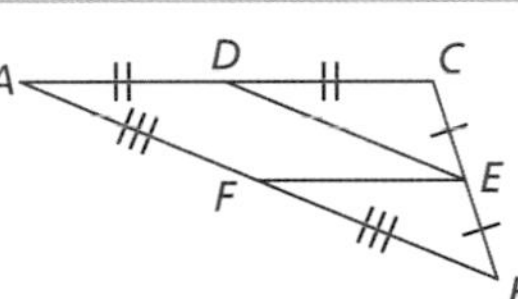

A Practice **Algebra** Find the value of x.

3.

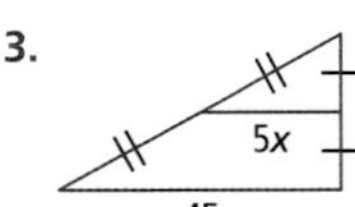

4.

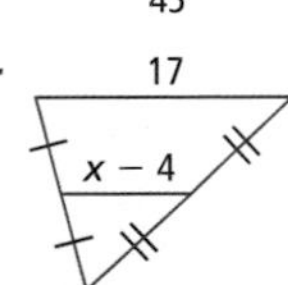

Problem 3 Using a Midsegment of a Triangle

Q What type of segment is $\overline{CD}$? Justify your answer. **[$\overline{CD}$ is a midsegment because it connects the midpoints of two sides of the triangle.]**

Q What is the relationship between *CD* and *AB*? **[$CD = \frac{1}{2}AB$]**

Got It?

Have students classify the segment which represents the new bridge. Ask them to state the relationship between the length of the new bridge and the side of the triangle to which the bridge will be parallel.

ANSWERS

Got It? 1320 ft

Practice

5. 156 m

▼ STUDENT PAGE 203

You can use the Triangle Midsegment Theorem to find lengths of segments that might be difficult to measure directly.

▼ DIGITAL

Problem 3 Using a Midsegment of a Triangle STEM

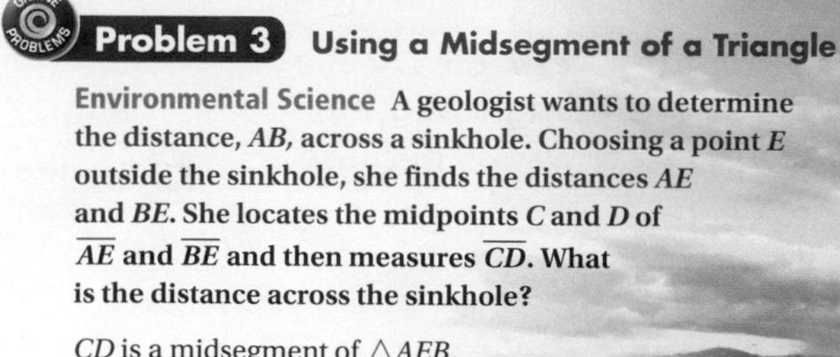

Environmental Science **A geologist wants to determine the distance, *AB*, across a sinkhole. Choosing a point *E* outside the sinkhole, she finds the distances *AE* and *BE*. She locates the midpoints *C* and *D* of $\overline{AE}$ and $\overline{BE}$ and then measures $\overline{CD}$. What is the distance across the sinkhole?**

CD is a midsegment of $\triangle AEB$.

$CD = \frac{1}{2}AB$	$\triangle$ Midsegment Thm.
$46 = \frac{1}{2}AB$	Substitute 46 for *CD*.
$92 = AB$	Multiply each side by 2.

The distance across the sinkhole is 92 ft.

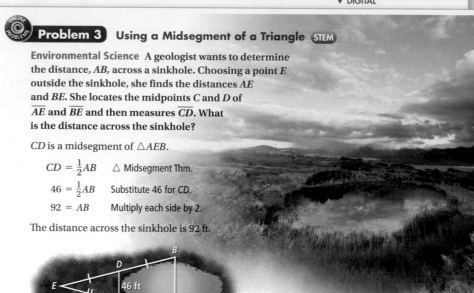

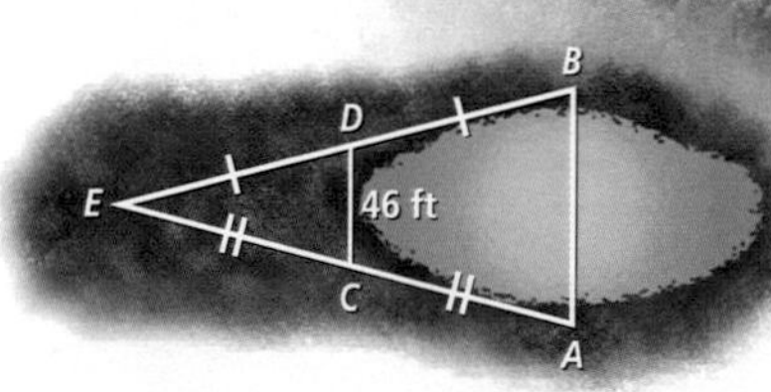

▼ STUDENT PAGE 203

Got It? $\overline{CD}$ is a bridge being built over a lake, as shown in the figure below. What is the length of the bridge?

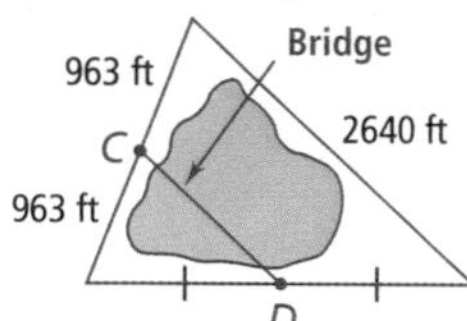

Think
Which theorem will help you solve this problem?

Practice

5. Surveying A surveyor needs to measure the distance *PQ* across the lake. Beginning at point *S*, she locates the midpoints of $\overline{SQ}$ and $\overline{SP}$ at *M* and *N*. She then measures $\overline{NM}$. What is *PQ*?

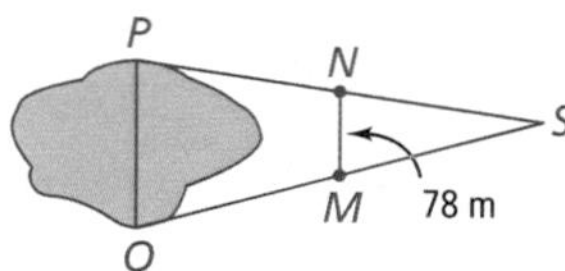

3 Lesson Check

Do you know HOW?
If students have difficulty with Exercise 6, then have them review Problem 1.

Do you UNDERSTAND?
If students have difficulty with Exercise 10, then have them review the Solve It.

Close

Q How is the length of a midsegment of a triangle related to the length of the third side? **[The length of the midsegment is half the length of the third side.]**

Q In the coordinate plane, how are the slopes of a midsegment and the third side of the triangle related? Explain. **[They are the same because the two segments are parallel.]**

ANSWERS

6. $\overline{NO}$ **7.** 23 **8.** 4

9. A midsegment is a segment whose endpoints are the midpoints of two sides of a triangle.

10. The segments are parallel.

11. The student is assuming that L is the midpoint of $\overline{OT}$, which is not given.

▼ STUDENT PAGES 203–204

Lesson Check

Do you know HOW?

Use the figure at the right for Exercises 6–8.

6. Which segment is parallel to $\overline{JK}$?

7. If $LK = 46$, what is NM?

8. If $JK = 5x + 20$ and $NO = 20$, what is the value of x?

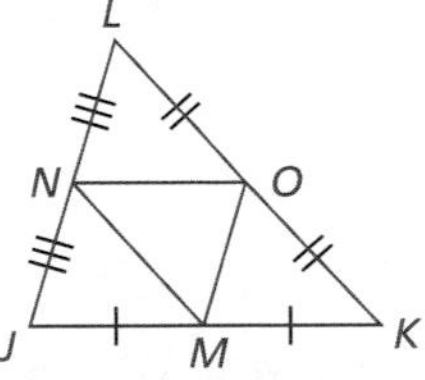

Do you UNDERSTAND?

9. Vocabulary How does the term *midsegment* describe the segments discussed in this lesson?

10. Reasoning If two noncollinear segments in the coordinate plane have slope 3, what can you conclude?

11. Error Analysis A student sees this figure and concludes that $\overline{PL} \parallel \overline{NO}$. What is the error in the student's reasoning?

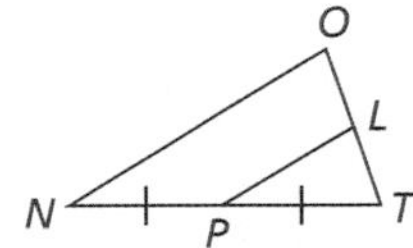

4 Practice

More Practice and Problem-Solving Exercises

ASSIGNMENT GUIDE
The assignments below are for the More Practice and Problem-Solving Exercises. You may also want to assign the A-Level Practice Exercises for homework if these are not used in class.
Average: 12–31
Advanced: 12–34

Mathematical Practices The exercises listed focus on the Standards for Mathematical Practices listed.

EX. 14: Persevere in Problem Solving (MP 1)
EX. 10, 32: Construct Arguments (MP 3)
EX. 11: Critique the Reasoning of Others (MP 3)
EX. 15: Communicate (MP 3)
EX. 12, 13, 23: Model (MP 4)
EX. 31: Use Appropriate Tools (MP 5)

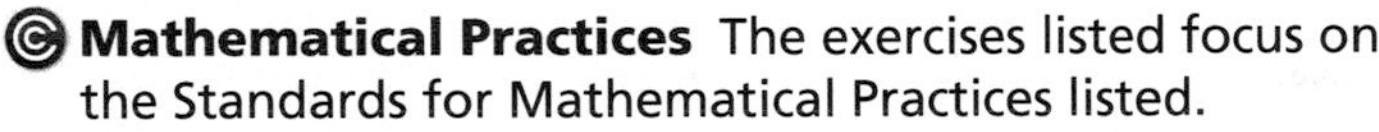
EXERCISE 16: Use the **Think About a Plan** worksheet in the Online Teacher Resources to further support students' development in becoming independent learners.

HOMEWORK QUICK CHECK
To check students' understanding of key skills and concepts, go over Exercises 14, 15, 16, 24, and 29.

ANSWERS

12. a. 1050 ft **b.** 437.5 ft

▼ STUDENT PAGE 205

More Practice and Problem-Solving Exercises

B Apply

12. Kayaking You want to paddle your kayak across a lake. To determine how far you must paddle, you pace out a triangle, counting the number of strides, as shown.

a. If your strides average 3.5 ft, what is the length of the longest side of the triangle?

b. What distance must you paddle across the lake?

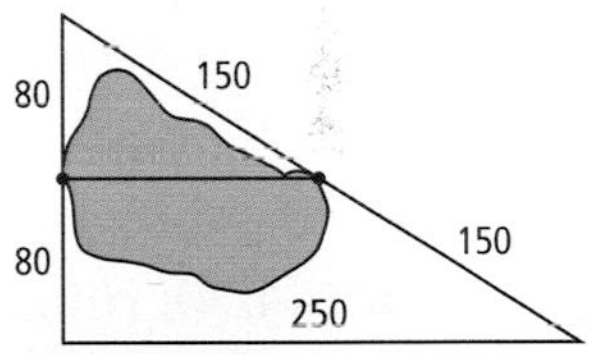

13. Architecture The triangular face of the Rock and Roll Hall of Fame in Cleveland, Ohio, is isosceles. The length of the base is 229 ft 6 in. Each leg is divided into four congruent parts by the red segments. What is the length of the white segment? Explain your reasoning.

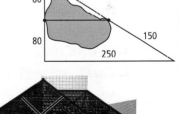

13. 114 ft 9 in.; because the red segments divide the legs into four ≅ parts, the white segment divides each leg into two ≅ parts. The white segment is a midsegment of the triangular face of the building, so its length is one half the length of the base.

14.

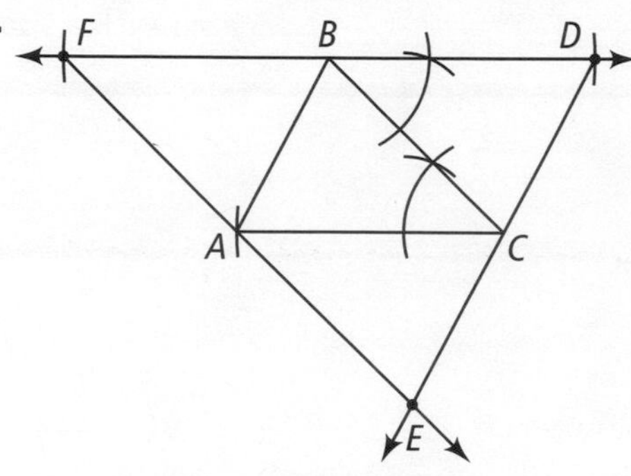

$\overline{FD} \parallel \overline{AC}$, $\overline{DE} \parallel \overline{AB}$, $\overline{FE} \parallel \overline{BC}$

15. 40; $\overline{ST}$ is a midsegment of $\triangle PQR$, so by the $\triangle$ Midseg. Thm., $\overline{ST} \parallel \overline{PR}$. Then $m\angle QPR = m\angle QST$ because corresp. $\angle$s of $\parallel$ lines are $\cong$.

16. **a.** $H(2, 0)$; $J(4, 2)$

b. Slope of $\overline{HJ} = \frac{2-0}{4-2} = 1$; slope of $\overline{EF} = \frac{6-2}{5-1} = 1$; the slopes are $=$, so $\overline{HJ} \parallel \overline{EF}$.

c. $HJ = \sqrt{(2-4)^2 + (0-2)^2} = \sqrt{8} = 2\sqrt{2}$ and $EF = \sqrt{(1-5)^2 + (2-6)^2} = \sqrt{32} = 4\sqrt{2}$, so $HJ = \frac{1}{2}EF$.

17. 60	**18.** 45
19. 100	**20.** 55
21. 18.5	**22.** 37
23. C	**24.** 60
25. 50	**26.** 10
27. $x = 6$; $y = 6.5$	**28.** 52
29. 24	**30.** 26

31. Draw $\overrightarrow{CA}$. Find P on $\overrightarrow{CA}$ such that $CA = AP$. Draw $\overline{PD}$. Construct the $\perp$ bisector of $\overline{PD}$. Label the intersection point B. Draw $\overline{AB}$. This is a midsegment of $\triangle CPD$. According to the $\triangle$ Midsegment Thm., $\overline{AB} \parallel \overline{CD}$ and $AB = \frac{1}{2}CD$.

32. 30 cm

33. $G(4, 4)$; $H(0, 2)$; $J(8, 0)$

34. $\triangle UTS$; answers may vary. Sample: $VS = SY = \frac{1}{2}VY$, $VU = UZ = \frac{1}{2}VZ$, and $YT = TZ = \frac{1}{2}YZ$ by the def. of midpt. Also $ST = \frac{1}{2}VZ$, $SU = \frac{1}{2}YZ$, and $TU = \frac{1}{2}VY$ by the $\triangle$ Midsegment Theorem. So $\triangle YST \cong \triangle TUZ \cong \triangle SVU \cong \triangle UTS$ by SSS.

14. Think About a Plan Draw $\triangle ABC$. Construct another triangle so that the three sides of $\triangle ABC$ are the midsegments of the new triangle.
- Can you visualize or sketch the final figure?
- Which segments in your final construction will be parallel?

15. Writing In the figure at the right, $m\angle QST = 40$. What is $m\angle QPR$? Explain how you know.

16. Coordinate Geometry The coordinates of the vertices of a triangle are $E(1, 2)$, $F(5, 6)$, and $G(3, -2)$.

a. Find the coordinates of H, the midpoint of $\overline{EG}$, and J, the midpoint of $\overline{FG}$.

b. Show that $\overline{HJ} \parallel \overline{EF}$.

c. Show that $HJ = \frac{1}{2}EF$.

X is the midpoint of $\overline{UV}$. Y is the midpoint of $\overline{UW}$.

17. If $m\angle UXY = 60$, find $m\angle V$.

18. If $m\angle W = 45$, find $m\angle UYX$.

19. If $XY = 50$, find VW.

20. If $VW = 110$, find XY.

$\overline{IJ}$ is a midsegment of $\triangle FGH$. $IJ = 7$, $FH = 10$, and $GH = 13$. Find the perimeter of each triangle.

21. $\triangle IJH$

22. $\triangle FGH$

23. Kite Design You design a kite to look like the one at the right. Its diagonals measure 64 cm and 90 cm. You plan to use ribbon, represented by the rectangle, to connect the midpoints of its sides. How much ribbon do you need?

 A 77 cm  B 122 cm  C 154 cm  D 308 cm

Algebra Find the value of each variable.

24.

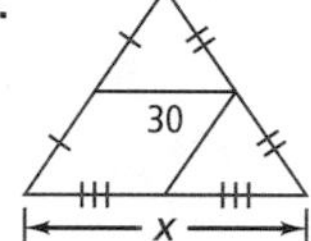

25.

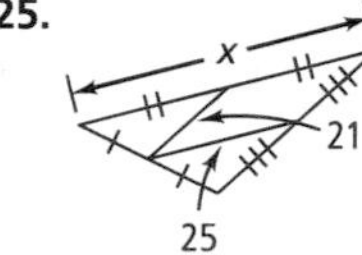

26.

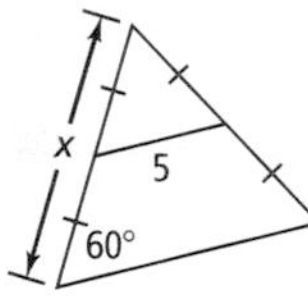

27.

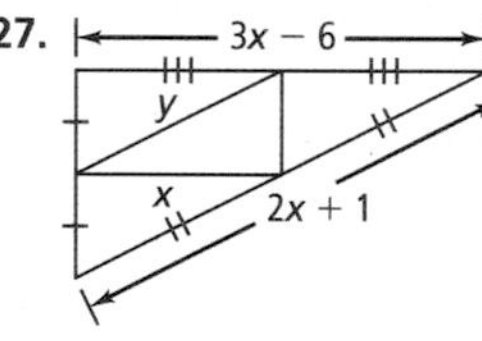

Use the figure at the right for Exercises 28–30.

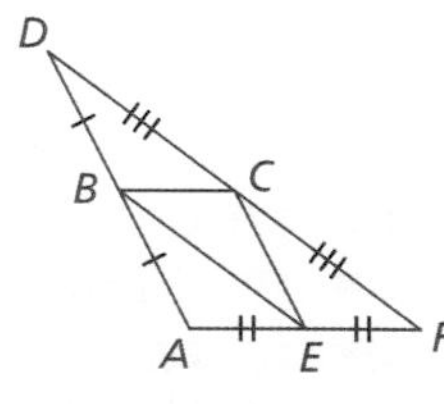

28. $DF = 24$, $BC = 6$, and $DB = 8$. Find the perimeter of $\triangle ADF$.

29. Algebra If $BE = 2x + 6$ and $DF = 5x + 9$, find DF.

30. Algebra If $EC = 3x - 1$ and $AD = 5x + 7$, find EC.

31. Open-Ended Explain how you could use the Triangle Midsegment Theorem as the basis for this construction: Draw $\overline{CD}$. Draw point A not on $\overline{CD}$. Construct $\overline{AB}$ so that $\overline{AB} \parallel \overline{CD}$ and $AB = \frac{1}{2}CD$.

Challenge

32. Reasoning In the diagram at the right, K, L, and M are the midpoints of the sides of $\triangle ABC$. The vertices of the three small red triangles are the midpoints of the sides of $\triangle KBL$, $\triangle AKM$, and $\triangle MLC$. The perimeter of $\triangle ABC$ is 24 cm. What is the perimeter of the shaded region?

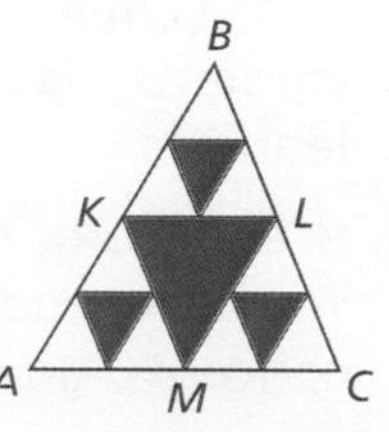

33. Coordinate Geometry In $\triangle GHJ$, $K(2, 3)$ is the midpoint of $\overline{GH}$, $L(4, 1)$ is the midpoint of $\overline{HJ}$, and $M(6, 2)$ is the midpoint of $\overline{GJ}$. Find the coordinates of G, H, and J.

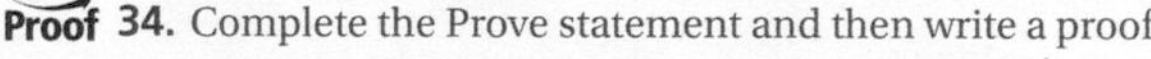

Proof 34. Complete the Prove statement and then write a proof.

Given: In $\triangle VYZ$, S, T, and U are midpoints.

Prove: $\triangle YST \cong \triangle TUZ \cong \triangle SVU \cong$ __?__

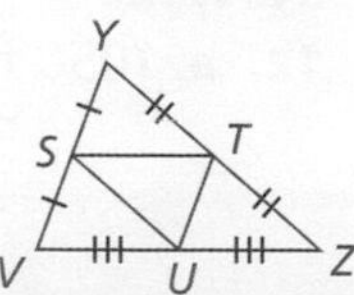

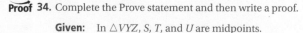

5 Assess and Remediate

Lesson Quiz

Use the triangle below for Questions 1–3.

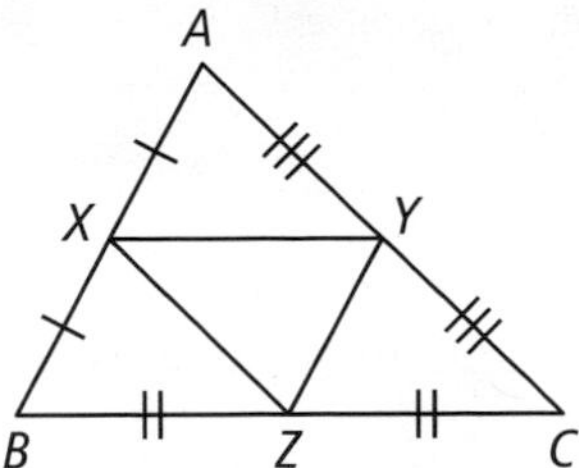

1. What are the three pairs of parallel segments in $\triangle ABC$?
2. If the length of $\overline{XZ}$ is known, to what other segment can you assign a length?
3. If it is given that $AX = 3.5$, what is the length of YZ?
4. **Do you UNDERSTAND?** In $\triangle MON$, J, K, and L are midpoints. If $JL = 11$, $LK = 13$, and $ON = 20$, and $\overline{JL} \parallel \overline{MN}$, $\overline{LK} \parallel \overline{MO}$, and $\overline{JK} \parallel \overline{ON}$, what are the lengths of MN, MO, and JK?

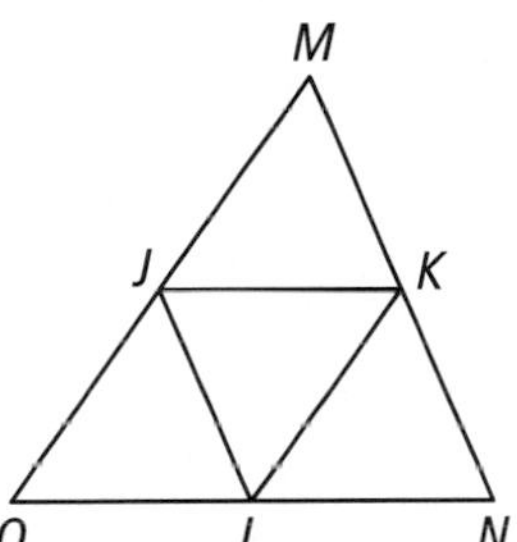

ANSWERS TO LESSON QUIZ

1. $\overline{AB} \parallel \overline{YZ}$; $\overline{BC} \parallel \overline{XY}$; $\overline{AC} \parallel \overline{XZ}$
2. $\overline{AC}$
3. 3.5
4. $MN = 22$, $MO = 26$, $JK = 10$

Prescription for Remediation

Use the student work on the Lesson Quiz to prescribe a differentiated assignment.

Points	Differentiated Remediation
0–2	Intervention
3	On-level
4	Extension

Differentiated Remediation

Intervention

- **RETEACHING** (2 pages) Provides reteaching and practice exercises for the key lesson concepts. Use with struggling students or absent students.
- **ENGLISH LANGUAGE LEARNER SUPPORT** Helps students develop and reinforce mathematical vocabulary and key concepts.

On-Level

- **PRACTICE** (2 pages) Provides extra practice for each lesson. For simpler practice exercises, use the Form K Practice pages found in the Online Teacher Resources.
- **THINK ABOUT A PLAN** Helps students develop specific problem-solving skills and strategies by providing scaffolded guiding questions.
- **STANDARDIZED TEST PREP** Focuses on all major exercises, all major question types, and helps students prepare for the high-stakes assessments.

Extension

- **ENRICHMENT** Provides students with interesting problems and activities that extend the concepts of the lesson.
- **ACTIVITIES, GAMES, AND PUZZLES** Worksheets that can be used for concept development, enrichment, and for fun!

Online Assessment

Assign the Lesson Quiz in Success Tracker on **pearsonsuccessnet.com**. Success Tracker will automatically score the quiz and assign appropriate intervention or enrichment to each student based on the results. The compiled data appear in three different reports for instant analysis of whole class and individual student performance.

4-2 Perpendicular and Angle Bisectors

Common Core State Standards
G.CO.9 Prove theorems about lines and angles . . . points on a perpendicular bisector of a line segment are exactly those equidistant from the segment's endpoints. **Also G.CO.12, G.SRT.5**

Preparing to Teach

BIG ideas Reasoning and Proof
Measurement

ESSENTIAL UNDERSTANDING

There is a special relationship between the points on the perpendicular bisector of a segment and the endpoints of the segment. There is a special relationship between the points on the bisector of an angle and the sides of the angle.

Math Background

In this lesson, students should begin to see the perpendicular bisector of a segment and the bisector of an angle as a locus of points. The perpendicular bisector of a segment contains all points which are equidistant from the endpoints of the segment.

The bisector of an angle represents all points which are equidistant from the sides of the angle. Loci of points are useful in many real-world applications. They aid surveyors, architects, and designers in locating points central to segments and angles.

ELL Support

USE GRAPHIC ORGANIZERS Have students verbalize their knowledge of triangles as they work with peers. Have students work in groups of four or five to make graphic organizers showing facts they have learned about triangles. Students should include:

- different kinds of triangles.
- facts about right triangles.
- postulates and theorems about triangle congruence.
- facts about triangle midsegments.

Encourage students to use illustrations and familiar language to make formal mathematical terms more understandable.

Have each group show their completed graphic organizer to another group. Allow students to add to their graphic organizers as they learn more about triangles.

Lesson Vocabulary

- equidistant
- distance from a point to a line

Mathematical Practices

LOOK FOR AND EXPRESS REGULARITY IN REPEATED REASONING. In the Solve It, students will evaluate the reasonableness of the Perpendicular Bisector Theorem.

1 Interactive Learning

Solve It!

▼ DIGITAL (STUDENT WORK SPACE PAGE 207)

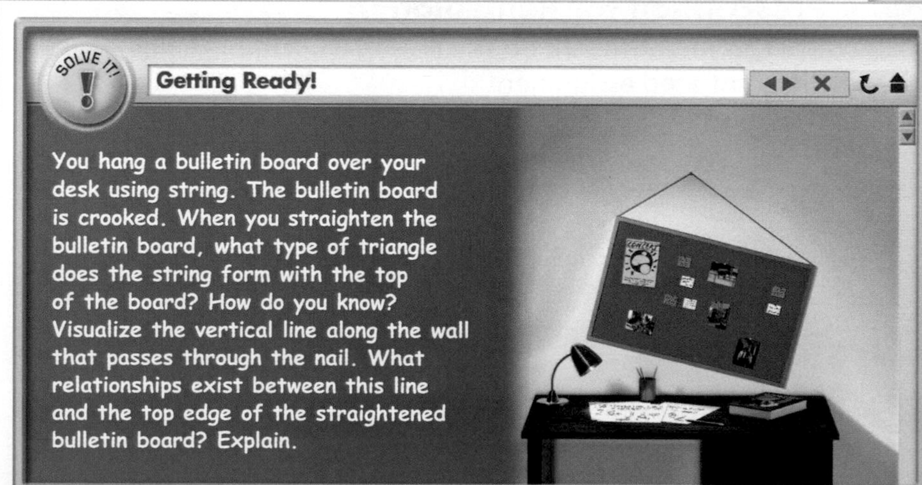

PURPOSE To discover properties of the perpendicular bisector of a segment

PROCESS Students may

- use concepts of triangle properties to make a conjecture.
- use logical reasoning to determine the best location to hang the bulletin board.

Q Why is the bulletin board crooked? **[The string is longer on the right side of the nail than it is on the left side of the nail.]**

Q What relationship must exist for the lengths of the string on each side of the nail for the bulletin board to hang straight? **[The lengths of the string must be equal.]**

Q If a line is drawn from the nail directly below to the top of a level bulletin board, where will it touch the bulletin board? **[At a point equidistant from the top corners of the bulletin board.]**

ANSWER Isosceles; the board will be straight when its weight is evenly balanced on either side of the nail, so the string will need to be touching the nail at the point that divides the length of the string in half. The line is perpendicular to and bisects the top edge of the straightened bulletin board; label the top corners of the bulletin board A and B, the nail N, and the point where the vertical line through N intersects the straightened bulletin board M. When the bulletin board is straight, $\overline{AB}$ is horizontal, so $\overleftrightarrow{NM} \perp \overline{AB}$ because a vertical line is perpendicular to a horizontal line. $\overline{AN} \cong \overline{BN}$ and $\overline{NM} \cong \overline{NM}$ (Refl. Prop. of $\cong$), so $\triangle ANM \cong \triangle BNM$ (HL) and $\overline{MA} \cong \overline{MB}$ (Corresp. parts of $\cong \triangle$ are $\cong$.). So, $\overleftrightarrow{NM}$ bisects $\overline{AB}$.

CONNECT THE MATH Students should conjecture that points on the perpendicular bisector of a segment are equidistant from the endpoints of that segment. In the lesson, students learn a theorem that relates a segment and its perpendicular bisector.

2 Guided Instruction

Problem 1 Using the Perpendicular Bisector Theorem

Have students write a proof to show that $\triangle CAD \cong \triangle CBD$ using the SAS Postulate.

Take Note

Have students compare and contrast the theorems presented in the Take Note section. Ask them to explain why Theorem 26 is called the converse of Theorem 25. Have them combine the two statements to form one biconditional statement.

▼ STUDENT PAGES 207–208

In the Solve It, you thought about the relationships that must exist in order for a bulletin board to hang straight. You will explore these relationships in this lesson.

Essential Understanding There is a special relationship between the points on the perpendicular bisector of a segment and the endpoints of the segment.

In the diagram below, $\overleftrightarrow{CD}$ is the perpendicular bisector of $\overline{AB}$. $\overleftrightarrow{CD}$ is perpendicular to $\overline{AB}$ at its midpoint. In the diagram on the right, $\overline{CA}$ and $\overline{CB}$ are drawn to complete $\triangle CAD$ and $\triangle CBD$.

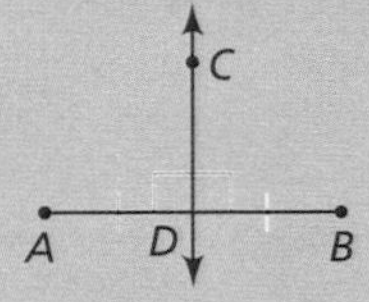

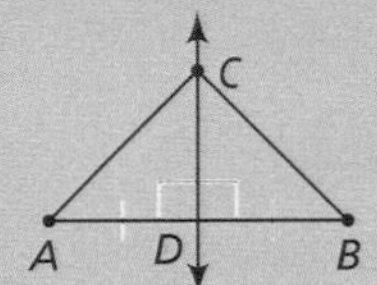

You should recognize from your work in Chapter 12 that $\triangle CAD \cong \triangle CBD$. So you can conclude that $\overline{CA} \cong \overline{CB}$, or that $CA = CB$. A point is **equidistant** from two objects if it is the same distance from the objects. So point C is equidistant from points A and B.

This suggests a proof of Theorem 25, the Perpendicular Bisector Theorem. Its converse is also true and is stated as Theorem 26.

take note

Theorem 25 Perpendicular Bisector Theorem

Theorem	If . . .	Then . . .
If a point is on the perpendicular bisector of a segment, then it is equidistant from the endpoints of the segment.	$\overleftrightarrow{PM} \perp \overline{AB}$ and $MA = MB$	$PA = PB$

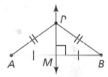

You will prove Theorem 25 in Exercise 26.

Theorem 26 Converse of the Perpendicular Bisector Theorem

Theorem	If . . .	Then . . .
If a point is equidistant from the endpoints of a segment, then it is on the perpendicular bisector of the segment.	$PA = PB$	$\overleftrightarrow{PM} \perp \overline{AB}$ and $MA = MB$

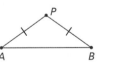

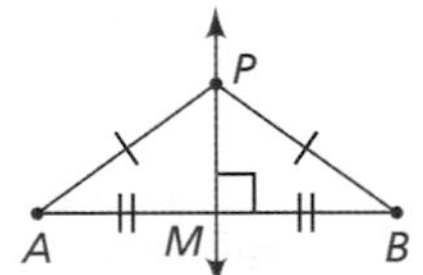

You will prove Theorem 26 in Exercise 27.

Problem 1 *continued*

Q What information is given in the diagram? **[$\overline{AD} \cong \overline{DC}$ and $\overline{BD} \perp \overline{AC}$]**

Q Which theorem can you apply? **[Theorem 25, the Perpendicular Bisector Theorem]**

Got It?

Have students classify $\overline{QS}$. Emphasize that $PQ = RQ$ by Theorem 25.

ANSWERS

Got It? 8

Practice

1. $\overline{MB}$ is the perpendicular bisector of $\overline{JK}$.
2. 9

▼ DIGITAL

Problem 1 Using the Perpendicular Bisector Theorem

Algebra What is the length of $\overline{AB}$?

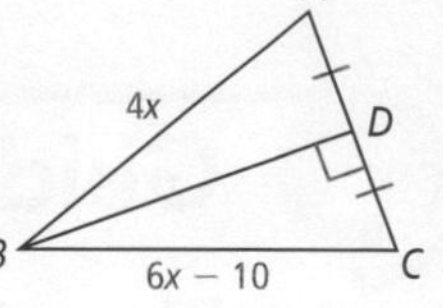

$\overline{BD}$ is the perpendicular bisector of $\overline{AC}$, so B is equidistant from A and C.

$BA = BC$	Perpendicular Bisector Theorem
$4x = 6x - 10$	Substitute $4x$ for BA and $6x - 10$ for BC.
$-2x = -10$	Subtract $6x$ from each side.
$x = 5$	Divide each side by -2.

Now find AB.

$AB = 4x$	
$AB = 4(5) = 20$	Substitute 5 for x.

▼ STUDENT PAGE 208

Got It? What is the length of $\overline{QR}$?

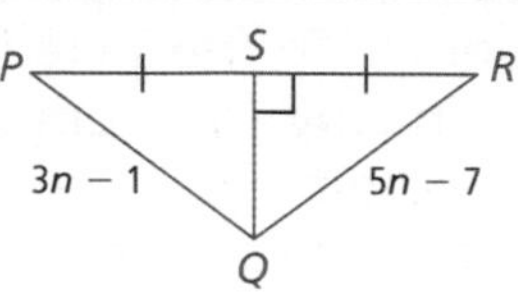

**Practice** Use the figure at the right for Exercises 1 and 2.

1. What is the relationship between $\overline{MB}$ and $\overline{JK}$?
2. Find JM.

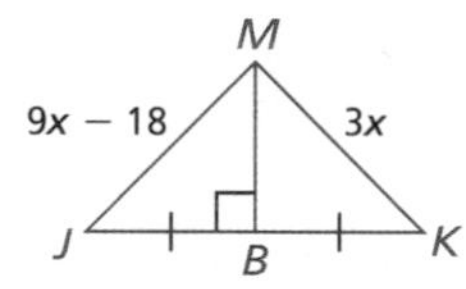

Problem 2 Using a Perpendicular Bisector

Have students sketch the triangle created by the locations of the Rollin' Coaster, the Spaceship Shoot, and each of the possible locations for the T-shirt stand.

Q How many possibilities are there for the location of the T-shirt stand? **[Infinite; any point along the perpendicular bisector of $\overline{RS}$ is a possibility.]**

Got It?

Have students sketch the triangle created by the locations of the paddle boats, the Spaceship Shoot, and the Rollin' Coaster. Then have them construct the perpendicular bisector of each side of the triangle.

Q What do you know about the point of intersection of three perpendicular bisectors and the three attractions? **[The point of intersection is the same distance from each of the three attractions.]**

Q Does your drawing model Theorem 25 or Theorem 26? Explain. **[Theorem 25; the theorem states that if you know the point is on the perpendicular bisector then it is equidistant from the endpoints. The perpendicular bisectors were constructed to find the point equidistant from the endpoints of the three segments.]**

▼ DIGITAL

**Problem 2** Using a Perpendicular Bisector

A park director wants to build a T-shirt stand equidistant from the Rollin' Coaster and the Spaceship Shoot. What are the possible locations of the stand? Explain.

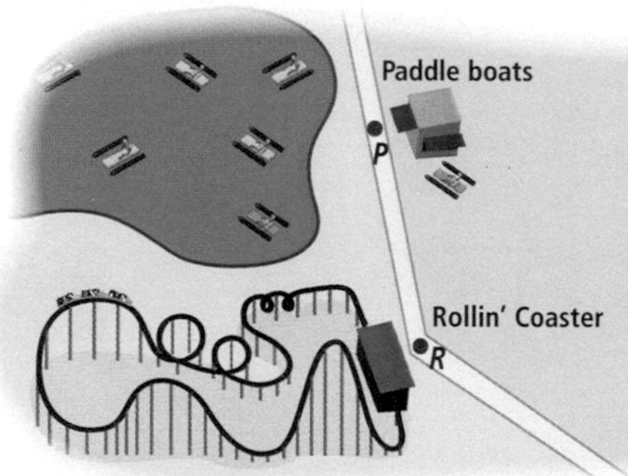

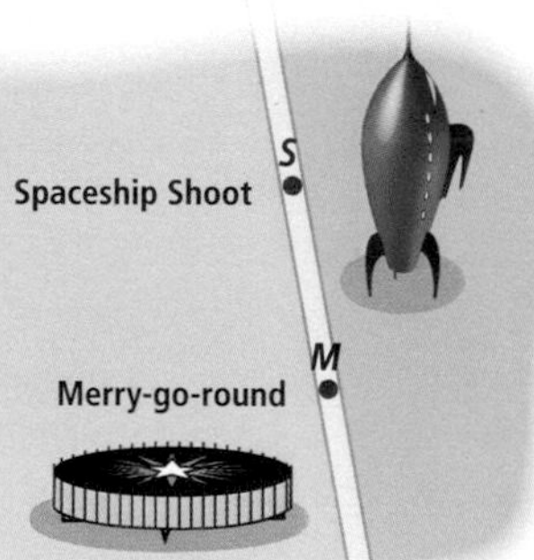

To be equidistant from the two rides, the stand should be on the perpendicular bisector of the segment connecting the rides. Find the midpoint A of $\overline{RS}$ and draw line ℓ through A perpendicular to $\overline{RS}$. The possible locations of the stand are all the points on line ℓ.

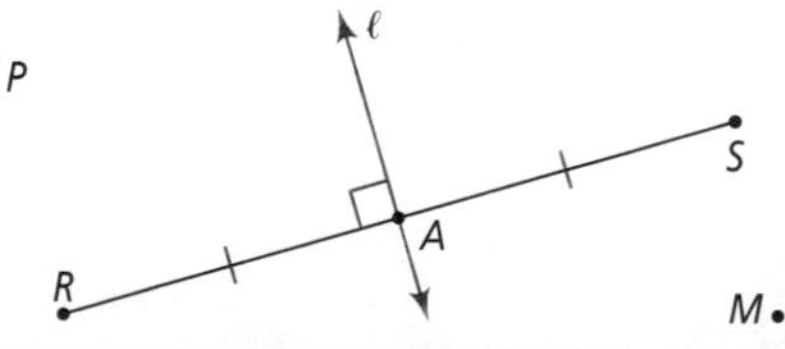

ANSWERS

Got It? a. any point on the ⊥ bis. of $\overline{PS}$ **b.** Yes, at the intersection point of ℓ and the perpendicular bisector of $\overline{PS}$. Let X be the intersection point of ℓ and the perpendicular bisector of $\overline{PS}$. By the ⊥ Bis. Thm., $XR = XS$ and $XS = XP$, so $XR = XS = XP$. Thus X is equidistant from R, S, and P.

Practice

3. No; it is not on the perpendicular bisector of the street connecting the two schools.
4. Draw $\overline{HS}$ and construct its midpoint, M. Through M, construct the line perpendicular to $\overline{HS}$. Any point on this line will be equidistant from H and S.

▼ STUDENT PAGE 209

Plan

How do you find points that are equidistant from two given points?

Got It? a. Suppose the director from Problem 2 wants the T-shirt stand to be equidistant from the paddle boats and the Spaceship Shoot. What are the possible locations?

b. **Reasoning** Can you place the T-shirt stand so that it is equidistant from the paddle boats, the Spaceship Shoot, and the Rollin' Coaster? Explain.

Practice 3. **Reading Maps** Use the map of a part of Manhattan. Is St. Vincent's Hospital equidistant from Village Kids Nursery School and Legacy School? How do you know?

4. **Writing** On a piece of paper, mark a point H for home and a point S for school. Describe how to find the set of points equidistant from H and S.

Problem 3 Using the Angle Bisector Theorem

Have a student stand at a point in the classroom where the students can model the distance between a point and a line on a wall in the classroom. Have another student describe how to find the student's distance from the wall. Guide the class to conclude that the distance must be measured on a segment that is perpendicular to the wall.

Take Note

Have students compare and contrast the theorems presented in the Take Note section. Ask them to explain why Theorem 28 is called the converse of Theorem 27. Have them combine the two statements to form one biconditional statement.

Emphasize to students that because $\overline{SP}$ and $\overline{SR}$ are perpendicular to the sides of the angles, SP and SR are the distance from point S to the sides of $\angle PQR$. Guide students to see that the points on an angle bisector are equidistant from the sides of the angle.

▼ STUDENT PAGE 201

Essential Understanding There is a special relationship between the points on the bisector of an angle and the sides of the angle.

The **distance from a point to a line** is the length of the perpendicular segment from the point to the line. This distance is also the length of the shortest segment from the point to the line. You will prove this in Lesson 4-6. In the figure at the right, the distances from A to ℓ and from B to ℓ are represented by the red segments.

In the diagram, $\overrightarrow{AD}$ is the bisector of $\angle CAB$. If you measure the lengths of the perpendicular segments from D to the two sides of the angle, you will find that the lengths are equal. Point D is equidistant from the sides of the angle.

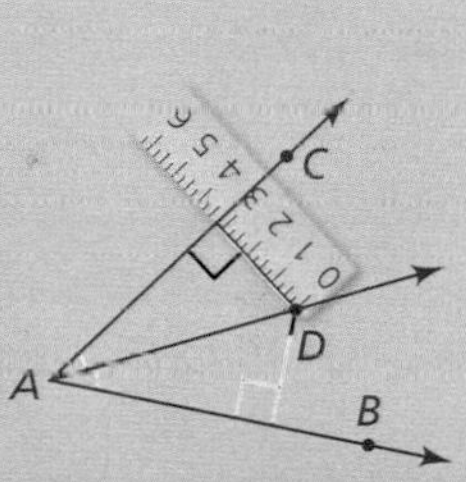

take note

Theorem 27 Angle Bisector Theorem

Theorem	If . . .	Then . . .
If a point is on the bisector of an angle, then the point is equidistant from the sides of the angle.	$\overrightarrow{QS}$ bisects $\angle PQR$, $\overline{SP} \perp \overrightarrow{QP}$, and $\overline{SR} \perp \overrightarrow{QR}$	$SP = SR$

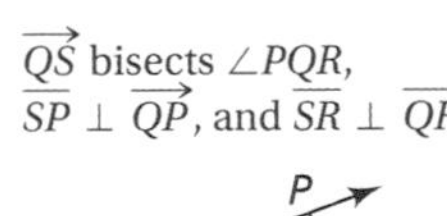

You will prove Theorem 27 in Exercise 28.

Theorem 28 Converse of the Angle Bisector Theorem

Theorem	If . . .	Then . . .
If a point in the interior of an angle is equidistant from the sides of the angle, then the point is on the angle bisector.	$\overline{SP} \perp \overrightarrow{QP}$, $\overline{SR} \perp \overrightarrow{QR}$, and $SP = SR$	$\overrightarrow{QS}$ bisects $\angle PQR$

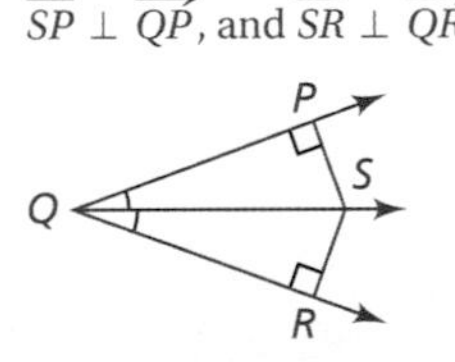

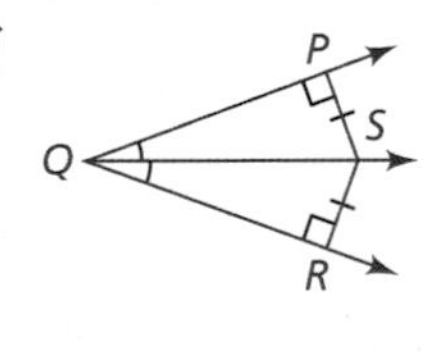

You will prove Theorem 28 in Exercise 29.

Problem 3 ***continued***

Q How can you classify $\overrightarrow{RN}$? Justify your answer. **[$\overrightarrow{RN}$ is the bisector of ∠*MNP* because ∠*MNR* ≅ ∠*PNR*.]**

Q What do *MR* and *PR* represent? **[They represent the distance between point *R* and the sides of the angle.]**

Got It?

Have students redraw the diagram and label the lengths of the segments as given. Ask students to classify $\overline{CF}$ as the angle bisector. Remind them to use the value they find for *x* to find *FB*.

ANSWERS

Got It? 21

Practice

5. 54; 54

6. $x = 12$, $JK = 17$, $JM = 17$

▼ DIGITAL

Problem 3 **Using the Angle Bisector Theorem**

Algebra What is the length of $\overline{RM}$?

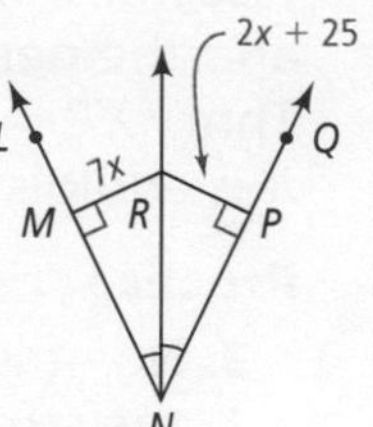

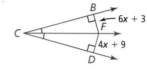

Know	Need	Plan
$\overrightarrow{NR}$ bisects ∠*LNQ*. $\overline{RM} \perp \overrightarrow{NL}$ and $\overline{RP} \perp \overrightarrow{NQ}$.	The length of $\overline{RM}$	Use the Angle Bisector Theorem to write an equation you can solve for *x*.

$RM = RP$ Angle Bisector Theorem

$7x = 2x + 25$ Substitute.

$5x = 25$ Subtract 2*x* from each side.

$x = 5$ Divide each side by 5.

Now find *RM*.

$RM = 7x$

$= 7(5) = 35$ Substitute 5 for *x*.

▼ STUDENT PAGE 211

Got It? What is the length of $\overline{FB}$?

Think

How can you use the expression for *FD* to check your answer?

Practice **5.** Find *m*∠*KHL* and *m*∠*FHL*.

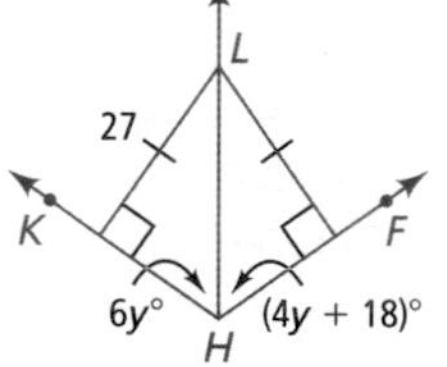

6. Algebra Find *x*, *JK*, and *JM*.

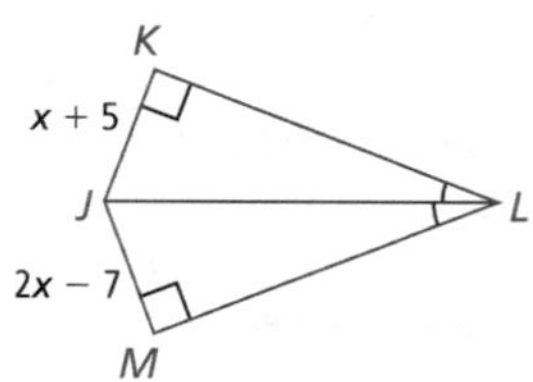

3 Lesson Check

Do you know HOW?
If students have difficulty with Exercises 7–9, then have them review Problem 1 to understand the relationship of a point on a perpendicular bisector to the endpoints of the bisected segment.

Do you UNDERSTAND?
If students have difficulty with Exercise 11, then have them review Theorem 27 and the diagram just above Theorem 27.

Close

Q What statement describes the points on the perpendicular bisector of a segment? **[They are equidistant from the endpoints of the segment.]**

Q What statement can be made about a point on the bisector of an angle? **[It is equidistant from the sides of the angle.]**

ANSWERS

7. $\overline{AC}$ is the perpendicular bisector of $\overline{BD}$.

8. 15 **9.** 18

10. Answers may vary. Sample:

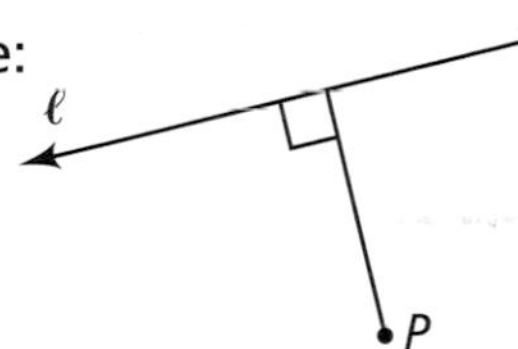

11. Draw the perpendicular segments that join P to $\overline{OL}$ and $\overline{OX}$. Use a ruler to determine if $OL = OX$. If $OL = OX$, then P is on the bisector of $\angle LOX$.

▼ STUDENT PAGES 211–212

Lesson Check

Do you know HOW?

Use the figure at the right for Exercises 7–9.

7. What is the relationship between $\overline{AC}$ and $\overline{BD}$?

8. What is the length of $\overline{AB}$?

9. What is the length of $\overline{DC}$?

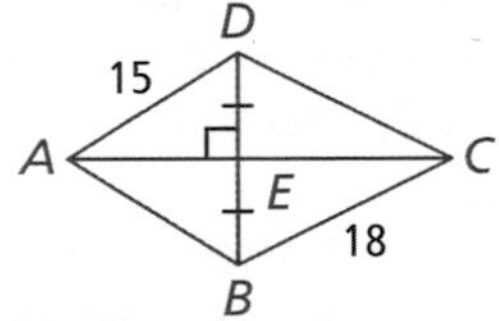

Do you UNDERSTAND?

10. Vocabulary Draw a line and a point not on the line. Draw the segment that represents the distance from the point to the line.

11. Writing Point P is in the interior of $\angle LOX$. Describe how you can determine whether P is on the bisector of $\angle LOX$ without drawing the angle bisector.

4 Practice

More Practice and Problem-Solving Exercises

ASSIGNMENT GUIDE
The assignments below are for the More Practice and Problem-Solving Exercises. You may also want to assign the A-Level Practice Exercises for homework if these are not used in class.
Average: 12–30
Advanced: 12–32

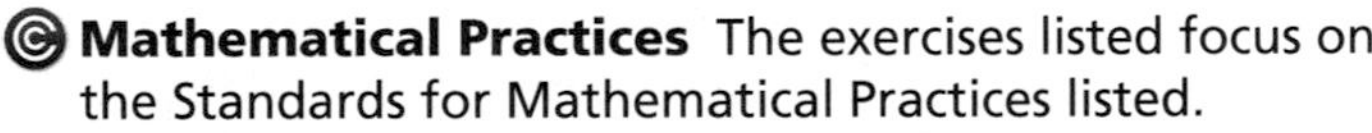

Mathematical Practices The exercises listed focus on the Standards for Mathematical Practices listed.

EX. 17: Make Sense of Problems (MP 1)
EX. 18b, 19b, 23–25, 32: Construct Arguments (MP 3)
EX. 11: Communicate (MP 3)
EX. 22: Critique the Reasoning of Others (MP 3)
EX. 18a, 19a: Use Appropriate Tools (MP 5)

EXERCISE 19: Use the **Think About a Plan** worksheet in the Online Teacher Resources to further support students' development in becoming independent learners.

HOMEWORK QUICK CHECK
To check students' understanding of key skills and concepts, go over Exercises 17, 19, 22, 28, and 30.

ANSWERS

12. 5 **13.** 10 **14.** 10

▼ STUDENT PAGE 213

More Practice and Problem-Solving Exercises

B Apply

Algebra **Use the figure at the right for Exercises 12–16.**

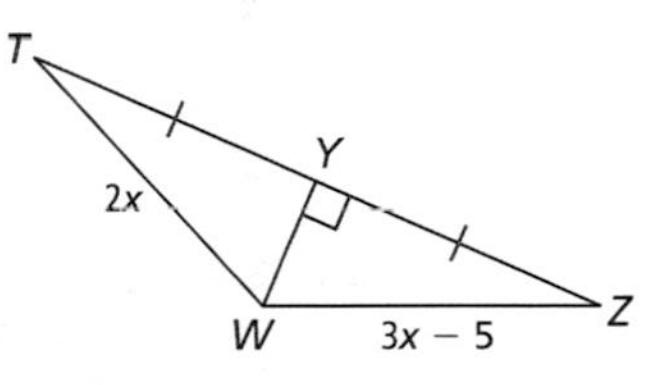

12. Find the value of x.

13. Find TW.

14. Find WZ.

15. What kind of triangle is $\triangle TWZ$? Explain.

16. If R is on the perpendicular bisector of $\overline{TZ}$, then R is ___?___ from T and Z, or ___?___ = ___?___.

17. Think About a Plan In the diagram at the right, the soccer goalie will prepare for a shot from the player at point P by moving out to a point on $\overline{XY}$. To have the best chance of stopping the ball, should the goalie stand at the point on $\overline{XY}$ that lies on the perpendicular bisector of $\overline{GL}$ or at the point on $\overline{XY}$ that lies on the bisector of $\angle GPL$? Explain your reasoning.

- How can you draw a diagram to help?
- Would the goalie want to be the same distance from G and L or from $\overline{PG}$ and $\overline{PL}$?

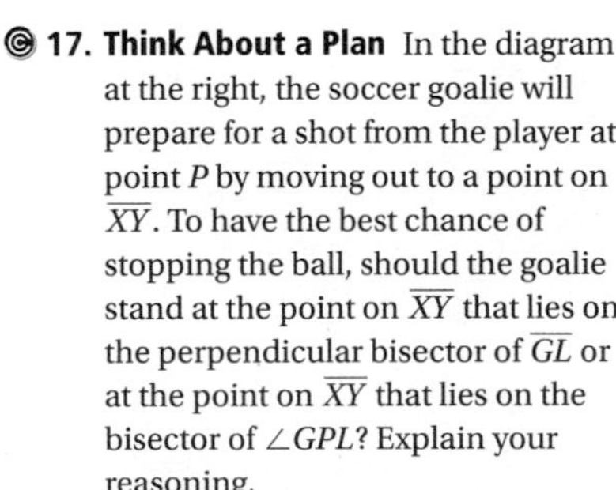

18. a. Constructions Draw $\angle CDE$. Construct the angle bisector of the angle.
b. Reasoning Use the converse of the Angle Bisector Theorem to justify your construction.

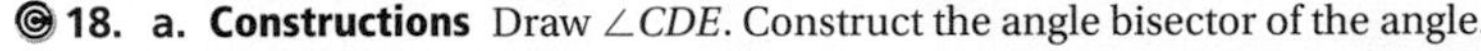

More Practice and Problem-Solving Exercises *continued*

15. isosc., because $TW = ZW$

16. equidistant; RT; RZ

17. At the point on $\overline{XY}$ that lies on the bisector of $\angle GPL$; the goalie does not know to which side of her the player will aim her shot, so she should keep herself equidistant from the sides of $\angle GPL$. Points on the bisector of $\angle GPL$ are equidistant from $\overline{PG}$ and $\overline{PL}$. If she moves to a point on the $\perp$ bisector of $\overline{GL}$, she will be closer to $\overline{PL}$ than to $\overline{PG}$.

18. a.

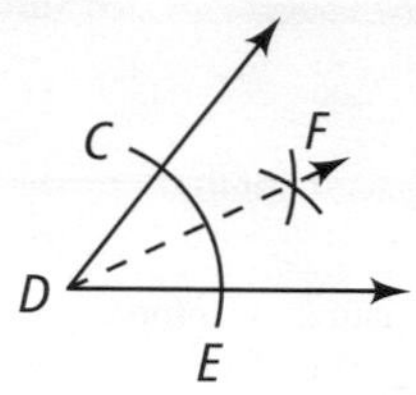

b. Answers may vary. Sample: Since the same radius is used to create the arc from point C to point F and from point E to point F, the distance from C to F is equal to the distance from E to F. By the Converse of the Angle Bisector Theorem, ray DF is the angle bisector of angle CDE.

19. a.

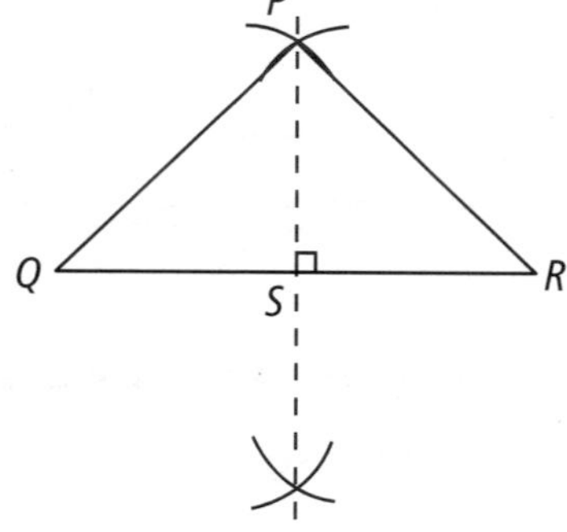

b. Answers may vary. Sample: Since P is on the perpendicular bisector of $\overline{QR}$, it is equidistant from Q and R by the Perpendicular Bisector Theorem.

20. A pt. is on the perpendicular bisector of a seg. if and only if it is equidistant from the endpoints of the seg.

21. A pt. is on the bisector of an angle if and only if it is equidistant from the sides of the angle.

22. To conclude that Q is equidistant from P and R, you must know that $\overline{QS} \perp \overline{PR}$ and that $\overline{QS}$ bisects $\overline{PR}$. The diagram does not show that $PS = SR$.

▼ STUDENT PAGE 213

19. a. Constructions Draw $\overline{QR}$. Construct the perpendicular bisector of $\overline{QR}$ to construct $\triangle PQR$.

b. Reasoning Use the Perpendicular Bisector Theorem to justify that your construction is an isosceles triangle.

20. Write Theorems 25 and 26 as a single biconditional statement.

21. Write Theorems 27 and 28 as a single biconditional statement.

22. Error Analysis To prove that $\triangle PQR$ is isosceles, a student began by stating that since Q is on the segment perpendicular to $\overline{PR}$, Q is equidistant from the endpoints of $\overline{PR}$. What is the error in the student's reasoning?

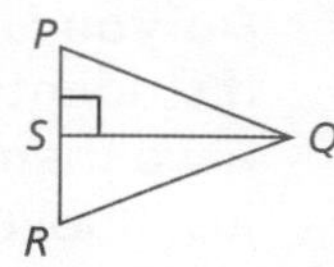

23. No; A is not equidistant from the sides of $\angle TXR$.

24. Yes; the markings show that $\angle TXA \cong \angle RXA$, so $\overline{XA}$ is the bisector of $\angle TXR$.

25. Yes; A is equidistant from the sides of $\angle TXR$.

26. $\overline{AM} \cong \overline{BM}$ by definition of bisector. $\overleftrightarrow{PM} \perp \overline{AB}$, so $\angle PMA$ and $\angle PMB$ are rt. $\angle$s. Therefore, $\angle PMA \cong \angle PMB$ because all rt. $\angle$s are $\cong$. $\overline{PM} \cong \overline{PM}$ by the Refl. Prop. of $\cong$. So $\triangle PMA \cong \triangle PMB$ by SAS, and $\overline{AP} \cong \overline{BP}$ (or $AP = BP$) because corresp. parts of $\cong$ $\triangle$s are $\cong$.

27. $\overline{PA} \cong \overline{PB}$ (Given) and $\angle AMP \cong \angle BMP$ because all rt. $\angle$s are $\cong$. Also, $\overline{PM} \cong \overline{PM}$ by the Refl. Prop. of $\cong$. So rt. $\triangle PMA \cong$ rt. $\triangle PMB$ by HL and $\overline{AM} \cong \overline{BM}$ because corresp. part of $\cong$ $\triangle$s are $\cong$. Therefore, $\overleftrightarrow{PM}$ is the $\perp$ bisector of $\overline{AB}$, by the def. of $\perp$ bisector.

28. In rt. $\triangle SPQ$ and rt. $\triangle SRQ$, $\angle PQS \cong \angle RQS$ (Given), $\angle QPS \cong \angle QRS$ (All rt. $\angle$s are $\cong$.), and $\overline{QS} \cong \overline{QS}$ (Refl. Prop. of $\cong$). So $\triangle SPQ \cong \triangle SRQ$ by AAS, and $\overline{SP} \cong \overline{SR}$ (or $SP = SR$) because corresp. parts of $\cong$ $\triangle$s are $\cong$.

29. In rt. $\triangle SPQ$ and rt. $\triangle SRQ$, $\overline{SP} \cong \overline{SR}$ (Given) and $\overline{QS} \cong \overline{QS}$ (Refl. Prop. of $\cong$), so $\triangle SPQ \cong \triangle SRQ$ by HL. Thus $\angle PQS \cong \angle RQS$ because corresp. parts of $\cong$ $\triangle$s are $\cong$, and $\overrightarrow{QS}$ bisects $\angle PQR$ by the def. of $\angle$ bisector.

30. a. ℓ: $y = -\frac{3}{4}x + \frac{25}{2}$; m: $x = 10$

b. $C(10, 5)$

c. $CA = \sqrt{(10-6)^2 + (5-8)^2} = 5$;
$CB = \sqrt{(10-10)^2 + (5-0)^2} = 5$

d. C is equidistant from the sides of $\angle AOB$, so C is on the bisector of $\angle AOB$ by the Converse of the $\angle$ Bisector Thm.

31. Line ℓ through the midpts. of two sides of $\triangle ABC$ is equidistant from A, B, and C. This is because $\triangle 1 \cong \triangle 2$ and $\triangle 3 \cong \triangle 4$ by AAS. $\overline{AD} \cong \overline{BE}$ and $\overline{BE} \cong \overline{CF}$ because corresp. parts of $\cong$ $\triangle$s are $\cong$. By the Trans. Prop. of $\cong$, $\overline{AD} \cong \overline{BE} \cong \overline{CF}$. By the def. of $\cong$, $AD = BE = CF$, so points A, B, and C are equidistant from line ℓ.

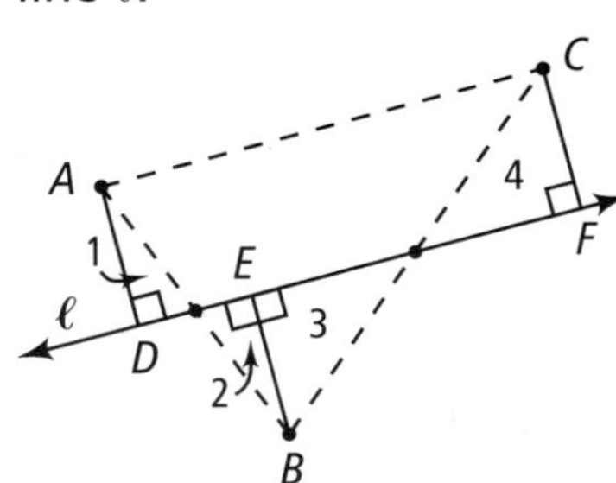

Writing Determine whether A must be on the bisector of $\angle TXR$. Explain.

23.

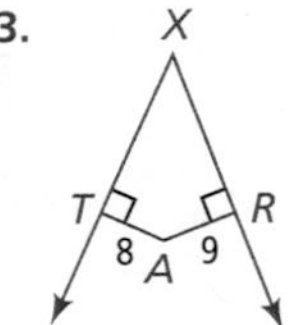

24.

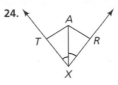

25.

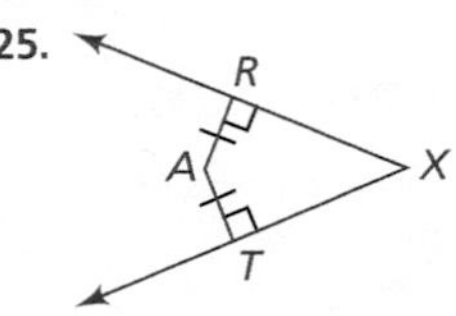

Proof 26. Prove the Perpendicular Bisector Theorem.

Given: $\overleftrightarrow{PM} \perp \overline{AB}$, $\overleftrightarrow{PM}$ bisects $\overline{AB}$

Prove: $AP = BP$

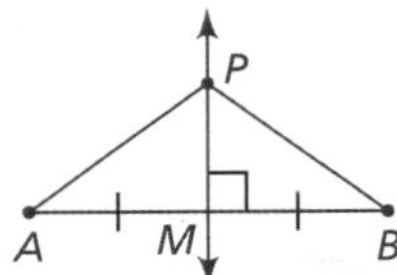

Proof 27. Prove the Converse of the Perpendicular Bisector Theorem.

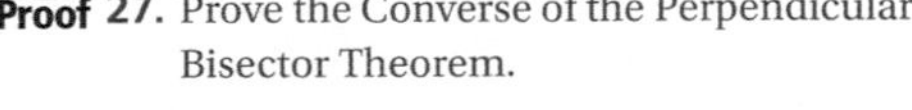

Given: $PA = PB$, with $\overline{PM} \perp \overline{AB}$ at M.

Prove: P is on the perpendicular bisector of $\overline{AB}$.

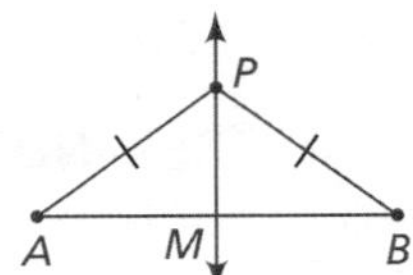

Proof 28. Prove the Angle Bisector Theorem.

Given: $\overrightarrow{QS}$ bisects $\angle PQR$, $\overline{SP} \perp \overrightarrow{QP}$, $\overline{SR} \perp \overrightarrow{QR}$

Prove: $SP = SR$

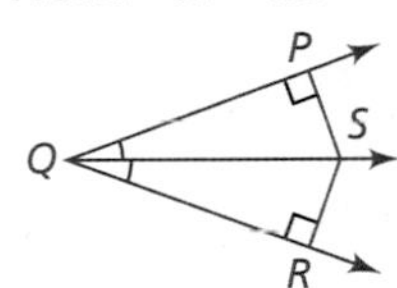

Proof 29. Prove the Converse of the Angle Bisector Theorem.

Given: $\overline{SP} \perp \overrightarrow{QP}$, $\overline{SR} \perp \overrightarrow{QR}$, $SP = SR$

Prove: $\overrightarrow{QS}$ bisects $\angle PQR$.

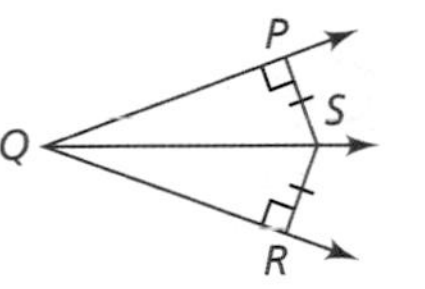

30. **Coordinate Geometry** Use points $A(6, 8)$, $O(0, 0)$, and $B(10, 0)$.

a. Write equations of lines ℓ and m such that $\ell \perp \overleftrightarrow{OA}$ at A and $m \perp \overleftrightarrow{OB}$ at B.

b. Find the intersection C of lines ℓ and m.

c. Show that $CA = CB$.

d. Explain why C is on the bisector of $\angle AOB$.

Challenge

31. A, B, and C are three noncollinear points. Describe and sketch a line in plane ABC such that points A, B, and C are equidistant from the line. Justify your response.

32. **Reasoning** M is the intersection of the perpendicular bisectors of two sides of $\triangle ABC$. Line ℓ is perpendicular to plane ABC at M. Explain why a point E on ℓ is equidistant from A, B, and C. (*Hint:* See Lesson 10-1, Exercise 30. Explain why $\triangle EAM \cong \triangle EBM \cong \triangle ECM$.)

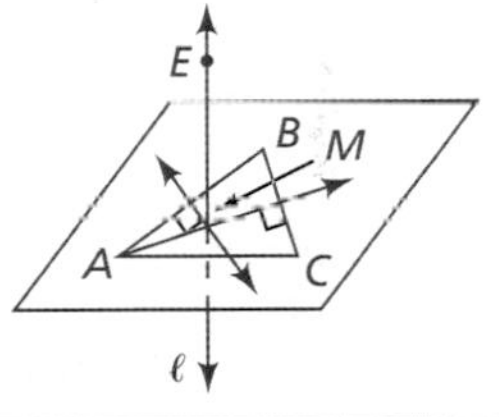

32. M is on the $\perp$ bisectors of $\overline{AB}$ and $\overline{BC}$, so $MA = MB$ and $MB = MC$ by the $\perp$ Bis. Thm. So $MA = MB = MC$ by the Transitive Prop. of Eq. $\angle AME \cong \angle BME \cong \angle CME$ because if a line is $\perp$ to a plane then it is $\perp$ to every line in the plane that contains the intersection of the plane and the line (and all rt. $\angle$s are $\cong$). $\overline{EM} \cong \overline{EM}$ by the Refl. Prop. of $\cong$. So $\triangle EAM \cong \triangle EBM \cong \triangle ECM$ by SAS. Therefore, $\overline{EA} \cong \overline{EB} \cong \overline{EC}$, since corresp. parts of $\cong$ $\triangle$s are $\cong$. So $EA = EB = EC$.

5 Assess and Remediate

Lesson Quiz

1. What is RU?

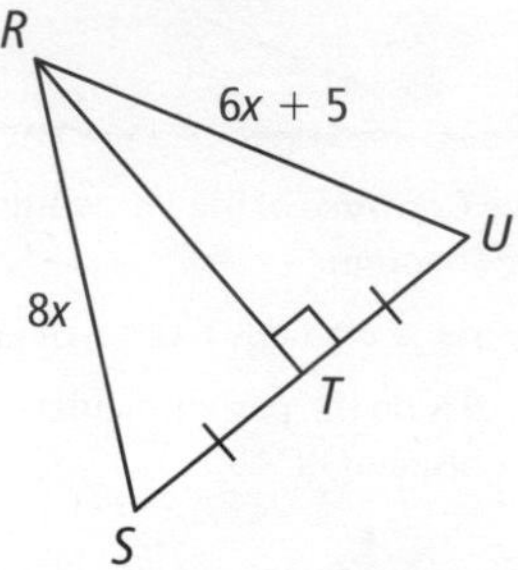

2. **Do you UNDERSTAND?** In the diagram above, if $\overline{RT}$ is extended to contain a point W so that $\overline{UW}$ has a length of 8, what is the length of $\overline{SW}$?
3. What is CD?

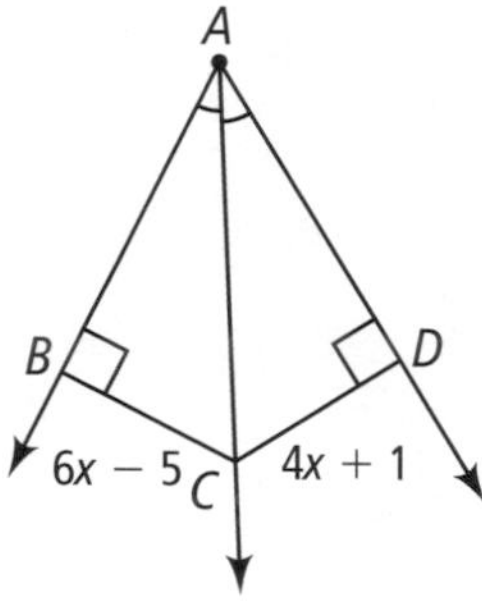

ANSWERS TO LESSON QUIZ

1. 20
2. 8
3. 13

Prescription for Remediation

Use the student work on the Lesson Quiz to prescribe a differentiated assignment.

Points	Differentiated Remediation
0–1	Intervention
2	On-level
3	Extension

Online Assessment

Assign the Lesson Quiz in Success Tracker on **pearsonsuccessnet.com**. Success Tracker will automatically score the quiz and assign appropriate intervention or enrichment to each student based on the results. The compiled data appear in three different reports for instant analysis of whole class and individual student performance.

Differentiated Remediation

Intervention

- **RETEACHING** (2 pages) Provides reteaching and practice exercises for the key lesson concepts. Use with struggling students or absent students.
- **ENGLISH LANGUAGE LEARNER SUPPORT** Helps students develop and reinforce mathematical vocabulary and key concepts.

On-Level

- **PRACTICE** (2 pages) Provides extra practice for each lesson. For simpler practice exercises, use the Form K Practice pages found in the Online Teacher Resources.
- **THINK ABOUT A PLAN** Helps students develop specific problem-solving skills and strategies by providing scaffolded guiding questions.
- **STANDARDIZED TEST PREP** Focuses on all major exercises, all major question types, and helps students prepare for the high-stakes assessments.

Extension

- **ENRICHMENT** Provides students with interesting problems and activities that extend the concepts of the lesson.
- **ACTIVITIES, GAMES, AND PUZZLES** Worksheets that can be used for concept development, enrichment, and for fun!

4-3 Bisectors in Triangles

Common Core State Standards
G.CO.10 Prove theorems about triangles . . . **Also G.C.3**

Preparing to Teach

BIG ideas Reasoning and Proof
Measurement

ESSENTIAL UNDERSTANDING

A triangle's three perpendicular bisectors are always concurrent. A triangle's three angle bisectors are always concurrent.

Math Background

A circumcenter is so named because it is the center of a circumscribed circle.

Similarly, an incenter is so named because it is the center of an inscribed circle.

Points of concurrency are useful in locating a point that is equidistant from three points or three segments. Architects, landscapers, and city planners can use these points to determine the location of key points.

Lesson 4-4 will present the points of concurrency of the medians and altitudes of a triangle.

Make sure students understand that the point of concurrency for angle bisectors is equidistant from the sides and that the point of concurrency for perpendicular bisectors of sides is equidistant from the vertices. This is often a point of confusion for students.

ELL Support

ASSESS UNDERSTANDING Assign groups of three students to draw acute, right, or obtuse triangles. Next, have each group find and label the circumcenter and incenter of the triangles that they have drawn.

Have groups exchange triangles. Each group should

- verify the other group's work.
- compare and contrast the triangle that they drew and the triangle the other group gave to them.
- discuss what might be true about the circumcenter and incenter of every triangle.

Have each group write and illustrate a short report on what they have learned about triangles.

Lesson Vocabulary

- concurrent
- point of concurrency
- circumcenter of a triangle
- circumscribed about
- incenter of a triangle
- inscribed in

Mathematical Practices

LOOK FOR AND MAKE USE OF STRUCTURE. Students will construct the perpendicular bisectors of a triangle, adding the circumcenter of the triangle and the circle circumscribed about it.

1 Interactive Learning

Solve It!

PURPOSE To discover the relationship between the center of a circle and the perpendicular bisectors of an inscribed triangle

PROCESS Students may

- sketch the diagram as described.
- measure the segments created by the perpendicular segments.

Q What is true about the distance from *C* to the vertices? Explain. **[*C* is equidistant from each vertex because each vertex is on circle *C*.]**

Q How are the perpendicular segments through *C* related to the sides of the triangle? Explain. **[By Theorem 26, the segments are the perpendicular bisectors of the sides.]**

ANSWER They are ≅. Draw radii from *C* to each vertex of the △. This forms two right triangles along each side. In any pair, the shared leg is ≅ to itself by the Refl. Prop. of ≅. The two hypotenuses are ≅, because all radii of a ⊙ are ≅. So the two right triangles are ≅ by HL. The two segments are corresp. parts of ≅ triangles.

▼ DIGITAL (STUDENT WORK SPACE PAGE 215)

Getting Ready!

Construct a circle and label its center C. Choose any three points on the circle and connect them to form a triangle. Draw three lines from C such that each line is perpendicular to one side of the triangle. What conjecture can you make about the two segments into which each side of the triangle is divided? Justify your reasoning.

CONNECT THE MATH In the Solve It, students should realize that the perpendicular bisectors of the sides of a triangle are concurrent at a point which is the center of a circumscribed circle. In the lesson, theorems are presented to prove this.

2 Guided Instruction

Problem 1 Finding the Circumcenter of a Triangle

Take Note

Ask students to relate the conclusion of the theorem to the diagram they drew in the Solve It. Encourage them to connect the phrase "equidistant from the vertices" to the circumscribed circle. The distance from the center of the circle to each vertex is the same because it represents the radius of the circle.

Have students sketch each segment and its perpendicular bisector separately. Students should use information from the previous lesson to identify congruent segments in their diagram. Then, they can transfer these congruent marks to the larger diagram associated with the proof.

Problem 1

Q Why is it sufficient to find the intersection of two of the three perpendicular bisectors? **[The third perpendicular bisector will intersect at the same point.]**

Q Why is the perpendicular bisector of $\overline{PO}$ a horizontal line? **[$\overline{PO}$ is a vertical line segment, so a line perpendicular to $\overline{PO}$ must be horizontal.]**

Q What is the equation of a horizontal line? **[$y = a$ where a is the y-coordinate of every point on the line.]**

Q What segment represents the radius of the circle that could circumscribe $\triangle POS$? **[the segment from the center of the hypotenuse to any vertex]**

Q What is the length of the radius? **[$\sqrt{13}$]**

▼ STUDENT PAGES 215–216

In the Solve It, the three lines you drew intersect at one point, the center of the circle. When three or more lines intersect at one point, they are **concurrent.** The point at which they intersect is the **point of concurrency.**

Essential Understanding For any triangle, certain sets of lines are always concurrent. Two of these sets of lines are the perpendicular bisectors of the triangle's three sides and the bisectors of the triangle's three angles.

take note

Theorem 29 Concurrency of Perpendicular Bisectors Theorem

Theorem	Diagram	Symbols
The perpendicular bisectors of the sides of a triangle are concurrent at a point equidistant from the vertices.		Perpendicular bisectors $\overline{PX}$, $\overline{PY}$, and $\overline{PZ}$ are concurrent at P. $PA = PB = PC$

The point of concurrency of the perpendicular bisectors of a triangle is called the **circumcenter of the triangle.**

Since the circumcenter is equidistant from the vertices, you can use the circumcenter as the center of the circle that contains each vertex of the triangle. You say the circle is **circumscribed about** the triangle.

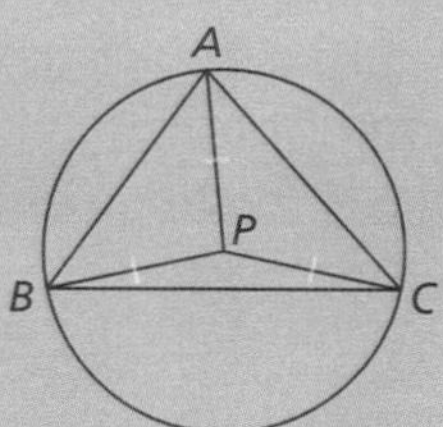

Proof of Theorem 29

Given: Lines ℓ, m, and n are the perpendicular bisectors of the sides of $\triangle ABC$. P is the intersection of lines ℓ and m.

Prove: Line n contains point P, and $PA = PB = PC$.

Proof: A point on the perpendicular bisector of a segment is equidistant from the endpoints of the segment. Point P is on ℓ, which is the perpendicular bisector of $\overline{AB}$, so $PA = PB$. Using the same reasoning, since P is on m, and m is the perpendicular bisector of $\overline{BC}$, $PB = PC$. Thus, $PA = PC$ by the Transitive Property. Since $PA = PC$, P is equidistant from the endpoints of $\overline{AC}$. Then, by the Converse of the Perpendicular Bisector Theorem, P is on line n, the perpendicular bisector of $\overline{AC}$.

The circumcenter of a triangle can be inside, on, or outside a triangle.

Acute triangle

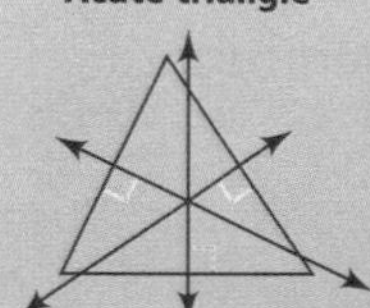

Right triangle

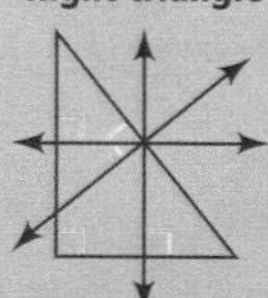

Obtuse triangle

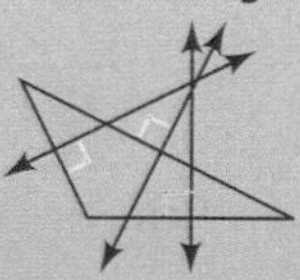

Got It?
Have students sketch the triangle in the coordinate plane. Ask students to identify the equations of the perpendicular bisectors of the horizontal and vertical sides of the triangle, and then use these equations to identify the point of concurrency.

ANSWERS

Got It? (6, 5)

Practice

1. (0, 0)
2. (−3, 1.5)

▼ DIGITAL

Problem 1 **Finding the Circumcenter of a Triangle**

What are the coordinates of the circumcenter of the triangle with vertices $P(0, 6)$, $O(0, 0)$, and $S(4, 0)$?

Find the intersection point of two of the triangle's perpendicular bisectors. Here, it is easiest to find the perpendicular bisectors of $\overline{PO}$ and $\overline{OS}$.

Step 1 (0, 3) is the midpoint of $\overline{PO}$. The line through (0, 3) that is perpendicular to $\overline{PO}$ is $y = 3$.

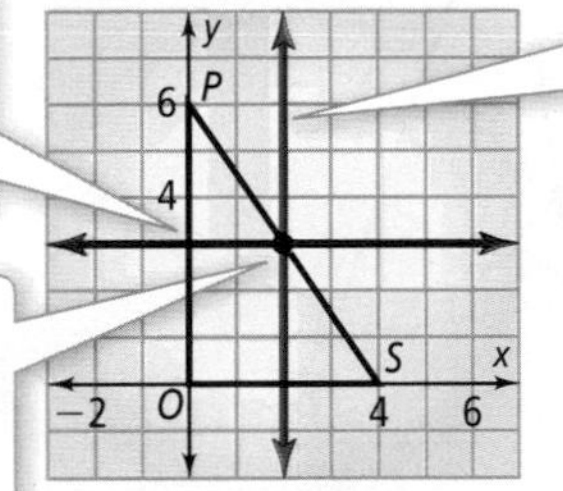

Step 2 (2, 0) is the midpoint of $\overline{OS}$. The line through (2, 0) that is perpendicular to $\overline{OS}$ is $x = 2$.

Step 3 Find the point where the two perpendicular bisectors intersect. $x = 2$ and $y = 3$ intersect at (2, 3).

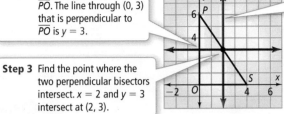

The coordinates of the circumcenter of the triangle are (2, 3).

▼ STUDENT PAGES 216–217

Got It? What are the coordinates of the circumcenter of the triangle with vertices $A(2, 7)$, $B(10, 7)$, and $C(10, 3)$?

Practice

1. **Coordinate Geometry** Find the coordinates of the circumcenter of the triangle.

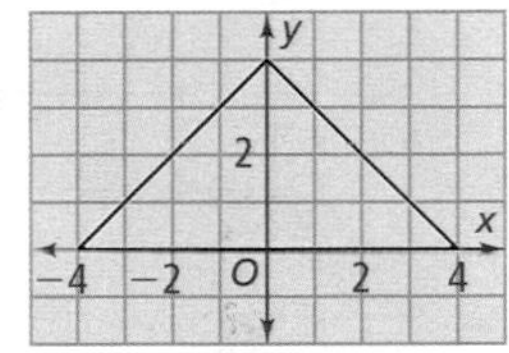

2. **Coordinate Geometry** Find the coordinates of the circumcenter of the triangle with vertices $A(-4, 5)$, $B(-2, 5)$, and $C(-2, -2)$

Problem 2 Using a Circumcenter

Q Why is the point of concurrency of the perpendicular bisectors equidistant from the three buildings? **[The circumcenter is equidistant from the vertices of the triangle. In this problem, the buildings represent the vertices of the triangle.]**

Got It?
Have students make a statement about the location of the bench in relation to the triangle formed by the three trees. Be sure that students can explain how to choose the location.

▼ DIGITAL

Problem 2 **Using a Circumcenter**

A town planner wants to locate a new fire station equidistant from the elementary, middle, and high schools. Where should he locate the station?

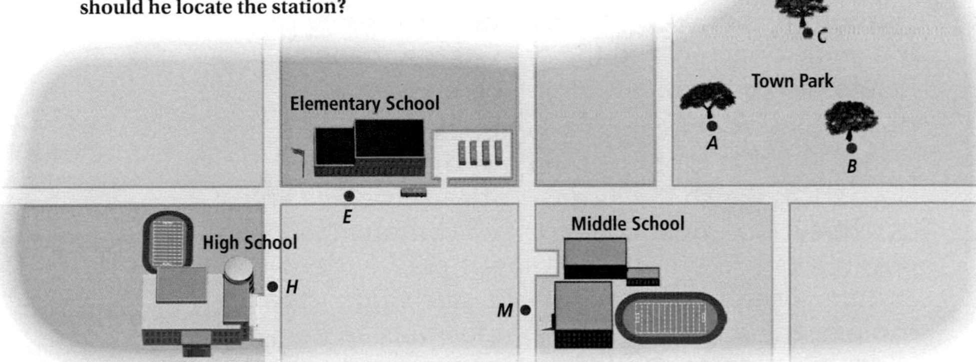

The three schools form the vertices of a triangle. The planner should locate the fire station at P, the point of concurrency of the perpendicular bisectors of $\triangle EMH$. This point is the circumcenter of $\triangle EMH$ and is equidistant from the three schools at E, M, and H.

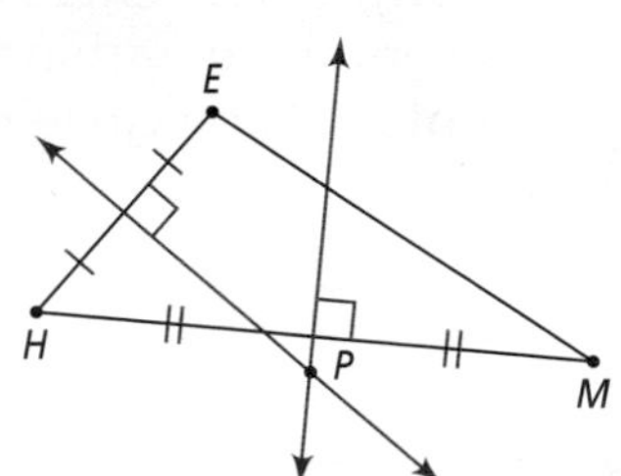

Problem 2 *continued*

ANSWERS

Got It? at the circumcenter of the triangle whose vertices are the three trees

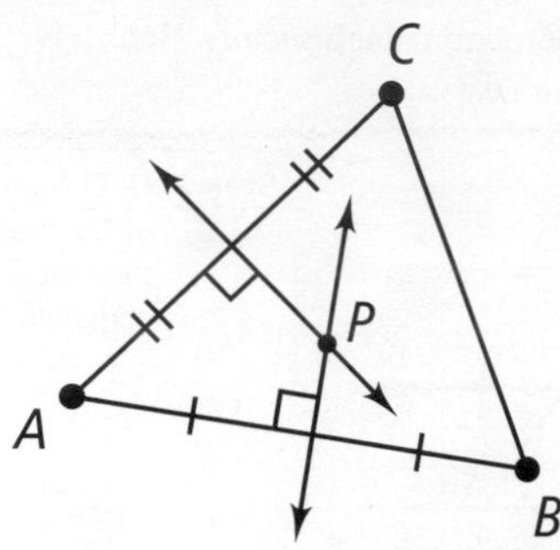

Practice

3. The circumcenter of the △ formed by the lifeguard chair, snack bar, and volleyball court is equidistant from the vertices of the △. Place the recycling barrel at the intersection pt. of two of the triangle's ⊥ bisectors.

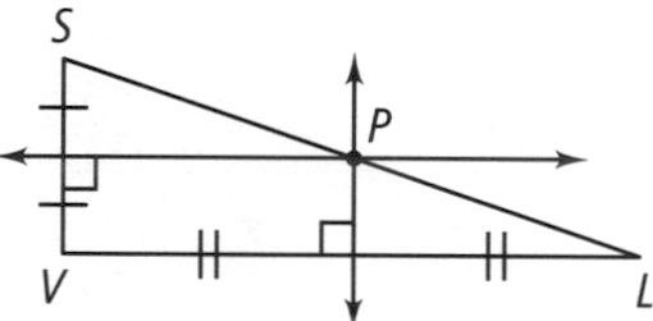

▼ STUDENT PAGES 217–218

Got It? In Problem 2, the town planner wants to place a bench equidistant from the three trees in the park. Where should he place the bench?

Think How do you find a point equidistant from three points?

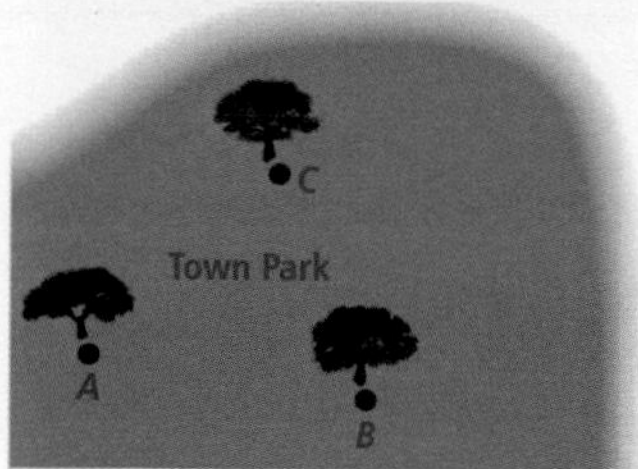

A Practice **3. City Planning** Show where town officials should place a recycling barrel so that it is equidistant from the lifeguard chair, the snack bar, and the volleyball court. Explain.

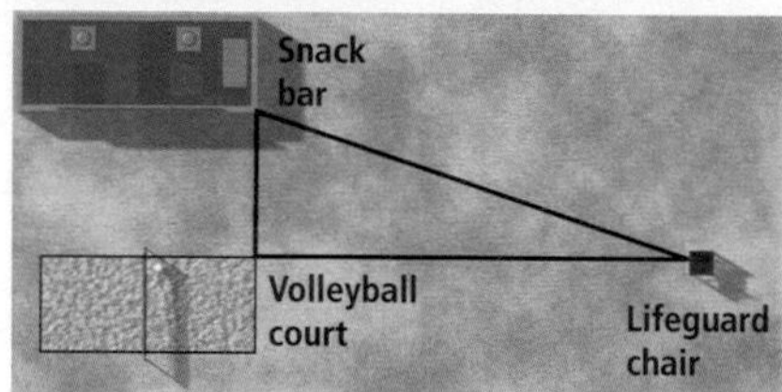

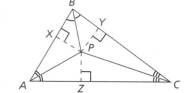

Problem 3 Identifying and Using the Incenter of a Triangle

Take Note

Ask students to use the Angle Bisector Theorem to justify the conclusion of Theorem 30. They may need to redraw the triangle and focus on one angle bisector at a time. Emphasize the relationship between the point of concurrency of the angle bisectors and the sides of the triangle. Relate this to the radius of an inscribed circle.

Have students draw three triangles: one that is acute, one that is obtuse, and one that is right. Have them sketch the incenter of each triangle and describe its location. Compare and contrast the possible locations of the circumcenter of a triangle and the incenter of a triangle. Be sure students can explain why the incenter cannot fall outside the triangle. Students should know an inscribed circle is contained within the triangle. Therefore, the center of the circle must also be inside the triangle.

▼ STUDENT PAGE 218

take note

Theorem 30 Concurrency of Angle Bisectors Theorem

Theorem	Diagram	Symbols
The bisectors of the angles of a triangle are concurrent at a point equidistant from the sides of the triangle.		Angle bisectors $\overline{AP}$, $\overline{BP}$, and $\overline{CP}$ are concurrent at P. $PX = PY = PZ$

You will prove Theorem 30 in Exercise 17.

The point of concurrency of the angle bisectors of a triangle is called the **incenter of the triangle**. For any triangle, the incenter is always inside the triangle. In the diagram, points X, Y, and Z are equidistant from P, the incenter of $\triangle ABC$. P is the center of the circle that is **inscribed in** the triangle.

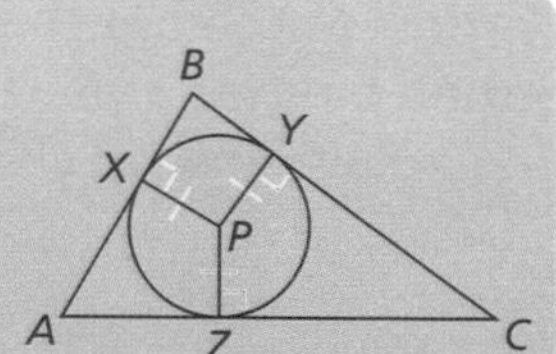

Problem 3

Q How can you justify the statement that G is the point of concurrency of the angle bisectors? **[Each angle of the triangle is bisected.]**

Q Which segments in the diagram are congruent? **[$\overline{GF} \cong \overline{GD} \cong \overline{GE}$]**

Got It?

Q What type of triangle is formed by the segments $\overline{QN}$ and $\overline{QP}$? Explain. **[A right triangle is formed because $\overline{QN} \perp \overline{KL}$.]**

ANSWERS

Got It? a. 61 **b.** No; answers may vary. Sample: The distance from Q to $\overline{KL}$ is QN, the length of the shortest segment from Q to $\overline{KL}$. From part (a), $QN = 61$, so $QP > 61$.

Practice

4. Z

5. 4

▼ DIGITAL

Problem 3 Identifying and Using the Incenter of a Triangle

Algebra $GE = 2x - 7$ and $GF = x + 4$. What is GD?

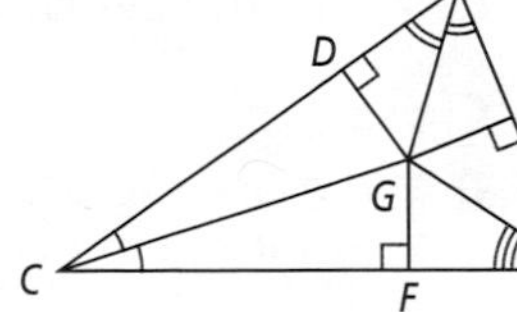

G is the incenter of $\triangle ABC$ because it is the point of concurrency of the angle bisectors. By the Concurrency of Angle Bisectors Theorem, the distances from the incenter to the three sides of the triangle are equal, so $GE = GF = GD$. Use this relationship to find x.

$2x - 7 = x + 4$ $\quad$ $GE = GF$

$2x = x + 11$ $\quad$ Add 7 to each side.

$x = 11$ $\quad$ Subtract x from each side.

Now find GF.

$GF = x + 4$

$= 11 + 4 = 15$ $\quad$ Substitute 11 for x.

Since $GF = GD$, $GD = 15$.

▼ STUDENT PAGE 219

Think Which segments in the diagram are congruent?

Got It? **a.** $QN = 5x + 36$ and $QM = 2x + 51$. What is QO?

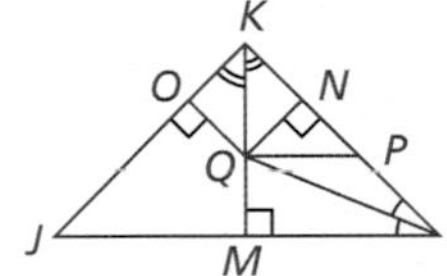

b. Reasoning Is it possible for QP to equal 50? Explain.

Practice **4.** Name the point of concurrency of the angle bisectors.

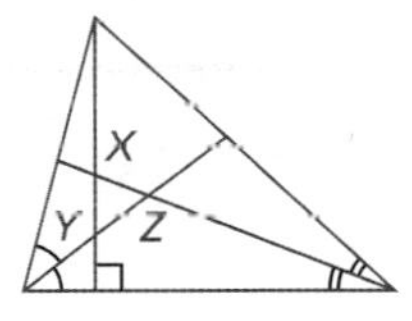

5. Find the value of x.

$RS = 4(x - 3) + 6$ and $RT = 5(2x - 6)$

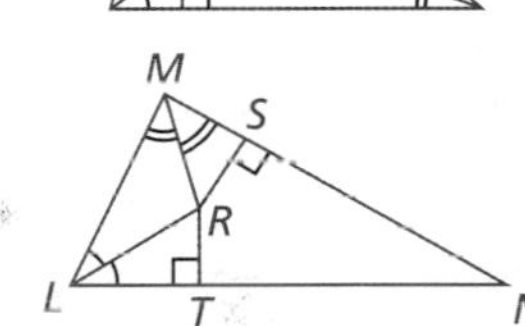

3 Lesson Check

Do you know HOW?

If students have difficulty with Exercise 6, then have them review Problem 1 to see that they must find the center of the circle that circumscribes the triangle.

▼ STUDENT PAGE 220

Lesson Check

Do you know HOW?

6. What are the coordinates of the circumcenter of the triangle at the right?

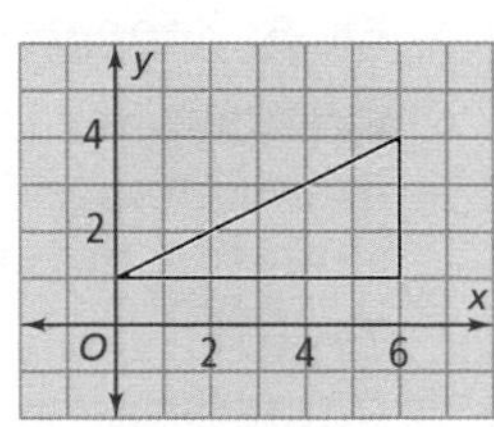

7. In the figure at the right, $TV = 3x - 12$ and $TU = 5x - 24$. What is the value of x?

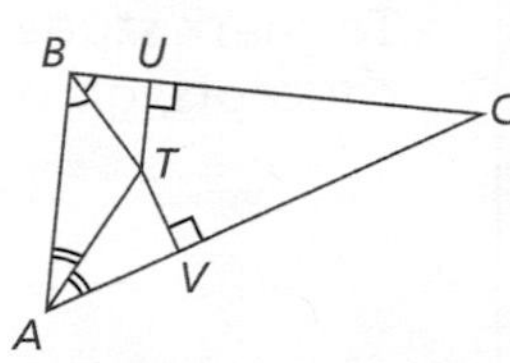

Lesson Check *continued*

Do you UNDERSTAND?

If students have difficulty with Exercise 10, then have them review Problem 3.

Close

Q What are the properties of the circumcenter of a triangle? **[It is equidistant from the vertices of the triangle and is contained in the perpendicular bisectors of the sides of the triangle.]**

Q What are the properties of the incenter of a triangle? **[It is equidistant from the sides of the triangle and contained in the bisectors of the angles of the triangle.]**

ANSWERS

6. (3, 2.5)

7. 6

8. obtuse △

9. Since the three ⊥ bisectors of a △ are concurrent, the third ⊥ bisector goes through the pt. of intersection of the other two ⊥ bisectors.

10. Answers may vary. Sample: The diagram does not show that $\overline{QC}$ bisects ∠*SQR*, so you cannot conclude that point *C* is equidistant from the sides of ∠*SQR*.

▼ STUDENT PAGES 220–221

Do you UNDERSTAND?

8. Vocabulary A triangle's circumcenter is outside the triangle. What type of triangle is it?

9. Reasoning You want to find the circumcenter of a triangle. Why do you only need to find the intersection of two of the triangle's perpendicular bisectors, instead of all three?

10. Error Analysis Your friend sees the triangle at the right and concludes that $CT = CP$. What is the error in your friend's reasoning?

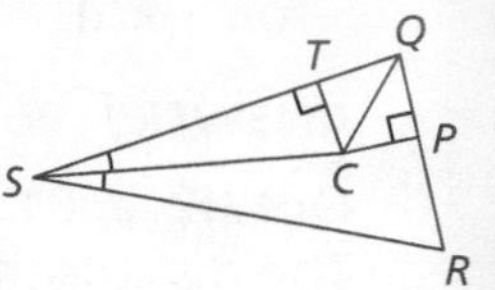

11. Compare and Contrast How are the circumcenter and incenter of a triangle alike? How are they different?

11. Each one is a point of concurrency of bisectors of parts of a △, each is equidistant from three parts of the △, and each is the center of a ⊙ that contains three points of the △. The circumcenter is equidistant from three points, while the incenter is equidistant from three segments. The △ is inside the ⊙ centered at the circumcenter and outside the ⊙ centered at the incenter.

4 Practice

More Practice and Problem-Solving Exercises

ASSIGNMENT GUIDE

The assignments below are for the More Practice and Problem-Solving Exercises. You may also want to assign the A-Level Practice Exercises for homework if these are not used in class.

Average: 12–22

Advanced: 12–25

Mathematical Practices The exercises listed focus on the Standards for Mathematical Practices listed.

EX. 11, 12, 16: Make Sense of Problems (MP 1)

EX. 19–22, 23: Construct Arguments (MP 3)

EX. 10: Critique the Reasoning of Others (MP 3)

EX. 18: Model (MP 4)

EX. 9: Repeated Reasoning (MP 8)

EXERCISE 16: Use the **Think About a Plan** worksheet in the Online Teacher Resources to further support students' development in becoming independent learners.

HOMEWORK QUICK CHECK

To check students' understanding of key skills and concepts, go over Exercises 12, 15, 16, 17, and 19.

▼ STUDENT PAGE 221

More Practice and Problem-Solving Exercises

B Apply

12. Think About a Plan In the figure at the right, *P* is the incenter of isosceles △*RST*. What type of triangle is △*RPT*? Explain.

- What segments determine the incenter of a triangle?
- What do you know about the base angles of an isosceles triangle?

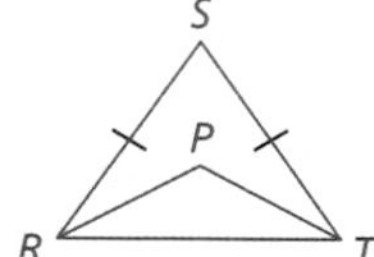

ANSWERS

12. Isosceles; $SR = ST$, so $\angle SRT \cong \angle STR$ (Isosc. △ Thm). Since *P* is the incenter of △*RST*, $\overline{PR}$ and $\overline{PT}$ are ∠ bisectors. So $m\angle PRT = \frac{1}{2}m\angle SRT = \frac{1}{2}m\angle STR = m\angle PTR$. Thus $PR = PT$ by the Converse of the Isosc. △ Thm.

13. Inscribed circle: Construct two ∠ bisectors. Their intersection is the center of the circle. Construct a ⊥ to any side from the center. The distance to the side is the radius. Construct a circle with this center and radius. Circumscribed circle: Construct two ⊥ bisectors. Their intersection is the center of the circle. Draw a circle from that center passing through the vertices.

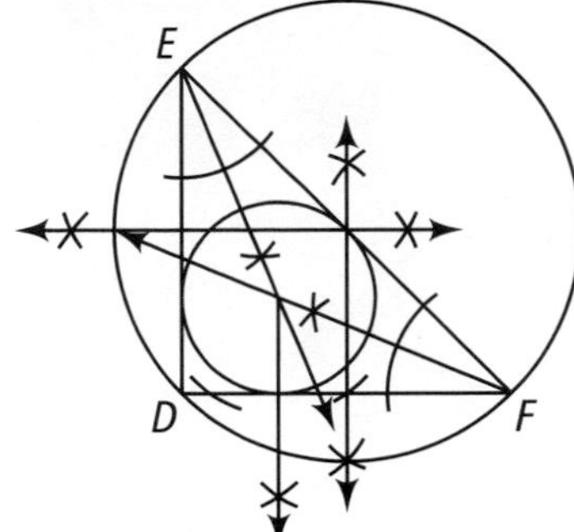

14. Same method as for Exercise 13.

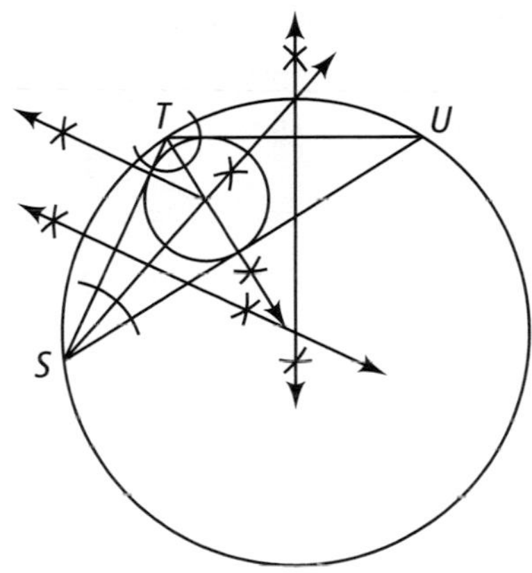

15. $m\angle DGE = 130$, $m\angle DGF = 120$, $m\angle EGF = 110$

16. An interpretation of the passage is that the treasure is equidistant from three Norway pines. To find the treasure, Karl can find the circumcenter of the △ whose vertices are the three pines.

17. From the given information, $\angle XBF \cong \angle XBE$ and $\angle XAE \cong \angle XAD$; also, $\angle XFB \cong \angle XEB \cong \angle XEA \cong \angle XDA$ because ⊥ lines form rt. angles, which are ≅. $\overline{XB} \cong \overline{XB}$ and $\overline{XA} \cong \overline{XA}$ by the Reflexive Prop. of ≅, so $\triangle XFB \cong \triangle XEB$ and $\triangle XEA \cong \triangle XDA$ by AAS. Thus $XF = XE$ and $XE = XD$ because corresp. parts of ≅ triangles are ≅, and $XF = XD$ by the Transitive Prop. of Equality. Thus X is on the bisector of $\angle BCA$ by the Converse of the ∠ Bisector Thm. Since n is the bisector of $\angle BCA$ (Given), then n contains X.

Constructions Draw a triangle that fits the given description. Then construct the inscribed circle and the circumscribed circle. Describe your method.

13. right triangle, $\triangle DEF$

14. obtuse triangle, $\triangle STU$

15. Algebra In the diagram at the right, G is the incenter of $\triangle DEF$, $m\angle DEF = 60$, and $m\angle EFD = 2 \cdot m\angle EDF$. What are $m\angle DGE$, $m\angle DGF$, and $m\angle EGF$?

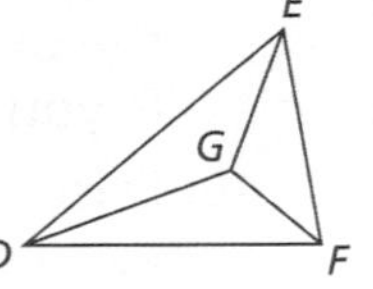

16. Writing Ivars found an old piece of paper inside an antique book.

It read,

From the spot I buried Olaf's treasure, equal sets of paces did I measure; each of three directions in a line, there to plant a seedling Norway pine. I could not return for failing health; now the hounds of Haiti guard my wealth. —*Karl*

After searching Caribbean islands for five years, Ivars found an island with three tall Norway pines. How might Ivars find where Karl buried Olaf's treasure?

Proof **17.** Use the diagram at the right to prove the Concurrrency of Angle Bisectors Theorem.

Given: Rays ℓ, m, and n are bisectors of the angles of $\triangle ABC$. X is the intersection of rays ℓ and m, $\overline{XD} \perp \overline{AC}$, $\overline{XE} \perp \overline{AB}$, and $\overline{XF} \perp \overline{BC}$.

Prove: Ray n contains point X, and $XD = XE = XF$.

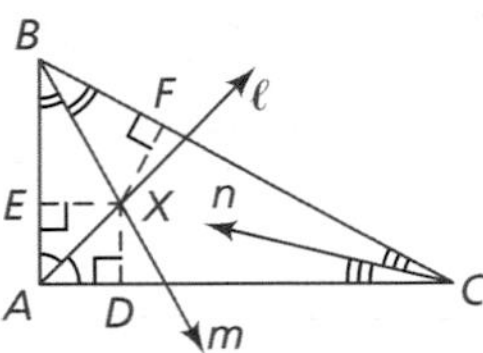

More Practice and Problem-Solving Exercises *continued*

18. *P*; the markings in the diagram show that *P* is the incenter of the triangular station and *C* is the circumcenter. If you stand at *P*, you will be equidistant from the three sides along which the buses are parked. If you move away from *P*, you will move closer to some of the buses.

19. False; the circumcenter is equidistant from the vertices, and the incenter and circumcenter are different (unless the triangle is an equilateral triangle).

20. true

21. False; if the points are collinear, then the $\perp$ bisectors of the segments determined by the points will be $\parallel$. Since the $\perp$ bisectors are $\parallel$, they will not intersect, so there is no point that is equidistant from all 3 points.

22. False;

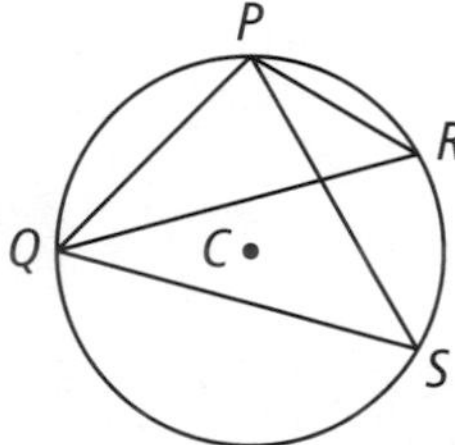

As the diagram shows, circle *C* is circumscribed about both $\triangle PQR$ and $\triangle PQS$, so points *R* and *S* do not have to coincide.

23. Answers may vary. Sample: The two midsegments that extend from the midpt. of the hypotenuse are $\parallel$ to the two legs by the Triangle Midsegment Thm. Since the two legs form a right $\angle$, the midsegments therefore form right angles with the legs (Corresp. Angles Thm.). Hence, they are the $\perp$ bisectors of the legs (Def. of $\perp$ bis.). Their meeting point—the midpt. of the hypotenuse—is the circumcenter (Def.).

24. Never; if you have three $\parallel$ lines ℓ, *m*, and *n*, with *m* in between ℓ and *n*, then a point equidistant from ℓ and *m* would be (midway) between them. A point equidistant from *m* and *n* would be (midway) between those two lines. A point equidistant from all three would therefore have to be on both sides of *m*! This is impossible.

25. Sometimes; the circumcenter and the incenter of a triangle are the same if the triangle is an equilateral triangle.

▼ STUDENT PAGE 222

18. Noise Control You are trying to talk to a friend on the phone in a busy bus station. The buses are so loud that you can hardly hear. Referring to the figure at the right, should you stand at *P* or *C* to be as far as possible from all the buses? Explain.

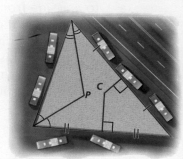

Reasoning Determine whether each statement is *true* or *false*. If the statement is false, give a counterexample.

19. The incenter of a triangle is equidistant from all three vertices.

20. The incenter of a triangle always lies inside the triangle.

21. You can circumscribe a circle about any three points in a plane.

22. If point *C* is the circumcenter of $\triangle PQR$ and the circumcenter of $\triangle PQS$, then *R* and *S* must be the same point.

Challenge

23. Reasoning Explain why the circumcenter of a right triangle is on one of the triangle's sides.

Determine whether each statement is *always*, *sometimes*, or *never* true. Explain.

24. It is possible to find a point equidistant from three parallel lines in a plane.

25. The circles inscribed in and circumscribed about an isosceles triangle have the same center.

Assess and Remediate

Lesson Quiz

1. What congruence statements can you write for the inscribed triangle below?

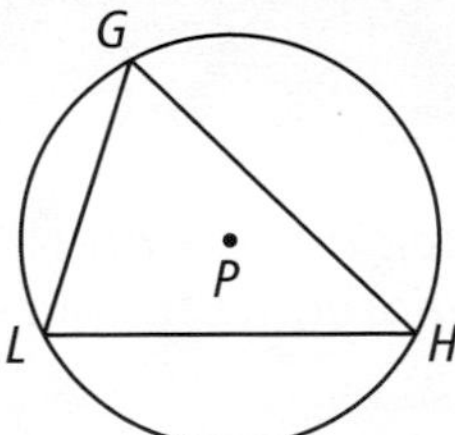

2. What is the center of the circle that you can circumscribe about a triangle with vertices $A(2, 6)$, $B(2, 0)$, and $C(10, 0)$?
3. **Do you UNDERSTAND?** A landscaper wants to build a goldfish pond that is equidistant from the gazebo, the rose garden, and the bench. How should the landscaper determine where to build the goldfish pond?

Bench

Gazebo

Rose Garden

ANSWERS TO LESSON QUIZ

1. $\overline{GP} \cong \overline{LP}$; $\overline{GP} \cong \overline{HP}$; $\overline{HP} \cong \overline{LP}$
2. (6, 3)
3. The landscaper should locate the goldfish pond at the point of concurrency of the triangle's perpendicular bisectors.

Prescription for Remediation

Use the student work on the Lesson Quiz to prescribe a differentiated assignment.

Points	Differentiated Remediation
0–1	Intervention
2	On-level
3	Extension

Online Assessment

Assign the Lesson Quiz in Success Tracker on **pearsonsuccessnet.com**. Success Tracker will automatically score the quiz and assign appropriate intervention or enrichment to each student based on the results. The compiled data appear in three different reports for instant analysis of whole class and individual student performance.

Differentiated Remediation

Intervention

- **RETEACHING** (2 pages) Provides reteaching and practice exercises for the key lesson concepts. Use with struggling students or absent students.
- **ENGLISH LANGUAGE LEARNER SUPPORT** Helps students develop and reinforce mathematical vocabulary and key concepts.

On-Level

- **PRACTICE** (2 pages) Provides extra practice for each lesson. For simpler practice exercises, use the Form K Practice pages found in the Online Teacher Resources.
- **THINK ABOUT A PLAN** Helps students develop specific problem-solving skills and strategies by providing scaffolded guiding questions.
- **STANDARDIZED TEST PREP** Focuses on all major exercises, all major question types, and helps students prepare for the high-stakes assessments.

Extension

- **ENRICHMENT** Provides students with interesting problems and activities that extend the concepts of the lesson.
- **ACTIVITIES, GAMES, AND PUZZLES** Worksheets that can be used for concept development, enrichment, and for fun!

Medians and Altitudes

Common Core State Standards
G.CO.10 Prove theorems about triangles . . . the medians of a triangle meet at a point. **Also G.SRT.5**

Preparing to Teach

BIG ideas Reasoning and Proof
Measurement

ESSENTIAL UNDERSTANDING

A triangle's three medians are always concurrent. The lines containing a triangle's altitudes are always concurrent.

Math Background

Students can use inductive reasoning to hypothesize that particular segments in a triangle such as altitudes, medians, angle bisectors, or perpendicular bisectors are always concurrent.

The point of concurrency of the medians of a triangle is the centroid. This point represents the center of gravity of the triangle. The median of a triangle occurs on the segment $\frac{2}{3}$ of the distance from the vertex to the midpoint opposite it. The lines containing the altitudes of a triangle are concurrent at a point called the orthocenter of the triangle. The orthocenter of a triangle can be located using coordinate geometry. Students will learn that all four types of special segments in triangles have a point of concurrency.

ELL Support

FOCUS ON LANGUAGE Have pairs of students work together to make word cards for the chapter vocabulary. Remind students to include the words: *incenter, circumcenter, orthocenter, concurrency, centroid, altitude, median, midsegment,* and *equidistant*.

Students should write the vocabulary word on one side of the card. On the other side they should write a formal definition and illustrations and familiar words which will help them understand the word's meaning.

Each pair of students should compare their vocabulary cards with those of another group. Students can change their cards to include ideas suggested by the other group.

Lesson Vocabulary

- median of a triangle
- centroid of a triangle
- altitude of a triangle
- orthocenter of a triangle

Mathematical Practices

LOOK FOR AND MAKE USE OF STRUCTURE. Using medians and altitudes of a triangle, students will label the centroid and orthocenter of that triangle.

Interactive Learning

Solve It!

PURPOSE To find the point of concurrency of the medians of a triangle

PROCESS Students investigate the intersection of segments drawn from the vertices to the sides of a triangle as the point on the side gets closer and closer to the midpoint.

Q What would be a logical first step for this Solve It? **[Measure the length of each side of the triangle.]**

Q What unit of measure makes the most sense to use? Explain. **[Answers will vary. Sample answer: millimeters because it is a precise measure and the measurements will be whole numbers.]**

Q What do you notice as the segments drawn from the vertices to opposite sides get closer to the midpoint of the opposite sides? **[The triangles formed get smaller and smaller.]**

ANSWER Check students' work; the three segments will be concurrent.

▼ DIGITAL (STUDENT WORK SPACE PAGE 223)

Getting Ready!

Draw a large acute scalene $\triangle ABC$. On each side, mark the point that is $\frac{1}{5}$ of the distance from one of the side's endpoints, as shown in the diagram. Connect each of these points to the opposite vertex. Repeat this process for $\frac{1}{4}$ and $\frac{1}{3}$. What do you think the result will be for $\frac{1}{2}$? Check your answer. Were you correct?

CONNECT THE MATH In the Solve It, students made a conjecture about the concurrency of the medians of a triangle. In this lesson their conjecture will be confirmed. They will also study the point of concurrency for altitudes of a triangle.

2 Guided Instruction

Problem 1 Finding the Length of a Median

Take Note

Have students label the lengths of each segment of the medians. If the median lengths are x, y, and z, then the longest sections should be labeled $\frac{2}{3}x$, $\frac{2}{3}y$, and $\frac{2}{3}z$, respectively.

Problem 1

Q How do you know that the segments $\overline{XB}$ and $\overline{ZC}$ are medians? **[Points *B* and *C* are the midpoints of the sides.]**

Got It?

ERROR PREVENTION

For part (b), let $ZC = x$. Write a ratio that relates the lengths of the two segments. Have students simplify the ratio and then explain the result. Because $ZA = \frac{2}{3}ZC$, it is twice AC.

ANSWERS

Got It? a. 13.5 **b.** 2 : 1; $ZA = \frac{2}{3}CZ$ and $AC = \frac{1}{3}CZ$, so $ZA : AC = \frac{2}{3} : \frac{1}{3} = 2 : 1$

Practice

1. $ZY = 1.8$, $ZU = 5.4$
2. $VY = 6$, $YX = 3$

▼ STUDENT PAGE 223

In the Solve It, the last set of segments you drew are the triangle's medians. A **median of a triangle** is a segment whose endpoints are a vertex and the midpoint of the opposite side.

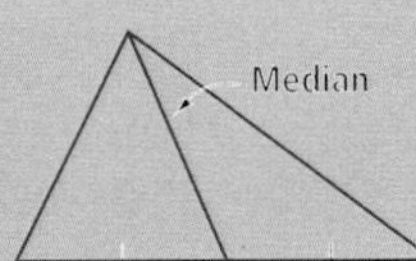

Essential Understanding A triangle's three medians are always concurrent.

take note

Theorem 31 Concurrency of Medians Theorem

The medians of a triangle are concurrent at a point that is two thirds the distance from each vertex to the midpoint of the opposite side.

$DC = \frac{2}{3}DJ$ $EC = \frac{2}{3}EG$ $FC = \frac{2}{3}FH$

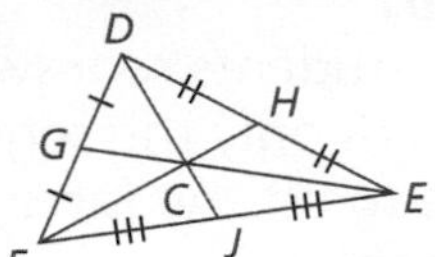

You will prove Theorem 31 in Lesson 5-8.

In a triangle, the point of concurrency of the medians is the **centroid of the triangle**. The point is also called the *center of gravity* of a triangle because it is the point where a triangular shape will balance. For any triangle, the centroid is always inside the triangle.

▼ DIGITAL

Problem 1 Finding the Length of a Median GRIDDED RESPONSE

In the diagram at the right, $XA = 8$. What is the length of $\overline{XB}$?

A is the centroid of $\triangle XYZ$ because it is the point of concurrency of the triangle's medians.

$XA = \frac{2}{3}XB$	Concurrency of Medians Theorem
$8 = \frac{2}{3}XB$	Substitute 8 for *XA*.
$\left(\frac{3}{2}\right)8 = \left(\frac{3}{2}\right)\frac{2}{3}XB$	Multiply each side by $\frac{3}{2}$.
$12 = XB$	Simplify.

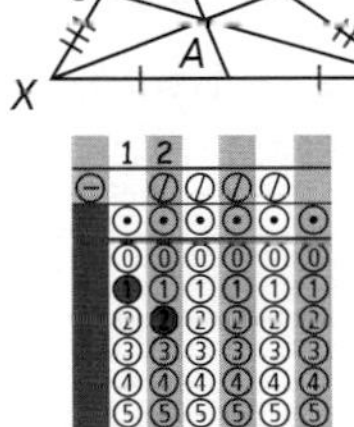

▼ STUDENT PAGE 224

Got It? **a.** If $ZA = 9$, what is the length of $\overline{ZC}$?

b. Reasoning What is the ratio of *ZA* to *AC*? Explain.

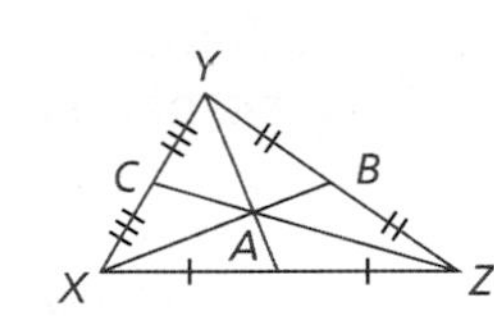

A Practice In $\triangle TUV$, *Y* is the centroid.

1. If $YU = 3.6$, find *ZY* and *ZU*.
2. If $VX = 9$, find *VY* and *YX*.

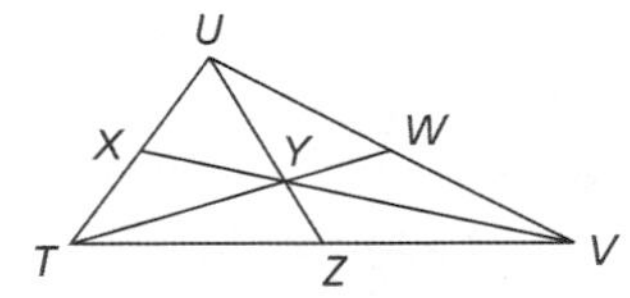

Problem 2 Identifying Medians and Altitudes

Q What is the relationship between $\overline{PR}$ and $\overline{QR}$? **[They are perpendicular.]**

Q What type of segment is perpendicular to a side of a triangle? **[an altitude]**

Q What is the relationship between $\overline{PT}$ and $\overline{ST}$? **[They are congruent.]**

Q What type of segment joins a vertex and the midpoint of the opposite side? **[a median]**

Got It? **SYNTHESIZING**

Have students redraw the triangle so that it contains only the segment they are examining. Ask them to list the facts that help them to classify the segment.

ANSWERS

Got It?

a. A median; it connects a vertex of $\triangle ABC$ and the midpt. of the opposite side.

b. Neither; *E* is a midpt. of $\triangle ABC$, but *G* is not a vertex of $\triangle ABC$.

c. An altitude; it extends from a vertex of $\triangle ABC$ and is $\perp$ to the opposite side.

Practice

3. Neither; it does not have a vertex of $\triangle ABC$ as an endpoint.

4. Altitude; it extends from a vertex of $\triangle ABC$ and is $\perp$ to the opposite side.

▼ STUDENT PAGE 225

An **altitude of a triangle** is the perpendicular segment from a vertex of the triangle to the line containing the opposite side. An altitude of a triangle can be inside or outside the triangle, or it can be a side of the triangle.

▼ DIGITAL

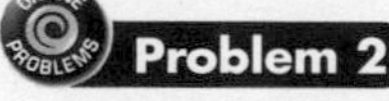

Problem 2 **Identifying Medians and Altitudes**

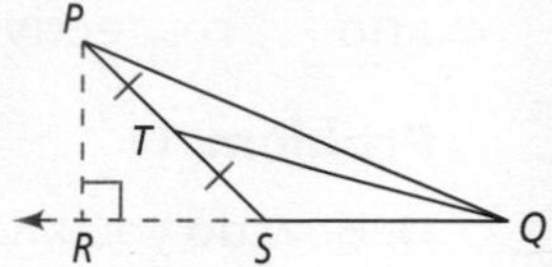

A **For $\triangle PQS$, is $\overline{PR}$ a *median*, an *altitude*, or *neither*? Explain.**

$\overline{PR}$ is a segment that extends from vertex *P* to the line containing $\overline{SQ}$, the side opposite *P*. $\overline{PR} \perp \overleftrightarrow{QR}$, so $\overline{PR}$ is an altitude of $\triangle PQS$.

B **For $\triangle PQS$, is $\overline{QT}$ a *median*, an *altitude*, or *neither*? Explain.**

$\overline{QT}$ is a segment that extends from vertex *Q* to the side opposite *Q*. Since $\overline{PT} \cong \overline{TS}$, *T* is the midpoint of $\overline{PS}$. So $\overline{QT}$ is a median of $\triangle PQS$.

▼ STUDENT PAGE 225

Got It? For $\triangle ABC$, is each segment a *median*, an *altitude*, or *neither*? Explain.

a. $\overline{AD}$

b. $\overline{EG}$

c. $\overline{CF}$

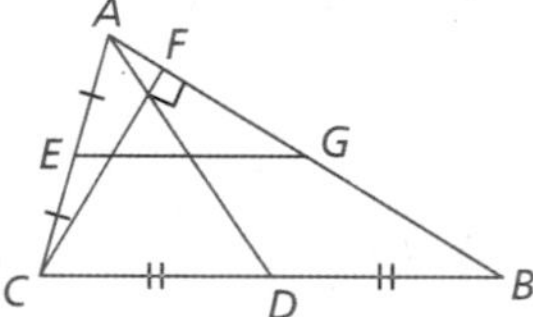

Plan

How do you determine whether a segment is an altitude or a median?

Practice For $\triangle ABC$, is the red segment a *median*, an *altitude*, or *neither*? Explain.

3.

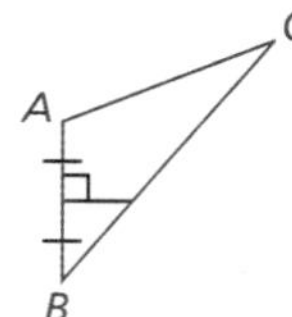

4.

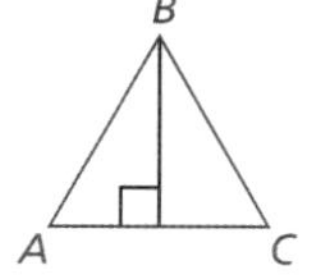

Problem 3 Finding the Orthocenter

Ask students to compare and contrast an altitude with a perpendicular bisector. Both segments are perpendicular to one side of the triangle. A perpendicular bisector does not necessarily pass through the vertex of the opposite side. An altitude must pass through the opposite vertex. Challenge students to identify a triangle in which an altitude and a perpendicular bisector are the same segment.

▼ STUDENT PAGE 226

take note

Theorem 32 **Concurrency of Altitudes Theorem**

The lines that contain the altitudes of a triangle are concurrent.

You will prove Theorem 32 in Lesson 5-8.

The lines that contain the altitudes of a triangle are concurrent at the **orthocenter of the triangle**. The orthocenter of a triangle can be inside, on, or outside the triangle.

Acute triangle

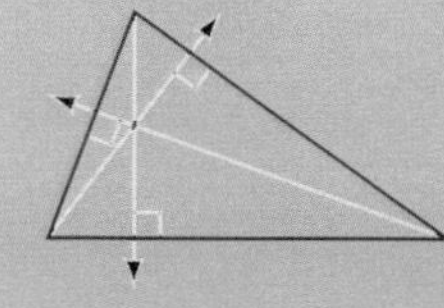

Right triangle

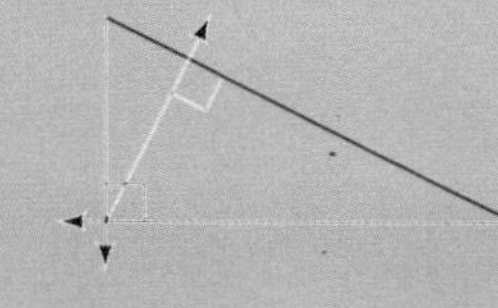

Obtuse triangle

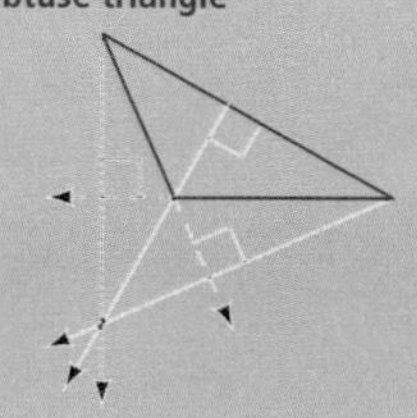

Problem 3

Q What linear equations do you need to find the coordinates of the orthocenter? **[the equations that represent at least two altitudes of the triangle]**

Q How are the slopes of the altitudes related to the slope of the sides to which they are perpendicular? **[The slopes are opposite reciprocals. Their product equals −1.]**

Q How can you identify the point where two lines intersect? **[Solve the system of equations using substitution, elimination, or graphing.]**

Got It?

Because the triangle is a right triangle, the legs are also the altitudes. Consequently, the orthocenter is the vertex of the right angle.

ANSWERS

Got It? (1, 2)

Practice

5. (4, 0)

6. (−2, 0)

Take Note

Ask students to define each of the special segments in triangles. They should be able to identify their characteristics, their points of concurrency, and list any special characteristics of these points.

▼ DIGITAL

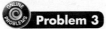

Problem 3 Finding the Orthocenter

$\triangle ABC$ has vertices $A(1, 3)$, $B(2, 7)$, and $C(6, 3)$. What are the coordinates of the orthocenter of $\triangle ABC$?

Know	Need	Plan
The coordinates of the three vertices	The intersection point of the triangle's altitudes	Write the equations of the lines that contain two of the altitudes. Then solve the system of equations.

Step 1 Find the equation of the line containing the altitude to $\overline{AC}$. Since $\overline{AC}$ is horizontal, the line containing the altitude to $\overline{AC}$ is vertical. The line passes through the vertex $B(2, 7)$. The equation of the line is $x = 2$.

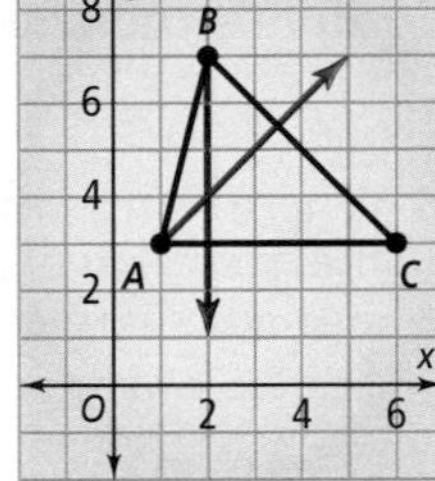

Step 2 Find the equation of the line containing the altitude to $\overline{BC}$. The slope of the line containing $\overline{BC}$ is $\frac{3-7}{6-2} = -1$. Since the product of the slopes of two perpendicular lines is -1, the line containing the altitude to $\overline{BC}$ has slope 1.

The line passes through the vertex $A(1, 3)$. The equation of the line is $y - 3 = 1(x - 1)$, which simplifies to $y = x + 2$.

Step 3 Find the orthocenter by solving this system of equations: $x = 2$, $y = x + 2$

$y = 2 + 2$ Substitute 2 for x in the second equation.

$y = 4$ Simplify.

The coordinates of the orthocenter are (2, 4).

▼ STUDENT PAGES 226–227

Got It? $\triangle DEF$ has vertices $D(1, 2)$, $E(1, 6)$, and $F(4, 2)$. What are the coordinates of the orthocenter of $\triangle DEF$?

Think Which two altitudes of $\triangle DEF$ should you choose?

Practice **Coordinate Geometry** **In Exercises 5 and 6, find the coordinates of the orthocenter of $\triangle ABC$ with the given vertices.**

5. $A(0, 0)$, $B(4, 0)$, and $C(4, 2)$

6. $A(0, -2)$, $B(4, -2)$, and $C(-2, -8)$

▼ STUDENT PAGE 227

take note **Concept Summary** Special Segments and Lines in Triangles

Perpendicular Bisectors	Angle Bisectors	Medians	Altitudes
Circumcenter	Incenter	Centroid	Orthocenter

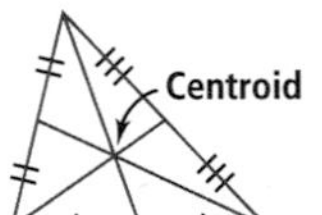

3 Lesson Check

Do you know HOW?
If students have difficulty with Exercise 7, then have them review Problem 2 to make of a list of the needed information.

Do you UNDERSTAND?
If students have difficulty with Exercise 13, then have them review the Got It after Problem 3. Compare the triangles and their characteristics.

Close

Q Where do the medians of a triangle intersect? Does the point have any special characteristics? **[The medians intersect at a point called the centroid. It is located $\frac{2}{3}$ of the way from a vertex to its opposite side.]**

Q Where do the altitudes of a triangle intersect? **[The altitudes intersect at a point called the orthocenter.]**

ANSWERS

7. median
8. 6
9. 7.5
10. $\overline{AB}$, $\overline{AC}$
11. $\overline{HJ}$ does not contain a vertex of $\triangle ABC$, so it is not an altitude of $\triangle ABC$.
12. No; any pair of altitudes meet at the orthocenter of the triangle.

▼ STUDENT PAGES 227–229

Lesson Check

Do you know HOW?

Use $\triangle ABC$ for Exercises 7–10.

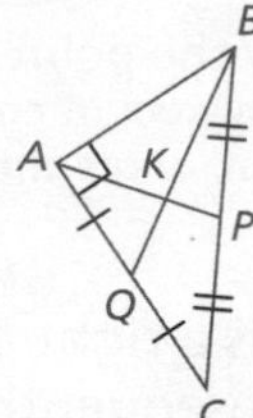

7. Is $\overline{AP}$ a *median* or an *altitude*?
8. If $AP = 18$, what is KP?
9. If $BK = 15$, what is KQ?
10. Which two segments are altitudes?

Do you UNDERSTAND?

MATHEMATICAL PRACTICES

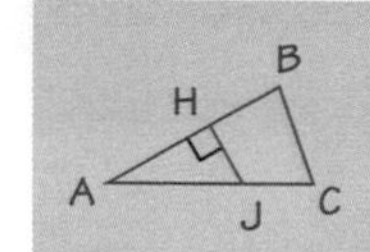

11. Error Analysis Your classmate says she drew $\overline{HJ}$ as an altitude of $\triangle ABC$. What error did she make?

12. Reasoning Does it matter which two altitudes you use to locate the orthocenter of a triangle? Explain.

13. Reasoning The orthocenter of $\triangle ABC$ lies at vertex A. What can you conclude about $\overline{BA}$ and $\overline{AC}$? Explain.

13. They are ⊥; since A lies on the altitude from B to $\overline{AC}$, B also lies on this altitude, so the altitude from B to $\overline{AC}$ must be $\overline{BA}$. Therefore, $\overline{BA} \perp \overline{AC}$.

4 Practice

More Practice and Problem-Solving Exercises

ASSIGNMENT GUIDE
The assignments below are for the More Practice and Problem-Solving Exercises. You may also want to assign the A-Level Practice Exercises for homework if these are not used in class.
Average: 14–31
Advanced: 14–36

Mathematical Practices The exercises listed focus on the Standards for Mathematical Practices listed.

EX. 18: Make Sense of Problems (MP 1)
EX. 13, 25, 29, 30: Construct Arguments (MP 3)
EX. 11: Critique the Reasoning of Others (MP 3)
EX. 26, 27, 32: Use Appropriate Tools (MP 5)
EX. 12: Repeated Reasoning (MP 8)

EXERCISE 31: Use the **Think About a Plan** worksheet in the Online Teacher Resources to further support students' development in becoming independent learners.

HOMEWORK QUICK CHECK
To check students' understanding of key skills and concepts, go over Exercises 17, 18, 23, 25, and 31.

▼ STUDENT PAGE 229

More Practice and Problem-Solving Exercises

B Apply

Name the centroid.

14.

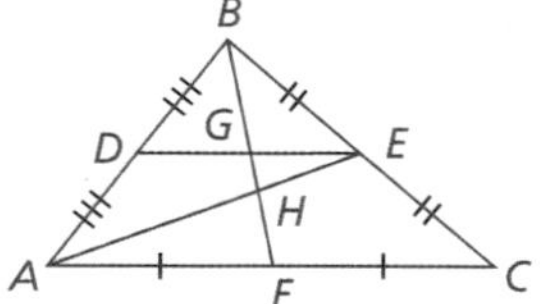

15.

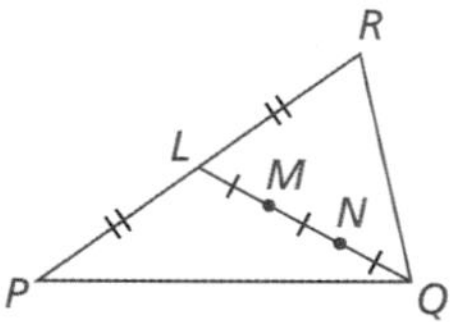

Name the orthocenter of $\triangle XYZ$.

16.

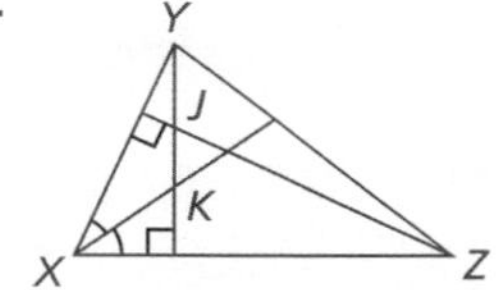

17.

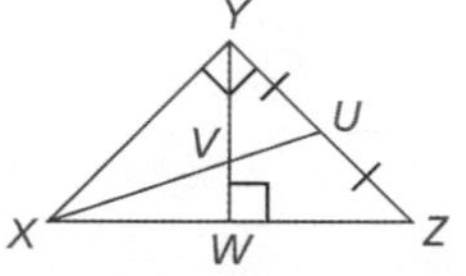

ANSWERS

14. *H* **15.** *M*
16. *J* **17.** *Y*

18. 125

19.

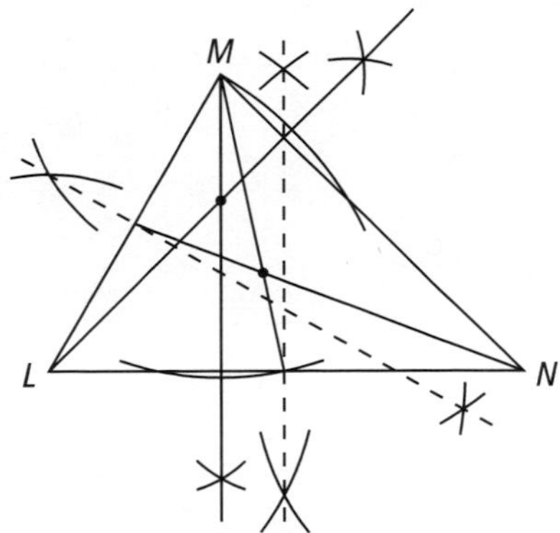

20.

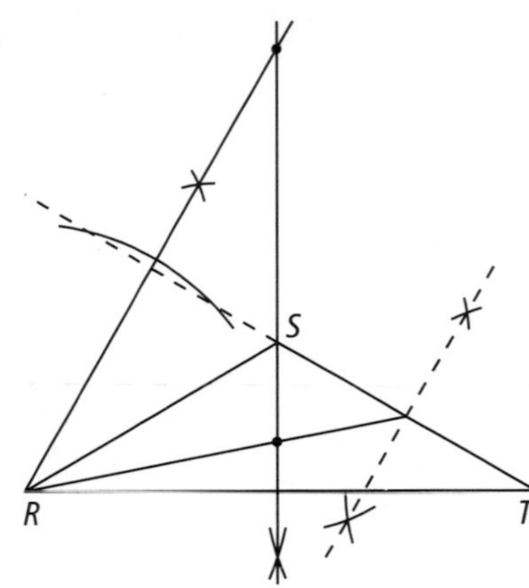

21. $\overline{AE}$

22. $\overline{BD}$

23. $\overline{DE}$

24. $\overline{OD}$

25. 1 : 2

26. Check students' work. The folds should show the ⊥ bisectors of the sides to identify the midpt. of each side, and also show the fold through each vertex and the midpt. of the opposite side.

27. Check students' work. The folds should show three lines where each contains a vertex and is ⊥ to the opposite side.

28. B

29. an obtuse triangle

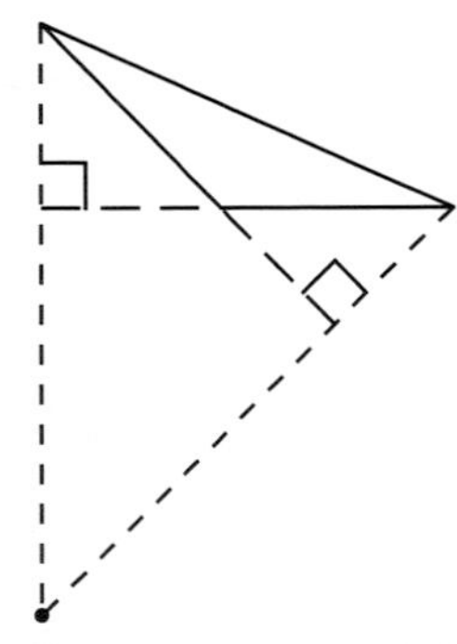

30. Answers may vary. Sample: The ∠ bisector of the vertex ∠ forms two triangles that are ≅ by SAS. Therefore the 2 segments formed on the base are ≅ (so the ∠ bisector contains a median), and the two angles formed by the ∠ bisector and the base are rt. angles (so the ∠ bisector contains an altitude). Thus the median and the altitude are the same.

18. Think About a Plan In the diagram at the right, $\overline{QS}$ and $\overline{PT}$ are altitudes and $m\angle R = 55$. What is $m\angle POQ$?
- What does it mean for a segment to be an altitude?
- What do you know about the sum of the angle measures in a triangle?
- How do you sketch overlapping triangles separately?

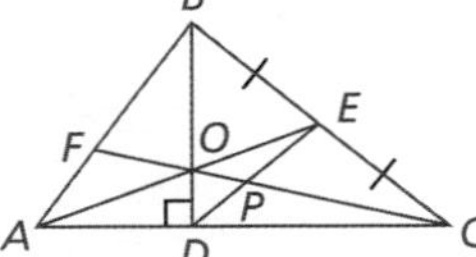

Constructions **Draw a triangle that fits the given description. Then construct the centroid and the orthocenter.**

19. acute scalene triangle, $\triangle LMN$

20. obtuse isosceles triangle, $\triangle RST$

In Exercises 21–24, name each segment.

21. a median in $\triangle ABC$

22. an altitude in $\triangle ABC$

23. a median in $\triangle BDC$

24. an altitude in $\triangle AOC$

25. Reasoning A centroid separates a median into two segments. What is the ratio of the length of the shorter segment to the length of the longer segment?

Paper Folding **The figures below show how to construct altitudes and medians by paper folding. Refer to them for Exercises 26 and 27.**

Folding an Altitude

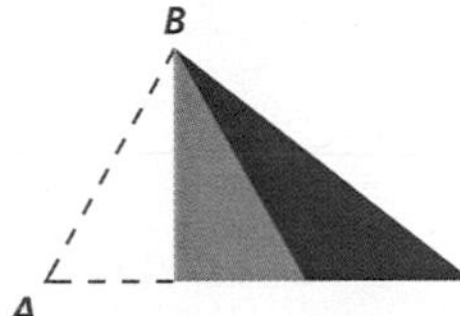

Fold the triangle so that a side $\overline{AC}$ overlaps itself and the fold contains the opposite vertex B.

Folding a Median

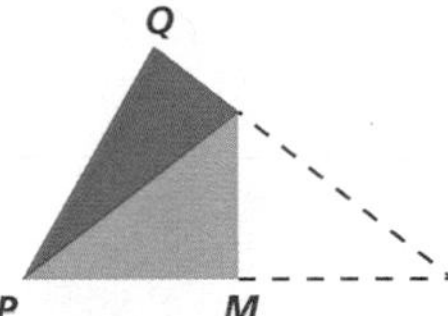

Fold one vertex R to another vertex P. This locates the midpoint M of a side.

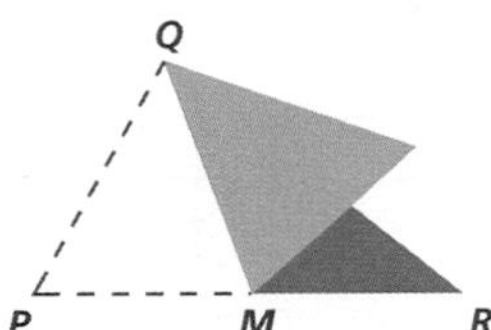

Unfold the triangle. Then fold it so that the fold contains the midpoint M and the opposite vertex Q.

26. Cut out a large triangle. Fold the paper carefully to construct the three medians of the triangle and demonstrate the Concurrency of Medians Theorem. Use a ruler to measure the length of each median and the distance of each vertex from the centroid.

27. Cut out a large acute triangle. Fold the paper carefully to construct the three altitudes of the triangle and demonstrate the Concurrency of Altitudes Theorem.

28. In the figure at the right, C is the centroid of $\triangle DEF$. If $GF = 12x^2 + 6y$, which expression represents CF?

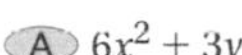

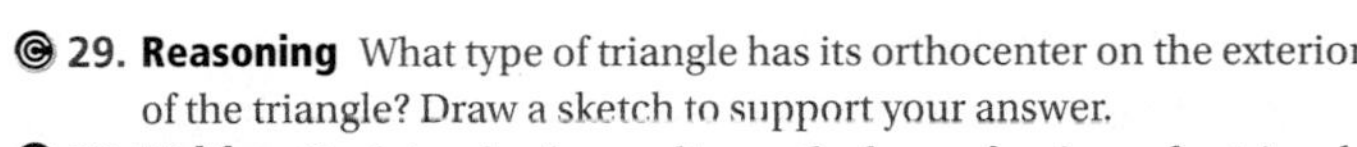

Ⓐ $6x^2 + 3y$ Ⓒ $4x^2 + 2y$

Ⓑ $8x^2 + 4y$ Ⓓ $8x^2 + 3y$

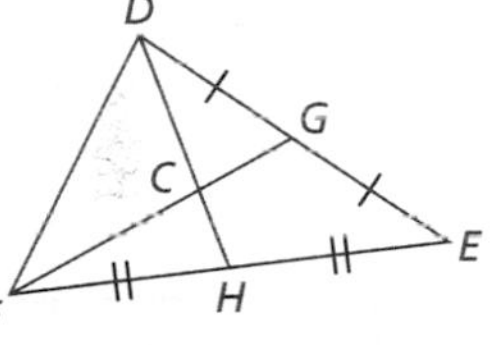

29. Reasoning What type of triangle has its orthocenter on the exterior of the triangle? Draw a sketch to support your answer.

30. Writing Explain why the median to the base of an isosceles triangle is also an altitude.

More Practice and Problem-Solving Exercises *continued*

31. a. $L(1, 3)$; $M(5, 3)$; $N(4, 0)$

b. $\overleftrightarrow{AM}: y = \frac{3}{5}x$; $\overleftrightarrow{BN}: y = -3x + 12$; $\overleftrightarrow{CL}: y = -\frac{3}{7}x + \frac{24}{7}$

c. $\left(\frac{10}{3}, 2\right)$

d. $-\frac{3}{7}\left(\frac{10}{3}\right) + \frac{24}{7} = -\frac{10}{7} + \frac{24}{7} = \frac{14}{7} = 2$

e. $AM = \sqrt{34}$, $AP = \sqrt{\frac{136}{9}} = \frac{2}{3}\sqrt{34}$; $CL = \sqrt{58}$, $CP = \sqrt{\frac{232}{9}} = \frac{2}{3}\sqrt{58}$; $BN = \sqrt{40} = 2\sqrt{10}$, $BP = \sqrt{\frac{160}{9}} = \frac{4}{3}\sqrt{10}$

32.

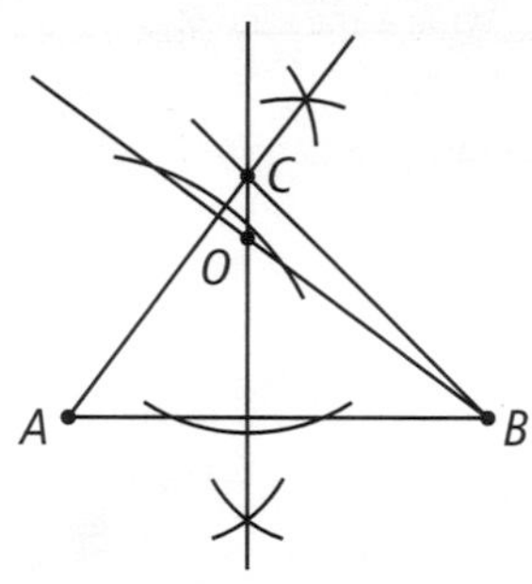

Draw $\overleftrightarrow{AB}$. Construct the $\perp$ to $\overleftrightarrow{AB}$ through O. Draw $\overleftrightarrow{BO}$. Construct the $\perp$ to $\overleftrightarrow{BO}$ through A. The two perpendiculars intersect at C. Draw $\overline{BC}$.

33. Answers may vary. Sample: The answer to Ex. 30 shows that if line ℓ is the $\angle$ bisector of the vertex $\angle$ of an isosc. triangle, then ℓ contains the median and the altitude. That same line ℓ is the $\perp$ bisector of the base because it bisects the base (it contains the median) and it is $\perp$ to the base (it contains the altitude to the base). Since the circumcenter, incenter, centroid, and orthocenter must all be on line ℓ, the four points must be collinear.

34. *A* is the intersection of the altitudes, so it is the orthocenter; *B* is the intersection of the $\angle$ bisectors, so it is the incenter; *C* is the intersection of the medians, so it is the centroid; *D* is the intersection of the $\perp$ bisectors of the sides, so it is the circumcenter.

35. *A* is the intersection of the $\perp$ bisectors of the sides, so it is the circumcenter; *B* is the intersection of the medians, so it is the centroid; *C* is the intersection of the $\angle$ bisectors, so it is the incenter; *D* is the intersection of the altitudes, so it is the orthocenter.

36. incenter

31. Coordinate Geometry $\triangle ABC$ has vertices $A(0, 0)$, $B(2, 6)$, and $C(8, 0)$. Complete the following steps to verify the Concurrency of Medians Theorem for $\triangle ABC$.

a. Find the coordinates of midpoints *L*, *M*, and *N*.
b. Find equations of $\overleftrightarrow{AM}$, $\overleftrightarrow{BN}$, and $\overleftrightarrow{CL}$.
c. Find the coordinates of *P*, the intersection of $\overleftrightarrow{AM}$ and $\overleftrightarrow{BN}$. This point is the centroid.
d. Show that point *P* is on $\overleftrightarrow{CL}$.
e. Use the Distance Formula to show that point *P* is two-thirds of the distance from each vertex to the midpoint of the opposite side.

Challenge

32. Constructions *A*, *B*, and *O* are three noncollinear points. Construct point *C* such that *O* is the orthocenter of $\triangle ABC$. Describe your method.

33. Reasoning In an isosceles triangle, show that the circumcenter, incenter, centroid, and orthocenter can be four different points, but all four must be collinear.

***A*, *B*, *C*, and *D* are points of concurrency for the triangle. Determine whether each point is a *circumcenter*, *incenter*, *centroid*, or *orthocenter*. Explain.**

34.

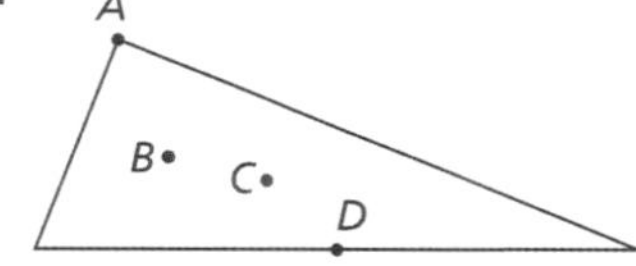

35.

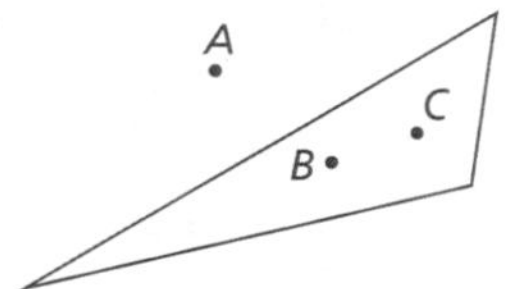

D

36. History In 1765, Leonhard Euler proved that, for any triangle, three of the four points of concurrency are collinear. The line that contains these three points is known as Euler's Line. Use Exercises 34 and 35 to determine which point of concurrency does not necessarily lie on Euler's Line.

Assess and Remediate

Lesson Quiz

1. Is $\overline{AC}$ a median, an altitude, or neither?

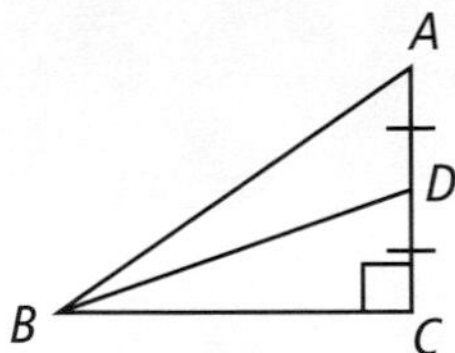

2. **Do you UNDERSTAND?** What are the coordinates of the orthocenter of $\triangle LMN$?

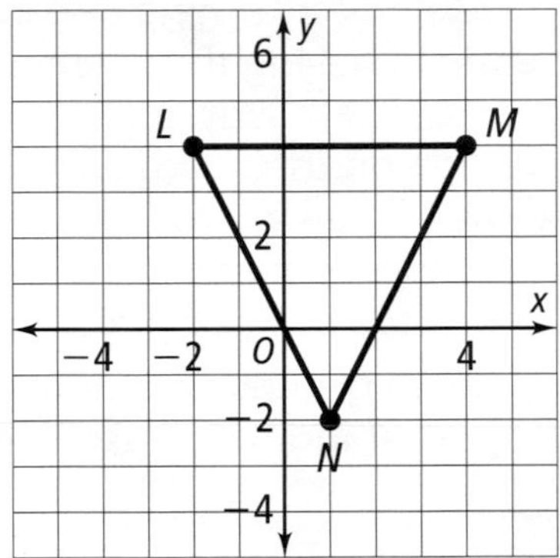

3. In the triangle shown in Question 2, which altitude length can be found without using the Distance Formula? What is the length?

ANSWERS TO LESSON QUIZ

1. altitude
2. (1, 2.5)
3. the altitude from N to $\overline{LM}$; 6 units

Prescription for Remediation

Use the student work on the Lesson Quiz to prescribe a differentiated assignment.

Points	Differentiated Remediation
0–1	Intervention
2	On-level
3	Extension

Online Assessment

Assign the Lesson Quiz in Success Tracker on **pearsonsuccessnet.com**. Success Tracker will automatically score the quiz and assign appropriate intervention or enrichment to each student based on the results. The compiled data appear in three different reports for instant analysis of whole class and individual student performance.

Differentiated Remediation

Intervention

- **RETEACHING** (2 pages) Provides reteaching and practice exercises for the key lesson concepts. Use with struggling students or absent students.
- **ENGLISH LANGUAGE LEARNER SUPPORT** Helps students develop and reinforce mathematical vocabulary and key concepts.

On-Level

- **PRACTICE** (2 pages) Provides extra practice for each lesson. For simpler practice exercises, use the Form K Practice pages found in the Online Teacher Resources.
- **THINK ABOUT A PLAN** Helps students develop specific problem-solving skills and strategies by providing scaffolded guiding questions.
- **STANDARDIZED TEST PREP** Focuses on all major exercises, all major question types, and helps students prepare for the high-stakes assessments.

Extension

- **ENRICHMENT** Provides students with interesting problems and activities that extend the concepts of the lesson.
- **ACTIVITIES, GAMES, AND PUZZLES** Worksheets that can be used for concept development, enrichment, and for fun!

Indirect Proof

Common Core State Standard
G.CO.10 Prove theorems about triangles . . .

Preparing to Teach

BIG idea Reasoning and Proof

ESSENTIAL UNDERSTANDING

In indirect reasoning, all possibilities are considered and then all but one are proved false. The remaining possibility must be true. An essential element of an indirect proof is showing a contradiction.

Math Background

Indirect Proof is another method of proof that students can add to their repertoire of logic skills. Also called Proof by Contradiction, the negation of the desired conclusion is assumed to be true and then it is shown that the negation of the premise is false. Thus, the contrapositive of the original statement is proven true, so the original statement must be true (because they have the same truth value).

Indirect proofs can be very challenging for students who find it confusing to argue validly by beginning with a negation. In this lesson the emphasis is on writing portions of indirect proofs, such as the first sentence of the proof (the negation of the Prove statement). Generally, negations are easier for students to write than contrapositives because a contrapositive requires students to negate both phrases of a conditional and then to form converses of the resulting negations. It may help to review Lesson 1-3.

ELL Support

USE ROLE PLAYING Have students write the names of different plants, different animals, and different machines on pieces of paper. Demonstrate the game *20 Questions*, attaching one of the pieces of paper behind a student and having the student ask Yes/No questions such as: Am I an animal? Write the information learned from each question on the board and point out how indirect reasoning can be used when a "No" answer eliminates some possibility, e.g.: I am a plant, animal, or a machine. I am not a plant or an animal, so I must be a machine.

Now have the students play the game in groups of four or five. Have each group report examples of indirect reasoning that came up as they played.

Lesson Vocabulary

- indirect reasoning
- indirect proof

Mathematical Practices

CONSTRUCT VIABLE ARGUMENTS AND CRITIQUE THE REASONING OF OTHERS. Students will use a counterexample as the basis for an indirect proof.

Interactive Learning

Solve It!

PURPOSE To use indirect reasoning to complete the number squares

PROCESS Students may use a process of elimination to fill in the squares.

Q What number must go in the second square of the first row? **[3; The numbers 3 and 4 are the numbers left for that row. 4 already appears in the column, so it must be 3.]**

Q How can you determine which number goes in each square? **[Compare the numbers that already exist in that column and row and write the remaining number.]**

ANSWER

Game A

1	3	4	2
4	2	1	3
2	4	3	1
3	1	2	4

Game B

1	2	4	3
4	1	3	2
2	3	1	4
3	4	2	1

▼ DIGITAL (STUDENT WORK SPACE PAGE 232)

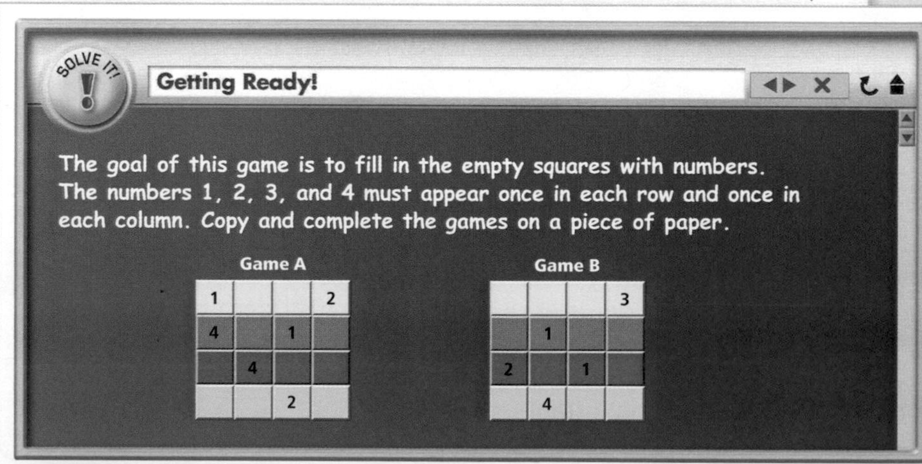

CONNECT THE MATH Students should realize that they are indirectly proving which number must go in each box by eliminating other possibilities. In this lesson, students study indirect proofs.

Guided Instruction

Problem 1 Writing the First Step of an Indirect Proof

Take Note

Practice identifying negations of statements with students. Give them a statement and have them identify the opposite. Discuss the concept that if the negation of a statement is false, then the statement itself is true.

Problem 1

Q What is the opposite of "divisible by 5?" **[not divisible by 5]**

Q What is the opposite of "do not have?" **[do have]**

Got It? — ERROR PREVENTION

In part (b), some students may write the negation as "At least one pair of shoes you bought did not cost more than $25." Point out that this is not the negation because both it and the original statement can be true.

ANSWERS

Got It? a. Assume temporarily that $\triangle BOX$ is acute. **b.** Assume temporarily that no pair of shoes you bought cost more than $25.

Practice

1. Assume temporarily that no $\angle$ is obtuse.
2. Assume temporarily that $m\angle 2 \leq 90$.

▼ STUDENT PAGE 232

In the Solve It, you can conclude that a square must contain a certain number if you can eliminate the other three numbers as possibilities. This type of reasoning is called indirect reasoning. In **indirect reasoning,** all possibilities are considered and then all but one are proved false. The remaining possibility must be true.

Essential Understanding You can use indirect reasoning as another method of proof.

A proof involving indirect reasoning is an **indirect proof.** Often in an indirect proof, a statement and its negation are the only possibilities. When you see that one of these possibilities leads to a conclusion that contradicts a fact you know to be true, you can eliminate that possibility. For this reason, indirect proof is sometimes called *proof by contradiction.*

Key Concept Writing an Indirect Proof

Step 1 State as a temporary assumption the opposite (negation) of what you want to prove.

Step 2 Show that this temporary assumption leads to a contradiction.

Step 3 Conclude that the temporary assumption must be false and that what you want to prove must be true.

In the first step of an indirect proof you assume as true the opposite of what you want to prove.

▼ DIGITAL

Problem 1 Writing the First Step of an Indirect Proof

Suppose you want to write an indirect proof of each statement. As the first step of the proof, what would you assume?

A An integer *n* is divisible by 5.

The opposite of "is divisible by" is "is not divisible by."
Assume temporarily that n is not divisible by 5.

B You do not have soccer practice today.

The opposite of "do not have" is "do have."
Assume temporarily that you do have soccer practice today.

▼ STUDENT PAGE 233

Got It? Suppose you want to write an indirect proof of each statement. As the first step of the proof, what would you assume?

a. $\triangle BOX$ is not acute.

b. At least one pair of shoes you bought cost more than $25.

A Practice **Write the first step of an indirect proof of the given statement.**

1. At least one angle is obtuse.
2. $m\angle 2 > 90$

Problem 2 Identifying Contradictions

Have students sketch a diagram of each statement. Then, they can try to combine the sketches. If it is not possible to combine two sketches, those two statements are contradictions.

Q Which two statements are mutually exclusive? Explain. **[Two segments cannot be both parallel and perpendicular because perpendicular lines intersect and parallel lines do not intersect.]**

Got It?

Have students sketch a diagram that combines two of the three statements."

Q Can you draw an acute triangle that is scalene? **[yes]**

Q Can you draw a scalene triangle that is equiangular? **[no]**

Q Can you draw an acute triangle that is equiangular? **[yes]**

In part (b), students should realize that contradicting statements are not necessarily negations of each other.

ANSWERS

Got It? a. II and III **b.** No; if $\triangle ABC$ is an isosc., nonequilateral triangle, then Statement III is true but Statement II is not true. Therefore, Statements II and III are not equivalent.

Practice

3. II and III

4. I and II

▼ STUDENT PAGE 234

To write an indirect proof, you have to be able to identify a contradiction.

▼ DIGITAL

Problem 2 Identifying Contradictions

Which two statements contradict each other?

I. $\overline{FG} \parallel \overline{KL}$ **II.** $\overline{FG} \cong \overline{KL}$ **III.** $\overline{FG} \perp \overline{KL}$

Segments can be parallel and congruent. Statements I and II do not contradict each other.

Segments can be congruent and perpendicular. Statements II and III do not contradict each other.

Parallel segments do not intersect, so they cannot be perpendicular. Statements I and III contradict each other.

▼ STUDENT PAGE 234

Got It? **a.** Which two statements contradict each other?

I. $\triangle XYZ$ is acute.

II. $\triangle XYZ$ is scalene.

III. $\triangle XYZ$ is equiangular.

Think

How do you know that two statements contradict each other?

b. Reasoning Statements I and II below contradict each other. Statement III is the negation of Statement I. Are Statements II and III equivalent? Explain your reasoning.

I. $\triangle ABC$ is scalene.

II. $\triangle ABC$ is equilateral.

III. $\triangle ABC$ is not scalene.

**Practice** **Identify the two statements that contradict each other.**

3. **I.** Each of the two items that Val bought costs more than \$10.

II. Val spent \$34 for the two items.

III. Neither of the two items that Val bought costs more than \$15.

4. **I.** In right $\triangle ABC$, $m\angle A = 60$.

II. In right $\triangle ABC$, $\angle A \cong \angle C$.

III. In right $\triangle ABC$, $m\angle B = 90$.

Problem 3 Writing an Indirect Proof

Q What is the opposite of "have different measures?" **[have the same measures]**

Q Where is the contradiction in the proof? **[If a triangle has congruent angles, then it cannot be a scalene triangle.]**

Got It?

Q What statement should be negated to begin the proof? **[$y \neq 6$ should be $y = 6$]**

Q Where is the contradiction in the proof? **[If $y = 6$, then $x = 4$.]**

ANSWERS

Got It? Assume temporarily that $y = 6$. Then $7(x + 6) = 70$; divide each side by 7 to get $x + 6 = 10$ and so $x = 4$. But this contradicts the given statement that $x \neq 4$. The temporary assumption that $y = 6$ led to a contradiction, so we can conclude that $y \neq 6$.

Practice

5. **a.** 20 or more
   b. The total membership is fewer than 20.
   c. The Yoga Club has fewer than 10 members.
6. **a.** right angle
   b. right angles
   c. 90
   d. 180
   e. 90
   f. 90
   g. 0
   h. more than one right angle
   i. at most one right angle

▼ DIGITAL

Proof  **Problem 3** **Writing an Indirect Proof**

Given: $\triangle ABC$ is scalene.

Prove: $\angle A$, $\angle B$, and $\angle C$ all have different measures.

Think	Write
Assume temporarily the opposite of what you want to prove.	Assume temporarily that two angles of $\triangle ABC$ have the same measure. Assume that $m\angle A = m\angle B$.
Show that this assumption leads to a contradiction.	By the Converse of the Isosceles Triangle Theorem, the sides opposite $\angle A$ and $\angle B$ are congruent. This contradicts the given information that $\triangle ABC$ is scalene.
Conclude that the temporary assumption must be false and that what you want to prove must be true.	The assumption that two angles of $\triangle ABC$ have the same measure must be false. Therefore, $\angle A$, $\angle B$, and $\angle C$ all have different measures.

▼ STUDENT PAGES 235–236

Got It? **Given:** $7(x + y) = 70$ and $x \neq 4$.

Prove: $y \neq 6$

Plan
What statement should be negated to begin the proof?

A Practice

5. **Developing Proof** Fill in the blanks to prove the following statement. If the Yoga Club and Go Green Club together have fewer than 20 members and the Go Green Club has 10 members, then the Yoga Club has fewer than 10 members.

   Given: The total membership of the Yoga Club and the Go Green Club is fewer than 20. The Go Green Club has 10 members.

   Prove: The Yoga Club has fewer than 10 members.

   Proof: Assume temporarily that the Yoga Club has 10 or more members.

   This means that together the two clubs have **a.** ________ members. This contradicts the given information that **b.** ________.

   The temporary assumption is false. Therefore, it is true that **c.** ________.

6. **Developing Proof** Fill in the blanks to prove the following statement. In a given triangle, $\triangle LMN$, there is at most one right angle.

   Given: $\triangle LMN$

   Prove: $\triangle LMN$ has at most one right angle.

   Proof: Assume temporarily that $\triangle LMN$ has more than one **a.** ________. That is, assume that both $\angle M$ and $\angle N$ are **b.** ________. If $\angle M$ and $\angle N$ are both right angles, then $m\angle M = m\angle N =$ **c.** ________. By the Triangle Angle-Sum Theorem, $m\angle L + m\angle M + m\angle N =$ **d.** ________. Use substitution to write the equation $m\angle L +$ **e.** ________ $+$ **f.** ________ $= 180$. When you solve for $m\angle L$, you find that $m\angle L =$ **g.** ________. This means that there is no $\triangle LMN$, which contradicts the given statement. So the temporary assumption that $\triangle LMN$ has **h.** ________ must be false. Therefore, $\triangle LMN$ has **i.** ________.

3 Lesson Check

Do you know HOW?

If students have difficulty with Exercise 7, then have them review Problem 1.

Do you UNDERSTAND?

If students have difficulty with Exercise 9, then have them review Problem 2 Got It, part (b) to review the different types of triangles.

Close

Q How does an indirect proof lead to the desired conclusion? **[The assumption of the opposite statement leads to a contradiction with some of the given information.]**

ANSWERS

7. Assume temporarily that at least one ∠ in quadrilateral *ABCD* is not a rt. ∠.

8. Lines *a* and *b* intersect at *P*.

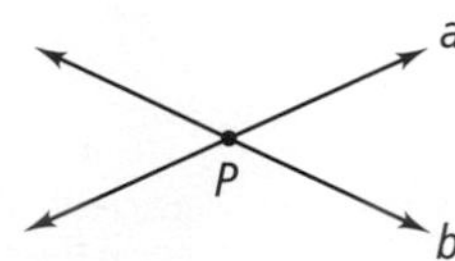

9. The angle could be acute, right, or straight.

▼ STUDENT PAGES 236–237

Lesson Check

Do you know HOW?

7. Suppose you want to write an indirect proof of the following statement. As the first step of the proof, what would you assume?

Quadrilateral *ABCD* has four right angles.

8. Write a statement that contradicts the following statement. Draw a diagram to support your answer.

Lines *a* and *b* are parallel.

Do you UNDERSTAND?

9. Error Analysis A classmate began an indirect proof as shown at the right. Explain and correct your classmate's error.

~~Given: △ABC~~
~~Prove: ∠A is obtuse.~~
~~Assume temporarily that ∠A is acute.~~

Practice

More Practice and Problem-Solving Exercises

ASSIGNMENT GUIDE

The assignments below are for the More Practice and Problem-Solving Exercises. You may also want to assign the A-Level Practice Exercises for homework if these are not used in class.
Average: 10–22
Advanced: 10–24

Mathematical Practices The exercises listed focus on the Standards for Mathematical Practices listed.

EX. 11: Make Sense of Problems (MP 1)
EX. 15: Construct Arguments (MP 3)
EX. 9, 20: Critique the Reasoning of Others (MP 3)
EX. 21: Model with Mathematics (MP 4)

STEM exercises focus on science or engineering applications.

EXERCISE 17: Use the **Think About a Plan** worksheet in the Online Teacher Resources to further support students' development in becoming independent learners.

HOMEWORK QUICK CHECK

To check students' understanding of key skills and concepts, go over Exercises 11, 13, 15, 17, and 20.

▼ STUDENT PAGE 237

More Practice and Problem-Solving Exercises

MATHEMATICAL PRACTICES

B Apply

10. History Use indirect reasoning to eliminate all but one of the following answers. In what year was George Washington born?

Ⓐ 1492 Ⓑ 1732 Ⓒ 1902 Ⓓ 2002

11. Think About a Plan Write an indirect proof.

Given: $\angle 1 \ncong \angle 2$

Prove: $\ell \nparallel p$

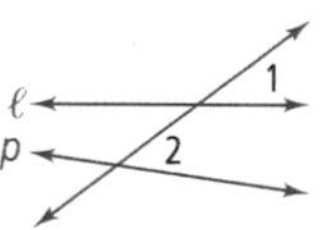

- What assumption should be the first step of your proof?
- In the figure, what type of angle pair do ∠1 and ∠2 form?

ANSWERS

10. B

11. Assume temporarily $\ell \parallel p$. Then $\angle 1 \cong \angle 2$ because if lines are ∥, then corresp. angles are ≅. But this contradicts the given statement that $\angle 1 \ncong \angle 2$. Therefore the temporary assumption is false, and we can conclude that $\ell \nparallel p$.

12. Assume temporarily that the number is divisible by 2.
13. Assume temporarily that $\overline{XB} \ncong \overline{XA}$.
14. Assume temporarily that two alt. ext. angles are not $\cong$.
15. I and III
16. Assume temporarily that $\angle A \cong \angle B$. Then $BC = AC$ by the Converse of the Isosc. Triangle Thm. But this contradicts the given statement that $BC > AC$. Therefore the temporary assumption is false, and we can conclude that $\angle A$ is not $\cong$ to $\angle B$.
17. Assume temporarily that at least one base $\angle$ is a rt. $\angle$. Then both base angles must be rt. angles, by the Isosc. Triangle Thm. But this contradicts the fact that a triangle is formed, because in a plane, two lines $\perp$ to the same line are $\parallel$. Therefore the temporary assumption is false that at least one base $\angle$ is a rt. $\angle$, and we can conclude that neither base $\angle$ is a rt. $\angle$.
18. Answers may vary. Sample: Assume temporarily that the temperature is greater than 32°F. This is above the freezing pt. of water. Thus, ice cannot form at that temperature, which contradicts the given statement that ice is forming. Therefore the temporary assumption that the temperature is greater than 32°F is incorrect, and we can conclude that the temperature is 32°F or lower.
19. Assume temporarily that an obtuse triangle can contain a rt. $\angle$. Then the measure of the obtuse $\angle$ plus the measure of the rt. $\angle$ must be greater than $90 + 90 = 180$. This contradicts the Triangle Angle-Sum Thm., so the temporary assumption that an obtuse triangle can contain a rt. $\angle$ is incorrect. We can conclude that an obtuse triangle cannot contain a rt. $\angle$.
20. He is omitting the possibility of the triangle being isosceles. He could instead write, "Assume temporarily that $\triangle ABC$ has two sides that are not congruent."
21. The culprit entered the room through a hole in the roof; all the other possibilities were ruled out.

Write the first step of an indirect proof of the given statement.

12. If a number n ends in 5, then it is not divisible by 2.
13. If point X is on the perpendicular bisector of $\overline{AB}$, then $\overline{XB} \cong \overline{XA}$.
14. If a transversal intersects two parallel lines, then alternate exterior angles are congruent.
15. **Reasoning** Identify the two statements that contradict each other.
    I. The orthocenter of $\triangle JRK$ is on the triangle.
    II. The centroid of $\triangle JRK$ is inside the triangle.
    III. $\triangle JRK$ is an obtuse triangle.

Write an indirect proof.

Proof 16. Use the figure at the right.
Given: $\triangle ABC$ with $BC > AC$
Prove: $\angle A \ncong \angle B$

C B A

Proof 17. **Given:** $\triangle XYZ$ is isosceles.
Prove: Neither base angle is a right angle.

Writing For Exercises 18 and 19, write a convincing argument that uses indirect reasoning.

STEM 18. **Chemistry** Ice is forming on the sidewalk in front of Toni's house. Show that the temperature of the sidewalk surface must be 32°F or lower.

19. Show that an obtuse triangle cannot contain a right angle.

20. **Error Analysis** Your friend wants to prove indirectly that $\triangle ABC$ is equilateral. For a first step, he writes, "Assume temporarily that $\triangle ABC$ is scalene." What is wrong with your friend's statement? How can he correct himself?

21. **Literature** In Arthur Conan Doyle's story "The Sign of the Four," Sherlock Holmes talks to his friend Watson about how a culprit enters a room that has only four entrances: a door, a window, a chimney, and a hole in the roof.

"You will not apply my precept," he said, shaking his head. "How often have I said to you that when you have eliminated the impossible, whatever remains, however improbable, must be the truth? We know that he did not come through the door, the window, or the chimney. We also know that he could not have been concealed in the room, as there is no concealment possible. Whence, then, did he come?"

How did the culprit enter the room? Explain.

More Practice and Problem-Solving Exercises *continued*

22. Refer to the figure in the statement of the theorem. Given: $\angle 2 \cong \angle 6$; Prove: $\ell \parallel m$. Assume that ℓ and m are not parallel. Then ℓ and m intersect at some point P. (Suppose that P is on the same side of the transversal as $\angle 2$ and $\angle 6$.) The sum of the angles of the triangle formed by ℓ, m, and the transversal is $m\angle 6 + (180° - m\angle 2) + m\angle P = m\angle 6 + (180° - m\angle 6) + m\angle P = 180° + m\angle P$. But $m\angle P > 0$, so the sum of the angle measures of the triangle is greater than 180°. This contradicts the Triangle Angle-Sum Theorem, which says that the angle sum of all triangles is 180°. Therefore lines ℓ and m are parallel. (The case where P is on the opposite side of the transversal is similar.)

23. Assume temporarily $\overline{XB} \perp \overline{AC}$. Then $\angle BXA \cong \angle BXC$ (All rt. angles are $\cong$.), $\angle ABX \cong \angle CBX$ (Given), and $\overline{BX} \cong \overline{BX}$ (Reflexive Prop. of $\cong$), so $\triangle BXA \cong \triangle BXC$ by ASA and $BA = BC$ because corresp. parts of $\cong$ triangles are $\cong$. But this contradicts the given statement that $\triangle ABC$ is scalene. Therefore the temporary assumption that $\overline{XB} \perp \overline{AC}$ is wrong, and we can conclude that $\overline{XB}$ is not $\perp$ to $\overline{AC}$.

24.

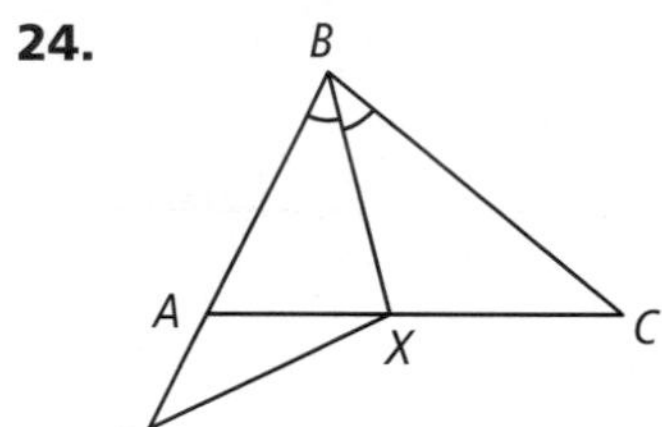

Assume temporarily that $\overline{AX} \cong \overline{XC}$. Since the $\triangle$ is scalene, we may suppose that $BA < BC$. Find D on $\overrightarrow{BA}$ so that $BD = BC$. We have $\angle DBX \cong \angle CBX$ (Given) and $\overline{BX} \cong \overline{BX}$ (Refl. Prop. of $\cong$). So $\triangle DBX \cong \triangle CBX$ by SAS. Then $\overline{DX} \cong \overline{CX}$ (Corresp. parts of $\cong$ ⚠ are $\cong$.) so $\overline{DX} \cong \overline{AX}$ (Trans. Prop. of $\cong$). Let $m\angle BDX = q$. Then $m\angle BCX = q$ (Corresp. parts of $\cong$ ⚠ are $\cong$.) and $m\angle XAD = q$ (Isosc. $\triangle$ Thm.). Therefore, $m\angle BAX = 180 - q$. Now the sum of the $\angle$ measures in $\triangle ABC$ is $180 - q + 72 + q = 252$. This contradicts the $\triangle$ Angle-Sum Thm. Therefore, the temporary assumption that $\overline{AX} \cong \overline{XC}$ is incorrect. So $\overline{AX} \ncong \overline{XC}$.

▼ STUDENT PAGE 238

Proof 22. Prove Theorem 9, the Converse of the Corresponding Angles Theorem. (*Hint:* Use the Triangle Angle-Sum Theorem.)

Challenge

Use the figure at the right for Exercises 23 and 24.

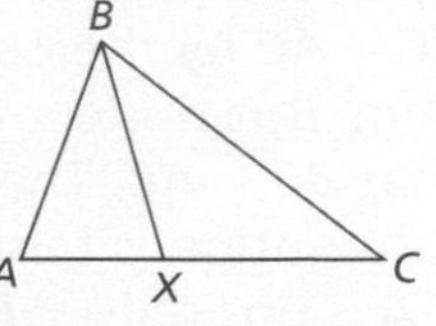

Proof 23. **Given:** $\triangle ABC$ is scalene, $m\angle ABX = 36$, $m\angle CBX = 36$
Prove: $\overline{XB}$ is not perpendicular to $\overline{AC}$.

Proof 24. **Given:** $\triangle ABC$ is scalene, $m\angle ABX = 36$, $m\angle CBX = 36$
Prove: $\overline{AX} \ncong \overline{XC}$

Assess and Remediate

Lesson Quiz

1. What is the first step of the indirect proof?
   - **a.** Given: There are 12 dogs and cats at a veterinarian's office. There are more dogs than cats.
     Prove: There are at least 7 dogs.
   - **b.** Given: an integer n
     Prove: n is odd.
2. Which two statements contradict each other?
   - **I.** $\overline{RS}$ is an altitude.
   - **II.** $\overline{RS}$ is a median.
   - **III.** $\overline{RS}$ is a side of $\triangle RST$.
3. **Do you UNDERSTAND?** Given:
   $8(x + y) = 48$ and $y \neq 2$
   Prove: $x \neq 4$

ANSWERS TO LESSON QUIZ

1. **a.** Assume that there are fewer than 7 dogs.
   b. Assume that n is even.
2. II and III
3. Assume that $x = 4$. Then substitute 4 for x in the equation and solve for y. This results in $y = 2$, which is a contradiction. So, $x \neq 4$.

Prescription for Remediation

Use the student work on the Lesson Quiz to prescribe a differentiated assignment.

Points	Differentiated Remediation
0–1	Intervention
2	On-level
3	Extension

Online Assessment

Assign the Lesson Quiz in Success Tracker on **pearsonsuccessnet.com**. Success Tracker will automatically score the quiz and assign appropriate intervention or enrichment to each student based on the results. The compiled data appear in three different reports for instant analysis of whole class and individual student performance.

Differentiated Remediation

Intervention

- **RETEACHING** (2 pages) Provides reteaching and practice exercises for the key lesson concepts. Use with struggling students or absent students.
- **ENGLISH LANGUAGE LEARNER SUPPORT** Helps students develop and reinforce mathematical vocabulary and key concepts.

On-Level

- **PRACTICE** (2 pages) Provides extra practice for each lesson. For simpler practice exercises, use the Form K Practice pages found in the Online Teacher Resources.
- **THINK ABOUT A PLAN** Helps students develop specific problem-solving skills and strategies by providing scaffolded guiding questions.
- **STANDARDIZED TEST PREP** Focuses on all major exercises, all major question types, and helps students prepare for the high-stakes assessments.

Extension

- **ENRICHMENT** Provides students with interesting problems and activities that extend the concepts of the lesson.
- **ACTIVITIES, GAMES, AND PUZZLES** Worksheets that can be used for concept development, enrichment, and for fun!

4-6 Inequalities in One Triangle

Common Core State Standard
G.CO.10 Prove theorems about triangles . . .

Preparing to Teach

BIG idea Reasoning and Proof

ESSENTIAL UNDERSTANDING

The measures of the angles of a triangle are related to the lengths of the opposite sides. The sum of the lengths of two sides of a triangle is related to the length of the third side.

Math Background

In this lesson, students will learn about the relationships between the lengths of sides and the measures of angles in triangles. The Triangle Inequality Theorem places restrictions on the length of the longest side of a triangle given the lengths of the two shortest sides. In addition to an upper bound, students can use the theorem to find lower bounds. You can challenge students to write formulas for the upper and lower bounds of the third side of a triangle.

Many of the theorems presented here could be introduced by asking students for an intuitive description of the relationship. For example, the Triangle Inequality Theorem formalizes the concept of the distance between two points. Students intuitively know that the shortest distance between two points is a straight line. It stands to reason that the distance from A to C is longer if you have to go through another point, B, first.

ELL Support

USE ROLE PLAYING Help students to internalize their understanding of the inequality relationships in a triangle. Assign students in groups of six to play the roles of the following parts of a triangle: longest side, medium side, shortest side, largest angle, medium angle, smallest angle. Have the students form a circle so that they are in the correct relationship. The largest angle should be opposite the longest side, and so forth.

Next have each group think of their own way to illustrate that the longer side of a triangle is opposite the larger angle. Allow the groups to demonstrate their way to other students.

Mathematical Practices

MAKE SENSE OF PROBLEMS AND PERSEVERE IN SOLVING THEM. Students will analyze constraints on the lengths of triangle sides and discover relationships between the relative length of a side and the relative measure of its opposite angle.

Interactive Learning

Solve It!

PURPOSE To recognize that only certain side lengths will form a triangle

PROCESS Students may cut out or sketch segments with the given lengths and determine which of the lengths will form a triangle.

Q Which side lengths cannot be used to make a triangle? **[2 ft and 15 ft]**

Q Why do you think the lengths will not work to create a triangle? **[2 ft is too short and 15 ft is too long.]**

ANSWER 5-ft, 8-ft, or 12-ft; the 2-ft board is too short to form a triangle with the 5-ft board and the 8-ft board, and the 15-ft board is too long.

CONNECT THE MATH In Solve It, students realize that there is a relationship between the lengths of the sides in a triangle. In the lesson, students learn a corollary and theorems to support this finding.

▼ DIGITAL (STUDENT WORK SPACE PAGE 239)

SOLVE IT! **Getting Ready!**

For a neighborhood improvement project, you volunteer to help build a new sandbox at the town playground. You have two boards that will make up two sides of the triangular sandbox. One is 5 ft long and the other is 8 ft long. Boards come in the lengths shown. Which boards can you use for the third side of the sandbox? Explain.

15 ft
12 ft
8 ft
5 ft
2 ft

2 Guided Instruction

Problem 1 Applying the Corollary

Take Note

Comparison Property of Inequality
Students may benefit from substituting numbers for the variables in the property. Be sure that the numbers they choose satisfy all the conditions given.

Q What happens when $c \leq 0$? **[When $c = 0$, $a = b$. When $c < 0$, $b > a$.]**

Take Note

Corollary to the Triangle Exterior Angle Theorem
Have students state the Triangle Exterior Angle Theorem. Invite them to describe how the Comparison Property of Inequality will help prove the Corollary to the Triangle Exterior Angle Theorem. Have them compare their statements with the proof.

Problem 1

Q What type of triangle is $\triangle CBD$? **[isosceles]**

Q What congruency statement can you write about angles in $\triangle CBD$? Explain. **[$\angle 1 \cong \angle 2$; base angles of an isosceles triangle are congruent.]**

Q Because $\angle 1$ is an exterior angle of $\triangle ABD$, what two inequality statements can you write? **[$m\angle 1 > m\angle 3$ and $m\angle 1 > m\angle 4$]**

Got It? ERROR PREVENTION

Have students write an angle addition statement about $m\angle 5$. Since $m\angle 5 = m\angle C + m\angle 3$, $m\angle 5$ must be greater than $m\angle C$.

▼ STUDENT PAGES 239–240

In the Solve It, you explored triangles formed by various lengths of board. You may have noticed that changing the angle formed by two sides of the sandbox changes the length of the third side.

Essential Understanding The angles and sides of a triangle have special relationships that involve inequalities.

take note **Property** Comparison Property of Inequality

If $a = b + c$ and $c > 0$, then $a > b$.

Proof **Proof of the Comparison Property of Inequality**

Given: $a = b + c, c > 0$
Prove: $a > b$

Statements	Reasons
1) $c > 0$	1) Given
2) $b + c > b + 0$	2) Addition Property of Inequality
3) $b + c > b$	3) Identity Property of Addition
4) $a = b + c$	4) Given
5) $a > b$	5) Substitution

The Comparison Property of Inequality allows you to prove the following corollary to the Triangle Exterior Angle Theorem (Theorem 17).

take note **Corollary** Corollary to the Triangle Exterior Angle Theorem

Corollary	If . . .	Then . . .
The measure of an exterior angle of a triangle is greater than the measure of each of its remote interior angles.	$\angle 1$ is an exterior angle. 	$m\angle 1 > m\angle 2$ and $m\angle 1 > m\angle 3$

Proof **Proof of the Corollary**

Given: $\angle 1$ is an exterior angle of the triangle.
Prove: $m\angle 1 > m\angle 2$ and $m\angle 1 > m\angle 3$.

Proof: By the Triangle Exterior Angle Theorem, $m\angle 1 = m\angle 2 + m\angle 3$. Since $m\angle 2 > 0$ and $m\angle 3 > 0$, you can apply the Comparison Property of Inequality and conclude that $m\angle 1 > m\angle 2$ and $m\angle 1 > m\angle 3$.

▼ DIGITAL

Problem 1 **Applying the Corollary**

Use the figure at the right. Why is $m\angle 2 > m\angle 3$?

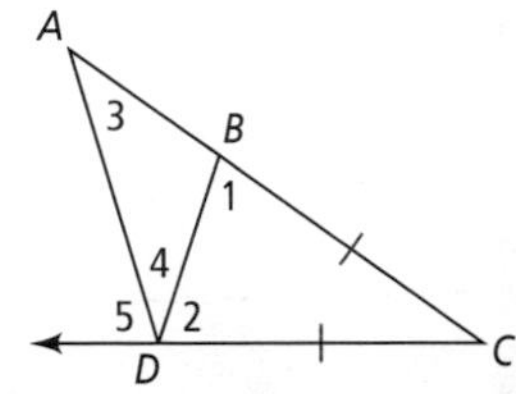

In $\triangle ACD$, $\overline{CB} \cong \overline{CD}$, so by the Isosceles Triangle Theorem, $m\angle 1 = m\angle 2$. $\angle 1$ is an exterior angle of $\triangle ABD$, so by the Corollary to the Triangle Exterior Angle Theorem, $m\angle 1 > m\angle 3$. Then $m\angle 2 > m\angle 3$ by substitution.

Problem 1 *continued*

ANSWERS

Got It? $\angle 5$ is an ext. angle of $\triangle ACD$, so by the Corollary to the Triangle Exterior Angle Theorem, $m\angle 5 > m\angle C$.

Practice

1. $m\angle 1 > m\angle 3$ by the Corollary to the Triangle Ext. $\angle$ Thm. $m\angle 3 = m\angle 2$, because they are vertical angles. Thus, $m\angle 1 > m\angle 2$ by substitution.
2. $m\angle 2 = m\angle 4$ because $\parallel$ lines form alt. int. angles that are $\cong$, and $m\angle 1 > m\angle 4$ by the Corollary to the Triangle Ext. $\angle$ Thm. So $m\angle 1 > m\angle 2$ by substitution.

▼ STUDENT PAGE 240

Got It? Why is $m\angle 5 > m\angle C$?

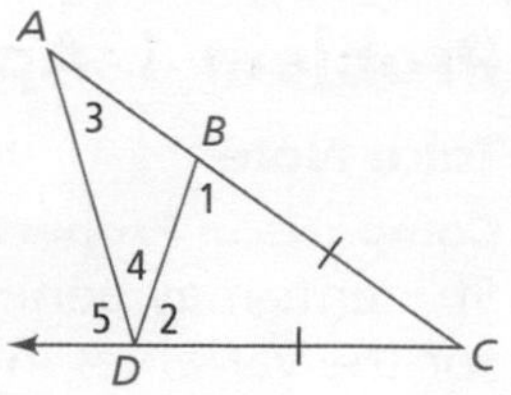

Practice Explain why $m\angle 1 > m\angle 2$.

1.

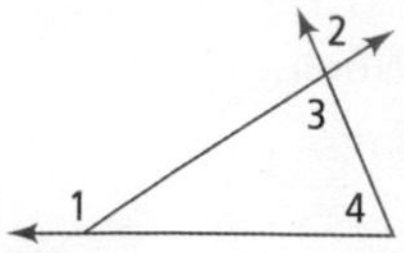

2.

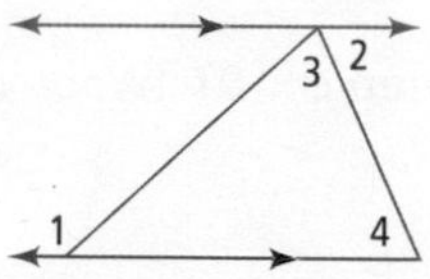

Problem 2 Using Theorem 33

Take Note

Draw several examples of triangles on the board. Have students practice identifying the longest side of the triangle and the largest angle.

Problem 2

Q Which road represents the longest side of the triangle? **[Hollingsworth Rd.]**

Got It?

Ask students to write an inequality statement that includes all three sides of the triangle. They can use this to write an inequality statement with the opposite angles.

ANSWERS

Got It? Hollingsworth Rd. and MLK Blvd.

Practice

3. $\angle M$, $\angle L$, $\angle K$
4. $\angle A$, $\angle B$, $\angle C$

▼ STUDENT PAGE 241

You can use the corollary to Theorem 17 to prove the following theorem.

take note

Theorem 33

Theorem	If . . .	Then . . .
If two sides of a triangle are not congruent, then the larger angle lies opposite the longer side.	$XZ > XY$	$m\angle Y > m\angle Z$

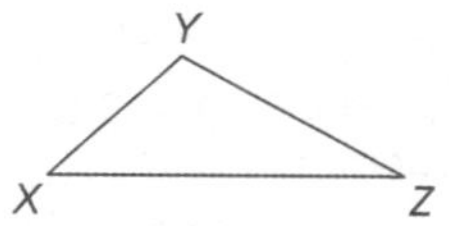

You will prove Theorem 33 in Exercise 23.

▼ DIGITAL

ONLINE PROBLEMS **Problem 2** Using Theorem 33

A town park is triangular. A landscape architect wants to place a bench at the corner with the largest angle. Which two streets form the corner with the largest angle?

Hollingsworth Road is the longest street, so it is opposite the largest angle. MLK Boulevard and Valley Road form the largest angle.

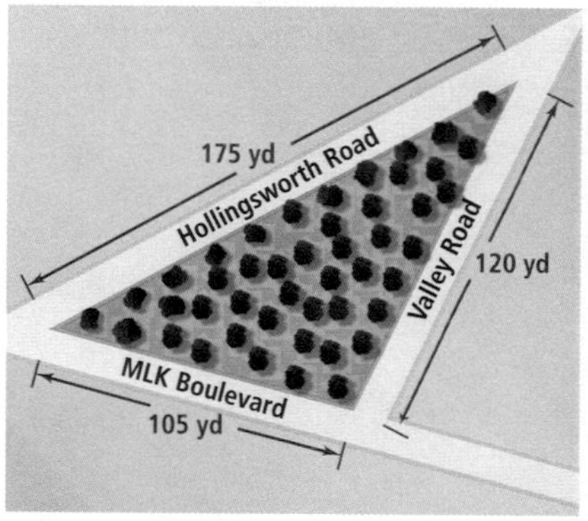

▼ STUDENT PAGE 241

Got It? Suppose the landscape architect from Problem 2 wants to place a drinking fountain at the corner with the second-largest angle. Which two streets form the corner with the second-largest angle?

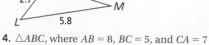

Practice **For Exercises 3 and 4, list the angles of each triangle in order from smallest to largest.**

3.

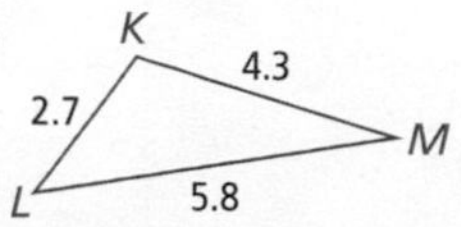

4. $\triangle ABC$, where $AB = 8$, $BC = 5$, and $CA = 7$

Problem 3 Using Theorem 34

VISUALIZATION

Before discussing the rest of this page, have students close their books. Distribute rulers and lengths of straws or uncooked spaghetti. Ask students to choose three lengths and record whether the lengths will form a triangle. Repeat until students see a pattern. Have them write a conjecture about the lengths of the sides that will form a triangle. Share conjectures.

Take Note

Have students write the Converse of Theorem 33.

Q What is a problem where you would use the Converse? **[Answers will vary. Sample: Any situation in which you know the angle measures in a triangle and want to compare the side lengths.]**

Q What are the hypothesis and conclusion? **[hypothesis: The measure of one angle of a triangle is greater than the measure of another angle.; conclusion: The side opposite the larger angle is longer than the side opposite the smaller angle.]**

Remind students that an indirect proof involves assuming the conclusion is not true and looking for a contradiction. Have students identify the assumption and the contradiction in the proof of Theorem 34.

Problem 3

Q What is the measure of the unmarked angle in the triangle? **[By the Triangle Angle-Sum Theorem, $m\angle T = 180 - (m\angle U + m\angle V) = 180 - (58 + 62) = 60$.]**

Q What inequality can be written using the measures of the angles? **[$m\angle V > m\angle T > m\angle U$]**

Got It?

Have students find the missing angle measure. They can write an inequality with the three angle measures to use when listing the sides.

ANSWERS

Got It? $\overline{OX}$; $m\angle X = 180 - (130 + 24) = 26$ so $m\angle O > m\angle X > m\angle S$. By Theorem 34, $SX > OS > OX$.

Practice

5. $\overline{TU}$, $\overline{UV}$, $\overline{TV}$
6. $\overline{EF}$, $\overline{DE}$, $\overline{DF}$

▼ STUDENT PAGE 242

Theorem 34 below is the converse of Theorem 33. The proof of Theorem 34 relies on indirect reasoning.

take note **Theorem 34**

Theorem	If . . .	Then . . .
If two angles of a triangle are not congruent, then the longer side lies opposite the larger angle.	$m\angle A > m\angle B$	$BC > AC$

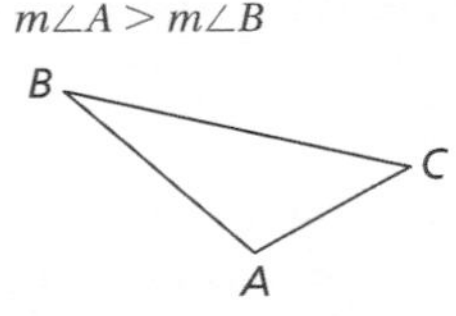

Proof Indirect Proof of Theorem 34

Given: $m\angle A > m\angle B$
Prove: $BC > AC$

Step 1 Assume temporarily that BC is not greater than AC. That is, assume temporarily that either $BC < AC$ or $BC = AC$.

Step 2 If $BC < AC$, then $m\angle A < m\angle B$ (Theorem 33). This contradicts the given fact that $m\angle A > m\angle B$. Therefore, $BC < AC$ must be false.

If $BC = AC$, then $m\angle A = m\angle B$ (Isosceles Triangle Theorem). This also contradicts $m\angle A > m\angle B$. Therefore, $BC = AC$ must be false.

Step 3 The temporary assumption $BC \ngtr AC$ is false, so $BC > AC$.

▼ DIGITAL

Problem 3 Using Theorem 34

Multiple Choice **Which choice shows the sides of $\triangle TUV$ in order from shortest to longest?**

Ⓐ $\overline{TV}$, $\overline{UV}$, $\overline{UT}$ Ⓒ $\overline{UV}$, $\overline{UT}$, $\overline{TV}$
Ⓑ $\overline{UT}$, $\overline{UV}$, $\overline{TV}$ Ⓓ $\overline{TV}$, $\overline{UT}$, $\overline{UV}$

By the Triangle Angle-Sum Theorem, $m\angle T = 60$. $58 < 60 < 62$, so $m\angle U < m\angle T < m\angle V$. By Theorem 34, $TV < UV < UT$. Choice A is correct.

T
U 58° 62° V

▼ STUDENT PAGES 242–243

Plan
How do you use the angle measures to order the side lengths?

Got It? **Reasoning** In the figure below, $m\angle S = 24$ and $m\angle O = 130$. Which side of $\triangle SOX$ is the shortest side? Explain your reasoning.

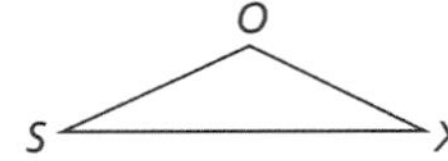

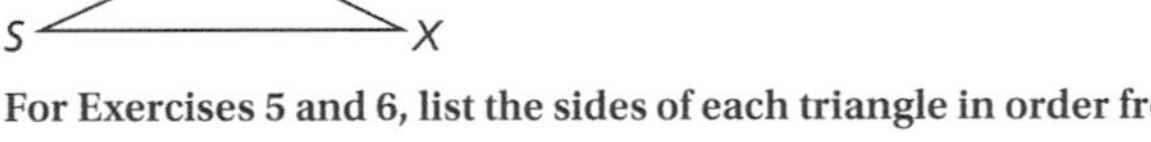

Practice **For Exercises 5 and 6, list the sides of each triangle in order from shortest to longest.**

5.
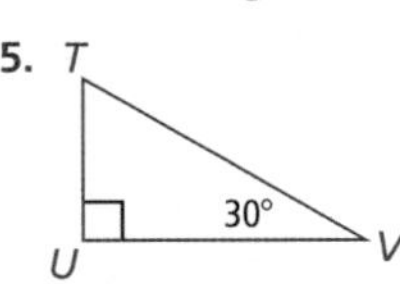

6. $\triangle DEF$, with $m\angle D = 20$, $m\angle E = 120$, and $m\angle F = 40$

Problem 4 Using the Triangle Inequality Theorem

Take Note

Ask students to choose side lengths which would satisfy the Triangle Inequality Theorem. Invite volunteers to give their lengths and check them as a class.

Problem 4

Q What must be true about the side lengths of a triangle? **[The sum of any two sides must be greater than the length of the third side.]**

Q How can you determine if the lengths can form a triangle? **[Find the sum of each pair of sides and verify that the sum is greater than the third side.]**

Got It?

Point out to students that they only need to check that the sum of the two shorter sides is greater than the length of the longest side.

ANSWERS

Got It? a. No; $2 + 6 \ngtr 9$. **b.** Yes; the sum of the lengths of any two sides is greater than the length of the third side.

Practice

7. No; $2 + 3 \ngtr 6$.

8. Yes; $11 + 12 > 15$, $11 + 15 > 12$, and $12 + 15 > 11$.

▼ STUDENT PAGE 243

For three segments to form a triangle, their lengths must be related in a certain way. Notice that only one of the sets of segments below can form a triangle. The sum of the smallest two lengths must be greater than the greatest length.

take note

Theorem 35 Triangle Inequality Theorem

The sum of the lengths of any two sides of a triangle is greater than the length of the third side.

$XY + YZ > XZ$ $\quad$ $YZ + XZ > XY$ $\quad$ $XZ + XY > YZ$

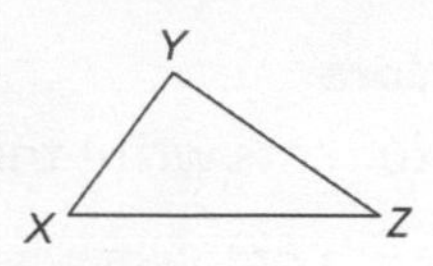

You will prove Theorem 35 in Exercise 28.

▼ DIGITAL

Problem 4 Using the Triangle Inequality Theorem

Can a triangle have sides with the given lengths? Explain.

A 3 ft, 7 ft, 8 ft

$3 + 7 > 8$ $\quad$ $7 + 8 > 3$ $\quad$ $8 + 3 > 7$

$10 > 8$ $\quad$ $15 > 3$ $\quad$ $11 > 7$

Yes. The sum of the lengths of any two sides is greater than the length of the third side.

B 5 ft, 10 ft, 15 ft

$5 + 10 \ngtr 15$

$15 \ngtr 15$

No. The sum of 5 and 10 is not greater than 15. This contradicts Theorem 35.

▼ STUDENT PAGE 244

Got It? Can a triangle have sides with the given lengths? Explain.

a. 2 m, 6 m, and 9 m

b. 4 yd, 6 yd, and 9 yd

Think

How can you determine if the lengths can form a triangle?

Practice Can a triangle have sides with the given lengths? Explain.

7. 2 in., 3 in., 6 in.

8. 11 cm, 12 cm, 15 cm

Problem 5 Finding Possible Side Lengths

Q What do you notice about the lower bound for the third side length? **[It is the difference between the two given side lengths.]**

Q What do you notice about the upper bound? **[It is the sum of the two given side lengths.]**

Got It?

It may help some students to sketch a diagram of the triangle. Have students write and solve inequalities to find the range of lengths.

ANSWERS

Got It? 3 in. $< x <$ 11 in.

Practice

9. 5 m $< x <$ 41 m

10. 15 km $< x <$ 55 km

▼ DIGITAL

Problem 5 **Finding Possible Side Lengths**

Algebra **In the Solve It, you explored the possible dimensions of a triangular sandbox. Two of the sides are 5 ft and 8 ft long. What is the range of possible lengths for the third side?**

Know	Need	Plan
The lengths of two sides of the triangle are 5 ft and 8 ft.	The range of possible lengths of the third side	Use the Triangle Inequality Theorem to write three inequalities. Use the solutions of the inequalities to determine the greatest and least possible lengths.

Let x represent the length of the third side. Use the Triangle Inequality Theorem to write three inequalities. Then solve each inequality for x.

$x + 5 > 8$ $\quad x + 8 > 5$ $\quad 5 + 8 > x$

$x > 3$ $\quad x > -3$ $\quad x < 13$

Numbers that satisfy $x > 3$ and $x > -3$ must be greater than 3. So, the third side must be greater than 3 ft and less than 13 ft.

▼ STUDENT PAGE 245

Got It? A triangle has side lengths of 4 in. and 7 in. What is the range of possible lengths for the third side?

Practice **Algebra** **The lengths of two sides of a triangle are given. Find the range of possible lengths for the third side.**

9. 18 m, 23 m

10. 20 km, 35 km

3 Lesson Check

Do you know HOW?

If students have difficulty with Exercise 13, remind them that they must make comparisons using each pair of the three sides.

Do you UNDERSTAND?

If students have difficulty with Exercise 14, then have them sketch a diagram of the triangle.

Close

Q What is the relationship between the lengths of the sides and the measures of the angles in a triangle? **[The longest side is across from the largest angle and the shortest side is across from the smallest angle.]**

Q How can you find the range of values for the third side of a triangle when you are given the lengths of the other two sides? **[Find the sum and the difference of the two side lengths.]**

ANSWERS

11. $\overline{BC}$ **12.** $\angle C$

13. No; $5 + 4 \not> 10$.

14. If the perimeter is 16 and the length of one side is 8, then the sum of the lengths of the other two sides is $16 - 8 = 8$. However, the Triangle Inequality Thm. tells you that if the length of one side is 8, then the sum of the lengths of the other two sides is greater than 8. So the friend is incorrect.

▼ STUDENT PAGES 246–247

Lesson Check

Do you know HOW?

Use $\triangle ABC$ for Exercises 11 and 12.

11. Which side is the longest?

12. Which angle is the smallest?

13. Can a triangle have sides of lengths 4, 5, and 10? Explain.

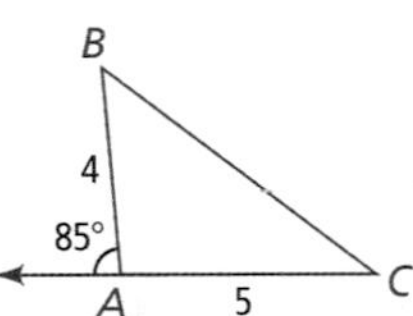

Do you UNDERSTAND?

14. Error Analysis A friend tells you that she drew a triangle with perimeter 16 and one side of length 8. How do you know she made an error in her drawing?

15. Reasoning Is it possible to draw a right triangle with an exterior angle measuring 88? Explain your reasoning.

15. No; the adjacent interior $\angle$ would measure 92. Then, because a second $\angle$ of the triangle measures 90, the sum of the $\angle$ measures would exceed 180, which contradicts the Triangle Angle-Sum Thm.

Practice

More Practice and Problem-Solving Exercises

ASSIGNMENT GUIDE
The assignments below are for the More Practice and Problem-Solving Exercises. You may also want to assign the A-Level Practice Exercises for homework if these are not used in class.
Average: 16–24
Advanced: 16–28

Mathematical Practices The exercises listed focus on the Standards for Mathematical Practices listed.

EX. 16, 18: Make Sense of Problems (MP 1)
EX. 15, 20–23: Construct Arguments (MP 3)
EX. 14, 19: Critique the Reasoning of Others (MP 3)

EXERCISE 24: Use the **Think About a Plan** worksheet in the Online Teacher Resources to further support students' development in becoming independent learners.

HOMEWORK QUICK CHECK
To check students' understanding of key skills and concepts, go over Exercises 16, 17, 19, 20, and 24.

ANSWERS

16. Place the computer at the corner that forms a rt. ∠; place the bookshelf along the wall opposite the rt. ∠. In a rt. triangle the rt. ∠ is the largest ∠, and the longest side of a triangle is opposite the largest ∠.
17. $\overline{AB}$
18. The dashed red line and the courtyard walkway determine three sides of a triangle, so by the Triangle Inequality Thm., the path that follows the dashed red line is longer than the courtyard walkway.
19. The sign, Topeka, and Wichita are either collinear or they determine the vertices of a triangle. If D is the distance between Topeka and Wichita, then $20 \leq D \leq 200$.
20. $\overline{RS}$ 21. $\overline{CD}$ 22. $\overline{XY}$
23. a. $m\angle OTY$
 b. $m\angle 3$
 c. Isosc. Triangle Thm.
 d. ∠ Addition Post.
 e. Comparison Prop. of Inequality
 f. Substitution
 g. Corollary to Triangle Ext. ∠ Thm.
 h. Transitive Prop. of Inequality
24. Answers may vary. Sample: The sum of the ∠ measures of a triangle is 180, so $m\angle T + m\angle P + m\angle A = 180$. Since $m\angle T = 90$, $m\angle P + m\angle A = 90$ and so $m\angle T > m\angle A$ (Comparison Prop. of Inequality). Therefore $PA > PT$ by Thm. 34.

More Practice and Problem-Solving Exercises

B Apply

16. **Think About a Plan** You are setting up a study area where you will do your homework each evening. It is triangular with an entrance on one side. You want to put your computer in the corner with the largest angle and a bookshelf on the longest side. Where should you place your computer? On which side should you place the bookshelf? Explain.
 - What type of triangle is shown in the figure?
 - Once you find the largest angle of a triangle, how do you find the longest side?

Entrance
7 ft

17. **Algebra** Find the longest side of $\triangle ABC$, with $m\angle A = 70$, $m\angle B = 2x - 10$, and $m\angle C = 3x + 20$.

18. **Writing** You and a friend compete in a scavenger hunt at a museum. The two of you walk from the Picasso exhibit to the Native American gallery along the dashed red line. When he sees that another team is ahead of you, your friend says, "They must have cut through the courtyard." Explain what your friend means.

19. **Error Analysis** Your family drives across Kansas on Interstate 70. A sign reads, "Wichita 90 mi, Topeka 110 mi." Your little brother says, "I didn't know that it was only 20 miles from Wichita to Topeka." Explain why the distance between the two cities does not have to be 20 mi.

Reasoning Determine which segment is shortest in each diagram.

20. 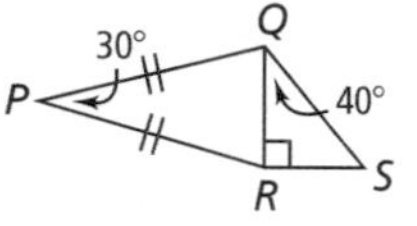

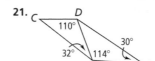

21.
C D 110° 30° 32° 114° B A

22. 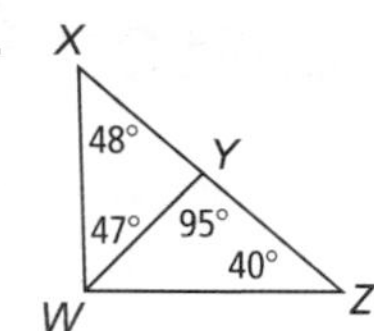

23. **Developing Proof** Fill in the blanks for a proof of Theorem 33: If two sides of a triangle are not congruent, then the larger angle lies opposite the longer side.

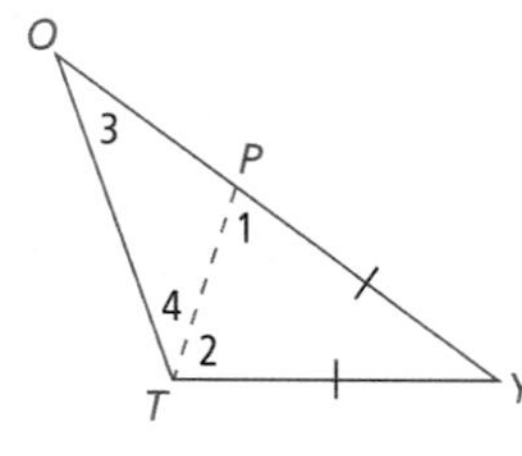

Given: $\triangle TOY$, with $YO > YT$
Prove: a. __?__ > b. __?__

Mark P on $\overline{YO}$ so that $\overline{YP} \cong \overline{YT}$. Draw $\overline{TP}$.

Statements	Reasons
1) $\overline{YP} \cong \overline{YT}$	1) Ruler Postulate
2) $m\angle 1 = m\angle 2$	2) c. __?__
3) $m\angle OTY = m\angle 4 + m\angle 2$	3) d. __?__
4) $m\angle OTY > m\angle 2$	4) e. __?__
5) $m\angle OTY > m\angle 1$	5) f. __?__
6) $m\angle 1 > m\angle 3$	6) g. __?__
7) $m\angle OTY > m\angle 3$	7) h. __?__

Proof 24. Prove this corollary to Theorem 34: The perpendicular segment from a point to a line is the shortest segment from the point to the line.

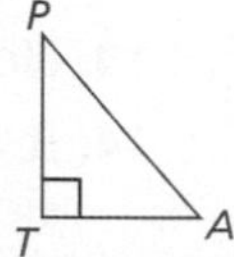

Given: $\overline{PT} \perp \overline{TA}$
Prove: $PA > PT$

▼ STUDENT PAGE 248

25. 0.5; the lengths of two sides of the △ are 6 cm and 9 cm, so the length of the third side of the △ must be greater than 3 cm and less than 15 cm, by the △ Inequality Thm. Since 2 of the 4 straws satisfy that condition, the probability that she can form a △ is $\frac{2}{4}$, or $\frac{1}{2}$.

26. (2, 4), (2, 5), (2, 6), (3, 3), (3, 4), (3, 5), (3, 6), (3, 7), (4, 3), (4, 4), (4, 5), (4, 6), (4, 7), (4, 8)

27. $\frac{5}{18}$

28. Answers may vary. Sample:

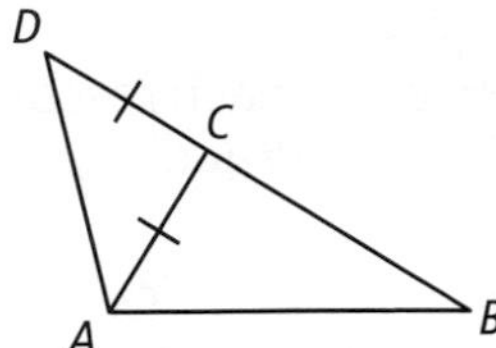

Find point D on $\overrightarrow{BC}$ such that $DC = AC$. $m\angle D = m\angle DAC$ by the Isosc. △ Thm. Now $m\angle DAB > m\angle DAC$ by the Comparison Prop. of Inequality, and so $m\angle DAB > m\angle D$ by substitution. Thus $DB > AB$ by Thm. 34. We know $DC + CB = DB$ by the Segment Add. Post., so $DC + CB > AB$ (Substitution) and $AC + CB > AB$ (Substitution).

Challenge

25. Probability A student has two straws. One is 6 cm long and the other is 9 cm long. She picks a third straw at random from a group of four straws whose lengths are 3 cm, 5 cm, 11 cm, and 15 cm. What is the probability that the straw she picks will allow her to form a triangle? Justify your answer.

For Exercises 26 and 27, x and y are integers such that $1 < x < 5$ and $2 < y < 9$.

26. The sides of a triangle are 5 cm, x cm, and y cm. List all possible (x, y) pairs.

27. Probability What is the probability that you can draw an isosceles triangle that has sides 5 cm, x cm, and y cm, with x and y chosen at random?

Proof **28.** Prove the Triangle Inequality Theorem: The sum of the lengths of any two sides of a triangle is greater than the length of the third side.

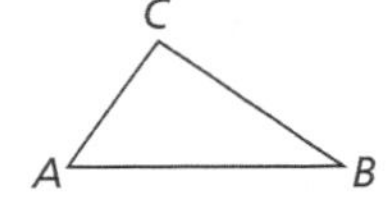

Given: $\triangle ABC$

Prove: $AC + CB > AB$

(*Hint:* On $\overrightarrow{BC}$, mark a point D not on $\overline{BC}$, so that $DC = AC$. Draw $\overline{DA}$ and use Theorem 34 with $\triangle ABD$.)

5 Assess and Remediate

Lesson Quiz

1. Which is the smallest angle in $\triangle MNO$?

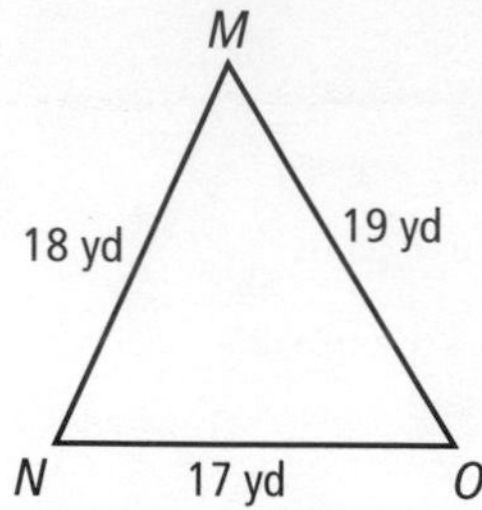

2. Order the sides of $\triangle DEF$ from shortest to longest.

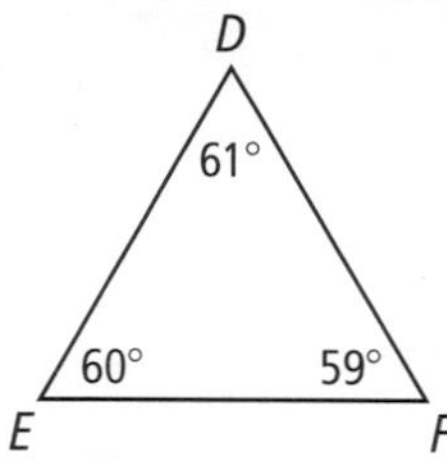

3. Do you UNDERSTAND? Two sides of a triangle are 5 inches and 10 inches long. What is the range of possible lengths for the third side?

ANSWERS TO LESSON QUIZ

1. $\angle M$

2. $\overline{DE}$, $\overline{DF}$, $\overline{EF}$

3. 5 in. $< x <$ 15 in.

Prescription for Remediation

Use the student work on the Lesson Quiz to prescribe a differentiated assignment.

Points	Differentiated Remediation
0–1	Intervention
2	On-level
3	Extension

Online Assessment

Assign the Lesson Quiz in Success Tracker on **pearsonsuccessnet.com**. Success Tracker will automatically score the quiz and assign appropriate intervention or enrichment to each student based on the results. The compiled data appear in three different reports for instant analysis of whole class and individual student performance.

Differentiated Remediation

Intervention

- **RETEACHING** (2 pages) Provides reteaching and practice exercises for the key lesson concepts. Use with struggling students or absent students.
- **ENGLISH LANGUAGE LEARNER SUPPORT** Helps students develop and reinforce mathematical vocabulary and key concepts.

On-Level

- **PRACTICE** (2 pages) Provides extra practice for each lesson. For simpler practice exercises, use the Form K Practice pages found in the Online Teacher Resources.
- **THINK ABOUT A PLAN** Helps students develop specific problem-solving skills and strategies by providing scaffolded guiding questions.
- **STANDARDIZED TEST PREP** Focuses on all major exercises, all major question types, and helps students prepare for the high-stakes assessments.

Extension

- **ENRICHMENT** Provides students with interesting problems and activities that extend the concepts of the lesson.
- **ACTIVITIES, GAMES, AND PUZZLES** Worksheets that can be used for concept development, enrichment, and for fun!

4-7 Inequalities in Two Triangles

Common Core State Standard
G.CO.10 Prove theorems about triangles . . .

Preparing to Teach

BIG ideas Reasoning and Proof
Measurement

ESSENTIAL UNDERSTANDING

In triangles that have two pairs of congruent sides, there is a relationship between the included angles and the third pair of sides.

Math Background

Relationships between angles and sides in triangles follow several rules. Students have already learned that the side lengths are related by inequalities. They know that the largest angle of a triangle is located across from the longest side. In this lesson, they will see that they can compare two triangles with two pairs of congruent sides. The triangle with the longest noncongruent side will also contain the largest included angle. Properties of triangles will be used to examine properties of other geometric figures.

Illustrate the Hinge Theorem with the hands of two students. Show that as one hand opens wider (the angle), the side opposite the hands must get longer.

ELL Support

FOCUS ON LANGUAGE Arrange students into groups of 2–5. Assign each group a lesson to list its vocabulary words and then define them. A student from each of these groups will then form new groups so there is one student in each of the second groups that has worked on a different lesson. Students combine their definitions to make their own flashcards which can be used to quiz each other and for review later.

USE MULTIPLE REPRESENTATIONS There are two identical cabinet doors, one that opens to the right and the other opens to the left. The right door is opened halfway and the left door is open all the way. Draw a picture to show which has the larger angle at the cabinet door's hinge.

Mathematical Practices

CONSTRUCT VIABLE ARGUMENTS AND CRITIQUE THE REASONING OF OTHERS. Using the relationship between the longest side of a triangle and the relative measure of its opposite angle, students will construct the SAS Inequality Theorem.

1 Interactive Learning

Solve It!

PURPOSE To discover the Hinge Theorem

PROCESS Students may

- draw each time on the clock and measure x.
- use algebra to find the measures of the angles at each time.

Q Is x greater at 1:00 or 3:00? Explain. **[x is greater at 3:00 because the hands are farther apart.]**

Q What part of the clock affects the length of x? **[On a clock, the angle between the hour and minute hands changes the length of x.]**

ANSWER The order of the times is 1:00, 8:30, 3:00, 12:20, 1:30, 5:00; the measures of the angles between the clock hands for these times are 30, 75, 90, 110, 135, 150. The larger the ∠ between the clock hands, the greater the distance x.

CONNECT THE MATH In the Solve It, students use a clock face to investigate properties of angles in a triangle. In the lesson, students learn a theorem that relates angle measures and side lengths in triangles.

▼ DIGITAL (STUDENT WORK SPACE PAGE 249)

SOLVE IT! **Getting Ready!**

Think of a clock or watch that has an hour hand and a minute hand. As minutes pass, the distance between the tip of the hour hand and the tip of the minute hand changes. This distance is x in the figure at the right. What is the order of the times below from least to greatest length of x? How do you know?

1:00, 3:00, 5:00, 8:30, 1:30, 12:20

2 Guided Instruction

Problem 1 Using the Hinge Theorem

Take Note

Have students review the definition of an included angle. Then, have them sketch a triangle with side lengths 3 cm and 4 cm. Have students compare the third side lengths with those around them. They should be able to make a statement about the sizes of the angles.

Problem 1

Q Which two pairs of sides are marked congruent? **[$\overline{SA} \cong \overline{OY}$ and $\overline{AK} \cong \overline{OU}$]**

Q Which angles are included between these pairs of sides? **[$\angle A$ and $\angle O$]**

Q Which angle is larger? **[$\angle A$]**

Got It? **ERROR PREVENTION**

Have students identify the congruent pairs of sides and their included angles. Then, have students identify the larger angle.

ANSWERS

Got It? a. $LN > OQ$ **b.** Assume temporarily that $m\angle P \not> m\angle A$. If $m\angle P = m\angle A$, then $\triangle ABC \cong \triangle PQR$ (SAS), but this contradicts the fact that $BC \neq QR$. If $m\angle P < m\angle A$, then by the Hinge Thm., $QR < BC$. This contradicts the fact that $QR > BC$. Therefore $m\angle P > m\angle A$.

Practice

1. $LM < KL$
2. no conclusion

▼ STUDENT PAGE 249

In the Solve It, the hands of the clock and the segment labeled x form a triangle. As the time changes, the shape of the triangle changes, but the lengths of two of its sides do not change.

Essential Understanding In triangles that have two pairs of congruent sides, there is a relationship between the included angles and the third pair of sides.

When you close a door, the angle between the door and the frame (at the hinge) gets smaller. The relationship between the measure of the hinge angle and the length of the opposite side is the basis for the SAS Inequality Theorem, also known as the Hinge Theorem.

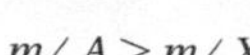

Theorem 36 The Hinge Theorem (SAS Inequality Theorem)

Theorem	If . . .	Then . . .
If two sides of one triangle are congruent to two sides of another triangle, and the included angles are not congruent, then the longer third side is opposite the larger included angle.	$m\angle A > m\angle X$	$BC > YZ$

You will prove Theorem 36 in Exercise 21.

▼ DIGITAL

Problem 1 Using the Hinge Theorem

Multiple Choice Which of the following statements must be true?

Ⓐ $AS < YU$ Ⓑ $SK > YU$ Ⓒ $SK < YU$ Ⓓ $AK = YU$

$\overline{SA} \cong \overline{YO}$ and $\overline{AK} \cong \overline{OU}$, so the triangles have two pairs of congruent sides. The included angles, $\angle A$ and $\angle O$, are not congruent. Since $m\angle A > m\angle O$, $SK > YU$ by the Hinge Theorem. The correct answer is B.

▼ STUDENT PAGE 250

Got It? **a.** What inequality relates LN and OQ in the figure at the right?

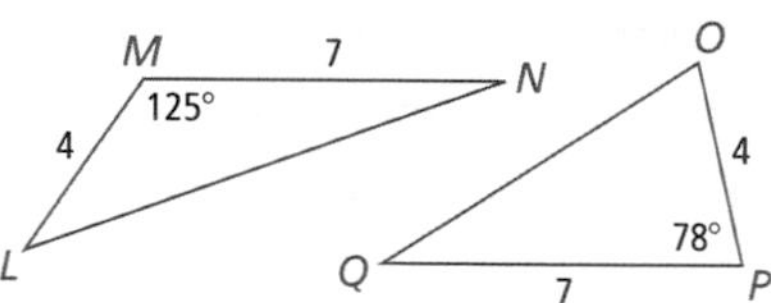

b. Reasoning In $\triangle ABC$, $AB = 3$, $BC = 4$, and $CA = 6$. In $\triangle PQR$, $PQ = 3$, $QR = 5$, and $RP = 6$. How can you use indirect reasoning to explain why $m\angle P > m\angle A$?

Practice Write an inequality relating the given side lengths. If there is not enough information to reach a conclusion, write *no conclusion.*

1. LM and KL

2. YZ and UV

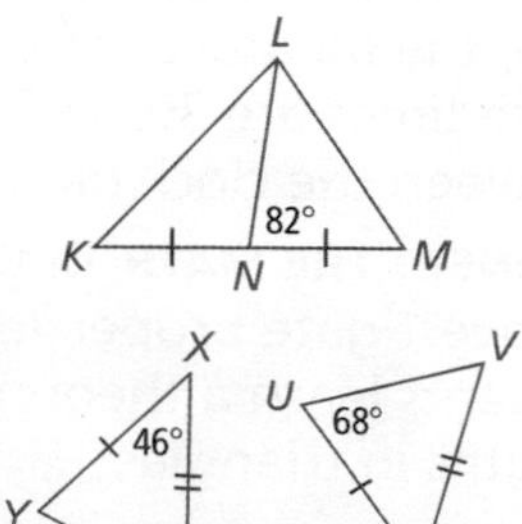

Problem 2 Applying the Hinge Theorem

Q Which segments remain the same throughout the ride? **[$\overline{AB}$ and the length of the swing's chain, $\overline{BC}$]**

Q What changes throughout the ride? **[The angle between $\overline{AB}$ and the swing gets larger.]**

Got It?

Q What does not change about both pairs of scissors in the diagram? **[the length of the blade parts of the scissors]**

Q Why can you use the Hinge Theorem to answer this question? **[The diagram shows the same scissors twice, so the "sides" of two triangles are congruent. The diagram also shows that the included angles are not congruent.]**

ANSWERS

Got It? The 40° opening; the lengths of the blades do not change as the scissors open. The included angle between the blades of the 40° opening is greater than the included angle of the 35° opening, so by the Hinge Thm., the distance between the blades is greater for the 40° opening.

Practice

3. The 40° opening; the lengths of the two sections of the robotic arm do not change as the arm moves. The included angle between the arm sections of the 60° opening is greater than the included angle of the 40° opening, so by the Hinge Thm., the tip of the arm is closer to the base for the 40° opening.

▼ DIGITAL

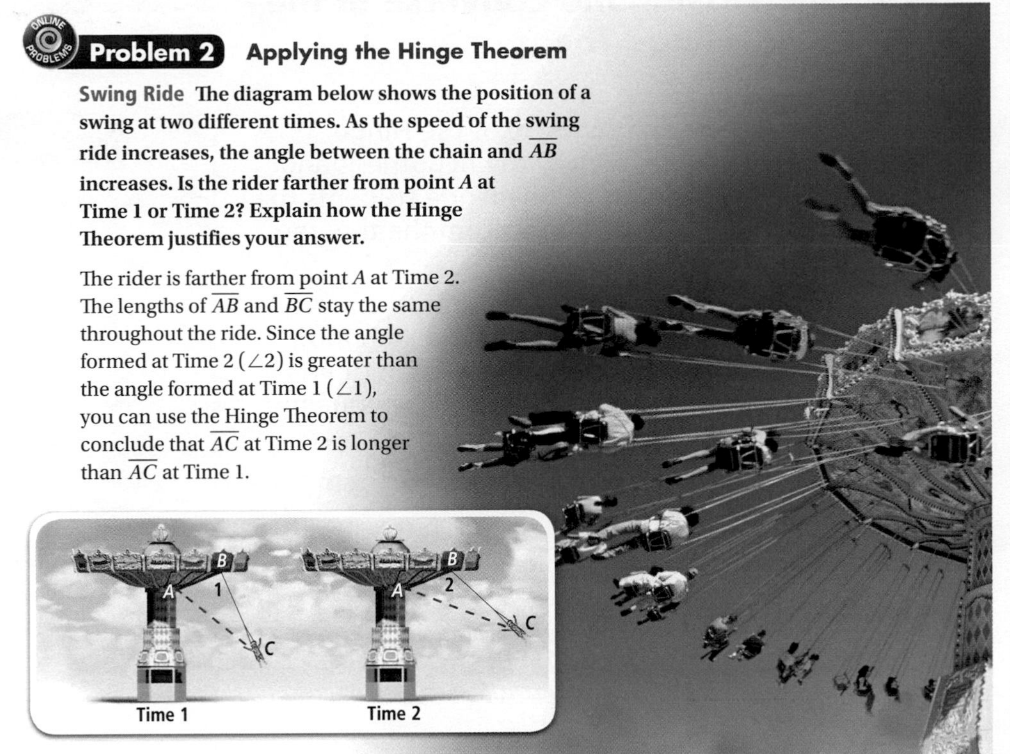

Problem 2 Applying the Hinge Theorem
Swing Ride The diagram below shows the position of a swing at two different times. As the speed of the swing ride increases, the angle between the chain and $\overline{AB}$ increases. Is the rider farther from point A at Time 1 or Time 2? Explain how the Hinge Theorem justifies your answer.
The rider is farther from point A at Time 2. The lengths of $\overline{AB}$ and $\overline{BC}$ stay the same throughout the ride. Since the angle formed at Time 2 ($\angle 2$) is greater than the angle formed at Time 1 ($\angle 1$), you can use the Hinge Theorem to conclude that $\overline{AC}$ at Time 2 is longer than $\overline{AC}$ at Time 1.
A
B
1
C
2
Time 1
Time 2

▼ STUDENT PAGE 251

Think What does not change about both pairs of scissors in the diagram?

Got It? The diagram below shows a pair of scissors in two different positions. In which position is the distance between the tips of the two blades greater? Use the Hinge Theorem to justify your answer.

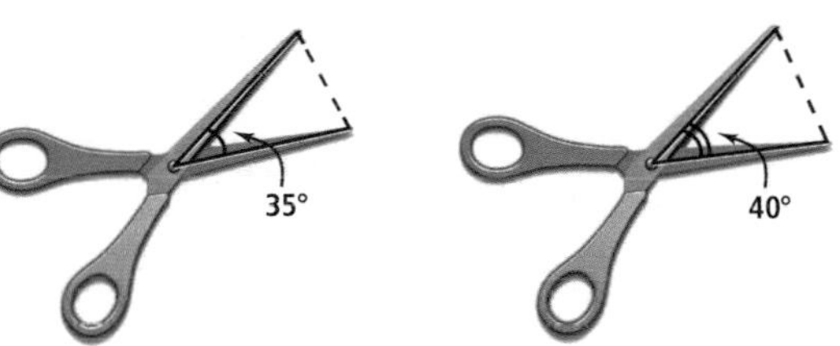

35°
40°

Practice 3. The diagram below shows a robotic arm in two different positions. In which position is the tip of the robotic arm closer to the base? Use the Hinge Theorem to justify your answer.

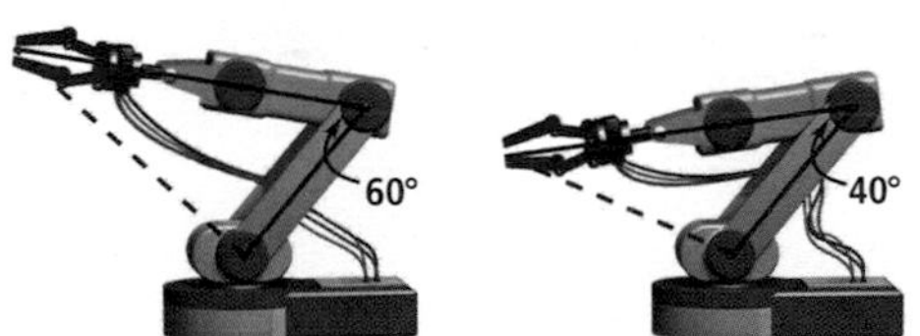

60°
40°

Problem 3 Using the Converse of the Hinge Theorem

Take Note

Have students state the converse of the Hinge Theorem. Ask them to identify the hypothesis and conclusion to the statement. Challenge students to create a biconditional statement from the theorem and its converse.

Remind students how an indirect proof is constructed. Ask them to identify the assumption. Be sure that they understand the negation of an inequality is the reverse inequality OR the equality. Ask them to identify both contradictions in the proof of the Converse of the Hinge Theorem.

Problem 3

Q Which pairs of sides are congruent in the two triangles? **[$\overline{RU} \cong \overline{TU}$ and $\overline{US} \cong \overline{US}$]**

Q What is the relationship between the included angles for these pairs of sides? Justify your answer. **[By the Converse of the Hinge Theorem, $m\angle RUS > m\angle TUS$.]**

▼ STUDENT PAGE 252

The Converse of the Hinge Theorem is also true. The proof of the converse is an indirect proof.

take note

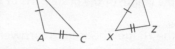

Theorem 37 Converse of the Hinge Theorem (SSS Inequality)

Theorem	If . . .	Then . . .
If two sides of one triangle are congruent to two sides of another triangle, and the third sides are not congruent, then the larger included angle is opposite the longer third side.	$BC > YZ$	$m\angle A > m\angle X$

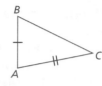

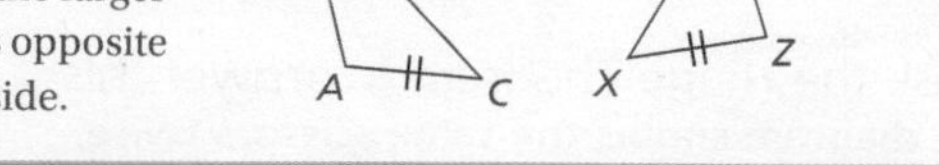

Proof Indirect Proof of the Converse of the Hinge Theorem (SSS Inequality)

Given: $\overline{AB} \cong \overline{XY}$, $\overline{AC} \cong \overline{XZ}$, $BC > YZ$
Prove: $m\angle A > m\angle X$

Step 1 Assume temporarily that $m\angle A \ngtr m\angle X$. This means either $m\angle A < m\angle X$ or $m\angle A = m\angle X$.

Step 2 If $m\angle A < m\angle X$, then $BC < YZ$ by the Hinge Theorem. This contradicts the given information that $BC > YZ$. Therefore, the assumption that $m\angle A < m\angle X$ must be false.

If $m\angle A = m\angle X$, then $\triangle ABC \cong \triangle XYZ$ by SAS. If the two triangles are congruent, then $BC = YZ$ because corresponding parts of congruent triangles are congruent. This contradicts the given information that $BC > YZ$. Therefore, the assumption that $m\angle A = m\angle X$ must be false.

Step 3 The temporary assumption that $m\angle A \ngtr m\angle X$ is false. Therefore, $m\angle A > m\angle X$.

▼ DIGITAL

Problem 3 Using the Converse of the Hinge Theorem

Algebra **What is the range of possible values for x?**

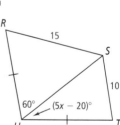

Step 1 Find an upper limit for the value of x. $\overline{UT} \cong \overline{UR}$ and $\overline{US} \cong \overline{US}$, so $\triangle TUS$ and $\triangle RUS$ have two pairs of congruent sides. $RS > TS$, so you can use the Converse of the Hinge Theorem to write an inequality.

$m\angle RUS > m\angle TUS$	Converse of the Hinge Theorem
$60 > 5x - 20$	Substitute.
$80 > 5x$	Add 20 to each side.
$16 > x$	Divide each side by 5.

Step 2 Find a lower limit for the value of x.

$m\angle TUS > 0$	The measure of an angle of a triangle is greater than 0.
$5x - 20 > 0$	Substitute.
$5x > 20$	Add 20 to each side.
$x > 4$	Divide each side by 5.

Rewrite $16 > x$ and $x > 4$ as $4 < x < 16$.

Got It?
Have students identify the pairs of congruent sides in the diagram. Then, ask them to write an inequality that relates the included angles. Finally, remind students that an angle in a triangle must have a measure greater than 0°.

ANSWERS

Got It? $-6 < x < 24$

Practice

4. $6 < x < 24$

5. $2.5 < x < 15$

▼ STUDENT PAGES 252–253

Got It? What is the range of possible values for x in the figure at the right?

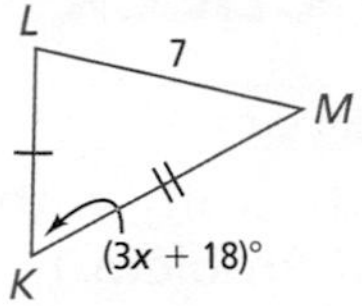

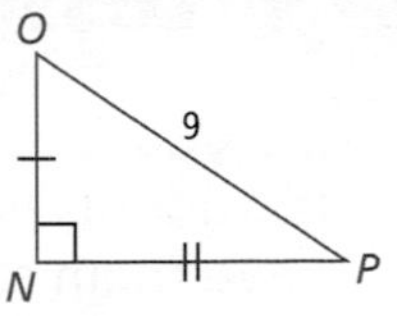

Practice **Algebra** Find the range of possible values for each variable.

4.
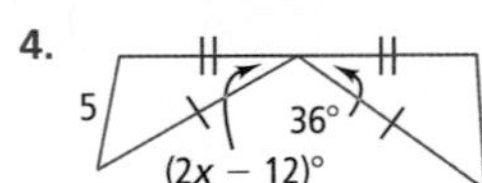

5.
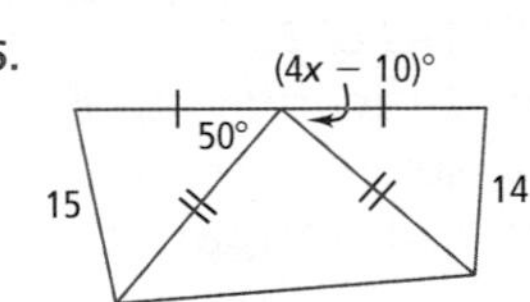

Problem 4 Proving Relationships in Triangles

Q Which pairs of sides are congruent in the two triangles? **[$\overline{BA} \cong \overline{DE}$ and $\overline{AE} \cong \overline{AE}$]**

Q Which angles are across from the unequal sides in the triangles? **[$\angle BAE$ and $\angle DEA$]**

Q Which of these angles appears to be smaller? **[$\angle DEA$]**

Q What theorem can you use to prove this fact? **[Converse of the Hinge Theorem]**

Got It?

Q Which segments are congruent in the diagram? Justify your answer. **[$\overline{MO} \cong \overline{MO}$ by the Reflexive Property of Congruence. $\overline{LO} \cong \overline{NO}$ because O is the midpoint of the segment.]**

ANSWERS

Got It? From the given information, $LO = NO$ (Def. of midpt.) and $m\angle MOL = 100$ (Suppl. $\angle$ to $\angle MON$). Since $\overline{MO} \cong MO$, and $m\angle MOL > m\angle MON$, the Hinge Thm. yields $LM > MN$.

Practice

6. **a.** Converse of Isosc. Triangle Thm.
b. Given
c. Def. of midpt.
d. $BC = CD$
e. Given
f. Hinge Theorem

▼ DIGITAL

Proof **Problem 4** **Proving Relationships in Triangles**

Given: $BA = DE$, $BE > DA$

Prove: $m\angle BAE > m\angle BEA$

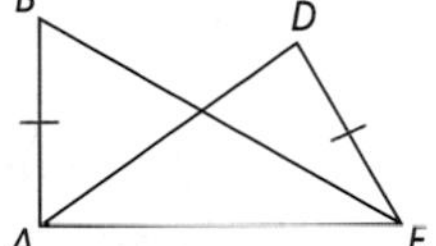

Statement	Reasons
1) $BA = DE$	1) Given
2) $AE = AE$	2) Reflexive Property of Equality
3) $BE > DA$	3) Given
4) $m\angle BAE > m\angle DEA$	4) Converse of the Hinge Theorem
5) $m\angle DEA = m\angle DEB + m\angle BEA$	5) Angle Addition Postulate
6) $m\angle DEA > m\angle BEA$	6) Comparison Property of Inequality
7) $m\angle BAE > m\angle BEA$	7) Transitive Property of Inequality

▼ STUDENT PAGES 253–254

Got It? **Given:** $m\angle MON = 80$, O is the midpoint of $\overline{LN}$

Prove: $LM > MN$

Think How can you find the measure of $\angle MOL$?

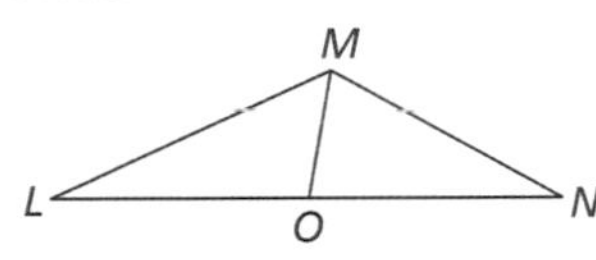
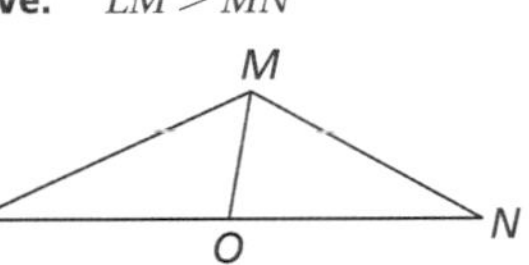

Practice

6. Developing Proof Complete the following proof.

Given: C is the midpoint of $\overline{BD}$,
$m\angle EAC = m\angle AEC$,
$m\angle BCA > m\angle DCE$

Prove: $AB > ED$

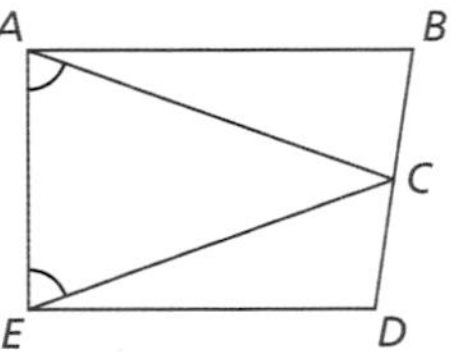

Statements	Reasons
1) $m\angle EAC = m\angle AEC$	1) Given
2) $AC = EC$	2) **a.** ______
3) C is the midpoint of $\overline{BD}$.	3) **b.** ______
4) $\overline{BC} \cong \overline{CD}$	4) **c.** ______
5) **d.** ______	5) $\cong$ segments have $=$ length.
6) $m\angle BCA > m\angle DCE$	6) **e.** ______
7) $AB > ED$	7) **f.** ______

Lesson Check

Do you know HOW?
If students have difficulty with Exercise 7, then have them review Problem 1 and list everything they know from the markings on the diagram.

Do you UNDERSTAND?
If students have difficulty with Exercise 10, then have them draw several triangles with two congruent sides and compare them.

Close

Q If each of two triangles has two congruent sides, how are their included angles related? **[The largest included angle is located in the triangle with the longest noncongruent side.]**

ANSWERS

7. $FD > BC$
8. $m\angle UST > m\angle VST$
9. Answers may vary. Sample: As a door opens, and the angle between the door and doorway increases, the distance between the doorjamb and the nonhinge vertical edge of the door increases.
10. The two angles that are formed by ≅ sides are $\angle ABD$ and $\angle CDB$. Since the side opposite $\angle ABD$ is longer than the side opposite $\angle CDB$, the correct conclusion is $m\angle ABD > m\angle CDB$.
11. Answers may vary. Sample: Both deal with a pair of triangles that have two pairs of ≅ corresponding sides along with a relationship between the angles formed by those sides.

▼ STUDENT PAGES 254–255

Lesson Check

Do you know HOW?

Write an inequality relating the given side lengths or angle measures.

7. FD and BC

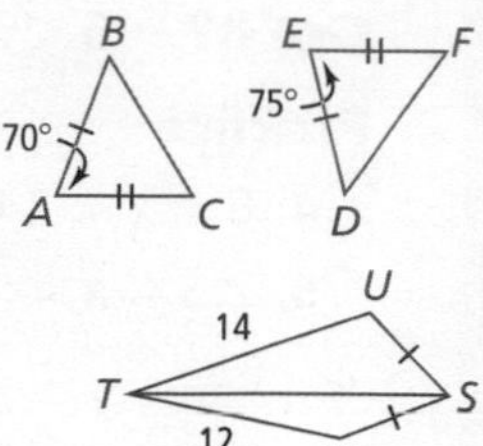

8. $m\angle UST$ and $m\angle VST$

Do you UNDERSTAND? MATHEMATICAL PRACTICES

9. **Vocabulary** Explain why *Hinge Theorem* is an appropriate name for Theorem 36.

10. **Error Analysis** From the figure at the right, your friend concludes that $m\angle BAD > m\angle BCD$. How would you correct your friend's mistake?

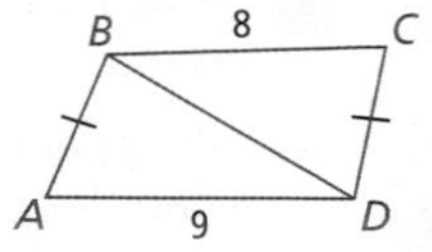

11. **Compare and Contrast** How are the Hinge Theorem and the SAS Congruence Postulate similar?

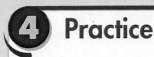

Practice

More Practice and Problem-Solving Exercises

ASSIGNMENT GUIDE

The assignments below are for the More Practice and Problem-Solving Exercises. You may also want to assign the A-Level Practice Exercises for homework if these are not used in class.

Average: 12–19

Advanced: 12–21

Mathematical Practices The exercises listed focus on the Standards for Mathematical Practices listed.

EX. 11, 17: Make Sense of Problems (MP 1)

EX. 15b, 16: Construct Arguments (MP 3)

EX. 10, 15a: Critique the Reasoning of Others (MP 3)

EXERCISE 16: Use the **Think About a Plan** worksheet in the Online Teacher Resources to further support students' development in becoming independent learners.

HOMEWORK QUICK CHECK

To check students' understanding of key skills and concepts, go over Exercises 13, 15, 16, 18, and 19.

ANSWERS

12. $PT < QR$; $QP = TR$, $QT = TQ$, and $m\angle PQT < m\angle RTQ$, so $PT < QR$ by the Hinge Thm.

13. $m\angle QTR > m\angle RTS$; $m\angle PTQ + m\angle QTR + m\angle RTS = 180$, so $m\angle PTQ + m\angle RTS = 88$. Thus $m\angle RTS < 88$ by the Comparison Prop. of Inequality, so $m\angle QTR > m\angle RTS$ by the Transitive Prop. of Inequality.

14. $PT > RS$; $QP = TR$, $QT = TS$, and $m\angle PQT > m\angle RTS$ (from Ex. 13), so $PT > RS$ by the Hinge Thm.

15. a. The two labeled angles are formed by ≅ corresp. sides of the two triangles, so the side opposite the 94°-∠ should be longer than the side opposite the 91°-∠, by the Hinge Thm. Thus the side labeled "13" must be longer than the side labeled "14."

b. Answers may vary. Sample: Switch the angle labels 91° and 94°.

16. The rt. isosc. triangle; two pairs of legs are ≅, and the hypotenuse of the rt. triangle is longer than the third side of the other triangle, by the Hinge Thm.

17. Ship A; the two triangles in the diagram have two pairs of ≅ corresp. sides. The included ∠ for Ship A measures $180 - 65 = 115$ and the included ∠ for Ship B measures $180 - 70 = 110$. Since $115 > 110$, the side opposite 115 is longer than the side opposite 110, by the Hinge Thm.

▼ STUDENT PAGES 255–256

More Practice and Problem-Solving Exercises

B Apply

Copy and complete with > or <. Explain your reasoning.

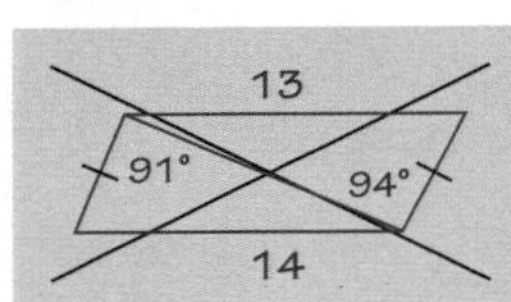

12. $PT \blacksquare QR$

13. $m\angle QTR \blacksquare m\angle RTS$

14. $PT \blacksquare RS$

15. a. Error Analysis Your classmate draws the figure at the right. Explain why the figure cannot have the labeled dimensions.

b. Open-Ended Describe a way you could change the dimensions to make the figure possible.

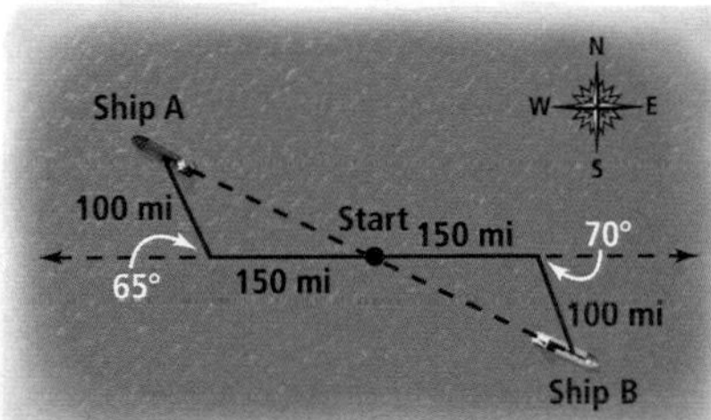

16. Reasoning The legs of a right isosceles triangle are congruent to the legs of an isosceles triangle with an 80° vertex angle. Which triangle has a greater perimeter? How do you know?

17. Think About a Plan Ship A and Ship B leave from the same point in the ocean. Ship A travels 150 mi due west, turns 65° toward north, and then travels another 100 mi. Ship B travels 150 mi due east, turns 70° toward south, and then travels another 100 mi. Which ship is farther from the starting point? Explain.

- How can you use the given angle measures?
- How does the Hinge Theorem help you to solve this problem?

More Practice and Problem-Solving Exercises *continued*

18. D

19. $\triangle ABE \cong \triangle CBD$ (Given) so $\triangle ABE$ and $\triangle CBD$ are isosc. with $AB = EB = DB = CB$. Since $m\angle EBD > m\angle ABE$ (Given), $ED > AE$ by the Hinge Thm.

20. In $\triangle AOB$ and $\triangle AOC$, $AO = AO = 7$, $OB = OC = \sqrt{5}$, $AB = \sqrt{82}$, and $AC = \sqrt{68}$. Since $AB > AC$, then $m\angle AOB > m\angle AOC$ by the Converse of the Hinge Thm.

21. Using the diagram in the Plan for Proof, $BC = YZ$, $BD = YX$, and $m\angle ZYX = m\angle CBD$, so $\triangle DBC \cong \triangle XYZ$ by SAS. $\angle FBA \cong \angle FBD$ (Def. of $\angle$ bisector), $\overline{BD} \cong \overline{BA}$ (because each is $\cong$ to $\overline{XY}$), and $\overline{BF} \cong \overline{BF}$, so $\triangle ABF \cong \triangle DBF$ by SAS. $\overline{AF} \cong \overline{DF}$, because corresp. parts of $\cong$ ⚠ are $\cong$. $AF + FC = AC$ (Segment Addition Post.), so $DF + FC = AC$. Using the $\triangle$ Inequality Thm. in $\triangle FDC$, $DF + FC > DC$. Now $AC > DC$ by substitution. Since $DC = XZ$ (Corresp. parts of $\cong$ ⚠ are $\cong$.), it follows that $AC > XZ$ by substitution.

▼ STUDENT PAGE 256

18. Which of the following lists the segment lengths in order from least to greatest?

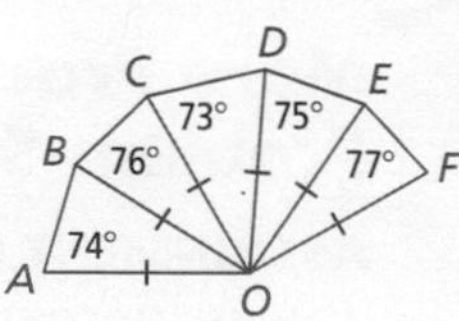

Ⓐ CD, AB, DE, BC, EF Ⓒ BC, DE, EF, AB, CD

Ⓑ EF, DE, AB, BC, CD Ⓓ EF, BC, DE, AB, CD

Proof 19. Use the figure at the right.

Given: $\triangle ABE$ is isosceles with vertex $\angle B$, $\triangle ABE \cong \triangle CBD$, $m\angle EBD > m\angle ABE$

Prove: $ED > AE$

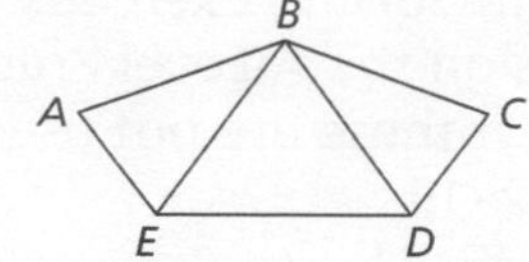

Challenge

20. Coordinate Geometry $\triangle ABC$ has vertices $A(0, 7)$, $B(-1, -2)$, $C(2, -1)$, and $O(0, 0)$. Show that $m\angle AOB > m\angle AOC$.

Proof 21. Use the plan below to complete a proof of the Hinge Theorem: If two sides of one triangle are congruent to two sides of another triangle and the included angles are not congruent, then the longer third side is opposite the larger included angle.

Given: $\overline{AB} \cong \overline{XY}$, $\overline{BC} \cong \overline{YZ}$, $m\angle B > m\angle Y$

Prove: $AC > XZ$

Plan for proof:

- Copy $\triangle ABC$. Locate point D outside $\triangle ABC$ so that $m\angle CBD = m\angle ZYX$ and $BD = YX$. Show that $\triangle DBC \cong \triangle XYZ$.
- Locate point F on $\overline{AC}$, so that $\overline{BF}$ bisects $\angle ABD$.
- Show that $\triangle ABF \cong \triangle DBF$ and that $\overline{AF} \cong \overline{DF}$.
- Show that $AC = FC + DF$.
- Use the Triangle Inequality Theorem to write an inequality that relates DC to the lengths of the other sides of $\triangle FCD$.
- Relate DC and XZ.

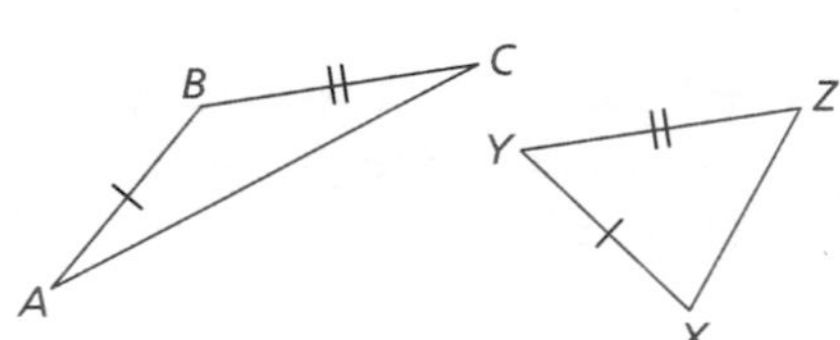

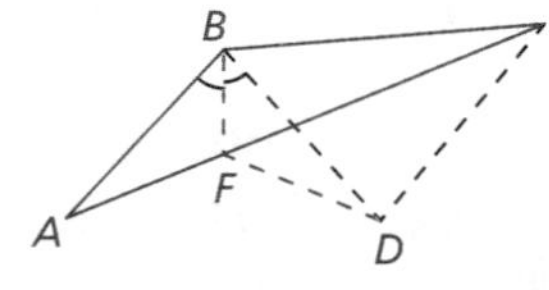

Assess and Remediate

Lesson Quiz

1. Which of the following statements must be true?

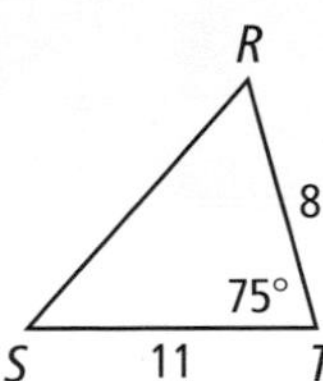

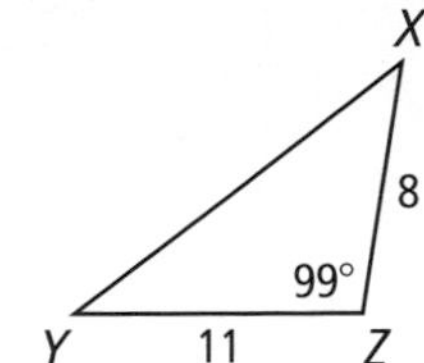

A. $XZ > ST$

B. $XY = RS$

C. $XY > RS$

D. $RS > XY$

2. Do you UNDERSTAND? What is the range of possible values for x?

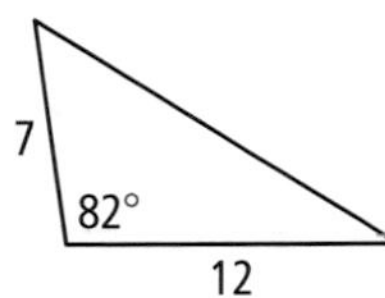

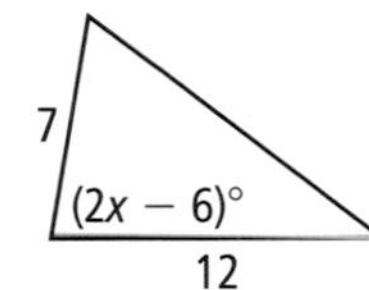

ANSWERS TO LESSON QUIZ

1. C

2. $3 < x < 44$

Prescription for Remediation

Use the student work on the Lesson Quiz to prescribe a differentiated assignment.

Points	Differentiated Remediation
0	Intervention
1	On-level
2	Extension

Online Assessment

Assign the Lesson Quiz in Success Tracker on **pearsonsuccessnet.com**. Success Tracker will automatically score the quiz and assign appropriate intervention or enrichment to each student based on the results. The compiled data appear in three different reports for instant analysis of whole class and individual student performance.

Differentiated Remediation

Intervention

- **RETEACHING** (2 pages) Provides reteaching and practice exercises for the key lesson concepts. Use with struggling students or absent students.
- **ENGLISH LANGUAGE LEARNER SUPPORT** Helps students develop and reinforce mathematical vocabulary and key concepts.

On-Level

- **PRACTICE** (2 pages) Provides extra practice for each lesson. For simpler practice exercises, use the Form K Practice pages found in the Online Teacher Resources.
- **THINK ABOUT A PLAN** Helps students develop specific problem-solving skills and strategies by providing scaffolded guiding questions.
- **STANDARDIZED TEST PREP** Focuses on all major exercises, all major question types, and helps students prepare for the high-stakes assessments.

Extension

- **ENRICHMENT** Provides students with interesting problems and activities that extend the concepts of the lesson.
- **ACTIVITIES, GAMES, AND PUZZLES** Worksheets that can be used for concept development, enrichment, and for fun!

Chapter Review

Essential Questions

BIG idea Coordinate Geometry

ESSENTIAL QUESTION How do you use coordinate geometry to find relationships within triangles?

ANSWER Use parallel and perpendicular lines, and the slope, midpoint, and distance formulas to find intersection points and unknown lengths.

BIG idea Measurement

ESSENTIAL QUESTION How do you solve problems that involve measurements of triangles?

ANSWER Use theorems about perpendicular bisectors, angle bisectors, medians, and altitudes to find points of concurrency, angle measures, and segment lengths.

BIG idea Reasoning and Proof

ESSENTIAL QUESTION How do you write indirect proofs?

ANSWER You can write an indirect proof by showing that a temporary assumption is false.

Summative Questions

Use the following prompts as you review this chapter with your students. The prompts are designed to help you assess your students' understanding of the Big Ideas they have studied.

- What is a midsegment of a triangle?
- What relationship does the midsegment make in a triangle?
- What are the concurrent lines in triangles?
- How do you write an indirect proof?
- What must be true about the length of the sides of a triangle?

4-1 Midsegments of Triangles

ANSWERS

1. 15
2. 11
3. $L\left(\frac{5}{2}, -\frac{1}{2}\right)$; $M\left(\frac{7}{2}, \frac{1}{2}\right)$; slope of $\overline{AB} = 1$ and slope of $\overline{LM} = 1$, so $\overline{LM} \parallel \overline{AB}$; $AB = 2\sqrt{2}$ and $LM = \sqrt{2}$, so $LM = \frac{1}{2}AB$.

▼ STUDENT PAGE 257

4-1 Midsegments of Triangles

Quick Review

A **midsegment of a triangle** is a segment that connects the midpoints of two sides. A midsegment is parallel to the third side and is half as long.

Example

Algebra Find the value of x.

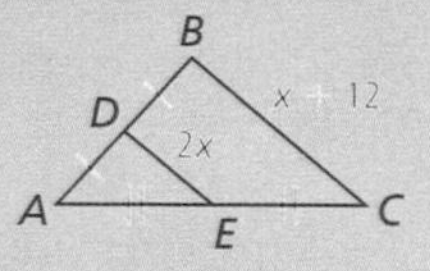

$\overline{DE}$ is a midsegment because D and E are midpoints.

$DE = \frac{1}{2}BC$	△ Midsegment Theorem
$2x = \frac{1}{2}(x + 12)$	Substitute.
$4x = x + 12$	Multiply each side by 2.
$3x = 12$	Subtract x from each side.
$x = 4$	Divide each side by 3.

Exercises

Algebra Find the value of x.

1.

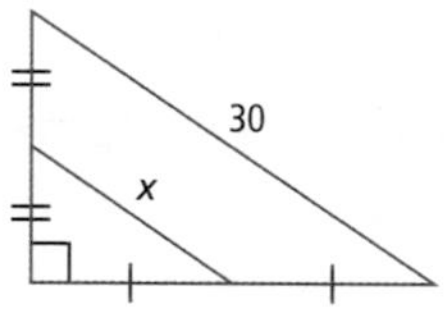

2.

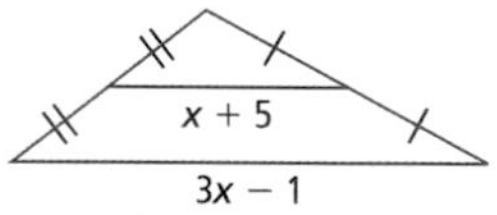

3. $\triangle ABC$ has vertices $A(0, 0)$, $B(2, 2)$, and $C(5, -1)$. Find the coordinates of L, the midpoint of $\overline{AC}$, and M, the midpoint of $\overline{BC}$. Verify that $\overline{LM} \parallel \overline{AB}$ and $LM = \frac{1}{2}AB$.

4-2 Perpendicular and Angle Bisectors

ANSWERS

4. Let point S be second base and point T be third base. Find the midpt. M of $\overline{ST}$ and then through M construct the line $\ell \perp$ to $\overline{ST}$. Points of the baseball field that are on line ℓ are equidistant from second and third base.

5. 40

6. 40

7. 6

8. 11

9. 33

10. 33

▼ STUDENT PAGE 257

4-2 Perpendicular and Angle Bisectors

Quick Review

The **Perpendicular Bisector Theorem** together with its converse states that P is equidistant from A and B if and only if P is on the perpendicular bisector of $\overline{AB}$.

The **distance from a point to a line** is the length of the perpendicular segment from the point to the line.

The **Angle Bisector Theorem** together with its converse states that P is equidistant from the sides of an angle if and only if P is on the angle bisector.

Example

In the figure, $QP = 4$ and $AB = 8$. Find QR and CB.

Q is on the bisector of $\angle ABC$, so $QR = QP = 4$. B is on the perpendicular bisector of $\overline{AC}$, so $CB = AB = 8$.

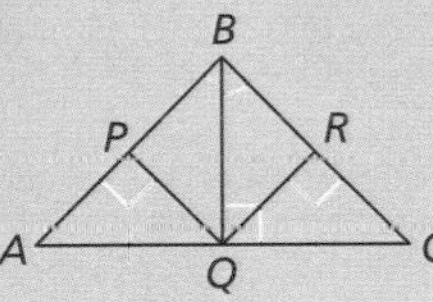

Exercises

4. Writing Describe how to find all the points on a baseball field that are equidistant from second base and third base.

In the figure, $m\angle DBE = 50$. Find each of the following.

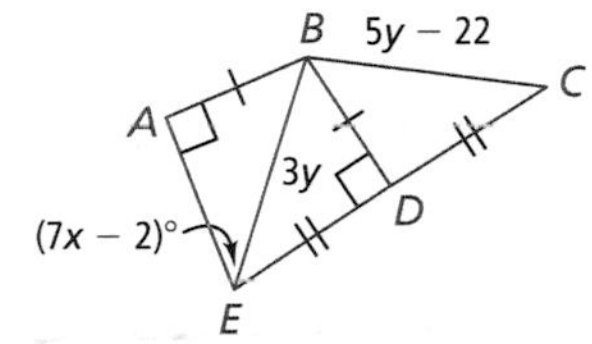

5. $m\angle BED$ **6.** $m\angle BEA$ **7.** x

8. y **9.** BE **10.** BC

4-3 Bisectors in Triangles

ANSWERS

11. (0, 0)

12. (3, 2)

13. (4, 4)

14. (5, 1)

15. 45

16. 40

17. 25

▼ STUDENT PAGE 258

4-3 Bisectors in Triangles

Quick Review

When three or more lines intersect in one point, they are **concurrent.**

- The point of concurrency of the perpendicular bisectors of a triangle is the **circumcenter of the triangle.**
- The point of concurrency of the angle bisectors of a triangle is the **incenter of the triangle.**

Example

Identify the incenter of the triangle.

The incenter of a triangle is the point of concurrency of the angle bisectors. $\overline{MR}$ and $\overline{LQ}$ are angle bisectors that intersect at Z. So, Z is the incenter.

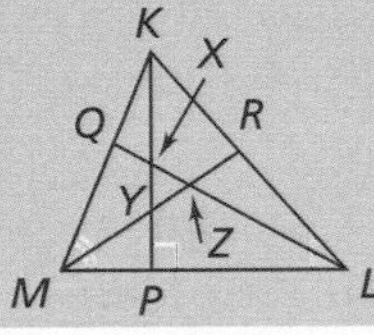

Exercises

Find the coordinates of the circumcenter of $\triangle DEF$.

11. $D(6, 0)$, $E(0, 6)$, $F(-6, 0)$

12. $D(0, 0)$, $E(6, 0)$, $F(0, 4)$

13. $D(5, -1)$, $E(-1, 3)$, $F(3, -1)$

14. $D(2, 3)$, $E(8, 3)$, $F(8, -1)$

P is the incenter of $\triangle XYZ$. Find the indicated angle measure.

15. $m\angle PXY$

16. $m\angle XYZ$

17. $m\angle PZX$

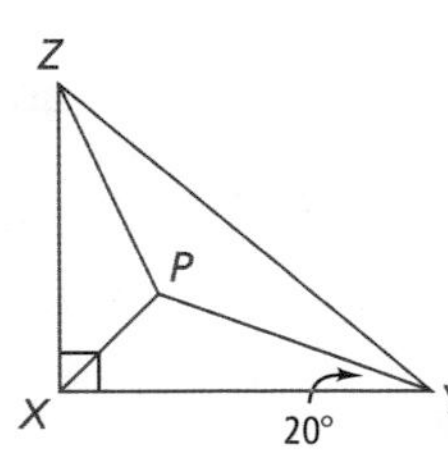

Chapter Review *(continued)*

4-4 Medians and Altitudes

ANSWERS

18. $\overline{AB}$ is an altitude; it is a segment from a vertex that is $\perp$ to the opposite side.

19. $\overline{AB}$ is a median; it is a segment from a vertex to the midpt. of the opposite side.

20. $QZ = 8$, $QM = 12$

21. $(0, -1)$

22. $(2, -3)$

▼ STUDENT PAGE 258

4-4 Medians and Altitudes

Quick Review

A **median of a triangle** is a segment from a vertex to the midpoint of the opposite side. An **altitude of a triangle** is a perpendicular segment from a vertex to the line containing the opposite side.

- The point of concurrency of the medians of a triangle is the **centroid of the triangle.** The centroid is two thirds the distance from each vertex to the midpoint of the opposite side.
- The point of concurrency of the altitudes of a triangle is the **orthocenter of the triangle.**

Example

If $PB = 6$, what is SB?

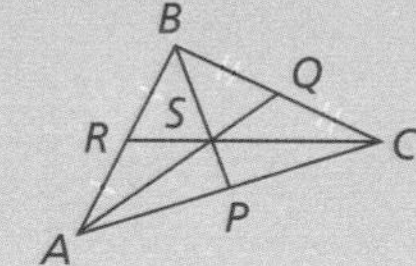

S is the centroid because $\overline{AQ}$ and $\overline{CR}$ are medians. So, $SB = \frac{2}{3}PB = \frac{2}{3}(6) = 4$.

Exercises

Determine whether $\overline{AB}$ is a *median*, an *altitude*, or *neither*. Explain.

18.

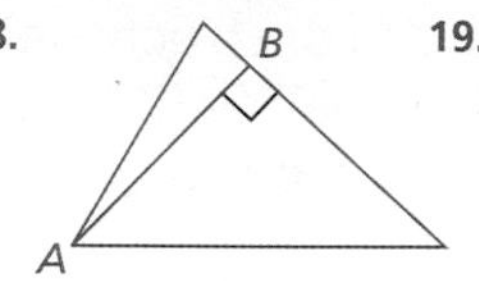

19.

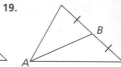

20. $\triangle PQR$ has medians $\overline{QM}$ and $\overline{PN}$ that intersect at Z. If $ZM = 4$, find QZ and QM.

$\triangle ABC$ has vertices $A(2, 3)$, $B(-4, -3)$, and $C(2, -3)$. Find the coordinates of each point of concurrency.

21. centroid

22. orthocenter

4-5 Indirect Proof

ANSWERS

23. Assume temporarily that neither of the two numbers is even. That means each number is odd, so the product of the two numbers must be odd. That contradicts the statement that the product of the two numbers is even. Thus the temporary assumption is false, and we can conclude that at least one of the numbers must be even.

24. Assume temporarily that the third line intersects neither of the first two. Then it is $\parallel$ to both of them. Since the first two lines are $\parallel$ to the same line, they are $\parallel$ to each other. This contradicts the given information. Therefore the temporary assumption is false, and the third line must intersect at least one of the two others.

25. Assume temporarily that there is a triangle with two obtuse angles. Then the sum of the measures of those two angles is greater than 180, which contradicts the Triangle Angle-Sum Thm. Therefore the temporary assumption is false, and a triangle can have at most one obtuse $\angle$.

▼ STUDENT PAGE 259

4-5 Indirect Proof

Quick Review

In an **indirect proof**, you first assume temporarily the opposite of what you want to prove. Then you show that this temporary assumption leads to a contradiction.

Example

Which two statements contradict each other?

I. The perimeter of $\triangle ABC$ is 14.
II. $\triangle ABC$ is isosceles.
III. The side lengths of $\triangle ABC$ are 3, 5, and 6.

An isosceles triangle can have a perimeter of 14.

The perimeter of a triangle with side lengths 3, 5, and 6 is 14.

An isosceles triangle must have two sides of equal length. Statements II and III contradict each other.

Exercises

Write a convincing argument that uses indirect reasoning.

23. The product of two numbers is even. Show that at least one of the numbers must be even.

24. Two lines in the same plane are not parallel. Show that a third line in the plane must intersect at least one of the two lines.

25. Show that a triangle can have at most one obtuse angle.

26. Show that an equilateral triangle cannot have an obtuse angle.

27. The sum of three integers is greater than 9. Show that one of the integers must be greater than 3.

26. Assume temporarily that an equilateral triangle has an obtuse ∠. Since all the angles are ≅ in an equilateral triangle, then all three angles must be obtuse. But we showed in Ex. 25 that a triangle can have at most one obtuse ∠. Therefore the temporary assumption is false, and an equilateral triangle cannot have an obtuse ∠.

27. Assume temporarily that each of the three integers is less than or equal to 3. Then the sum of the three integers must be less than or equal to 3 • 3, or 9. This contradicts the given statement that the sum of the three integers is greater than 9. Therefore the temporary assumption is false, and you can conclude that one of the integers must be greater than 3.

4-6 and 4-7 Inequalities in Triangles

ANSWERS

28. $\overline{RS}$, $\overline{ST}$, $\overline{RT}$

29. No; $5 + 8 \not> 15$.

30. Yes; $10 + 12 > 20$, $10 + 20 > 12$, and $12 + 20 > 10$.

31. $1 \text{ ft} < x < 25 \text{ ft}$

32. $<$

33. $>$

34. $<$

▼ STUDENT PAGE 259

4-6 and 4-7 Inequalities in Triangles

Quick Review

For any triangle,

- the measure of an exterior angle is greater than the measure of each of its remote interior angles
- if two sides are not congruent, then the larger angle lies opposite the longer side
- if two angles are not congruent, then the longer side lies opposite the larger angle
- the sum of any two side lengths is greater than the third

The **Hinge Theorem** states that if two sides of one triangle are congruent to two sides of another triangle, and the included angles are not congruent, then the longer third side is opposite the larger included angle.

Example

Which is greater, *BC* or *AD*?

$\overline{BA} \cong \overline{CD}$ and $\overline{BD} \cong \overline{DB}$, so $\triangle ABD$ and $\triangle CDB$ have two pairs of congruent corresponding sides. Since $60 > 45$, you know $BC > AD$ by the Hinge Theorem.

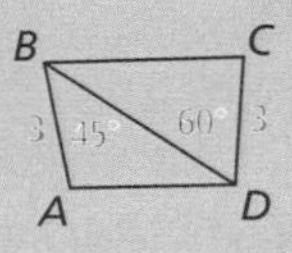

Exercises

28. In $\triangle RST$, $m\angle R = 70$ and $m\angle S = 80$. List the sides of $\triangle RST$ in order from shortest to longest.

Is it possible for a triangle to have sides with the given lengths? Explain.

29. 5 in., 8 in., 15 in.

30. 10 cm, 12 cm, 20 cm

31. The lengths of two sides of a triangle are 12 ft and 13 ft. Find the range of possible lengths for the third side.

Use the figure below. Complete each statement with >, <, or =.

32. $m\angle BAD$ ■ $m\angle ABD$

33. $m\angle CBD$ ■ $m\angle BCD$

34. $m\angle ABD$ ■ $m\angle CBD$

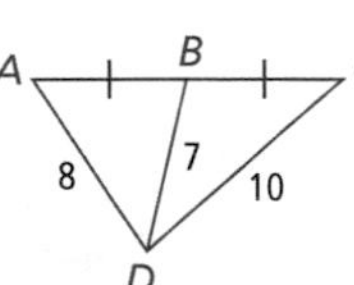

Pull It All Together

Common Core State Standard
Extends G.CO.10 Prove theorems about triangles.

Using Performance Tasks

Understanding by Design® principles support using performance tasks to assess students' progress toward mastering content standards and developing proficiency with the Mathematical Practices.

Mathematical Practices

- Make sense of problems and persevere in solving them.
- Model with mathematics.
- Construct viable arguments.

Assessing Performance

See the Implementation Guide for a holistic scoring rubric to use in assessing students' work on the performance task.

Guiding Questions

Q What is the Hinge Theorem?

Q Which of the three segments of the trail is not part of a triangle?

Q Could the length of the first segment of the trail from the lookout tower be 7 km?

Solution Outline

To help determine a range for each part of the trail, label the vertices shown and draw an additional line segment $\overline{BC}$. The total distance is equal to $AB + BD + DE$.

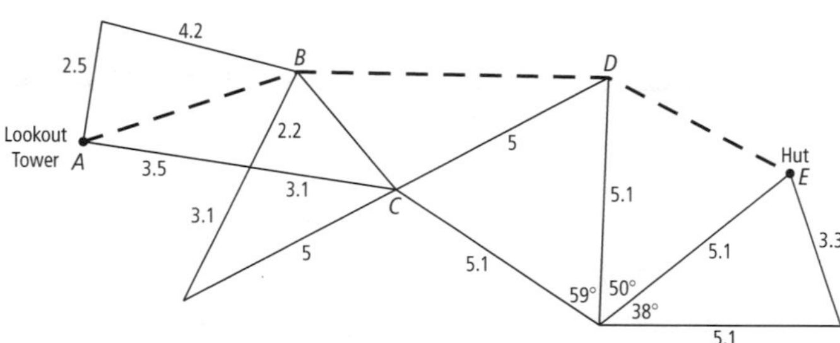

AB: *AB* is a side length of two different triangles. By the Triangle Inequality Theorem, *AB* is between 4.2 km − 2.5 km = 1.7 km and 2.5 km + 4.2 km = 6.7 km. Therefore 1.7 km < *AB* < 6.7 km. Similarly, *AB* is between 3.5 km − 2.2 km = 1.3 km and 3.5 km + 2.2 km = 5.7 km. So 1.3 km < *AB* < 5.7 km. These two inequalities can be written as the single inequality 1.7 km < *AB* < 5.7 km.

BD: First, determine the range for *BC*, which by the Triangle Inequality Theorem is 0.9 km < *BC* < 5.3 km. *CD* = 5 km, so applying the theorem again gives 4.1 km < *BD* < 5.9 km (using 0.9 km for *BC*) or 0.3 km < *BD* < 10.3 km (using 5.3 km for *BC*). Therefore 4.1 km < *BD* < 5.9 km covers all possibilities.

▼ STUDENT PAGE 260

Estimating the Length of a Hiking Trail

A group of hikers plan to hike from the campground lookout tower to the hut. To challenge the group, the leader gives them the diagram below. (All distances are given in kilometers.) The dashed line shows the trail they will take, but the distances along the trail are unknown.

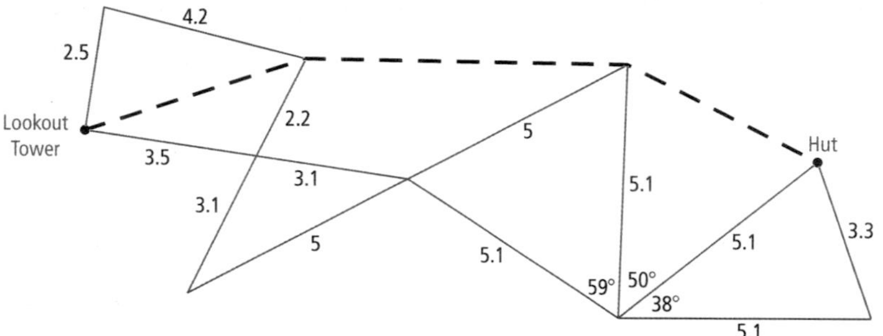

The group must determine the best lower bound and the best upper bound for the length of the trail. To do this, they are allowed to use the Triangle Inequality Theorem and the Hinge Theorem.

Task Description

Find a range in kilometers for the length of the trail.

- Do you need to draw any additional segments in the diagram to help you estimate the length of the trail?
- The trail from the lookout tower to the hut includes three segments. How can you find a range for each segment? How do these ranges lead you to determine the lower and upper bounds for the length of the trail?

DE: The map shows 3 isosceles triangles with leg lengths of 5.1 km. Applying the Hinge Theorem, *DE* < 5 km because 50° < 59°. Similarly, *DE* > 3.3 km because 50° > 38°. So 3.3 km < *DE* < 5 km.

The best lower bound for *AB* + *BD* + *DE* is 1.7 km + 4.1 km + 3.3 km = 9.1 km. The best upper bound is 5.7 km + 5.9 km + 5 km = 16.6 km.

Get Ready!

Using This Diagnostic Assessment

Assign this diagnostic assessment to determine if students have the prerequisite skills for Chapter 5.

Lesson	Skill
2-2	Properties of Parallel Lines
2-3	Proving Lines Parallel
Previous Course	Using Slope to Determine Parallel and Perpendicular Lines
3-2 and 3-3	Proving Triangles Congruent

To remediate students, select from these resources (available for every lesson).

- Online Problems (pearsonsuccessnet.com)
- Reteaching (Online Teacher Resources)
- Practice (Online Teacher Resources)

Why Students Need These Skills

PROPERTIES OF PARALLEL LINES Students will use properties of parallel lines to find missing angle measures in quadrilaterals.

PROVING LINES PARALLEL Students will use parallel lines to prove that a given quadrilateral is a specific type of parallelogram.

USING SLOPE TO DETERMINE PARALLEL AND PERPENDICULAR LINES Students will use slope in proofs involving coordinate geometry.

PROVING TRIANGLES CONGRUENT When a diagonal of a quadrilateral is drawn, two triangles are formed. Students will generate congruence statements to prove parts of the triangles congruent, which in turn will reveal information about the original quadrilateral.

Looking Ahead Vocabulary

EQUIANGULAR Ask students to give examples of other words that use the prefix *equi-*.

CONSECUTIVE Have students name consecutive numbers.

ANSWERS

1. 30
2. 42
3. 22
4. yes
5. no
6. yes
7. $\parallel$
8. $\perp$
9. neither
10. ASA
11. SAS
12. AAS
13. Answers may vary. Sample: polygon in which all the angles are $\cong$
14. Answers may vary. Sample: angles that follow one right after the other

▼ STUDENT PAGE 261

Properties of Parallel Lines

Algebra Use properties of parallel lines to find the value of x.

1. 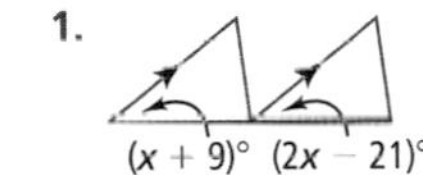

2. 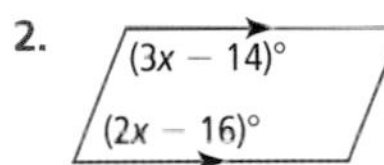

3. 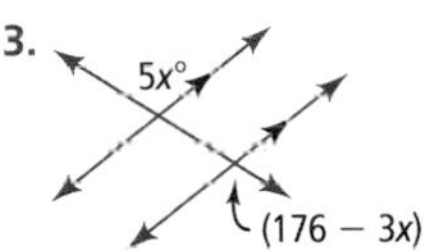

Proving Lines Parallel

Algebra Determine whether $\overline{AB}$ is parallel to $\overline{CD}$.

4. 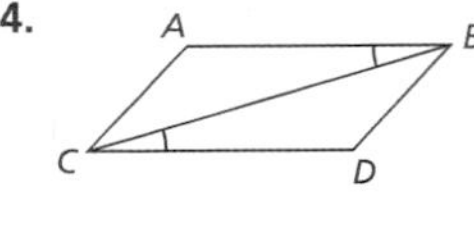

5. 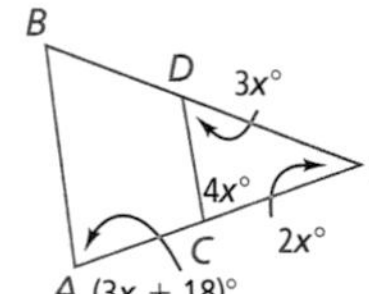

6. 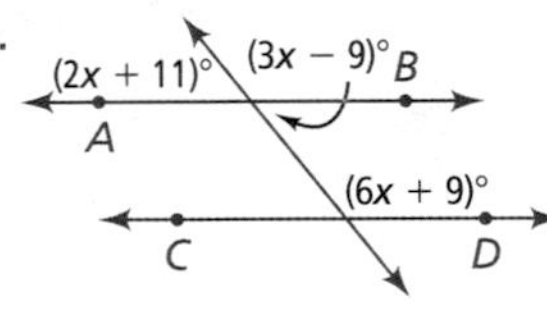

Using Slope to Determine Parallel and Perpendicular Lines

Algebra Determine whether each pair of lines is *parallel*, *perpendicular*, or *neither*.

7. $y = -2x;\ y = -2x + 4$
8. $y = -\frac{3}{5}x + 1;\ y = \frac{5}{3}x - 3$
9. $2x - 3y = 1;\ 3x - 2y = 8$

Proving Triangles Congruent

Determine the postulate or theorem that makes each pair of triangles congruent.

10. 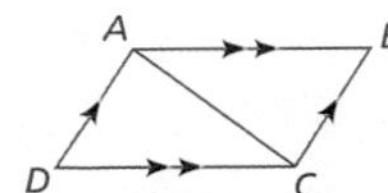

11. 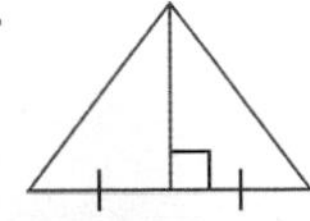

12. 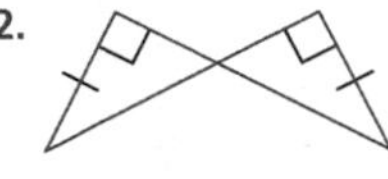

Looking Ahead Vocabulary

13. You know the meaning of *equilateral*. What do you think an *equiangular* polygon is?
14. When a team wins two *consecutive* gold medals, it means they have won two gold medals in a row. What do you think two *consecutive* angles in a quadrilateral means?

CHAPTER
5

PROVING THEOREMS ABOUT QUADRILATERALS

Chapter 5 Overview

Interactive Digital Path
Log in to pearsonsuccessnet.com and click on Interactive Digital Path to access the Solve Its and animated Problems.

In Chapter 5 students examine properties of quadrilaterals and use the properties to prove special types of quadrilaterals. In this chapter, students will develop the answers to the Essential Questions posed below as they learn the bulleted concepts and skills.

BIG idea Measurement

ESSENTIAL QUESTION How can you find the sum of the measures of polygon angles?

- The formula for angle measures of a polygon will be derived using diagonals.

BIG idea Reasoning and Proof

ESSENTIAL QUESTION How can you classify quadrilaterals?

- Students will use the properties of parallel and perpendicular lines and diagonals to classify quadrilaterals.
- Students will use coordinate geometry to classify special parallelograms.

BIG idea Coordinate Geometry

ESSENTIAL QUESTION How can you use coordinate geometry to prove general relationships?

- Students will examine slope and segment length in the coordinate plane.
- Students will use the Distance and Midpoint Formulas in the coordinate plane.

Chapter Preview

Dynamic Activity

Use the Dynamic Activity, an interactive math tool with guided instruction, to have students explore concepts visually and support the development of the Standards for Mathematical Practice.

Content Standards

Following are the key standards covered in this chapter.

Conceptual Category Geometry

DOMAIN Congruence G.CO
CLUSTER Prove geometric theorems (Standards G.CO.9, G.CO.10, G.CO.11) **LESSONS** 5-1, 5-2, 5-3, 5-4, 5-5, 5-6, 5-7, 5-8

DOMAIN Similarity, Right Triangles, and Trigonometry G.SRT
CLUSTER Prove theorems involving similarity (Standard G.SRT.5) **LESSONS** 5-1, 5-2, 5-3, 5-4, 5-5, 5-6

Vocabulary

English/Spanish Vocabulary Audio Online:

English	Spanish
coordinate proof, *p. 318**	prueba de coordenadas
equiangular polygon, *p. 264*	polígono equiángulo
equilateral polygon, *p. 264*	polígono equilátero
isosceles trapezoid, *p. 306*	trapecio isósceles
kite, *p. 310*	cometa
midsegment of a trapezoid, *p. 308*	segmento medio de un trapecio
parallelogram, *p. 270*	paralelogramo
rectangle, *p. 289*	rectángulo
regular polygon, *p. 264*	polígono regular
rhombus, *p. 289*	rombo
trapezoid, *p. 306*	trapecio

**All page numbers refer to the Student Edition.*

PROVING THEOREMS ABOUT QUADRILATERALS

Math Background

Understanding by Design® principles were central to the development of the Big Ideas and the Essential Understandings. These will help your students build a structure on which to make connections to prior learning.*

Measurement

BIG idea Some attributes of geometric figures, such as length, area, volume, and angle measure, are measurable. Units are used to describe these attributes.

ESSENTIAL UNDERSTANDINGS

5-1 The sum of the angle measures of a polygon depends on the number of sides the polygon has.

Reasoning and Proof

BIG idea Definitions establish meanings and remove possible misunderstandings. Other truths are more complex and difficult to see. It is often possible to verify complex truths by reasoning from simpler ones using deductive reasoning.

ESSENTIAL UNDERSTANDINGS

5-2 Parallelograms have special properties regarding their sides, angles, and diagonals.

5-3 If a quadrilateral's sides, angles, and diagonals have certain properties, it can be shown that the quadrilateral is a parallelogram.

5-4 to 5-5 The special parallelograms, rhombus, rectangle, and square, have basic properties of their sides, angles, and diagonals that help identify them.

5-6 The angles, sides, and diagonals of a trapezoid have certain properties.

5-7 to 5-8 Variables can be used to name the coordinates of a figure in the coordinate plane. This allows relationships to be shown to be true for a general case.

Coordinate Geometry

BIG idea A coordinate system in a plane is formed by two perpendicular lines, called the *x*- and *y*-axes. It is possible to verify some complex truths using deductive reasoning in combination with the Distance, Midpoint, and Slope formulas.

ESSENTIAL UNDERSTANDINGS

5-7 to 5-8 The formulas for slope, distance and midpoint can be used to classify and to prove geometric relationships for figures in the coordinate plane. Using variables to name the coordinates of a figure allows relationships to be shown to be true for a general case.

*UNDERSTANDING BY DESIGN® and UbD™ are trademarks of ASCD, and are used under license.

Properties of Parallelograms

If you know that this quadrilateral is a parallelogram, then you can use properties of parallelograms to find the missing measurements.

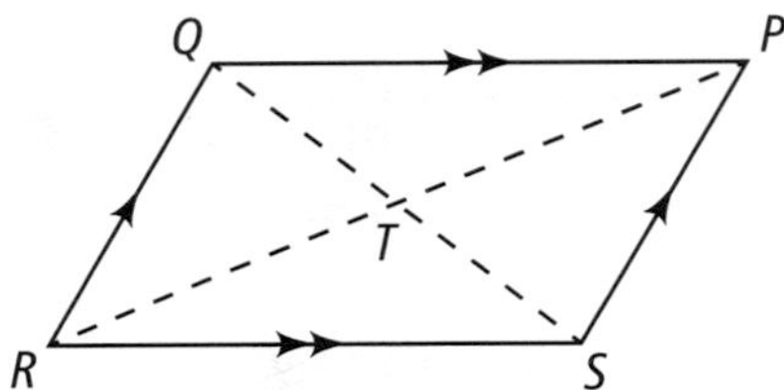

Property: Opposite sides are congruent.

$\overline{QR} \cong \overline{PS}$ and $\overline{SR} \cong \overline{PQ}$

Property: Consecutive angles are supplementary.

$m\angle P + m\angle Q = 180^\circ$, $m\angle Q + m\angle R = 180^\circ$,
$m\angle R + m\angle S = 180^\circ$, $m\angle S + m\angle P = 180^\circ$

Property: Opposite angles are congruent.

$\angle P \cong \angle R$ and $\angle Q \cong \angle S$

Property: Diagonals bisect each other.

$\overline{QT} \cong \overline{TS}$ and $\overline{RT} \cong \overline{TP}$

Common Errors With Properties of Parallelograms

If it is known that two sides of a quadrilateral are parallel, but it is not known if they are congruent, then it cannot be determined from that information alone whether the quadrilateral is a parallelogram.

For example, if it is given that $\overline{PQ} \parallel \overline{SR}$, but it is not known if $\overline{PQ} \cong \overline{SR}$, it would be incorrect to assume that the quadrilateral is a parallelogram.

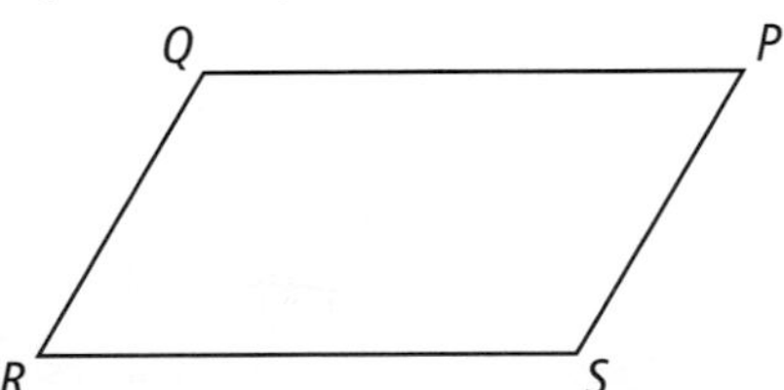

Mathematical Practices

Look for and make use of structure. In learning about properties of parallelograms students are constructing new results by building on their understanding of congruent triangles and parallel lines and transversals. They further develop conclusions by proving the converses of these theorems, again reasoning from previous theorems and postulates.

Math Background *(continued)*

Special Parallelograms

There are three special parallelograms: rhombus, rectangle, and square. One way to classify rhombuses, rectangles, and squares is by their diagonals.

Rhombus

A rhombus is a parallelogram with all four sides congruent. The diagonals of a rhombus are perpendicular.

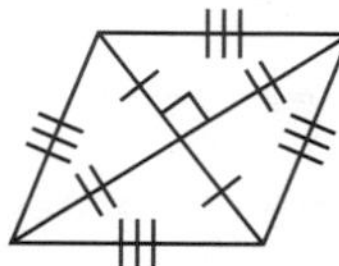

Rectangle

A rectangle is a parallelogram whose angles are right angles. The diagonals are congruent.

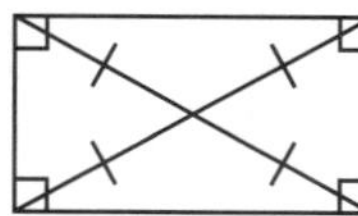

Square

A square is a parallelogram with all four sides congruent and its angles are right angles.

The diagonals are perpendicular and congruent.

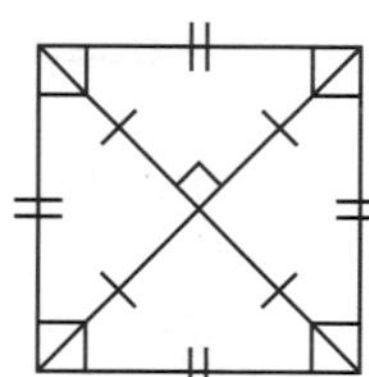

Common Errors With Special Parallelograms

Students may get confused about all the properties of special parallelograms. One way to help them see the relationship between the figures is with a Venn diagram.

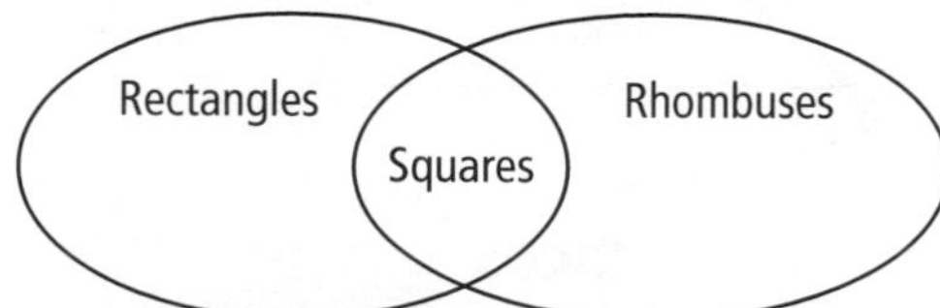

Mathematical Practices

Attend to precision. Students learn precise definitions for special parallelograms and again apply previously developed ideas to proving theorems about their properties as well as the converses of those theorems.

Coordinate Geometry

A coordinate plane can be used to classify quadrilaterals. Students can verify properties of special quadrilaterals using the Midpoint, Slope, and Distance Formulas in the coordinate plane.

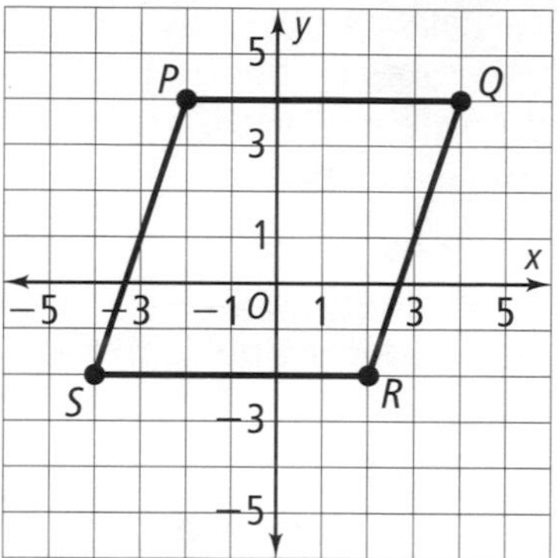

Figure *PQRS* appears to be a parallelogram. If one pair of opposite sides is parallel and congruent, then the quadrilateral is a parallelogram.

Find and compare the slopes of $\overline{SP}$ and $\overline{RQ}$.

$\overline{SP}: m = \frac{4-(-2)}{-2-(-4)} = \frac{6}{2} = 3$

$\overline{RQ}: m = \frac{4-(-2)}{4-2} = \frac{6}{2} = 3$

Their slopes are equal so they are parallel.

Find and compare the lengths of $\overline{SP}$ and $\overline{RQ}$.

$\overline{SP}: d = \sqrt{(-2-(-4))^2 + (4-(-2))^2} = \sqrt{40}$

$\overline{RQ}: d = \sqrt{(4-2)^2 + (4-(-2))^2} = \sqrt{40}$

Their lengths are equal so they are congruent. Figure *PQRS* is a parallelogram.

Common Errors With Coordinate Geometry

Figure *PQRS* is a parallelogram. Students might make the mistake of classifying it as a rhombus, either because its shape is close to that of a rhombus or because it has been shown that one pair of sides is parallel and congruent. However, proving one pair of sides is congruent and parallel is not sufficient to classify the figure as a rhombus. To do that, all four sides need to be proved congruent.

Mathematical Practices

Construct viable arguments and critique the reasoning of others. In coordinate geometry students move from the quantitative to the abstract. They look at numerical examples from which they inductively reason results. Then they structure diagrams with variables and ultimately use the tool of coordinate geometry to prove results, some of which they have already confirmed deductively. This allows students to view ideas from both algebraic and geometric perspectives.

5-1 The Polygon Angle-Sum Theorems

Common Core State Standards
G.CO.9 Prove theorems about lines and angles . . . **Also G.SRT.5**

Preparing to Teach

BIG idea Measurement

ESSENTIAL UNDERSTANDING

The sum of the angle measures of a polygon depends on the number of sides the polygon has.

Math Background

The hierarchy of quadrilaterals can help students who are troubled by questions such as "Is a square always a rectangle?" or "Is a rectangle always a square?" Students may gain insight by making a Venn diagram. Practice in learning definitions and theorems will help students classify quadrilaterals.

The Polygon Angle-Sum Theorems are extensions of the Triangle Angle-Sum Theorems. These theorems can be developed through inductive reasoning by examining examples or proved using deductive reasoning. The rest of this chapter will focus on polygons with four sides, or quadrilaterals. Quadrilaterals have the property that the sum of the interior angles as well as the sum of the exterior angles is 360.

ELL Support

ASSESS UNDERSTANDING Draw a triangle on the board. Trace the interior angles of the triangle and ask: How many interior angles are in a triangle? What is the sum of the measures of those angle measures? How do you know? Then draw a rectangle on the board. Ask: How many interior angles are in a rectangle? What is the sum of those angle measures? Draw a diagonal and trace it with your finger. Ask: What do you notice about the rectangle with a diagonal?

USE MANIPULATIVES Arrange students in mixed pairs. Have them draw polygons with 5, 6, 7, 8, 9, and 10 sides. Model how to draw a diagonal from one vertex to each of the other vertices. Ask them to do the same. Tell them to discuss their results and make a conjecture about the sum of the angle measures in a polygon.

Lesson Vocabulary

- equilateral polygon
- equiangular polygon
- regular polygon

Mathematical Practices

CONSTRUCT VIABLE ARGUMENTS AND CRITIQUE THE REASONING OF OTHERS. By drawing diagonals from the vertices of polygons of *n* sides, students will justify the Polygon Angle-Sum Theorem.

1 Interactive Learning

Solve It!

PURPOSE To familiarize students with the process of dividing the interior of any polygon into nonoverlapping triangles

PROCESS Students may use inductive reasoning to make conjectures after drawing the diagonals to collect data.

Q What is a diagonal of a polygon? **[a segment that connects two nonconsecutive vertices]**

Q What is a convex pentagon? **[a five-sided figure that has no diagonal with points outside the polygon]**

ANSWER Answers may vary. Sample:

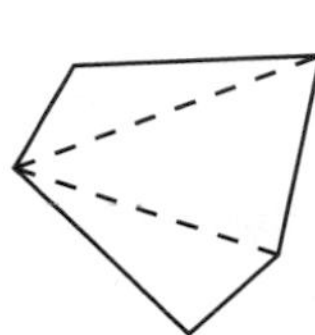
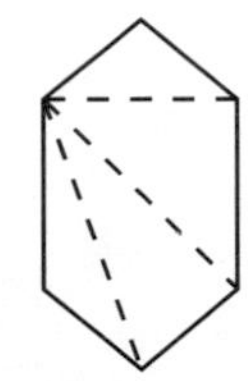
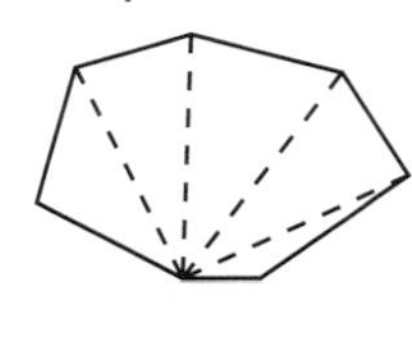

The number of triangles formed by the diagonals is 2 less than the number of sides of the polygon.

▼ DIGITAL (STUDENT WORK SPACE PAGE 263)

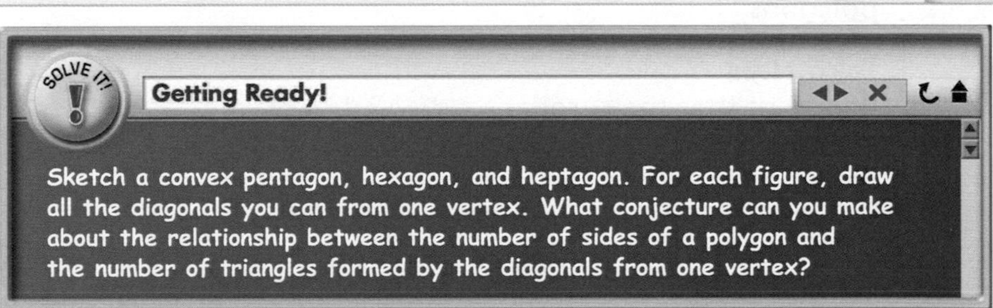

SOLVE IT!
Getting Ready!
Sketch a convex pentagon, hexagon, and heptagon. For each figure, draw all the diagonals you can from one vertex. What conjecture can you make about the relationship between the number of sides of a polygon and the number of triangles formed by the diagonals from one vertex?

CONNECT THE MATH In the Solve It students investigate the number of triangles contained in convex polygons. In the lesson, students use this relationship to understand the Polygon Angle-Sum Theorem.

2 Guided Instruction

Problem 1 Finding a Polygon Angle Sum

Q How many nonoverlapping triangles can a nonagon be divided into? Explain. **[7, because the number of triangles is always 2 less than the number of sides.]**

Got It?
Students may attempt to use trial and error to answer part (b). Help students to write the equation $1980 = (n-2)180$.

ANSWERS

Got It? a. 2700 **b.** Answers may vary. Sample: Divide 1980 by 180, and then add 2.

Practice

1. 5940 **2.** 3240

▼ STUDENT PAGE 263

The Solve It is related to a formula for the sum of the interior angle measures of a polygon. (In this textbook, a polygon is convex unless otherwise stated.)

Essential Understanding The sum of the interior angle measures of a polygon depends on the number of sides the polygon has.

By dividing a polygon with n sides into $(n - 2)$ triangles, you can show that the sum of the interior angle measures of any polygon is a multiple of 180.

take note

Theorem 38 Polygon Angle-Sum Theorem

The sum of the measures of the interior angles of an n-gon is $(n - 2)180$.

▼ DIGITAL

Problem 1 Finding a Polygon Angle Sum

What is the sum of the interior angle measures of a heptagon?

Sum	$= (n - 2)180$	Polygon Angle-Sum Theorem
	$= (7 - 2)180$	Substitute 7 for n.
	$= 5 \cdot 180$	Simplify.
	$= 900$	

The sum of the interior angle measures of a heptagon is 900.

▼ STUDENT PAGES 263–264

Got It? a. What is the sum of the interior angle measures of a 17-gon?

b. Reasoning The sum of the interior angle measures of a polygon is 1980. How can you find the number of sides in the polygon?

Practice Find the sum of the interior angle measures of each polygon.

1. 35-gon **2.** 20-gon

Problem 2 Using the Polygon Angle-Sum Theorem

Ask students to create a Venn diagram to show the relationships among polygons, equilateral polygons, equiangular polygons, and regular polygons.

Take Note
Point out that the corollary is derived by starting with the formula given in the theorem, and dividing the sum of the measures by the number of sides (which is the same as the number of angles).

▼ STUDENT PAGE 264

An **equilateral polygon** is a polygon with all sides congruent.

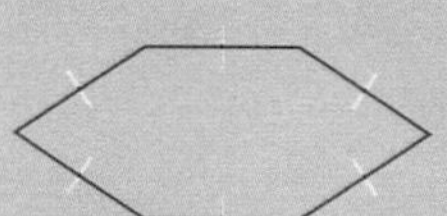

An **equiangular polygon** is a polygon with all angles congruent.

A **regular polygon** is a polygon that is both equilateral and equiangular.

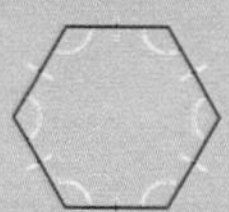

take note

Corollary to the Polygon Angle-Sum Theorem

The measure of each interior angle of a regular n-gon is $\frac{(n-2)180}{n}$.

You will prove the Corollary to the Polygon Angle-Sum Theorem in Exercise 36.

Problem 2

Q Is the sum of the measures of the interior angles of a hexagon different from the sum of the measures of the interior angles of a regular hexagon? Explain. **[No, the sum of the measures of the interior angles of any hexagon is the same.]**

Q How many interior angles does a hexagon have? **[six]**

Q Could you solve this problem if you were told that the hexagons are NOT regular? Explain. **[No, you must know that all angles are congruent to be able to divide by 6 to determine the measure of each individual angle.]**

Got It?

Q What is the sum of the measures of the interior angles of a regular nonagon? Explain. **[The sum is 1260 because (9 – 2)180 = 1260.]**

ANSWERS

Got It? 140

Practice

3. 150 **4.** 108

▼ DIGITAL

Problem 2 Using the Polygon Angle-Sum Theorem STEM

Biology The common housefly, *Musca domestica*, has eyes that consist of approximately 4000 facets. Each facet is a regular hexagon. What is the measure of each interior angle in one hexagonal facet?

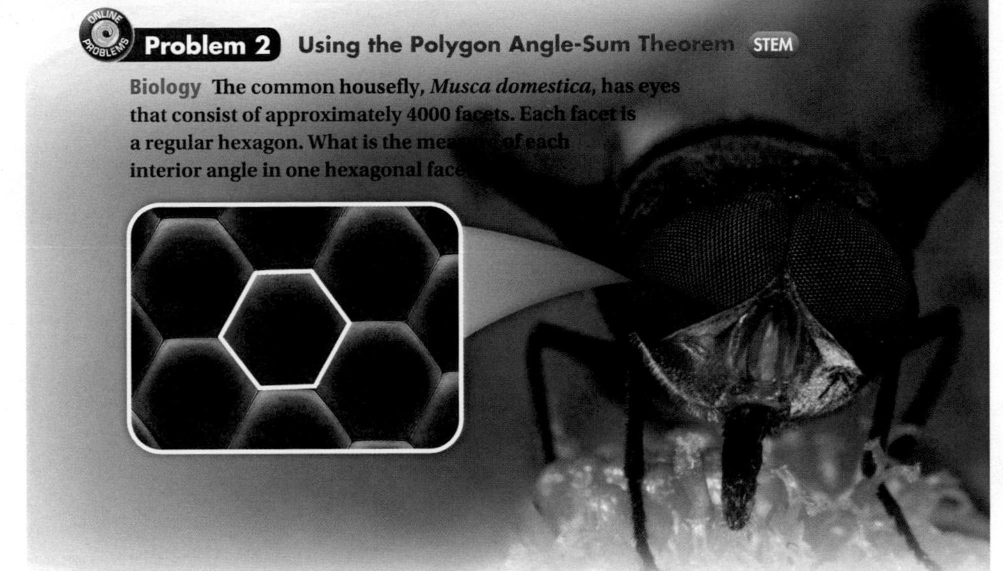

Measure of an angle	$= \frac{(n-2)180}{n}$	Corollary to the Polygon Angle-Sum Theorem
	$= \frac{(6-2)180}{6}$	Substitute 6 for n.
	$= \frac{4 \cdot 180}{6}$	Simplify.
	$= 120$	

The measure of each interior angle in one hexagonal facet is 120.

▼ STUDENT PAGES 264–265

Got It? What is the measure of each interior angle in a regular nonagon?

Think
How does the word *regular* help you answer the question?

A Practice Find the measure of one interior angle in each regular polygon.

3. 

4. 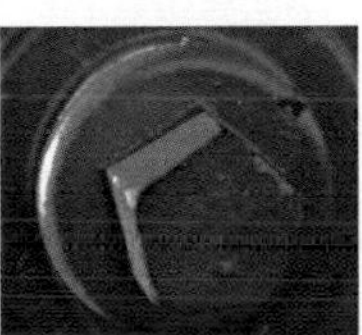

Problem 3 Using the Polygon Angle-Sum Theorem

Q What is the sum of the labeled angles in the pentagon *TODAY*? **[The sum of the measures is 470.]**

Q What is the sum of the measures of all five of the interior angles of a pentagon? **[540°]**

Q How can you determine the measure of the unlabeled angle? **[You can subtract 470 from 540.]**

▼ DIGITAL

Problem 3 Using the Polygon Angle-Sum Theorem

What is $m\angle Y$ in pentagon *TODAY*?

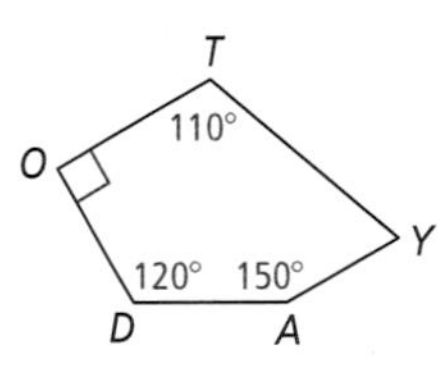

Use the Polygon Angle-Sum Theorem for $n = 5$.

$m\angle T + m\angle O + m\angle D + m\angle A + m\angle Y = (5-2)180$

$110 + 90 + 120 + 150 + m\angle Y = 3 \cdot 180$	Substitute.
$470 + m\angle Y = 540$	Simplify.
$m\angle Y = 70$	Subtract 470 from each side.

Problem 3 *continued*

Got It?

Remind students that the sum of the measures of the angles of any quadrilateral is the same. Ask them the sum of the angle measures in a square.

ANSWERS

Got It? 102

Practice

5. 60, 120, 120, 60 **6.** 145

▼ STUDENT PAGE 265

Got It? What is $m\angle G$ in quadrilateral *EFGH*?

Think What is the sum of the measures of the angles of a quadrilateral?

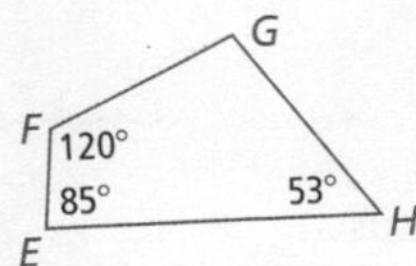

Practice **Algebra** In Exercises 5 and 6, find the missing angle measures.

5.

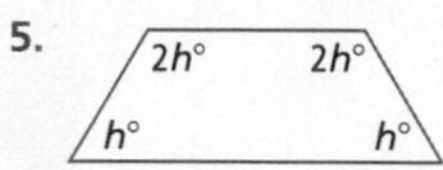

6.

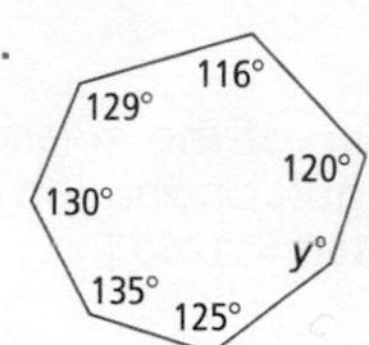

Problem 4 Finding an Exterior Angle Measure

Take Note

Students may be confused with the phrase "one at each vertex." Draw a polygon on the board and remind students that at each vertex there are two ways to draw an exterior angle.

Problem 4

Students may wish to solve this problem using the following alternate method: First, determine that the measure of each interior angle is 135 using the Polygon Angle-Sum Theorem. Second, determine the measure of $\angle 1$ by considering that it is supplementary to an angle that measures 135.

Got It?

Q What is the sum of the exterior angle measures for a regular nonagon? **[360]**

ANSWERS

Got It? 40

Practice

7. 10 **8.** 3.6

▼ STUDENT PAGE 266

You can draw exterior angles at any vertex of a polygon. The figures below show that the sum of the measures of the exterior angles, one at each vertex, is 360.

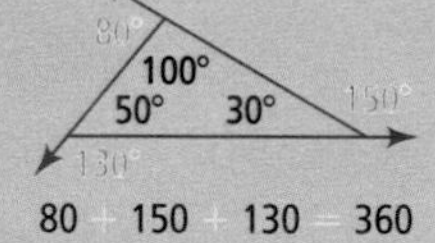

80 + 150 + 130 = 360

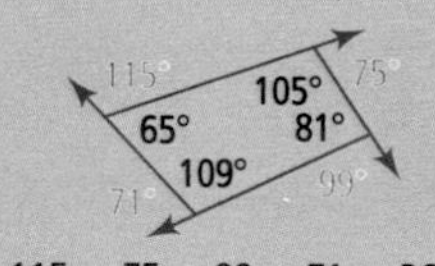

115 + 75 + 99 + 71 = 360

take note

Theorem 39 Polygon Exterior Angle-Sum Theorem

The sum of the measures of the exterior angles of a polygon, one at each vertex, is 360.

For the pentagon, $m\angle 1 + m\angle 2 + m\angle 3 + m\angle 4 + m\angle 5 = 360$.

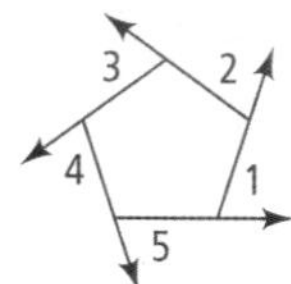

You will prove Theorem 39 in Exercise 32.

▼ DIGITAL

Problem 4 **Finding an Exterior Angle Measure**

What is $m\angle 1$ in the regular octagon at the right?

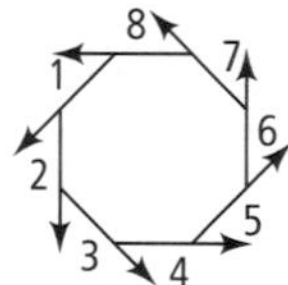

By the Polygon Exterior Angle-Sum Theorem, the sum of the exterior angle measures is 360. Since the octagon is regular, the interior angles are congruent. So their supplements, the exterior angles, are also congruent.

$m\angle 1 = \frac{360}{8}$ Divide 360 by 8, the number of sides in an octagon.

$= 45$ Simplify.

▼ STUDENT PAGE 266

Got It? What is the measure of an exterior angle of a regular nonagon?

Practice **Find the measure of an exterior angle of each regular polygon.**

7. 36-gon **8.** 100-gon

Lesson Check

Do you know HOW?
If students have difficulty with Exercise 9, then remind them how to use the Polygon Angle-Sum Theorem.

Do you UNDERSTAND?
If students have difficulty with Exercise 12, then provide them with the familiar examples of a square and a rectangle.

Close

Q For what n-gon is the sum of the measures of the interior angles equal to the sum of the measures of the exterior angles? Explain. **[The sum of the exterior angles is always 360, so find an n-gon such that $(n - 2)180 = 360$. Solving this equation gives $n = 4$. A quadrilateral has the same sum for the measures of the interior angles and the measures of the exterior angles.]**

ANSWERS

9. 1620 **10.** 360

11. 144, 36

12. Yes; explanations may vary. Sample: rectangle that is not square

▼ STUDENT PAGES 267–268

Lesson Check

Do you know HOW?

9. What is the sum of the interior angle measures of an 11-gon?

10. What is the sum of the measures of the exterior angles of a 15-gon?

11. Find the measures of an interior angle and an exterior angle of a regular decagon.

Do you UNDERSTAND?

12. Vocabulary Can you draw an equiangular polygon that is not equilateral? Explain.

13. Reasoning Which angles are the exterior angles for ∠1? What do you know about their measures? Explain.

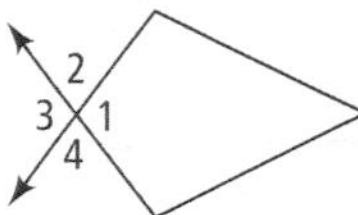

14. Error Analysis Your friend says that she measured an interior angle of a regular polygon as 130. Explain why this result is impossible.

13. ∠2 and ∠4; their measures are equal; answers may vary. Sample: Two angles suppl. to the same ∠ must be ≅.

14. Answers may vary. Sample: ext. ∠ would measure 50, which is not a factor of 360.

Practice

More Practice and Problem-Solving Exercises

ASSIGNMENT GUIDE
The assignments below are for the More Practice and Problem-Solving Exercises. You may also want to assign the A-Level Practice Exercises for homework if these are not used in class.
Average: 15–34
Advanced: 15–37

Mathematical Practices The exercises listed focus on the Standards for Mathematical Practices listed.

EX. 21: Make Sense of Problems (MP 1)
EX. 19: Persevere in Solving Problems (MP 1)
EX. 13, 31: Construct Arguments (MP 3)
EX. 14, 33: Critique the Reasoning of Others (MP 3)
EX. 20, 30: Model (MP 4)

EXERCISE 33: Use the **Think About a Plan** worksheet in the Online Teacher Resources to further support students' development in becoming independent learners.

HOMEWORK QUICK CHECK
To check students' understanding of key skills and concepts, go over Exercises 19, 21, 25, 30, and 33.

▼ STUDENT PAGE 268

More Practice and Problem-Solving Exercises

B Apply

The sum of the interior angle measures of a polygon with n sides is given. Find n.

15. 180 **16.** 1080 **17.** 1980 **18.** 2880

19. Open-Ended Sketch an equilateral polygon that is not equiangular.

20. Stage Design A theater-in-the-round allows for a play to have an audience on all sides. The diagram at the right shows a platform constructed for a theater-in-the-round stage. What type of regular polygon is the largest platform? Find the measure of each numbered angle.

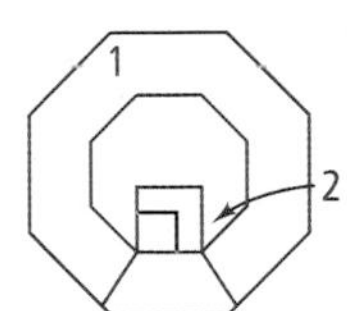

ANSWERS

15. 3 **16.** 8

17. 13 **18.** 18

19. Answers may vary. Sample:

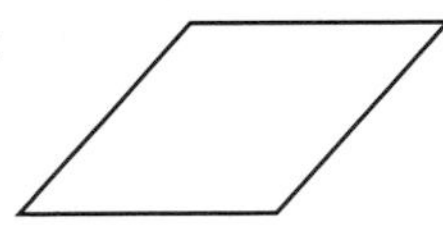

20. octagon; $m\angle 1 = 135$, $m\angle 2 = 45$

More Practice and Problem-Solving Exercises *continued*

21. 20, 80, 80; 80, 50, 50
22. $y = 103$, $z = 70$
23. $w = 72$, $x = 59$, $y = 49$, $z = 121$
24. 36
25. 108; 5
26. 144; 10
27. 162; 20
28. 150; 12
29. $180 - x$; $\frac{360}{x}$
30. 45, 45, 90
31. 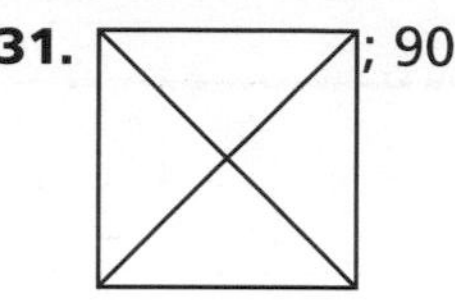 ; 90

32. a. $180n$
b. $(n-2) \cdot 180$
c. $180n - [(n-2) \cdot 180] = 360$
d. Polygon Ext. Angle-Sum Theorem

33. Yes; answers may vary. Sample: Sum of interior angle measures = sum of int. angle measures of triangles − sum of angle measures with a vertex at the interior point = $n \cdot 180 - 360 = (n-2)180$.
34. octagon
35. 0.8
36. a. Answers may vary. Sample: The sum of the interior ∠ measures = $(n-2)180$. All angles of a regular n-gon are ≅. So each interior ∠ measures = $\frac{180(n-2)}{n}$, and $\frac{180(n-2)}{n} = \frac{180n - 360}{n} = 180 - \frac{360}{n}$.
b. As n gets larger, $\frac{360}{n}$ gets smaller. The interior angle measure gets closer to 180. The polygon becomes more like a circle.
37. 36

21. Think About a Plan A triangle has two congruent interior angles and an exterior angle that measures 100. Find two possible sets of interior angle measures for the triangle.
- How can a diagram help you?
- What is the sum of the angle measures in a triangle?

Algebra Find the value of each variable.

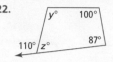

22. **23.** **24.**

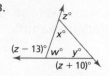

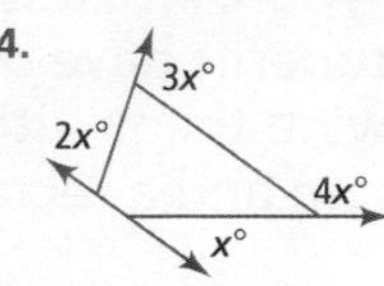

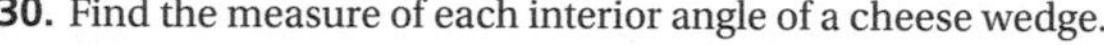

The measure of an exterior angle of a regular polygon is given. Find the measure of an interior angle. Then find the number of sides.

25. 72 **26.** 36 **27.** 18 **28.** 30 **29.** x

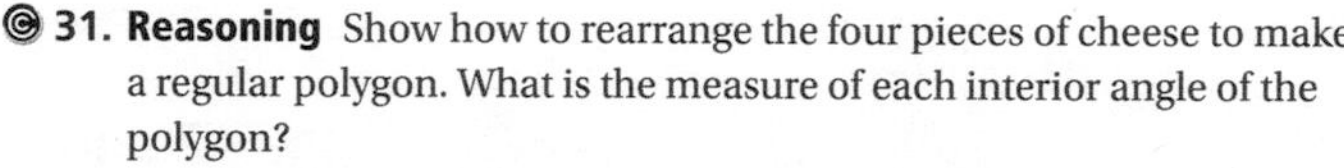

Packaging **The gift package at the right contains fruit and cheese. The fruit is in a container that has the shape of a regular octagon. The fruit container fits in a square box. A triangular cheese wedge fills each corner of the box.**

30. Find the measure of each interior angle of a cheese wedge.

31. Reasoning Show how to rearrange the four pieces of cheese to make a regular polygon. What is the measure of each interior angle of the polygon?

32. Algebra A polygon has n sides. An interior angle of the polygon and an adjacent exterior angle form a straight angle.
a. What is the sum of the measures of the n straight angles?
b. What is the sum of the measures of the n interior angles?
c. Using your answers above, what is the sum of the measures of the n exterior angles?
d. What theorem do the steps above prove?

33. Reasoning Your friend says she has another way to find the sum of the interior angle measures of a polygon. She picks a point inside the polygon, draws a segment to each vertex, and counts the number of triangles. She multiplies the total by 180, and then subtracts 360 from the product. Does her method work? Explain.

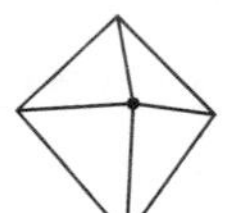
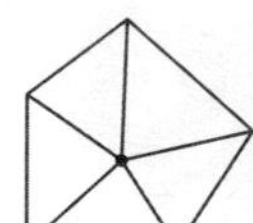

34. Algebra The measure of an interior angle of a regular polygon is three times the measure of an exterior angle of the same polygon. What is the name of the polygon?

Challenge

35. Probability Find the probability that the measure of an interior angle of a regular n-gon is a positive integer when n is an integer and $3 \le n \le 12$.

36. a. In the Corollary to the Polygon Angle-Sum Theorem, explain why the measure of an interior angle of a regular n-gon is given by the formulas $\frac{180(n-2)}{n}$ and $180 - \frac{360}{n}$.
b. Use the second formula to explain what happens to the measures of the interior angles of regular n-gons as n becomes a large number. Explain also what happens to the polygons.

37. *ABCDEFGHJK* is a regular decagon. A ray bisects ∠*C*, and another ray bisects ∠*D*. The two rays intersect in the decagon's interior. Find the measure of the acute angles formed by the intersecting rays.

Assess and Remediate

Lesson Quiz

1. What is the sum of the interior angle measures of a 14-gon?
2. What is the measure of each interior angle of a regular pentagon?
3. What is $m\angle C$ in pentagon *ABCDE*?

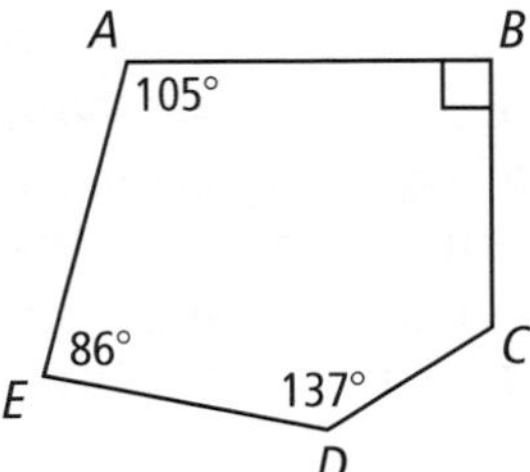

4. What is the measure of an exterior angle of a regular pentagon?

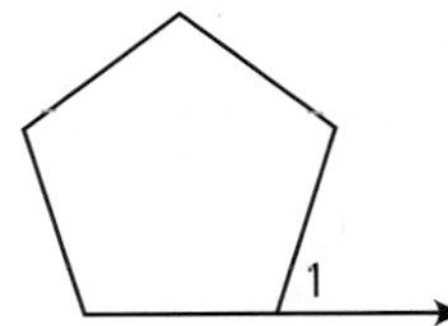

5. **Do you UNDERSTAND?** How many sides does a regular polygon have if each exterior angle is 24°? How do you know?

ANSWERS TO LESSON QUIZ

1. 2160
2. 108
3. 122
4. 72
5. The sum of the exterior angles of any polygon is 360°, so the number of sides is $\frac{360}{24}$, or 15.

Prescription for Remediation

Use the student work on the Lesson Quiz to prescribe a differentiated assignment.

Points	Differentiated Remediation
0–2	Intervention
3–4	On-level
5	Extension

Online Assessment

Assign the Lesson Quiz in Success Tracker on **pearsonsuccessnet.com**. Success Tracker will automatically score the quiz and assign appropriate intervention or enrichment to each student based on the results. The compiled data appear in three different reports for instant analysis of whole class and individual student performance.

Differentiated Remediation

Intervention

- **RETEACHING** (2 pages) Provides reteaching and practice exercises for the key lesson concepts. Use with struggling students or absent students.
- **ENGLISH LANGUAGE LEARNER SUPPORT** Helps students develop and reinforce mathematical vocabulary and key concepts.

On-Level

- **PRACTICE** (2 pages) Provides extra practice for each lesson. For simpler practice exercises, use the Form K Practice pages found in the Online Teacher Resources.
- **THINK ABOUT A PLAN** Helps students develop specific problem-solving skills and strategies by providing scaffolded guiding questions.
- **STANDARDIZED TEST PREP** Focuses on all major exercises, all major question types, and helps students prepare for the high-stakes assessments.

Extension

- **ENRICHMENT** Provides students with interesting problems and activities that extend the concepts of the lesson.
- **ACTIVITIES, GAMES, AND PUZZLES** Worksheets that can be used for concept development, enrichment, and for fun!

5-2 Properties of Parallelograms

Common Core State Standards
G.CO.11 Prove theorems about parallelogram. Theorems include: opposite sides are congruent, opposite angles are congruent, the diagonals of a parallelogram bisect each other . . . **Also G.SRT.5**

Preparing to Teach

BIG idea Reasoning and Proof

ESSENTIAL UNDERSTANDING

Parallelograms have special properties regarding their sides, angles, and diagonals. Parallelograms can be used to prove theorems about parallel lines and their transversals.

Math Background

The study of polygons is a study of hierarchy. Quadrilaterals are a subset of polygons and parallelograms are a subset of quadrilaterals. Thus parallelograms have all properties of polygons and quadrilaterals as well as special properties of their own. Parallelograms themselves contain several subsets. Each of these subsets will have all properties of polygons, quadrilaterals, and parallelograms.

Remind students that they have seen properties similar to those in this lesson in Chapter 3 when studying congruent triangles. Exploring such properties can be made easier by using geometry software.

ELL Support

FOCUS ON LANGUAGE Explore the word *opposite*. Ask: What other words sound like *opposite*? (*opposing, oppositional*) As a noun, *opposite* means a person or thing that is contrary. As an adjective, *opposite* means the other of two related or corresponding things. The word *opposite* is from the Latin *oppositus*, meaning "placed across from."

USE MULTIPLE REPRESENTATIONS Have other materials available of varied instructional levels. This text should describe the properties of parallelograms using the relationships between sides and angles, and the diagonals of a parallelogram.

Lesson Vocabulary

- parallelogram
- opposite sides
- opposite angles
- consecutive angles

Mathematical Practices

CONSTRUCT VIABLE ARGUMENTS AND CRITIQUE THE REASONING OF OTHERS. Using the definition of a parallelogram, students will construct several theorems regarding the congruence of sides, congruence of angles, and common midpoint of diagonals.

1 Interactive Learning

Solve It!

PURPOSE To familiarize students with the characteristics of a parallelogram

PROCESS Students may use previous knowledge of congruent triangle theorems and properties of parallel lines.

Q Are there any angles in the diagram that you know are congruent? Explain. **[Yes, vertical angles and alternate interior angles are congruent.]**

Q Can you make a conjecture about the congruence of any segments? Explain. **[Yes, The opposite sides appear congruent and the diagonals appear to bisect each other.]**

Q Based on your conjectures, what triangle congruence postulates or theorems might you use to determine congruent triangles? **[ASA and AAS]**

ANSWER You can show $\triangle BAD \cong \triangle DCB$ and $\triangle BAC \cong \triangle DCA$ by ASA. Then you can use the fact that corresp. parts of $\cong$ $\triangle$s are $\cong$ and that vert. angles are $\cong$ to show that $\triangle ABE \cong \triangle CDE$ by ASA or AAS, and $\triangle BCE \cong \triangle DAE$ by ASA, AAS, or SAS.

▼ DIGITAL (STUDENT WORK SPACE PAGE 270)

Getting Ready!

Use the information given in the diagram. Which triangles are congruent? How do you know?

CONNECT THE MATH In the Solve It, students identify congruent angles and make conjectures about congruent segments. In the lesson, students learn properties of parallelograms and theorems related to quadrilaterals.

2 Guided Instruction

Problem 1 Using Consecutive Angles

Take Note
Theorem 40
Some students may ask if a quadrilateral in which all sides are congruent rather than just opposite sides being congruent is also considered a parallelogram. This special case will be considered in subsequent lessons.

Proof
Because you are given that *ABCD* is a parallelogram, you know that 2 pairs of segments are parallel. Therefore, the diagonal of the parallelogram can serve as a transversal.

Take Note
Theorem 41 **TACTILE LEARNERS**
Have students cut out two identical parallelograms. Students can use the parallelograms to "test" the supplementary relationship of the consecutive angles.

▼ STUDENT PAGES 270–271

A **parallelogram** is a quadrilateral with both pairs of opposite sides parallel. In the Solve It, you made some conjectures about the characteristics of a parallelogram. In this lesson, you will verify whether your conjectures are correct.

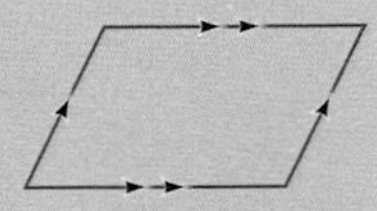

Essential Understanding Parallelograms have special properties regarding their sides, angles, and diagonals.

In a quadrilateral, **opposite sides** do not share a vertex and **opposite angles** do not share a side.

You can abbreviate *parallelogram* with the symbol ▱ and *parallelograms* with the symbol ▱s. You can use what you know about parallel lines and transversals to prove some theorems about parallelograms.

take note Theorem 40

Theorem	If . . .	Then . . .
If a quadrilateral is a parallelogram, then its opposite sides are congruent.	*ABCD* is a ▱	$\overline{AB} \cong \overline{CD}$ and $\overline{BC} \cong \overline{DA}$

Proof Proof of Theorem 40

Given: ▱*ABCD*
Prove: $\overline{AB} \cong \overline{CD}$ and $\overline{BC} \cong \overline{DA}$

Statements	Reasons
1) *ABCD* is a parallelogram.	1) Given
2) $\overline{AB} \parallel \overline{CD}$ and $\overline{BC} \parallel \overline{DA}$	2) Definition of parallelogram
3) $\angle 1 \cong \angle 4$ and $\angle 3 \cong \angle 2$	3) If lines are $\parallel$, then alt. int. ∠s are $\cong$.
4) $\overline{AC} \cong \overline{AC}$	4) Reflexive Property of $\cong$
5) $\triangle ABC \cong \triangle CDA$	5) ASA
6) $\overline{AB} \cong \overline{CD}$ and $\overline{BC} \cong \overline{DA}$	6) Corresp. parts of $\cong$ △s are $\cong$.

Angles of a polygon that share a side are **consecutive angles**. In the diagram, ∠*A* and ∠*B* are consecutive angles because they share side $\overline{AB}$.

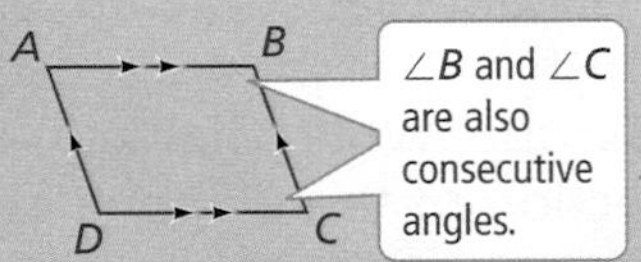

The theorem below uses the fact that consecutive angles of a parallelogram are same-side interior angles of parallel lines.

take note Theorem 41

Theorem	If . . .	Then . . .
If a quadrilateral is a parallelogram, then its consecutive angles are supplementary.	*ABCD* is a ▱ 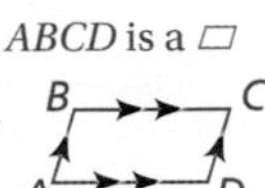	$m\angle A + m\angle B = 180$ $m\angle B + m\angle C = 180$ $m\angle C + m\angle D = 180$ $m\angle D + m\angle A = 180$

You will prove Theorem 41 in Exercise 23.

Problem 1 *continued*

Q How are $\angle S$ and $\angle P$ related? **[They are consecutive angles of a parallelogram. They are supplementary.]**

Q What other angle in the diagram is also supplementary to $\angle S$ and is therefore congruent to $\angle P$? **[$\angle R$]**

Got It?

Q What is the relationship of $\angle S$ and $\angle R$? Explain. **[The angles are consecutive angles and therefore are supplementary.]**

ANSWERS

Got It? 94

Practice

1. 127 **2.** 67

▼ DIGITAL

Problem 1 Using Consecutive Angles

Multiple Choice What is $m\angle P$ in ▱$PQRS$?

A 26 C 116

B 64 D 126

$m\angle P + m\angle S = 180$	Consecutive angles of a ▱ are suppl.
$m\angle P + 64 = 180$	Substitute.
$m\angle P = 116$	Subtract 64 from each side.

The correct answer is C.

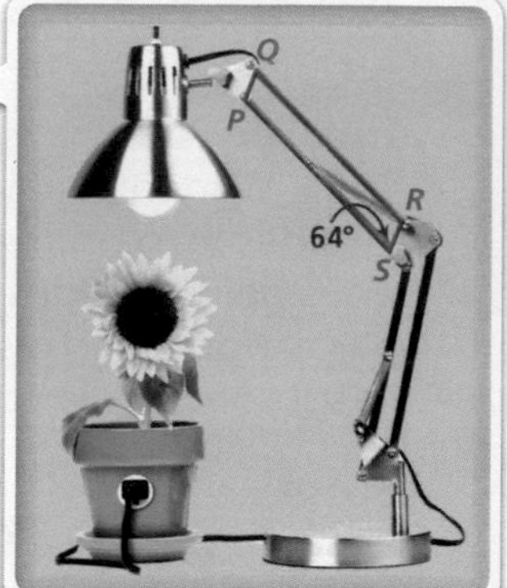

▼ STUDENT PAGES 271–272

Got It? Suppose you adjust the lamp in Problem 1 so that $m\angle S = 86$. What is $m\angle R$ in ▱$PQRS$?

Think
What is the relationship between $\angle R$ and $\angle S$?

Practice **Algebra** Find the value of x in each parallelogram.

1. (53°, x°)

2. (113°, x°)

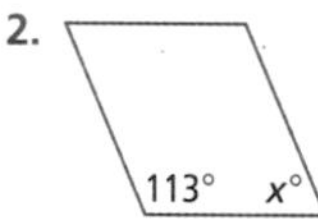

Problem 2 Using Properties of Parallelograms in a Proof

Take Note

Theorem 42

Make sure that students understand that consecutive angles are angles that share a side, while opposite angles are angles that do not share a side.

Take Note

Theorem 43

Make certain that students realize what relationships this theorem describes and does not describe. While the segments created by the intersection of the diagonals are congruent, the diagonals themselves are not congruent.

▼ STUDENT PAGE 272

Parallelograms have some other special properties.

take note

Theorem 42

Theorem	If . . .	Then . . .
If a quadrilateral is a parallelogram, then its opposite angles are congruent.	$ABCD$ is a ▱	$\angle A \cong \angle C$ and $\angle B \cong \angle D$

Theorem 43

Theorem	If . . .	Then . . .
If a quadrilateral is a parallelogram, then its diagonals bisect each other.	$ABCD$ is a ▱	$\overline{AE} \cong \overline{CE}$ and $\overline{BE} \cong \overline{DE}$

You will prove Theorem 43 in Exercise 3.

A proof of Theorem 42 in Problem 2 uses the consecutive angles of a parallelogram and the fact that supplements of the same angle are congruent.

Problem 2

Show students that Theorem 42 could also be proved similarly to the way Theorem 40 was proved using congruent triangles.

Q Does the order of the boxes in the second row of the flow proof matter? Can they be interchanged? **[no; yes]**

Q If the order of these boxes is changed, what must change accordingly? Explain. **[The order of the boxes in the third row; the box stating the angles are consecutive must connect to the box stating the same angles are supplementary.]**

Got It? **ERROR PREVENTION**

If students have trouble constructing the proof, tell them to make sure that they identify the isosceles triangle in the diagram.

ANSWERS

Got It?

1. $ABCD$ is a ▱ and $\overline{AK} \cong \overline{MK}$. (Given)
2. $\angle A \cong \angle BCD$ (Opp. ∠s of a ▱ are ≅.)
3. $\angle A \cong \angle CMD$ (Isosc. △ Theorem)
4. $\angle BCD \cong \angle CMD$ (Transitive Prop. of ≅)

Practice

3. a Def. of ▱
   b. If lines are ∥, then alt. int. angles are ≅.
   c. Opp. sides of a ▱ are ≅.
   d. $\triangle ABE \cong \triangle CDE$
   e. Corresp. parts of ≅ triangles are ≅.
   f. $\overline{AC}$ and $\overline{BD}$ bisect each other at E.

▼ DIGITAL

Problem 2 Using Properties of Parallelograms in a Proof

Given: ▱$ABCD$

Prove: $\angle A \cong \angle C$ and $\angle B \cong \angle D$

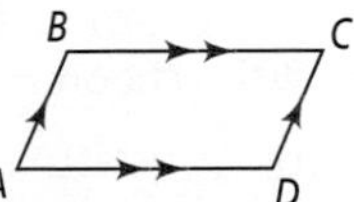

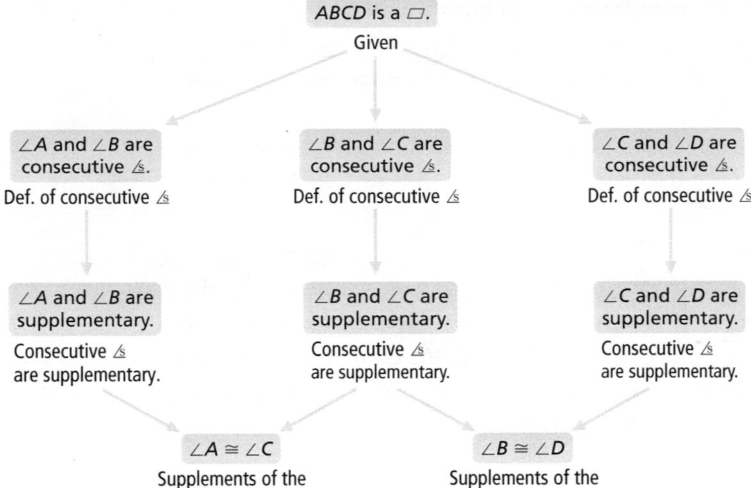

▼ STUDENT PAGE 273

Think What kind of triangle is △*AKM*?

Got It? Use the diagram at the right.

Given: ▱$ABCD$, $\overline{AK} \cong \overline{MK}$

Prove: $\angle BCD \cong \angle CMD$

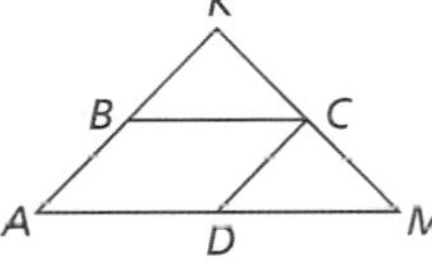

Practice 3. **Developing Proof** Complete this two-column proof of Theorem 43.

Given: ▱$ABCD$

Prove: $\overline{AC}$ and $\overline{BD}$ bisect each other at E.

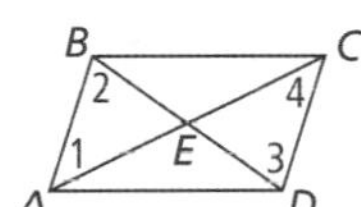

Statements	Reasons
1) $ABCD$ is a parallelogram.	1) Given
2) $\overline{AB} \parallel \overline{DC}$	2) a. ________
3) $\angle 1 \cong \angle 4$; $\angle 2 \cong \angle 3$	3) b. ________
4) $\overline{AB} \cong \overline{DC}$	4) c. ________
5) d. ________	5) ASA
6) $\overline{AE} \cong \overline{CE}$; $\overline{BE} \cong \overline{DE}$	6) e. ________
7) f. ________	7) Definition of bisector

Problem 3 Using Algebra to Find Lengths

Q What theorem allows you to write $KP = MP$ and $LP = NP$? **[Theorem 43]**

Q Can you substitute 14 for y in equation 1 to determine the value of x? Explain. **[Yes, the solution is the common ordered pair of both equations.]**

Q What other methods are available for solving the system of equations? **[graphing method or elimination method]**

Q What are three algebraic expressions that represent KM? LN? **[KM: $2(y + 10)$, $y + 2x + 2$, $2(2x - 8)$; LN: $2x$, $2(y + 2)$, $x + y + 2$]**

Got It? **ERROR PREVENTION**

In part (a), if students give answers of 4 and 5, then they likely thought they had finished the problem once they had solved the system of equations. Tell students to make sure that they use the values of x and y to determine PR and SQ.

ANSWERS

Got It? a. $x = 4$, $y = 5$, $PR = 16$, $SQ = 10$
b. No; answers may vary. Sample: Solutions to a system of equations do not depend on the method used to solve it.

Practice

4. $x = 6$, $y = 8$ **5.** $x = 5$, $y = 7$

▼ STUDENT PAGE 274

You can use Theorem 43 to find unknown lengths in parallelograms.

▼ DIGITAL

Problem 3 **Using Algebra to Find Lengths**

Solve a system of linear equations to find the values of x and y in ▱$KLMN$. What are KM and LN?

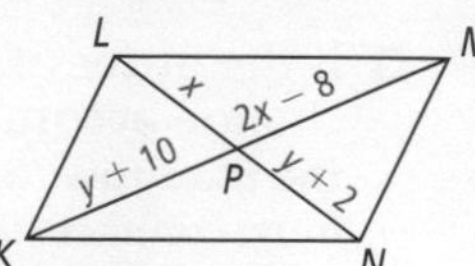

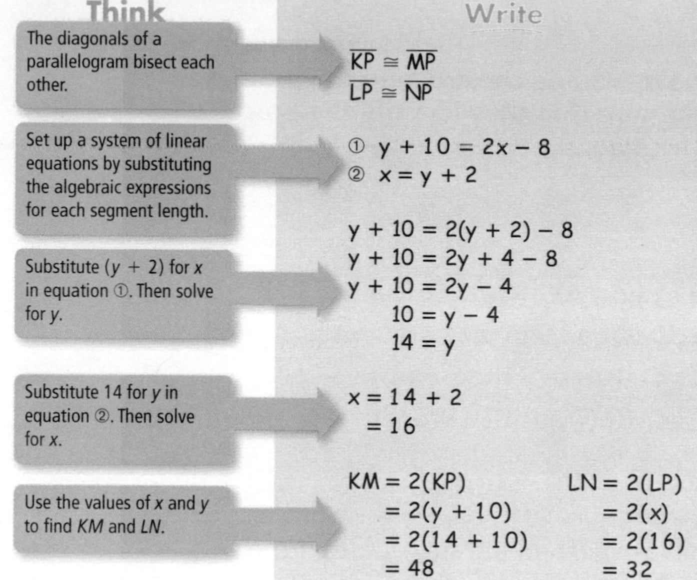

Think	Write
The diagonals of a parallelogram bisect each other.	$\overline{KP} \cong \overline{MP}$ $\overline{LP} \cong \overline{NP}$
Set up a system of linear equations by substituting the algebraic expressions for each segment length.	① $y + 10 = 2x - 8$ ② $x = y + 2$
Substitute $(y + 2)$ for x in equation ①. Then solve for y.	$y + 10 = 2(y + 2) - 8$ $y + 10 = 2y + 4 - 8$ $y + 10 = 2y - 4$ $10 = y - 4$ $14 = y$
Substitute 14 for y in equation ②. Then solve for x.	$x = 14 + 2$ $= 16$
Use the values of x and y to find KM and LN.	$KM = 2(KP)$ $= 2(y + 10)$ $= 2(14 + 10)$ $= 48$ $LN = 2(LP)$ $= 2(x)$ $= 2(16)$ $= 32$

▼ STUDENT PAGE 274

Got It? **a.** Find the values of x and y in ▱$PQRS$ at the right. What are PR and SQ?

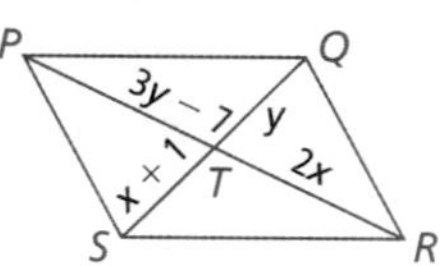

b. Reasoning In Problem 3, does it matter which variable you solve for first? Explain.

Practice **Algebra** Find the values of x and y in ▱$PQRS$.

4. $PT = 2x$, $TR = y + 4$, $QT = x + 2$, $TS = y$

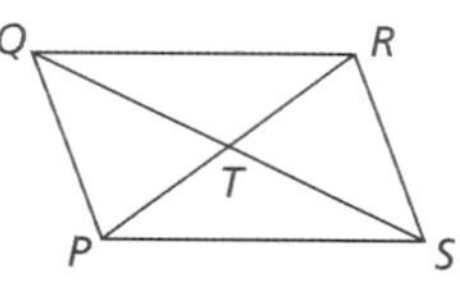

5. $PT = x + 2$, $TR = y$, $QT = 2x$, $TS = y + 3$

Problem 4 Using Parallel Lines and Transversals

Take Note

The theorem states that if $\overline{AC} \cong \overline{CE}$, then $\overline{BD} \cong \overline{DF}$, not that $\overline{AC} \cong \overline{BD}$ or $\overline{CE} \cong \overline{DF}$.

▼ STUDENT PAGE 275

You will use parallelograms to prove the following theorem.

take note **Theorem 44**

Theorem	If . . .	Then . . .
If three (or more) parallel lines cut off congruent segments on one transversal, then they cut off congruent segments on every transversal.	$\overleftrightarrow{AB} \parallel \overleftrightarrow{CD} \parallel \overleftrightarrow{EF}$ and $\overline{AC} \cong \overline{CE}$ 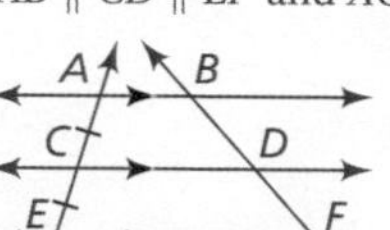	$\overline{BD} \cong \overline{DF}$ 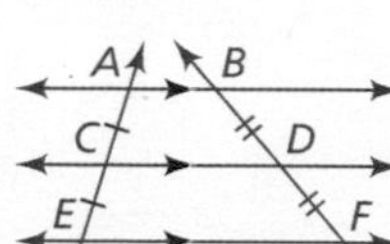

You will prove Theorem 44 in Exercise 34.

Problem 4

Q What does the Segment Addition Postulate state? **[The sum of all lengths of the parts of a segment equals the length of the segment.]**

Q What segment addition equation can be used to find *AD*? **[$AD = AB + BC + CD$]**

Got It?

Q Does $AB = BC = CD$? Explain. **[Yes, if the segments cut from the transversal $\overline{EH}$ are congruent, the segments cut from the transversal $\overline{AD}$ are also congruent.]**

ANSWERS

Got It? 5

Practice

6. 3 **7.** 6.75

▼ DIGITAL

Problem 4 **Using Parallel Lines and Transversals**

In the figure, $\overleftrightarrow{AE} \parallel \overleftrightarrow{BF} \parallel \overleftrightarrow{CG} \parallel \overleftrightarrow{DH}$, $AB = BC = CD = 2$, and $EF = 2.25$. What is *EH*?

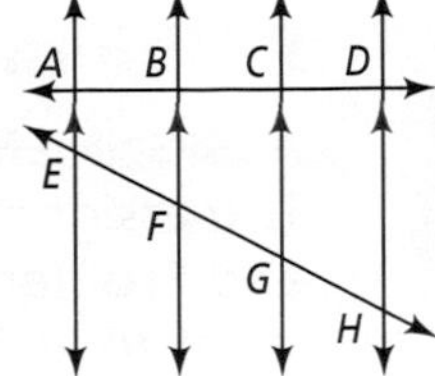

$EF = FG = GH$	Since ∥ lines divide $\overline{AD}$ into equal parts, they also divide $\overline{EH}$ into equal parts.
$EH = EF + FG + GH$	Segment Addition Postulate
$EH = 2.25 + 2.25 + 2.25 = 6.75$	Substitute.

▼ STUDENT PAGE 275

Got It? Use the figure in Problem 4, shown at the right. If $EF = FG = GH = 6$ and $AD = 15$, what is *CD*?

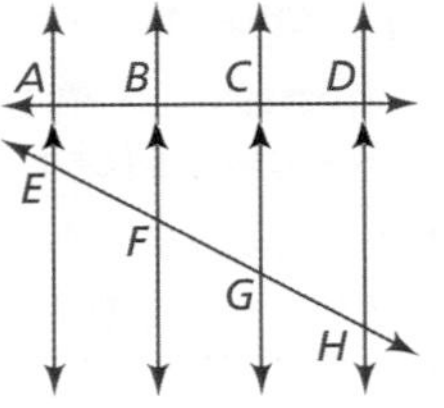

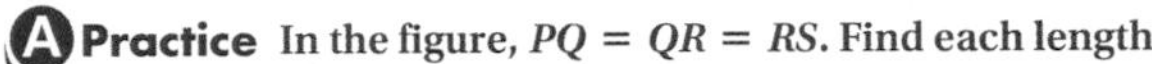

Practice In the figure, $PQ = QR = RS$. Find each length.

6. *ZU*

7. *WV*

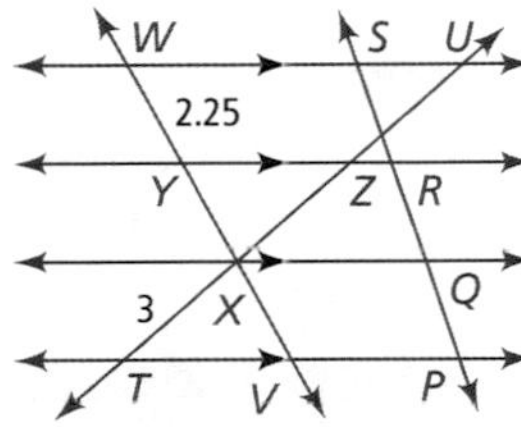

Lesson Check

Do you know HOW?

If students have difficulty with Exercises 8–9, then have them review Problem 1 to learn which angles are consecutive and what that means in terms of writing an equation.

Do you UNDERSTAND?

If students have difficulty with Exercise 14, then have them make sketches of both shapes.

Close

Q What are the distinguishing properties of a parallelogram? **[In a parallelogram, opposite sides are congruent and parallel, opposite angles are congruent, consecutive angles are supplementary, and diagonals bisect each other.]**

ANSWERS

8. 53

9. 127

10. 5

11. 7

12. $ED = 12$, $FD = 24$

13. Answers may vary. Sample: The ∠ opposite the given ∠ is congruent to it. The other two angles and the given ∠ are consecutive angles, so they are supplements of the given ∠.

14. A ▱ is a special quadrilateral. A ▱ is a quadrilateral with both pairs of opp. sides ∥.

15. It is not given that $\overleftrightarrow{PQ}$, $\overleftrightarrow{RS}$, and $\overleftrightarrow{TV}$ are ∥.

▼ STUDENT PAGES 276–277

Lesson Check

Do you know HOW?

For Exercises 8–11, use the diagram of ▱*ABCD* to find each value.

8. $m\angle A$ **9.** $m\angle D$

10. x **11.** AB

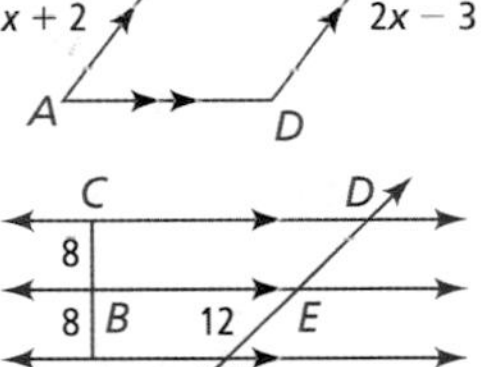

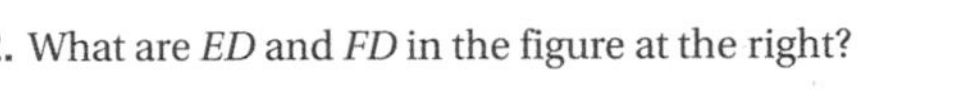

12. What are *ED* and *FD* in the figure at the right?

Do you UNDERSTAND? MATHEMATICAL PRACTICES

13. Reasoning If you know one angle measure of a parallelogram, how do you find the other three angle measures? Explain.

14. Compare and Contrast What is the difference between a quadrilateral and a parallelogram?

15. Error Analysis Your classmate says that $QV = 10$. Explain why the statement may not be correct.

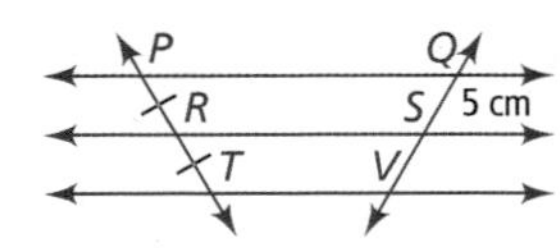

4 Practice

More Practice and Problem-Solving Exercises

ASSIGNMENT GUIDE

The assignments below are for the More Practice and Problem-Solving Exercises. You may also want to assign the A-Level Practice Exercises for homework if these are not used in class.

Average: 16–32

Advanced: 16–35

Mathematical Practices The exercises listed focus on the Standards for Mathematical Practices listed.

EX. 13, 14, 19: Make Sense of Problems (MP 1)

EX. 33: Construct Arguments (MP 3)

EX. 15: Critique the Reasoning of Others (MP 3)

EX. 22: Model (MP 4)

EXERCISE 32: Use the **Think About a Plan** worksheet in the Online Teacher Resources to further support students' development in becoming independent learners.

HOMEWORK QUICK CHECK

To check students' understanding of key skills and concepts, go over Exercises 18, 19, 21, 23, and 32.

ANSWERS

16. 20 **17.** 17

18. $x = 12$, $y = 4$ **19.** $x = 15$, $y = 45$

20. 22, $AB = 23.6$, $BC = 18.5$, $CD = 23.6$, $AD = 18.5$

21. 6, $m\angle H = 30$, $m\angle G = 150$, $m\angle J = 30$, $m\angle K = 150$

22. **a.** 2.5 ft

b. 129

c. Answers may vary. Sample: As $m\angle E$ increases, $m\angle D$ decreases. $\angle E$ and $\angle D$ are suppl.

23. **1.** ▱$ABCD$ (Given)

2. $\overline{AB} \parallel \overline{CD}$ and $\overline{BC} \parallel \overline{DA}$. (Def. of a ▱)

3. $\angle A$ is suppl. to $\angle B$ and $\angle A$ is suppl. to $\angle D$. (Same-side int. ∠s are suppl.)

▼ STUDENT PAGE 278

More Practice and Problem-Solving Exercises

B Apply

Algebra Find the value(s) of the variable(s) in each parallelogram.

16. $(6a + 10)°$, $130°$

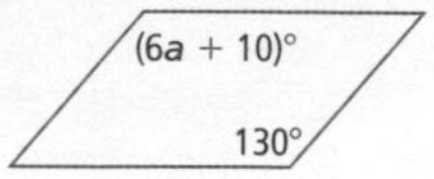

17. $(4a - 4)°$, $(2a + 30)°$

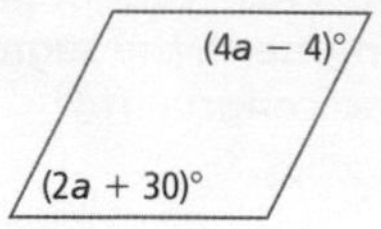

18. $6y + 1$, $x + 7$, $2x - 5$, $4y + 9$

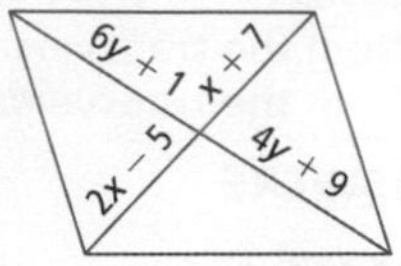

19. Think About a Plan What are the values of x and y in the parallelogram?
- How are the angles related?
- Which variable should you solve for first?

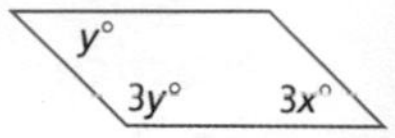

$y°$, $3y°$, $3x°$

Algebra Find the value of a. Then find each side length or angle measure.

20.

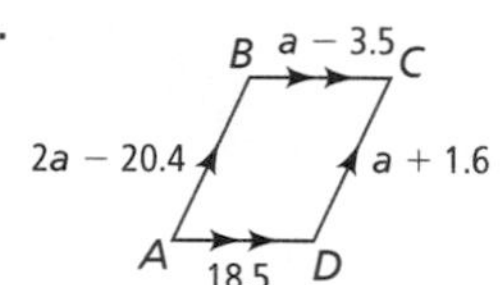

21.

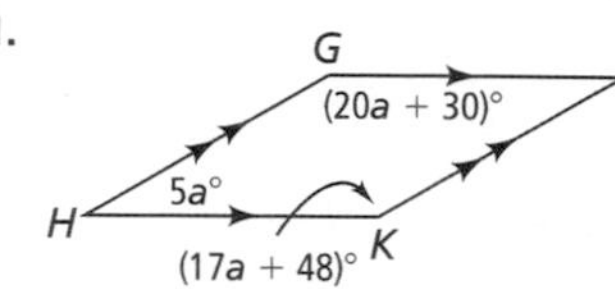

22. Studio Lighting A pantograph is an expandable device shown at the right. Pantographs are used in the television industry in positioning lighting and other equipment. In the photo, points D, E, F, and G are the vertices of a parallelogram. ▱$DEFG$ is one of many parallelograms that change shape as the pantograph extends and retracts.

a. If $DE = 2.5$ ft, what is FG?

b. If $m\angle E = 129$, what is $m\angle G$?

c. What happens to $m\angle D$ as $m\angle E$ increases or decreases? Explain.

Proof **23. Prove Theorem 41.**

Given: ▱$ABCD$

Prove: $\angle A$ is supplementary to $\angle B$. $\angle A$ is supplementary to $\angle D$.

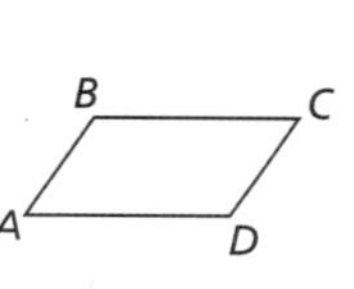

24. Answers may vary. Sample:

1. ▱ *LENS* and *NGTH* (Given)
2. $\angle L \cong \angle ENS$ and $\angle GNH \cong \angle T$. (Opp. △s of a ▱ are ≅.)
3. $\angle ENS \cong \angle GNH$ (Vert. △s are ≅.)
4. $\angle L \cong \angle T$ (Transitive Prop. of ≅)

25. Answers may vary. Sample:

1. ▱ *LENS* and *NGTH* (Given)
2. $\overline{LS} \parallel \overline{EN}$ and $\overline{NH} \parallel \overline{GT}$. (Def. of ▱)
3. $\overline{LS} \parallel \overline{GT}$ (If two lines are ∥ to the same line, then they are ∥ to each other.)

26. Answers may vary. Sample:

1. ▱ *LENS* and *NGTH* (Given)
2. $\angle E$ is suppl. to $\angle ENS$. (Consecutive △s in a ▱ are suppl.)
3. $\angle GNH \cong \angle ENS$ (Vert. △s are ≅.)
4. $\angle GNH \cong \angle T$ (Opp. △s of a ▱ are ≅.)
5. $\angle ENS \cong \angle T$ (Transitive Prop. of ≅)
6. $\angle E$ is suppl. to $\angle T$. (Substitution Prop.)

27. Answers may vary. Sample:

1. ▱ *RSTW* and *XYTZ* (Given)
2. $\angle R \cong \angle T$ and $\angle T \cong \angle X$. (Opp. △s of a ▱ are ≅.)
3. $\angle R \cong \angle X$ (Transitive Prop. of ≅)

28.

1. ▱ *RSTW* and *XYTZ* (Given)
2. $\overline{XY} \parallel \overline{TZ}$ and $\overline{TZ} \parallel \overline{RS}$. (Def. of ▱)
3. $\overline{XY} \parallel \overline{RS}$ (If two lines are ∥ to the same line, then they are ∥ to each other.)

29. $m\angle 1 = 38$, $m\angle 2 = 32$, $m\angle 3 = 110$

30. $m\angle 1 = 71$, $m\angle 2 = 28$, $m\angle 3 = 81$

31. $m\angle 1 = 95$, $m\angle 2 = 37$, $m\angle 3 = 37$

32. $AB = CD = 13$ cm, $BC = AD = 33$ cm

33. No; answers may vary. Sample: Corresponding sides ≅ does not prove parallelograms ≅, since corresponding angles are not necessarily congruent.

34. Answers may vary. Sample:

1. $\overline{AB} \parallel \overline{CD}$, $\overline{CD} \parallel \overline{EF}$ (Given)
2. $\overline{BG} \parallel \overline{AC}$, $\overline{DH} \parallel \overline{CE}$ (Construction)
3. *ABGC* and *CDHE* are ▱s. (Def. of ▱)
4. $\overline{AC} \cong \overline{BG}$, $\overline{CE} \cong \overline{DH}$ (Opp. sides of a ▱ are ≅.)
5. $\overline{AC} \cong \overline{CE}$ (Given)
6. $\overline{BG} \cong \overline{DH}$ (Trans. Prop. of ≅)
7. $\overline{BG} \parallel \overline{DH}$ (If two lines are ∥ to the same line, then they are ∥ to each other.)
8. $\angle 3 \cong \angle 6$ and $\angle GBD \cong \angle HDF$. (If lines are ∥, corresp. △s are ≅.)
9. $\triangle GBD \cong \triangle HDF$ (AAS)
10. $\overline{BD} \cong \overline{DF}$ (Corresp. parts of ≅ △s are ≅.)

Proof In the figure at the right, $\overline{GS}$ and $\overline{EH}$ intersect at point *N*. Use the diagram at the right to complete Exercises 24–26.

24. Given: ▱*LENS* and ▱*NGTH*
Prove: $\angle L \cong \angle T$

25. Given: ▱*LENS* and ▱*NGTH*
Prove: $\overline{LS} \parallel \overline{GT}$

26. Given: ▱*LENS* and ▱*NGTH*
Prove: $\angle E$ is supplementary to $\angle T$.

Proof In the figure at the right, points *S*, *Y*, and *T* are collinear, and points *T*, *Z*, and *W* are collinear. Use the figure for Exercises 27 and 28.

27. Given: ▱*RSTW* and ▱*XYTZ*
Prove: $\angle R \cong \angle X$

28. Given: ▱*RSTW* and ▱*XYTZ*
Prove: $\overline{XY} \parallel \overline{RS}$

Find the measures of the numbered angles for each parallelogram.

29.

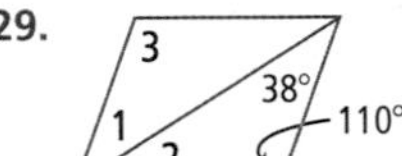

30.

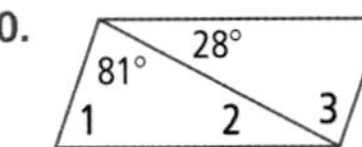

31.

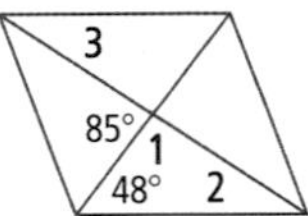

32. Algebra The perimeter of ▱*ABCD* is 92 cm. *AD* is 7 cm more than twice *AB*. Find the lengths of all four sides of ▱*ABCD*.

Challenge

33. Writing Is there an SSSS congruence theorem for parallelograms? Explain.

Proof **34.** Prove Theorem 44. Use the diagram at the right.

Given: $\overleftrightarrow{AB} \parallel \overleftrightarrow{CD} \parallel \overleftrightarrow{EF}$, $\overline{AC} \cong \overline{CE}$
Prove: $\overline{BD} \cong \overline{DF}$
(*Hint:* Draw lines through *B* and *D* parallel to $\overleftrightarrow{AE}$ and intersecting $\overleftrightarrow{CD}$ at *G* and $\overleftrightarrow{EF}$ at *H*.)

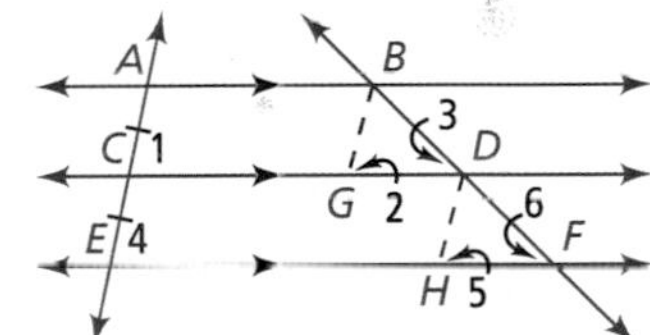

35. Measurement Explain how to separate a blank card into three strips that are the same height by using lined paper, a straightedge, and Theorem 44.

35. Answers may vary. Sample: The lines of the paper are ∥ and equally spaced. Place the right corner of the top edge of the card on the first line of the paper. Place the right corner of the bottom edge on the fourth line. Mark the points where the second and third lines intersect the card. The marks will be equally spaced because the edge of the card is a transversal for the equally spaced ∥ lines of the paper. Repeat for the left side of the card. Connect the marks using a straightedge.

5 Assess and Remediate

Lesson Quiz

1. What is $m\angle O$ in ▱ $LMNO$?

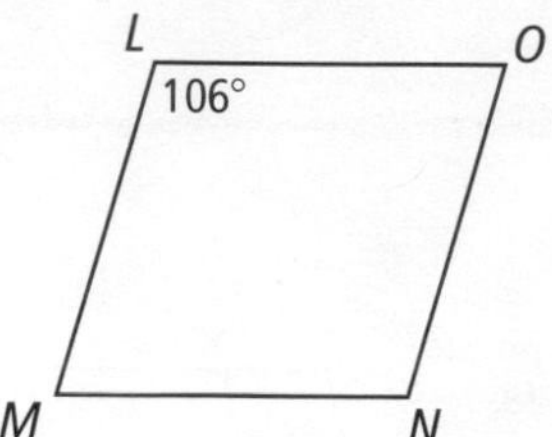

2. Solve a system of linear equations to find the values of a and b in ▱ $EFGH$. What are EG and FH?

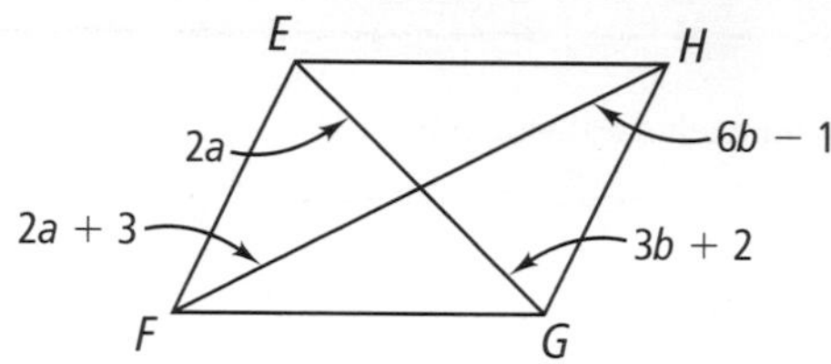

3. **Do you UNDERSTAND?** If $MQ = 29.5$, what is MN?

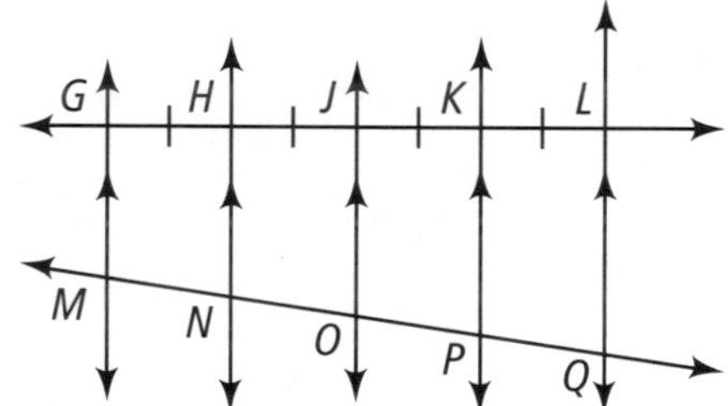

ANSWERS TO LESSON QUIZ

1. 74
2. $a = 4$, $b = 2$, $EG = 16$, $FH = 22$
3. 7.375

Prescription for Remediation

Use the student work on the Lesson Quiz to prescribe a differentiated assignment.

Points	Differentiated Remediation
0–1	Intervention
2	On-level
3	Extension

Online Assessment

Assign the Lesson Quiz in Success Tracker on **pearsonsuccessnet.com**. Success Tracker will automatically score the quiz and assign appropriate intervention or enrichment to each student based on the results. The compiled data appear in three different reports for instant analysis of whole class and individual student performance.

Differentiated Remediation

Intervention

- **RETEACHING** (2 pages) Provides reteaching and practice exercises for the key lesson concepts. Use with struggling students or absent students.
- **ENGLISH LANGUAGE LEARNER SUPPORT** Helps students develop and reinforce mathematical vocabulary and key concepts.

On-Level

- **PRACTICE** (2 pages) Provides extra practice for each lesson. For simpler practice exercises, use the Form K Practice pages found in the Online Teacher Resources.
- **THINK ABOUT A PLAN** Helps students develop specific problem-solving skills and strategies by providing scaffolded guiding questions.
- **STANDARDIZED TEST PREP** Focuses on all major exercises, all major question types, and helps students prepare for the high-stakes assessments.

Extension

- **ENRICHMENT** Provides students with interesting problems and activities that extend the concepts of the lesson.
- **ACTIVITIES, GAMES, AND PUZZLES** Worksheets that can be used for concept development, enrichment, and for fun!

5-3 Proving That a Quadrilateral Is a Parallelogram

Common Core State Standards
G.CO.11 Prove theorems about parallelograms . . . the diagonals of a parallelogram bisect each other . . . **Also G.SRT.5**

Preparing to Teach

BIG idea Reasoning and Proof

ESSENTIAL UNDERSTANDING

If a quadrilateral's sides, angles, and diagonals have certain properties, it can be shown that the quadrilateral is a parallelogram. The properties of parallelograms and algebra can be used to find the lengths of some sides and the measures of some angles of some parallelograms.

Math Background

A definition in geometry is a biconditional statement. Thus, the definition of a parallelogram given in Lesson 5-2 could be read as "A quadrilateral is a parallelogram if and only if both pairs of opposite sides are parallel." The theorems presented in Lesson 5-2 concerning the properties of parallelograms were only stated as conditional statements and thus could not be interpreted as biconditional statements. However, the theorems presented and proven in Lesson 5-3 are their converses, so now many properties of parallelograms can be written as biconditional statements.

Students need to distinguish between the properties and their converses in writing proofs as they examine more complex diagrams.

ELL Support

USE GRAPHIC ORGANIZERS Have students fold a sheet of paper in half widthwise and then lengthwise so there are 4 equal sections. Ask students to write Theorems 40 through 43 in their own words in each of the sections. Throughout this lesson, have them fill in the appropriate section with the converse of that theorem. Students can use different colored pencils to visually differentiate the theorems.

For example, in the first section, students would rephrase Theorem 40, and then write Theorem 45. Use the strategy of Compare and Contrast by asking what is similar and different about the two theorems.

Mathematical Practices

CONSTRUCT VIABLE ARGUMENTS AND CRITIQUE THE REASONING OF OTHERS. Using Lesson 5-2, students will prove geometric figures with certain congruent sides or angles to be parallelograms.

1 Interactive Learning

Solve It!

PURPOSE To use properties of geometric figures to show that lines are parallel

PROCESS Students may use previous knowledge of congruent triangle theorems and properties of parallel lines and equilateral triangles.

Q What are the properties of an equilateral triangle? **[All angles are congruent and all sides are congruent. Each angle has a measure of 60.]**

Q Are all of the equilateral triangles in the diagram congruent? Explain. **[Yes, the triangles share one side and have congruent angles, so they are congruent by ASA.]**

Q Can you identify parallel lines cut by a transversal in the diagram? Explain. **[Yes, the angles of the triangles are congruent. They form corresponding and alternate interior angles.]**

ANSWER Yes; explanations may vary. Sample: angles are ≅ corresp. angles, so the horizontal lines are ∥, or alt. int. angles are ≅, so the lines are ∥.

▼ DIGITAL (STUDENT WORK SPACE PAGE 280)

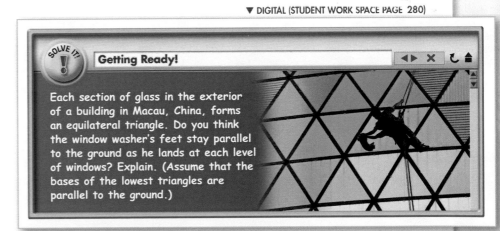

Getting Ready!

Each section of glass in the exterior of a building in Macau, China, forms an equilateral triangle. Do you think the window washer's feet stay parallel to the ground as he lands at each level of windows? Explain. (Assume that the bases of the lowest triangles are parallel to the ground.)

CONNECT THE MATH In the Solve It, equilateral triangles and their properties are used to prove lines parallel. In the lesson, similar approaches will be used to prove a quadrilateral is a parallelogram.

Guided Instruction

Problem 1 Finding Values for Parallelograms

Take Note

Theorem 45

Students may recognize that Theorem 45 is the converse of Theorem 40.

Take Note

Theorem 46

Emphasize the importance of the word *both* in this theorem. Ask students to sketch a counterexample to the conclusion of this theorem if the word *both* is not included.

Take Note

Theorem 47

Q The diagram shows two sets of congruent angles. What relationship do you know about all four angles of the quadrilateral? **[The sum of the measures of the angles is 360.]**

▼ STUDENT PAGES 280–281

In the Solve It, you used angle properties to show that lines are parallel. In this lesson, you will apply the same properties to show that a quadrilateral is a parallelogram.

Essential Understanding You can decide whether a quadrilateral is a parallelogram if its sides, angles, and diagonals have certain properties.

In Lesson 5-2, you learned theorems about the properties of parallelograms. In this lesson, you will learn the converses of those theorems. That is, if a quadrilateral has certain properties, then it must be a parallelogram. Theorem 45 is the converse of Theorem 40.

take note

Theorem 45

Theorem	If . . .	Then . . .
If both pairs of opposite sides of a quadrilateral are congruent, then the quadrilateral is a parallelogram.	$\overline{AB} \cong \overline{CD}$ $\overline{BC} \cong \overline{DA}$	$ABCD$ is a ▱

You will prove Theorem 45 in Exercise 15.

Theorems 46 and 47 are the converses of Theorems 41 and 42, respectively. They use angle relationships to conclude that a quadrilateral is a parallelogram.

take note

Theorem 46

Theorem	If . . .	Then . . .
If an angle of a quadrilateral is supplementary to both of its consecutive angles, then the quadrilateral is a parallelogram.	$m\angle A + m\angle B = 180$ $m\angle A + m\angle D = 180$	$ABCD$ is a ▱

You will prove Theorem 46 in Exercise 16.

Theorem 47

Theorem	If . . .	Then . . .
If both pairs of opposite angles of a quadrilateral are congruent, then the quadrilateral is a parallelogram.	$\angle A \cong \angle C$ $\angle B \cong \angle D$	$ABCD$ is a ▱

You will prove Theorem 47 in Exercise 13.

You can use algebra together with Theorems 45, 46, and 47 to find segment lengths and angle measures that assume that a quadrilateral is a parallelogram.

Problem 1

Q For quadrilateral *PQRS* to be a parallelogram, what relationship must exist between the opposite sides of the quadrilateral? **[Pairs of opposite sides must be congruent.]**

Q What equations represent that the opposite sides are congruent? **[$3x - 5 = 2x + 1$ and $y = x + 2$]**

Q How can you find the value of *x*? **[Solve the equation $3x - 5 = 2x + 1$.]**

Q How can you find the value of *y* in the diagram? **[Substitute the value for *x* into the equation $y = x + 2$.]**

Got It?

Q Which theorem should you use? Explain. **[The diagram gives you information about the angles, so you should use Theorem 47.]**

ANSWERS

Got It? $x = 10$, $y = 43$

Practice

1. $x = 21$, $y = 39$

2. $x = 5$

▼ DIGITAL

Problem 1 Finding Values for Parallelograms — GRIDDED RESPONSE

For what value of *y* must *PQRS* be a parallelogram?

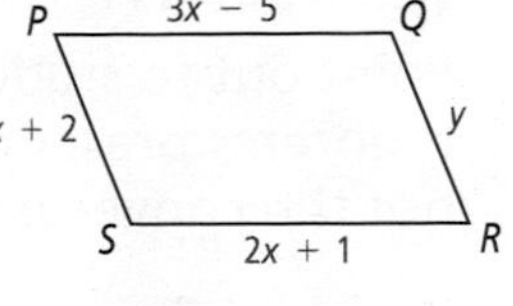

Step 1 Find *x*.

$3x - 5 = 2x + 1$ — If opp. sides are ≅, then the quad. is a ▱.

$x - 5 = 1$ — Subtract 2*x* from each side.

$x = 6$ — Add 5 to each side.

Step 2 Find *y*.

$y = x + 2$ — If opp. sides are ≅, then the quad. is a ▱.

$= 6 + 2$ — Substitute 6 for *x*.

$= 8$ — Simplify.

For *PQRS* to be a parallelogram, the value of *y* must be 8.

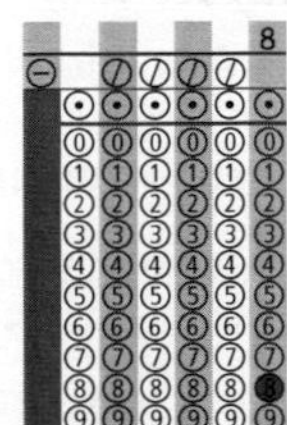

▼ STUDENT PAGES 281–282

Plan
What theorem should you use?

Got It? Use the diagram below. For what values of *x* and *y* must *EFGH* be a parallelogram?

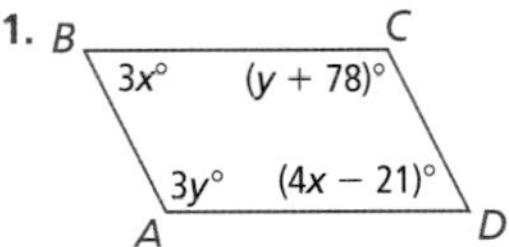

A Practice **Algebra** In Exercises 1 and 2, for what values of *x* and *y* must *ABCD* be a parallelogram?

1.

2.

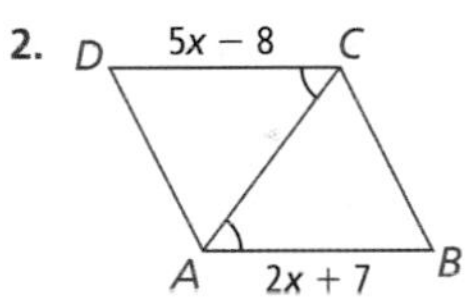

Problem 2 Deciding Whether a Quadrilateral Is a Parallelogram

Take Note

Theorem 48

Ask students the following questions to prepare them for the logical reasoning presented in the proof for this theorem.

Q Which angles in the diagram do you know are congruent? **[The pairs of vertical angles formed by the intersection of the diagonals are congruent.]**

Q Can you determine by visual inspection that the opposite sides of the quadrilateral *BCDA* are congruent? Explain. **[No, it is not known if the quadrilateral is a parallelogram.]**

Q Do any triangles in the diagram appear to be congruent? How can you prove them to be congruent? Explain. **[Yes, △*BEC* appears congruent to △*DEA* and △*BEA* appears congruent to △*DEC*. You can prove them congruent using SAS.]**

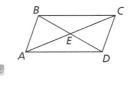

▼ STUDENT PAGE 282

You know that the converses of Theorems 40, 41, and 42 are true. Using what you have learned, you can show that the converse of Theorem 43 is also true.

take note **Theorem 48**

Theorem	If . . .		Then . . .
If the diagonals of a quadrilateral bisect each other, then the quadrilateral is a parallelogram.	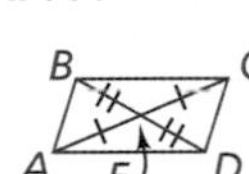	$\overline{AE} \cong \overline{CE}$ $\overline{BE} \cong \overline{DE}$	*ABCD* is a ▱ 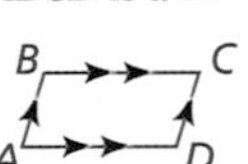

Proof **Proof of Theorem 48**

Given: $\overline{AC}$ and $\overline{BD}$ bisect each other at *E*.

Prove: *ABCD* is a parallelogram.

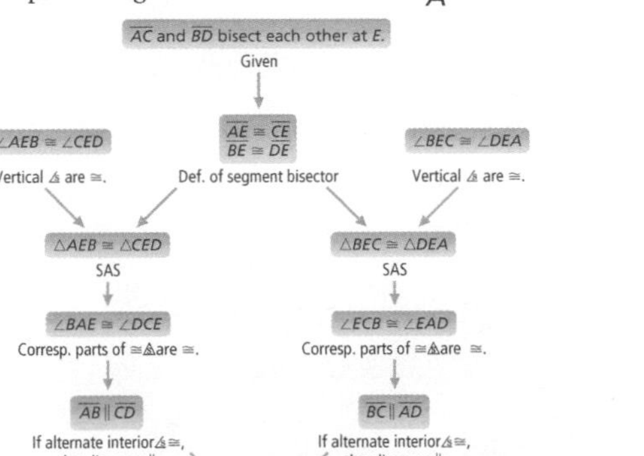

Problem 2 *continued*

Take Note

Theorem 49

Point out to students that unlike all of the other theorems presented in this lesson, Theorem 49 is not the converse of a previous theorem.

Problem 2

Q In 2A, which lines in the diagram must be parallel? Explain. **[$\overline{AB}$ and $\overline{CD}$ must be parallel, because $\angle A$ and $\angle D$ are supplementary.]**

Ask students to create a quadrilateral with given information that would allow a classmate to determine that the quadrilateral is a parallelogram using Theorem 45.

Got It? **ERROR PREVENTION**

Q Can you prove that $\triangle ALN \cong \triangle DNL$ in the diagram given for part (b)? Explain. **[Yes, by using ASA.]**

Q Can you prove that $\triangle ALD \cong \triangle DNA$? Explain. **[Yes, by using the Angle Addition Postulate.]**

ANSWERS

Got It? a. No; *DEFG* could be an isosc. trapezoid. (One pair of sides must be both $\cong$ and $\parallel$.) **b.** yes;

1. $\angle ALN \cong \angle DNL$; $\angle ANL \cong \angle DLN$ (Given)
2. $\overline{AN} \parallel \overline{LD}$ and $\overline{AL} \parallel \overline{ND}$. (If alt. int. $\angle$s are $\cong$, then lines are $\parallel$.)
3. *LAND* is a ▱. (Def. of ▱)

Practice

3. Yes; both pairs of opp. angles are $\cong$.
4. No; only one diagonal is bisected.

▼ STUDENT PAGE 283

Theorem 49 suggests that if you keep two objects of the same length parallel, such as cross-country skis, then the quadrilateral formed by connecting their endpoints is always a parallelogram.

take note **Theorem 49**

Theorem	If . . .	Then . . .
If one pair of opposite sides of a quadrilateral is both congruent and parallel, then the quadrilateral is a parallelogram.	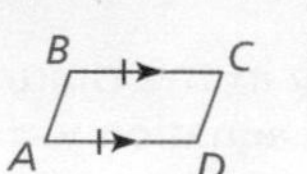 $\overline{BC} \cong \overline{DA}$, $\overline{BC} \parallel \overline{DA}$	*ABCD* is a ▱ 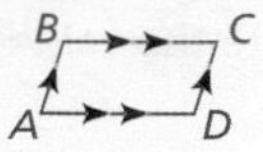 

You will prove Theorem 49 in Exercise 14.

▼ DIGITAL

Problem 2 **Deciding Whether a Quadrilateral Is a Parallelogram**

Can you prove that the quadrilateral is a parallelogram based on the given information? Explain.

A Given: $AB = 5$, $CD = 5$, $m\angle A = 50$, $m\angle D = 130$

Prove: *ABCD* is a parallelogram.

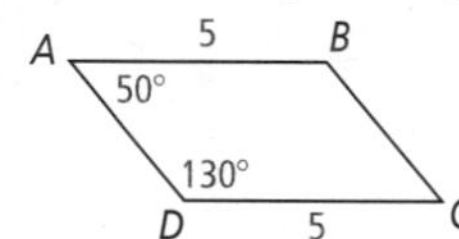

Yes. Same-side interior angles *A* and *D* are supplementary, so $\overline{AB} \parallel \overline{CD}$. Since $\overline{AB} \cong \overline{CD}$, *ABCD* is a parallelogram by Theorem 49.

B Given: $\overline{HI} \cong \overline{HK}$, $\overline{JI} \cong \overline{JK}$

Prove: *HIJK* is a parallelogram.

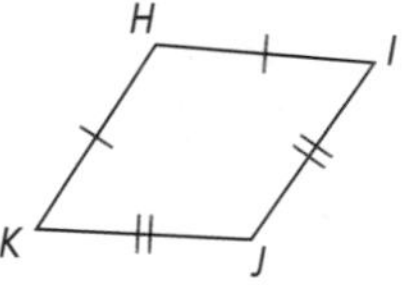

No. By Theorem 45, you need to show that both pairs of *opposite* sides are congruent, not consecutive sides.

▼ STUDENT PAGES 283–284

Got It? Can you prove that the quadrilateral is a parallelogram based on the given information? Explain.

Think: How do you decide if you have enough information?

a. Given: $\overline{EF} \cong \overline{GD}$, $\overline{DE} \parallel \overline{FG}$

Prove: *DEFG* is a parallelogram.

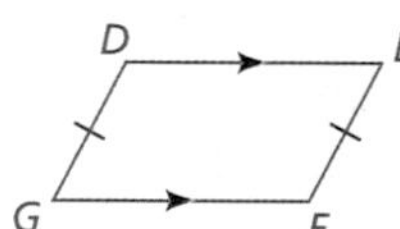

b. Given: $\angle ALN \cong \angle DNL$, $\angle ANL \cong \angle DLN$

Prove: *LAND* is a parallelogram.

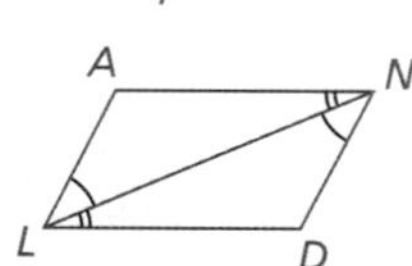

A Practice **Algebra Can you prove that the quadrilateral is a parallelogram based on the given information? Explain.**

3.

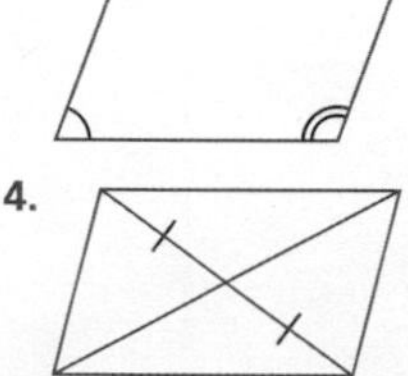

4.

Problem 3 Identifying Parallelograms

TACTILE LEARNERS

Cut the bottom out of a shoebox to use as a model for exploring this problem. Students will be able to manipulate the angles of the quadrilateral while still maintaining the parallel and congruent relationships of the sides.

Got It? **TACTILE LEARNERS**

Remind students that while the lengths of $\overline{QP}$ and $\overline{RS}$ remain constant as the lift raises, the length of a segment perpendicular to both $\overline{QR}$ and $\overline{PS}$ does not remain constant as the lift raises.

ANSWERS

Got It? 6 ft; explanations may vary. Sample: The maximum height occurs when $\overline{QP}$ is vertical.

Practice

5. The connecting pieces $\overline{AD}$ and $\overline{BC}$ are ≅, and the distances AB and CD between where the two pieces attach are =. The side lengths of $ABCD$ do not change as the tackle box opens and closes. Since both pairs of opp. sides are ≅, $ABCD$ is always a ▱. By def. of ▱, $\overline{AB} \parallel \overline{CD}$, so the shelves are always ∥ to each other.

Take Note

Remind students that all but one of the sources presented in this table was already presented in the form of its converse in Lesson 5-2. For example, in Lesson 5-2, if you knew a quadrilateral was a parallelogram, then you could conclude that both pairs of opposite angles were congruent. In this lesson, if you know that both pairs of opposite angles in a quadrilateral are congruent, then you can conclude that the quadrilateral is a parallelogram.

▼ DIGITAL

Problem 3 Identifying Parallelograms

Vehicle Lifts **A truck sits on the platform of a vehicle lift. Two moving arms raise the platform until a mechanic can fit underneath. Why will the truck always remain parallel to the ground as it is lifted? Explain.**

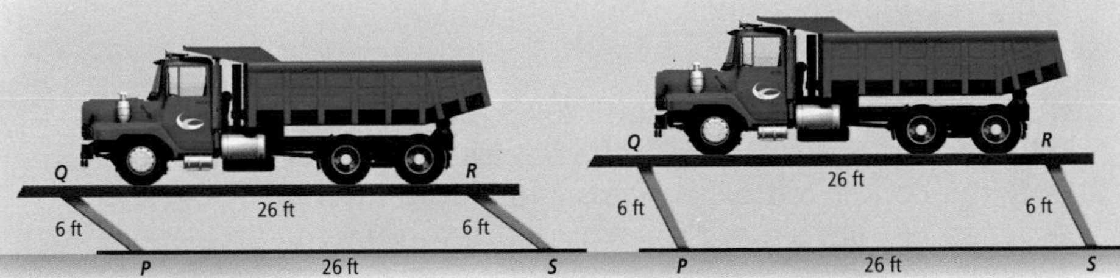

The angles of $PQRS$ change as platform $\overline{QR}$ rises, but its side lengths remain the same. Both pairs of opposite sides are congruent, so $PQRS$ is a parallelogram by Theorem 6-8. By the definition of a parallelogram, $\overline{PS} \parallel \overline{QR}$. Since the base of the lift $\overline{PS}$ lies along the ground, platform $\overline{QR}$, and therefore the truck, will always be parallel to the ground.

▼ STUDENT PAGES 284–285

Got It? **Reasoning** What is the maximum height that the vehicle lift can elevate the truck? Explain.

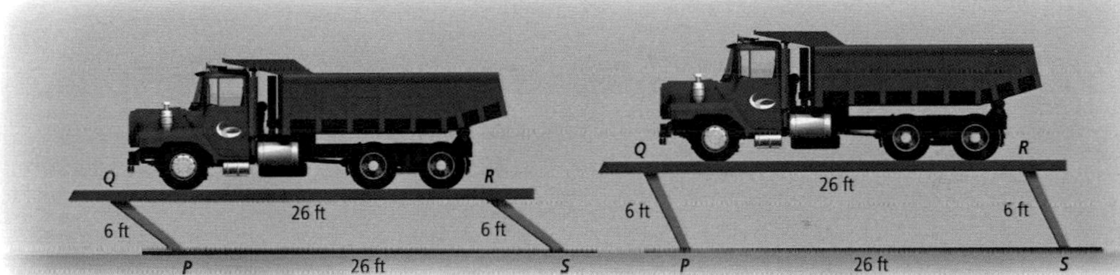

Practice

5. **Fishing** Quadrilaterals are formed on the side of this fishing tackle box by the adjustable shelves and connecting pieces. Explain why the shelves are always parallel to each other no matter what their position is.

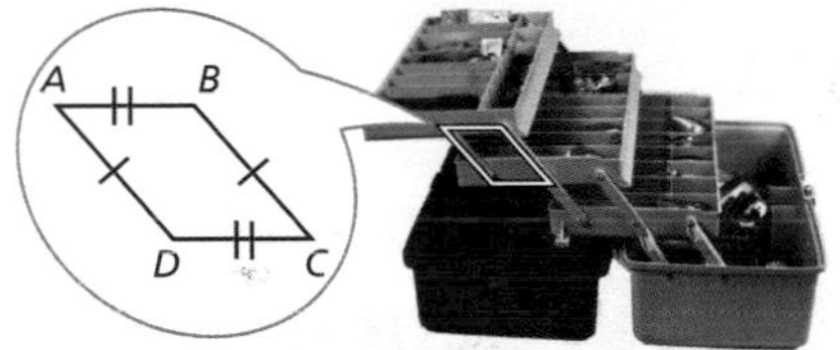

▼ STUDENT PAGE 285

take note

Concept Summary Proving That a Quadrilateral Is a Parallelogram

Method	Source	Diagram
Prove that both pairs of opposite sides are parallel.	Definition of parallelogram	
Prove that both pairs of opposite sides are congruent.	Theorem 45	
Prove that an angle is supplementary to both of its consecutive angles.	Theorem 46	75° 75° 105°
Prove that both pairs of opposite angles are congruent.	Theorem 47	
Prove that the diagonals bisect each other.	Theorem 48	
Prove that one pair of opposite sides is congruent and parallel.	Theorem 49	

Lesson Check

Do you know HOW?
If students have difficulty with Exercises 7–8, then have them revise the diagrams as necessary so that the given information is sufficient.

Do you UNDERSTAND?
If students have difficulty with Exercise 11, then tell them to make a sketch of a diagram that meets only the conditions of the classmate's statement in order to visually show the error in the statement.

Close

Q What biconditional can you write concerning a parallelogram and its opposite angles? **[A quadrilateral is a parallelogram if and only if both pairs of opposite angles are congruent.]**

ANSWERS

6. 112

7. Yes; opp. angles are ≅.

8. No; the diagonals may not bisect each other.

9. because Thm. 40 and its converse are both true

10. Thm. 48 and Thm. 43 are converses of each other. Use Thm. 48 if you need to show the figure is a ▱. Use Thm. 43 if it is given that the figure is a ▱.

11. It is a ▱ only if the same pair of opp. sides are ≅ and ∥.

▼ STUDENT PAGES 286–287

Lesson Check

Do you know HOW?

6. For what value of y must $LMNP$ be a parallelogram?

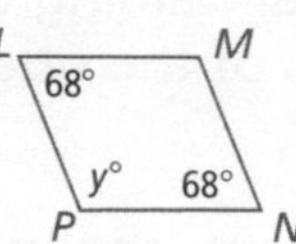

For Exercises 7 and 8, is the given information enough to prove that $ABCD$ is a parallelogram? Explain.

7.

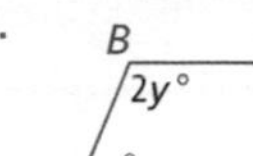

8.

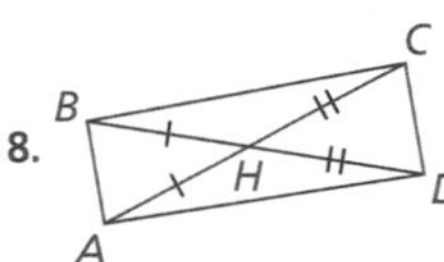

Do you UNDERSTAND?

9. Vocabulary Explain why you can now write a biconditional statement regarding opposite sides of a parallelogram.

10. Compare and Contrast How is Theorem 48 in this lesson different from Theorem 43 in the previous lesson? In what situations should you use each theorem? Explain.

11. Error Analysis Your friend says, "If a quadrilateral has a pair of opposite sides that are congruent and a pair of opposite sides that are parallel, then it is a parallelogram." What is your friend's error? Explain.

Practice

More Practice and Problem-Solving Exercises

ASSIGNMENT GUIDE

The assignments below are for the More Practice and Problem-Solving Exercises. You may also want to assign the A-Level Practice Exercises for homework if these are not used in class.
Average: 12–21
Advanced: 12–23

Mathematical Practices The exercises listed focus on the Standards for Mathematical Practices listed.

EX. 10: Make Sense of Problems (MP 1)
EX. 14, 21: Persevere in Solving Problems (MP 1)
EX. 13: Construct Arguments (MP 3)
EX. 12: Communicate (MP 3)
EX. 11: Critique the Reasoning of Others (MP 3)

EXERCISE 15: Use the **Think About a Plan** worksheet in the Online Teacher Resources to further support students' development in becoming independent learners.

▼ STUDENT PAGE 287

More Practice and Problem-Solving Exercises

Apply

12. Writing Combine each of Theorems 40, 41, 42, and 43 with its converse from this lesson into biconditional statements.

13. Developing Proof Complete this two-column proof of Theorem 47.

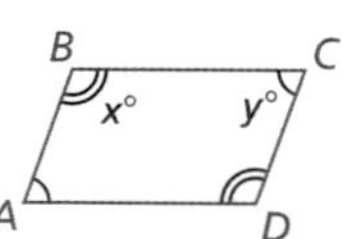

Given: $\angle A \cong \angle C$, $\angle B \cong \angle D$

Prove: $ABCD$ is a parallelogram.

Statements	Reasons
1) $x + y + x + y = 360$	1) The sum of the measures of the angles of a quadrilateral is 360.
2) $2(x + y) = 360$	2) a. __?__
3) $x + y = 180$	3) b. __?__
4) $\angle A$ and $\angle B$ are supplementary. $\angle A$ and $\angle D$ are supplementary.	4) Definition of supplementary
5) c. __?__ ∥ __?__, __?__ ∥ __?__	5) d. __?__
6) $ABCD$ is a parallelogram.	6) e. __?__

HOMEWORK QUICK CHECK
To check students' understanding of key skills and concepts, go over Exercises 13, 14, 15, 17, and 18.

ANSWERS

12. A quad. is a ▱ if and only if its opp. sides are ≅; a quad. is a ▱ if and only if its consecutive angles are suppl.; a quad. is a ▱ if and only if its opp. angles are ≅; a quad. is a ▱ if and only if its diagonals bisect each other.

13. **a.** Distr. Prop.
b. Div. Prop. of Eq.
c. $\overline{AD} \parallel \overline{BC}$, $\overline{AB} \parallel \overline{DC}$
d. If same-side int. angles are suppl., then lines are ∥.
e. Def. of ▱

14. Answers may vary. Sample:
1. Draw $\overline{BD}$. (Through any two points there is exactly one line.)
2. $\angle CBD \cong \angle ADB$ (Alt. int. ∠s are ≅.)
3. $\overline{BC} \cong \overline{DA}$ (Given)
4. $\overline{BD} \cong \overline{BD}$ (Refl. Prop. of ≅)
5. $\triangle BCD \cong \triangle DAB$ (SAS)
6. $\angle BDC \cong \angle DBA$ (Corresp. parts of ≅ △s are ≅.)
7. $\overline{AB} \parallel \overline{CD}$ (If alt. int. ∠s are ≅, then lines are ∥.)
8. *ABCD* is a ▱. (Def. of ▱)

15. Answers may vary. Sample:
1. Draw $\overline{BD}$. (Through any two points there is exactly one line.)
2. $\overline{AB} \cong \overline{CD}$ and $\overline{BC} \cong \overline{DA}$. (Given)
3. $\overline{BD} \cong \overline{BD}$ (Refl. Prop. of ≅)
4. $\triangle ABD \cong \triangle CDB$ (SSS)
5. $\angle ADB \cong \angle CBD$ and $\angle CDB \cong \angle ABD$. (Corresp. parts of ≅ △s are ≅.)
6. $\overline{AB} \parallel \overline{DC}$ and $\overline{BC} \parallel \overline{AD}$. (Converse of Corresp. ∠s Thm.)
7. *ABCD* is a ▱. (Def. of ▱)

16. Answers may vary. Sample:
1. ∠*A* is suppl. to ∠*B*. (Given)
2. $\overline{BC} \parallel \overline{AD}$ (If same-side int. ∠s are suppl., then lines are ∥.)
3. ∠*A* is suppl. to ∠*D*. (Given)
4. $\overline{AB} \parallel \overline{DC}$ (If same-side int. ∠s are suppl., then lines are ∥.)
5. *ABCD* is a ▱. (Def. of ▱)

17. $x = 15$, $y = 25$ **18.** $x = 3$, $y = 11$

19. 24

14. Think About a Plan Prove Theorem 49.
Proof **Given:** $\overline{BC} \parallel \overline{DA}$, $\overline{BC} \cong \overline{DA}$
Prove: *ABCD* is a parallelogram.
- How can drawing diagonals help you?
- How can you use triangles in this proof?

Proof 15. Prove Theorem 45.
Given: $\overline{AB} \cong \overline{CD}$, $\overline{BC} \cong \overline{DA}$
Prove: *ABCD* is a parallelogram.

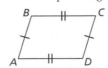

Proof 16. Prove Theorem 46.
Given: ∠*A* is supplementary to ∠*B*.
∠*A* is supplementary to ∠*D*.
Prove: *ABCD* is a parallelogram.

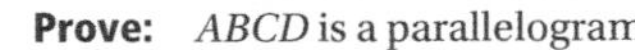

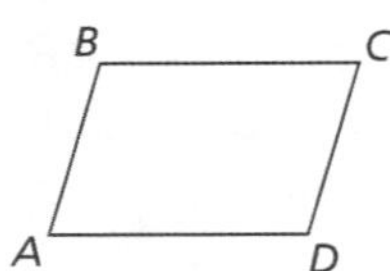

Algebra For what values of the variables must *ABCD* be a parallelogram?

17.

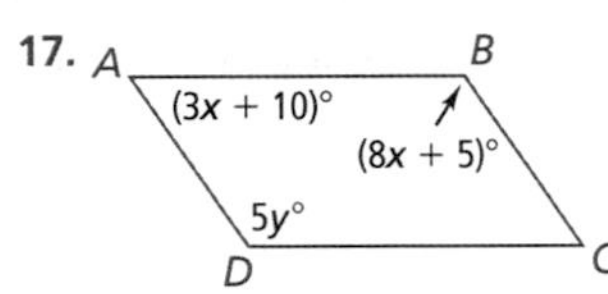

18.

19.

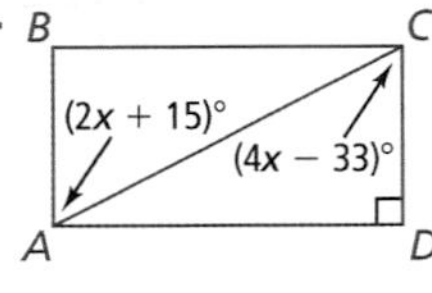

Proof 20. Given: $\triangle TRS \cong \triangle RTW$
Prove: *RSTW* is a parallelogram.

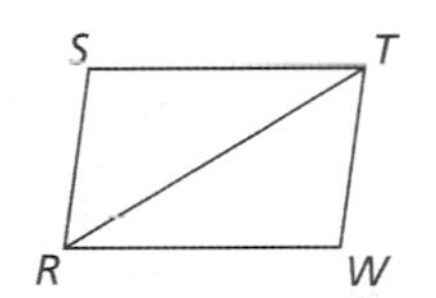

21. Open-Ended Sketch two noncongruent parallelograms *ABCD* and *EFGH* such that $\overline{AC} \cong \overline{EG}$ and $\overline{BD} \cong \overline{FH}$.

Challenge

Proof 22. Construction In the figure at the right, point *D* is constructed by drawing two arcs. One has center *C* and radius *AB*. The other has center *B* and radius *AC*. Prove that $\overline{AM}$ is a median of △*ABC*.

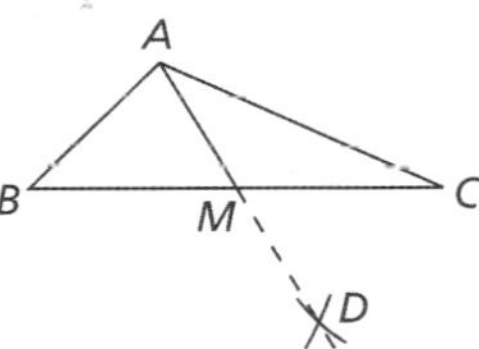

23. Probability If two opposite angles of a quadrilateral measure 120 and the measures of the other angles are multiples of 10, what is the probability that the quadrilateral is a parallelogram?

20. Answers may vary. Sample:
1. $\triangle TRS \cong \triangle RTW$ (Given)
2. $\overline{SR} \cong \overline{WT}$ and $\overline{ST} \cong \overline{WR}$. (Corresp. parts of ≅ △s are ≅.)
3. *RSTW* is a ▱. (If both pairs of opp. sides of a quad. are ≅, then the quad. is a ▱.)

21. Check students' work.

22. Answers may vary. Sample:
1. $\overline{AB} \cong \overline{CD}$, $\overline{AC} \cong \overline{BD}$ (Construction)
2. *ABCD* is a ▱ (Opp. sides of a ▱ are ≅.)
3. *M* is the midpt. of $\overline{BC}$. (Diagonals of a ▱ bisect each other.)
4. $\overline{AM}$ is a median. (Def. of median)

23. $\frac{1}{6}$

5 Assess and Remediate

Lesson Quiz

1. For what value of a must *LMNO* be a parallelogram?

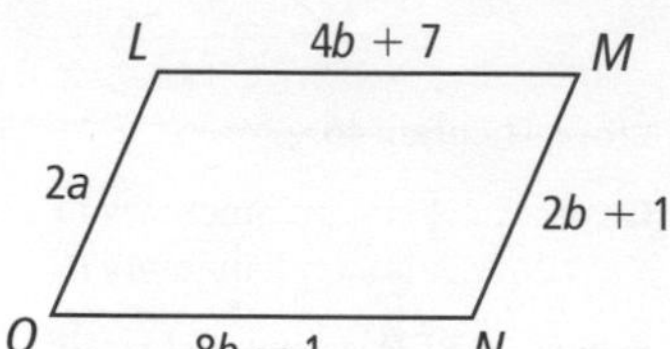

2. Can you prove *ABCD* is a parallelogram based on the given information? Explain.

Given: $x = 5$, $y = 4$

Prove: *ABCD* is a parallelogram.

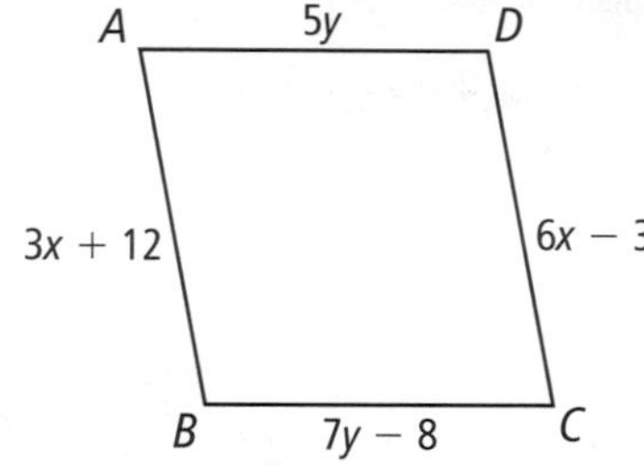

3. Do you UNDERSTAND? Quadrilateral *QRST* has two pairs of congruent sides. Is it a parallelogram? If not, what additional information do you need to conclude that it is a parallelogram?

ANSWERS TO LESSON QUIZ

1. 2.5

2. Yes, by Theorem 45

3. No. To be a parallelogram, *QRST* must have two pairs of opposite sides congruent.

Prescription for Remediation

Use the student work on the Lesson Quiz to prescribe a differentiated assignment.

Points	Differentiated Remediation
0–1	Intervention
2	On-level
3	Extension

Online Assessment

Assign the Lesson Quiz in Success Tracker on **pearsonsuccessnet.com**. Success Tracker will automatically score the quiz and assign appropriate intervention or enrichment to each student based on the results. The compiled data appear in three different reports for instant analysis of whole class and individual student performance.

Differentiated Remediation

Intervention

- **RETEACHING** (2 pages) Provides reteaching and practice exercises for the key lesson concepts. Use with struggling students or absent students.
- **ENGLISH LANGUAGE LEARNER SUPPORT** Helps students develop and reinforce mathematical vocabulary and key concepts.

On-Level

- **PRACTICE** (2 pages) Provides extra practice for each lesson. For simpler practice exercises, use the Form K Practice pages found in the Online Teacher Resources.
- **THINK ABOUT A PLAN** Helps students develop specific problem-solving skills and strategies by providing scaffolded guiding questions.
- **STANDARDIZED TEST PREP** Focuses on all major exercises, all major question types, and helps students prepare for the high-stakes assessments.

Extension

- **ENRICHMENT** Provides students with interesting problems and activities that extend the concepts of the lesson.
- **ACTIVITIES, GAMES, AND PUZZLES** Worksheets that can be used for concept development, enrichment, and for fun!

5-4 Properties of Rhombuses, Rectangles, and Squares

Common Core State Standards
G.CO.11 Prove theorems about parallelograms . . . rectangles are parallelograms with congruent diagonals. **Also G.SRT.5**

Preparing to Teach

BIG idea Reasoning and Proof

ESSENTIAL UNDERSTANDING

The special parallelograms (rhombus, rectangle, and square) have basic properties about their sides, angles, and diagonals that help identify them.

Math Background

In Chapter 3, students were introduced to the hierarchical classification of triangles. Equilateral and isosceles triangles had all of the properties of any triangle as well as their own special properties. Likewise, the special parallelograms introduced in this lesson have all of the properties of parallelograms as well as their own special properties.

It is important to treat proofs as a means to an end and not as the goal of this lesson. Remind students that, for example, because a square is a special rhombus, it has all the properties of a rhombus. This relationship holds true for all special quadrilaterals in the hierarchy of quadrilaterals.

ELL Support

FOCUS ON LANGUAGE Place the lesson on an overhead and read the essential portions, including the direction lines. Use your finger to point at each word as students follow along.

Ask students to analyze the key words such as *characteristics*, *properties*, and *congruent*. Ask students to clarify the meanings of these words in their own words.

USE MANIPULATIVES Cut out a variety of rhombuses, rectangles, and squares from construction paper. Divide students into pairs of mixed abilities. Give each student pair several quadrilaterals. Ask them to classify each of the shapes they receive as a rhombus, a rectangle, or a square. Invite students to share their reasoning. Use the sharing as an instructional opportunity as well as peer teaching.

Lesson Vocabulary

- rhombus
- rectangle
- square

Mathematical Practices

MAKE SENSE OF PROBLEMS AND PERSEVERE IN SOLVING THEM. Students will analyze relationships between rhombuses, rectangles, and squares. They will also recognize the significance of sides, angles, etc. within each figure and be able to add auxiliary elements to each.

1 Interactive Learning

Solve It!

PURPOSE To explore the properties of a rhombus

PROCESS Students may use previous knowledge of the properties of parallelograms as well as visual inspection.

Q How can you tell that all four sides are congruent? **[When the quadrilateral is folded along both diagonals, all four sides overlap entirely.]**

Q How can you tell that the resulting figure is a parallelogram? **[When both pairs of opposite sides are congruent, the quadrilateral is a parallelogram.]**

Q Are consecutive angles congruent? How can you tell? **[No, when you fold the figure such that one angle is lying on top of another, the angles are not congruent.]**

ANSWER The quadrilateral has $\cong$ sides. Diagonals are $\perp$ bis. of each other, and each diagonal bisects two angles.

CONNECT THE MATH In the Solve It, students manipulated a paper figure to learn its special characteristics. In this lesson, students will learn the names of special parallelograms that have these characteristics.

▼ DIGITAL (STUDENT WORK SPACE PAGE 289)

Getting Ready!

Fold a piece of notebook paper in half. Fold it in half again in the other direction. Draw a diagonal line from one vertex to the other. Cut through the folded paper along that line. Unfold the paper. What do you notice about the sides and about the diagonals of the figure you formed?

2 Guided Instruction

Problem 1 Classifying Special Parallelograms

Take Note

Have students create a hierarchical chart showing the relationships between the special parallelograms listed and the classifications: parallelogram, quadrilateral, and polygon. Make sure that students realize that in a hierarchical chart any figure listed must be a special case of all figures listed above it.

Problem 1

Q What conclusions can you draw regarding the angles of ▱*ABCD*? **[All angles are congruent and measure 90°.]**

Q What conclusions can you draw regarding the sides of ▱*ABCD*? **[Opposite sides are congruent and parallel.]**

▼ STUDENT PAGES 289–290

In the Solve It, you formed a special type of parallelogram with characteristics that you will study in this lesson.

Essential Understanding The parallelograms in the Take Note box below have basic properties about their sides and angles that help identify them. The diagonals of these parallelograms also have certain properties.

take note

Key Concept Special Parallelograms

Definition	Diagram
A **rhombus** is a parallelogram with four congruent sides.	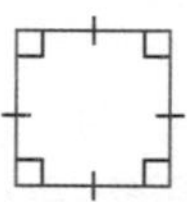
A **rectangle** is a parallelogram with four right angles.	
A **square** is a parallelogram with four congruent sides and four right angles.	

The Venn diagram at the right shows the relationships among special parallelograms.

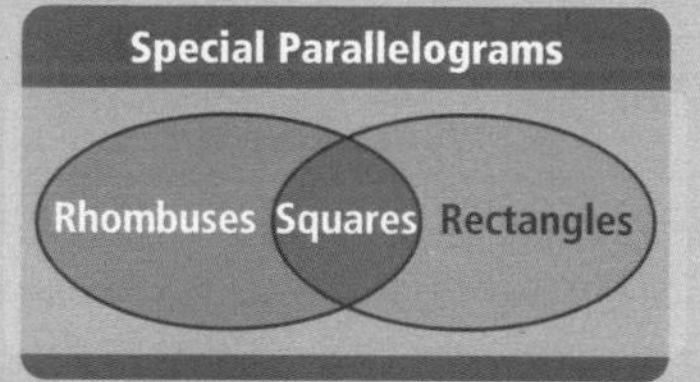

▼ DIGITAL

Problem 1 Classifying Special Parallelograms

Is ▱*ABCD* a rhombus, a rectangle, or a square? Explain.

▱*ABCD* is a rectangle. Opposite angles of a parallelogram are congruent so $m\angle D$ is 90. By the Same-Side Interior Angles Theorem, $m\angle A = 90$ and $m\angle C = 90$. Since ▱*ABCD* has four right angles, it is a rectangle. You cannot conclude that *ABCD* is a square because you do not know its side lengths.

Got It?

Q Can the parallelogram be classified as more than one of the quadrilaterals listed? Explain. **[Yes; every square is both a rhombus and a rectangle.]**

ANSWERS

Got It? Rhombus; opp. sides of a ▱ are ≅, so all sides of *EFGH* are ≅, and there are no rt. angles.

Practice

1. Rectangle; the ▱ has ≅ opp. ∠s and supp. consecutive ∠s. So the ▱ has 4 rt. ∠s and does not have 4 ≅ sides.
2. Rhombus; the ▱ has 4 ≅ sides and no rt. angles.

▼ STUDENT PAGE 290

Got It? Is ▱*EFGH* in Problem 1 a rhombus, a rectangle, or a square? Explain.

Think How do you decide whether *EFGH* is a rhombus, rectangle, or square?

A Practice **Decide whether the parallelogram is a rhombus, a rectangle, or a square. Explain.**

1. 

2.

Problem 2 Finding Angle Measures

Take Note

Theorem 50

Ask students the following questions in preparation for the proof of the theorem.

Q What does the Perpendicular Bisector Theorem state? **[If a point is on the perpendicular bisector of a segment, then it is equidistant from the endpoints of the segment.]**

Q Which labeled points are equidistant from the endpoints of segment *BD*? Explain. **[Since *ABCD* is a rhombus and all sides are congruent, points *A* and *C* are equidistant from the endpoints of $\overline{BD}$.]**

Take Note

Theorem 51

Ask students the following question in preparation for the proof of the theorem.

Q What are the properties of an isosceles triangle? **[Isosceles triangles have two congruent sides and two congruent base angles that are opposite those sides by the Isosceles Triangle Theorem.]**

Proof

Have students make all the geometric markings that identify special characteristics, given that *ABCD* is a rhombus. Then have them identify what information might be useful in the proof. The following marks can be added to the diagram.

- Parallel line indicators on $\overline{AD}$ and $\overline{BC}$, and $\overline{BA}$ and $\overline{CD}$
- Congruence marks on $\overline{AD}$, $\overline{CD}$, $\overline{BC}$, $\overline{AB}$
- Congruence marks on ∠*ADB* and ∠*DBC*, ∠*BDC* and ∠*DBA*, ∠*DAC* and ∠*BCA*, ∠*CAB* and ∠*ACD*

▼ STUDENT PAGE 291

take note **Theorem 50**

Theorem	If . . .	Then . . .
If a parallelogram is a rhombus, then its diagonals are perpendicular.	*ABCD* is a rhombus	$\overline{AC} \perp \overline{BD}$

Theorem 51

Theorem	If . . .	Then . . .
If a parallelogram is a rhombus, then each diagonal bisects a pair of opposite angles.	*ABCD* is a rhombus	∠1 ≅ ∠2 ∠3 ≅ ∠4 ∠5 ≅ ∠6 ∠7 ≅ ∠8

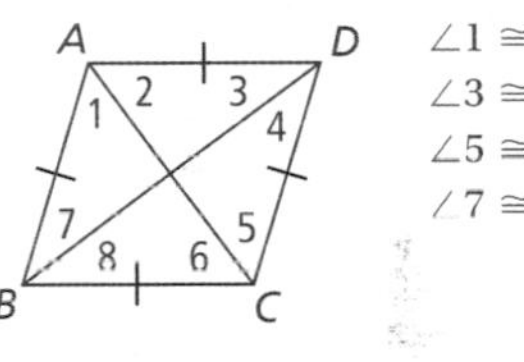

You will prove Theorem 51 in Exercise 34.

Proof **Proof of Theorem 50**

Given: *ABCD* is a rhombus.

Prove: The diagonals of *ABCD* are perpendicular.

Statements	Reasons
1) *A* and *C* are equidistant from *B* and *D*; *B* and *D* are equidistant from *A* and *C*.	1) All sides of a rhombus are ≅.
2) *A* and *C* are on the perpendicular bisector of $\overline{BD}$; *B* and *D* are on the perpendicular bisector of $\overline{AC}$.	2) Converse of the Perpendicular Bisector Theorem
3) $\overline{AC} \perp \overline{BD}$	3) Through two points, there is one unique line perpendicular to a given line.

You can use Theorems 50 and 51 to find angle measures in a rhombus.

Problem 2 *continued*

Q What is the measure of $\angle DBC$? Explain. **[58; $\overline{BD}$ is a diagonal of rhombus *ABCD*.]**

Q What is the sum of the measures of $\angle 4$ and $\angle 3$? Explain. **[90, since $\angle 1$ is a rt. $\angle$.]**

Got It? **ERROR PREVENTION**

Remind students that the sum of all four angles in rhombus *PQRS* is 360 because the figure is a quadrilateral. Hence, the sum of the measures of angles 3 and 4 must be 76. Diagonals bisect the opposite angles of a rhombus, so the measures of angles 3 and 4 are both 38.

Alternatively, point out that $\triangle PQR$ is an isosceles triangle with a vertex angle of 104°, so the two base angles, $\angle 1$ and $\angle 3$, would each have a measure of $\frac{180 - 104}{2} = 38$.

ANSWERS

Got It? $m\angle 1 = m\angle 2 = m\angle 3 = m\angle 4 = 38$

Practice

3. $m\angle 1 = 32$, $m\angle 2 = 90$, $m\angle 3 = 58$, $m\angle 4 = 32$
4. $m\angle 1 = 60$, $m\angle 2 = 90$, $m\angle 3 = 30$

▼ DIGITAL

Problem 2 Finding Angle Measures

What are the measures of the numbered angles in rhombus *ABCD*?

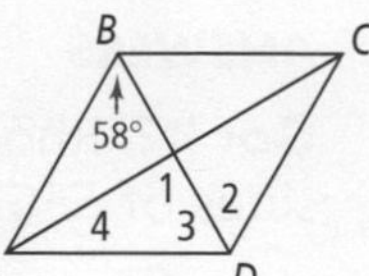

$m\angle 1 = 90$	The diagonals of a rhombus are $\perp$.
$m\angle 2 = 58$	Alternate Interior Angles Theorem
$m\angle 3 = 58$	Each diagonal of a rhombus bisects a pair of opposite angles.
$m\angle 1 + m\angle 3 + m\angle 4 = 180$	Triangle Angle-Sum Theorem
$90 + 58 + m\angle 4 = 180$	Substitute.
$148 + m\angle 4 = 180$	Simplify.
$m\angle 4 = 32$	Subtract 148 from each side.

▼ STUDENT PAGE 292

Got It? What are the measures of the numbered angles in rhombus *PQRS*?

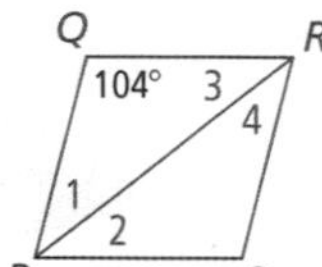

Think What type of triangle is $\triangle PQR$?

A Practice **Find the measures of the numbered angles in each rhombus.**

3. 58°

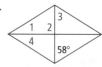

4.

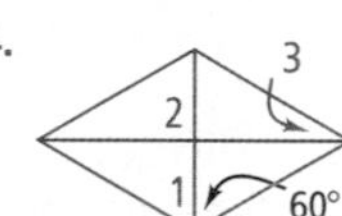

Problem 3 Finding Diagonal Length

Take Note

Ask students the following question in preparation for the proof of the theorem.

Q What congruence theorem can you use to prove that $\triangle ABC \cong \triangle DCB$? Explain. **[SAS, you know that $\overline{AB} \cong \overline{DC}$, $\overline{BC} \cong \overline{BC}$, and $\angle ABC \cong \angle DCB$.]**

▼ STUDENT PAGE 292

The diagonals of a rectangle also have a special property.

take note

Theorem 52

Theorem	If . . .	Then . . .
If a parallelogram is a rectangle, then its diagonals are congruent.	*ABCD* is a rectangle	$\overline{AC} \cong \overline{BD}$

You will prove Theorem 52 in Exercise 30.

Problem 3 **TACTILE LEARNERS**

Q If a student selects answer choice B, what mistake is he or she likely making? **[The student is likely indicating the value of x rather than the length of $\overline{RB}$.]**

Q Could you also substitute the value of x into the expression $2x + 15$ to find RB? Explain. **[Yes, $RB = SF$, so you can use either expression.]**

Got It? **DESCRIPTOR**

Q What is the length of $\overline{PM}$? of $\overline{PN}$? Explain. **[The length of both segments is 21.5. $\overline{MO}$ and $\overline{LN}$ are bisectors of each other and $MO = LN = 43$.]**

ANSWERS

Got It? a. 43 **b.** Isosc.; diagonals of a rectangle are ≅ and bisect each other.

Practice

5. $x = 3$; $LN = MP = 7$ **6.** $x = 1$; $LN = MP = 4$

▼ DIGITAL

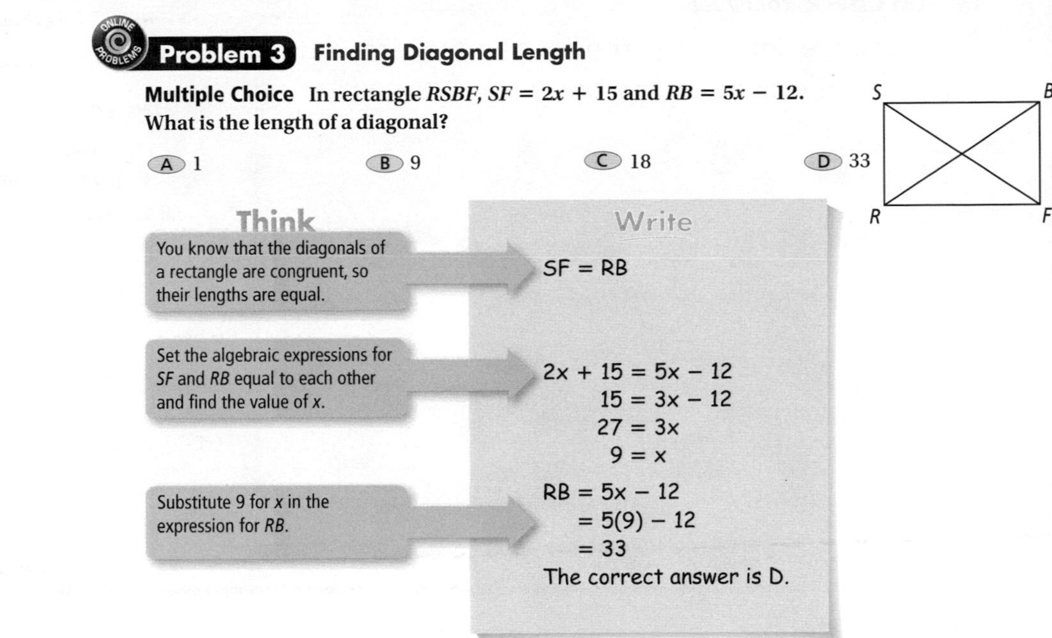

Problem 3 Finding Diagonal Length
Multiple Choice In rectangle RSBF, SF = 2x + 15 and RB = 5x − 12. What is the length of a diagonal?
A 1
B 9
C 18
D 33
S
B
R
F
Think
Write
You know that the diagonals of a rectangle are congruent, so their lengths are equal.
SF = RB
Set the algebraic expressions for SF and RB equal to each other and find the value of x.
2x + 15 = 5x − 12
15 = 3x − 12
27 = 3x
9 = x
Substitute 9 for x in the expression for RB.
RB = 5x − 12
= 5(9) − 12
= 33
The correct answer is D.

▼ STUDENT PAGE 293

Got It? **a.** If $LN = 4x - 17$ and $MO = 2x + 13$, what are the lengths of the diagonals of rectangle $LMNO$?

b. Reasoning What type of triangle is $\triangle PMN$? Explain.

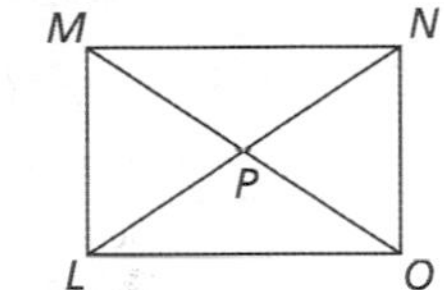

Practice **Algebra** $LMNP$ is a rectangle. Find the value of x and the length of each diagonal.

5. $LN = 5x - 8$ and $MP = 2x + 1$

6. $LN = 3x + 1$ and $MP = 8x - 4$

3 Lesson Check

Do you know HOW?

If students have difficulty with Exercise 9, then have them identify which angles are congruent and which angles are supplementary.

Do you UNDERSTAND?

If students have difficulty with Exercise 12, then have them identify the special parallelogram that the classmate was likely thinking of when he wrote the equation $2x + 8 = 9x - 6$.

Close

Q Why can quadrilaterals that are squares be considered the intersection of parallelograms, rhombuses, and rectangles? **[A quadrilateral that is a square must have all properties of parallelograms, rhombuses, and rectangles.]**

ANSWERS

7. Square. Since opp. angles of a ▱ are ≅ and consec. angles are supp., the ▱ has 4 rt. angles. Since the opp. sides of a ▱ are ≅, the ▱ has 4 ≅ sides. So the ▱ is a square. Because it is a square it is also a rhombus and a rectangle.

8. Rhombus; it has 4 ≅ sides, and no rt. angles.

9. $m\angle 1 = 40$, $m\angle 2 = 90$, $m\angle 3 = 50$

10. 4, 4

▼ STUDENT PAGE 294

Lesson Check

Do you know HOW?

Is each parallelogram a rhombus, rectangle, or square? Explain.

7.

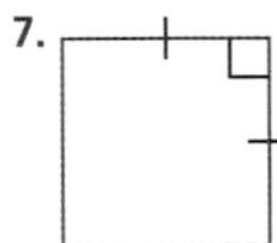

8.

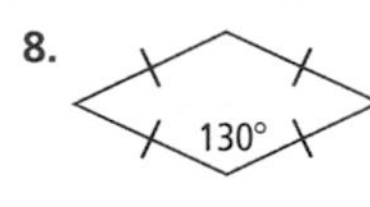

9. What are the measures of the numbered angles in the rhombus?

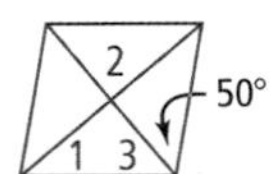

10. Algebra $JKLM$ is a rectangle. If $JL = 4x - 12$ and $MK = x$, what is the value of x? What is the length of each diagonal?

Lesson Check *continued*

11. rectangle and square; rhombus and square

12. The first step should be $2x + 8 + 9x - 6 = 90$.

▼ STUDENT PAGE 295

Do you UNDERSTAND?

11. Vocabulary Which special parallelograms are equiangular? Which special parallelograms are equilateral?

12. Error Analysis Your class needs to find the value of x for which ▱$DEFG$ is a rectangle. A classmate's work is shown at the right. What is the error? Explain.

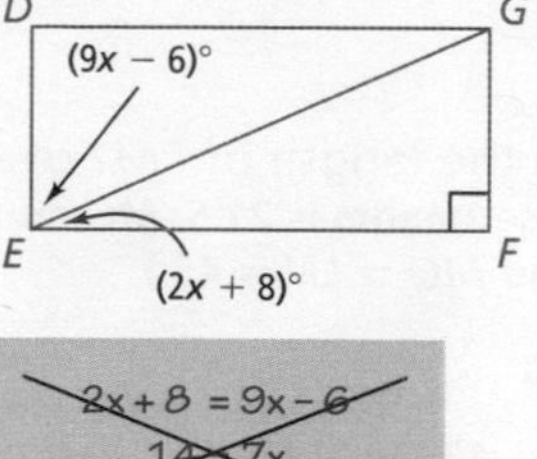

$2x + 8 = 9x - 6$

$14 = 7x$

$2 = x$

4 Practice

More Practice and Problem-Solving Exercises

ASSIGNMENT GUIDE

The assignments below are for the More Practice and Problem-Solving Exercises. You may also want to assign the A-Level Practice Exercises for homework if these are not used in class.

Average: 13–41

Advanced: 13–43

Mathematical Practices The exercises listed focus on the Standards for Mathematical Practices listed.

EX. 29: Make Sense of Problems (MP 1)

EX. 37: Persevere in Solving Problems (MP 1)

EX. 30: Construct Arguments (MP 3)

EX. 35: Communicate (MP 3)

EX. 12: Critique the Reasoning of Others (MP 3)

EXERCISE 36: Use the **Think About a Plan** worksheet in the Online Teacher Resources to further support students' development in becoming independent learners.

HOMEWORK QUICK CHECK

To check students' understanding of key skills and concepts, go over Exercises 19, 23, 31, 35, and 36.

ANSWERS

13. rhombus

14. ▱

15. rhombus

16. rectangle

17. rhombus, square

18. ▱, rhombus, rectangle, square

▼ STUDENT PAGES 295–296

More Practice and Problem-Solving Exercises

B Apply

Determine the most precise name for each quadrilateral.

13. **14.** 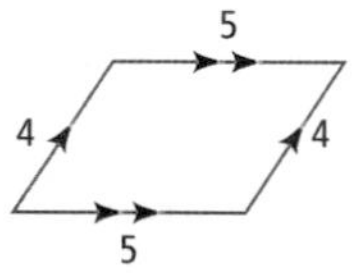 **15.** 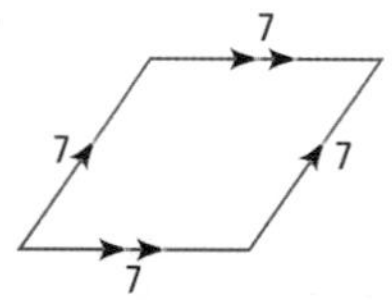 **16.**

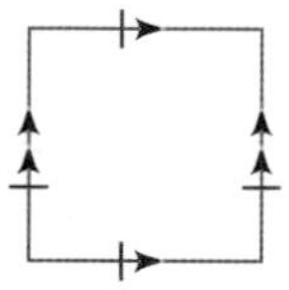

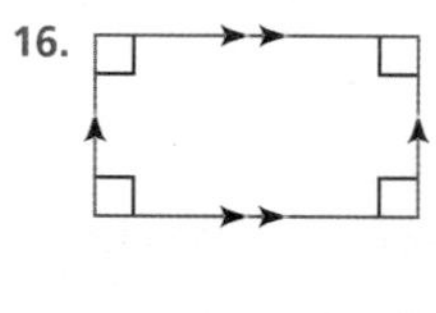

List the quadrilaterals that have the given property. Choose among *parallelogram, rhombus, rectangle,* and *square.*

17. All sides are ≅.

18. Opposite sides are ≅.

19. ▱, rhombus, rectangle, square
20. ▱, rhombus, rectangle, square
21. rectangle, square
22. ▱, rhombus, rectangle, square
23. ▱, rhombus, rectangle, square
24. rectangle, square
25. rhombus, square
26. rhombus, square
27. $x = 3$, $y = 5$; all sides are 15.
28. $x = 5$, $y = 4$; all sides are 3.
29. Answers may vary. Sample:
   1. *PLAN* is a rectangle. (Given)
   2. $\overline{PA} \cong \overline{LN}$ (Diagonals of a rectangle are ≅.)
   3. $TP = TL = TN = TA$ (Diagonals of a ▱ bisect each other.)
   4. $\angle LTP \cong \angle ATN$ (Vert. ∠s are ≅.)
   5. $\triangle LTP \cong \triangle NTA$ (SAS)
30. **a.** Given
   b. Def. of rectangle
   c. Refl. Prop. of ≅
   d. Def. of rectangle
   e. $\overline{AB} \cong \overline{DC}$
   f. $\triangle ABC \cong \triangle DCB$
   g. All rt. ∠s are ≅.
   h. Corresp. parts of ≅ △s are ≅.
31. 30
32. $x = 5$, $y = 32$, $z = 7.5$
33. $x = 7.5$, $y = 3$

19. Opposite sides are ∥.
20. Opposite ∠s are ≅.
21. All ∠s are right ∠s.
22. Consecutive ∠s are supplementary.
23. Diagonals bisect each other.
24. Diagonals are ≅.
25. Diagonals are ⊥.
26. Each diagonal bisects opposite ∠s.

Algebra **Find the values of the variables. Then find the side lengths.**

27. rhombus

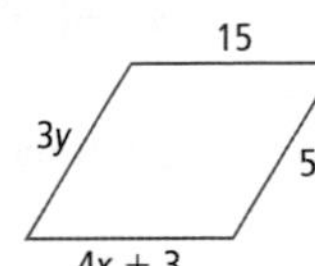

28. square

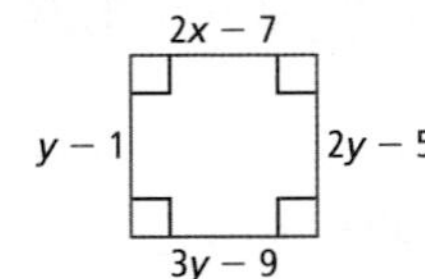

29. Think About a Plan Write a proof.
Proof

Given: Rectangle *PLAN*

Prove: $\triangle LTP \cong \triangle NTA$

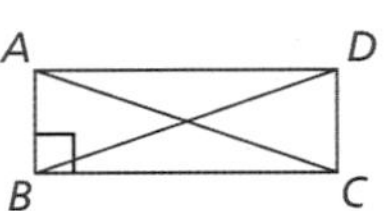

- What do you know about the diagonals of rectangles?
- Which triangle congruence postulate or theorem can you use?

30. Developing Proof Complete the flow proof of Theorem 52.

Given: *ABCD* is a rectangle.

Prove: $\overline{AC} \cong \overline{BD}$

A D B C

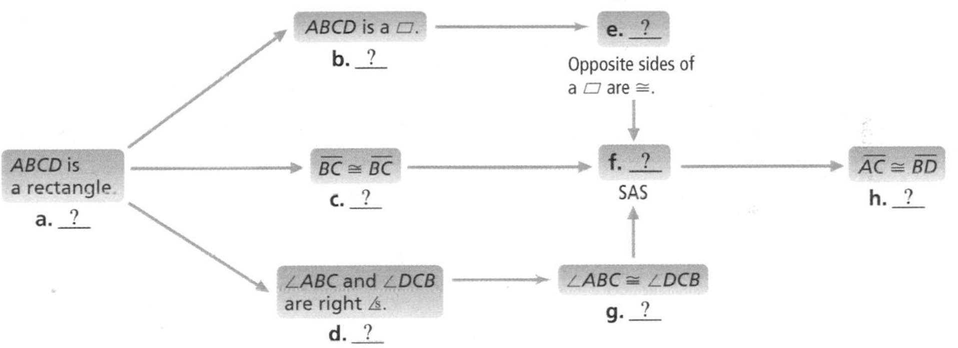

Algebra **Find the value(s) of the variable(s) for each parallelogram.**

31. $RZ = 2x + 5$, $SW = 5x - 20$

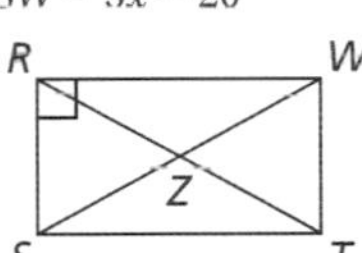

32. $m\angle 1 = 3y - 6$

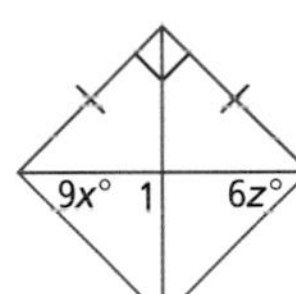

33. $BD = 4x - y + 1$

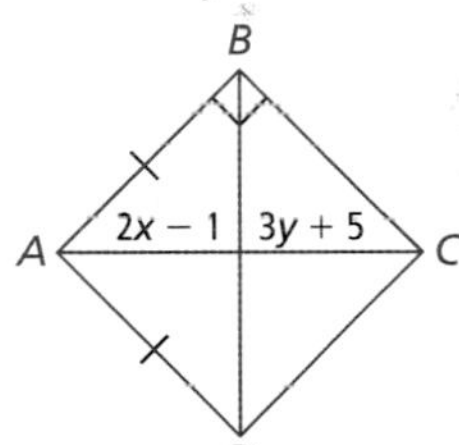

More Practice and Problem-Solving Exercises *continued*

34. Answers may vary. Sample:

1. $ABCD$ is a rhombus. (Given)
2. $\overline{AB} \cong \overline{AD}$ and $\overline{CB} \cong \overline{CD}$ (Def. of rhombus)
3. $\overline{AC} \cong \overline{AC}$ (Refl. Prop. of $\cong$)
4. $\triangle ABC \cong \triangle ADC$ (SSS)
5. $\angle 3 \cong \angle 4$ and $\angle 2 \cong \angle 1$. (Corresp. parts of $\cong$ ▲s are $\cong$.)
6. $\overline{AC}$ bisects $\angle BAD$ and $\angle BCD$. (Def. of $\angle$ bisector)

35. a. Opp. sides are $\cong$ and $\parallel$; opp. ∠s are $\cong$; consecutive ∠s are supp.; diagonals bisect each other.

b. All 4 sides are $\cong$; diagonals are $\perp$ and bisect opp. ∠s.

c. All 4 ∠s are rt. ∠s; diagonals are $\cong$.

36. $m\angle H = m\angle J = 58$, $m\angle K = m\angle G = 122$, $HK = KJ = JG = GH = 6$

37. Answers may vary. Sample:

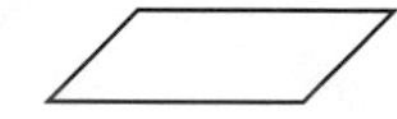

38. $AC = BC = 16$

39. $AC = BD = 2$

40. $AC = BD = 1$

41. $AC = BD = 1$

42. 4

43. 6

▼ STUDENT PAGE 297

34. Prove Theorem 51.
Proof

Given: $ABCD$ is a rhombus.

Prove: $\overline{AC}$ bisects $\angle BAD$ and $\angle BCD$.

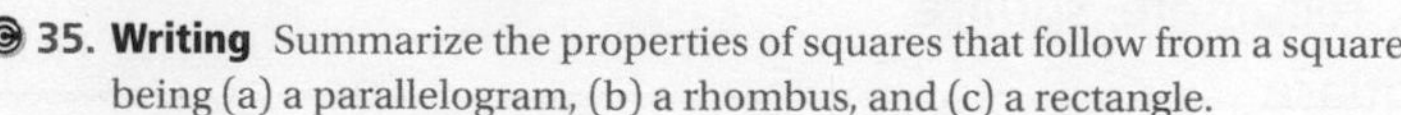

35. Writing Summarize the properties of squares that follow from a square being (a) a parallelogram, (b) a rhombus, and (c) a rectangle.

36. Algebra Find the angle measures and the side lengths of the rhombus at the right.

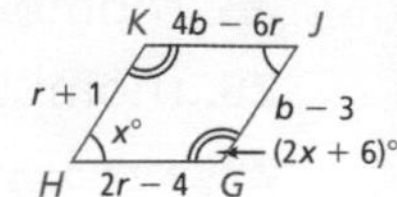

37. Open-Ended On graph paper, draw a parallelogram that is neither a rectangle nor a rhombus.

Algebra $ABCD$ **is a rectangle. Find the length of each diagonal.**

38. $AC = 2(x - 3)$ and $BD = x + 5$

39. $AC = 2(5a + 1)$ and $BD = 2(a + 1)$

40. $AC = \frac{3y}{5}$ and $BD = 3y - 4$

41. $AC = \frac{3c}{9}$ and $BD = 4 - c$

Challenge

Algebra Find the value of x in the rhombus.

42. $(7x + 10)°$ $(3x + 6)°$

43.

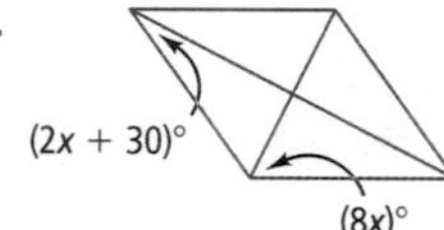

5 Assess and Remediate

Lesson Quiz

1. Is parallelogram *KLMN* a rhombus, a rectangle, or a square? Explain.

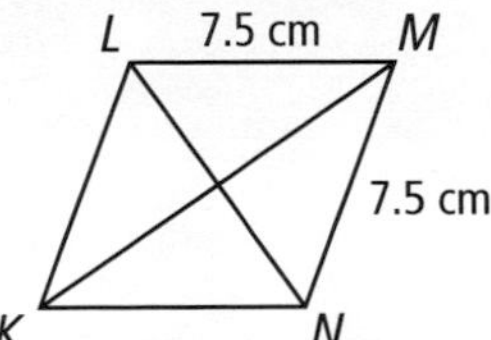

2. In the parallelogram above, if $m\angle KLN = 63$, what is $m\angle MNL$?
3. In square *ABCD*, $AE = 3x + 5$ and $BD = 10x + 2$. What is the length of $\overline{AC}$?

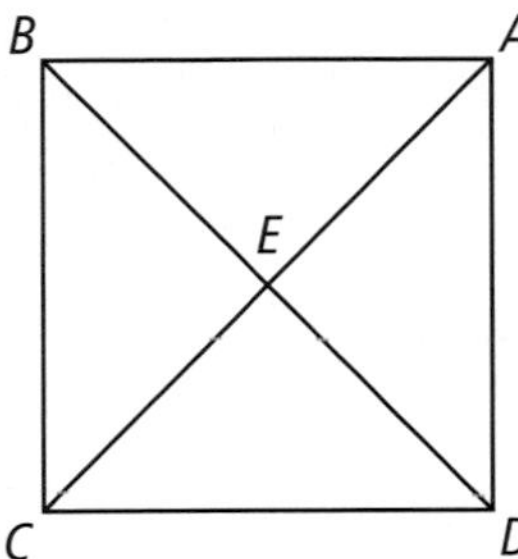

4. **Do you UNDERSTAND?** You are asked to draw an equiangular rhombus, an equilateral rectangle, and a parallelogram with four right angles. Will all three figures be squares?

ANSWERS TO LESSON QUIZ

1. rhombus; The opposite sides of a parallelogram are congruent, so the figure has 4 congruent sides.
2. 63
3. 22
4. A parallelogram with four right angles is a rectangle but not necessarily a square.

Prescription for Remediation

Use the student work on the Lesson Quiz to prescribe a differentiated assignment.

Points	Differentiated Remediation
0–2	Intervention
3	On-level
4	Extension

Online Assessment

Assign the Lesson Quiz in Success Tracker on **pearsonsuccessnet.com**. Success Tracker will automatically score the quiz and assign appropriate intervention or enrichment to each student based on the results. The compiled data appear in three different reports for instant analysis of whole class and individual student performance.

Differentiated Remediation

Intervention

- **RETEACHING** (2 pages) Provides reteaching and practice exercises for the key lesson concepts. Use with struggling students or absent students.
- **ENGLISH LANGUAGE LEARNER SUPPORT** Helps students develop and reinforce mathematical vocabulary and key concepts.

On-Level

- **PRACTICE** (2 pages) Provides extra practice for each lesson. For simpler practice exercises, use the Form K Practice pages found in the Online Teacher Resources.
- **THINK ABOUT A PLAN** Helps students develop specific problem-solving skills and strategies by providing scaffolded guiding questions.
- **STANDARDIZED TEST PREP** Focuses on all major exercises, all major question types, and helps students prepare for the high-stakes assessments.

Extension

- **ENRICHMENT** Provides students with interesting problems and activities that extend the concepts of the lesson.
- **ACTIVITIES, GAMES, AND PUZZLES** Worksheets that can be used for concept development, enrichment, and for fun!

5-5 Conditions for Rhombuses, Rectangles, and Squares

Common Core State Standards
G.CO.11 Prove theorems about parallelograms . . . rectangles are parallelograms with congruent diagonals. **Also G.SRT.5**

Preparing to Teach

BIG idea Reasoning and Proof

ESSENTIAL UNDERSTANDING

A parallelogram can be shown to be a rhombus, rectangle, or square based on the properties of its diagonals.

Math Background

In this lesson, students expand their understanding of special quadrilaterals to include rhombuses, rectangles, and squares. They explore the relationship between side lengths and diagonals of these figures. If students were to draw a Venn diagram to demonstrate the relationship between rhombuses, rectangles, and squares, they would see that rhombuses and rectangles have different characteristics. However, since squares are both rectangles and rhombuses, the intersection of the two figures is the set of all squares.

ELL Support

FOCUS ON COMMUNICATION Summarize the most important concepts. Because Theorems 53, 54, and 55 are important for students to know, either tell students repeatedly of their importance, or have a place on the board labeled "Important" and write the concepts, theorems, or key words that are the most important for students to learn.

ASSESS UNDERSTANDING Have students draw a diagram for the following word problem.

Mr. Brown is building a shed with a square floor. If one wall of the shed is 8 ft, how can Mr. Brown make sure the shed is a square?

Mathematical Practices

MODEL WITH MATHEMATICS. In Problem 3, students will utilize their knowledge of the relationship of rectangular diagonals in setting up an appropriate space for a patio.

1 Interactive Learning

Solve It!

PURPOSE To explore how to determine if a given figure is a rhombus

PROCESS Students may use previous knowledge of the properties of rhombuses and parallelograms and visual inspection.

Q What formula can you use to examine whether points form a rhombus? **[the Distance Formula]**

Q What formula can you use to examine whether points form a rectangle? **[the Slope Formula]**

ANSWER square: *OEFA*, because it has 4 rt. angles and 4 ≅ sides; rhombus: *OEDG*, because it has 4 ≅ sides of length 5; rectangle: *EHDL*, because it has 4 rt. angles and opp. sides ≅.

CONNECT THE MATH In the Solve It, students identify figures that satisfy the definitions of rhombuses, rectangles, and squares. In this lesson, students use properties of diagonals to classify special parallelograms.

▼ DIGITAL (STUDENT WORK SPACE PAGE 298)

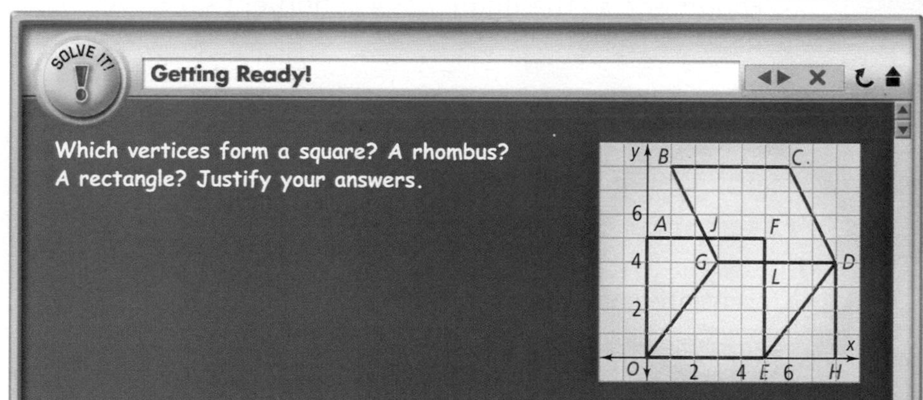

2 Guided Instruction

▼ STUDENT PAGES 298–299

Problem 1 Identifying Special Parallelograms

Take Note

Theorem 53

Point out to students that although the theorem states the parallelogram is a rhombus, that rhombus could be a square if the necessary conditions are met.

Take Note

Theorem 54

Q Is $\angle 1$ congruent to any other angles in the diagram? Explain. **[$\angle ABC$ and $\angle CDA$ are congruent; $\angle 1$ is congruent to $\angle 3$ because $m\angle 1 = \frac{1}{2}m\angle ABC$ and $m\angle 3 = \frac{1}{2}m\angle CDA$. Also, $\angle 4 \cong \angle 1$ by the Alternate Interior Angles Theorem.]**

Q Are the two triangles formed by the diagonal congruent? Explain. **[Yes, they are congruent by ASA.]**

Take Note

Theorem 55

Point out to students that this theorem is the converse of Theorem 52 from Lesson 5-4. Remind students that these two theorems can be stated as the biconditional "A parallelogram is a rectangle if and only if its diagonals are congruent."

Essential Understanding You can determine whether a parallelogram is a rhombus or a rectangle based on the properties of its diagonals.

take note — Theorem 53

Theorem	If . . .	Then . . .
If the diagonals of a parallelogram are perpendicular, then the parallelogram is a rhombus.	$ABCD$ is a ▱ and $\overline{AC} \perp \overline{BD}$	$ABCD$ is a rhombus

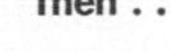
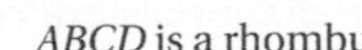
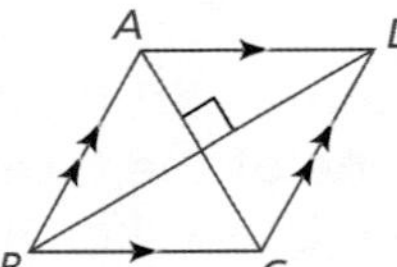

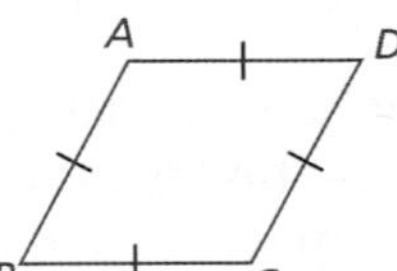

Proof Proof of Theorem 53

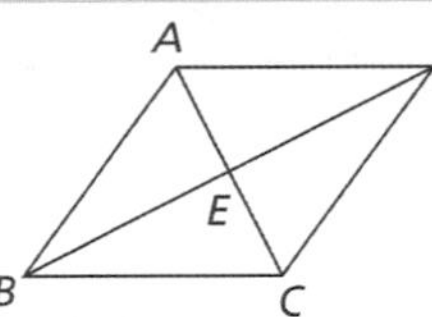

Given: $ABCD$ is a parallelogram, $\overline{AC} \perp \overline{BD}$

Prove: $ABCD$ is a rhombus.

Since $ABCD$ is a parallelogram, $\overline{AC}$ and $\overline{BD}$ bisect each other, so $\overline{BE} \cong \overline{DE}$. Since $\overline{AC} \perp \overline{BD}$, $\angle AED$ and $\angle AEB$ are congruent right angles. By the Reflexive Property of Congruence, $\overline{AE} \cong \overline{AE}$.

So $\triangle AEB \cong \triangle AED$ by SAS. Corresponding parts of congruent triangles are congruent, so $\overline{AB} \cong \overline{AD}$. Since opposite sides of a parallelogram are congruent, $\overline{AB} \cong \overline{DC} \cong \overline{BC} \cong \overline{AD}$. By definition, $ABCD$ is a rhombus.

take note — Theorem 54

Theorem	If . . .	Then . . .
If one diagonal of a parallelogram bisects a pair of opposite angles, then the parallelogram is a rhombus.	$ABCD$ is a ▱, $\angle 1 \cong \angle 2$, and $\angle 3 \cong \angle 4$	$ABCD$ is a rhombus

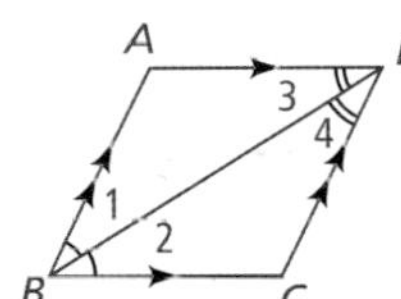

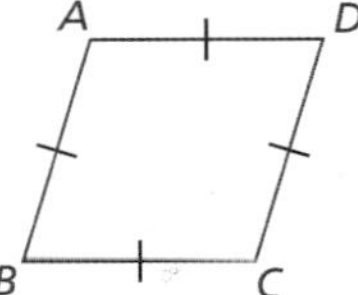

You will prove Theorem 54 in Exercise 21.

Theorem 55

Theorem	If . . .	Then . . .
If the diagonals of a parallelogram are congruent, then the parallelogram is a rectangle.	$ABCD$ is a ▱, and $\overline{AC} \cong \overline{BD}$	$ABCD$ is a rectangle

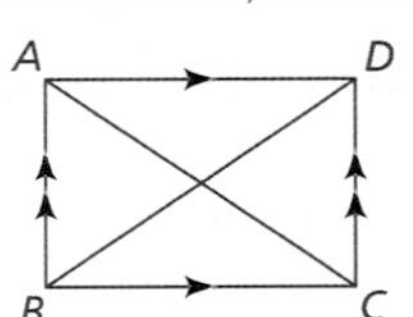

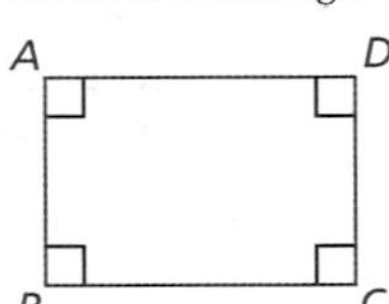

You will prove Theorem 55 in Exercise 22.

Problem 1 *continued*

Q What two conditions concerning the diagonals of a parallelogram indicate that the figure is also a rhombus? **[You can conclude that the parallelogram is a rhombus if a diagonal bisects the opposite angles or if the diagonals are shown to be perpendicular.]**

Q What conditions concerning the diagonals of a parallelogram indicate that the figure is also a rectangle? **[You can conclude that the parallelogram is a rectangle if the diagonals are congruent.]**

Got It?

Students may have difficulty answering part (b) if they think that they must choose one of the three quadrilaterals given as their answer. Use a sketch to remind students that all parallelograms have diagonals that bisect each other.

ANSWERS

Got It? a. The ▱ is not a rectangle or a square because angles are not rt. angles. It might be a rhombus. **b.** No; the fact that the diagonals bisect each other is true of all parallelograms.

Practice

1. Rhombus; one diagonal bisects a pair of opp. angles.
2. No; you only know that the diagonals bisect each other, which is true of all parallelograms.

▼ STUDENT PAGE 299

You can use Theorems 53, 54, and 55 to classify parallelograms. Notice that if a parallelogram is both a rectangle and a rhombus, then it is a square.

▼ DIGITAL

Problem 1 Identifying Special Parallelograms

Can you conclude that the parallelogram is a rhombus, a rectangle, or a square? Explain.

A

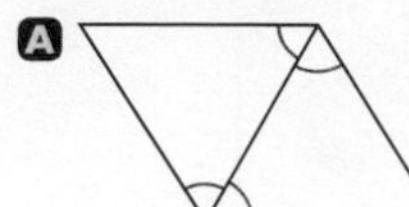

Yes. A diagonal bisects two angles. By Theorem 54, this parallelogram is a rhombus.

B

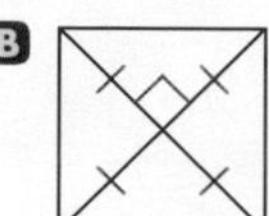

Yes. The diagonals are congruent, so by Theorem 55, this parallelogram is a rectangle. The diagonals are perpendicular, so by Theorem 53, it is a rhombus. Therefore, this parallelogram is a square.

▼ STUDENT PAGES 299–300

Got It? **a.** A parallelogram has angle measures of 20, 160, 20, and 160. Can you conclude that it is a rhombus, a rectangle, or a square? Explain.

b. Reasoning Suppose the diagonals of a quadrilateral bisect each other. Can you conclude that it is a rhombus, a rectangle, or a square? Explain.

Think

How can you determine whether a figure is a special parallelogram?

Practice **Can you conclude that the parallelogram is a rhombus, a rectangle, or a square? Explain.**

1.

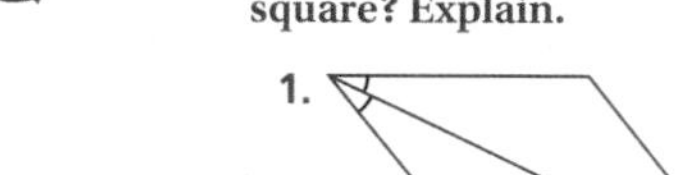

2.

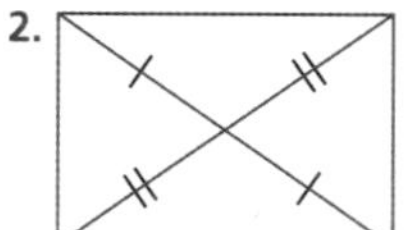

Problem 2 Using Properties of Special Parallelograms

Q Is ▱$ABCD$ also a square? Explain. **[No, the measure of ∠B is 56 degrees given that $x = 5$.]**

Q What equation can you use to determine for what value of x ▱$ABCD$ is a rectangle? **[$6x - 2 + 4x + 8 = 90$]**

▼ DIGITAL

Problem 2 Using Properties of Special Parallelograms

Algebra **For what value of *x* is ▱*ABCD* a rhombus?**

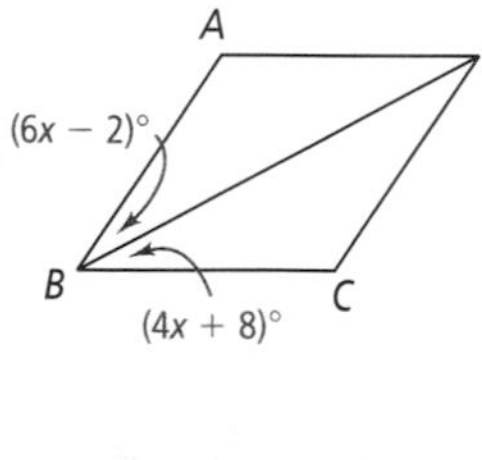

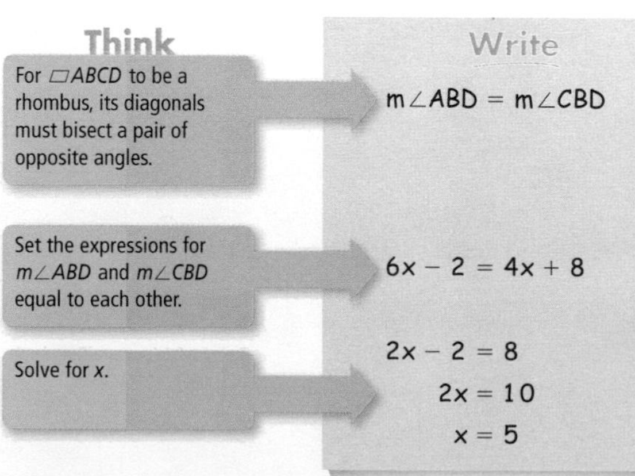

Think
Write
For ▱ABCD to be a rhombus, its diagonals must bisect a pair of opposite angles.
m∠ABD = m∠CBD
Set the expressions for m∠ABD and m∠CBD equal to each other.
6x − 2 = 4x + 8
Solve for x.
2x − 2 = 8
2x = 10
x = 5

Got It?

Q What statements are true about the diagonals of a rectangle? **[The diagonals bisect each other and are congruent.]**

Q What equation can you use to determine for what value of y ▱$DEFG$ is a rectangle? **[$5y + 3 = 7y - 5$]**

ANSWERS

Got It? 4

Practice

3. 12

4. 10

▼ STUDENT PAGES 300–301

Think

What do you know about the diagonals of a rectangle?

Got It? For what value of y is ▱$DEFG$ a rectangle?

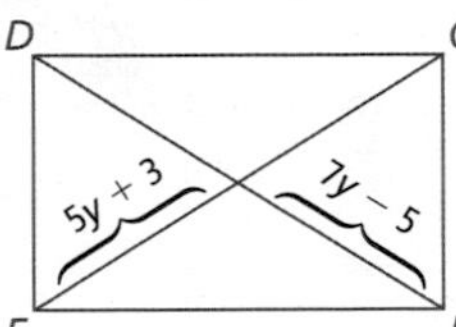

Practice **For what value of x is the figure the given special parallelogram?**

3. rhombus

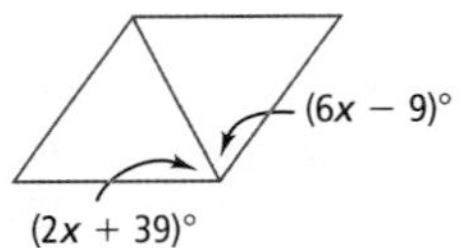

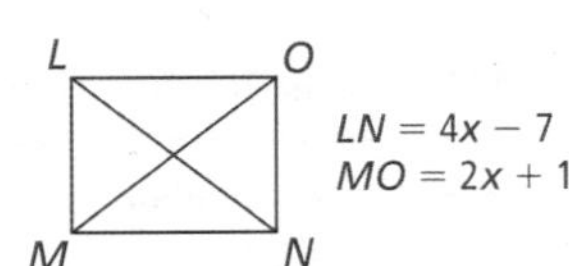

4. rectangle

Problem 3 Using Properties of Parallelograms

Q What kind of shape(s) can be formed if the ropes are made to bisect each other but are not congruent? **[Only rhombuses or other parallelograms can be formed.]**

Q What kind of shape(s) can be formed if the ropes are congruent but do not bisect each other? **[Only quadrilaterals can be formed.]**

Got It? **TACTILE LEARNERS**

Ask students to use strands of spaghetti to form a square as in Problem 3. State all conditions the diagonals must meet in order to make the square.

ANSWERS

Got It? Yes; make diagonals ⊥. The result will be a rectangle and a rhombus, so it is a square.

Practice

5. Answers may vary. Sample: Measure opp. sides; if they are ≅, then it is a ▱ by Thm. 45. Then measure the diagonals; if they are ≅, then the bookshelf is a rectangle by Thm. 55.

▼ DIGITAL

Problem 3 **Using Properties of Parallelograms**

Community Service **Builders use properties of diagonals to "square up" rectangular shapes like building frames and playing-field boundaries. Suppose you are on the volunteer building team at the right. You are helping to lay out a rectangular patio for a youth center. How can you use properties of diagonals to locate the four corners?**

You can use two theorems.

- Theorem 48: If the diagonals of a quadrilateral bisect each other, then the quadrilateral is a parallelogram.
- Theorem 55: If the diagonals of a parallelogram are congruent, then the parallelogram is a rectangle.

Step 1 Cut two pieces of rope that will be the diagonals of the foundation rectangle. Cut them the same length because of Theorem 55.

Step 2 Join the two pieces of rope at their midpoints because of Theorem 48.

Step 3 Pull the ropes straight and taut. The ends of the ropes will be the corners of a rectangle.

▼ STUDENT PAGE 301

Got It? Can you adapt the method described in Problem 3 to stake off a square play area? Explain.

Practice **5. Carpentry** A carpenter is building a bookcase. How can the carpenter use a tape measure to check that the bookshelf is rectangular? Justify your answer and name any theorems used.

3 Lesson Check

Do you know HOW?
If students have difficulty with Exercises 8–9, then have them review the definitions of rhombus and rectangle from Problem 1.

Do you UNDERSTAND?
If students have difficulty with Exercise 10, then remind them that there may be more than one special parallelogram for each property. For example, both squares and rectangles have diagonals that are congruent.

Close

Q If you conclude that quadrilateral *ABCD* is a square, what other names can be used to describe *ABCD*? **[If *ABCD* is a square, then it is also a parallelogram, a rhombus, and a rectangle.]**

ANSWERS

6. Rectangle; diagonals are ≅.
7. Rhombus; diagonals are ⊥.
8. 2
9. 3
10. a. rhombus, square
b. rectangle, square
c. rhombus, square
d. rectangle, rhombus, square
e. rhombus, square
11. The only parallelograms with ⊥ diagonals are rhombuses and squares.
12. Rectangle; diagonals are ≅.

▼ STUDENT PAGES 302–304

Lesson Check

Do you know HOW?

Can you conclude that the parallelogram is a rhombus, a rectangle, or a square? Explain.

6.

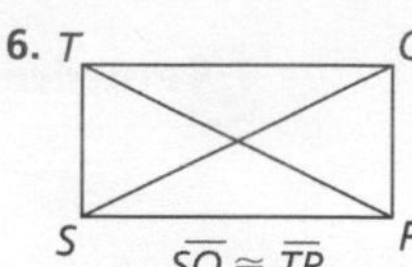

7.

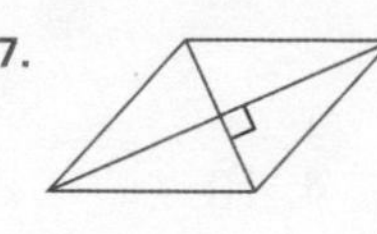

For what value of x is the figure the given special parallelogram?

8. rhombus

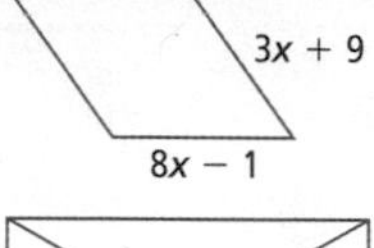

9. rectangle

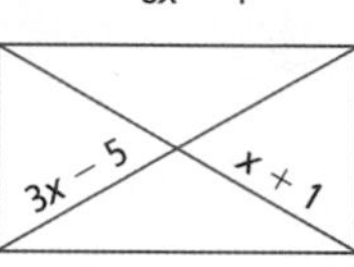

Do you UNDERSTAND?

10. Name all of the special parallelograms that have each property.
a. Diagonals are perpendicular.
b. Diagonals are congruent.
c. Diagonals are angle bisectors.
d. Diagonals bisect each other.
e. Diagonals are perpendicular bisectors of each other.

11. Error Analysis Your friend says, "A parallelogram with perpendicular diagonals is a rectangle." What is your friend's error? Explain.

12. Reasoning When you draw a circle and two of its diameters and connect the endpoints of the diameters, what quadrilateral do you get? Explain.

Practice

More Practice and Problem-Solving Exercises

ASSIGNMENT GUIDE
The assignments below are for the More Practice and Problem-Solving Exercises. You may also want to assign the A-Level Practice Exercises for homework if these are not used in class.
Average: 13–25
Advanced: 13–29

Mathematical Practices The exercises listed focus on the Standards for Mathematical Practices listed.

EX. 12: Make Sense of Problems (MP 1)
EX. 23–25: Persevere in Solving Problems (MP 1)
EX. 14, 18–20: Construct Arguments (MP 3)
EX. 11: Critique the Reasoning of Others (MP 3)
EX. 13: Model (MP 4)

STEM exercises focus on science or engineering applications.

EXERCISE 22: Use the **Think About a Plan** worksheet in the Online Teacher Resources to further support students' development in becoming independent learners.

HOMEWORK QUICK CHECK
To check students' understanding of key skills and concepts, go over Exercises 14, 16, 18, 22, and 23.

ANSWERS

13. Answers may vary. Sample: Measure the lengths of the frame's diagonals. If they are ≅, then the frame has the shape of a rectangle, and therefore a parallelogram; measure the two pairs of alt. int. angles formed by the turnbuckle (the transversal). If both pairs of angles are ≅, then both pairs of opposite sides of the frame are ∥.

14. Square; since it is a rhombus and a rectangle, it must be a square.

15. 11

16. 7

17. 16

18. Rectangle, square; answers may vary. Sample:

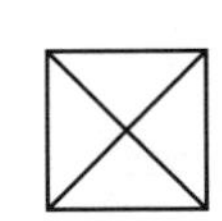

19. Rhombus; answers may vary. Sample:

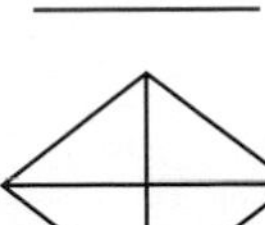

More Practice and Problem-Solving Exercises

B Apply

13. Hardware You can use a simple device called a turnbuckle to "square up" structures that are parallelograms. For the gate pictured at the right, you tighten or loosen the turnbuckle on the diagonal cable so that the rectangular frame will keep the shape of a parallelogram when it sags. What are two ways you can make sure that the turnbuckle works? Explain.

14. Reasoning Suppose the diagonals of a parallelogram are both perpendicular and congruent. What type of special quadrilateral is it? Explain your reasoning.

Algebra For what value of x is the figure the given special parallelogram?

15. rectangle **16.** rhombus **17.** rectangle

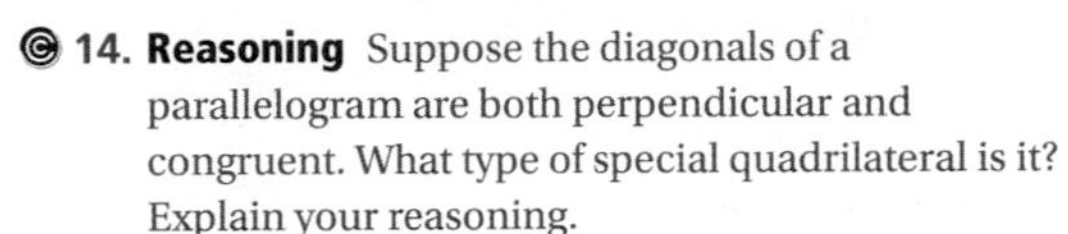

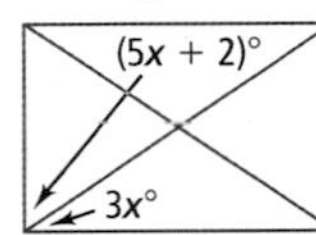

Open-Ended Given two segments with lengths a and b ($a \neq b$), what special parallelograms meet the given conditions? Show each sketch.

18. Both diagonals have length a.

19. The two diagonals have lengths a and b.

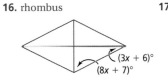

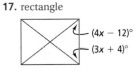

More Practice and Problem-Solving Exercises *continued*

20. Rectangle, rhombus, square; answers may vary. Sample:

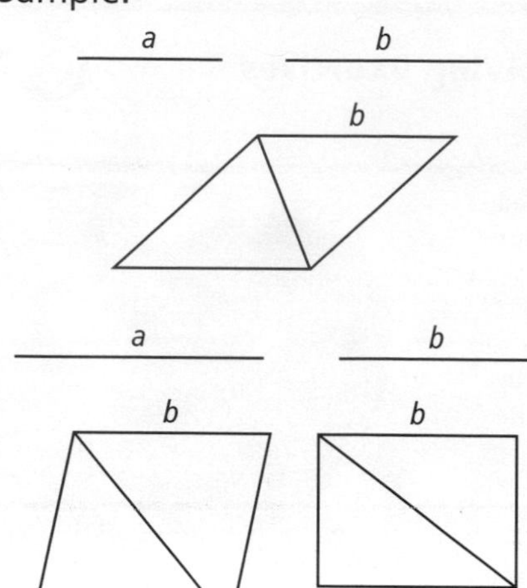

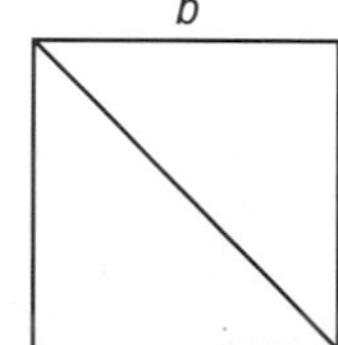

21. Answers may vary. Sample:
    1. $\overline{AC}$ bisects $\angle BAD$ and $\angle BCD$. (Given)
    2. $\angle 1 \cong \angle 2$ and $\angle 3 \cong \angle 4$. (Def. of bisect)
    3. $\overline{AC} \cong \overline{AC}$ (Refl. Prop. of $\cong$)
    4. $\triangle ABC \cong \triangle ADC$ (ASA)
    5. $\overline{AB} \cong \overline{AD}$ and $\overline{BC} \cong \overline{DC}$. (Corresp. parts of $\cong$ △s are $\cong$.)
    6. $\overline{AB} \cong \overline{CD}$ and $\overline{BC} \cong \overline{AD}$. (Opp. sides of a ▱ are $\cong$.)
    7. $\overline{AB} \cong \overline{AD} \cong \overline{BC} \cong \overline{CD}$ (Trans. Prop. of $\cong$)
    8. $ABCD$ is a rhombus. (Def. of rhombus)
22. Answers may vary. Sample:
    1. $\overline{AC} \cong \overline{BD}$, ▱$ABCD$ (Given)
    2. $\overline{AD} \cong \overline{BC}$ (Opposite sides of a ▱ are $\cong$.)
    3. $\overline{DC} \cong \overline{DC}$ (Refl. Prop. of $\cong$)
    4. $\triangle ADC \cong \triangle BCD$ (SSS)
    5. $\angle ADC \cong \angle BCD$ (Corresp. parts of $\cong$ △s are $\cong$.)
    6. $m\angle ADC + m\angle BCD = 180$ (Same-side int. ∠s are suppl.)
    7. $\angle ADC$ and $\angle BCD$ are rt. ∠s (Def. of rt. ∠)
    8. $ABCD$ is a rectangle. (Def. of rectangle)
23. Construct the midpt. of each diagonal. Copy the diagonals so the two midpts. coincide. Connect the endpoints of the diagonals.
24. Construct the midpt. of $\cong$ diagonals. Copy the diagonals so the two midpts. coincide. Connect the endpoints of the diagonals.

▼ STUDENT PAGE 305

20. One diagonal has length a, and one side of the quadrilateral has length b.

Proof 21. Prove Theorem 54.

Given: $ABCD$ is a parallelogram. $\overline{AC}$ bisects $\angle BAD$ and $\angle BCD$.

Prove: $ABCD$ is a rhombus.

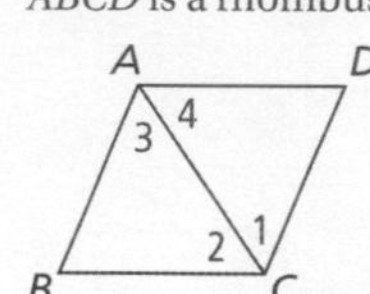

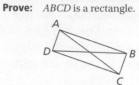

Proof 22. Prove Theorem 55.

Given: ▱$ABCD$, $\overline{AC} \cong \overline{BD}$

Prove: $ABCD$ is a rectangle.

Think About a Plan **Explain how to construct each figure given its diagonals.**
- What do you know about the diagonals of each figure?
- How can you apply constructions to what you know about the diagonals?

23. parallelogram
24. rectangle
25. rhombus

Challenge

Determine whether the quadrilateral can be a parallelogram. Explain.

26. The diagonals are congruent, but the quadrilateral has no right angles.
27. Each diagonal is 3 cm long and two opposite sides are 2 cm long.
28. Two opposite angles are right angles, but the quadrilateral is not a rectangle.

Proof 29. In Theorem 54, replace "a pair of opposite angles" with "one angle." Write a paragraph that proves this new statement to be true, or give a counterexample to prove it to be false.

25. Construct the midpts. of each diagonal. Construct two ⊥ lines, and mark off diagonal lengths on the ⊥ lines. Connect the endpoints of the diagonals.
26. No; if the diagonals of a ▱ are $\cong$, then it would have to be a rectangle and have rt. angles.
27. Yes; $\cong$ diagonals in a ▱ mean it can be a rectangle with 2 opp. sides 2 cm long.
28. No; in a ▱, consecutive angles must be suppl., so all angles must be rt. This would make it a rectangle.
29. "If one diagonal of a ▱ bisects one ∠, then the ▱ is a rhombus." The new statement is true. If $\overline{AC}$ bisects $\angle BCD$, then $\angle BCA \cong \angle DCA$. (Def. of ∠ bisector) $ABCD$ is a ▱, so $\angle B \cong \angle D$. (Opp. ∠s of a ▱ are $\cong$.) $\overline{AC} \cong \overline{AC}$ (Reflexive Prop. of $\cong$), so $\triangle BCA \cong \triangle DCA$ (AAS) and $\overline{BC} \cong \overline{DC}$. (Corresp. parts of $\cong$ △s are $\cong$.) Since opp. sides of a ▱ are $\cong$, $\overline{AB} \cong \overline{CD}$ and $\overline{BC} \cong \overline{DA}$. So $\overline{AB} \cong \overline{BC} \cong \overline{CD} \cong \overline{DA}$, and ▱$ABCD$ is a rhombus. (Def. of rhombus)

Assess and Remediate

Lesson Quiz

1. Can you conclude that the parallelogram is a rhombus, a rectangle, or a square? Explain.

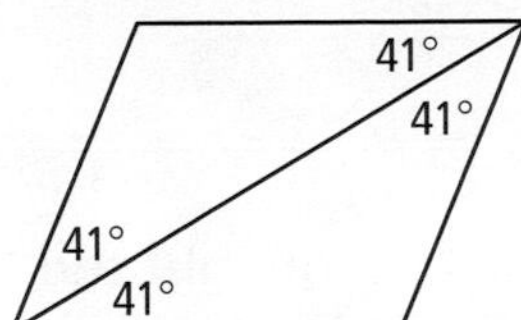

2. For what value of x is parallelogram $ABCD$ a rectangle?

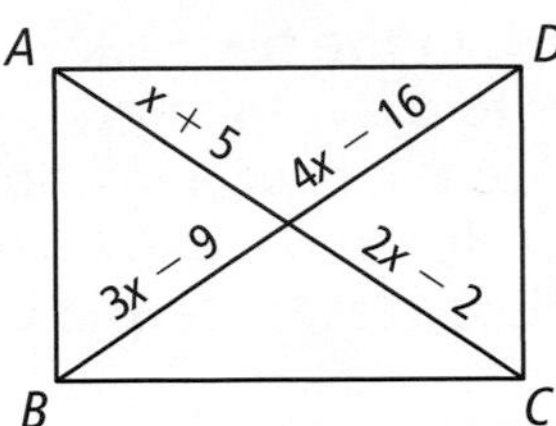

3. **Do you UNDERSTAND?** Given $WRST$ is a parallelogram and $\overline{WS} \cong \overline{RT}$, how can you classify $WRST$? Explain.

ANSWERS TO LESSON QUIZ

1. Rhombus; the diagonal bisects a pair of opposite angles, so the figure is a rhombus by Theorem 54. Also, by ASA and the converse of the Isosceles Triangle Theorem, all four sides are congruent.
2. 7
3. Rectangle; $\overline{WS}$ and $\overline{RT}$ are congruent diagonals, and by Theorem 55, $WRST$ is a rectangle.

Prescription for Remediation

Use the student work on the Lesson Quiz to prescribe a differentiated assignment.

Points	Differentiated Remediation
0–1	Intervention
2	On-level
3	Extension

Online Assessment

Assign the Lesson Quiz in Success Tracker on **pearsonsuccessnet.com**. Success Tracker will automatically score the quiz and assign appropriate intervention or enrichment to each student based on the results. The compiled data appear in three different reports for instant analysis of whole class and individual student performance.

Differentiated Remediation

Intervention

- **RETEACHING** (2 pages) Provides reteaching and practice exercises for the key lesson concepts. Use with struggling students or absent students.
- **ENGLISH LANGUAGE LEARNER SUPPORT** Helps students develop and reinforce mathematical vocabulary and key concepts.

On-Level

- **PRACTICE** (2 pages) Provides extra practice for each lesson. For simpler practice exercises, use the Form K Practice pages found in the Online Teacher Resources.
- **THINK ABOUT A PLAN** Helps students develop specific problem-solving skills and strategies by providing scaffolded guiding questions.
- **STANDARDIZED TEST PREP** Focuses on all major exercises, all major question types, and helps students prepare for the high-stakes assessments.

Extension

- **ENRICHMENT** Provides students with interesting problems and activities that extend the concepts of the lesson.
- **ACTIVITIES, GAMES, AND PUZZLES** Worksheets that can be used for concept development, enrichment, and for fun!

5-6 Trapezoids and Kites

Common Core State Standards
G.SRT.5 Use congruence . . . criteria . . . to solve problems and to prove relationships in geometric figures. **Also G.CO.9**

Preparing to Teach

BIG idea Reasoning and Proof

ESSENTIAL UNDERSTANDING

The angles, sides, and diagonals of a trapezoid have certain properties.

Math Background

A kite is introduced in this lesson as the union of two isosceles triangles that share a common base. Construction methods for kites depend on a kite's relationship to circles. A kite can be formed by constructing two noncongruent intersecting circles. The sides of the kite are the radii connecting the centers of the two circles to the two intersection points of the circles.

Having studied all properties of all special quadrilaterals, students can now make a list of figures with common properties (congruent diagonals, perpendicular diagonals, mutually bisecting diagonals, reflectional symmetries).

ELL Support

FOCUS ON LANGUAGE Project the Essential Understanding paragraphs on the board and point to each word as you read the text, as students follow. Point out that vocabulary words are in boldface. Model how to underline or highlight the key words. Ask students to name cognates (same base word) of any key words.

As you encounter the vocabulary words in the text, ask: What is a *trapezoid*? Invite volunteers to draw the figure on the board and point out as you trace the base, legs, and base angles. Do the same with an isosceles trapezoid. Invite students to compare and contrast an isosceles trapezoid with other trapezoids.

Lesson Vocabulary

- trapezoid
- base
- leg
- base angle
- isosceles trapezoid
- midsegment of a trapezoid
- kite

Mathematical Practices

ATTEND TO PRECISION. Students will use clear definitions of kites and trapezoids in finding relationships between certain sides, angles, and so on.

Interactive Learning

Solve It!

PURPOSE To explore the properties of isosceles trapezoids

PROCESS Students may use previous knowledge of isosceles triangles, midsegments of triangles, and angle pairs formed when parallel lines are cut by a transversal.

Q How are the midsegments related to the base of each isosceles triangle? Explain. **[The midsegments are parallel to the base of each isosceles triangle by the Triangle Midsegment Theorem.]**

Q What are same-side interior angles? What property do they have? **[Same side interior angles are the angles formed along one side of the transversal when a transversal cuts two parallel lines. They are supplementary.]**

▼ DIGITAL (STUDENT WORK SPACE PAGE 306)

Getting Ready!

Two isosceles triangles form the figure at the right. Each white segment is a midsegment of a triangle. What can you determine about the angles in the orange region? In the green region? Explain.

ANSWER In each region, angles are either suppl. or ≅; the midsegment of each isosc. △ is ∥ to its base, so same-side int. angles in each region are suppl. Since the angles sharing the base of each isosc. △ are ≅, the angles sharing the midsegment of each △ are also ≅.

CONNECT THE MATH In the Solve It, students explore the midsegments of isosceles triangles. In this lesson, students learn the characteristics of trapezoids and kites, including the midsegments of trapezoids.

2 Guided Instruction

Problem 1 Finding Angle Measures in Trapezoids

Take Note

Drawing and labeling isosceles trapezoids in many different orientations can help students identify base angles of trapezoids.

Problem 1

Q How are the opposite angles in an isosceles trapezoid related? Explain. **[They are supplementary. Each pair of base angles is congruent and each pair of base angles is supplementary to the other same-side interior angle formed along the same leg.]**

Q What is the sum of the measures of all of the angles of an isosceles trapezoid? Explain. **[360, because it is a quadrilateral.]**

Got It?

Q What are the pairs of base angles in the diagram? **[$\angle Q$ and $\angle P$ are a pair of base angles and $\angle R$ and $\angle S$ are a pair of base angles.]**

Q What is the sum of $m\angle Q$ and $m\angle R$? Explain. **[The sum is 180, because these are same-side interior angles.]**

ANSWERS

Got It?

a. $m\angle P = m\angle Q = 74$, $m\angle S = 106$

b. Yes; $\overline{DE} \parallel \overline{CF}$ so same-side int. angles are suppl.

Practice

1. $m\angle 1 = 77$, $m\angle 2 = 103$, $m\angle 3 = 103$

2. $m\angle 1 = 49$, $m\angle 2 = 131$, $m\angle 3 = 131$

▼ STUDENT PAGE 306

In the Solve It, the orange and green regions are trapezoids. The entire figure is a kite. In this lesson, you will learn about these special quadrilaterals that are not parallelograms.

Essential Understanding The angles, sides, and diagonals of a trapezoid have certain properties.

A **trapezoid** is a quadrilateral with exactly one pair of parallel sides. The parallel sides of a trapezoid are called **bases**. The nonparallel sides are called **legs**. The two angles that share a base of a trapezoid are called **base angles**. A trapezoid has two pairs of base angles.

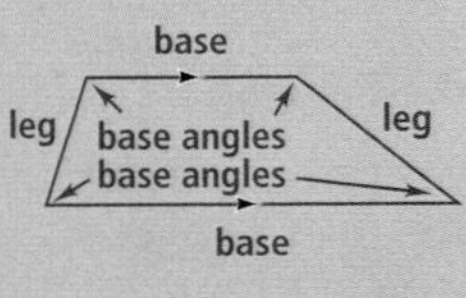

An **isosceles trapezoid** is a trapezoid with legs that are congruent. *ABCD* at the right is an isosceles trapezoid. The angles of an isosceles trapezoid have some unique properties.

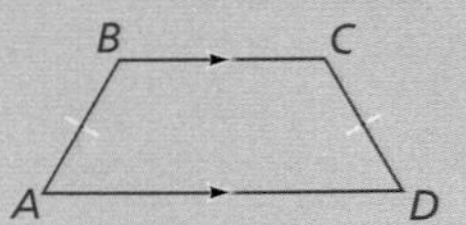

take note **Theorem 56**

Theorem	If . . .	Then . . .
If a quadrilateral is an isosceles trapezoid, then each pair of base angles is congruent.	*TRAP* is an isosceles trapezoid with bases $\overline{RA}$ and $\overline{TP}$ 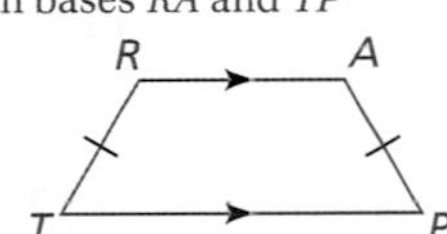	$\angle T \cong \angle P$, $\angle R \cong \angle A$ 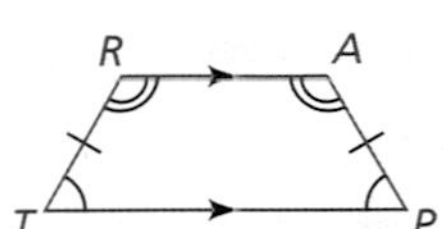

You will prove Theorem 56 in Exercise 35.

▼ DIGITAL

Problem 1 Finding Angle Measures in Trapezoids

***CDEF* is an isosceles trapezoid and $m\angle C = 65$. What are $m\angle D$, $m\angle E$, and $m\angle F$?**

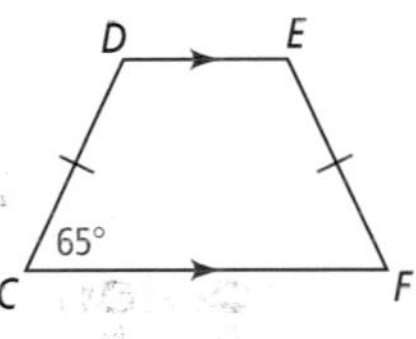

$m\angle C + m\angle D = 180$ Two angles that form same-side interior angles along one leg are supplementary.

$65 + m\angle D = 180$ Substitute.

$m\angle D = 115$ Subtract 65 from each side.

Since each pair of base angles of an isosceles trapezoid is congruent, $m\angle C = m\angle F = 65$ and $m\angle D = m\angle E = 115$.

▼ STUDENT PAGE 307

Got It? **a.** In the diagram, *PQRS* is an isosceles trapezoid and $m\angle R = 106$. What are $m\angle P$, $m\angle Q$, and $m\angle S$?

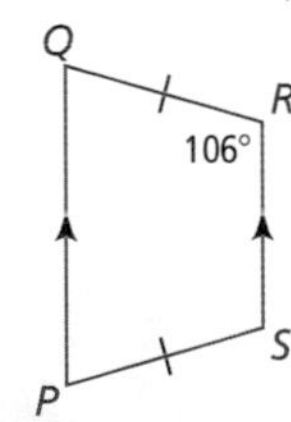

Think What do you know about the angles of an isosceles trapezoid?

b. Reasoning In Problem 1, if *CDEF* were not an isosceles trapezoid, would $\angle C$ and $\angle D$ still be supplementary? Explain.

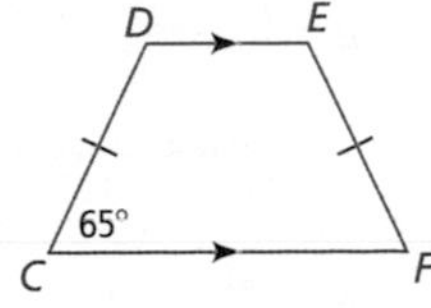

A Practice Find the measures of the numbered angles in each isosceles trapezoid.

1.

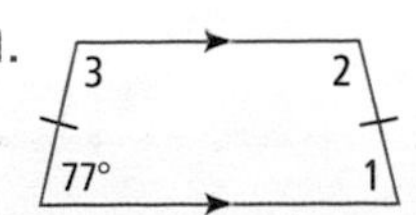

2.

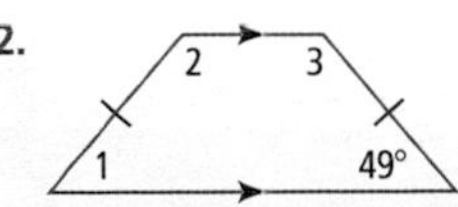

Problem 2 Finding Angle Measures in Isosceles Trapezoids

Q What figures are formed in the first ring of the paper fan? How many are formed? **[Twenty isosceles triangles are formed.]**

Q How are the base angles of the isosceles triangles related to the adjacent base angles of the isosceles trapezoids created in the second ring? Explain. **[The base angles are supplementary because they form a straight angle.]**

Q How are the obtuse base angles of the isosceles trapezoids related to the acute base angles of the isosceles trapezoids? Explain. **[They are supplementary. They form same-side interior angles.]**

Got It?

Direct students to verify that the total measure of the interior angles of a 15-sided polygon is the same as the sum of the measures of the base angles of the isosceles triangles and the same as the sum of the measures of the acute base angles of the isosceles trapezoids.

ANSWERS

Got It? Obtuse base angles measure 102; acute base angles measure 78.

Practice

3. $m\angle 1 = 105$, $m\angle 2 = m\angle 3 = 75$

4. $m\angle 1 = m\angle 2 = 120$, $m\angle 3 = 60$

▼ DIGITAL

Problem 2 Finding Angle Measures in Isosceles Trapezoids

Paper Fans The second ring of the paper fan shown at the right consists of 20 congruent isosceles trapezoids that appear to form circles. What are the measures of the base angles of these trapezoids?

Step 1 Find the measure of each angle at the center of the fan. This is the measure of the vertex angle of an isosceles triangle.

$$m\angle 1 = \frac{360}{20} = 18$$

Step 2 Find the measure of each acute base angle of an isosceles triangle.

$18 + x + x = 180$ Triangle Angle-Sum Theorem

$18 + 2x = 180$ Combine like terms.

$2x = 162$ Subtract 18 from each side.

$x = 81$ Divide each side by 2.

Step 3 Find the measure of each obtuse base angle of the isosceles trapezoid.

$81 + y = 180$ Two angles that form same-side interior angles along one leg are supplementary.

$y = 99$ Subtract 81 from each side.

Each acute base angle measures 81. Each obtuse base angle measures 99.

▼ STUDENT PAGE 308

Got It? A fan like the one in Problem 2 has 15 angles meeting at the center. What are the measures of the base angles of the trapezoids in its second ring?

Practice Find the measures of the numbered angles in each isosceles trapezoid.

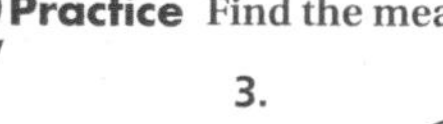

3.

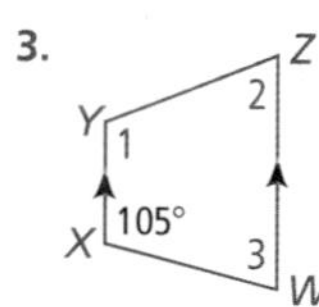

4.

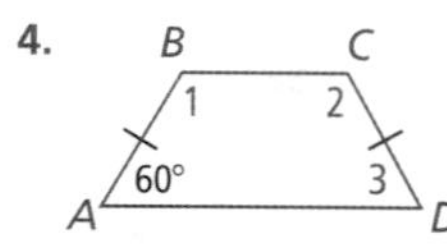

Problem 3 Using the Midsegment of a Trapezoid

Take Note

Theorem 57

Ask students the following questions in preparation for proving the theorem.

Q Do $\triangle ABD$ and $\triangle DCA$ have any congruent angles? Explain. **[Yes, $\angle BAD \cong \angle CDA$, Base angles of an isosceles trapezoid are congruent.]**

Q Do $\triangle ABD$ and $\triangle DCA$ have any congruent sides? Explain. **[Yes, the side they share, $\overline{AD}$, is congruent to itself and $\overline{AB} \cong \overline{CD}$ by def. of isosc. trap.]**

Take Note

Theorem 58

Ask students to compare and contrast this theorem with the Triangle Midsegment Theorem. This comparison will aid students in understanding and retaining the theorem.

▼ STUDENT PAGES 308–309

take note **Theorem 57**

Theorem	If . . .	Then . . .
If a quadrilateral is an isosceles trapezoid, then its diagonals are congruent.	*ABCD* is an isosceles trapezoid	$\overline{AC} \cong \overline{BD}$

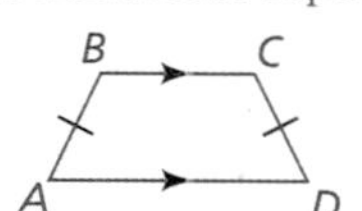

You will prove Theorem 57 in Exercise 43.

In Lesson 4-1, you learned about midsegments of triangles. Trapezoids also have midsegments. The **midsegment of a trapezoid** is the segment that joins the midpoints of its legs. The midsegment has two unique properties.

take note **Theorem 58** Trapezoid Midsegment Theorem

Theorem	If . . .	Then . . .
If a quadrilateral is a trapezoid, then (1) the midsegment is parallel to the bases, and (2) the length of the midsegment is half the sum of the lengths of the bases.	*TRAP* is a trapezoid with midsegment $\overline{MN}$	(1) $\overline{MN} \parallel \overline{TP}$, $\overline{MN} \parallel \overline{RA}$, and (2) $MN = \frac{1}{2}(TP + RA)$

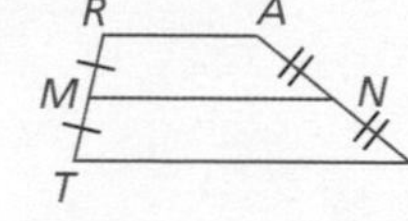

You will prove Theorem 58 in Lesson 14-8.

Problem 3

Q What is another way to describe the relationship of the midsegment and the bases? **[The length of the midsegment is equal to the mean of the lengths of the two bases.]**

Q How can you use the value of x to verify Theorem 58? **[Substitute 3 into the expressions and verify the relationship. $LM = 2$, $QR = 5$, so $(LM + PN) \div 2 = (2 + 8) \div 2 = 5$, which is the length of $\overline{QR}$.]**

Got It?

Q Is $\overline{MN} \parallel \overline{PS}$? Explain. **[Yes, The midsegment of a trapezoid is parallel to the bases of a trapezoid.]**

Q How is $\angle QMN$ related to $\angle MPS$? Explain. **[The angles are congruent because they are corresponding angles formed by parallel lines and a transversal.]**

ANSWERS

Got It? **a.** 6; 23 **b.** 3; 1; A △ has 3 midsegments joining any pair of side midpts. A trapezoid has 1 midsegment joining the midpts. of the two legs.

Practice

5. 11 **6.** 9

▼ DIGITAL

Problem 3 Using the Midsegment of a Trapezoid

Algebra $\overline{QR}$ is the midsegment of trapezoid $LMNP$. What is x?

$QR = \frac{1}{2}(LM + PN)$	Trapezoid Midsegment Theorem
$x + 2 = \frac{1}{2}[(4x - 10) + 8]$	Substitute.
$x + 2 = \frac{1}{2}(4x - 2)$	Simplify.
$x + 2 = 2x - 1$	Distributive Property
$3 = x$	Subtract x and add 1 to each side.

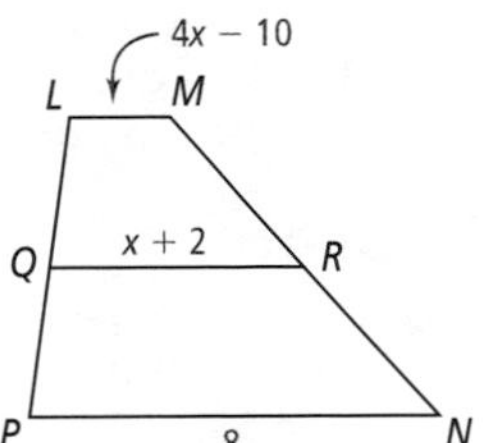

▼ STUDENT PAGES 309–310

Got It? **a. Algebra** $\overline{MN}$ is the midsegment of trapezoid $PQRS$. What is x? What is MN?

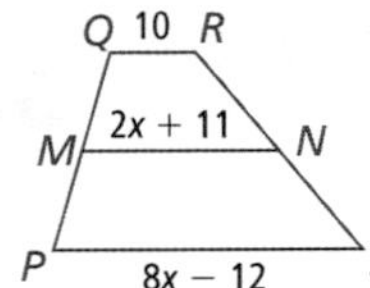

Think How can you check your answer?

b. Reasoning How many midsegments can a triangle have? How many midsegments can a trapezoid have? Explain.

Practice Find EF in each trapezoid.

5. 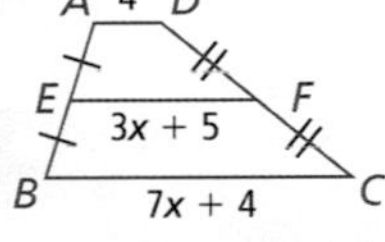

6. 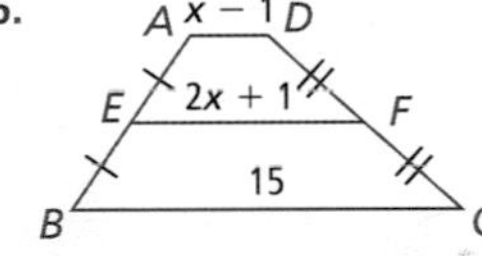

Problem 4 Finding Angle Measures in Kites

Take Note

Ask students to identify other quadrilaterals whose diagonals are perpendicular bisectors. Ask students to compare and contrast the other properties of those quadrilaterals.

▼ STUDENT PAGE 310

A **kite** is a quadrilateral with two pairs of consecutive sides congruent and no opposite sides congruent.

Essential Understanding The angles, sides, and diagonals of a kite have certain properties.

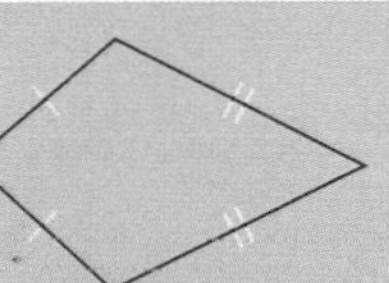

take note **Theorem 59**

Theorem	If . . .	Then . . .
If a quadrilateral is a kite, then its diagonals are perpendicular.	$ABCD$ is a kite	$\overline{AC} \perp \overline{BD}$

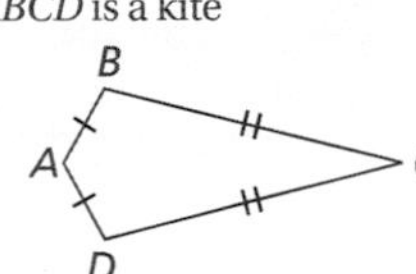

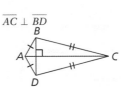

Proof **Proof of Theorem 59**

Given: Kite $ABCD$ with $\overline{AB} \cong \overline{AD}$ and $\overline{CB} \cong \overline{CD}$

Prove: $\overline{AC} \perp \overline{BD}$

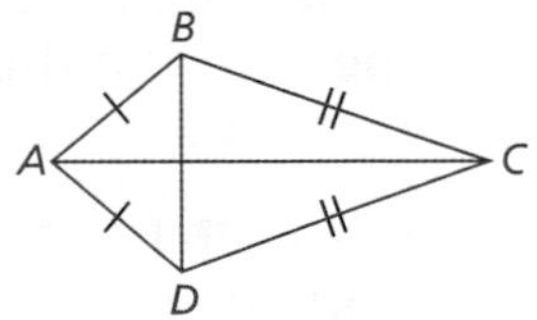

Statements	Reasons
1) Kite $ABCD$ with $\overline{AB} \cong \overline{AD}$ and $\overline{CB} \cong \overline{CD}$	1) Given
2) A and C lie on the perpendicular bisector of $\overline{BD}$.	2) Converse of Perpendicular Bisector Theorem
3) $\overline{AC}$ is the perpendicular bisector of $\overline{BD}$.	3) Two points determine a line.
4) $\overline{AC} \perp \overline{BD}$	4) Definition of perpendicular bisector

Problem 4 *continued*

Q Is $\angle DEF \cong \angle DGF$? Explain. **[Yes, $\triangle DEF \cong \triangle DGF$ by SSS, and the angles are corresponding parts.]**

Q What is the sum of $m\angle EGF$ and $m\angle GFD$? Explain. **[The sum of the angles is 90 because the third angle of the triangle is a right angle.]**

Got It?

Q What theorems can you use to find the measure of each of the angles? **[$\angle 1$ by Theorem 59, $\angle 3$ by CPCTC from SSS; $\angle 2$ by the Triangle Angle-Sum Theorem.]**

ANSWERS

Got It? $m\angle 1 = 90$, $m\angle 2 = 54$, $m\angle 3 = 36$

Practice

7. $m\angle 1 = 90$, $m\angle 2 = 45$, $m\angle 3 = 45$

8. $m\angle 1 = 90$, $m\angle 2 = 90$, $m\angle 3 = 90$, $m\angle 4 = 90$, $m\angle 5 = 46$, $m\angle 6 = 34$, $m\angle 7 = 56$, $m\angle 8 = 44$, $m\angle 9 = 56$, $m\angle 10 = 44$

Take Note

Students can use the Concept Summary to help them remember the characteristics of special quadrilaterals.

▼ DIGITAL

Problem 4 **Finding Angle Measures in Kites**

Quadrilateral *DEFG* is a kite. What are $m\angle 1$, $m\angle 2$, and $m\angle 3$?

$m\angle 1 = 90$	Diagonals of a kite are $\perp$.
$90 + m\angle 2 + 52 = 180$	Triangle Angle-Sum Theorem
$142 + m\angle 2 = 180$	Simplify.
$m\angle 2 = 38$	Subtract 142 from each side.

$\triangle DEF \cong \triangle DGF$ by SSS. Since corresponding parts of congruent triangles are congruent, $m\angle 3 = m\angle GDF = 52$.

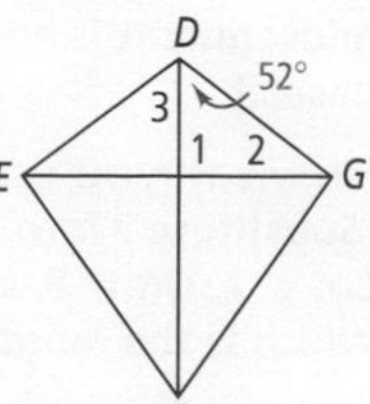

▼ STUDENT PAGE 311

Got It? Quadrilateral *KLMN* is a kite. What are $m\angle 1$, $m\angle 2$, and $m\angle 3$?

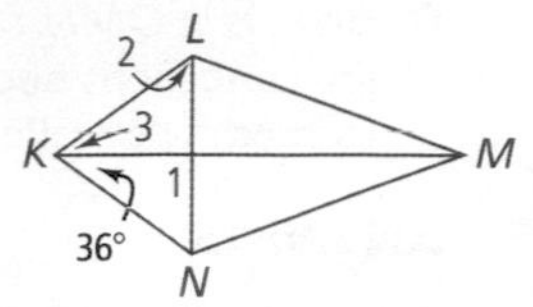

A Practice Find the measures of the numbered angles in each kite.

7.

8.

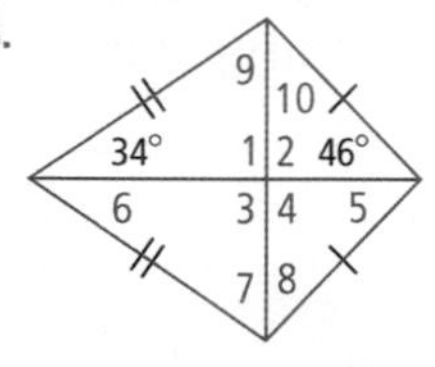

▼ STUDENT PAGE 312

take note **Concept Summary** Relationships Among Quadrilaterals

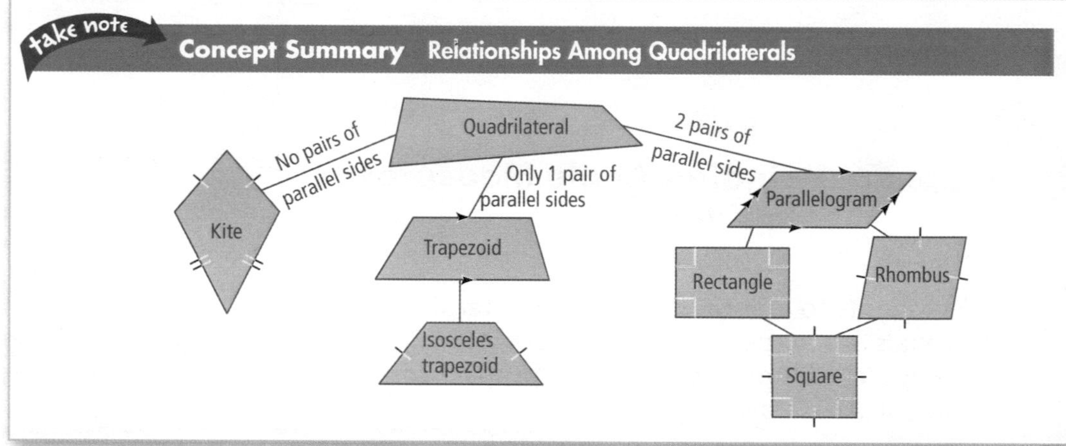

3 Lesson Check

Do you know HOW?

If students have difficulty with Exercise 10, then tell them that the trapezoid is not an isosceles trapezoid, and thus the base angles will not be congruent.

Do you UNDERSTAND?

If students have difficulty with Exercise 14, then have them review the definition of a trapezoid given on page 894. Students need to make note of the word *exactly*.

Close

Q Are either kites or trapezoids a subset of parallelograms? Explain. **[No, neither figure meets the conditions for being a parallelogram.]**

▼ STUDENT PAGE 312

Lesson Check

Do you know HOW?

What are the measures of the numbered angles?

9.

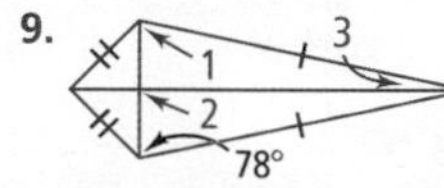

10.

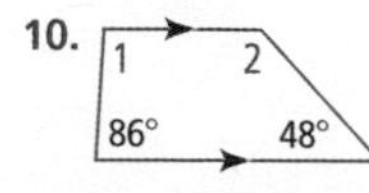

11. What is the length of the midsegment of a trapezoid with bases of lengths 14 and 26?

ANSWERS

9. $m\angle 1 = 78$, $m\angle 2 = 90$, $m\angle 3 = 12$

10. $m\angle 1 = 94$, $m\angle 2 = 132$

11. 20

12. No; a kite's opp. sides are not ≅ or ∥.
13. Answers may vary. Sample: Similar: diagonals are ⊥, consecutive sides ≅. Different: one diagonal of a kite bisects opp. angles but the other diagonal does not; all sides of a rhombus are ≅.
14. Def. of trapezoid is a quad. with exactly one pair of ∥ sides. A ▱ has two pairs of ∥ sides, so a ▱ is not a trapezoid.

▼ STUDENT PAGE 313

Do you UNDERSTAND?

12. **Vocabulary** Is a kite a parallelogram? Explain.
13. **Compare and Contrast** How is a kite similar to a rhombus? How is it different? Explain.
14. **Error Analysis** Since a parallelogram has two pairs of parallel sides, it certainly has one pair of parallel sides. Therefore, a parallelogram must also be a trapezoid. What is the error in this reasoning? Explain.

4 Practice

More Practice and Problem-Solving Exercises

ASSIGNMENT GUIDE
The assignments below are for the More Practice and Problem-Solving Exercises. You may also want to assign the A-Level Practice Exercises for homework if these are not used in class.
Average: 15–52
Advanced: 15–56

Mathematical Practices The exercises listed focus on the Standards for Mathematical Practices listed.

EX. 13, 16: Make Sense of Problems (MP 1)
EX. 15: Persevere in Solving Problems (MP 1)
EX. 17, 29–35: Construct Arguments (MP 3)
EX. 14: Critique the Reasoning of Others (MP 3)
EX. 27, 28: Model (MP 4)

STEM exercises focus on science or engineering applications.

EXERCISE 36: Use the **Think About a Plan** worksheet in the Online Teacher Resources to further support students' development in becoming independent learners.

HOMEWORK QUICK CHECK
To check students' understanding of key skills and concepts, go over Exercises 16, 22, 24, 30, and 36.

ANSWERS

15. Answers may vary. Sample:

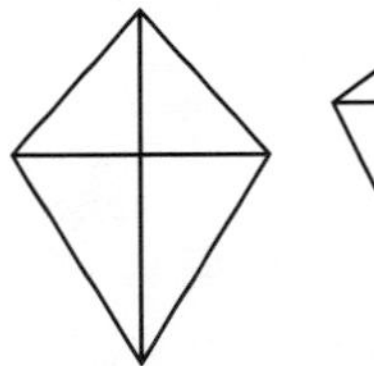
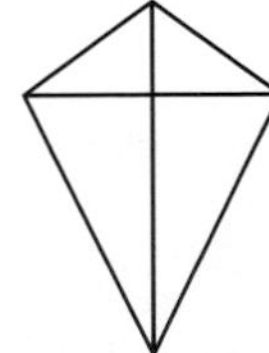

16. 12 cm, 12 cm, 21cm, 21 cm
17. No; explanations may vary. Sample: Assume $\overline{KM}$ bisects both ⦣s. Then $\angle MKL \cong \angle MKN \cong \angle KML \cong \angle KMN$. Both pairs of sides of $KLMN$ would be ∥, and $KLMN$ would be a ▱. It is impossible for an isosc. trap. to also be a ▱, so $\overline{KM}$ cannot bis. $\angle LMN$ and $\angle LKN$.

▼ STUDENT PAGE 313

More Practice and Problem-Solving Exercises

B Apply

15. **Open-Ended** Sketch two noncongruent kites such that the diagonals of one are congruent to the diagonals of the other.
16. **Think About a Plan** The perimeter of a kite is 66 cm. The length of one of its sides is 3 cm less than twice the length of another. Find the length of each side of the kite.
    - Can you draw a diagram?
    - How can you write algebraic expressions for the lengths of the sides?
17. **Reasoning** If $KLMN$ is an isosceles trapezoid, is it possible for $\overline{KM}$ to bisect $\angle LMN$ and $\angle LKN$? Explain.

More Practice and Problem-Solving Exercises *continued*

18. 12
19. 15
20. 1
21. $AD = 4$, $EF = 9$, $BC = 14$
22. $EF = 1$, $CD = 6$, $HG = 11$
23. $HG = 2$, $CD = 5$, $EF = 8$
24. 28
25. $x = 35$, $y = 30$
26. $x = 18$, $y = 108$
27. Isosc. trapezoid; $\overline{AB} \parallel \overline{DC}$ (If alt. int. ∠s are ≅, then lines are ∥.) and $\overline{AD} \cong \overline{BC}$. (Corresp. parts of ≅ △s are ≅.)
28. $m\angle A = m\angle B = 60$, $m\angle CDA = 120$
29. Yes; the ≅ angles can be obtuse.
30. Yes; the ≅ angles and one other ∠ can be obtuse.
31. Yes; if two ≅ angles are rt. angles, they are suppl. The other two angles are also suppl.
32. No; if two consecutive angles are suppl., then another pair must also be suppl. because one pair of opp. angles is ≅. Therefore the opp. angles would be ≅, which means the figure would be a ▱ and not a kite.
33. Yes; for example, if the ≅ angles each have measure 45.
34. No; if consecutive angles are compl., the figure is concave, so not a kite.
35. Answers may vary. Sample:
1. Draw $\overline{AE} \parallel \overline{DC}$. (Parallel Post.)
2. $AECD$ is a ▱. (Def. of ▱)
3. $\overline{AE} \cong \overline{DC}$ (Opp. sides of a ▱ are ≅.)
4. $\angle 1 \cong \angle C$ (If ∥ lines, corresp. ∠s are ≅.)
5. $\angle B \cong \angle 1$ (Isosc. △ Thm.)
6. $\angle B \cong \angle C$ (Transitive Prop. of ≅)
7. $\angle D$ and $\angle C$ are suppl. (If ∥ lines, same-side int. ∠s are suppl.)
8. $\angle BAD$ and $\angle B$ are suppl. (If ∥ lines, same-side int. ∠s are suppl.)
9. $\angle BAD \cong \angle D$ (∠s suppl. to ≅ ∠s are ≅.)

▼ STUDENT PAGE 314

Algebra Find the value of the variable in each isosceles trapezoid.

18.
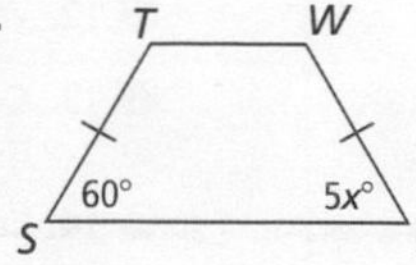

19.
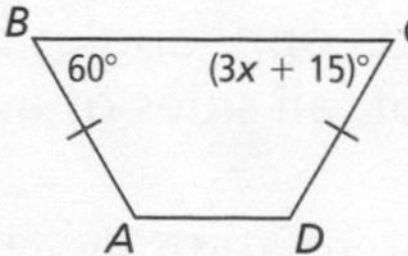

20.
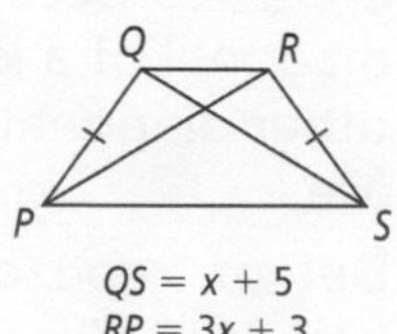

Algebra Find the lengths of the segments with variable expressions.

21.
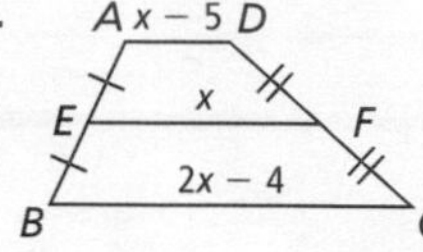

22.
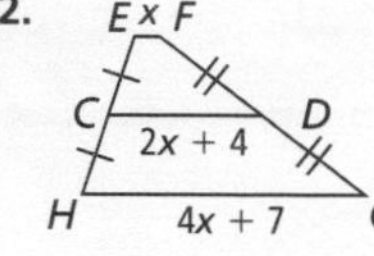

23.
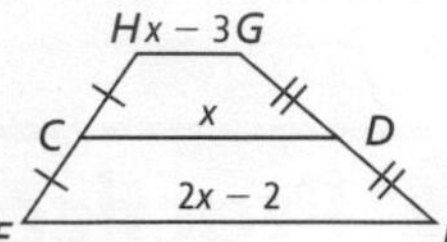

Algebra Find the value(s) of the variable(s) in each kite.

24.
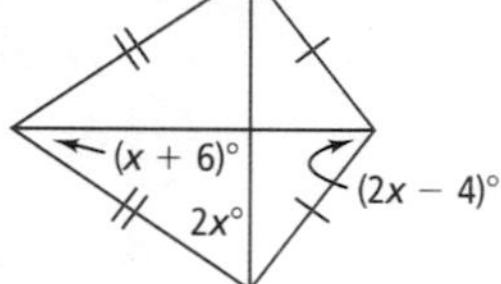

25.
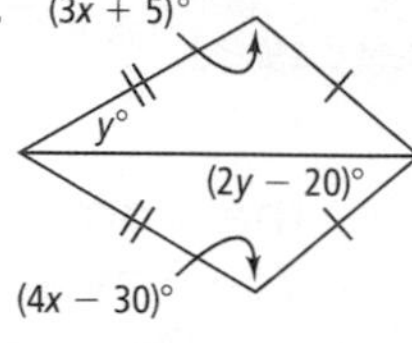

26.
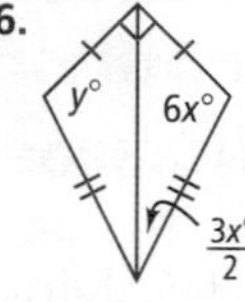

STEM **Bridge Design** The beams of the bridge at the right form quadrilateral $ABCD$. $\triangle AED \cong \triangle CDE \cong \triangle BEC$ and $m\angle DCB = 120$.

27. Classify the quadrilateral. Explain your reasoning.

28. Find the measures of the other interior angles of the quadrilateral.

Reasoning Can two angles of a kite be as follows? Explain.

29. opposite and acute
30. consecutive and obtuse
31. opposite and supplementary
32. consecutive and supplementary
33. opposite and complementary
34. consecutive and complementary

35. Developing Proof The plan suggests a proof of Theorem 56. Write a proof that follows the plan.

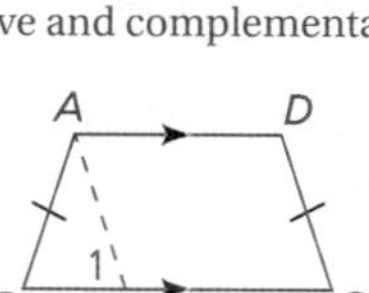

Given: Isosceles trapezoid $ABCD$ with $\overline{AB} \cong \overline{DC}$

Prove: $\angle B \cong \angle C$ and $\angle BAD \cong \angle D$

Plan: Begin by drawing $\overline{AE} \parallel \overline{DC}$ to form parallelogram $AECD$ so that $\overline{AE} \cong \overline{DC} \cong \overline{AB}$. $\angle B \cong \angle C$ because $\angle B \cong \angle 1$ and $\angle 1 \cong \angle C$. Also, $\angle BAD \cong \angle D$ because they are supplements of the congruent angles, $\angle B$ and $\angle C$.

Proof 36. Prove the converse of Theorem 56: If a trapezoid has a pair of congruent base angles, then the trapezoid is isosceles.

Name each type of special quadrilateral that can meet the given condition. Make sketches to support your answers.

37. exactly one pair of congruent sides

38. two pairs of parallel sides

39. four right angles

40. adjacent sides that are congruent

41. perpendicular diagonals

42. congruent diagonals

Proof 43. Prove Theorem 57.

Given: Isosceles trapezoid $ABCD$ with $\overline{AB} \cong \overline{DC}$

Prove: $\overline{AC} \cong \overline{DB}$

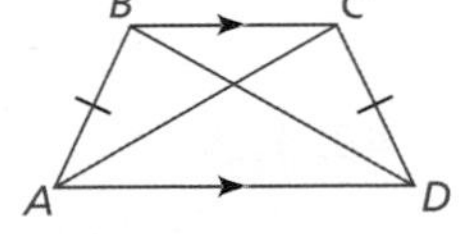

Proof 44. Prove the converse of Theorem 57: If the diagonals of a trapezoid are congruent, then the trapezoid is isosceles.

36. Answers may vary. Sample:

Given: Trapezoid $ABCD$ with $\overline{BC} \parallel \overline{AD}$, $\angle A \cong \angle D$

Prove: $ABCD$ is an isosc. trapezoid.

1. $\overleftrightarrow{AB}$ is not $\parallel$ to $\overleftrightarrow{DC}$. (Def. of trapezoid)
2. Extend $\overleftrightarrow{AB}$ and $\overleftrightarrow{DC}$ to meet at point T. (Construction)
3. $\angle A \cong \angle D$ (Given)
4. $\overline{AT} \cong \overline{DT}$ (Converse of Isosc. △ Thm.)
5. $\angle TBC \cong \angle A$ and $\angle TCB \cong \angle D$ (If $\parallel$ lines, then corresp. ∠s are $\cong$.)
6. $\angle TBC \cong \angle TCB$ (Transitive Prop. of $\cong$)
7. $\overline{TB} \cong \overline{TC}$ (Converse of Isosc. △ Thm.)
8. $AT = AB + BT$, $DT = DC + CT$ (Seg. Add. Post.)
9. $AB = AT - BT$, $DC = DT - CT$ (Subtr. Prop. of Eq.)
10. $AB = DC$ (Subst. Prop. of Eq.)
11. $ABCD$ is an isosc. trapezoid. (Def. of isosc. trapezoid)

37. Isosc. trapezoid; answers may vary. Sample:

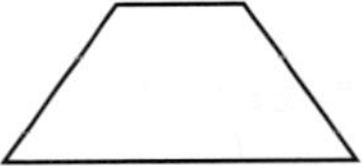

38. ▱, rhombus, rectangle, square; answers may vary. Sample:

39. Rectangle, square; answers may vary. Sample:

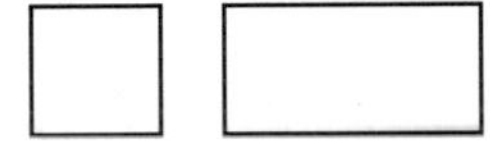

40. Kite, isosc. trapezoid, rhombus, square; answers may vary. Sample:

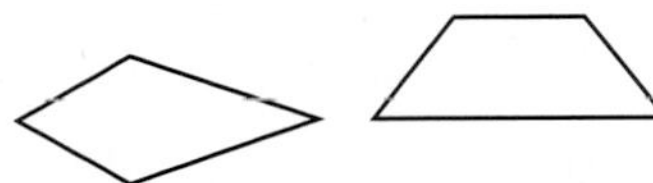

41. Kite, rhombus, square; answers may vary. Sample:

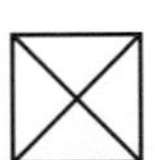

42. Rectangle, isosc. trapezoid, kite; answers may vary. Sample:

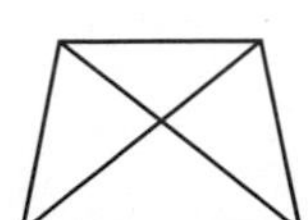
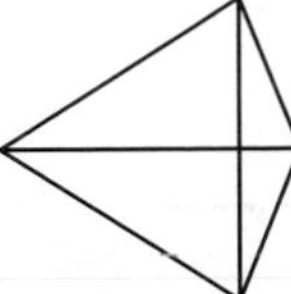

43. Answers may vary. Sample:

1. $\overline{AB} \cong \overline{DC}$ (Given)
2. $\angle BAD \cong \angle CDA$ (Base ∠s of an isosc. trapezoid are $\cong$.)
3. $\overline{AD} \cong \overline{AD}$ (Refl. Prop. of $\cong$)
4. $\triangle BAD \cong \triangle CDA$ (SAS)
5. $\overline{BD} \cong \overline{CA}$ (Corresp. parts of $\cong$ △s are $\cong$.)

44. Given: Trapezoid $ABCD$ with $\overline{BC} \parallel \overline{AD}$, $\overline{BD} \cong \overline{AC}$

Prove: $\overline{AB} \cong \overline{DC}$

1. Draw $\overline{BP} \perp \overline{AD}$ and $\overline{CQ} \perp \overline{AD}$. (Construction)
2. $\overline{BP} \cong \overline{CQ}$ (Opp. sides of a rectangle are $\cong$.)
3. $\overline{BD} \cong \overline{AC}$ (Given)
4. $\triangle BPD \cong \triangle CQA$ (HL)
5. $\angle BDP \cong \angle CAQ$ (Corresp. parts of $\cong$ △s are $\cong$.)
6. $\overline{AD} \cong \overline{DA}$ (Refl. Prop. of $\cong$)
7. $\triangle BAD \cong \triangle CDA$ (SAS)
8. $\overline{AB} \cong \overline{DC}$ (Corresp. parts of $\cong$ △s are $\cong$.)

More Practice and Problem-Solving Exercises *continued*

▼ STUDENT PAGE 315

Proof 45. Given: Isosceles trapezoid *TRAP* with $\overline{TR} \cong \overline{PA}$

Prove: $\angle RTA \cong \angle APR$

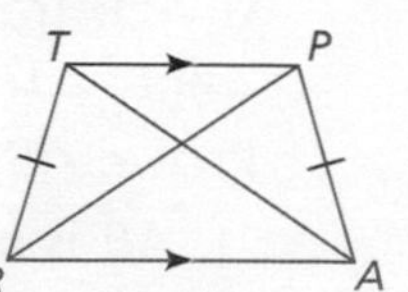

Proof 46. Prove that the angles formed by the noncongruent sides of a kite are congruent. (*Hint:* Draw a diagonal of the kite.)

Determine whether each statement is *true* or *false*. Justify your response.

47. All squares are rectangles.

48. A trapezoid is a parallelogram.

49. A rhombus can be a kite.

50. Some parallelograms are squares.

51. Every quadrilateral is a parallelogram.

52. All rhombuses are squares.

Proof 53. Given: Isosceles trapezoid *TRAP* with $\overline{TR} \cong \overline{PA}$; $\overline{BI}$ is the perpendicular bisector of $\overline{RA}$, intersecting $\overline{RA}$ at *B* and $\overline{TP}$ at *I*.

Prove: $\overline{BI}$ is the perpendicular bisector of $\overline{TP}$.

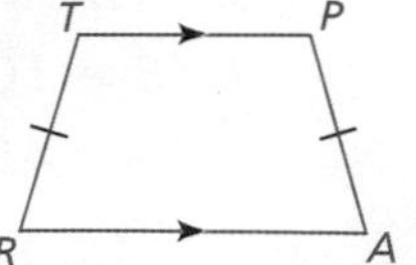

For a trapezoid, consider the segment joining the midpoints of the two given segments. How are its length and the lengths of the two parallel sides of the trapezoid related? Justify your answer.

54. the two nonparallel sides

55. the diagonals

56. $\overleftrightarrow{BN}$ is the perpendicular bisector of $\overline{AC}$ at *N*. Describe the set of points, *D*, for which *ABCD* is a kite.

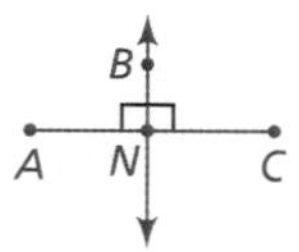

45. Answers may vary. Sample:
1. Draw $\overline{TA}$ and $\overline{PR}$. (Construction)
2. $\overline{TR} \cong \overline{PA}$ (Given)
3. $\angle TRA \cong \angle PAR$ (Base ∠s of an isosc. trapezoid are ≅.)
4. $\overline{RA} \cong \overline{RA}$ (Refl. Prop. of ≅)
5. $\triangle TRA \cong \triangle PAR$ (SAS)
6. $\angle RTA \cong \angle APR$ (Corresp. parts of ≅ △s are ≅.)

46. 1. kite *ABCD* with $\overline{AB} \cong \overline{AD}$, $\overline{BC} \cong \overline{CD}$ (Given)
2. Draw $\overline{AC}$. (Construction)
3. $\triangle ABC \cong \triangle ADC$ (SSS)
4. $\angle B \cong \angle D$ (Corresp. parts of ≅ △s are ≅.)

47. True; a square is a ▱ with 4 rt. angles.

48. False; a trapezoid has exactly one pair of ∥ sides.

49. False; a rhombus has 4 ≅ sides, and a kite does not.

50. True; a square is a ▱ that has four ≅ sides and four rt. angles.

51. False; counterexample: kites and trapezoids are not parallelograms.

52. False; a rhombus without 4 rt. angles is not a square.

53. Answers may vary. Sample:
1. $\overline{RT}$ and $\overline{PA}$ are not ∥. (Def. of trapezoid)
2. Extend $\overline{RT}$ and $\overline{PA}$ to meet at *M*. (Construction)
3. $\angle MTP \cong \angle R$ and $\angle MPT \cong \angle A$. (If ∥ lines, then corresp. ∠s are ≅.)
4. $\angle MTP \cong \angle MPT$ (Trans. Prop. of ≅)
5. $\overline{MT} \cong \overline{MP}$ (Converse of Isosc. △ Thm.)
6. $\angle MIT$ and $\angle MIP$ are rt. ∠s. (In a plane, a line ⊥ to one of two ∥ lines is also ⊥ to the other line.)
7. $\overline{MI} \cong \overline{MI}$ (Refl. Prop. of ≅)
8. $\triangle MIT \cong \triangle MIP$ (HL)
9. $\overline{TI} \cong \overline{PI}$ (Corresp. parts of ≅ △s are ≅.)
10. $\overline{BI}$ is the ⊥ bis. of $\overline{TP}$. (Def. of ⊥ bis.)

54. half the sum of the bases; Trapezoid Midsegment Thm.

55. half the difference of the bases; Consider trap. *ABCD* with diagonals $\overline{AC}$ and $\overline{BD}$. Let *P* and *Q* be the midpoints of $\overline{AC}$ and, $\overline{BD}$ respectively. The line through *P* and *Q* is parallel to both bases of *TRAP* and contains the midpoint *M* of $\overline{AB}$ and the midpoint *N* of $\overline{CD}$. $MN = \frac{1}{2}(BC + AD)$, $MP = \frac{1}{2}BC = QN$. $PQ = MN - MP - QN = \frac{1}{2}(BC + AD) - \frac{1}{2}BC - \frac{1}{2}BC = \frac{1}{2}(AD - BC)$.

56. *D* is a point on $\overline{BN}$ such that $ND \neq BN$, and *B* and *D* are on opp. sides of *N*.

5 Assess and Remediate

Lesson Quiz

1. *QRST* is an isosceles trapezoid and $m\angle R = 116$. What are $m\angle Q$, $m\angle T$, and $m\angle S$?

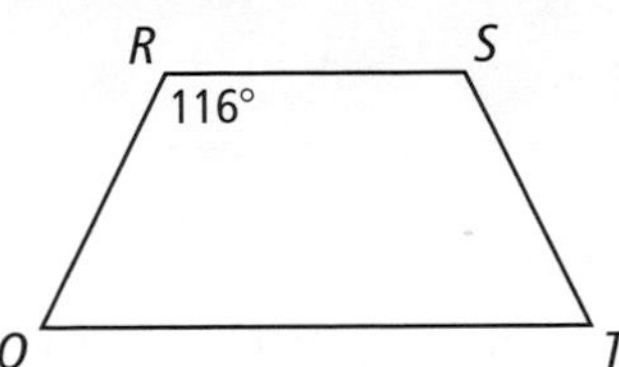

2. $\overline{AB}$ is the midsegment of trapezoid *DEFG*. What is *x*?

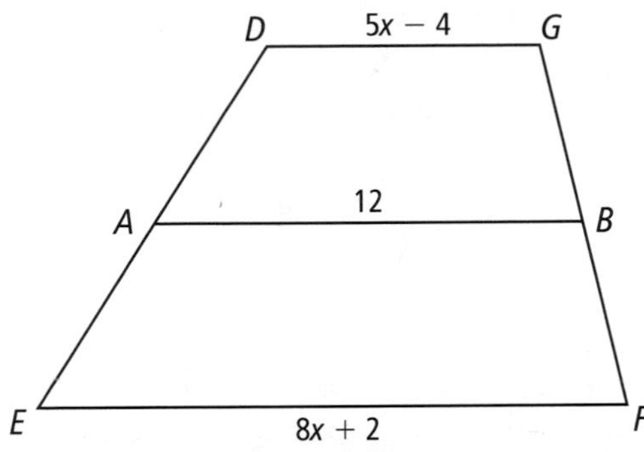

3. **Do you UNDERSTAND?** In kite *NPRQ*, what is $m\angle RPT$?

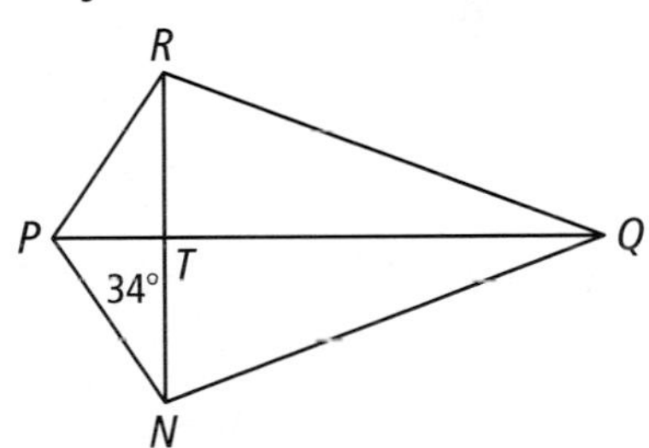

ANSWERS TO LESSON QUIZ

1. $m\angle S = 116$, $m\angle Q = 64$, $m\angle T = 64$
2. 2
3. 56

Prescription for Remediation

Use the student work on the Lesson Quiz to prescribe a differentiated assignment.

Points	Differentiated Remediation
0–1	Intervention
2	On-level
3	Extension

Online Assessment

Assign the Lesson Quiz in Success Tracker on **pearsonsuccessnet.com**. Success Tracker will automatically score the quiz and assign appropriate intervention or enrichment to each student based on the results. The compiled data appear in three different reports for instant analysis of whole class and individual student performance.

Differentiated Remediation

Intervention

- **RETEACHING** (2 pages) Provides reteaching and practice exercises for the key lesson concepts. Use with struggling students or absent students.
- **ENGLISH LANGUAGE LEARNER SUPPORT** Helps students develop and reinforce mathematical vocabulary and key concepts.

On-Level

- **PRACTICE** (2 pages) Provides extra practice for each lesson. For simpler practice exercises, use the Form K Practice pages found in the Online Teacher Resources.
- **THINK ABOUT A PLAN** Helps students develop specific problem-solving skills and strategies by providing scaffolded guiding questions.
- **STANDARDIZED TEST PREP** Focuses on all major exercises, all major question types, and helps students prepare for the high-stakes assessments.

Extension

- **ENRICHMENT** Provides students with interesting problems and activities that extend the concepts of the lesson.
- **ACTIVITIES, GAMES, AND PUZZLES** Worksheets that can be used for concept development, enrichment, and for fun!

5-7 Applying Coordinate Geometry

Common Core State Standards
G.CO.11 Prove theorems about parallelograms. Theorems include: opposite sides are congruent . . . **Also G.CO.10**

Preparing to Teach

BIG ideas Coordinate Geometry
Reasoning and Proof

ESSENTIAL UNDERSTANDING

Using variables to name the coordinates of a figure allows relationships to be shown to be true for a general case.

Math Background

In the seventeenth century, René Descartes blended algebraic principles with geometry to create what is called analytic geometry. Analytic geometry is also commonly referred to as coordinate geometry since geometric figures are placed in the coordinate plane. Learning to use variables to represent a figure in the coordinate plane is an important first step in completing proofs using coordinate geometry.

Students will need assistance in the logical placement of quadrilaterals. Show students when it makes sense to place a segment on an axis. Encourage students to think about why it is not practical to place one side of a rhombus or one diagonal of a parallelogram on the *x*-axis. Have them list advantages of a square or rectangle model in the first quadrant versus one symmetrically placed in all four quadrants.

Coordinate geometry can be used to prove some results more easily than a standard deductive proof. For example, coordinate geometry can be used to prove that the midpoint of the hypotenuse of a right triangle is equidistant from its vertices, or that the centroid of a triangle is $\frac{2}{3}$ of the distance from any vertex to the midpoint of the opposite side.

ELL Support

ASSESS UNDERSTANDING Place students in pairs of mixed abilities. Write Theorem 57 on the board. Students will plan a coordinate proof of the theorem. Invite students to draw their isosceles trapezoid on the board, including the axes and coordinates, to explain their work.

FOCUS ON LANGUAGE After this lesson, have students write why it is better for a figure to be on an axis when on the coordinate plane. Ask them to include examples and sketches to show their thinking.

Lesson Vocabulary

- coordinate proof

Mathematical Practices

MAKE SENSE OF PROBLEMS AND PERSEVERE IN SOLVING THEM. In Problem 3, students will adapt their knowledge of geometric proofs to figures in a coordinate plane to plan a coordinate proof.

Interactive Learning

Solve It!

PURPOSE To apply knowledge of the properties of parallelograms to determine the unknown vertex of the parallelogram

PROCESS Students may use previous knowledge of slope, Distance Formula, parallelograms, and visual discretion.

Q How many sides of the parallelogram can be formed using points *A, B,* and *C*? Explain. **[Two; a third segment would form a triangle.]**

Q How many ways are there to form two sides of the parallelogram using points *A, B,* and *C*? **[Three: $\overline{AB}$ and $\overline{BC}$; $\overline{AB}$ and $\overline{AC}$; $\overline{AC}$ and $\overline{BC}$.]**

Q Given that $\overline{AB}$ and $\overline{BC}$ are adjacent sides of the parallelogram, what requirements must be met for placing point *D*? **[$\overline{AD}$ must be parallel and congruent to $\overline{BC}$. $\overline{AB}$ must be parallel and congruent to $\overline{CD}$.]**

ANSWER (8, 6), (6, 0), (−4, 4); each forms a quad. with opp. sides that are ∥ and ≅.

CONNECT THE MATH In the Solve It, students look at a diagram showing all three parallelograms on the same coordinate plane. The original points *A, B,* and *C* form a triangle. The three placements of point *D* form three additional congruent triangles that share a side with △*ABC*.

▼ DIGITAL (STUDENT WORK SPACE PAGE 316)

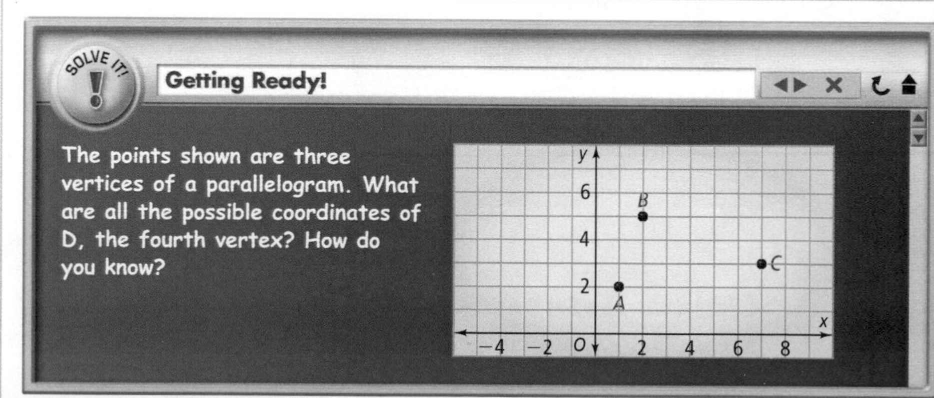

SOLVE IT!
Getting Ready!
The points shown are three vertices of a parallelogram. What are all the possible coordinates of D, the fourth vertex? How do you know?
y
x
6
4
2
−4
−2
O
2
4
6
8
A
B
C

2 Guided Instruction

▼ STUDENT PAGE 316

Problem 1 Naming Coordinates

Intro Text

Ask students to use the variables for Figure 1 to write the coordinates of M and N.

Problem 1

Q In 1A, if $SQ = 2a$, what are QR, RE, and SE? Explain. **[They are all $2a$, because all four sides of a square are congruent.]**

Q Can you use the Distance Formula for a number line to show that $SQ = 2a$? Explain. **[Yes, $|a - (-a)| = |a + a| = 2a$]**

Q Can you use the Distance Formula to show that $SQ = 2a$? Explain. **[Yes, $\sqrt{(-a-a)^2 + (a-a)^2} = \sqrt{(-2a)^2 + (0)^2} = \sqrt{4a^2} = 2a$]**

Q In 1B, what is a median of a triangle? **[A median is a segment whose endpoints are a vertex and the midpoint of the opposite side.]**

Q If given that the length of the median is c, then what point represents vertex R? **[(0, c)]**

In the Solve It, you found coordinates of a point and named it using numbers for the x- and y-coordinates. In this lesson, you will learn to use variables for the coordinates.

Essential Understanding You can use variables to name the coordinates of a figure. This allows you to show that relationships are true for a general case.

In Chapter 4, you learned about the segment joining the midpoints of two sides of a triangle. Here are three possible ways to place a triangle and its midsegment.

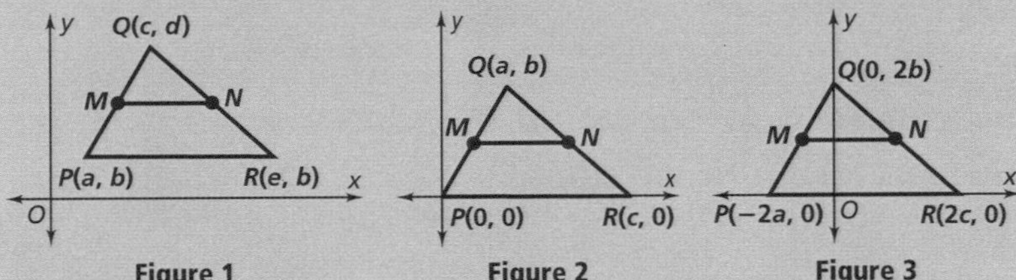

Figure 1 does not use the axes, so it requires more variables. Figures 2 and 3 have good placement. In Figure 2, the midpoint coordinates are $M\left(\frac{a}{2}, \frac{b}{2}\right)$ and $N\left(\frac{a+c}{2}, \frac{b}{2}\right)$. In Figure 3, the coordinates are $M(-a, b)$ and $N(c, b)$. You can see that Figure 3 is the easiest to work with.

To summarize, to place a figure in the coordinate plane, it is usually helpful to place at least one side on an axis or to center the figure at the origin. For the coordinates, try to anticipate what you will need to do in the problem. Then multiply the coordinates by the appropriate number to make your work easier.

▼ DIGITAL

Problem 1 Naming Coordinates

What are the coordinates of the vertices of each figure?

A ***SQRE* is a square where $SQ = 2a$. The axes bisect each side.**

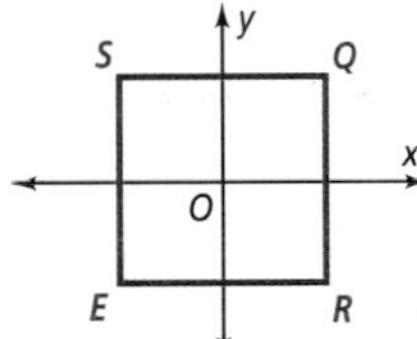

Since $SQRE$ is a square centered at the origin and $SQ = 2a$, S and Q are each a units from each axis. The same is true for the other vertices.

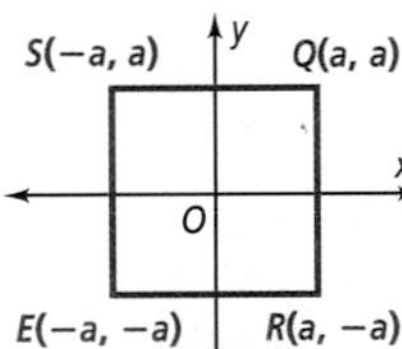

B ***TRI* is an isosceles triangle where $TI = 2a$. The y-axis is a median.**

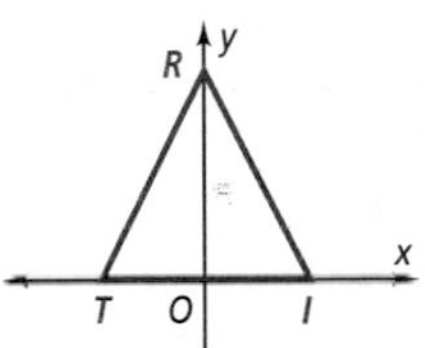

The y-axis is a median, so it bisects $\overline{TI}$. $TI = 2a$, so T and I are both a units from the y-axis. The height of TRI does not depend on a, so use a different variable for R.

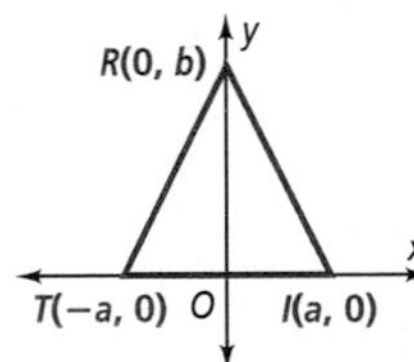

Problem 1 *continued*

Got It?

Students may be confused when determining the coordinates for points *K* and *T* in part (b). Remind students that the length of $\overline{KT}$ is not dependent on the length of $\overline{IE}$ and therefore new variables must be used. Also, remind students that by definition, a kite must have two pairs of congruent adjacent sides and no opposite congruent sides.

ANSWERS

Got It?

a. $R(-b, 0)$, $E(-b, a)$, $C(b, a)$, $T(b, 0)$

b. $K(-b, 0)$, $I(0, a)$, $T(c, 0)$, $E(0, -a)$

Practice

1. $Z(b, 0)$, $W(b + c, 0)$, $T(c, a)$, $S(0, a)$
2. $S(-a, 0)$, $Z(a, 0)$, $W(b, c)$, $T(-b, c)$. Another variable for *b* is acceptable.

▼ STUDENT PAGE 317

Got It? What are the coordinates of the vertices of each figure?

a. *RECT* is a rectangle with height *a* and length 2*b*. The *y*-axis bisects $\overline{EC}$ and $\overline{RT}$.

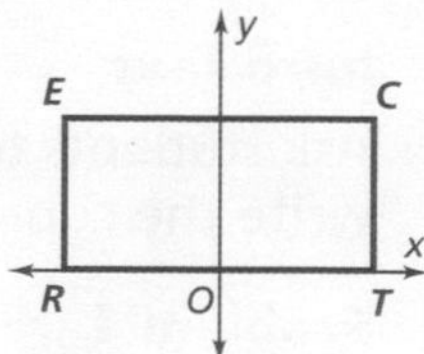

b. *KITE* is a kite where $IE = 2a$, $KO = b$, and $OT = c$. The *x*-axis bisects $\overline{IE}$.

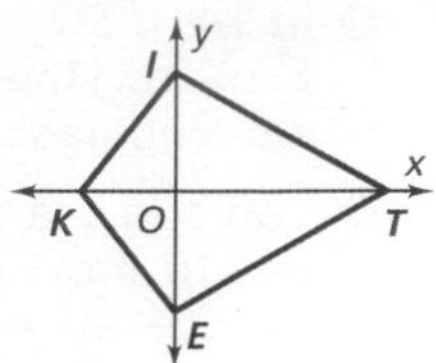

A Practice **Algebra** What are the coordinates of the vertices of each figure?

1. parallelogram where *S* is *a* units from the origin and *Z* is *b* units from the origin

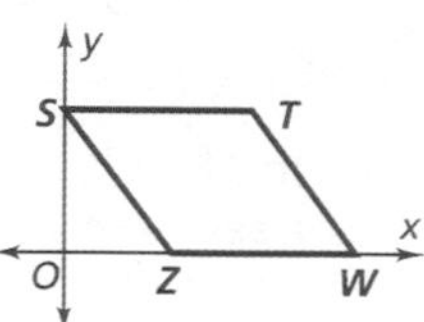

2. isosceles trapezoid with base centered at the origin, with base 2*a* and $OR = c$

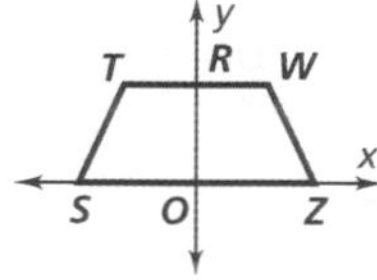

Problem 2 Using Variable Coordinates

Q What do you know about the diagonals of a parallelogram? **[The diagonals of a parallelogram bisect each other.]**

Q How do you simplify the expression $\frac{2a + 2b}{2}$? **[You must factor the numerator and rewrite it as 2(*a* + *b*), then cancel the common factor of 2 in the numerator and denominator.]**

Q If you were to determine the midpoint of $\overline{OB}$, would you arrive at the same answer? Explain. **[Yes, because the diagonals bisect each other, the point of intersection is the midpoint of each diagonal.]**

▼ DIGITAL

Problem 2 **Using Variable Coordinates**

The diagram shows a general parallelogram with a vertex at the origin and one side along the *x*-axis. What are the coordinates of *D*, the point of intersection of the diagonals of ▱*ABCO*? How do you know?

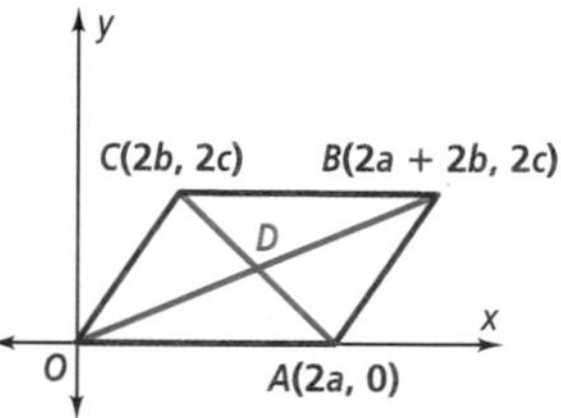

Know
- The coordinates of the vertices of ▱*ABCO*
- $\overline{OB}$ bisects $\overline{AC}$ and $\overline{AC}$ bisects $\overline{OB}$

Need
The coordinates of *D*

Plan
Since the diagonals of a parallelogram bisect each other, the midpoint of each segment is their point of intersection. Use the Midpoint Formula to find the midpoint of one diagonal.

Use the Midpoint Formula to find the midpoint of $\overline{AC}$.

$$D = \text{midpoint of } \overline{AC} = \left(\frac{2a + 2b}{2}, \frac{0 + 2c}{2}\right) = (a + b, c)$$

The coordinates of the point of intersection of the diagonals of ▱*ABCO* are $(a + b, c)$.

Got It?

Q Given that the figure is a trapezoid, what must be true about the diagonals in order for it to be an isosceles trapezoid? **[The diagonals must be congruent.]**

Q What are the lengths of $\overline{RP}$ and $\overline{TA}$? Explain. **[Using the Distance Formula,** $RP = \sqrt{(b-a)^2 + (c-0)^2} = \sqrt{b^2 + 2ab + a^2 + c^2}$ **and** $TA = \sqrt{(b-(-a))^2 + (c-0)^2} = \sqrt{b^2 + 2ab + a^2 + c^2}$.**]**

ANSWERS

Got It? a. Answers may vary. Sample: *x*-coordinate of *B* is 2*a* more than *x*-coordinate of *C*. **b.** yes; $TR = AP = \sqrt{a^2 - 2ab + b^2 + c^2}$

Practice

3. Yes, *ABCD* is a rhombus. The slope of $\overline{AC} = -1$, and the slope of $\overline{BD} = 1$, so the diagonals are $\perp$.

▼ STUDENT PAGE 318

Got It? a. **Reasoning** In Problem 2, explain why the *x*-coordinate of *B* is the sum of 2*a* and 2*b*.

b. The diagram below shows a trapezoid with the base centered at the origin. Is the trapezoid isosceles? Explain.

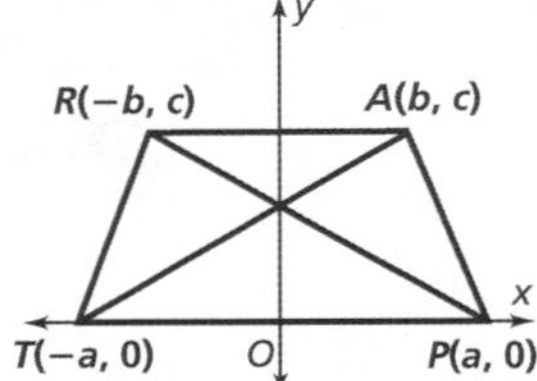

Plan

Which formula should you use to show that the trapezoid is isosceles?

Practice 3. The diagram at the right shows a parallelogram. Without using the Distance Formula, determine whether the parallelogram is a rhombus. How do you know?

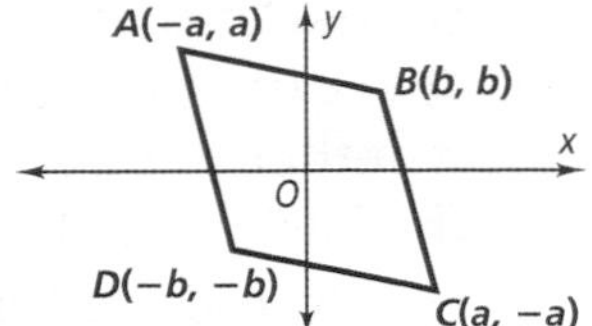

Problem 3 Planning a Coordinate Proof

Q What are the coordinates of *M*? **[(*b*, *c*)]**

Q Considering how the figure is placed in the coordinate plane, what is the slope of both bases and the midsegment? **[The slope for each is zero, since they are all horizontal.]**

Got It?

Q What conditions must be proved for the Triangle Midsegment Theorem? **[The midsegment is parallel to one of the sides of the triangle, and the midsegment is half the length of that side.]**

▼ STUDENT PAGE 319

You can use coordinate geometry and algebra to prove theorems in geometry. This kind of proof is called a **coordinate proof.** Sometimes it is easier to show that a theorem is true by using a coordinate proof rather than a standard deductive proof. It is useful to write a plan for a coordinate proof. Problem 3 shows you how.

▼ DIGITAL

Problem 3 Planning a Coordinate Proof

Plan a coordinate proof of the Trapezoid Midsegment Theorem (Theorem 58).
(1) The midsegment of a trapezoid is parallel to the bases.
(2) The length of the midsegment of a trapezoid is half the sum of the lengths of the bases.

Step 1 Draw and label a figure.

Midpoints will be involved, so use multiples of 2 to name coordinates.

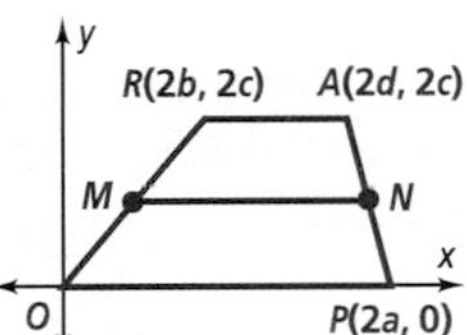

Step 2 Write the *Given* and *Prove* statements.

Use the information on the diagram to write the statements.

Given: $\overline{MN}$ is the midsegment of trapezoid *ORAP*.

Prove: $\overline{MN} \parallel \overline{OP}$, $\overline{MN} \parallel \overline{RA}$, $MN = \frac{1}{2}(OP + RA)$

Step 3 Determine the formulas you will need. Then write the plan.

- First, use the Midpoint Formula to find the coordinates of *M* and *N*.
- Then, use the Slope Formula to determine whether the slopes of $\overline{MN}$, $\overline{OP}$, and $\overline{RA}$ are equal. If they are, $\overline{MN}$, $\overline{OP}$, and $\overline{RA}$ are parallel.
- Finally, use the Distance Formula to find and compare the lengths of $\overline{MN}$, $\overline{OP}$, and $\overline{RA}$.

Problem 3 *continued*

ANSWERS

Got It?

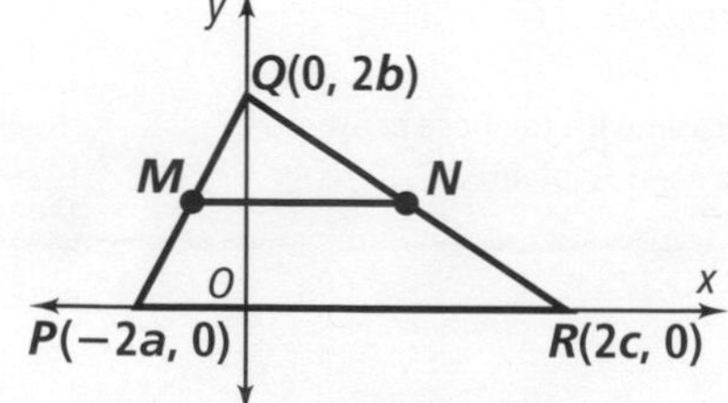

Given: $\triangle PQR$, midpoints M and N

Prove: $\overline{MN} \parallel \overline{PR}$ and $MN = \frac{1}{2}PR$

- First, use the Midpoint Formula to find the coordinates of M and N.
- Then, use the Slope Formula to determine whether the slopes of $\overline{MN}$ and $\overline{PR}$ are equal. If they are, then $\overline{MN} \parallel \overline{PR}$.
- Finally, use the Distance Formula to find and compare the lengths of $\overline{MN}$ and $\overline{PR}$.

Practice

4. a. $T(-2a, 0)$, $R(-2b, 2c)$, $A(2b, 2c)$, $P(2a, 0)$
   b. Given: $TRAP$ is an isosc. trapezoid, $\overline{TR} \cong \overline{PA}$, D, E, F, and G are midpts. of sides.
   Prove: $DEFG$ is a rhombus.
   c. Use the Midpoint Formula.
   d. Answers may vary. Sample: Use the Distance Formula to show $DEFG$ is equilateral.

▼ STUDENT PAGES 319–320

Got It? Plan a coordinate proof of the Triangle Midsegment Theorem (Theorem 24).

Think What conditions must be proved for the Triangle Midsegment Theorem?

A Practice 4. Plan a coordinate proof to show that the midpoints of the sides of an isosceles trapezoid form a rhombus.

a. Name the coordinates of isosceles trapezoid *TRAP* at the right, with bottom base length $4a$, top base length $4b$, and $EG = 2c$. The y-axis bisects the bases.

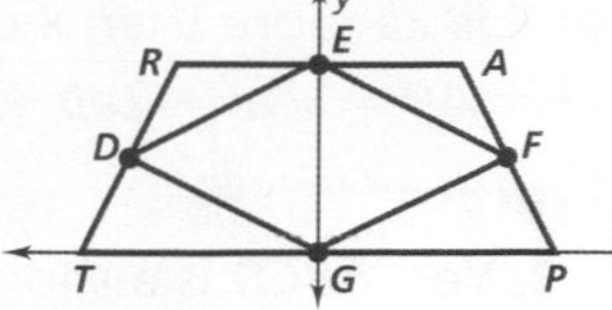

b. Write the *Given* and *Prove* statements.

c. How will you find the coordinates of the midpoints of each side?

d. How will you determine whether *DEFG* is a rhombus?

3 Lesson Check

Do you know HOW?

if students have difficulty with Exercise 6, then make sure they realize that the slopes of the diagonals of a parallelogram are never parallel and are perpendicular only when the parallelogram is a rhombus.

Do you UNDERSTAND?

If students have difficulty with Exercise 9, then have them choose sample values for the variables and then sketch the quadrilateral described.

Close

Q How many variables are needed to name the coordinates of a rectangle drawn with one vertex at the origin in a coordinate plane? Explain. **[two, one to represent the length and one to represent the height]**

ANSWERS

5. $K(2b, c)$, $M(2a, 0)$
6. The slope of $\overline{KM}$ is $\frac{c}{2b - 2a}$, and the slope of $\overline{OL}$ is $\frac{c}{2a + 2b}$.
7. $\left(a + b, \frac{c}{2}\right)$
8. Answers may vary. Sample: Using variables allows the figure to represent all possibilities.
9. rectangle
10. Answers may vary. Sample: Classmate ignored the coefficient 2 in the coordinates. The endpoints are (b, c) and $(a + d, c)$.

▼ STUDENT PAGES 320–322

Lesson Check

Do you know HOW?

Use the diagram at the right.

5. In $\square KLMO$, $OM = 2a$. What are the coordinates of K and M?

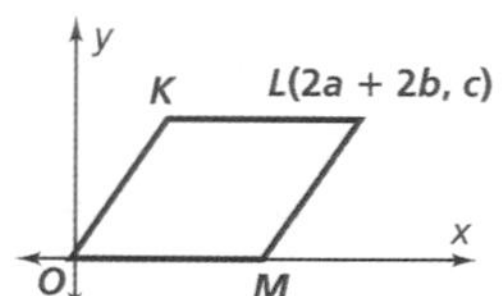

6. What are the slopes of the diagonals of *KLMO*?
7. What are the coordinates of the point of intersection of $\overline{KM}$ and $\overline{OL}$?

Do you UNDERSTAND?

8. **Reasoning** How do variable coordinates generalize figures in the coordinate plane?
9. **Reasoning** A vertex of a quadrilateral has coordinates (a, b). The x-coordinates of the other three vertices are a or $-a$, and the y-coordinates are b or $-b$. What kind of quadrilateral is the figure?
10. **Error Analysis** A classmate says the endpoints of the midsegment of the trapezoid in Problem 3 are $\left(\frac{b}{2}, \frac{c}{2}\right)$ and $\left(\frac{d+a}{2}, \frac{c}{2}\right)$. What is your classmate's error? Explain.

Practice

More Practice and Problem-Solving Exercises

ASSIGNMENT GUIDE
The assignments below are for the More Practice and Problem-Solving Exercises. You may also want to assign the A-Level Practice Exercises for homework if these are not used in class.
Average: 11–27
Advanced: 11–33

Mathematical Practices The exercises listed focus on the Standards for Mathematical Practices listed.

EX. 8, 19: Make Sense of Problems (MP 1)
EX. 11: Persevere in Solving Problems (MP 1)
EX. 9, 12, 16e: Construct Arguments (MP 3)
EX. 10: Critique the Reasoning of Others (MP 3)
EX. 27: Model (MP 4)

STEM exercises focus on science or engineering applications.

EXERCISE 20: Use the **Think About a Plan** worksheet in the Online Teacher Resources to further support students' development in becoming independent learners.

HOMEWORK QUICK CHECK
To check students' understanding of key skills and concepts, go over Exercises 11, 13, 19, 20, and 22.

ANSWERS

11. Answers may vary. Sample:

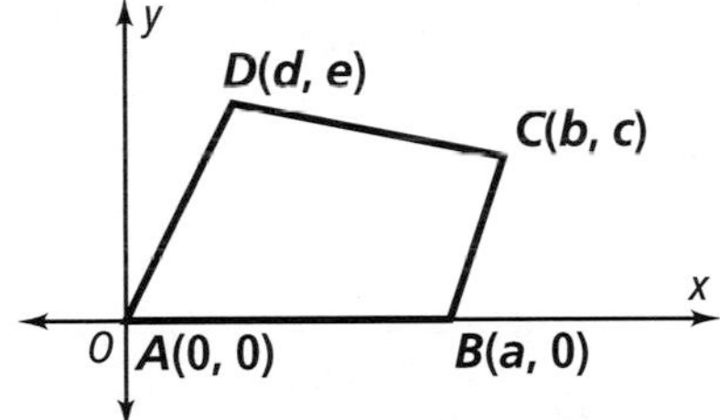

12. $P(-r, s)$
13. $P(c - a, b)$
14. $P(a, 0)$
15. $P(-b, 0)$
16. a. Answers may vary. Sample:

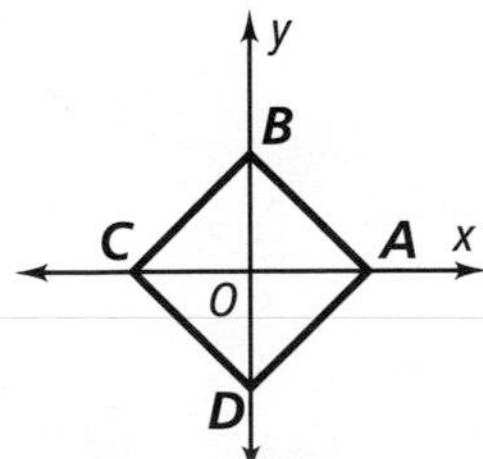

b. Answers may vary. Sample: $(-b, 0)$, $(0, -b)$, $(b, 0)$, $(0, b)$
c. $b\sqrt{2}$
d. 1, −1

▼ STUDENT PAGE 322

More Practice and Problem-Solving Exercises

B Apply

11. Open-Ended Place a general quadrilateral in the coordinate plane.

12. Reasoning A rectangle *LMNP* is centered at the origin with $M(r, -s)$. What are the coordinates of *P*?

Give the coordinates for point *P* without using any new variables.

13. isosceles trapezoid

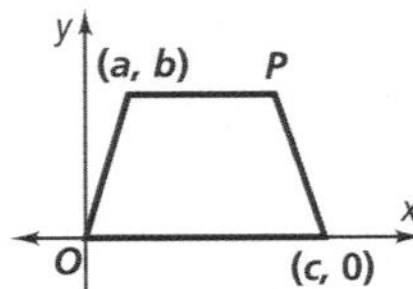

14. trapezoid with a right ∠

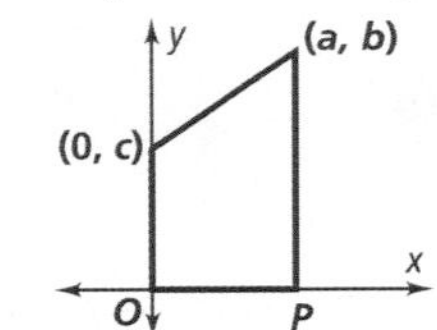

15. kite

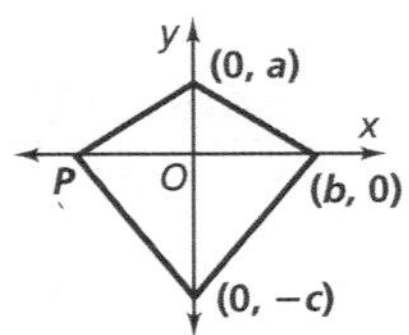

16. a. Draw a square whose diagonals of length $2b$ lie on the x- and y-axes.
b. Give the coordinates of the vertices of the square.
c. Compute the length of a side of the square.
d. Find the slopes of two adjacent sides of the square.
e. Writing Do the slopes show that the sides are perpendicular? Explain.

More Practice and Problem-Solving Exercises *continued*

e. Yes; product of the slopes is -1.

17. a. Answers may vary. Sample:

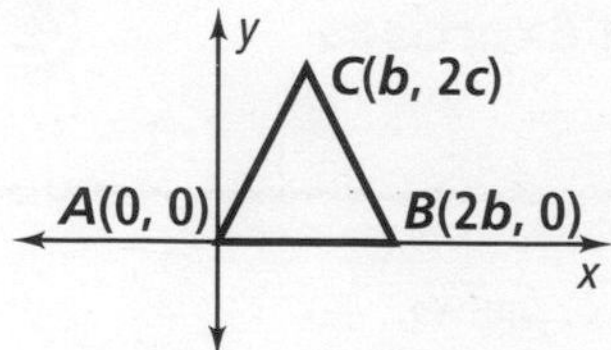

b. Answers may vary. Sample:

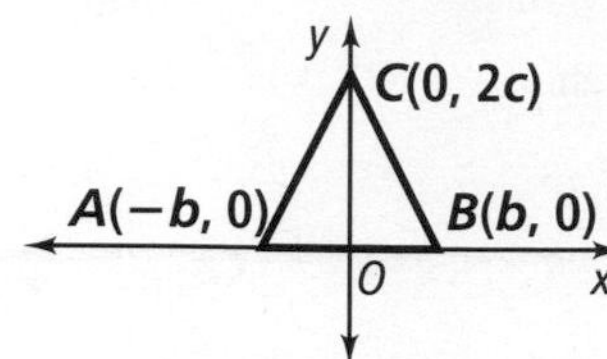

c. $\sqrt{b^2 + 4c^2}$, $\sqrt{b^2 + 4c^2}$

d. $\sqrt{b^2 + 4c^2}$, $\sqrt{b^2 + 4c^2}$

e. The results are the same.

18. a. $W\left(\frac{a}{2}, \frac{b}{2}\right)$, $Z\left(\frac{c+e}{2}, \frac{d}{2}\right)$

b. $W(a, b)$, $Z(c + e, d)$

c. $W(2a, 2b)$, $Z(2c + 2e, 2d)$

d. Answers may vary. Sample: Figure (c) avoids fractions.

19. Answers may vary. Sample: Place vertices at $A(0, 0)$, $B(a, 0)$, $C(a + b, c)$, and $D(b, c)$. Use the Distance Formula to find the lengths of opp. sides.

20. Answers may vary. Sample: Place vertices at $A(-a, -b)$, $B(-a, b)$, $C(a, b)$, and $D(a, -b)$. Show each diagonal has (0, 0) as its midpt.

21. Answers may vary. Sample: Place vertices at $A(0, 0)$, $B(0, a)$, $C(a, a)$, and $D(a, 0)$. Use the fact that a horizontal line is $\perp$ to a vertical line.

22. ▱

23. kite

24. isosc. trapezoid

25. square

26. The diagonals of a rhombus are $\perp$.

27. Answers may vary. Sample:

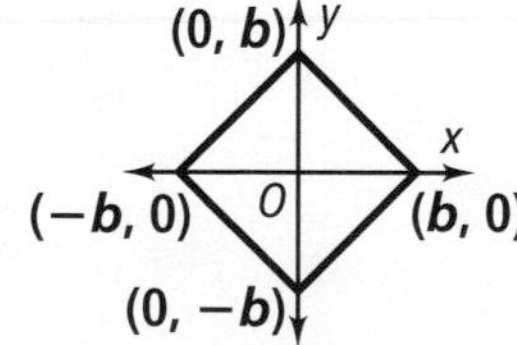

28. Answers may vary. Sample: *A, C, H, F*

29. Answers may vary. Sample: *B, D, H, F*

30. Answers may vary. Sample: *A, B, F, E*

31. Answers may vary. Sample: *A, C, G, E*

32. Answers may vary. Sample: *A, C, F, E*

33. Answers may vary. Sample: *A, D, G, F*

17. Make two drawings of an isosceles triangle with base length $2b$ and height $2c$.
- **a.** In one drawing, place the base on the x-axis with a vertex at the origin.
- **b.** In the second, place the base on the x-axis with its midpoint at the origin.
- **c.** Find the lengths of the legs of the triangle as placed in part (a).
- **d.** Find the lengths of the legs of the triangle as placed in part (b).
- **e.** How do the results of parts (c) and (d) compare?

18. W and Z are the midpoints of $\overline{OR}$ and $\overline{ST}$, respectively. In parts (a)–(c), find the coordinates of W and Z.

a.

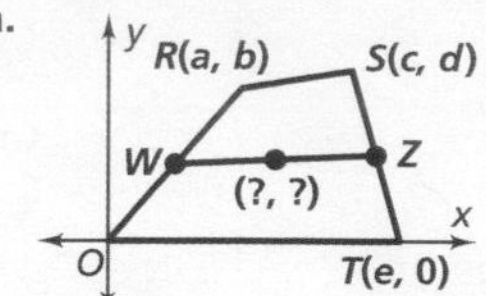

b.

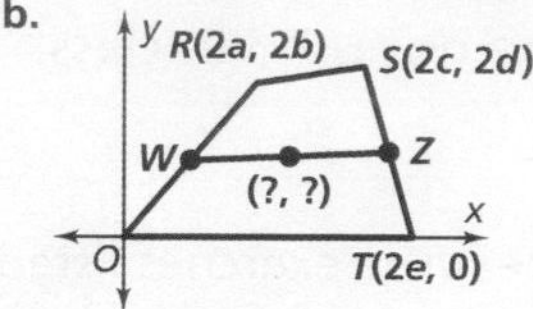

c.

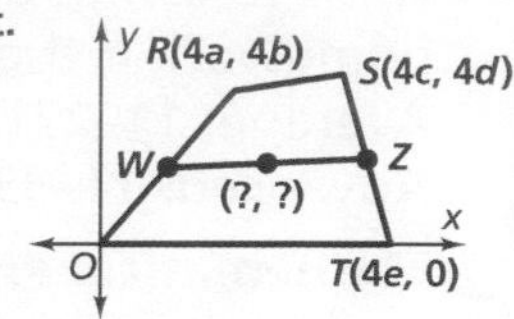

d. You are to plan a coordinate proof involving the midpoint of $\overline{WZ}$. Which of the figures (a)–(c) would you prefer to use? Explain.

Plan the coordinate proof of each statement.

19. Think About a Plan The opposite sides of a parallelogram are congruent (Theorem 40).
- How will you place the parallelogram in a coordinate plane?
- What formulas will you need to use?

20. The diagonals of a rectangle bisect each other.

21. The consecutive sides of a square are perpendicular.

Classify each quadrilateral as precisely as possible.

22. $A(b, 2c)$, $B(4b, 3c)$, $C(5b, c)$, $D(2b, 0)$

23. $E(a, b)$, $F(2a, 2b)$, $G(3a, b)$, $H(2a, -b)$

24. $O(0, 0)$, $P(t, 2s)$, $Q(3t, 2s)$, $R(4t, 0)$

25. $O(0, 0)$, $L(-e, f)$, $M(f - e, f + e)$, $N(f, e)$

26. What property of a rhombus makes it convenient to place its diagonals on the x- and y-axes?

STEM **27. Marine Archaeology** Marine archaeologists sometimes use a coordinate system on the ocean floor. They record the coordinates of points where artifacts are found. Assume that each diver searches a square area and can go no farther than b units from the starting point. Draw a model for the region one diver can search. Assign coordinates to the vertices without using any new variables.

Challenge

Here are coordinates for eight points in the coordinate plane ($q > p > 0$). $A(0, 0)$, $B(p, 0)$, $C(q, 0)$, $D(p + q, 0)$, $E(0, q)$, $F(p, q)$, $G(q, q)$, $H(p + q, q)$. Which four points, if any, are the vertices for each type of figure?

28. parallelogram **29.** rhombus **30.** rectangle

31. square **32.** trapezoid **33.** isosceles trapezoid

Assess and Remediate

Lesson Quiz

Plan a coordinate proof to show that the midpoints of the sides of an equilateral triangle form another equilateral triangle.

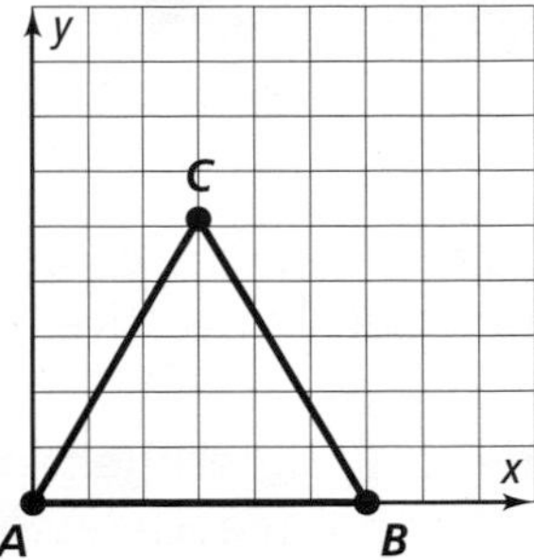

1. Name the coordinates of equilateral triangle *ABC* with base $AB = 2a$ along the *x*-axis and height $a\sqrt{3}$.
2. State the *Given* and *Prove*.
3. How will you find the coordinates of the midpoints of each side?
4. **Do you UNDERSTAND?** How will you determine whether the figure formed is an equilateral triangle?

ANSWERS TO LESSON QUIZ

1. $A(0, 0)$, $B(2a, 0)$, $C(a, a\sqrt{3})$
2. Given: $\triangle ABC$ is equilateral with vertices $A(0, 0)$, $B(2a, 0)$, $C(a, a\sqrt{3})$

   Prove: The midpoints of the sides of $\triangle ABC$ form the vertices of another equilateral triangle.
3. Use the Midpoint Formula.
4. Use the Distance Formula to show that the sides of the resulting triangle are all the same length.

Prescription for Remediation

Use the student work on the Lesson Quiz to prescribe a differentiated assignment.

Points	Differentiated Remediation
0–2	Intervention
3	On-level
4	Extension

Online Assessment

Assign the Lesson Quiz in Success Tracker on **pearsonsuccessnet.com**. Success Tracker will automatically score the quiz and assign appropriate intervention or enrichment to each student based on the results. The compiled data appear in three different reports for instant analysis of whole class and individual student performance.

Differentiated Remediation

Intervention

- **RETEACHING** (2 pages) Provides reteaching and practice exercises for the key lesson concepts. Use with struggling students or absent students.
- **ENGLISH LANGUAGE LEARNER SUPPORT** Helps students develop and reinforce mathematical vocabulary and key concepts.

On-Level

- **PRACTICE** (2 pages) Provides extra practice for each lesson. For simpler practice exercises, use the Form K Practice pages found in the Online Teacher Resources.
- **THINK ABOUT A PLAN** Helps students develop specific problem-solving skills and strategies by providing scaffolded guiding questions.
- **STANDARDIZED TEST PREP** Focuses on all major exercises, all major question types, and helps students prepare for the high-stakes assessments.

Extension

- **ENRICHMENT** Provides students with interesting problems and activities that extend the concepts of the lesson.
- **ACTIVITIES, GAMES, AND PUZZLES** Worksheets that can be used for concept development, enrichment, and for fun!

5-8 Proofs Using Coordinate Geometry

Common Core State Standards
G.CO.11 Prove theorems about parallelograms . . . **Also G.CO.10**

Preparing to Teach

BIG ideas Coordinate Geometry
Reasoning and Proof

ESSENTIAL UNDERSTANDING

Geometric relationships can be proven using variable coordinates for figures in the coordinate plane.

Math Background

Synthetic geometry is the branch of geometry which makes use of observations, postulates, and theorems. Euclid's geometry, which is the basis for this textbook, is a synthetic geometry. Proofs for some theorems in synthetic geometry can be very difficult to construct and understand. Using coordinate geometry provides a powerful and sometimes more understandable alternative to proving theorems in synthetic geometry.

Keys to effective coordinate proofs lie in confidently using the Distance Formula, the Midpoint Formula, and the Slope Formula.

Note to students that theorems about angles are generally not provable by coordinate geometry unless the angle is a right angle or a straight angle.

ELL Support

CONNECT TO PRIOR KNOWLEDGE Use the plans for the coordinate proofs created by students in the last lesson for practice writing coordinate proofs.

FOCUS ON COMMUNICATION Place students in heterogeneous groups. Have students write the theorems from each lesson on one side of an index card. Students discuss the theorems and then write a summary on the reverse side of the card. Encourage students to engage in discussion using questions. For example: What does this mean? How would you use that theorem? How are these two theorems related? Students can share the results of their discussions, particularly what they learned from each other. The cards can then be used for review.

Mathematical Practices

REASON ABSTRACTLY AND QUANTITATIVELY. In writing coordinate proofs, students will create a coherent representation of a geometric figure in algebraic terms.

1 Interactive Learning

Solve It!

PURPOSE To use knowledge of the properties of a rectangle that is represented by variables in the coordinate plane

PROCESS Students may use previous knowledge of the properties of rectangles and the Midpoint Formula.

Q What are the coordinates of the fourth vertex of the rectangle? Explain. **[$(-2a, 2b)$, since it must create sides that are congruent and parallel to the existing sides.]**

Q What are the endpoints of the diagonal for which we need to determine the midpoint? **[$(-2a, 2b)$ and $(2a, 0)$]**

ANSWER $(0, b)$; diagonals have the same midpoint. The midpoint of the diagonal joining $(-2a, 0)$ and $(2a, 2b)$ is $(0, b)$.

CONNECT THE MATH In the Solve It, students use coordinate geometry and facts about rectangles to find a midpoint. In the lesson, students will gain more experience with coordinate proofs.

▼ DIGITAL (STUDENT WORK SPACE PAGE 324)

Getting Ready!

The coordinates of three vertices of a rectangle are $(-2a, 0)$, $(2a, 0)$, and $(2a, 2b)$. A diagonal joins one of these points with the fourth vertex. What are the coordinates of the midpoint of the diagonal? Justify your answer.

2 Guided Instruction

Problem 1 Writing a Coordinate Proof

Q Why should you place the legs of the right triangle on the x- and y-axes? **[Placing the legs on the axes will make calculations involving the Midpoint Formula and the Distance Formula easier.]**

Got It?

To check understanding of the answer to this question, ask students to list another advantageous set of three points to use as the vertices for the right triangle.

ANSWERS

Got It? The factor 2 avoids fractions.

Practice

1. **a.** $M(-a, b)$, $N(a, b)$
   b. $PN = \sqrt{9a^2 + b^2}$, $RM = \sqrt{9a^2 + b^2}$
   c. The Distance Formula shows that $\overline{PN}$ and $\overline{RM}$ are the same length.

▼ STUDENT PAGE 324

In the Solve It, the coordinates of the points include variables. In this lesson, you will use coordinates with variables to write coordinate proofs.

Essential Understanding You can prove geometric relationships using variable coordinates for figures in the coordinate plane.

▼ DIGITAL

Problem 1 **Writing a Coordinate Proof**

Use coordinate geometry to prove that the midpoint of the hypotenuse of a right triangle is equidistant from the three vertices.

Given: $\triangle OEF$ is a right triangle.
M is the midpoint of $\overline{EF}$.

Prove: $EM = FM = OM$

Coordinate Proof:

By the Midpoint Formula, $M = \left(\frac{2a + 0}{2}, \frac{0 + 2b}{2}\right) = (a, b)$.

By the Distance Formula,

$OM = \sqrt{a^2 + b^2}$

$FM = \sqrt{(2a - a)^2 + (0 - b)^2} = \sqrt{a^2 + b^2}$

$EM = \sqrt{(0 - a)^2 + (2b - b)^2} = \sqrt{a^2 + b^2}$

Since $EM = FM = OM$, the midpoint of the hypotenuse is equidistant from the vertices of the right triangle.

▼ STUDENT PAGES 324–325

Got It? **Reasoning** Refer to the proof in Problem 1. What is the advantage of using coordinates $O(0, 0)$, $E(0, 2b)$, and $F(2a, 0)$ rather than $O(0, 0)$, $E(0, b)$, and $F(a, 0)$?

Think
What is the advantage of placing the legs of the right triangle on the axes?

Practice **Developing Proof** Complete the following coordinate proof.

1. The medians drawn to the congruent sides of an isosceles triangle are congruent.

   Given: $\triangle PQR$ with $\overline{PQ} \cong \overline{RQ}$, M is the midpoint of $\overline{PQ}$, N is the midpoint of $\overline{RQ}$

   Prove: $\overline{PN} \cong \overline{RM}$

   a. What are the coordinates of M and N?
   b. What are PN and RM?
   c. Explain why $\overline{PN} \cong \overline{RM}$.

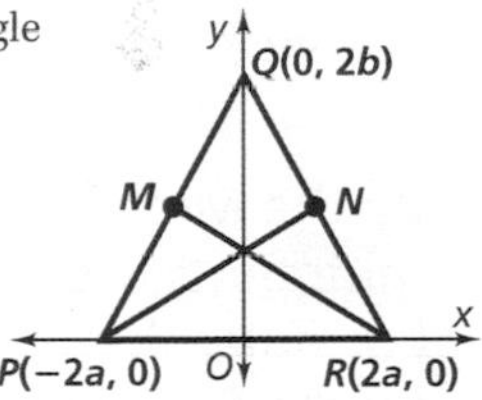

Problem 2 Writing a Coordinate Proof

Q How will the Slope Formula be used in this proof? **[The Slope Formula will be used to determine the slopes of the two bases and the midsegment. The slopes must be the same if the segments are parallel.]**

Q How will the Midpoint Formula be used in this proof? **[The Midpoint Formula will be used to determine the endpoints of the midsegment.]**

Q How will the Distance Formula be used in this proof? **[The Distance Formula will be used to determine the length of each base and the midsegment.]**

Q Should you remove the parentheses from the expression $(2d - 2b)^2$ prior to simplifying the expression $\sqrt{(2d - 2b)^2}$? Explain. **[No; $2d - 2b^2 \neq (2d - 2b)^2$.]**

Q Is it possible to use the Distance Formula for a number line instead of the Distance Formula for points on a coordinate plane? Explain. **[Yes; the segments are all horizontal.]**

Q What property do you use to simplify the expression $\frac{1}{2}[2a + (2d - 2b)]$. **[Distributive Property]**

Got It?

Students can use the proof of the Trapezoid Midsegment Theorem as a template for the proof of the Triangle Midsegment Theorem.

ANSWERS

Got It? Answers may vary. Sample:

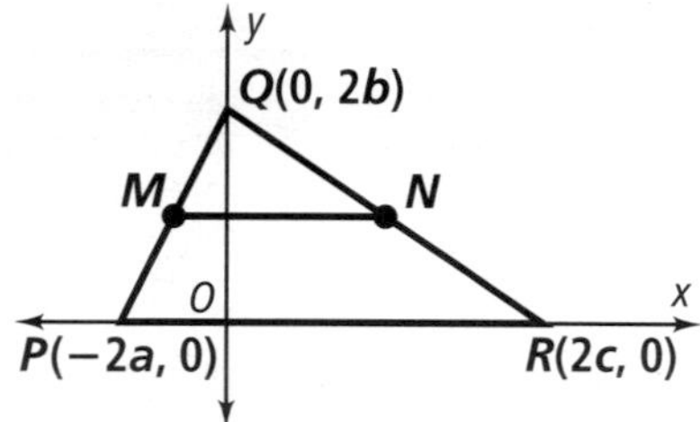

Given: $\triangle PQR$, midpoints M and N

Prove: $\overline{MN} \parallel \overline{PR}$, $MN = \frac{1}{2}PR$

By the Midpoint Formula, coordinates of the midpoints are $M(-a, b)$ and $N(c, b)$. By the Slope Formula, slope of $\overline{MN}$ = slope of $\overline{PR} = 0$, so $\overline{MN} \parallel \overline{PR}$. By the Distance Formula, $MN = c + a$ and $PR = 2c + 2a = 2 \cdot MN$, so $MN = \frac{1}{2}PR$.

Practice

2. a. $\sqrt{(b + a)^2 + c^2}$
   b. $\sqrt{(a + b)^2 + c^2}$
   c. The Distance Formula shows that $\overline{EG}$ and $\overline{FH}$ are the same length.

▼ STUDENT PAGE 325

In the previous lesson, you wrote a plan for the proof of the Trapezoid Midsegment Theorem. Now you will write the full coordinate proof.

▼ DIGITAL

Problem 2 Writing a Coordinate Proof

Write a coordinate proof of the Trapezoid Midsegment Theorem.

Given: $\overline{MN}$ is the midsegment of trapezoid *ORAP*.

Prove: $\overline{MN} \parallel \overline{OP}$, $\overline{MN} \parallel \overline{RA}$, $MN = \frac{1}{2}(OP + RA)$

y | R(2b, 2c) | A(2d, 2c) | M | N | x | O | P(2a, 0)

Coordinate Proof:

Use the Midpoint Formula to find the coordinates of *M* and *N*.

$$M = \left(\frac{2b + 0}{2}, \frac{2c + 0}{2}\right) = (b, c)$$

$$N = \left(\frac{2a + 2d}{2}, \frac{0 + 2c}{2}\right) = (a + d, c)$$

Use the Slope Formula to determine whether $\overline{MN}$ is parallel to $\overline{OP}$ and $\overline{RA}$.

$$\text{slope of } \overline{MN} = \frac{c - c}{(a + d) - b} = 0$$

$$\text{slope of } \overline{RA} = \frac{2c - 2c}{2d - 2b} = 0$$

$$\text{slope of } \overline{OP} = \frac{0 - 0}{2a - 0} = 0$$

The three slopes are equal, so $\overline{MN} \parallel \overline{OP}$ and $\overline{MN} \parallel \overline{RA}$.

Use the Distance Formula to find and compare *MN*, *OP*, and *RA*.

$$MN = \sqrt{[(a + d) - b)]^2 + (c - c)^2} = a + d - b$$

$$OP = \sqrt{(2a - 0)^2 + (0 - 0)^2} = 2a$$

$$RA = \sqrt{(2d - 2b)^2 + (2c - 2c)^2} = 2d - 2b$$

$MN \stackrel{?}{=} \frac{1}{2}(OP + RA)$	Check that $MN = \frac{1}{2}(OP + RA)$ is true.
$a + d - b \stackrel{?}{=} \frac{1}{2}[2a + (2d - 2b)]$	Substitute.
$a + d - b = a + d - b$ ✓	Simplify.

So, (1) the midsegment of a trapezoid is parallel to its bases, and
(2) the length of the midsegment of a trapezoid is half the sum of the lengths of the bases.

▼ STUDENT PAGE 326

Got It? Write a coordinate proof of the Triangle Midsegment Theorem (Theorem 24).

Think
How will you place the triangle in the coordinate plane and assign coordinates?

A Practice **Developing Proof** Complete the following coordinate proof.

2. The diagonals of an isosceles trapezoid are congruent.

   Given: Trapezoid *EFGH* with $\overline{EF} \cong \overline{GH}$

   Prove: $\overline{EG} \cong \overline{FH}$

   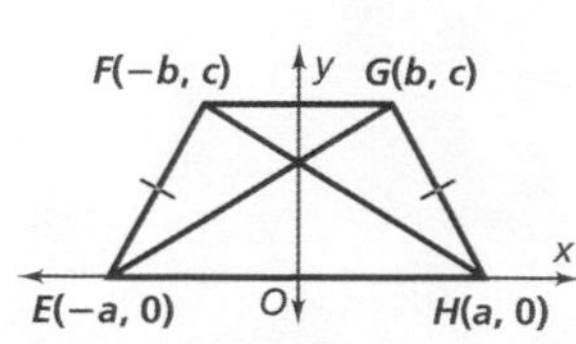

   a. Find *EG*.

   b. Find *FH*.

   c. Explain why $\overline{EG} \cong \overline{FH}$.

Lesson Check

Do you know HOW?

If students have difficulty with Exercise 3, then have them review Problem 1 to write a plan for the proof.

Do you UNDERSTAND?

If students have difficulty with Exercise 5, then have them choose sample values for the variables and try to draw a diagram that fits all the specifications of the given diagram.

Close

Q What three formulas are important for completing coordinate proofs? Explain the importance of each. **[The Slope Formula is important for proving segments parallel and perpendicular. The Distance Formula is important for determining and comparing the lengths of segments. The Midpoint Formula is important for constructing special points and segments on the given figure.]**

ANSWERS

3. a. Answers may vary. Sample:

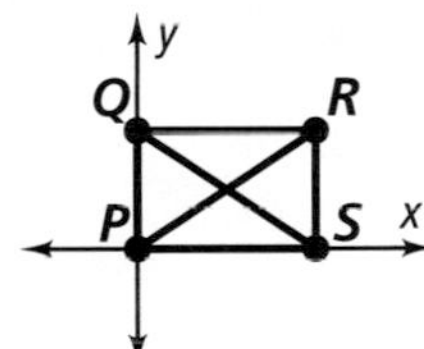

b. $Q(0, b)$, $R(a, b)$, and $S(a, 0)$

c. Given: Rectangle $PQRS$

Prove: $\overline{PR} \cong \overline{SQ}$

d. Answers may vary. Sample: By the Distance Formula,
$PR = \sqrt{(0-a)^2 + (0-b)^2} = \sqrt{a^2+b^2}$
and $SQ = \sqrt{(0-a)^2 + (b-0)^2} = \sqrt{a^2+b^2}$.
So $\overline{PR} \cong \overline{SQ}$.

4. Answers may vary. Sample: Place the vertices on the x- and y-axes so that the axes are the diagonals of the rhombus.

5. Your classmate assumes $PQRO$ is an isosc. trapezoid.

▼ STUDENT PAGES 327–328

Lesson Check

Do you know HOW?

3. Use coordinate geometry to prove that the diagonals of a rectangle are congruent.

a. Place rectangle $PQRS$ in the coordinate plane with P at $(0, 0)$.

b. What are the coordinates of Q, R, and S?

c. Write the *Given* and *Prove* statements.

d. Write a coordinate proof.

Do you UNDERSTAND?

4. Reasoning Describe a good strategy for placing the vertices of a rhombus for a coordinate proof.

5. Error Analysis Your classmate places a trapezoid on the coordinate plane. What is the error?

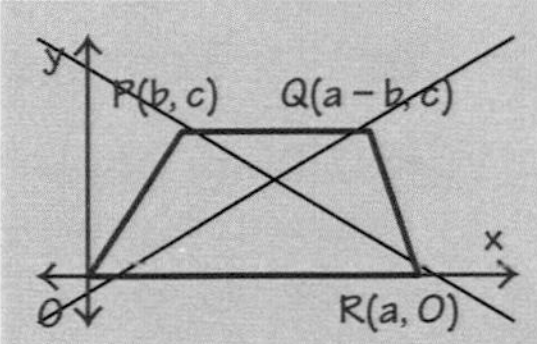

Practice

More Practice and Problem-Solving Exercises

ASSIGNMENT GUIDE

The assignments below are for the More Practice and Problem-Solving Exercises. You may also want to assign the A-Level Practice Exercises for homework if these are not used in class.

Average: 6–26

Advanced: 6–28

Mathematical Practices The exercises listed focus on the Standards for Mathematical Practices listed.

EX. 4, 21: Make Sense of Problems (MP 1)
EX. 20: Construct Arguments (MP 3)
EX. 5: Critique the Reasoning of Others (MP 3)
EX. 19: Model (MP 4)
EX. 27: Repeated Reasoning (MP 7)

EXERCISE 22: Use the **Think About a Plan** worksheet in the Online Teacher Resources to further support students' development in becoming independent learners.

HOMEWORK QUICK CHECK

To check students' understanding of key skills and concepts, go over Exercises 8, 20, 21, 22, and 25.

ANSWERS

6. Yes; use Distance Formula.
7. Yes; use Slope Formula.
8. Yes; use Slope Formula and property of ⊥ lines.
9. Yes; use Midpoint Formula.
10. Yes; show that a point on $\overline{AB}$ is equidistant from the sides of ∠CAD.
11. No; you need ∠ measures.
12. Yes; use Slope Formula and property of ⊥ lines.
13. Yes; use Distance Formula.
14. Yes; answers may vary. Sample: Show two sides ≅.
15. Yes; answers may vary. Sample: Show four sides have the same length or show diagonals ⊥.
16. Yes; show they have same midpt.
17. No; you need ∠ measures.
18. Yes; find intersection point of segments.

▼ STUDENT PAGE 328

More Practice and Problem-Solving Exercises

Apply

Tell whether you can reach each type of conclusion below using coordinate methods. Give a reason for each answer.

6. $\overline{AB} \cong \overline{CD}$
7. $\overline{AB} \parallel \overline{CD}$
8. $\overline{AB} \perp \overline{CD}$
9. $\overline{AB}$ bisects $\overline{CD}$.
10. $\overline{AB}$ bisects ∠CAD.
11. ∠A ≅ ∠B
12. ∠A is a right angle.
13. $AB + BC = AC$
14. △ABC is isosceles.
15. Quadrilateral ABCD is a rhombus.
16. $\overline{AB}$ and $\overline{CD}$ bisect each other.
17. ∠A is the supplement of ∠B.
18. $\overline{AB}$, $\overline{CD}$, and $\overline{EF}$ are concurrent.

Proof 19. **Flag Design** The flag design at the right is made by connecting the midpoints of the sides of a rectangle. Use coordinate geometry to prove that the quadrilateral formed is a rhombus.

20. **Open-Ended** Give an example of a statement that you think is easier to prove with a coordinate geometry proof than with a proof method that does not require coordinate geometry. Explain your choice.

19. Answers may vary. Sample:

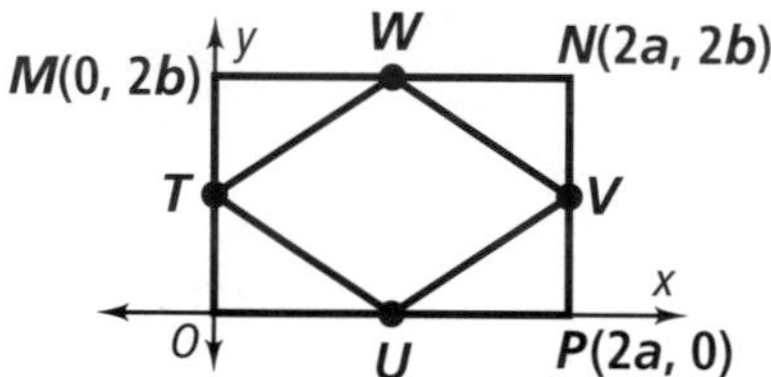

Given: MNPO is a rectangle.
T, W, V, U are midpoints of its sides.

Prove: TWVU is a rhombus.

By the Midpoint Formula, the coordinates of the midpoints are T(0, b), W(a, 2b), V(2a, b), and U(a, 0). By the Slope Formula,

slope of $\overline{TW} = \frac{2b-b}{a-0} = \frac{b}{a}$,

slope of $\overline{WV} = \frac{2b-b}{a-2a} = -\frac{b}{a}$,

slope of $\overline{VU} = \frac{b-0}{2a-a} = \frac{b}{a}$,

slope of $\overline{UT} = \frac{b-0}{0-a} = -\frac{b}{a}$.

So $\overline{TW} \parallel \overline{VU}$ and $\overline{WV} \parallel \overline{UT}$. Therefore TWVU is a ▱. By the Slope Formula, slope of $\overline{TV} = 0$, and slope of $\overline{WU}$ is undefined. $\overline{TV} \perp \overline{WU}$ because horiz. and vert. lines are ⊥. Since the diagonals of ▱TWVU are ⊥, it must be a rhombus.

20. Answers may vary. Sample: Lines are ⊥ when product of their slopes is −1; it is difficult to find the product without using coordinate methods.

21. Answers may vary. Sample:

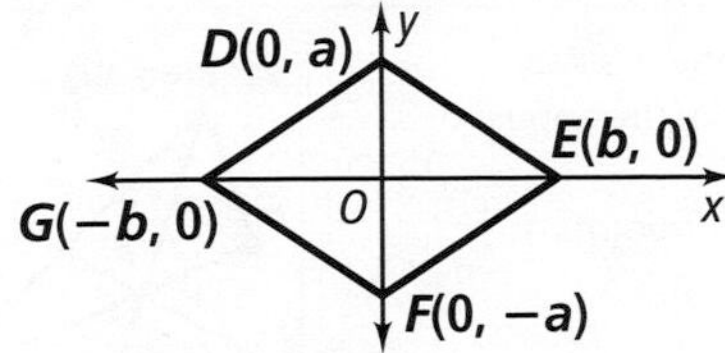

Given: *DEFG* is a rhombus.

Prove: $\overline{GE} \perp \overline{DF}$

By the Slope Formula, slope of $\overline{GE} = \frac{0-0}{b-(-b)} = 0$, and slope of $\overline{DF} = \frac{a-(-a)}{0-0}$, which is undefined. So $\overline{GE}$ must be horizontal and $\overline{DF}$ must be vertical. Therefore $\overline{GE} \perp \overline{DF}$ because horiz. and vert. lines are $\perp$.

22. Answers may vary. Sample:

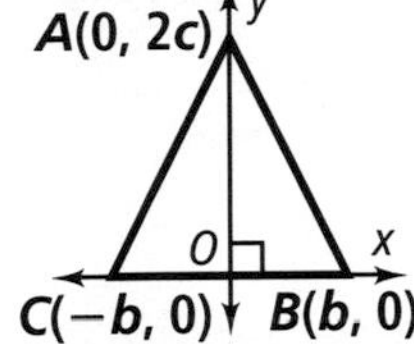

Given: Isosc. $\triangle ABC$ with base $\overline{BC}$ and altitude $\overline{AO}$

Prove: $\overline{AO}$ bisects $\overline{BC}$.

By the Distance Formula, $CO = \sqrt{[0-(-b)]^2 + (0-0)^2} = b$ and $BO = \sqrt{(b-0)^2 + (0-0)^2} = b$. Since $CO = BO$, $\overline{CO} \cong \overline{BO}$, so $\overline{AO}$ bisects $\overline{BC}$ by def. of seg. bisect.

23. Answers may vary. Sample:

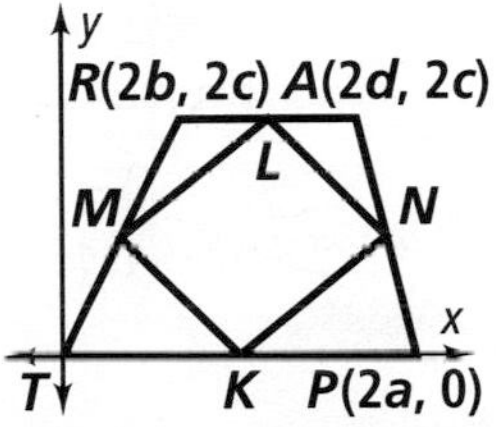

Given: Trapezoid *TRAP*; *M*, *L*, *N*, and *K* are midpoints of its sides.

Prove: *MLNK* is a ▱.

By the Midpoint Formula, the coordinates of the midpoints are $M(b, c)$, $L(b+d, 2c)$, $N(a+d, c)$, and $K(a, 0)$. By the Slope Formula, the slope of $\overline{ML} = \frac{c}{d}$, the slope of $\overline{LN} = \frac{c}{b-a}$, the slope of $\overline{NK} = \frac{c}{d}$, and the slope of $\overline{KM} = \frac{c}{b-a}$. Since slopes are =, $\overline{ML} \parallel \overline{NK}$ and $\overline{LN} \parallel \overline{KM}$. Therefore, *MLNK* is a ▱ by def. of ▱.

▼ STUDENT PAGE 328

Use coordinate geometry to prove each statement.

21. Think About a Plan If a parallelogram is a rhombus, its diagonals are perpendicular (Theorem 50).
- How will you place the rhombus in a coordinate plane?
- What formulas will you need to use?

22. The altitude to the base of an isosceles triangle bisects the base.

23. If the midpoints of a trapezoid are joined to form a quadrilateral, then the quadrilateral is a parallelogram.

24. One diagonal of a kite divides the kite into two congruent triangles.

24. Answers may vary. Sample:

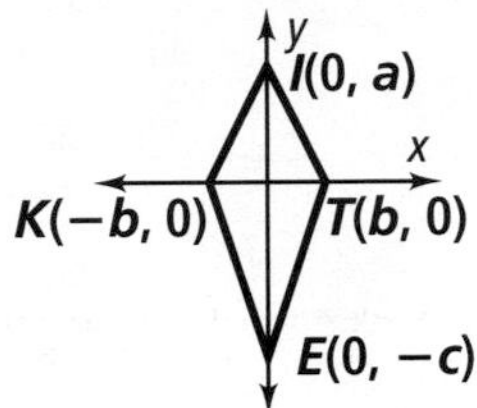

Given: Kite *KITE*

Prove: $\triangle KIE \cong \triangle TIE$

By the Distance Formula, $KI = IT = \sqrt{a^2 + b^2}$ and $KE = TE = \sqrt{b^2 + c^2}$. $\overline{IE} \cong \overline{IE}$ by the Refl. Prop. of $\cong$. So $\triangle KIE \cong \triangle TIE$ by SSS.

25. a. $L(3q, 3r)$, $M(3p + 3q, 3r)$, $N(3p, 0)$

b. equation of $\overleftrightarrow{AM}$: $y = \frac{r}{p + q}x$

equation of $\overleftrightarrow{BN}$: $y = \frac{2r}{2q - p}(x - 3p)$

equation of $\overleftrightarrow{CL}$: $y = \frac{r}{q - 2p}(x - 6p)$

c. $P(2p + 2q, 2r)$

d. The coordinates of P satisfy the equation for $\overleftrightarrow{CL}$: $y = \frac{r}{q - 2p}(x - 6p)$.

$2r = \frac{r}{q - 2p}(2p + 2q - 6p)$

$2r = \frac{r}{q - 2p}(2q - 4p)$

$2r = 2r$

e. $AM = \sqrt{(3p + 3q - 0)^2 + (3r - 0)^2} = \sqrt{(3p + 3q)^2 + (3r)^2}$;

$\frac{2}{3}AM = \frac{2}{3}\sqrt{(3p + 3q)^2 + (3r)^2} =$

$\sqrt{\frac{4}{9}\left[(3p + 3q)^2 + (3r)^2\right]} =$

$\sqrt{\left[\frac{4}{9}(3p + 3q)^2\right] + \left[\frac{4}{9}(3r)^2\right]} =$

$\sqrt{\left[\frac{4}{9}(9p^2 + 18pq + 9q^2)\right] + \left[\frac{4}{9}(9r^2)\right]} =$

$\sqrt{(4p^2 + 8pq + 4q^2) + (4r^2)} =$

$\sqrt{(2p + 2q)^2 + (2r)^2}$;

$AP = \sqrt{(2p + 2q - 0)^2 + (2r - 0)^2} = \sqrt{(2p + 2q)^2 + (2r)^2}$

So $AP = \frac{2}{3}AM$. You can find the other two distances similarly.

26. a. $\frac{b}{c}$

b. The point-slope formula for point $(a, 0)$ and $m = \frac{b}{c}$ is $y - 0 = \frac{b}{c}(x - a)$ or $y = \frac{b}{c}(x - a)$.

c. $x = 0$

d. The ordered pair $\left(0, \frac{-ab}{c}\right)$ satisfies the equation of line q, $x = 0$. When $x = 0$, $y = \frac{b}{c}(x - a) = \frac{b}{c}(0 - a) = \frac{-ab}{c}$. So p and q intersect at $\left(0, -\frac{ab}{c}\right)$.

e. $\frac{a}{c}$

f. The point-slope formula for point $(b, 0)$ and $m = \frac{a}{c}$ is $y - 0 = \frac{a}{c}(x - b)$ or $y = \frac{a}{c}(x - b)$.

g. The ordered pair $\left(0, \frac{-ab}{c}\right)$ satisfies the equation of line q, $x = 0$. When $x = 0$, $y = \frac{a}{c}(x - b) = \frac{a}{c}(0 - b) = \frac{-ab}{c}$. So q and r intersect at $\left(0, -\frac{ab}{c}\right)$.

h. $\left(0, \frac{-ab}{c}\right)$

27. a. Answers may vary. Sample: The area of a △ with base b and height c is $\frac{1}{2}bc$. The area of a △ with base d and height a is $\frac{1}{2}ad$. In both cases, the remaining area of the triangle has base $(b - d)$ and height a. Therefore $\frac{1}{2}ad = \frac{1}{2}bc$ by the Transitive Prop. of Eq. So $ad = bc$.

b. Slope of $\ell = \frac{a}{b}$ or $\frac{c}{d}$. So $\frac{a}{b} = \frac{c}{d}$ and $ad = bc$.

▼ STUDENT PAGE 329

Proof 25. You learned in Theorem 31 that the centroid of a triangle is two thirds the distance from each vertex to the midpoint of the opposite side. Complete the steps to prove this theorem.

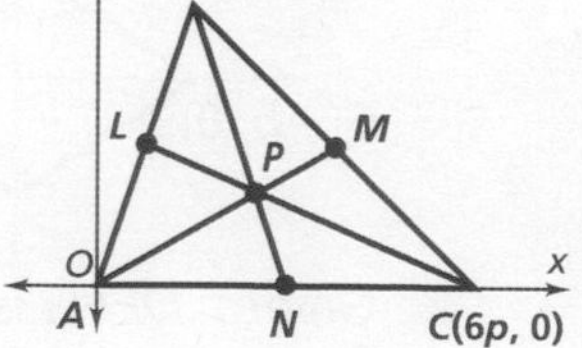

a. Find the coordinates of points L, M, and N, the midpoints of the sides of $\triangle ABC$.

b. Find equations of $\overleftrightarrow{AM}$, $\overleftrightarrow{BN}$, and $\overleftrightarrow{CL}$.

c. Find the coordinates of point P, the intersection of $\overleftrightarrow{AM}$ and $\overleftrightarrow{BN}$.

d. Show that point P is on $\overleftrightarrow{CL}$.

e. Use the Distance Formula to show that point P is two thirds the distance from each vertex to the midpoint of the opposite side.

Proof 26. Complete the steps to prove Theorem 32. You are given $\triangle ABC$ with altitudes p, q, and r. Show that p, q, and r intersect at a point (called the orthocenter of the triangle).

a. The slope of $\overline{BC}$ is $\frac{c}{-b}$. What is the slope of line p?

b. Show that the equation of line p is $y = \frac{b}{c}(x - a)$.

c. What is the equation of line q?

d. Show that lines p and q intersect at $\left(0, \frac{-ab}{c}\right)$.

e. The slope of $\overline{AC}$ is $\frac{c}{-a}$. What is the slope of line r?

f. Show that the equation of line r is $y = \frac{a}{c}(x - b)$.

g. Show that lines r and q intersect at $\left(0, \frac{-ab}{c}\right)$.

h. What are the coordinates of the orthocenter of $\triangle ABC$?

Challenge

27. Multiple Representations Use the diagram at the right.

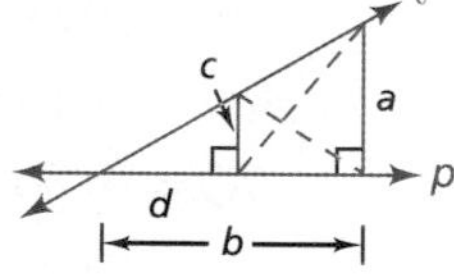

a. Explain using area why $\frac{1}{2}ad = \frac{1}{2}bc$ and therefore $ad = bc$.

b. Find two ratios for the slope of ℓ. Use these two ratios to show that $ad = bc$.

Proof 28. Prove: If two lines are perpendicular, the product of their slopes is -1.

a. Two nonvertical lines, ℓ_1 and ℓ_2, intersect as shown at the right. Find the coordinates of C.

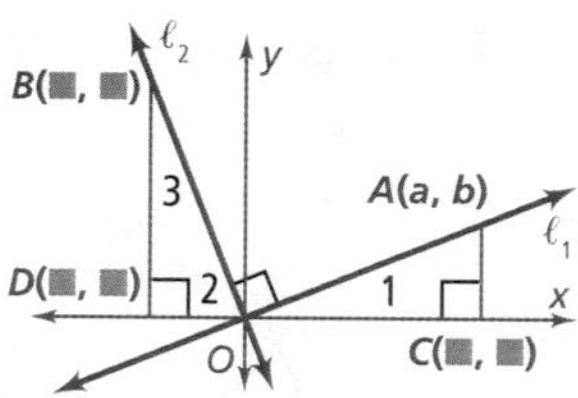

b. Choose coordinates for D and B. (*Hint:* Find the relationship between ∠1, ∠2, and ∠3. Then use congruent triangles.)

c. Complete the proof that the product of slopes is -1.

28. a. $(a, 0)$

b. $D(-b, 0)$, $B(-b, a)$

c. By the Slope Formula, the slope of ℓ_1 is $\frac{b}{a}$ and the slope of ℓ_2 is $\frac{a}{-b}$. So the product of the slopes is $\left(\frac{b}{a}\right)\left(\frac{a}{-b}\right) = \frac{ab}{-ab} = -1$.

Assess and Remediate

Lesson Quiz

1. Write a coordinate proof to show that the midpoints of the sides of an isos. rt. △ form another isos. rt. △.
   Given: *ABC* is an isosceles right triangle with coordinates *A*(0, 0), *B*(0, 2*a*), *C*(2*a*, 0).
   Prove: *LMN* is an isosceles right triangle.

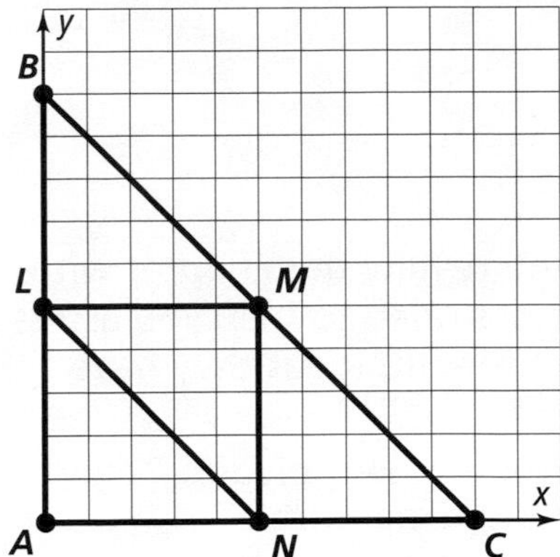

2. **Do you UNDERSTAND?** Why should you use variables as coordinates when writing a coordinate proof?

ANSWERS TO LESSON QUIZ

1. The midpoints of the sides of △*ABC* are *L*(0, *a*), *M*(*a*, *a*), and *N*(*a*, 0). By the Distance Formula, $LM = a$, $MN = a$, and $LN = a\sqrt{2}$. So, △*LMN* is isosceles since two of its sides are congruent. Since $\overline{LM}$ is horizontal and $\overline{MN}$ is vertical, they are ⊥ and form a right angle. So, *LMN* is an isos. rt. △.
2. You want to show that the relationships you demonstrate are true for any values of the variables.

Prescription for Remediation

Use the student work on the Lesson Quiz to prescribe a differentiated assignment.

Points	Differentiated Remediation
0	Intervention
1	On-level
2	Extension

Online Assessment

Assign the Lesson Quiz in Success Tracker on **pearsonsuccessnet.com**. Success Tracker will automatically score the quiz and assign appropriate intervention or enrichment to each student based on the results. The compiled data appear in three different reports for instant analysis of whole class and individual student performance.

Differentiated Remediation

Intervention

- **RETEACHING** (2 pages) Provides reteaching and practice exercises for the key lesson concepts. Use with struggling students or absent students.
- **ENGLISH LANGUAGE LEARNER SUPPORT** Helps students develop and reinforce mathematical vocabulary and key concepts.

On-Level

- **PRACTICE** (2 pages) Provides extra practice for each lesson. For simpler practice exercises, use the Form K Practice pages found in the Online Teacher Resources.
- **THINK ABOUT A PLAN** Helps students develop specific problem-solving skills and strategies by providing scaffolded guiding questions.
- **STANDARDIZED TEST PREP** Focuses on all major exercises, all major question types, and helps students prepare for the high-stakes assessments.

Extension

- **ENRICHMENT** Provides students with interesting problems and activities that extend the concepts of the lesson.
- **ACTIVITIES, GAMES, AND PUZZLES** Worksheets that can be used for concept development, enrichment, and for fun!

5 Chapter Review

Essential Questions

BIG idea Measurement

ESSENTIAL QUESTION How can you find the sum of the measures of polygon angles?

ANSWER You can find the sum of the measures of any convex polygon using a formula based on the number of its sides.

BIG idea Reasoning and Proof

ESSENTIAL QUESTION How can you classify quadrilaterals?

ANSWER If you know certain information about the sides, angles, or diagonals of a quadrilateral, you can classify it.

BIG idea Coordinate Geometry

ESSENTIAL QUESTION How can you use coordinate geometry to prove general relationships?

ANSWER Coordinate proofs use variable coordinates to prove relationships in the coordinate plane.

Summative Questions

Use the following prompts as you review this chapter with your students. The prompts are designed to help you assess your students' understanding of the BIG Ideas they have studied.

- How can you form triangles inside other polygons? How does this relate to the formula for angle measures?
- What are the special types of parallelograms?
- What formulas can you use to help with coordinate proofs?

5-1 The Polygon Angle-Sum Theorems

ANSWERS

1. 120, 60
2. 157.5, 22.5
3. 108, 72
4. 360, 360, 360
5. 159
6. 69

▼ STUDENT PAGE 330

5-1 The Polygon Angle-Sum Theorems

Quick Review

The sum of the measures of the interior angles of an n-gon is $(n - 2)180$. The measure of one interior angle of a regular n-gon is $\frac{(n-2)180}{n}$. The sum of the measures of the exterior angles of a polygon, one at each vertex, is 360.

Example

Find the measure of an interior angle of a regular 20-gon.

Measure $= \frac{(n-2)180}{n}$ Corollary to the Polygon Angle-Sum Theorem

$= \frac{(20-2)180}{20}$ Substitute.

$= \frac{18 \cdot 180}{20}$ Simplify.

$= 162$

The measure of an interior angle is 162.

Exercises

Find the measure of an interior angle and an exterior angle of each regular polygon.

1. hexagon
2. 16-gon
3. pentagon
4. What is the sum of the exterior angles for each polygon in Exercises 1–3?

Find the measure of the missing angle.

5. 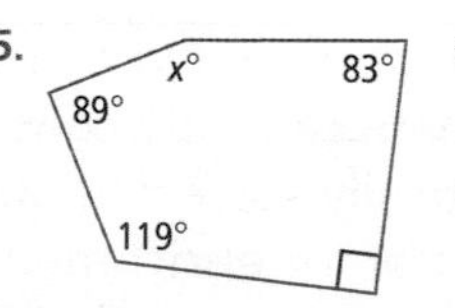

6. 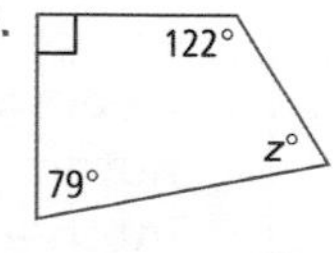

5-2 Properties of Parallelograms

ANSWERS

7. $m\angle 1 = 38$, $m\angle 2 = 43$, $m\angle 3 = 99$
8. $m\angle 1 = 101$, $m\angle 2 = 79$, $m\angle 3 = 101$
9. $m\angle 1 = 37$, $m\angle 2 = 26$, $m\angle 3 = 26$
10. $m\angle 1 = 45$, $m\angle 2 = 45$, $m\angle 3 = 45$
11. $x = 3$, $y = 7$
12. $x = 2$, $y = 5$

▼ STUDENT PAGE 330

5-2 Properties of Parallelograms

Quick Review

Opposite sides and **opposite angles** of a **parallelogram** are congruent. **Consecutive angles** in a parallelogram are supplementary. The diagonals of a parallelogram bisect each other. If three (or more) parallel lines cut off congruent segments on one transversal, then they cut off congruent segments on every transversal.

Example

Find the measures of the numbered angles in the parallelogram.

Since consecutive angles are supplementary, $m\angle 1 = 180 - 56$, or 124. Since opposite angles are congruent, $m\angle 2 = 56$ and $m\angle 3 = 124$.

Exercises

Find the measures of the numbered angles for each parallelogram.

7. 3 38° 2 1 99°

8. 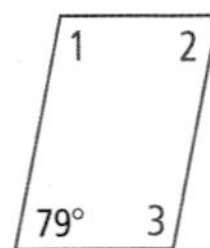

9. 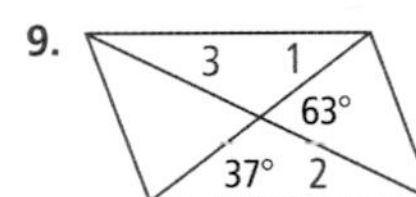

10. 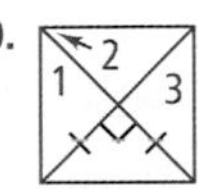

Find the values of *x* and *y* in ▱ *ABCD*.

11. $AB = 2y$, $BC = y + 3$, $CD = 5x - 1$, $DA = 2x + 4$

12. $AB = 2y + 1$, $BC = y + 1$, $CD = 7x - 3$, $DA = 3x$

5-3 Proving That a Quadrilateral Is a Parallelogram

ANSWERS

13. no
14. yes
15. $x = 29$, $y = 28$
16. $x = 4$, $y = 5$

▼ STUDENT PAGE 331

5-3 Proving That a Quadrilateral Is a Parallelogram

Quick Review

A quadrilateral is a parallelogram if any one of the following is true.

- Both pairs of opposite sides are parallel.
- Both pairs of opposite sides are congruent.
- Consecutive angles are supplementary.
- Both pairs of opposite angles are congruent.
- The diagonals bisect each other.
- One pair of opposite sides is both congruent and parallel.

Example

Must the quadrilateral be a parallelogram?

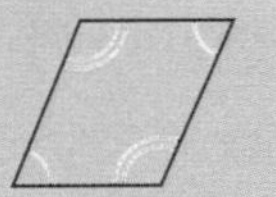

Yes, both pairs of opposite angles are congruent.

Exercises

Determine whether the quadrilateral must be a parallelogram.

13.

14. 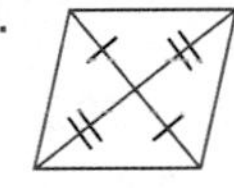

Algebra **Find the values of the variables for which *ABCD* must be a parallelogram.**

15. 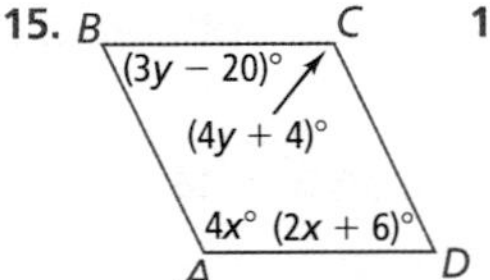

16. 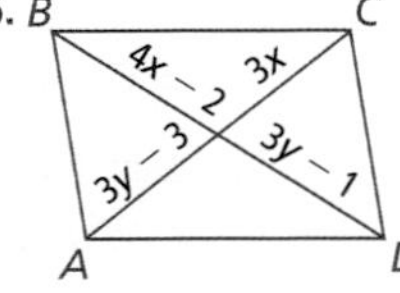

Chapter Review *(continued)*

5-4 Properties of Rhombuses, Rectangles, and Squares

ANSWERS

17. $m\angle 1 = 58$, $m\angle 2 = 32$, $m\angle 3 = 90$
18. $m\angle 1 = 124$, $m\angle 2 = 28$, $m\angle 3 = 62$
19. sometimes
20. always
21. sometimes
22. sometimes
23. sometimes
24. always

▼ STUDENT PAGE 331

5-4 Properties of Rhombuses, Rectangles, and Squares

Quick Review

A **rhombus** is a parallelogram with four congruent sides.

A **rectangle** is a parallelogram with four right angles.

A **square** is a parallelogram with four congruent sides and four right angles.

The diagonals of a rhombus are perpendicular. Each diagonal bisects a pair of opposite angles.

The diagonals of a rectangle are congruent.

Example

What are the measures of the numbered angles in the rhombus?

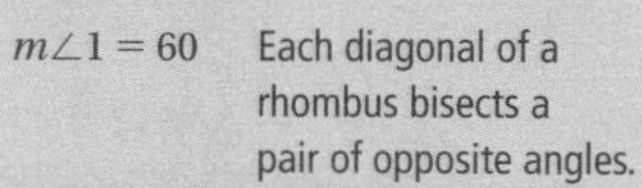

$m\angle 1 = 60$ Each diagonal of a rhombus bisects a pair of opposite angles.

$m\angle 2 = 90$ The diagonals of a rhombus are $\perp$.

$60 + m\angle 2 + m\angle 3 = 180$ Triangle Angle-Sum Thm.

$60 + 90 + m\angle 3 = 180$ Substitute.

$m\angle 3 = 30$ Simplify.

Exercises

Find the measures of the numbered angles in each special parallelogram.

17.

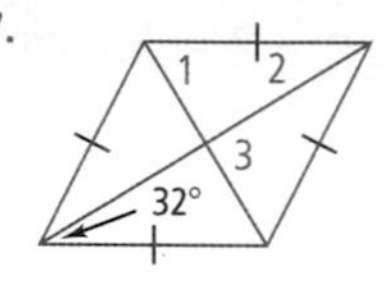

18.

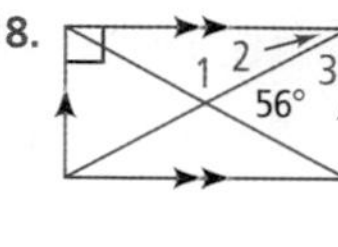

Determine whether each statement is *always, sometimes,* or *never* true.

19. A rhombus is a square.

20. A square is a rectangle.

21. A rhombus is a rectangle.

22. The diagonals of a parallelogram are perpendicular.

23. The diagonals of a parallelogram are congruent.

24. Opposite angles of a parallelogram are congruent.

5-5 Conditions for Rhombuses, Rectangles, and Squares

ANSWERS

25. No; two sides are $\parallel$ in all parallelograms.
26. Yes; the $\square$ is a rhombus and a rectangle so it must be a square.
27. $x = 18$; a diagonal bisects a pair of angles in a rhombus.
28. $x = 4$; a rectangle has $\cong$ diagonals that bisect each other.

▼ STUDENT PAGE 332

5-5 Conditions for Rhombuses, Rectangles, and Squares

Quick Review

If one diagonal of a parallelogram bisects two angles of the parallelogram, then the parallelogram is a rhombus. If the diagonals of a parallelogram are perpendicular, then the parallelogram is a rhombus. If the diagonals of a parallelogram are congruent, then the parallelogram is a rectangle.

Example

Can you conclude that the parallelogram is a rhombus, rectangle, or square? Explain.

Yes, the diagonals are perpendicular, so the parallelogram is a rhombus.

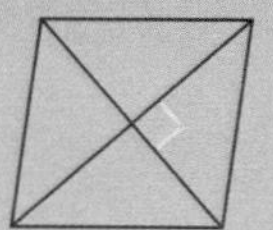

Exercises

Can you conclude that the parallelogram is a rhombus, rectangle, or square? Explain.

25.

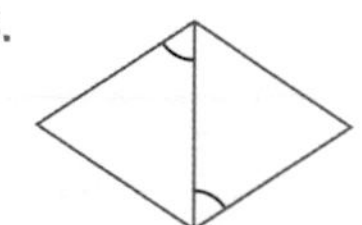

26.

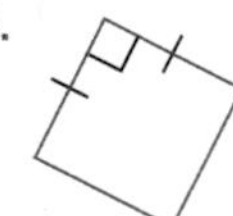

For what value of x is the figure the given parallelogram? Justify your answer.

27.

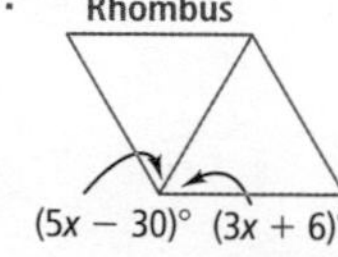

28.

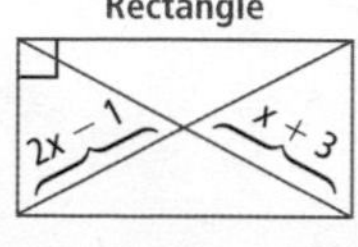

5-6 Trapezoids and Kites

ANSWERS

29. $m\angle 1 = 135$, $m\angle 2 = 135$, $m\angle 3 = 45$

30. $m\angle 1 = 80$, $m\angle 2 = 100$, $m\angle 3 = 100$

31. $m\angle 1 = 90$, $m\angle 2 = 25$

32. $m\angle 1 = 56$, $m\angle 2 = 52$

33. 2

▼ STUDENT PAGE 332

5-6 Trapezoids and Kites

Quick Review

The parallel sides of a **trapezoid** are its **bases** and the nonparallel sides are its **legs**. Two angles that share a base of a trapezoid are **base angles** of the trapezoid. The **midsegment of a trapezoid** joins the midpoints of its legs.

The base angles of an isosceles trapezoid are congruent.

The diagonals of an isosceles trapezoid are congruent.

The diagonals of a kite are perpendicular.

Example

***ABCD* is an isosceles trapezoid. What is $m\angle C$?**

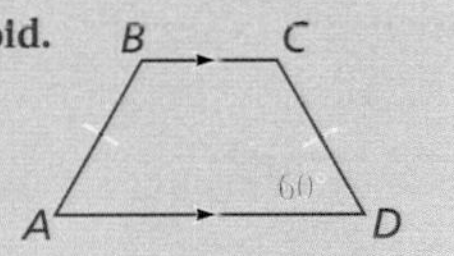

Since $\overline{BC} \parallel \overline{AD}$, $\angle C$ and $\angle D$ are same-side interior angles.

$m\angle C + m\angle D = 180$	Same-side interior angles are supplementary.
$m\angle C + 60 = 180$	Substitute.
$m\angle C = 120$	Subtract 60 from each side.

Exercises

Find the measures of the numbered angles in each isosceles trapezoid.

29.

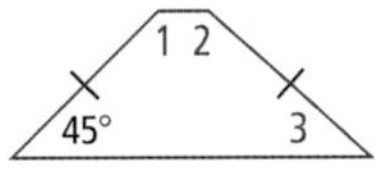

30.

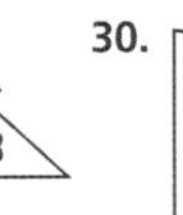

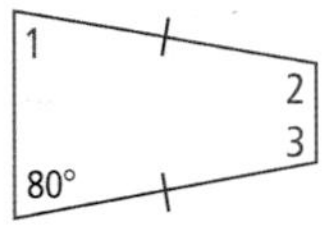

Find the measures of the numbered angles in each kite.

31.

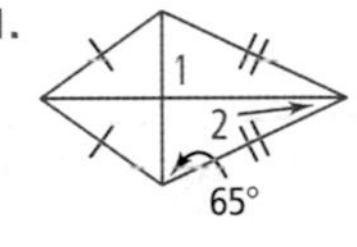

32.

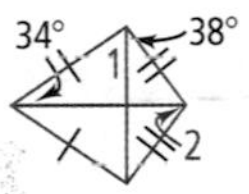

33. Algebra A trapezoid has base lengths of $(6x - 1)$ units and 3 units. Its midsegment has a length of $(5x - 3)$ units. What is the value of x?

5-7 and 5-8 Applying Coordinate Geometry and Proofs Using Coordinate Geometry

ANSWERS

34. $F(0, 2b)$, $L(a, 0)$, $P(0, -2b)$, $S(-a, 0)$

35. $(a - b, c)$

36. Answers may vary. Sample:

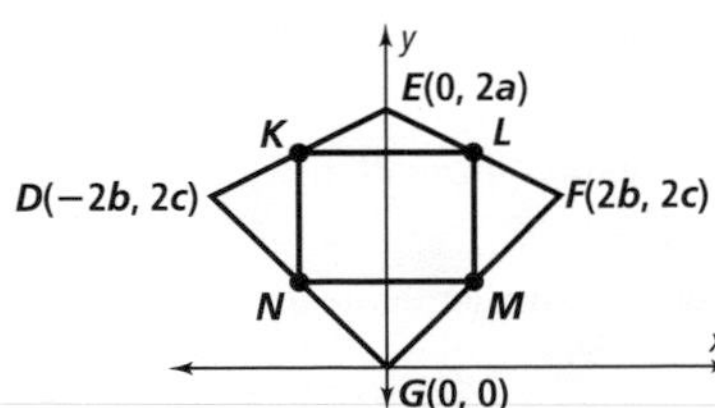

Given: Kite *DEFG*, *K*, *L*, *M*, *N* are midpoints of sides.

Prove: *KLMN* is a rectangle.

By the Midpoint Formula, coordinates of midpoints are $K(-b, a + c)$, $L(b, a + c)$, $M(b, c)$, and $N(-b, c)$. By the Slope Formula, slope of $\overline{KL}$ = slope of $\overline{NM} = 0$, and slope of $\overline{KN}$ and slope of $\overline{LM}$ are undefined. $\overline{KL} \parallel \overline{NM}$ and $\overline{KN} \parallel \overline{LM}$ so *KLMN* is a ▱. $\overline{KL} \perp \overline{LM}$, $\overline{LM} \perp \overline{NM}$, $\overline{KN} \perp \overline{NM}$, and $\overline{KN} \perp \overline{KL}$ so *KLMN* is a rectangle.

▼ STUDENT PAGE 333

5-7 and 5-8 Applying Coordinate Geometry and Proofs Using Coordinate Geometry

Quick Review

When placing a figure in the coordinate plane, it is usually helpful to place at least one side on an axis. Use variables when naming the coordinates of a figure in order to show that relationships are true for a general case.

Example

Rectangle *PQRS* has length *a* and width 4*b*. The *x*-axis bisects $\overline{PS}$ and $\overline{QR}$. What are the coordinates of the vertices?

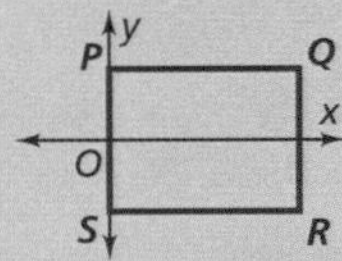

Since the width of *PQRS* is 4*b* and the *x*-axis bisects $\overline{PS}$ and $\overline{QR}$, all the vertices are 2*b* units from the *x*-axis. $\overline{PS}$ is on the *y*-axis, so $P = (0, 2b)$ and $S = (0, -2b)$. The length of *PQRS* is *a*, so $Q = (a, 2b)$ and $R = (a, -2b)$.

Exercises

34. In rhombus *FLPS*, the axes form the diagonals. If $SL = 2a$ and $FP = 4b$, what are the coordinates of the vertices?

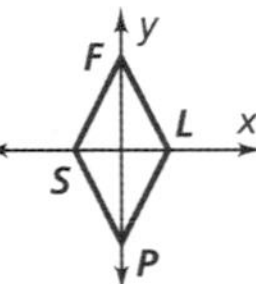

35. The figure at the right is a parallelogram. Give the coordinates of point *P* without using any new variables.

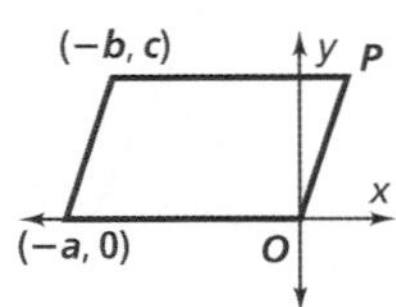

36. Use coordinate geometry to prove that the quadrilateral formed by connecting the midpoints of a kite is a rectangle.

Pull It All Together

Common Core State Standard
Extends G.SRT.5 Use congruence . . . criteria for triangles to solve problems and to prove relationships in geometric figures.

Using Performance Tasks

Understanding by Design® principles support using performance tasks to assess students' progress toward mastering content standards and developing proficiency with the Mathematical Practices.

Mathematical Practices

- Make sense of problems and persevere in solving them.
- Model with mathematics.
- Look for and make use of structure.

Assessing Performance

See the Implementation Guide for a holistic scoring rubric to use in assessing students' work on the performance task.

Guiding Questions

Q How do you know that the vertical support bisects the horizontal support?

Q How can you find the vertical support's length by thinking of the support as two smaller pieces? What theorem can you use to find the length?

Q How can the formula for the area of a triangle help you find the kite's area?

Solution Outline

Draw the vertical support, as shown. Each pair of right triangles is congruent by HL. So the kite's vertical support bisects its horizontal support into two segments that are each 12 in. long. Let y represent the shorter part of the vertical support, and let x represent the longer part.

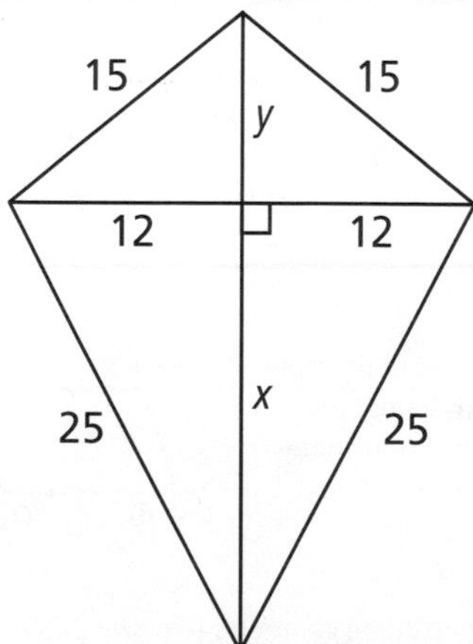

Since the diagonals of a kite are perpendicular, each length can be determined by the Pythagorean Theorem:

$$12^2 + y^2 = 15^2 \qquad 12^2 + x^2 = 25^2$$
$$y^2 = 81 \qquad x^2 = 481$$
$$y = 9 \qquad x \approx 21.9$$

▼ STUDENT PAGE 334

Building a Kite

ASSESSMENT

Charles is building a paper kite. He needs another dowel to make the vertical support for the frame. He gives his friend Amy the measurements below but neglects to include the length of the support.

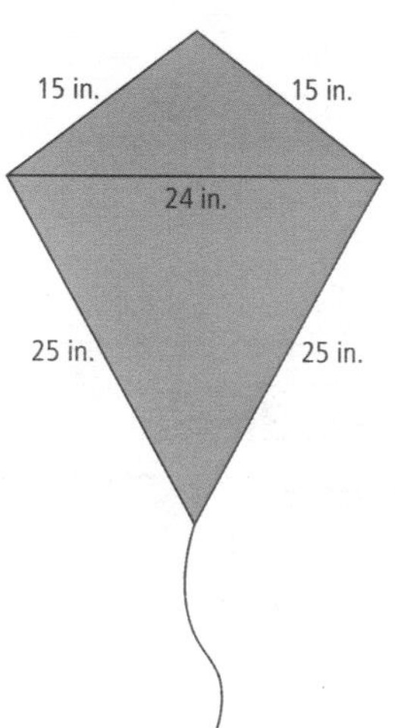

Task Description

Find the length of the vertical support for this kite and the area of the paper used to make the kite.

- What is true about the diagonals of a kite? How can you use this information to find the length of the vertical support?
- How can you find the kite's area by decomposing the kite into smaller figures?

To the nearest tenth of an inch, the length of the vertical support is $9 + 21.9 = 30.9$ inches.

The area of the kite can be found using two congruent triangles with the vertical support as a base. The height of each triangle is 12 inches. The area of paper used to make the kite is $2 \cdot \frac{1}{2}(30.9)(12) = 370.8$, or about 371 square inches.

Get Ready!

Using This Diagnostic Assessment

Assign this diagnostic assessment to determine if students have the prerequisite skills for Chapter 6.

Lesson	Skill
2-2	Properties of Parallel Lines
3-1	Naming Congruent Parts
3-2 and 3-3	Triangle Congruence
4-1	Midsegments of Triangles

To remediate students, select from these resources (available for every lesson).

- Online Problems (pearsonsuccessnet.com)
- Reteaching (Online Teacher Resources)
- Practice (Online Teacher Resources)

Why Students Need These Skills

PROPERTIES OF PARALLEL LINES Angle relationships will be extended to similar triangles.

NAMING CONGRUENT PARTS The order in which vertices are listed is important when identifying similar triangles.

TRIANGLE CONGRUENCE Congruence statements are formed by postulates. Likewise, similarity statements will be formed from the AA ~ postulate.

MIDSEGMENTS OF TRIANGLES Properties of proportionality within triangles will be explored.

Looking Ahead Vocabulary

PROPORTION Ask students to identify other real-world objects that are in proportion to one another.

SIMILAR Using the example of a golf ball and basketball, have students identify characteristics that define similarity.

SCALE Show examples of maps and blueprint drawings that use scales.

ANSWERS

1. 70; if lines are ∥, same-side int. angles are suppl.
2. 110; if lines are ∥, corresponding angles are ≅.
3. 70; adjacent angles forming a straight ∠ are suppl.
4. 70; it is a vert. ∠ with ∠1; vert. angles are ≅.
5. $\overline{DL}$
6. ∠*A*
7. ∠*DLH*
8. △*APC*
9. △*KNP* ≅ △*LNM* by SAS.
10. △*BAC* ≅ △*BED* by AAS.
11. △*UGH* ≅ △*UGB* by SSS.
12. 6, 6
13. 4.7, 9.4
14. Answers may vary. Sample: The relative sizes of the body parts in the drawing are the same as those of a real person.
15. Answers may vary. Sample: They might be similar if they have the same shape.
16. Answers may vary. Sample: Measure the number of inches on the map between the two cities, and multiply that number of inches by the number of miles represented by 1 in.

▼ STUDENT PAGE 335

Properties of Parallel Lines

Use the diagram at the right. Find the measure of each angle. Justify your answer.

1. ∠1 2. ∠2 3. ∠3 4. ∠4

Naming Congruent Parts

△*PAC* ≅ △*DHL*. Complete each congruence statement.

5. $\overline{PC}$ ≅ _?_ 6. ∠*H* ≅ _?_ 7. ∠*PCA* ≅ _?_ 8. △*HDL* ≅ _?_

Triangle Congruence

Write a congruence statement for each pair of triangles. Explain why the triangles are congruent.

9. 10.

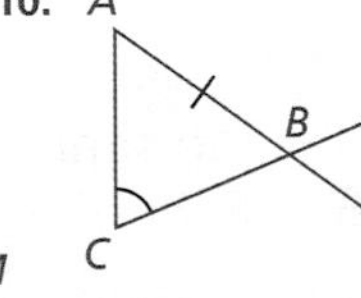

11.

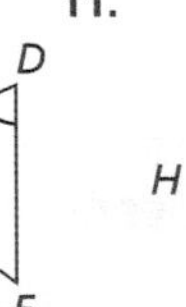

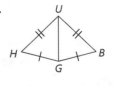

Midsegments of Triangles

Use the diagram at the right for Exercises 12–13.

12. If *BC* = 12, then *BF* = _?_ and *DE* = _?_.
13. If *EF* = 4.7, then *AD* = _?_ and *AC* = _?_.

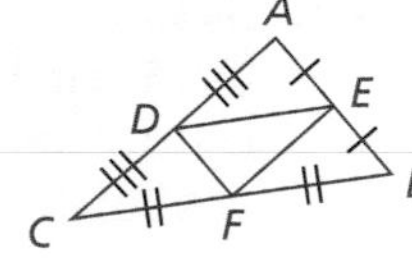

Looking Ahead Vocabulary

14. An artist sketches a person. She is careful to draw the different parts of the person's body in *proportion*. What does *proportion* mean in this situation?
15. Siblings often look *similar* to each other. How might two geometric figures be *similar*?
16. A road map has a *scale* on it that tells you how many miles are equivalent to a distance of 1 inch on the map. How would you use the *scale* to estimate the distance between two cities on the map?

CHAPTER
6

SIMILARITY

Chapter 6 Overview

Interactive Digital Path
Log in to pearsonsuccessnet.com and click on Interactive Digital Path to access the Solve Its and animated Problems.

Chapter 6 expands on students' understandings and skills related to similarity. In this chapter, students will develop the answers to the Essential Questions posed below as they learn the bulleted concepts and skills.

BIG idea Similarity

ESSENTIAL QUESTION How do you use proportions to find side lengths in similar polygons?

- Students will form proportions based on known lengths of corresponding sides.

BIG idea Reasoning and Proof

ESSENTIAL QUESTION How do you show two triangles are similar?

- Students will use the Angle-Angle Similarity Postulate.
- Students will use the Side-Angle-Side Similarity Theorem.
- Students will use the Side-Side-Side Similarity Theorem.

BIG idea Visualization

ESSENTIAL QUESTION How do you identify corresponding parts of similar triangles?

- A key to understanding corresponding parts of similar triangles is to show the triangles in like orientations.

Content Standards

Following are the key standards covered in this chapter.

Conceptual Category Geometry

DOMAIN Similarity, Right Triangles, and Trigonometry G.SRT

CLUSTER Understand similarity in terms of similarity transformations (Standards G.SRT.1.a, G.SRT.1.b, G.SRT.2, G.SRT.3) **LESSONS** AL 6-6, 6-6, 6-7

CLUSTER Prove theorems involving similarity (Standards G.SRT.4, G.SRT.5) **LESSONS** 6-1, 6-2, 6-3, 6-4, TL 6-5, 6-5

DOMAIN Expressing Geometric Properties with Equations G.GPE

CLUSTER Use coordinates to prove simple geometric theorems algebraically (Standards G.GPE.5, G.GPE.6) **LESSONS** 6-3, 6-4

Chapter Preview

DYNAMIC ACTIVITIES

Dynamic Activity

Use the Dynamic Activity, an interactive math tool with guided instruction, to have students explore concepts visually and support the development of the Standards for Mathematical Practice.

VOCABULARY

Vocabulary

English/Spanish Vocabulary Audio Online:

English	Spanish
dilation, *p. 393**	dilatación
extremes of a proportion, *p. 340*	valores extremos de una proporción
geometric mean, *p. 371*	media geométrica
indirect measurement, *p. 364*	medición indirecta
means of a proportion, *p. 340*	valores medios de una proporción
proportion, *p. 340*	proporción
ratio, *p. 337*	razón
scale drawing, *p. 352*	dibujo a escala
scale factor, *p. 348, 393*	factor de escala
similar, *p. 348, 403*	semejante
similar polygons, *p. 348*	polígonos semejantes

**All page numbers refer to the Student Edition.*

SIMILARITY

Math Background

Understanding by Design® principles were central to the development of the Big Ideas and the Essential Understandings. These will help your students build a structure on which to make connections to prior learning.*

Similarity

BIG idea Two geometric figures are similar when corresponding lengths are proportional and corresponding angles are congruent.

ESSENTIAL UNDERSTANDINGS

6-1 A proportion can be written stating that two ratios are equal, and if the proportion contains a variable, it can be solved to find the value of the variable.

6-2 Ratios and proportions can be used to decide whether two polygons are similar and to find unknown side lengths of similar figures.

6-4 Drawing in the altitude to the hypotenuse of a right triangle forms three pairs of similar right triangles.

6-5 When two or more parallel lines intersect other lines, proportional segments are formed.

Reasoning and Proof

BIG idea Definitions establish meanings and remove possible misunderstanding. Other truths are more complex and difficult to see. It is often possible to verify complex truths by reasoning from simpler ones by using deductive reasoning.

ESSENTIAL UNDERSTANDINGS

6-2 to 6-3 Ratios and proportions can be used to prove whether two polygons are similar and to find unknown side lengths. Triangles can be shown to be similar based on the relationship of two or three pairs of corresponding parts.

6-4 It can be proven that the three pairs of right triangles formed by drawing in the altitude to the hypotenuse are similar.

Visualization

BIG idea Visualization can help you see the relationships between two figures and help you connect the properties of real objects with two-dimensional drawings of these objects.

ESSENTIAL UNDERSTANDINGS

6-3 to 6-4 Two triangles can be shown to be similar. Drawing in the altitude to the hypotenuse of a right triangle forms three pairs of similar right triangles.

6-5 When two or more parallel lines intersect other lines, proportional segments are formed.

6-7 Two figures are similar if there is a similarity transformation that maps one to the other.

*UNDERSTANDING BY DESIGN® and UbD™ are trademarks of ASCD, and are used under license.

Ratios and Proportions

A *ratio* is a comparison of two numbers.

Cereal is on sale: 3 boxes for 5 dollars. This ratio can be written $\frac{5 \text{ dollars}}{3 \text{ boxes}}$.

You can make a table to show the cost of different numbers of boxes of cereal. Simple tables like this can help students see equivalent ratios.

Dollars	5	10	15	20
Boxes of Cereal	3	6	9	12

The two numbers in each column can be expressed as ratios: $\frac{5}{3}, \frac{10}{6}, \frac{15}{9}, \frac{20}{12}$

A proportion is a statement equating two ratios and can be used to solve problems. To find the cost of 5 boxes of cereal, use the proportion

extreme $\frac{3}{5} = \frac{5}{x}$ mean
mean extreme

The cross-products of proportions are equal. "The product of the means equals the product of the extremes." One way to find x is

$3x = 25$

$x = 8.33$

The cost of 5 boxes equals $8.33.

Common Errors With Ratios and Proportions

If two ratios are equal, $\frac{a}{b} = \frac{c}{d}$, their inverses are also equal, $\frac{b}{a} = \frac{d}{c}$. However, $\frac{a}{b} \neq \frac{d}{c}$. Cereal boxes must be the numerator in both ratios or the denominator in both ratios.

Mathematical Practices

Reason abstractly and quantitatively. Students decontextualize to represent the problem in terms of ratios, solve it, and then contextualize to make sense of their solution.

Look for and make use of structure. Students examine patterns in equivalent ratios, seeing the structure as shown in the table at the top of this column, as numerators increase by multiples of 5 and denominators increase by multiples of 3.

Math Background *(continued)*

Proving Similar Triangles

Two triangles are similar if and only if corresponding angles are congruent and corresponding sides are proportional.

Recall from Chapter 3 that SSS, SAS, ASA, AAS, and HL postulates could each be used to prove that triangles are congruent.

In the case of similarity, you can prove two triangles are similar if two angles are congruent, all three sides are proportional, or if one angle is congruent and the two adjacent sides are proportional.

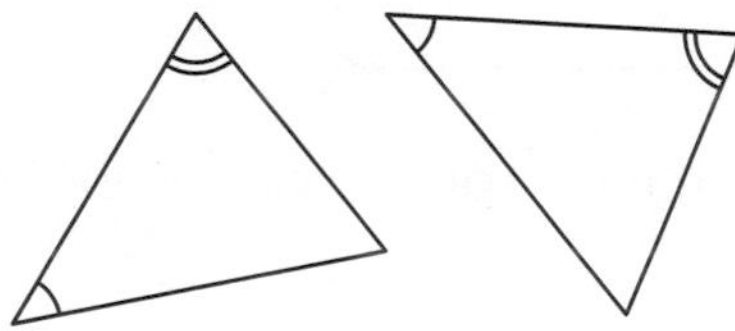

Common Errors With Proving Similar Triangles

If students are given similar triangles that are oriented in such a way that their corresponding sides are oriented differently, students may incorrectly conclude that the triangles are not similar based on incorrectly setting up the proportion.

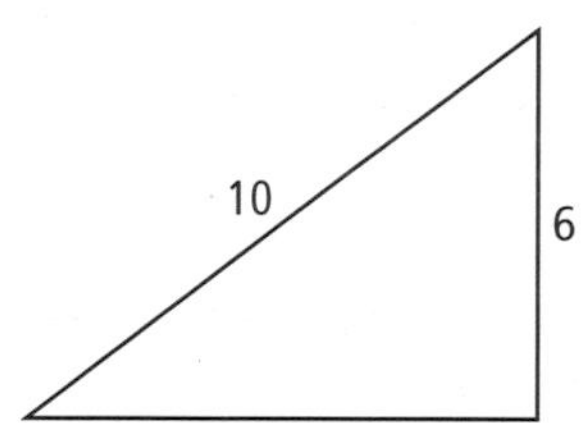

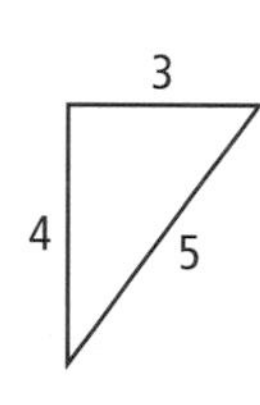

The two triangles above are similar. However, the student may set up the proportion $\frac{4}{6} = \frac{3}{8}$, and wrongly conclude that the two triangles are not similar. Students should always compare the longest side to the longest, the shortest side to the shortest, and the remaining sides to each other.

Mathematical Practices

Construct viable arguments and critique the reasoning of others. In working with similar triangles, students build on deductive arguments about congruent triangles to establish new results.

Look for and make use of structure. Students learn to see patterns in noncongruent triangles, matching corresponding sides or angles to make comparisons.

Proving Similar Triangles

Special segments in triangles divide the sides proportionally.

Angle Bisectors

If $\overrightarrow{AD}$ bisects $\angle CAB$, then $\frac{CD}{DB} = \frac{CA}{BA}$.

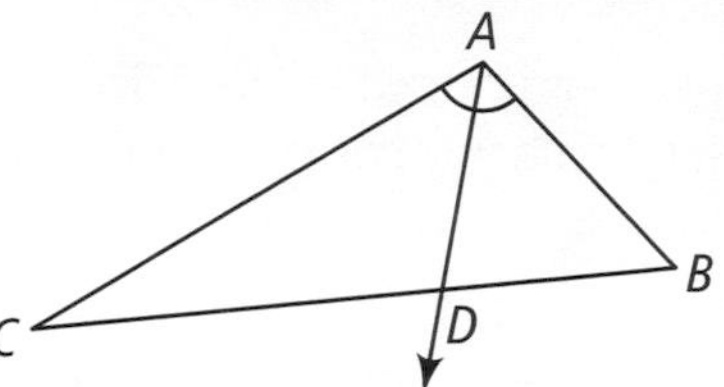

Altitudes in Right Triangles

If $\overline{CD}$ is the altitude drawn to the hypotenuse in a right triangle, then

1. $\frac{AD}{CD} = \frac{CD}{DB}$
2. $\frac{AB}{AC} = \frac{AC}{AD}$
3. $\frac{AB}{CB} = \frac{CB}{DB}$
4. $\triangle ABC \sim \triangle CBD \sim \triangle ACD$

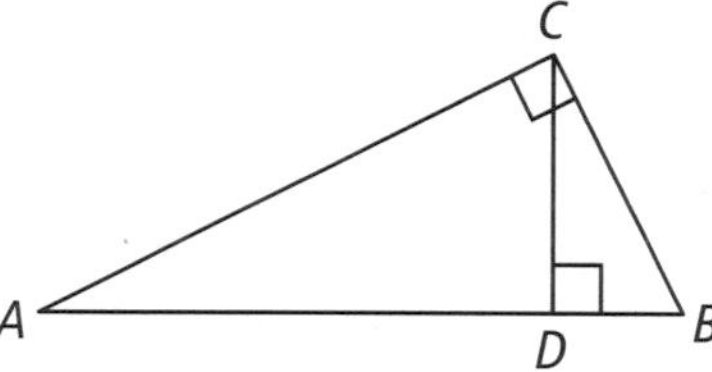

Side-Splitter Theorem

If $\overline{DE} \parallel \overline{AC}$, then $\frac{AD}{DB} = \frac{CE}{EB}$.

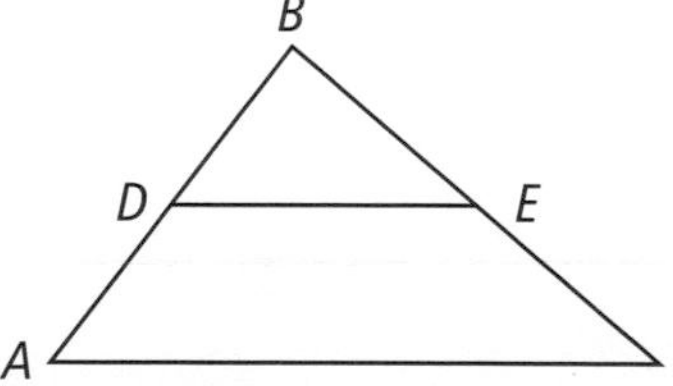

Common Errors With Bisectors

In the first triangle above, students might incorrectly assume that the angle bisector of $\angle CAB$ in $\triangle CAB$ divides $\overline{CB}$ into two equal parts. In fact, the parts are proportional to the sides $\overline{CA}$ and $\overline{AB}$.

Mathematical Practices

Construct viable arguments and critique the reasoning of others. Students use auxiliary lines to establish the Triangle Angle Bisector Theorem, building on a previously established result (the Side-Splitter Theorem) to make sense of an otherwise nonintuitive conclusion.

6-1 Ratios and Proportions

Common Core State Standards
Prepares for G.SRT.5 Use . . . similarity criteria for triangles to solve problems and to prove relationships in geometric figures. **Also N.Q.2**

Preparing to Teach

BIG idea Proportionality

ESSENTIAL UNDERSTANDING

A ratio can be written to compare two quantities. A proportion can be written stating that two ratios are equal. If the proportion contains a variable, it can be solved to find the value of the variable.

Math Background

The topic of ratios is an important foundation that leads to solving problems that involve scale drawings and similar figures. Students need to become comfortable with ratios written as fractions, as well as decimals and percents. They will need to identify equivalent ratios in order to determine when figures are similar. Students should not only be able to write proportions to show the relationship of similar figures and scale drawings, but should be able to solve proportions for a missing term.

ELL Support

USE GRAPHIC ORGANIZERS Tell students to make a 3-column KWL table. The columns are labeled "know," "want to know," and "learned." In the first column, have students write a declarative sentence about each of the following words: *ratio*, *proportion*, *extreme*, *mean*, and *cross product*. In the second column, have them write a question about each word.

Give the students an example to help them get started. Here is an example of what a student might write for ratio:

K: A ratio compares two numbers.
W: What ratios do triangles have?

After the lesson, ask students to write what they have learned about each word in the third column.

Lesson Vocabulary

- ratio
- extended ratio
- proportion
- extremes
- means
- Cross Products Property

Mathematical Practices

ATTEND TO PRECISION. Students will use colons and division to represent ratios and proportions. They will also set up algebraic expressions using ratios and proportions.

1 Interactive Learning

Solve It!

PURPOSE To use ratios to represent quantities and find equivalent ratios

PROCESS Students may find the ratios of wins to total games played in simplest form for each team or convert ratios to percents to compare each team's record.

Q How can each year's record be expressed as a ratio? **[Sample: It can be expressed as a ratio of wins to losses such as 60 : 24.]**

Q Is there an equivalent ratio for 60 : 24 for the year 1890? Explain. **[Yes; 60 : 24 can be divided by 12 on both sides to equal 5 : 2.]**

ANSWER 1890 and 1930; explanations may vary. Sample: In both years the team won $\frac{5}{7}$, or about 71.4% of the games they played.

CONNECT THE MATH Students should realize that even though the team did not play the same number of games in each of the four years, their win-to-loss ratios can be equivalent. To determine equivalent ratios, the ratios should be written in simplest form.

▼ DIGITAL (STUDENT WORK SPACE PAGE 337)

SOLVE IT! **Getting Ready!**

The table at the right gives the wins and losses of a baseball team. In which year(s) did the team have the best record? Explain.

Year	Wins	Losses
1890	60	24
1930	110	44
1970	110	52
2010	108	54

2 Guided Instruction

Problem 1 Writing a Ratio

Q What relationship does the conversion factor used in the problem describe? **[It shows the relationship 12 in. = 1 ft.]**

Got It? **ERROR PREVENTION**

Be sure that students remember to express the width and the height in the same unit.

ANSWERS

Got It? 3 : 4

Practice

1. $\frac{14}{5}$ or 14 : 5 **2.** $\frac{10}{17}$ or 10 : 17

▼ STUDENT PAGE 337

In the Solve It, you compared two quantities for four years.

Essential Understanding You can write a *ratio* to compare two quantities.

A **ratio** is a comparison of two quantities by division. You can write the ratio of two numbers a and b, where $b \neq 0$, in three ways: $\frac{a}{b}$, $a : b$, and a to b. You usually express a and b in the same unit and write the ratio in simplest form.

▼ DIGITAL

Problem 1 **Writing a Ratio**

Bonsai Trees **The bonsai bald cypress tree is a small version of a full-size tree. A Florida bald cypress tree called the Senator stands 118 ft tall. What is the ratio of the height of the bonsai to the height of the Senator?**

15 in.

Express both heights in the same unit. To convert 118 ft to inches, multiply by the conversion factor $\frac{12 \text{ in.}}{1 \text{ ft}}$.

$118 \text{ ft} = \frac{118 \cancel{\text{ft}}}{1} \cdot \frac{12 \text{ in.}}{1 \cancel{\text{ft}}} = (118 \cdot 12) \text{ in.} = 1416 \text{ in.}$

Write the ratio as a fraction in simplest form.

$$\begin{matrix}\text{height of bonsai} \rightarrow \\ \text{height of Senator} \rightarrow\end{matrix} \frac{15 \text{ in.}}{118 \text{ ft}} = \frac{15 \text{ in.}}{1416 \text{ in.}} = \frac{(\cancel{3} \cdot 5) \cancel{\text{in.}}}{(\cancel{3} \cdot 472) \cancel{\text{in.}}} = \frac{5}{472}$$

The ratio of the height of the bonsai to the height of the Senator is $\frac{5}{472}$ or 5 : 472.

▼ STUDENT PAGES 337–338

Got It? A bonsai tree is 18 in. wide and stands 2 ft tall. What is the ratio of the width of the bonsai to its height?

Think

How can you write the width and the height using the same units?

Practice **Write the ratio of the first measurement to the second measurement.**

1. length of a tennis racket: 2 ft 4 in.

   length of a table tennis paddle: 10 in.

2. diameter of a table tennis ball: 40 mm

   diameter of a tennis ball: 6.8 cm

Problem 2 Dividing a Quantity Into a Given Ratio

Students use ratios to write equations that show the relationship between two quantities.

Q In the ratio $\frac{2x}{3x}$, what does x represent? **[the common factor of the numerator and denominator]**

Q How many ratios can be written that equal $\frac{2}{3}$? Of these, how many meet the criteria of the number of pots bought? **[Infinitely many; only one ratio has a numerator and denominator that have a sum of 120.]**

▼ DIGITAL

Problem 2 **Dividing a Quantity Into a Given Ratio**

Fundraising **Members of the school band are buying pots of tulips and pots of daffodils to sell at their fundraiser. They plan to buy 120 pots of flowers. The ratio $\frac{\text{number of tulip pots}}{\text{number of daffodil pots}}$ will be $\frac{2}{3}$. How many pots of each type of flower should they buy?**

Think	Write
If the ratio $\frac{\text{number of tulip pots}}{\text{number of daffodil pots}}$ is $\frac{2}{3}$, it must be in the form $\frac{2x}{3x}$.	Let $2x =$ the number of tulip pots. Let $3x =$ the number of daffodil pots.
The total number of flower pots is 120. Use this fact to write an equation. Then solve for x.	$2x + 3x = 120$ $5x = 120$ $x = 24$
Substitute 24 for x in the expressions for the numbers of pots.	$2x = 2(24) = 48$ $3x = 3(24) = 72$
Write the answer in words.	The band members should buy 48 tulip pots and 72 daffodil pots.

Got It? VISUAL LEARNERS

Have students attempt to draw a pair of supplementary angles that fit this description before calculating the answer algebraically.

ANSWERS

Got It? 36, 144

Practice

3. won 110, lost 44 **4.** 105

▼ STUDENT PAGES 338–339

Got It? The measures of two supplementary angles are in the ratio 1 : 4. What are the measures of the angles?

Practice

3. **Baseball** A baseball team played 154 regular season games. The ratio of the number of games they won to the number of games they lost was $\frac{5}{2}$. How many games did they win? How many games did they lose?
4. The measures of two supplementary angles are in the ratio 5 : 7. What is the measure of the larger angle?

Problem 3 Using an Extended Ratio

Q What ratios are described by the extended ratio in Problem 3? **[$\frac{3x}{5x}$, $\frac{5x}{6x}$, and $\frac{3x}{6x}$]**

Q What steps are used to check the answer to this problem? **[Find the lengths of all three sides. Check that the sum is 98 and verify that the side lengths are in the proportion given by the extended ratio.]**

Got It? VISUAL LEARNERS

Have students sketch the triangle and label the side lengths using the ratio.

Q What equation can you write using the ratios and the perimeter? **[$4x + 7x + 9x = 60$]**

ANSWERS

Got It? 12 cm, 21 cm, 27 cm

Practice

5. 24 cm, 28 cm, 36 cm

6. 80

▼ STUDENT PAGE 339

An **extended ratio** compares three (or more) numbers. In the extended ratio $a : b : c$, the ratio of the first two numbers is $a : b$, the ratio of the last two numbers is $b : c$, and the ratio of the first and last numbers is $a : c$.

▼ DIGITAL

Problem 3 Using an Extended Ratio

The lengths of the sides of a triangle are in the extended ratio 3 : 5 : 6. The perimeter of the triangle is 98 in. What is the length of the longest side?

Sketch the triangle. Use the extended ratio to label the sides with expressions for their lengths.

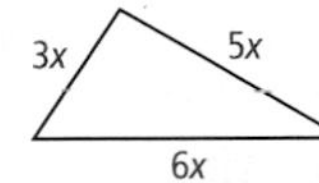

$3x + 5x + 6x = 98$	The perimeter is 98 in.
$14x = 98$	Simplify.
$x = 7$	Divide each side by 14.

The expression that represents the length of the longest side is $6x$. $6(7) = 42$, so the length of the longest side is 42 in.

▼ STUDENT PAGES 339–340

Got It? The lengths of the sides of a triangle are in the extended ratio 4 : 7 : 9. The perimeter is 60 cm. What are the lengths of the sides?

Think How do you use the extended ratio to write the equation?

Practice

5. The lengths of the sides of a triangle are in the extended ratio 6 : 7 : 9. The perimeter of the triangle is 88 cm. What are the lengths of the sides?
6. The measures of the angles of a triangle are in the extended ratio 4 : 3 : 2. What is the measure of the largest angle?

Problem 4 Solving a Proportion

Take Note

Have students write their own examples of proportions and verify that their examples are proportions using the Cross Products Property.

Here's Why It Works

Q What relationship does *bd* have with the proportion? **[*bd* is a common multiple for the two denominators.]**

Q Why is that relationship important? **[Multiplying both ratios by a common multiple eliminates the denominators.]**

Problem 4

Q Why is the Cross Products Property used to solve these proportions? **[The products of the means and extremes are used to write a linear equation.]**

Q In 4B, what property is used to find the product of the extremes? **[The extremes are 3 and $y + 4$. The Distributive Property is used to find the product.]**

Got It? ERROR PREVENTION

For part (b), if students give an answer of $\frac{1}{12}$, remind them to use the Distributive Property with 3 and $m + 1$. Have students check their answers by substituting their solutions back into the original proportion.

ANSWERS

Got It? a. 63 **b.** 0.25

Practice

7. 6 **8.** 4

▼ STUDENT PAGE 340

Essential Understanding If two ratios are equivalent, you can write an equation stating that the ratios are equal. If the equation contains a variable, you can solve the equation to find the value of the variable.

An equation that states that two ratios are equal is called a **proportion.** The first and last numbers in a proportion are the **extremes.** The middle two numbers are the **means.**

extremes: 2 : 3 = 4 : 6 (means: 3 and 4)

extremes → $\frac{2}{3} = \frac{4}{6}$ ← means

take note

Key Concept Cross Products Property

Words	Symbols	Example
In a proportion, the product of the extremes equals the product of the means.	If $\frac{a}{b} = \frac{c}{d}$, where $b \neq 0$ and $d \neq 0$, then $ad = bc$.	$\frac{2}{3} = \frac{4}{6}$ $2 \cdot 6 = 3 \cdot 4$ $12 = 12$

Here's Why It Works Begin with $\frac{a}{b} = \frac{c}{d}$, where $b \neq 0$ and $d \neq 0$.

$bd \cdot \frac{a}{b} = \frac{c}{d} \cdot bd$ Multiply each side of the proportion by *bd*.

$\frac{bd}{1} \cdot \frac{a}{b} = \frac{c}{d} \cdot \frac{bd}{1}$ Divide the common factors.

$ad = bc$ Simplify.

▼ DIGITAL

Problem 4 Solving a Proportion

Algebra What is the solution of each proportion?

A $\frac{6}{x} = \frac{5}{4}$

$6(4) = 5x$ Cross Products Property

$24 = 5x$ Simplify.

$x = \frac{24}{5}$ Solve for the variable.

The solution is $\frac{24}{5}$ or 4.8.

B $\frac{y + 4}{9} = \frac{y}{3}$

$3(y + 4) = 9y$

$3y + 12 = 9y$

$12 = 6y$

$y = 2$

The solution is 2.

▼ STUDENT PAGE 341

Got It? What is the solution of each proportion?

a. $\frac{9}{2} = \frac{a}{14}$

b. $\frac{15}{m + 1} = \frac{3}{m}$

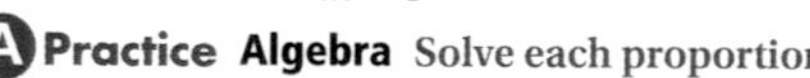

Practice **Algebra** Solve each proportion.

7. $\frac{y}{10} = \frac{15}{25}$

8. $\frac{n + 4}{8} = \frac{n}{4}$

Problem 5 Writing Equivalent Proportions

Take Note

Have students write their true proportions and then carry out the actions described in the properties.

Problem 5

Q In Method 1, why is Property (2) used? **[It shows the means in the two ratios changing places.]**

Got It?

Q Which property is applied in part (a)? Explain. **[Property (1) because it shows the proportion is preserved by taking the reciprocal of each ratio.]**

Q How is the expression $\frac{y+7}{7}$ written as the sum of two ratios? How can the sum of these ratios clarify property (3)? **[$\frac{y}{7} + \frac{7}{7}$; it shows that 1 (expressed as a fraction) is added to each side of the proportion.]**

ANSWERS

Got It? a. $\frac{7}{y}$; Prop. of Proportions (1) **b.** $\frac{x+6}{6}$; Prop. of Proportions (3) **c.** The proportion is equivalent to $\frac{x-6}{6} = \frac{y-7}{7}$ by Prop. of Proportions (1). Then by Prop. of Proportions (3), $\frac{x-6+6}{6} = \frac{y-7+7}{7}$, which simplifies to $\frac{x}{6} = \frac{y}{7}$.

Practice

9. $3b$; Cross Products Prop.

10. $\frac{7}{4}$; Prop. of Proportions (3)

▼ STUDENT PAGE 342

Using the Properties of Equality, you can rewrite proportions in equivalent forms.

take note **Key Concept** Properties of Proportions

a, b, c, and d do not equal zero.

Property	How to Apply It
(1) $\frac{a}{b} = \frac{c}{d}$ is equivalent to $\frac{b}{a} = \frac{d}{c}$.	Write the reciprocal of each ratio. $\frac{2}{3} = \frac{4}{6}$ becomes $\frac{3}{2} = \frac{6}{4}$.
(2) $\frac{a}{b} = \frac{c}{d}$ is equivalent to $\frac{a}{c} = \frac{b}{d}$.	Switch the means. $\frac{2}{3} = \frac{4}{6}$ becomes $\frac{2}{4} = \frac{3}{6}$.
(3) $\frac{a}{b} = \frac{c}{d}$ is equivalent to $\frac{a+b}{b} = \frac{c+d}{d}$.	In each ratio, add the denominator to the numerator. $\frac{2}{3} = \frac{4}{6}$ becomes $\frac{2+3}{3} = \frac{4+6}{6}$.

▼ DIGITAL

Problem 5 Writing Equivalent Proportions

In the diagram, $\frac{x}{6} = \frac{y}{7}$. What ratio completes the equivalent proportion $\frac{x}{y} = \frac{■}{■}$? Justify your answer.

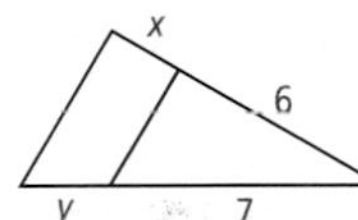

Method 1

$\frac{x}{6} = \frac{y}{7}$

$\frac{x}{y} = \frac{6}{7}$ Property of Proportions (2)

Method 2

$\frac{x}{6} = \frac{y}{7}$

$7x = 6y$ Cross Products Property

$\frac{7x}{7y} = \frac{6y}{7y}$ To solve for $\frac{x}{y}$, divide each side by $7y$.

$\frac{x}{y} = \frac{6}{7}$ Simplify.

The ratio that completes the proportion is $\frac{6}{7}$.

▼ STUDENT PAGES 342–343

Got It? For parts (a) and (b), use the proportion $\frac{x}{6} = \frac{y}{7}$. What ratio completes the equivalent proportion? Justify your answer.

a. $\frac{6}{x} = \frac{■}{■}$ **b.** $\frac{■}{■} = \frac{y+7}{7}$

c. Reasoning Explain why $\frac{6}{x-6} = \frac{7}{y-7}$ is an equivalent proportion to $\frac{x}{6} = \frac{y}{7}$. (Assume $x \neq 6$ and $y \neq 7$.)

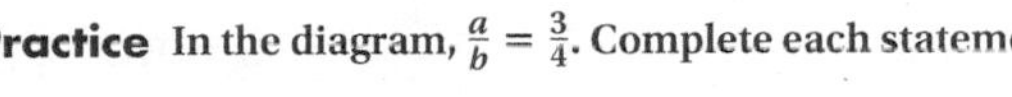

Practice **In the diagram, $\frac{a}{b} = \frac{3}{4}$. Complete each statement. Justify your answer.**

9. $4a = ■$

10. $\frac{a+b}{b} = \frac{■}{■}$

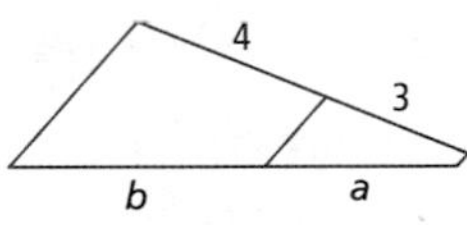

Lesson Check

Do you know HOW?
If students have difficulty with Exercise 14, then have them describe the change made to $\frac{a}{7}$ and then make the same change to $\frac{13}{b}$.

Do you UNDERSTAND?
If students have difficulty with Exercise 16, then remind them to rewrite the extended ratio as $3x : 6x : 7x$ and then choose two values for x.

Close

Q When two ratios are written as a proportion, what relationship must be true? **[The product of the means equals the product of the extremes.]**

Q When a proportion contains a variable, what property can be used to solve for the unknown quantity? **[Cross Products Property]**

ANSWERS

11. $23 : 42$, or $\frac{23}{42}$

12. $5x$, $9x$

13. 12

14. a. $\frac{a}{13} = \frac{7}{b}$ **b.** $\frac{a-7}{7} = \frac{13-b}{b}$ **c.** $\frac{7}{a} = \frac{b}{13}$

15. A ratio is a single comparison, while a proportion is a statement that two ratios are equal.

16. Answers may vary. Sample: 3 in., 6 in., 7 in.; or 6 in., 12 in., 14 in.

17. The second line should equate the product of the means and the product of the extremes: $7x = 12$. Then the third line would be $x = \frac{12}{7}$.

18. $\frac{9}{6} = \frac{18}{12}$, $\frac{9}{18} = \frac{6}{12}$, $\frac{12}{6} = \frac{18}{9}$, or $\frac{12}{18} = \frac{6}{9}$

▼ STUDENT PAGES 343–345

Lesson Check

Do you know HOW?

11. A cell phone is 84 mm long and 46 mm wide. What is the ratio of the width to the length?

12. Two angle measures are in the ratio 5 : 9. Write expressions for the two angle measures in terms of the variable x.

13. What is the solution of the proportion $\frac{20}{z} = \frac{5}{3}$?

14. For $\frac{a}{7} = \frac{13}{b}$ complete each equivalent proportion.

a. $\frac{a}{■} = \frac{7}{■}$

b. $\frac{a-7}{7} = \frac{■}{■}$

c. $\frac{7}{a} = \frac{■}{■}$

Do you UNDERSTAND?

15. Vocabulary What is the difference between a ratio and a proportion?

16. Open-Ended The lengths of the sides of a triangle are in the extended ratio 3 : 6 : 7. What are two possible sets of side lengths, in inches, for the triangle?

17. Error Analysis What is the error in the solution of the proportion shown at the right?

18. What is a proportion that has means 6 and 18 and extremes 9 and 12?

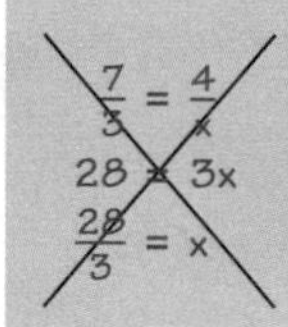

Practice

More Practice and Problem-Solving Exercises

ASSIGNMENT GUIDE
The assignments below are for the More Practice and Problem-Solving Exercises. You may also want to assign the A-Level Practice Exercises for homework if these are not used in class.
Average: 19–40
Advanced: 19–43

Mathematical Practices The exercises listed focus on the Standards for Mathematical Practices listed.

EX. 16, 23, 31: Make Sense of Problems (MP 1)
EX. 32: Persevere in Solving Problems (MP 1)
EX. 33: Communicate (MP 3)
EX. 17: Critique the Reasoning of Others (MP 3)
EX. 24, 25: Model (MP 4)
EX. 34: Use Structure (MP 7)

EXERCISE 32: Use the **Think About a Plan** worksheet in the Online Teacher Resources to further support students' development in becoming independent learners.

HOMEWORK QUICK CHECK
To check students' understanding of key skills and concepts, go over Exercises 23, 30, 32, 33, and 34.

ANSWERS

19. 1 **20.** $\frac{5}{4}$

21. 4 **22.** −2

23. length: 15 in.; width: 10 in.

24. $AB = 36$ cm, $BC = 18$ cm; $CD = 9$ cm, $DE = 9$ cm

25. **a.** 12 in. **b.** 1.5 in.

26. 2 **27.** 1.5

28. 0.5 **29.** 0.2

30. $\frac{9}{4} = \frac{x}{52}$; 117 mm

31.

72°
126°
72°

32. 1 and 60, 2 and 30, 3 and 20, 4 and 15, 5 and 12, 6 and 10

33. The product of the means is $26 \cdot 16 = 416$, and the product of the extremes is $10 \cdot 42 = 420$. Since $416 \neq 420$, it is not a valid proportion.

34. $\frac{3}{4} = \frac{12}{16}$ is equivalent to $\frac{3}{12} = \frac{4}{16}$ by Prop. of Proportions (2). $\frac{3}{12} = \frac{4}{16}$ is equivalent to $\frac{12}{3} = \frac{16}{4}$ by Prop. of Proportions (1).

35. $\frac{9}{4}$; divide each side by $4n$.

36. $\frac{30}{18}$; mult. each side by $\frac{t}{18}$.

37. $\frac{b}{2}$; Prop. of Proportions (3)

38. $\frac{b}{d}$; Prop. of Proportions (3) and (2)

39. $\frac{c}{d}$; Prop. of Proportions (2), then (3), then (2)

40. $\frac{c + 2d}{d}$; apply Prop. of Proportions (3) twice.

41. $\frac{a}{b} = \frac{c}{d}$ (given); $\frac{a}{b}(bd) = \frac{c}{d}(bd)$ (Mult. Prop. of =); $ad = bc$ (simplify and Commutative Prop. of Mult.); $bc = ad$ (Sym. Prop. of =); $\frac{bc}{ac} = \frac{ad}{ac}$ (Div. Prop. of =); $\frac{b}{a} = \frac{d}{c}$ (simplify)

42. $\frac{a}{b} = \frac{c}{d}$ (given); $\frac{a}{b}(bd) = \frac{c}{d}(bd)$ (Mult. Prop. of =); $ad = bc$ (simplify and Commutative Prop. of Mult.); $\frac{ad}{cd} = \frac{bc}{cd}$ (Div. Prop. of =); $\frac{a}{c} = \frac{b}{d}$ (simplify)

43. $\frac{a}{b} = \frac{c}{d}$ (given); $\frac{a}{b} + 1 = \frac{c}{d} + 1$ (Add. Prop. of Eq.); $\frac{a}{b} + \frac{b}{b} = \frac{c}{d} + \frac{d}{d}$ (Subst. Prop. of Eq.); $\frac{a + b}{b} = \frac{c + d}{d}$ (simplify)

More Practice and Problem-Solving Exercises

B Apply

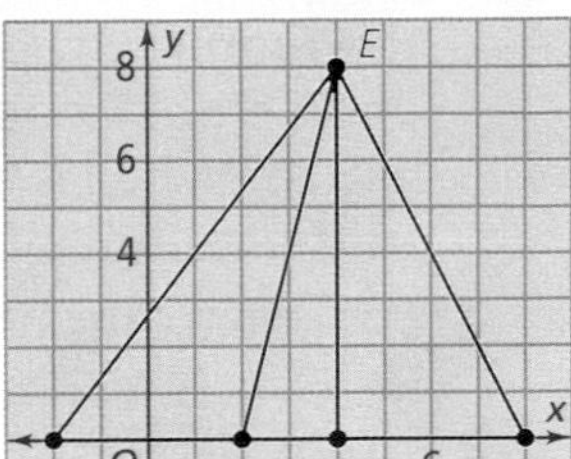

Coordinate Geometry Use the graph. Write each ratio in simplest form.

19. $\frac{AC}{BD}$ **20.** $\frac{AE}{EC}$ **21.** slope of $\overline{EB}$ **22.** slope of $\overline{ED}$

23. Think About a Plan The area of a rectangle is 150 in.². The ratio of the length to the width is 3 : 2. Find the length and the width.

- What is the formula for the area of a rectangle?
- How can you use the given ratio to write expressions for the length and width?

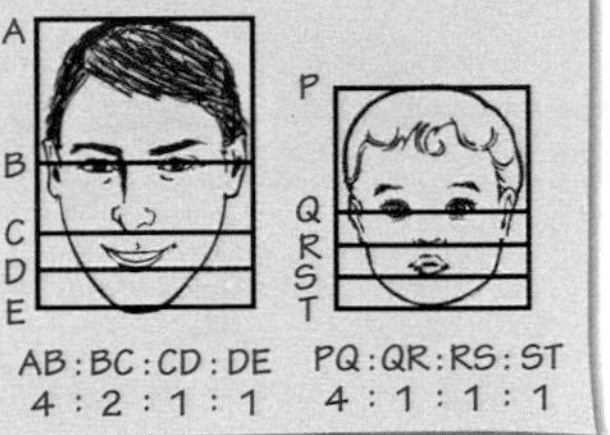

Art To draw a face, you can sketch the head as an oval and then lightly draw horizontal lines to help locate the eyes, nose, and mouth. You can use the extended ratios shown in the diagrams to help you place the lines for an adult's face or for a baby's face.

24. If $AE = 72$ cm in the diagram, find AB, BC, CD, and DE.

25. You draw a baby's head as an oval that is 21 in. from top to bottom.

a. How far from the top should you place the line for the eyes?

b. Suppose you decide to make the head an adult's head. How far up should you move the line for the eyes?

Algebra Solve each proportion.

26. $\frac{1}{7y - 5} = \frac{2}{9y}$ **27.** $\frac{4a + 1}{7} = \frac{2a}{3}$

28. $\frac{5}{x + 2} = \frac{3}{x + 1}$ **29.** $\frac{2b - 1}{4} = \frac{b - 2}{12}$

30. The ratio of the length to the width of a rectangle is 9 : 4. The width of the rectangle is 52 mm. Write and solve a proportion to find the length.

31. Open-Ended Draw a quadrilateral that satisfies this condition: The measures of the consecutive angles are in the extended ratio 4 : 5 : 4 : 7.

32. Reasoning The means of a proportion are 4 and 15. List all possible pairs of positive integers that could be the extremes of the proportion.

33. Writing Describe how to use the Cross Products Property to determine whether $\frac{10}{26} = \frac{16}{42}$ is a true proportion.

34. Reasoning Explain how to use two different properties of proportions to change the proportion $\frac{3}{4} = \frac{12}{16}$ into the proportion $\frac{12}{3} = \frac{16}{4}$.

Complete each statement. Justify your answer.

35. If $4m = 9n$, then $\frac{m}{n} = \frac{■}{■}$. **36.** If $\frac{30}{t} = \frac{18}{r}$, then $\frac{t}{r} = \frac{■}{■}$.

37. If $\frac{a + 5}{5} = \frac{b + 2}{2}$, then $\frac{a}{5} = \frac{■}{■}$. **38.** If $\frac{a}{b} = \frac{c}{d}$, then $\frac{a + b}{c + d} = \frac{■}{■}$.

39. If $\frac{a}{b} = \frac{c}{d}$, then $\frac{a + c}{b + d} = \frac{■}{■}$. **40.** If $\frac{a}{b} = \frac{c}{d}$, then $\frac{a + 2b}{b} = \frac{■}{■}$.

C Challenge

Algebra Use properties of equality to justify each property of proportions.

41. $\frac{a}{b} = \frac{c}{d}$ is equivalent to $\frac{b}{a} = \frac{d}{c}$.

42. $\frac{a}{b} = \frac{c}{d}$ is equivalent to $\frac{a}{c} = \frac{b}{d}$.

43. $\frac{a}{b} = \frac{c}{d}$ is equivalent to $\frac{a + b}{b} = \frac{c + d}{d}$.

Assess and Remediate

Lesson Quiz

1. **Do you UNDERSTAND?** Jessica is making a scale model of the Empire State Building. Her model will have a height of 16 cm. The actual height of the building is about 448 m. What is the ratio of the height of Jessica's model to the height of the building?
2. The measures of two supplementary angles are in the ratio 4 : 5. What are the measures of the angles?
3. In the diagram, $\frac{x}{15} = \frac{y}{6}$. What ratio completes the equivalent proportion $\frac{x}{y} = \frac{■}{■}$? Use one of the Properties of Proportions to justify your answer.

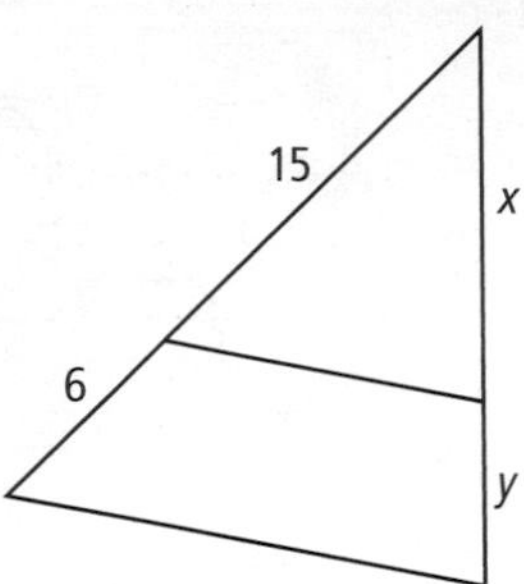

ANSWERS TO LESSON QUIZ

1. 1 : 2800
2. 80, 100
3. $\frac{x}{y} = \frac{15}{6}$

Prescription for Remediation

Use the student work on the Lesson Quiz to prescribe a differentiated assignment.

Points	Differentiated Remediation
0–1	Intervention
2	On-level
3	Extension

Online Assessment

Assign the Lesson Quiz in Success Tracker on **pearsonsuccessnet.com**. Success Tracker will automatically score the quiz and assign appropriate intervention or enrichment to each student based on the results. The compiled data appear in three different reports for instant analysis of whole class and individual student performance.

Differentiated Remediation

Intervention

- **RETEACHING** (2 pages) Provides reteaching and practice exercises for the key lesson concepts. Use with struggling students or absent students.
- **ENGLISH LANGUAGE LEARNER SUPPORT** Helps students develop and reinforce mathematical vocabulary and key concepts.

On-Level

- **PRACTICE** (2 pages) Provides extra practice for each lesson. For simpler practice exercises, use the Form K Practice pages found in the Online Teacher Resources.
- **THINK ABOUT A PLAN** Helps students develop specific problem-solving skills and strategies by providing scaffolded guiding questions.
- **STANDARDIZED TEST PREP** Focuses on all major exercises, all major question types, and helps students prepare for the high-stakes assessments.

Extension

- **ENRICHMENT** Provides students with interesting problems and activities that extend the concepts of the lesson.
- **ACTIVITIES, GAMES, AND PUZZLES** Worksheets that can be used for concept development, enrichment, and for fun!

6-2 Similar Polygons

Common Core State Standard
G.SRT.5 Use . . . similarity criteria for triangles to solve problems and to prove relationships in geometric figures.

Preparing to Teach

BIG ideas Proportionality
Reasoning and Proof

ESSENTIAL UNDERSTANDING

Ratios and proportions can be used to decide whether two polygons are similar and to find unknown side lengths of similar figures. All lengths in a scale drawing are proportional to their corresponding actual lengths.

Math Background

Scale drawings and similar figures appear in many real-world situations. Similar figures are used to create scale drawings, produce reductions or enlargements of existing figures, and conduct indirect measurement. Students should be comfortable with writing and simplifying ratios and using the Cross Products Property. Students will use these skills to solve problems involving unknown side lengths and to prove that figures are similar. Students should understand that proving figures similar is the necessary first step before using proportions to find missing dimensions. Any proportion can be set up in more than one correct way—and more than one incorrect way. Students may need extra guidance to be sure their ratios are written correctly.

ELL Support

FOCUS ON LANGUAGE Have groups of students list ways they have heard the word *similar* used. Tell each group: Use familiar words to write a definition for *similar*. Have students compare their list and definition with another group.

Say: In your group, list five examples of things that are similar. You may also draw pictures of similar things. Give examples, such as twins and two pencils, to help students get started.

Have a volunteer draw similar triangles on the board. Have each group write out answers to the following questions: Do the triangles fit your definition of *similar*? Ask: Is a large triangle similar to a small triangle?

Lesson Vocabulary

- similar figures
- similar polygons
- extended proportion
- scale factor
- scale drawing
- scale

Mathematical Practices

ATTEND TO PRECISION. Using a knowledge of extended proportions, students will define and make explicit use of the term "scale factor" between similar polygons. They will also solve situations involving scale factor.

Interactive Learning

Solve It!

PURPOSE To determine properties of similar polygons

PROCESS Students may find the ratios of heights and ratios of widths to see which screens have proportional sides or find the height-to-width ratios of all three screens.

Q If a video that is filmed for a movie theater screen is shown on a television that does not have the same height-to-width ratio, how might the images appear on the screen? **[You can display part of the theater image and fill the TV screen. The complete theater image cannot be made to fill a TV screen without distorting the image. You can scale the theater image to fit, but part of the TV screen will not be filled.]**

ANSWER The letterbox screen has the same ratio of width to height as the movie screen, 9 : 5 in both cases.

CONNECT THE MATH Students should recognize that the relationship between similar figures lies in the proportionality of their sides. This allows a movie filmed for a theater screen to be shrunk to fit on a television screen. "Letterbox" format is a video format that preserves the film's original aspect ratio.

▼ DIGITAL (STUDENT WORK SPACE PAGE 348)

SOLVE IT! **Getting Ready!**

A movie theater screen is in the shape of a rectangle 45 ft wide by 25 ft high. Which of the TV screen formats at the right do you think would show the most complete scene from a movie shown on the theater screen? Explain.

Standard: 36 in. wide, 27 in. high

Letterbox: 36 in. wide, 20 in. high

2 Guided Instruction

Problem 1 Understanding Similarity

Take Note
Ask students to describe the two conditions necessary for figures to be similar. Draw similar figures on the board and ask students to identify the conditions that show the figures are similar.

Problem 1

Q How do you know which angles are corresponding? **[The similarity statement shows the order in which the vertices correspond.]**

Q What is another way to write the extended ratio of corresponding sides? Explain. **[$\frac{RS}{NM} = \frac{RT}{NP} = \frac{ST}{MP}$; the sides of the larger triangle are in the numerators of these ratios.]**

Got It? **ERROR PREVENTION**
Remind students that there will be four pairs of corresponding sides and corresponding angles, because the figures are quadrilaterals.

ANSWERS

Got It? a. $\angle D \cong \angle H$, $\angle E \cong \angle J$, $\angle F \cong \angle K$, $\angle G \cong \angle L$ **b.** $\frac{DE}{HJ} = \frac{EF}{JK} = \frac{FG}{KL} = \frac{GD}{LH}$

Practice

1. $\angle R \cong \angle D$, $\angle S \cong \angle E$, $\angle T \cong \angle F$, $\angle V \cong \angle G$; $\frac{RS}{DE} = \frac{ST}{EF} = \frac{TV}{FG} = \frac{VR}{GD}$
2. $\angle K \cong \angle H$, $\angle L \cong \angle G$, $\angle M \cong \angle F$, $\angle N \cong \angle D$, $\angle P \cong \angle C$; $\frac{KL}{HG} = \frac{LM}{GF} = \frac{MN}{FD} = \frac{NP}{DC} = \frac{PK}{CH}$

▼ STUDENT PAGE 348

Similar figures have the same shape but not necessarily the same size. You can abbreviate *is similar to* with the symbol ~.

Essential Understanding You can use ratios and proportions to decide whether two polygons are similar and to find unknown side lengths of similar figures.

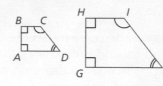

take note **Key Concept** Similar Polygons

Define	Diagram	Symbols
Two polygons are **similar polygons** if corresponding angles are congruent and if the lengths of corresponding sides are proportional.	$ABCD \sim GHIJ$ 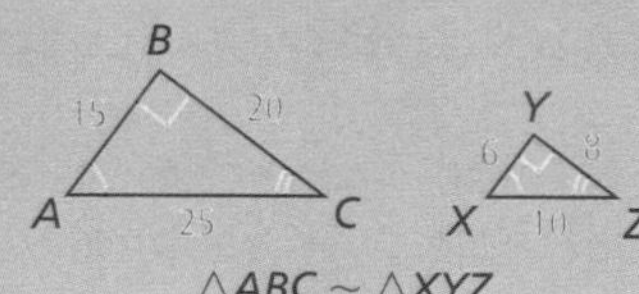	$\angle A \cong \angle G$ $\angle B \cong \angle H$ $\angle C \cong \angle I$ $\angle D \cong \angle J$ $\frac{AB}{GH} = \frac{BC}{HI} = \frac{CD}{IJ} = \frac{AD}{GJ}$

You write a similarity statement with corresponding vertices in order, just as you write a congruence statement. When three or more ratios are equal, you can write an **extended proportion.** The proportion $\frac{AB}{GH} = \frac{BC}{HI} = \frac{CD}{IJ} = \frac{AD}{GJ}$ is an extended proportion.

A **scale factor** is the ratio of corresponding linear measurements of two similar figures. The ratio of the lengths of corresponding sides $\overline{BC}$ and $\overline{YZ}$, or more simply stated, the ratio of corresponding sides, is $\frac{BC}{YZ} = \frac{20}{8} = \frac{5}{2}$. So the scale factor of $\triangle ABC$ to $\triangle XYZ$ is $\frac{5}{2}$, or 5 : 2.

$\triangle ABC \sim \triangle XYZ$

▼ DIGITAL

Problem 1 Understanding Similarity

$\triangle MNP \sim \triangle SRT$

A What are the pairs of congruent angles?

$\angle M \cong \angle S$, $\angle N \cong \angle R$, and $\angle P \cong \angle T$

B What is the extended proportion for the ratios of corresponding sides?

$\frac{MN}{SR} = \frac{NP}{RT} = \frac{MP}{ST}$

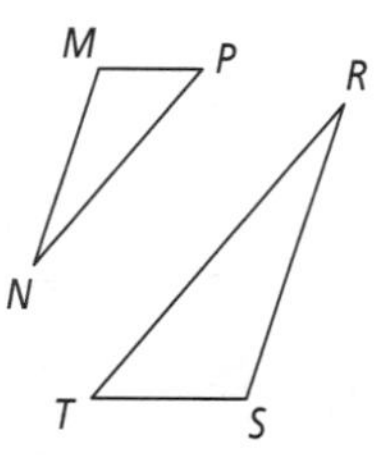

▼ STUDENT PAGE 349

Got It? *DEFG ~ HJKL*

a. What are the pairs of congruent angles?

b. What is the extended proportion for the ratios of the lengths of corresponding sides?

Think How can you use the similarity statement to write ratios of corresponding sides?

A Practice List the pairs of congruent angles and the extended proportion that relates the corresponding sides for the similar polygons.

1. *RSTV ~ DEFG*

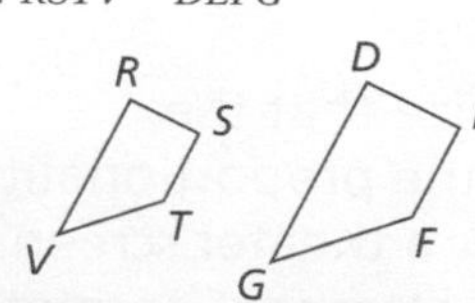

2. *KLMNP ~ HGFDC*

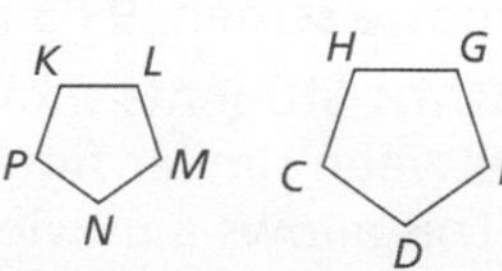

Problem 2 Determining Similarity

Use ratios to write equations that show the relationship between two quantities.

Q In 2A, for the figures to be similar, what angle must be congruent to $\angle L$? **[$\angle V$]**

Q For 2B, what triangle is similar to $\triangle CAB$? **[$\triangle FDE$]**

Q What other scale factor may be used in 2B? Explain. **[A scale factor of 5 : 4 may be used if the larger triangle is listed first in the similarity statement.]**

Got It? **VISUAL LEARNERS**

Remind students to determine which sides are proportional before writing the similarity statement. The vertices should be listed in corresponding order.

ANSWERS

Got It? a. not similar **b.** *ABCDE* ~ *SRVUT* or *ABCDE* ~ *UVRST*; 2 : 1

Practice

3. $\triangle JKL \sim \triangle PQR$; scale factor is 2 : 1.
4. Not similar; sample explanation: The $\angle$ measures are not the same.

▼ DIGITAL

Problem 2 **Determining Similarity**

Are the polygons similar? If they are, write a similarity statement and give the scale factor.

A ***JKLM* and *TUVW***

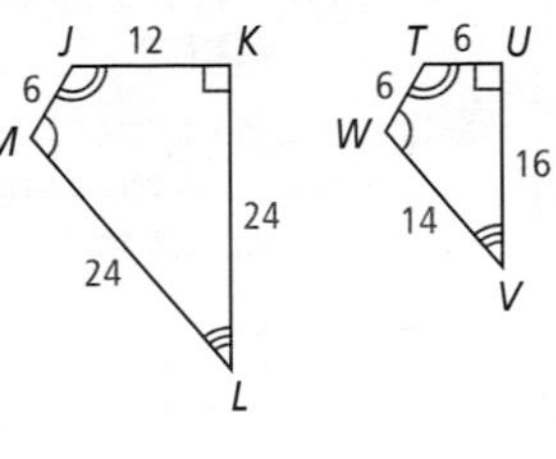

Step 1 Identify pairs of congruent angles.

$\angle J \cong \angle T$, $\angle K \cong \angle U$, $\angle L \cong \angle V$, and $\angle M \cong \angle W$

Step 2 Compare the ratios of corresponding sides.

$\frac{JK}{TU} = \frac{12}{6} = \frac{2}{1}$ $\quad \frac{KL}{UV} = \frac{24}{16} = \frac{3}{2}$

$\frac{LM}{VW} = \frac{24}{14} = \frac{12}{7}$ $\quad \frac{JM}{TW} = \frac{6}{6} = \frac{1}{1}$

Corresponding sides are not proportional, so the polygons are not similar.

B **$\triangle ABC$ and $\triangle EFD$**

Step 1 Identify pairs of congruent angles.

$\angle A \cong \angle D$, $\angle B \cong \angle E$, and $\angle C \cong \angle F$

Step 2 Compare the ratios of corresponding sides.

$\frac{AB}{DE} = \frac{12}{15} = \frac{4}{5}$ $\quad \frac{BC}{EF} = \frac{16}{20} = \frac{4}{5}$ $\quad \frac{AC}{DF} = \frac{8}{10} = \frac{4}{5}$

Yes; $\triangle ABC \sim \triangle DEF$ and the scale factor is $\frac{4}{5}$ or 4 : 5.

▼ STUDENT PAGE 350

Think How do you identify corresponding sides?

Got It? Are the polygons similar? If they are, write a similarity statement and give the scale factor.

a.

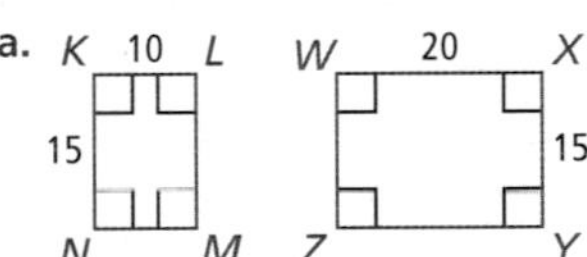

b.

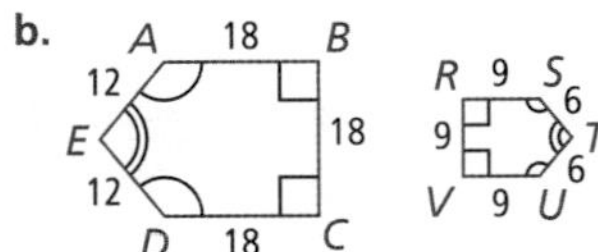

Practice **Determine whether the polygons are similar. If so, write a similarity statement and give the scale factor. If not, explain.**

3.

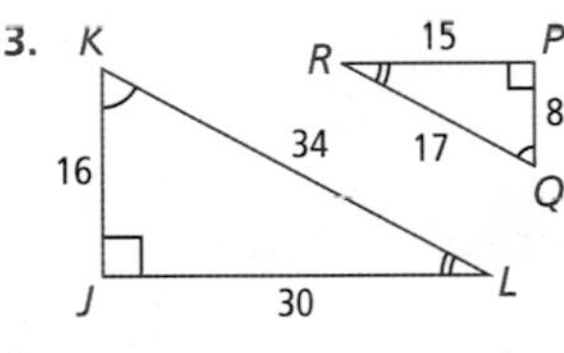

4.

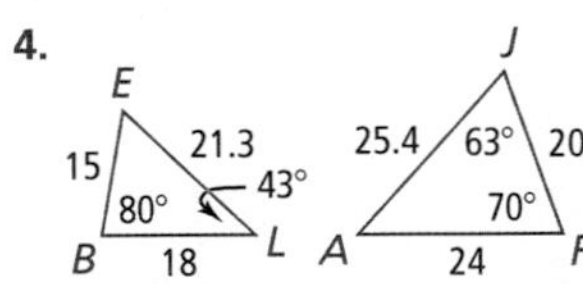

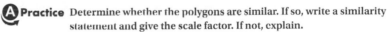

Problem 3 Using Similar Polygons

Q What four sides should be included in the proportion to solve for x and why? **[FG, BC, ED, AD; The unknown segment length x is the length of $\overline{FG}$, which corresponds to $\overline{BC}$. The only known corresponding side lengths are ED and AD.]**

Q Can you check that your answer is correct? Explain. **[Yes; find the ratio of FG to BC and check that it is equivalent to the ratio of ED to AD.]**

Got It?

Point out to students there are two ways to find the value of y: Set up a proportion as in Problem 3 or multiply the scale factor by the corresponding side length.

ANSWERS

Got It? $\frac{10}{3}$

Practice

5. $x = 4$, $y = 3$

6. $x = 12.75$, $y = 18.5$

▼ DIGITAL

Problem 3 Using Similar Polygons

Algebra $ABCD \sim EFGD$. What is the value of x?

Ⓐ 4.5 Ⓑ 5 Ⓒ 7.2 Ⓓ 11.25

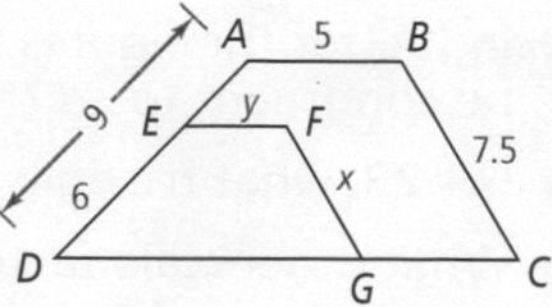

$\frac{FG}{BC} = \frac{ED}{AD}$ Corresponding sides of similar polygons are proportional.

$\frac{x}{7.5} = \frac{6}{9}$ Substitute.

$9x = 45$ Cross Products Property

$x = 5$ Divide each side by 9.

The value of x is 5. The correct answer is B.

▼ STUDENT PAGE 351

Got It? Use the diagram in Problem 3. $ABCD \sim EFGD$ What is the value of y?

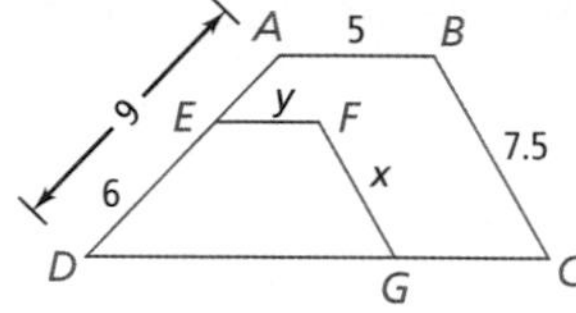

Practice **Algebra** The polygons are similar. Find the value of each variable.

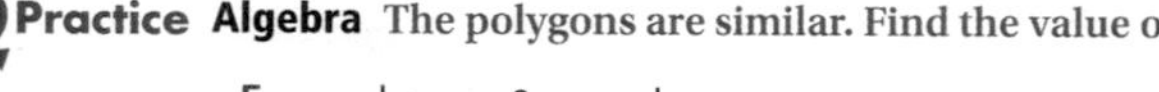

5.

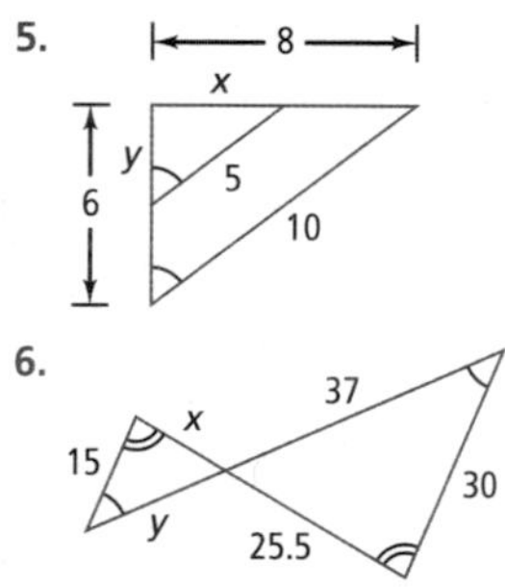

6.

Problem 4 Using Similarity

Q What happens if the width of the poster is maximized instead of the height? **[The new poster would have a height of 57.6 in. (4.8 ft), which would not fit the wall height of 48 in. (4 ft).]**

Got It?

Q By what scale factor can the poster be enlarged? **[4.8]**

ANSWERS

Got It? 28.8 in. high by 48 in. wide

Practice

7. 120 pixels wide by 90 pixels high

8. 288 in. wide, 162 in. high; or 24 ft wide, 13.5 ft high

▼ DIGITAL

Problem 4 Using Similarity

Design **Your class is making a rectangular poster for a rally. The poster's design is 6 in. high by 10 in. wide. The space allowed for the poster is 4 ft high by 8 ft wide. What are the dimensions of the largest poster that will fit in the space?**

Step 1 Determine whether the height or width will fill the space first.

Height: 4 ft = 48 in.; 48 in. ÷ 6 in. = 8

Width: 8 ft = 96 in.; 96 in. ÷ 10 in. = 9.6

The design can be enlarged at most 8 times.

Step 2 The greatest height is 48 in., so find the width.

$\frac{6}{48} = \frac{10}{x}$ Corresponding sides of similar polygons are proportional.

$6x = 480$ Cross Products Property

$x = 80$ Divide each side by 6.

The largest poster is 48 in. by 80 in. or 4 ft by $6\frac{2}{3}$ ft.

▼ STUDENT PAGES 351–352

Got It? A poster design is 6 in. high by 10 in. wide. What are the dimensions of the largest enlarged poster that will fit in a space 3 ft high by 4 ft wide?

Practice

7. **Web Page Design** The space allowed for the mascot on a school's Web page is 120 pixels wide by 90 pixels high. Its digital image is 500 pixels wide by 375 pixels high. What is the largest image of the mascot that will fit on the Web page?

8. **Art** The design for a mural is 16 in. wide and 9 in. high. What are the dimensions of the largest possible complete mural that can be painted on a wall 24 ft wide by 14 ft high?

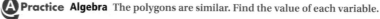

Problem 5 Using a Scale Drawing

Q How can the scale factor in the drawing be written as a ratio? **[$\frac{1\text{ cm}}{200\text{ m}}$]**

Q How does this ratio compare to the ratios used in Lesson 6-1? How do they differ? **[In Lesson 6-1, the units in the numerator and denominator were the same. In this ratio, the units are different.]**

Q How are units used when writing a proportion for this problem? **[Both ratios have the same units in the numerators and the same units in the denominators.]**

Q Is there another method you can use to solve this problem? Explain. **[Yes, you could multiply the length on the drawing by the scale factor of the drawing.]**

Got It?

For part (b), to solve the problem, students must decide whether to scale the height of the Space Needle to the width of the paper or to its length. Have students calculate the scale using first the length, then the width.

Q If the drawing is placed on the paper so that the height of the Space Needle fills the $8\frac{1}{2}$ in. of the width of the paper, what is the maximum height, drawn to scale, that will fit on the page? **[425 ft]**

Q If the drawing is placed on the paper so that the height of the Space Needle fills the 11 in. length of the paper, what is the maximum height, drawn to scale, that will fit on the page? **[550 ft]**

ANSWERS

Got It? a. Using 0.8 cm as the height of the towers, then $\frac{1}{200} = \frac{0.8}{h}$ and $h = 160$ m. **b.** No; using a scale of 1 in. = 50 ft, the paper must be more than 12 in. long.

Practice

9. 5 in. **10.** 9.5 in.

▼ STUDENT PAGE 352

In a **scale drawing**, all lengths are proportional to their corresponding actual lengths. The **scale** is the ratio that compares each length in the scale drawing to the actual length. The lengths used in a scale can be in different units. For example, a scale might be written as 1 cm to 50 km, 1 in. = 100 mi, or 1 in. : 10 ft.

You can use proportions to find the actual dimensions represented in a scale drawing.

▼ DIGITAL

Problem 5 Using a Scale Drawing STEM

Design **The diagram shows a scale drawing of the Golden Gate Bridge in San Francisco. The distance between the two towers is the main span. What is the actual length of the main span of the bridge?**

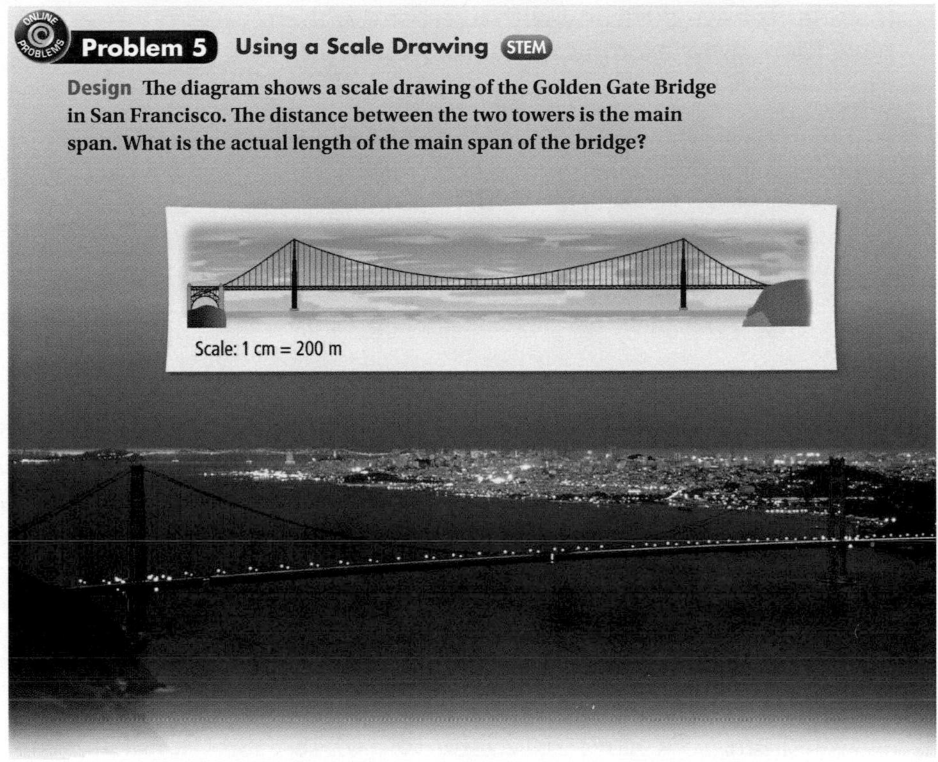

The length of the main span in the scale drawing is 6.4 cm. Let s represent the main span of the bridge. Use the scale to set up a proportion.

$\frac{1}{200} = \frac{6.4}{s}$ $\frac{\text{length in drawing (cm)}}{\text{actual length (m)}}$

$s = 1280$ Cross Products Property

The actual length of the main span of the bridge is 1280 m.

▼ STUDENT PAGES 352–353

Got It? **a.** Use the scale drawing in Problem 5. What is the actual height of the towers above the roadway?

b. **Reasoning** The Space Needle in Seattle is 605 ft tall. A classmate wants to make a scale drawing of the Space Needle on an $8\frac{1}{2}$ in.-by-11 in. sheet of paper. He decides to use the scale 1 in. = 50 ft. Is this a reasonable scale? Explain.

A Practice STEM

9. **Architecture** You want to make a scale drawing of New York City's Empire State Building using the scale 1 in. = 250 ft. If the building is 1250 ft tall, how tall should you make the building in your scale drawing?

10. **Cartography** A cartographer is making a map of Pennsylvania. She uses the scale 1 in. = 10 mi. The actual distance between Harrisburg and Philadelphia is about 95 mi. How far apart should she place the two cities on the map?

Lesson Check

Do you know HOW?
If students have difficulty with Exercise 13, then have them write and simplify the ratios of corresponding sides.

Do you UNDERSTAND?
If students have difficulty with Exercise 17, then have them draw examples of each property.

Close

Q What two conditions must be true for similar figures? **[Corresponding angles are congruent, and corresponding sides are proportional.]**

Q How can you use the scale factor between two similar figures to find an unknown side length? **[Set up a proportion between the scale factor and the corresponding side lengths or multiply the known side length by the scale factor.]**

ANSWERS

11. $\angle H$ **12.** JT

13. yes; $DEGH \sim PLQR$; 3 : 2

14. 6

15. Answers may vary. Sample: The scale indicates how many units of length of the actual object are represented by each unit of length in the drawing.

16. A is incorrect. Sample explanation: In the diagram, $\angle T$ corresp. to $\angle P$ (or to $\angle U$), but in the similarity statement $TRUV \sim NPQU$, $\angle T$ corresp. to $\angle N$.

17. Every figure is ~ to itself, so similarity is reflexive. If figure 1 ~ figure 2 and figure 2 ~ figure 3, then figure 1 ~ figure 3, so similarity is transitive. If figure 1 ~ figure 2, then figure 2 ~ figure 1, so similarity is symmetric.

18. any three of the following:
$\triangle ABS \sim \triangle PRS$, $\triangle ASB \sim \triangle PSR$, $\triangle SAB \sim \triangle SPR$, $\triangle SBA \sim \triangle SRP$, $\triangle BAS \sim \triangle RPS$, $\triangle BSA \sim \triangle RSP$

▼ STUDENT PAGES 354–355

Lesson Check

Do you know HOW?

$JDRT \sim WHYX$. **Complete each statement.**

11. $\angle D \cong$ ______

12. $\frac{RT}{YX} = \frac{\blacksquare}{WX}$

13. Are the polygons similar? If they are, write a similarity statement and give the scale factor.

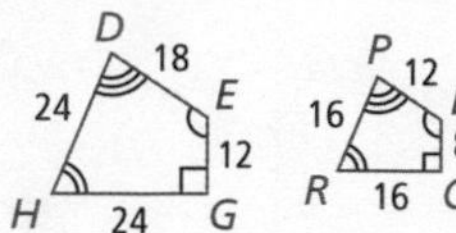

14. $\triangle FGH \sim \triangle MNP$. What is the value of x?

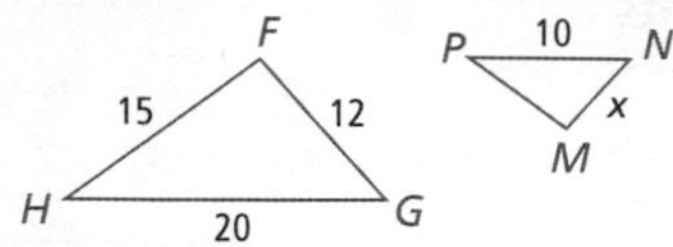

Do you UNDERSTAND?

15. Vocabulary What does the scale on a scale drawing indicate?

16. Error Analysis The polygons at the right are similar. Which similarity statement is *not* correct? Explain.

A. $TRUV \sim NPQU$ **B.** $RUVT \sim QUNP$

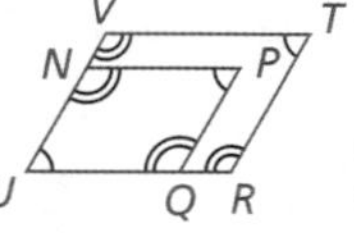

17. Reasoning Is similarity reflexive? Transitive? Symmetric? Justify your reasoning.

18. The triangles at the right are similar. What are three similarity statements for the triangles?

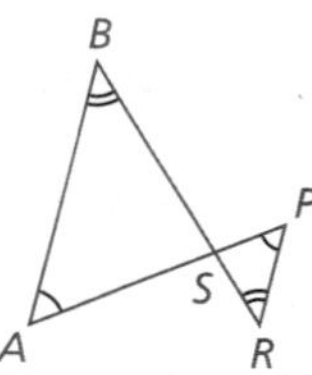

Practice

More Practice and Problem-Solving Exercises

ASSIGNMENT GUIDE
The assignments below are for the More Practice and Problem-Solving Exercises. You may also want to assign the A-Level Practice Exercises for homework if these are not used in class.
Average: 19–41
Advanced: 19–44

Mathematical Practices The exercises listed focus on the Standards for Mathematical Practices listed.

EX. 26, 30: Make Sense of Problems (MP 1)
EX. 17, 27, 28: Construct Arguments (MP 3)
EX. 16: Critique the Reasoning of Others (MP 3)
EX. 24, 33–36, 41: Model (MP 4)

STEM exercises focus on science or engineering applications.

EXERCISE 33: Use the **Think About a Plan** worksheet in the Online Teacher Resources to further support students' development in becoming independent learners.

HOMEWORK QUICK CHECK
To check students' understanding of key skills and concepts, go over Exercises 19, 26, 28, 31, and 33.

ANSWERS

19. 3 : 5 **20.** 51
21. 5 : 3 **22.** 16.5
23. 25 **24.** 60 ft

25. a. The slope of $\overline{AB}$, $\overline{CD}$, $\overline{AE}$, and $\overline{FG}$ is -2. The slope of $\overline{BC}$, $\overline{AD}$, $\overline{EF}$, and $\overline{AG}$ is $\frac{1}{2}$. For each pair of consecutive sides of $ABCD$, the slopes are negative reciprocals, so $ABCD$ has four rt. $\angle$s. Similarly, $AEFG$ has four rt. $\angle$s. The measure of $\angle A$, $\angle ABC$, $\angle BCD$, $\angle CDA$, $\angle E$, $\angle F$, and $\angle G$, is 90.

b. By the Distance Formula, $AB = BC = CD = AD = \sqrt{5}$ and $AE = EF = FG = AG = 2\sqrt{5}$.

c. All the angles of $AEFG$ and $ABCD$ are $\cong$. $\frac{AB}{AE} = \frac{BC}{EF} = \frac{CD}{FG} = \frac{AD}{AG} = \frac{\sqrt{5}}{2\sqrt{5}} = \frac{1}{2}$. The corresp. sides are proportional, so $AEFG \sim ABCD$.

26. The distance on the map is about 2.8 cm, so the actual distance is (2.8)(112), or about 314 km.

27. No; for polygons with more than 3 sides, you also need to know that corresp. $\angle$s are $\cong$ in order to state that the polygons are $\sim$.

28. Answers may vary. Sample: If two figures are $\cong$, then corresp. $\angle$s are $\cong$ and corresp. sides are $\cong$. Therefore the ratio of the lengths of each pair of corresp. sides is 1, so the sides are proportional with a scale factor of 1 : 1.

▼ STUDENT PAGES 355–356

More Practice and Problem-Solving Exercises

B Apply

In the diagram at the right, $\triangle DFG \sim \triangle HKM$. Find each of the following.

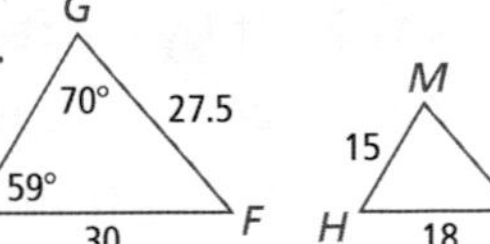

19. the scale factor of $\triangle HKM$ to $\triangle DFG$ **20.** $m\angle K$

21. $\frac{GD}{MH}$ **22.** MK **23.** GD

24. Flags A company produces a standard-size U.S. flag that is 3 ft by 5 ft. The company also produces a giant-size flag that is similar to the standard-size flag. If the shorter side of the giant-size flag is 36 ft, what is the length of its longer side?

25. a. Coordinate Geometry What are the measures of $\angle A$, $\angle ABC$, $\angle BCD$, $\angle CDA$, $\angle E$, $\angle F$, and $\angle G$? Explain.

b. What are the lengths of $\overline{AB}$, $\overline{BC}$, $\overline{CD}$, $\overline{DA}$, $\overline{AE}$, $\overline{EF}$, $\overline{FG}$, and $\overline{AG}$?

c. Is $ABCD$ similar to $AEFG$? Justify your answer.

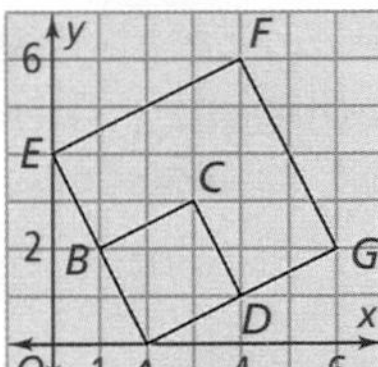

26. Think About a Plan The Davis family is planning to drive from San Antonio to Houston. About how far will they have to drive?

- How can you find the distance between the two cities on the map?
- What proportion can you set up to solve the problem?

27. Reasoning Two polygons have corresponding side lengths that are proportional. Can you conclude that the polygons are similar? Justify your reasoning.

28. Writing Explain why two congruent figures must also be similar. Include scale factor in your explanation.

More Practice and Problem-Solving Exercises *continued*

29. 1 : 3

30. Check students' work.

31. $x = 10$; 2 : 1

32. $x = 4.4$; 4 : 3

33–36. Check students' work.

37. always

38. never

39. sometimes

40. sometimes

41. 21 ft by 14 ft

42. **a.** 24 in., 32 in.

b. Ratio of perimeters: $\frac{54}{72} = \frac{3}{4}$, scale factor is $\frac{12}{16} = \frac{3}{4}$; they are the same.

43. All ∠s in any rectangle are right ∠s, so all corresp. ∠s are ≅. The ratio of two pair of consecutive sides for each rectangle is the same. Since opposite sides of a parallelogram are equal, the other two pair of sides will also have the same ratio. So corresp. sides form equal ratios and are proportional. So $BCEG \sim LJAW$.

44. If $\triangle ABC \sim \triangle DEF$ then $\angle A \cong \angle D$, $\angle B \cong \angle E$, $\angle C \cong \angle F$, and $\frac{AB}{DE} = \frac{BC}{EF} = \frac{AC}{DF}$. If $\triangle DEF \sim \triangle GHK$, then $\angle D \cong \angle G$, $\angle E \cong \angle H$, $\angle F \cong \angle K$, and $\frac{DE}{GH} = \frac{EF}{HK} = \frac{DF}{GK}$. Using Prop. of Proportions (2), you can write $\frac{AB}{BC} = \frac{DE}{EF}$ and $\frac{AB}{AC} = \frac{DE}{DF}$ from the first extended proportion and $\frac{DE}{EF} = \frac{GH}{HK}$ and $\frac{DE}{DF} = \frac{GH}{GK}$ from the second extended proportion. Then $\frac{AB}{BC} = \frac{GH}{HK}$ and $\frac{AB}{AC} = \frac{GH}{GK}$ by the Transitive Prop. of Equality; applying Prop. of Proportions (2) again gives $\frac{AB}{GH} = \frac{BC}{HK}$ and $\frac{AB}{GH} = \frac{AC}{GK}$. Since $\angle A \cong \angle G$, $\angle B \cong \angle H$, and $\angle C \cong \angle K$ by the Transitive Prop. of ≅, and $\frac{AB}{GH} = \frac{BC}{HK} = \frac{AC}{GK}$ by the Transitive Prop. of Equality, then $\triangle ABC \sim \triangle GHK$.

29. $\triangle JLK$ and $\triangle RTS$ are similar. The scale factor of $\triangle JLK$ to $\triangle RTS$ is 3 : 1. What is the scale factor of $\triangle RTS$ to $\triangle JLK$?

30. Open-Ended Draw and label two different similar quadrilaterals. Write a similarity statement for each and give the scale factor.

Algebra **Find the value of *x*. Give the scale factor of the polygons.**

31. $\triangle WLJ \sim \triangle QBV$

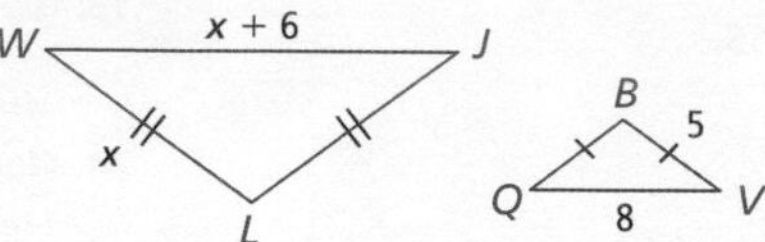

32. $GKNM \sim VRPT$

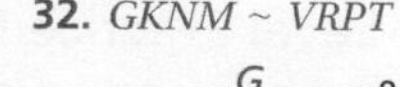

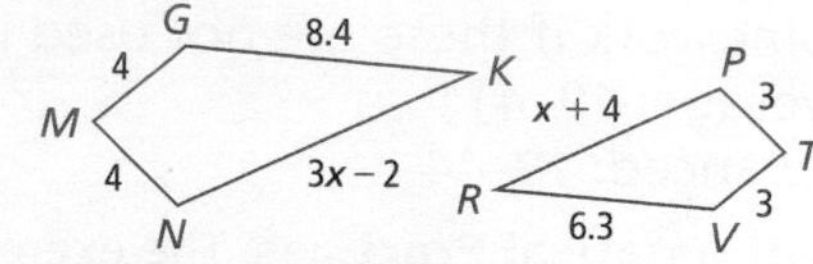

Sports **Choose a scale and make a scale drawing of each rectangular playing surface.**

33. A soccer field is 110 yd by 60 yd.

34. A volleyball court is 60 ft by 30 ft.

35. A tennis court is 78 ft by 36 ft.

36. A football field is 360 ft by 160 ft.

Determine whether each statement is always, sometimes, or never true.

37. Any two regular pentagons are similar.

38. A hexagon and a triangle are similar.

39. A square and a rhombus are similar.

40. Two similar rectangles are congruent.

STEM **41. Architecture** The scale drawing at the right is part of a floor plan for a home. The scale is 1 cm = 10 ft. What are the actual dimensions of the family room?

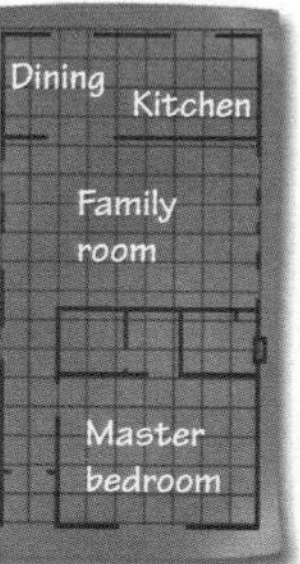

Challenge

42. The lengths of the sides of a triangle are in the extended ratio 2 : 3 : 4. The perimeter of the triangle is 54 in.

a. The length of the shortest side of a similar triangle is 16 in. What are the lengths of the other two sides of this triangle?

b. Compare the ratio of the perimeters of the two triangles to their scale factor. What do you notice?

43. In rectangle $BCEG$, $BC : CE = 2 : 3$. In rectangle $LJAW$, $LJ : JA = 2 : 3$. Show that $BCEG \sim LJAW$.

44. Prove the following statement: If $\triangle ABC \sim \triangle DEF$ and $\triangle DEF \sim \triangle GHK$, then $\triangle ABC \sim \triangle GHK$.

Assess and Remediate

Lesson Quiz

1. $\triangle HJK \sim \triangle CND$
   a. What are the pairs of congruent angles?
   b. What is the extended proportion for the ratios of corresponding sides?
2. Are the polygons similar? If they are, write a similarity statement and give the scale factor.

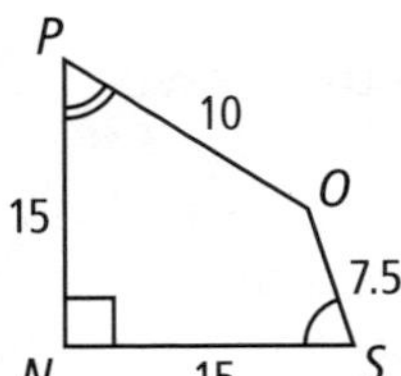

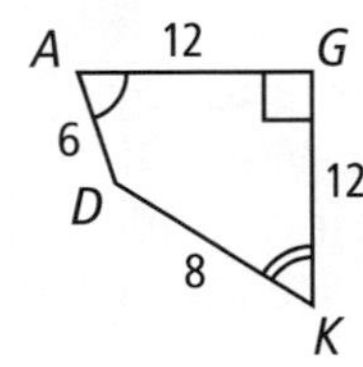

3. **Do you UNDERSTAND?** Harold has a photograph that is 8 in. × 10 in. that he wants to print at a reduced size to fit into a frame that is 6 in. tall. What will be the dimensions of the new photograph?

ANSWERS TO LESSON QUIZ

1. **a.** $\angle H \cong \angle C$, $\angle J \cong \angle N$, $\angle K \cong \angle D$
   b. $\frac{HJ}{CN} = \frac{JK}{ND} = \frac{HK}{CD}$
2. yes; $POSN \sim KDAG$, scale factor: 5 : 4
3. 4.8 in. × 6 in.

Prescription for Remediation

Use the student work on the Lesson Quiz to prescribe a differentiated assignment.

Points	Differentiated Remediation
0–1	Intervention
2	On-level
3	Extension

Online Assessment

Assign the Lesson Quiz in Success Tracker on **pearsonsuccessnet.com**. Success Tracker will automatically score the quiz and assign appropriate intervention or enrichment to each student based on the results. The compiled data appear in three different reports for instant analysis of whole class and individual student performance.

Differentiated Remediation

Intervention

- **RETEACHING** (2 pages) Provides reteaching and practice exercises for the key lesson concepts. Use with struggling students or absent students.
- **ENGLISH LANGUAGE LEARNER SUPPORT** Helps students develop and reinforce mathematical vocabulary and key concepts.

On-Level

- **PRACTICE** (2 pages) Provides extra practice for each lesson. For simpler practice exercises, use the Form K Practice pages found in the Online Teacher Resources.
- **THINK ABOUT A PLAN** Helps students develop specific problem-solving skills and strategies by providing scaffolded guiding questions.
- **STANDARDIZED TEST PREP** Focuses on all major exercises, all major question types, and helps students prepare for the high-stakes assessments.

Extension

- **ENRICHMENT** Provides students with interesting problems and activities that extend the concept of the lesson.
- **ACTIVITIES, GAMES, AND PUZZLES** Worksheets that can be used for concept development, enrichment, and for fun!

6-3 Proving Triangles Similar

Common Core State Standards
G.SRT.5 Use . . . similarity criteria for triangles to solve problems and to prove relationships in geometric figures. **Also G.GPE.5**

Preparing to Teach

BIG ideas Reasoning and Proof
Visualization

ESSENTIAL UNDERSTANDING

Triangles can be shown to be similar based on the relationship of two or three pairs of corresponding parts. Similar triangles can be used to find unknown measurements.

Math Background

The definition of similar triangles involves a complicated set of conditions. Postulates and theorems about similarity can provide a shortcut to proving triangles similar. Similar triangles can be used for indirect measurement in a variety of circumstances. Similar triangles are also part of the basic idea of proportionality, which extends through all areas of geometry. Proving statements in geometry helps students understand how to develop logical arguments in other areas of their lives.

ELL Support

USE ROLE PLAYING Divide students into small groups. Say: Draw two triangles. Make the length of each side of the second triangle one-and-a-half times the length of a side of the first triangle. Use one group's triangles for the next activity.

Hold up the two triangles and say, "I accuse these two triangles of being similar. We will hold a trial to see if the triangles are guilty of being similar." Assign students the roles of prosecutor, defense lawyer, witnesses, and members of the jury. Set a chair in front of the classroom for witnesses to sit. Have the prosecutor and defense lawyer question the witnesses. Then have the jury vote to determine whether the triangles are similar or not.

Lesson Vocabulary

- indirect measurement

Mathematical Practices

CONSTRUCT VIABLE ARGUMENTS AND CRITIQUE THE REASONING OF OTHERS. Students will prove the similarity of triangles using the stated assumptions provided by the AA ~ Postulate and the SAS ~ and SSS ~ Theorems.

1 Interactive Learning

Solve It!

PURPOSE To determine whether two triangles are similar

PROCESS Students may measure the side lengths and show that they are proportional or use the Triangle Sum Theorem to find the missing angle measures.

Q How can you determine whether the triangles are similar? **[Polygons are similar if corresponding angles are congruent and pairs of corresponding side lengths are proportional.]**

Q Are the unmarked angles in the triangles congruent? How do you know? **[Yes; by the Triangle Sum Theorem, both angle measures are 70°.]**

Q What must be true about the side lengths in similar triangles? **[Corresponding side lengths must be proportional.]**

ANSWER Yes; corresp. angles are congruent and corresp. sides are proportional.

CONNECT THE MATH Emphasize that proving triangles similar with the definition requires showing three pairs of angles are congruent, and that an extended proportion is true for corresponding side lengths. Learning the triangle similarity theorems will shorten this process.

▼ DIGITAL (STUDENT WORK SPACE PAGE 358)

SOLVE IT! **Getting Ready!**

Are the triangles similar? How do you know? (Hint: Use a centimeter ruler to measure the sides of each triangle.)

2 Guided Instruction

Problem 1 Using the AA ~ Postulate

Take Note
Emphasize that the Angle-Angle Similarity Postulate is stated in the form of an If-Then statement. Have students identify the hypothesis and conclusion of the postulate. Discuss the logic behind the postulate.

Problem 1

Q How many pairs of angles are labeled with the same measure? What does this mean about the angles? **[1; The angles are congruent.]**

Q How many pairs of angles are needed to use the AA ~ Postulate? **[2]**

Q What theorem relates the measures of the angles with vertex S? **[The Vertical Angles Theorem states that vertical angles are congruent.]**

Got It? SYNTHESIZING
Ask students to describe the types of triangles in each diagram. Have them list the properties of the triangles. Students should use the properties of these triangles to determine similarity.

ANSWERS

Got It? a. The measures of the two acute angles in each △ are 39 and 51, so the triangles are ~ by the AA ~ Post. **b.** Each of the base angles in the △ at the left measures 68, while each of the base angles in the △ at the right measures $\frac{1}{2}(180 - 62) = 59$; the triangles are not ~.

Practice

1. △FGH ~ △KJH; AA ~
2. Not ~; $m\angle U = 180 - (25 + 35) = 120$, while $m\angle A = 110$.

▼ STUDENT PAGE 358

In the Solve It, you determined whether the two triangles are similar. That is, you needed information about all three pairs of angles and all three pairs of sides. In this lesson, you'll learn an easier way to determine whether two triangles are similar.

Essential Understanding You can show that two triangles are similar when you know the relationships between only two or three pairs of corresponding parts.

take note **Postulate 17 Angle-Angle Similarity (AA ~) Postulate**

Postulate	If . . .	Then . . .
If two angles of one triangle are congruent to two angles of another triangle, then the triangles are similar.	$\angle S \cong \angle M$ and $\angle R \cong \angle L$	$\triangle SRT \sim \triangle MLP$

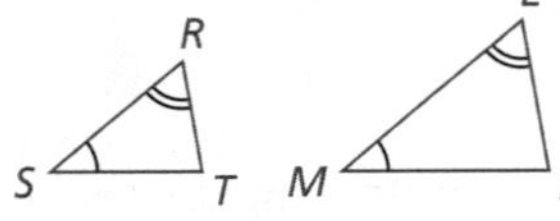

▼ DIGITAL

Problem 1 Using the AA ~ Postulate

Are the two triangles similar? How do you know?

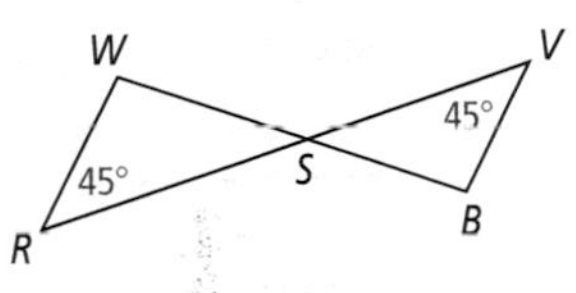

A $\triangle RSW$ **and** $\triangle VSB$

$\angle R \cong \angle V$ because both angles measure 45°.
$\angle RSW \cong \angle VSB$ because vertical angles are congruent.
So, $\triangle RSW \sim \triangle VSB$ by the AA ~ Postulate.

B $\triangle JKL$ **and** $\triangle PQR$

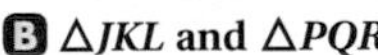

$\angle L \cong \angle R$ because both angles measure 70°.
By the Triangle Angle-Sum Theorem,
$m\angle K = 180 - 30 - 70 = 80$ and
$m\angle P = 180 - 85 - 70 = 25$. Only one pair of angles is congruent. So, $\triangle JKL$ and $\triangle PQR$ are *not* similar.

▼ STUDENT PAGE 359

Got It? Are the two triangles similar? How do you know?

a.
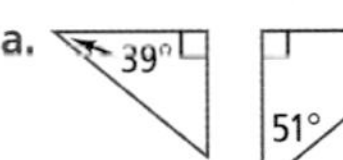

b.
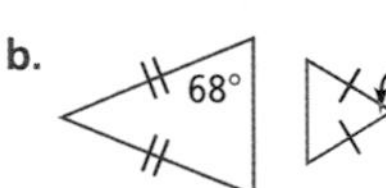

Plan
What do you need to show that the triangles are similar?

A Practice Determine whether the triangles are similar. If so, write a similarity statement and name the postulate you used. If not, explain.

1.
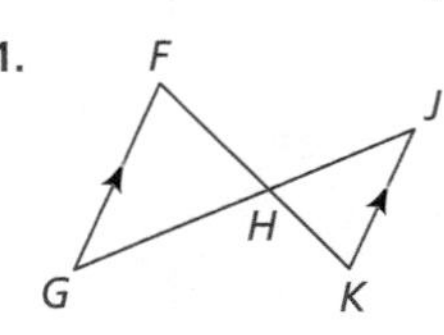

2.
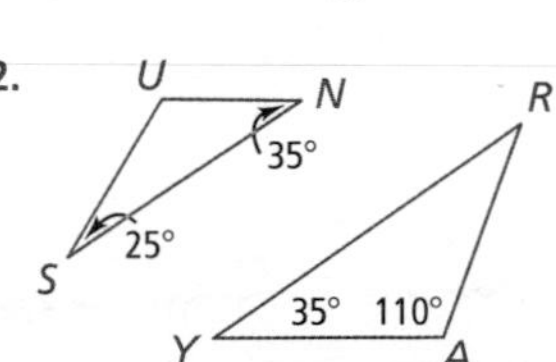

Problem 2 Verifying Triangle Similarity

Take Note
Review the concept of included angles. Ask students to explain in their own words why each theorem is true. Focus the discussion on how only three conditions can satisfy the full definition of similar triangles.

Problem 2

Q In 2A, what parts of the triangles are given? **[All six side measures are given.]**

Q What similarity postulate uses these measures? **[SSS ~ Theorem]**

Q In order to prove the triangles similar, what computation must be performed? Why? **[The ratios of corresponding side lengths must be simplified to show that the ratios are equivalent.]**

Q In 2B, what measurements of the triangles are given? **[Two sets of side lengths are given.]**

Q What further information do you need to prove the triangles are similar in 2B? **[One pair of congruent angles is needed to use the SAS ~ Theorem.]**

Q Is there a pair of congruent angles in the diagram? What theorem, postulate, or property confirms their congruence? **[Yes, ∠K is contained in both triangles. By the Reflexive Property of Congruence, ∠K ≅ ∠K.]**

▼ STUDENT PAGE 360

Here are two other ways to determine whether two triangles are similar.

take note

Theorem 60 Side-Angle-Side Similarity (SAS ~) Theorem

Theorem	If . . .	Then . . .
If an angle of one triangle is congruent to an angle of a second triangle, and the sides that include the two angles are proportional, then the triangles are similar.	$\frac{AB}{QR} = \frac{AC}{QS}$ and $\angle A \cong \angle Q$	$\triangle ABC \sim \triangle QRS$

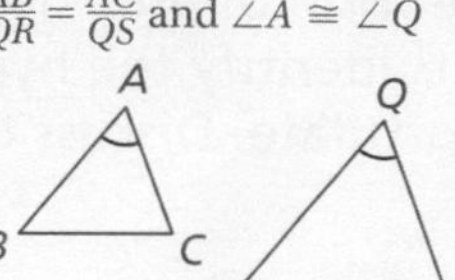

You will prove Theorem 60 in Exercise 32.

Theorem 61 Side-Side-Side Similarity (SSS ~) Theorem

Theorem	If . . .	Then . . .
If the corresponding sides of two triangles are proportional, then the triangles are similar.	$\frac{AB}{QR} = \frac{AC}{QS} = \frac{BC}{RS}$	$\triangle ABC \sim \triangle QRS$

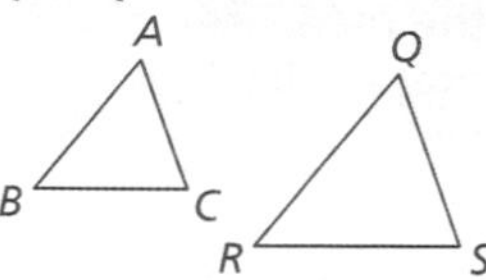

You will prove Theorem 61 in Exercise 33.

Proof Proof of Theorem 60: Side-Angle-Side Similarity Theorem

Given: $\frac{AB}{QR} = \frac{AC}{QS}$, $\angle A \cong \angle Q$

Prove: $\triangle ABC \sim \triangle QRS$

Plan for Proof: Choose X on $\overline{RQ}$ so that $QX = AB$. Draw $\overleftrightarrow{XY} \parallel \overline{RS}$. Show that $\triangle QXY \sim \triangle QRS$ by the AA ~ Postulate. Then use the proportion $\frac{QX}{QR} = \frac{QY}{QS}$ and the given proportion $\frac{AB}{QR} = \frac{AC}{QS}$ to show that $AC = QY$. Then prove that $\triangle ABC \cong \triangle QXY$. Finally, prove that $\triangle ABC \sim \triangle QRS$ by the AA ~ Postulate.

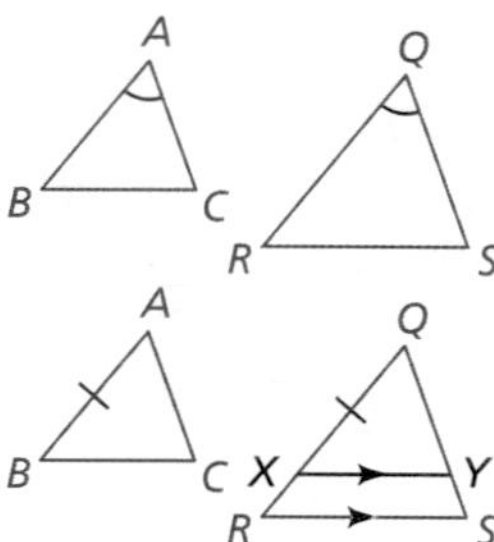

▼ DIGITAL

Problem 2 Verifying Triangle Similarity

Are the triangles similar? If so, write a similarity statement for the triangles.

A

S, U, T: 10, 6, 8; V, W, X: 12, 9, 15

Use the side lengths to identify corresponding sides. Then set up ratios for each pair of corresponding sides.

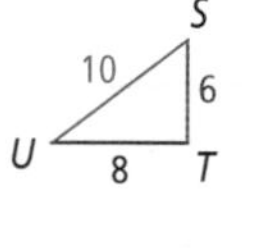

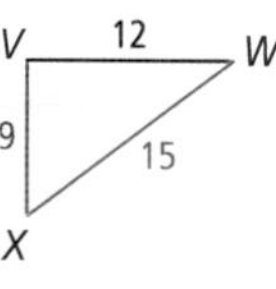

Shortest sides $\frac{ST}{XV} = \frac{6}{9} = \frac{2}{3}$

Longest sides $\frac{US}{WX} = \frac{10}{15} = \frac{2}{3}$

Remaining sides $\frac{TU}{VW} = \frac{8}{12} = \frac{2}{3}$

All three ratios are equal, so corresponding sides are proportional. $\triangle STU \sim \triangle XVW$ by the SSS ~ Theorem.

B

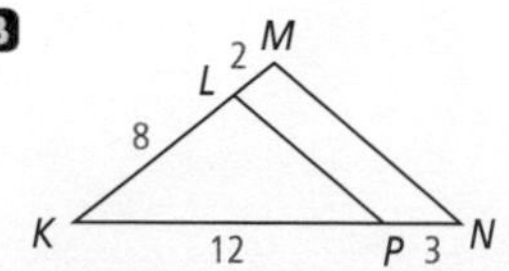

$\angle K \cong \angle K$ by the Reflexive Property of Congruence.

$\frac{KL}{KM} = \frac{8}{10} = \frac{4}{5}$ and $\frac{KP}{KN} = \frac{12}{15} = \frac{4}{5}$.

So, $\triangle KLP \sim \triangle KMN$ by the SAS ~ Theorem.

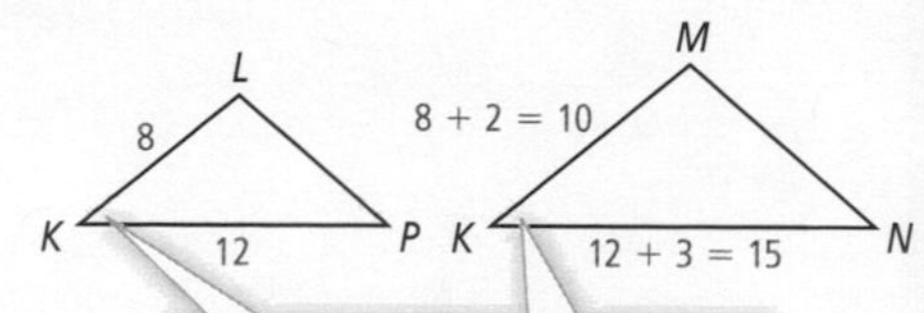

Got It? **VISUAL LEARNERS**

For part (b), have students draw each triangle separately to confirm which angles and sides are corresponding.

ANSWERS

Got It? a. The ratio for each of the three pairs of corresp. sides is 3 : 4, so $\triangle ABC \sim \triangle EFG$ by SSS ~.

b. $\angle A$ is in each triangle and $\frac{AL}{AC} = \frac{AW}{AE} = \frac{1}{2}$, so $\triangle ALW \sim \triangle ACE$ by SAS ~.

Practice

3. Not ~; using the sides that contain the rt. angles, the ratio of the shorter sides is 1 : 1, while the ratio of the longer sides is 5 : 4.
4. Not ~; $\frac{JL}{PQ} = \frac{KL}{PR} = \frac{3}{2}$, but $\frac{JK}{RQ} = \frac{16}{11}$.

▼ STUDENT PAGES 361–362

Got It? Are the triangles similar? If so, write a similarity statement for the triangles and explain how you know the triangles are similar.

Plan

How can you make it easier to identify corresponding sides and angles?

a. 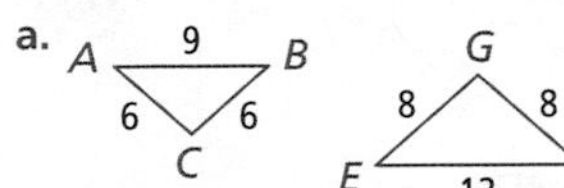
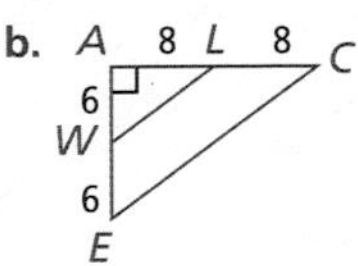

b. 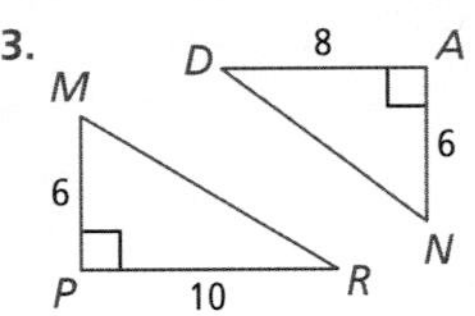

Practice Determine whether the triangles are similar. If so, write a similarity statement and name the postulate or theorem you used. If not, explain.

3. 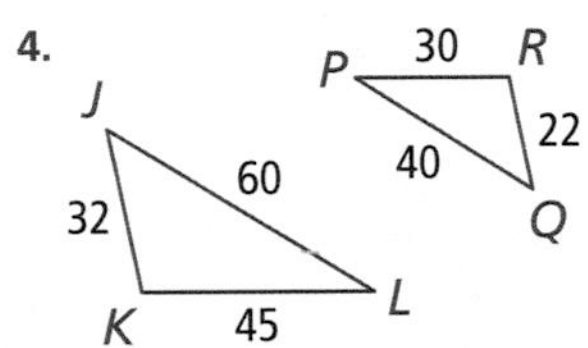

4.
J: 32, 60, K 45 L; P 30 R, 22, 40, Q

Problem 3 Proving Triangles Similar

When writing a proof, students may find it easier to make a plan that starts at the conclusion and work backward based on the information they need.

Q What information do you need to prove the triangles are similar? **[two pairs of congruent angles for the AA ~ Postulate, two pairs of proportional sides and the congruent included angles for the SAS ~ Theorem, or three pairs of proportional sides for the SSS ~ Theorem]**

Q What properties of an isosceles triangle help you prove that the triangles are similar? **[Isosceles triangles have one vertex angle and two congruent base angles.]**

Q Which pairs of angles are congruent within each triangle? **[$\angle F \cong \angle H$ and $\angle J \cong \angle L$]**

Got It?

Q What theorem about parallel lines may be useful in proving the triangles similar? **[When two parallel lines are cut by a transversal, alternate interior angles are congruent.]**

Q Are there any special pairs of angles present in the diagram? Explain. **[Yes; there are two pairs of alternate interior angles and one pair of vertical angles.]**

ANSWERS

Got It? a. $\overline{MP} \parallel \overline{AC}$ (given), so $\angle A \cong \angle P$ and $\angle C \cong \angle M$ because if two lines are ∥, then alt. int. angles are ≅. So $\triangle ABC \sim \triangle PBM$ by AA ~.

b. No; the ≅ vertical angles are not included by the proportional sides, so it is not possible to prove that the triangles are similar.

▼ DIGITAL

Problem 3 **Proving Triangles Similar**

Given: $\overline{FG} \cong \overline{GH}$, $\overline{JK} \cong \overline{KL}$, $\angle F \cong \angle J$

Prove: $\triangle FGH \sim \triangle JKL$

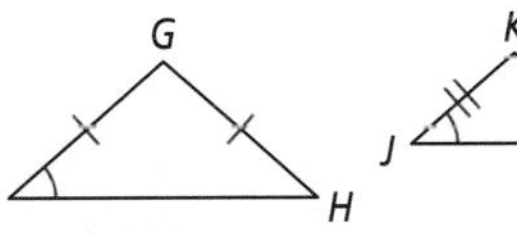
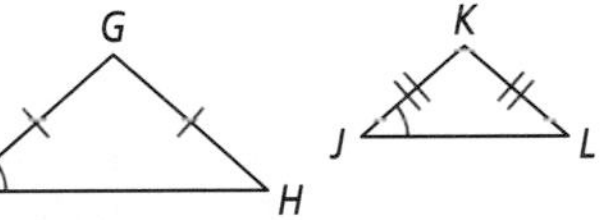

Know The triangles are isosceles, so the base angles are congruent.

Need You need to show that the triangles are similar.

Plan Find two pairs of corresponding congruent angles and use the AA ~ Postulate to prove the triangles are similar.

Statements	Reasons
1) $\overline{FG} \cong \overline{GH}$, $\overline{JK} \cong \overline{KL}$	1) Given
2) $\triangle FGH$ is isosceles. $\triangle JKL$ is isosceles.	2) Def. of an isosceles △
3) $\angle F \cong \angle H$, $\angle J \cong \angle L$	3) Base ∡ of an isosceles △ are ≅.
4) $\angle F \cong \angle J$	4) Given
5) $\angle H \cong \angle J$	5) Transitive Property of ≅
6) $\angle H \cong \angle L$	6) Transitive Property of ≅
7) $\triangle FGH \sim \triangle JKL$	7) AA ~ Postulate

▼ STUDENT PAGE 362

Got It? a. **Given:** $\overline{MP} \parallel \overline{AC}$

Prove: $\triangle ABC \sim \triangle PBM$

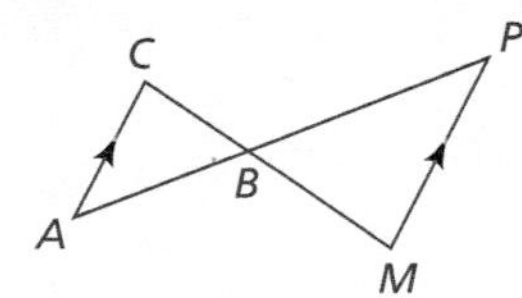

b. **Reasoning** For the figure above, suppose you are given only that $\frac{CA}{PM} = \frac{CB}{MB}$. Could you prove that the triangles are similar? Explain.

Problem 3 *continued*

Practice

5. $\angle A \cong \angle A$ (Refl. Prop. of $\cong$) and $\angle ABC \cong \angle ACD$ (given), so $\triangle ABC \sim \triangle ACD$ by AA $\sim$.
6. $\angle MPN \cong \angle QPR$ (Vert. angles are $\cong$.), and the given information tells us $\frac{PR}{PN} = \frac{PQ}{PM} = \frac{2}{1}$. So $\triangle MPN \sim \triangle QPR$ by SAS $\sim$.

▼ STUDENT PAGE 363

A Practice

Proof 5. Given: $\angle ABC \cong \angle ACD$

Prove: $\triangle ABC \sim \triangle ACD$

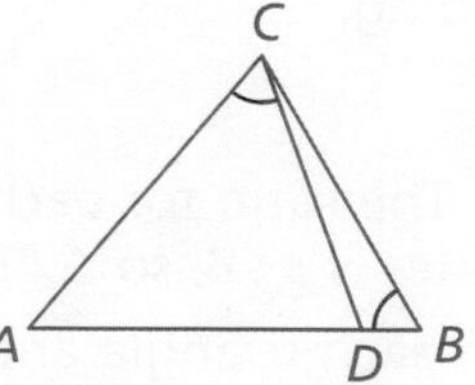

Proof 6. Given: $PR = 2NP$, $PQ = 2MP$

Prove: $\triangle MNP \sim \triangle QRP$

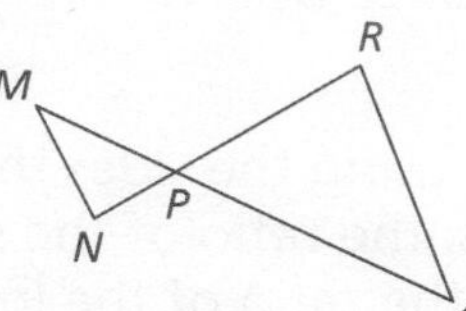

Problem 4 Finding Lengths in Similar Triangles

Q How can you tell the two triangles in the diagram are similar? **[They contain two pairs of congruent angles: the right angles formed at the ground and the angles at the mirror.]**

Q What postulate verifies that the triangles are similar? **[AA ~ Postulate]**

Q How do you know which sides are corresponding to set up a proportion? **[The corresponding sides are included between congruent angles.]**

Got It?

Q What characteristic needed to prove the triangles similar is not given directly by the problem? **[The angles of light entering and exiting the mirror are congruent.]**

▼ STUDENT PAGE 364

Essential Understanding Sometimes you can use similar triangles to find lengths that cannot be measured easily using a ruler or other measuring device.

You can use **indirect measurement** to find lengths that are difficult to measure directly. One method of indirect measurement uses the fact that light reflects off a mirror at the same angle at which it hits the mirror.

▼ DIGITAL

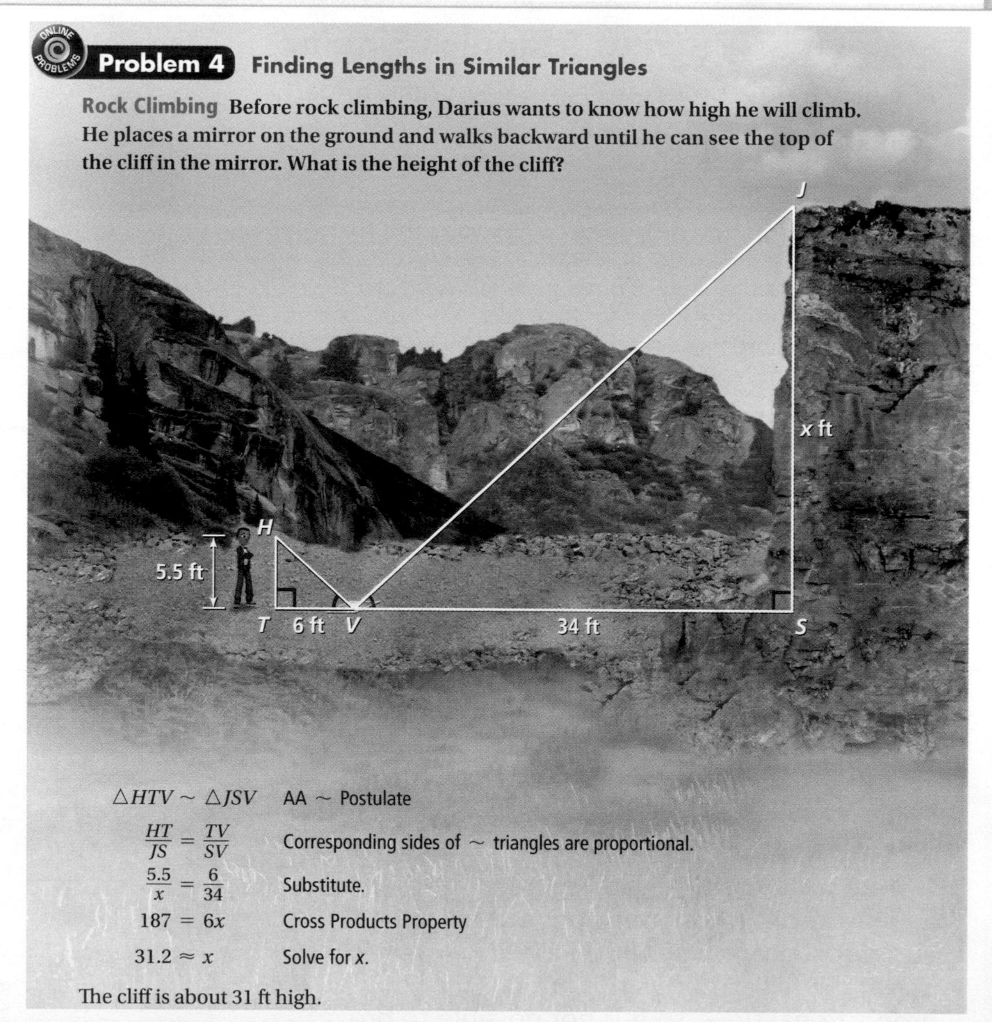

ONLINE PROBLEMS
Problem 4 Finding Lengths in Similar Triangles
Rock Climbing Before rock climbing, Darius wants to know how high he will climb. He places a mirror on the ground and walks backward until he can see the top of the cliff in the mirror. What is the height of the cliff?
J
x ft
H
5.5 ft
T
6 ft
V
34 ft
S
$\triangle HTV \sim \triangle JSV$ AA ~ Postulate
$\frac{HT}{JS} = \frac{TV}{SV}$ Corresponding sides of ~ triangles are proportional.
$\frac{5.5}{x} = \frac{6}{34}$ Substitute.
$187 = 6x$ Cross Products Property
$31.2 \approx x$ Solve for x.
The cliff is about 31 ft high.

ANSWERS

Got It? The triangles formed will not be similar unless both Darius and the cliff form right angles with the ground.

Practice

7. There are a pair of ≅ vert. angles and a pair of ≅ rt. angles, so the triangles are ~ by AA ~; 180 ft
8. about 169.2 m

▼ STUDENT PAGE 364

Got It? **Reasoning** Why is it important that the ground be flat to use the method of indirect measurement illustrated in Problem 4? Explain.

Practice

7. **Indirect Measurement** Explain why the triangles are similar. Then find the distance represented by x.

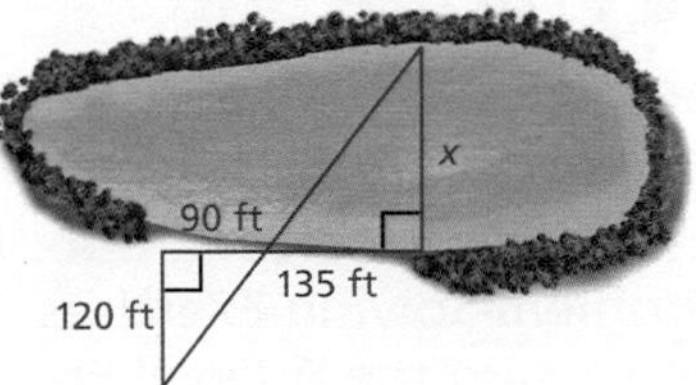

8. **Washington Monument** At a certain time of day, a 1.8-m-tall person standing next to the Washington Monument casts a 0.7-m shadow. At the same time, the Washington Monument casts a 65.8-m shadow. How tall is the Washington Monument?

3 Lesson Check

Do you know HOW?
If students have difficulty with Exercise 11, then have them redraw the triangles so that they are oriented the same way.

Do you UNDERSTAND?
If students have difficulty with Exercise 12, then have them review Problem 4.

Close

Q What is the minimum number of conditions necessary to prove two triangles similar? What are the conditions? **[Two pairs of congruent angles can prove two triangles similar.]**

Q What other sets of conditions will prove two triangles are similar? **[two pairs of proportional side lengths and the included angles congruent or three pairs of proportional side lengths]**

ANSWERS

9. Yes; $m\angle R = 180 - (35 + 45) - 100$, and $\angle AEZ \cong \angle REB$ (Vert. ⦞ are ≅.), so $\triangle AEZ \sim \triangle REB$ by AA ~.
10. Yes; the ratios of corresp. sides are all 2 : 3, so $\triangle ABC \sim \triangle FED$ by SSS ~.
11. Yes; $\angle G \cong \angle E$ and $\frac{UG}{FE} = \frac{AG}{BE} = \frac{4}{5}$, so $\triangle GUA \sim \triangle EFB$ by SAS ~.
12. Answers may vary. Sample: Measure your shadow and the flagpole's shadow. Use the proportion $\frac{\text{your shadow}}{\text{flagpole's shadow}} = \frac{\text{your height}}{\text{flagpole's height}}$
13. Method A is not correct because the ratio, $\frac{4}{8}$, does not use corresp. sides.
14. **a.** Answers may vary. Sample: Both use two pairs of corresp. sides and the angles included by those sides, but SAS ~ uses pairs of equal ratios, while SAS ≅ uses pairs of ≅ sides.
    b. Both involve all three sides of a triangle, but corresp. sides are proportional for SSS ~ and ≅ for SSS ≅.

▼ STUDENT PAGES 365–366

Lesson Check

Do you know HOW?

Are the triangles similar? If yes, write a similarity statement and explain how you know they are similar.

9.

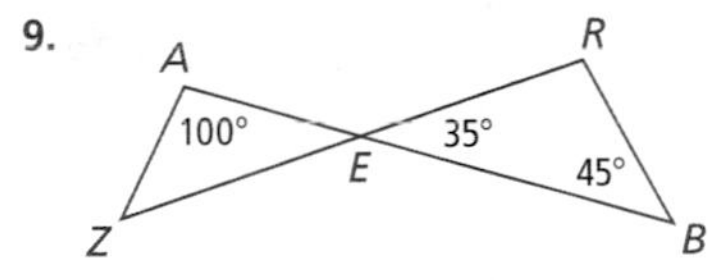

10.

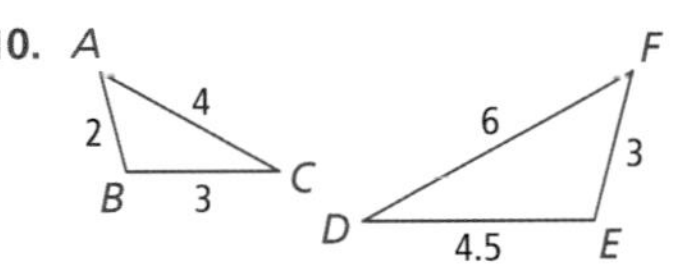

11.

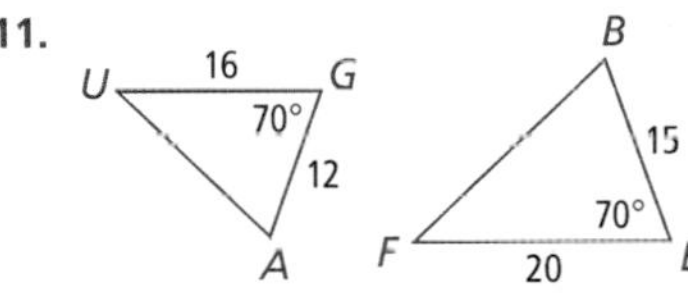

Do you UNDERSTAND? MATHEMATICAL PRACTICES

12. **Vocabulary** How could you use indirect measurement to find the height of the flagpole at your school?
13. **Error Analysis** Which solution for the value of x in the figure at the right is *not* correct? Explain.

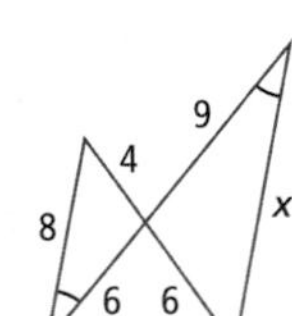

A.

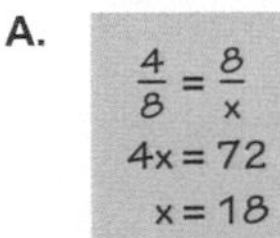

B.

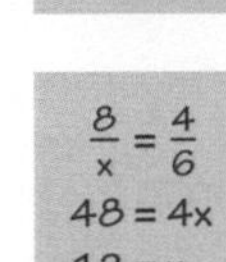

14. **a. Compare and Contrast** How are the SAS Similarity Theorem and the SAS Congruence Postulate alike? How are they different?
    b. How are the SSS Similarity Theorem and the SSS Congruence Postulate alike? How are they different?

Practice

More Practice and Problem-Solving Exercises

ASSIGNMENT GUIDE

The assignments below are for the More Practice and Problem-Solving Exercises. You may also want to assign the A-Level Practice Exercises for homework if these are not used in class.

Average: 15–29
Advanced: 15–33

Mathematical Practices The exercises listed focus on the Standards for Mathematical Practices listed.

EX. 14, 19: Make Sense of Problems (MP 1)
EX. 26, 28: Construct Arguments (MP 3)
EX. 13: Critique the Reasoning of Others (MP 3)
EX. 20: Model (MP 4)

EXERCISE 20: Use the **Think About a Plan** worksheet in the Online Teacher Resources to further support students' development in becoming independent learners.

HOMEWORK QUICK CHECK

To check students' understanding of key skills and concepts, go over Exercises 15, 19, 20, 24, and 29.

ANSWERS

15. Not ~; $\frac{AB}{DF} = \frac{BC}{EF} = \frac{4}{3}$, $\frac{AC}{FD} = \frac{48}{38} = \frac{24}{19}$

16. $\triangle LMN \sim \triangle SMT$ by AA ~

17. $\frac{NK}{NP} = \frac{GD}{GK}$ and $\angle N \cong \angle G$, so $\triangle NKP \sim \triangle GDK$ by SAS ~.

18. a. No; the ratios of the sides that form the vertex ∠s are =, but the vertex ∠s may not be ≅.

b. Yes; sample explanation: An isosc. rt. triangle has two ∠s 45°, so any two isosc. rt. triangles are ~ by AA~.

19. 15 ft

20. 180 ft

21. 6

22. 12

23. 4

24. In $\triangle PQR$ and $\triangle STV$, $\angle Q \cong \angle T$ because ⊥ lines form rt. ∠s, which are ≅. The sides that contain the ∠s are proportional (given). So $\triangle PQR \sim \triangle STV$ by SAS~, and $\angle KRV \cong \angle KVR$ because corresp. ∠s of ~ △s are ≅. Thus $\triangle VKR$ is isosc. by the Converse of Isosc. △ Thm.

25. $\angle A \cong \angle DCG$ and $\angle ACB \cong \angle G$ (If lines are ∥ then corresp. ∠s are ≅.). So $\triangle ABC \sim \triangle CDG$ by AA~. Then $\frac{AB}{CD} = \frac{AC}{CG}$ because corresp. sides of ~ △s are proportional, and $AB \cdot CG = CD \cdot AC$ by the Cross Products Prop.

26. Yes; the two ∥ lines and the two sides determine two pairs of ≅ corr. ∠s, so two triangles are ~ by AA~.

▼ STUDENT PAGE 367

More Practice and Problem-Solving Exercises

B Apply

Can you conclude that the triangles are similar? If so, state the postulate or theorem you used and write a similarity statement. If not, explain.

15.

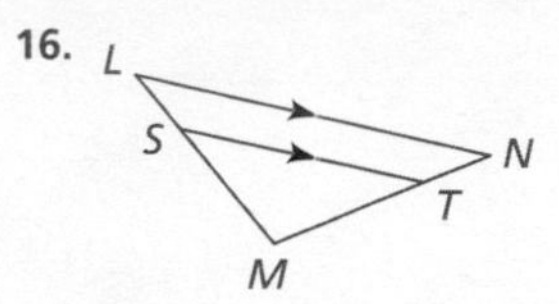

16.

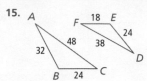

17.

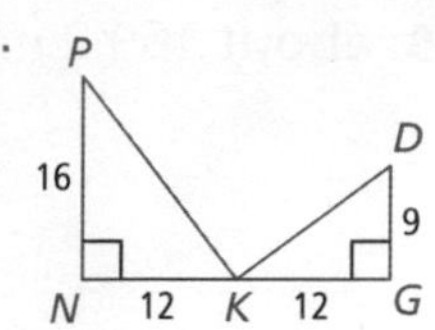

18. a. Are two isosceles triangles always similar? Explain.
b. Are two right isosceles triangles always similar? Explain.

19. Think About a Plan On a sunny day, a classmate uses indirect measurement to find the height of a building. The building's shadow is 12 ft long and your classmate's shadow is 4 ft long. If your classmate is 5 ft tall, what is the height of the building?

- Can you draw and label a diagram to represent the situation?
- What proportion can you use to solve the problem?

20. Indirect Measurement A 2-ft vertical post casts a 16-in. shadow at the same time a nearby cell phone tower casts a 120-ft shadow. How tall is the cell phone tower?

Algebra **For each pair of similar triangles, find the value of *x*.**

21.

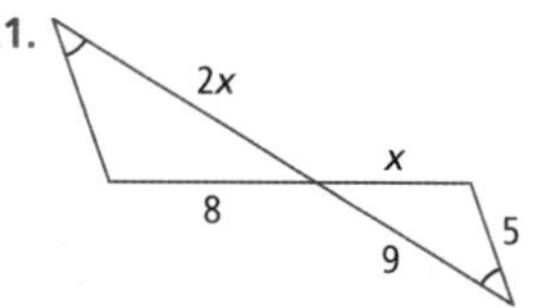

22.

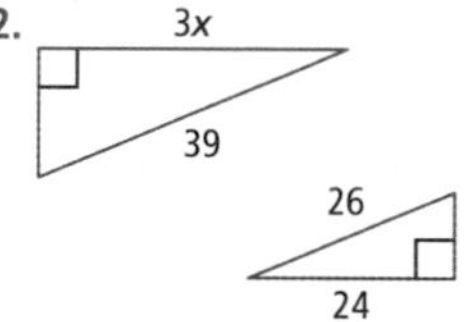

23.

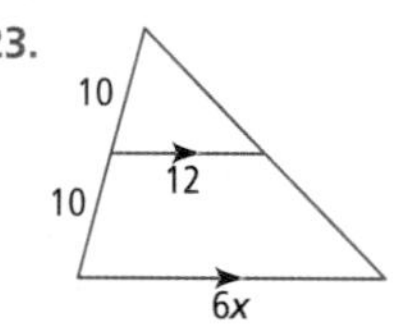

24. Given: $\overline{PQ} \perp \overline{QT}$, $\overline{ST} \perp \overline{TQ}$, $\frac{PQ}{ST} = \frac{QR}{TV}$
Proof
Prove: $\triangle VKR$ is isosceles.

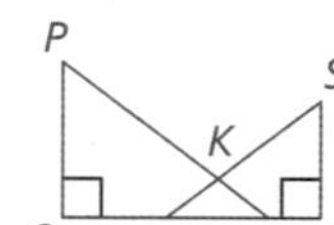

25. Given: $\overline{AB} \parallel \overline{CD}$, $\overline{BC} \parallel \overline{DG}$
Proof
Prove: $AB \cdot CG = CD \cdot AC$

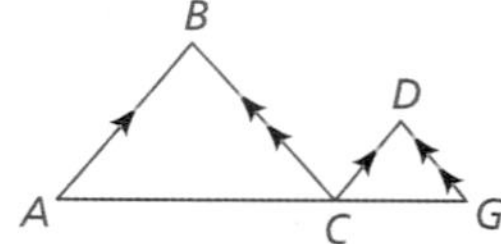

26. Reasoning Does any line that intersects two sides of a triangle and is parallel to the third side of the triangle form two similar triangles? Justify your reasoning.

27.

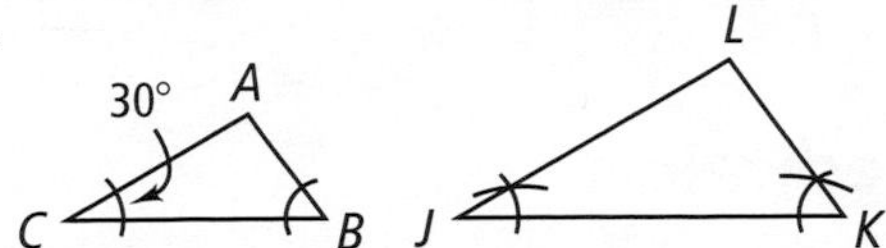

Draw a line segment $\overline{JK}$ of any length. At J, construct an angle ≅ to $\angle C$. At K, construct an angle ≅ to $\angle B$. Extend the sides of the angles till they intersect. Label the intersection point L. $\triangle LKJ \sim \triangle ABC$ by AA~.

28. 4 : 3; sample explanation: Since $\angle P \cong \angle S$ and $\angle PQM \cong \angle STR$, $\triangle PQM \sim \triangle STR$ by AA~. So the ratio $\frac{MQ}{RT} = \frac{PM}{SR}$ = the ratio of corresp. sides in $\triangle PMN$ and $\triangle SRW$ namely, 4 : 3.

29. Use the Distance Formula: $AB = AC = 2\sqrt{5}$ and $BC = 2\sqrt{2}$, while $RS = RT = \sqrt{5}$ and $ST = \sqrt{2}$. $\triangle ABC \sim \triangle RST$ (SSS~) because $\frac{AB}{RS} = \frac{BC}{ST} = \frac{AC}{RT} = 2$.

30. It is given that $\ell_1 \parallel \ell_2$, so $\angle BAC \cong \angle EDF$ because if lines are ∥, then corresponding ∡ are ≅. The given ⊥ lines mean $\angle ACB \cong \angle DFE$ because ⊥ lines form rt. ∡, which are ≅. So $\triangle ABC \sim \triangle DEF$ by AA~, and $\frac{BC}{EF} = \frac{AC}{DF}$ because corresp. sides of ~ ⊿ are proportional. Then Prop. of Proportions (2) lets us conclude that $\frac{BC}{AC} = \frac{EF}{DF}$.

31. $\frac{BC}{AC} = \frac{EF}{DF}$, $\overline{EF} \perp \overline{AF}$, $\overline{BC} \perp \overline{AF}$ (Given); $\angle ACB$ and $\angle DFE$ are rt. ∡. (Def. of ⊥); $\angle ACB \cong \angle DFE$ (All rt. ∡ are ≅.); $\triangle ABC \sim \triangle DEF$ (SAS ~); $\angle BAC \cong \angle EDF$ (Def. of similar); $\ell_1 \parallel \ell_2$ (If corr. ∡ are ≅, then lines are ∥.)

32.

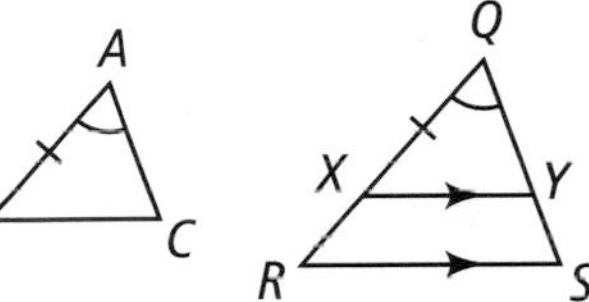

Choose point X on $\overline{QR}$ so that $QX = AB$. Then draw $\overline{XY} \parallel \overline{RS}$ (Through a point not on a line, there is exactly one line ∥ to the given line.). $\angle A \cong \angle Q$ (Given) and $\angle QXY \cong \angle R$ (If two lines are ∥, then corresp. ∡ are ≅.), so $\triangle QXY \sim \triangle QRS$ by AA~. Therefore, $\frac{QX}{QR} = \frac{XY}{RS} = \frac{QY}{QS}$ because corresp. sides of ~ ⊿ are proportional. Since $QX = AB$, substitute QX for AB in the given proportion $\frac{AB}{QR} = \frac{AC}{QS}$ to get $\frac{QX}{QR} = \frac{AC}{QS}$. Therefore, $\frac{QX}{QR} = \frac{QY}{QS} = \frac{AC}{QS}$, and $QY = AC$. So $\triangle ABC \cong \triangle QXY$ by SAS. $\angle B \cong \angle QXY$ (Corresp. parts of ≅ ⊿ are ≅.) and $\angle B \cong \angle R$ by the Transitive Prop. of ≅. Therefore, $\triangle ABC \sim \triangle QRS$ by AA~.

27. Constructions Draw any $\triangle ABC$ with $m\angle C = 30$. Use a straightedge and compass to construct $\triangle LKJ$ so that $\triangle LKJ \sim \triangle ABC$.

28. Reasoning In the diagram at the right, $\triangle PMN \sim \triangle SRW$. $\overline{MQ}$ and $\overline{RT}$ are altitudes. The scale factor of $\triangle PMN$ to $\triangle SRW$ is 4 : 3. What is the ratio of $\overline{MQ}$ to $\overline{RT}$? Explain how you know.

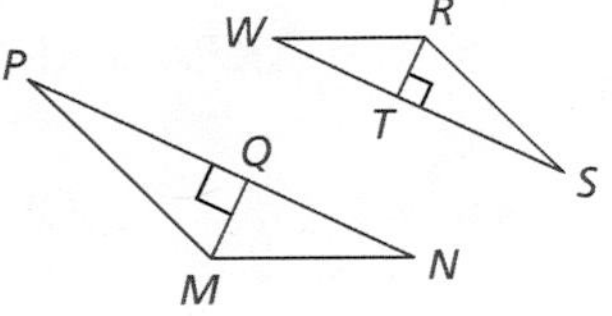

29. Coordinate Geometry $\triangle ABC$ has vertices $A(0, 0)$, $B(2, 4)$, and $C(4, 2)$. $\triangle RST$ has vertices $R(0, 3)$, $S(-1, 5)$, and $T(-2, 4)$. Prove that $\triangle ABC \sim \triangle RST$. (*Hint:* Graph $\triangle ABC$ and $\triangle RST$ in the coordinate plane.)

Challenge

30. Write a proof of the following: Any two nonvertical parallel lines have equal slopes.

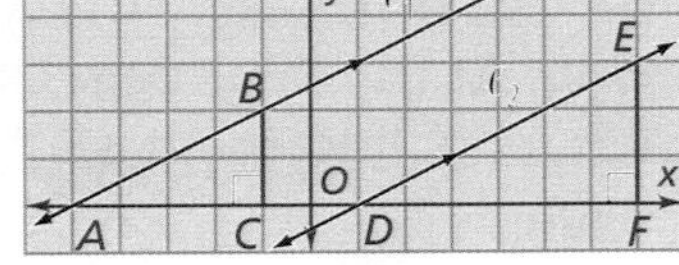

Given: Nonvertical lines ℓ_1 and ℓ_2, $\ell_1 \parallel \ell_2$, $\overline{EF}$ and $\overline{BC}$ are ⊥ to the x-axis

Prove: $\frac{BC}{AC} = \frac{EF}{DF}$

31. Use the diagram in Exercise 30. Prove: Any two nonvertical lines with equal slopes are parallel.

32. Prove the Side-Angle-Side Similarity Theorem (Theorem 60).

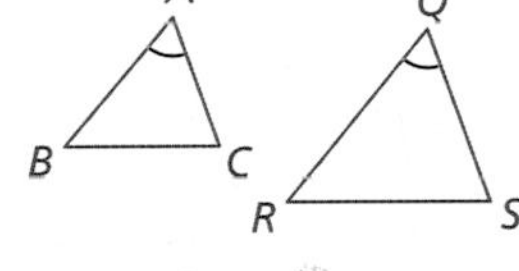

Given: $\frac{AB}{QR} = \frac{AC}{QS}$, $\angle A \cong \angle Q$

Prove: $\triangle ABC \sim \triangle QRS$

33. Proof Prove the Side-Side-Side Similarity Theorem (Theorem 61).

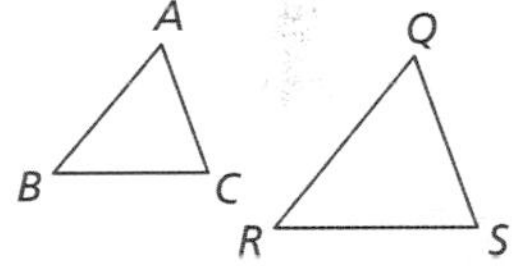

Given: $\frac{AB}{QR} = \frac{AC}{QS} = \frac{BC}{RS}$

Prove: $\triangle ABC \sim \triangle QRS$

33.

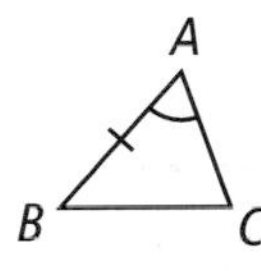

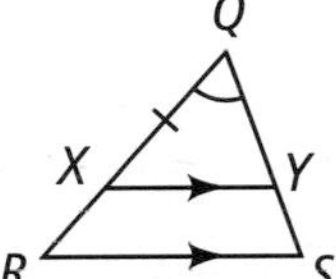

Choose point X on $\overline{QR}$ so that $QX = AB$. Then draw $\overline{XY} \parallel \overline{RS}$ (Through a point not on a line, there is exactly one line ∥ to the given line.). $\angle QYX \cong \angle S$ and $\angle QXY \cong \angle R$ (If lines are ∥, then corresp. ∡ are ≅.), so $\triangle QXY \sim \triangle QRS$ by AA~. Therefore, $\frac{QX}{QR} = \frac{XY}{RS} = \frac{QY}{QS}$ because corresp. sides of ~ ⊿ are proportional. Since $QX = AB$, substitute QX for AB in the given proportion $\frac{AB}{QR} = \frac{AC}{QS} = \frac{BC}{RS}$ to get $\frac{QX}{QR} = \frac{AC}{QS} = \frac{BC}{RS}$. Therefore, $\frac{AC}{QS} = \frac{QY}{QS}$ and $\frac{BC}{RS} = \frac{XY}{RS}$. So $BC = XY$ and $AC = QY$. Then $\triangle ABC \cong QXY$ by SSS ≅. $\angle B \cong \angle QXY$ and $\angle C \cong \angle QYX$ (Corresp. parts of ≅ ⊿ are ≅.). Since $\overline{XY} \parallel \overline{RS}$, $\angle QXY \cong \angle R$ and $\angle QYX \cong \angle S$ (If lines are ∥, then corresp. ∡ are ≅.). $\angle B \cong \angle R$ and $\angle C \cong \angle S$ (Transitive Prop.) Therefore, $\triangle ABC \sim \triangle QRS$ by AA~.

5 Assess and Remediate

Lesson Quiz

1. Are △*KRA* and △*FLN* similar? How do you know?

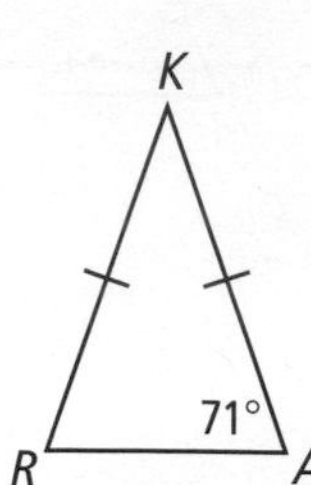

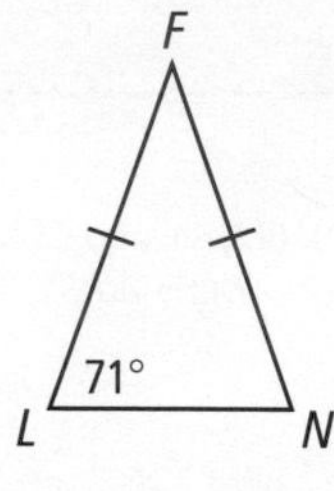

2. Do you UNDERSTAND? A flagpole casts a shadow 18 ft long. At the same time, Rachael casts a shadow that is 4 ft long. If Rachael is 5 ft tall, what is the height of the flagpole?

3. Are the triangles similar? If so, what is the similarity statement?

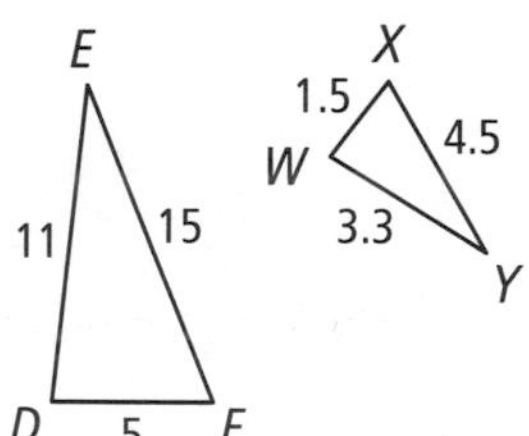

ANSWERS TO LESSON QUIZ

1. yes; by the AA Similarity Postulate

2. 22 ft 6 in.

3. yes; △*DEF* ~ △*WYX*

Prescription for Remediation

Use the student work on the Lesson Quiz to prescribe a differentiated assignment.

Points	Differentiated Remediation
0–1	Intervention
2	On-level
3	Extension

Online Assessment

Assign the Lesson Quiz in Success Tracker on **pearsonsuccessnet.com**. Success Tracker will automatically score the quiz and assign appropriate intervention or enrichment to each student based on the results. The compiled data appear in three different reports for instant analysis of whole class and individual student performance.

Differentiated Remediation

Intervention

- **RETEACHING** (2 pages) Provides reteaching and practice exercises for the key lesson concepts. Use with struggling students or absent students.
- **ENGLISH LANGUAGE LEARNER SUPPORT** Helps students develop and reinforce mathematical vocabulary and key concepts.

On-Level

- **PRACTICE** (2 pages) Provides extra practice for each lesson. For simpler practice exercises, use the Form K Practice pages found in the Online Teacher Resources.
- **THINK ABOUT A PLAN** Helps students develop specific problem-solving skills and strategies by providing scaffolded guiding questions.
- **STANDARDIZED TEST PREP** Focuses on all major exercises, all major question types, and helps students prepare for the high-stakes assessments.

Extension

- **ENRICHMENT** Provides students with interesting problems and activities that extend the concepts of the lesson.
- **ACTIVITIES, GAMES, AND PUZZLES** Worksheets that can be used for concept development, enrichment, and for fun!

Similarity in Right Triangles

Common Core State Standards
G.SRT.5 Use . . . similarity criteria for triangles to solve problems and to prove relationships in geometric figures. **Also G.GPE.5, G.GPE.6**

Preparing to Teach

BIG ideas Reasoning and Proof
Visualization
Proportionality

ESSENTIAL UNDERSTANDING

Drawing in the altitude to the hypotenuse of a right triangle forms three pairs of similar right triangles. The altitude to the hypotenuse of a right triangle, the segments formed by the altitude, and the sides of the right triangle have lengths that are related using geometric means.

Math Background

Similar triangles are created when the altitude of a right triangle is drawn to the hypotenuse. The segments created in and existing in these triangles are related to the concept of geometric mean. A geometric mean is an average of factors that contribute to a specific product. It is used throughout geometry and mathematics to average quantities that are multiplied together. The relationship between the segments in right triangles with an altitude can be used for indirect measurement as well.

ELL Support

FOCUS ON COMMUNICATION Have a volunteer draw a right triangle on the board. Point to a leg of the triangle. Ask: What is the name of this side?

Point to the hypotenuse and repeat the question. Draw the altitude perpendicular to the hypotenuse and touching the corner between the two legs. Ask: What is the name of this line? [the altitude to the hypotenuse] Ask volunteers to point to the two right triangles that the altitude forms.

Have small groups draw a right triangle like the one on the board. Say: Label your triangle, then list the similar triangles. Pair groups together. Have one group describe its triangle and the other group draw a copy based on the description.

Lesson Vocabulary

- geometric mean

Mathematical Practices

MAKE SENSE OF PROBLEMS AND PERSEVERE IN SOLVING THEM. Students will use the special case of drawing an altitude in right triangles to find similar triangles. They will also define and make explicit use of the term "geometric mean" based on this altitude.

1 Interactive Learning

Solve It!

PURPOSE To show that the triangles created by drawing altitudes in a right triangle are similar

PROCESS Students may align the right angles of each triangle to see which angles are corresponding, may redraw the triangles so they are oriented the same way, or use properties of complementary angles to show that the acute angles are congruent.

Q What is the relationship of the angles that are produced by cutting apart the corners of the paper? **[They are complementary.]**

Q How are the opposite sides of the paper related? **[They are parallel.]**

Q What type of line is formed by the first cut in relationship to the parallel lines? **[It is a transversal.]**

ANSWER

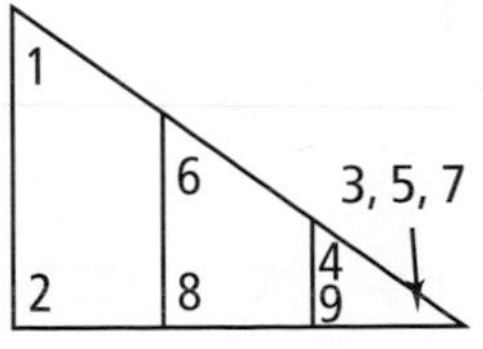

1
6
3, 5, 7
2
8
4
9

▼ DIGITAL (STUDENT WORK SPACE PAGE 369)

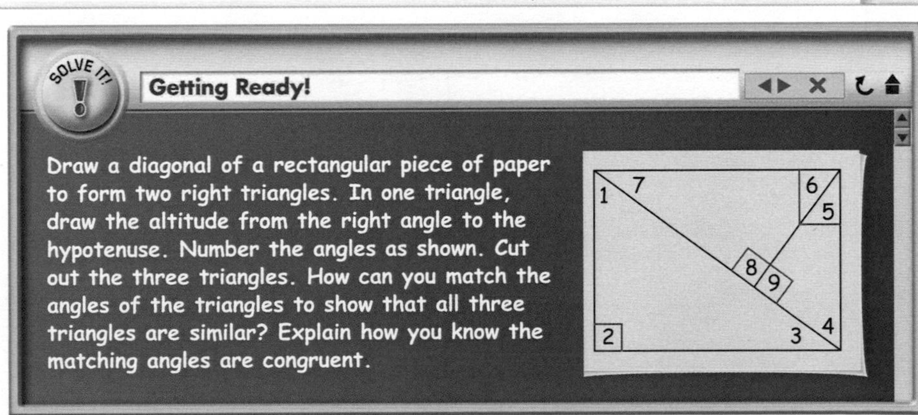

SOLVE IT!
Getting Ready!
Draw a diagonal of a rectangular piece of paper to form two right triangles. In one triangle, draw the altitude from the right angle to the hypotenuse. Number the angles as shown. Cut out the three triangles. How can you match the angles of the triangles to show that all three triangles are similar? Explain how you know the matching angles are congruent.
1
7
6
5
8
9
2
3
4

$\angle 2 \cong \angle 8 \cong \angle 9$ because all rt. △ are congruent. In the original diagram, $\angle 1 \cong \angle 4$ and $\angle 3 \cong \angle 7$ because they are alt. int. △of ∥ lines. By the Triangle-Angle-Sum Thm. you can show that $\angle 1 \cong \angle 6$ and $\angle 3 \cong \angle 5$.

CONNECT THE MATH Ask students to identify the type of line that was drawn to separate the upper right-hand triangle into two similar triangles. Review the definition of an altitude. They will be using properties of this line to show that triangles are similar.

Guided Instruction

Problem 1 Identifying Similar Triangles

Take Note

Have students use the congruence statements to write angle-congruence and side-proportionality statements. Be sure that students understand how each triangle is related to the other triangles.

It may help students to reorganize the statement to address one set of triangles at a time. Begin by having students draw each triangle separately with the right angle pointing upward. They should first show that $\triangle ACD \sim \triangle ABC$ by finding two angles in those triangles congruent and proving the triangles similar by AA~. Next, they can show that $\triangle CBD \sim \triangle ABC$. Finally, have students show $\triangle ACD \sim \triangle CBD$ by AA~. Note that in the proof $\angle B$ is only shown as $\angle B$. As students examine their separated triangles, make sure they know $\angle CBA$ and $\angle CBD$ are the same angle.

Problem 1

Q Which angles are congruent based on the diagram? Why? **[$\angle XYZ$, $\angle XWY$, and $\angle YWZ$; all three are right angles.]**

Q According to the Reflexive Property, which pairs of angles are congruent? **[$\angle Z \cong \angle Z$, $\angle X \cong \angle X$]**

Q How do you know the order in which to list the vertices? **[When there is a correspondence between figures, corresponding vertices should be listed in the same order.]**

▼ STUDENT PAGES 369–370

In the Solve It, you looked at three similar right triangles. In this lesson, you will learn new ways to think about the proportions that come from these similar triangles. You began with three separate, nonoverlapping triangles in the Solve It. Now you will see the two smaller right triangles fitting side by side to form the largest right triangle.

Essential Understanding When you draw the *altitude to the hypotenuse* of a right triangle, you form three pairs of similar right triangles.

take note

Theorem 62

Theorem	If . . .	Then . . .
The altitude to the hypotenuse of a right triangle divides the triangle into two triangles that are similar to the original triangle and to each other.	$\triangle ABC$ is a right triangle with right $\angle ACB$, and $\overline{CD}$ is the altitude to the hypotenuse	$\triangle ABC \sim \triangle ACD$ $\triangle ABC \sim \triangle CBD$ $\triangle ACD \sim \triangle CBD$

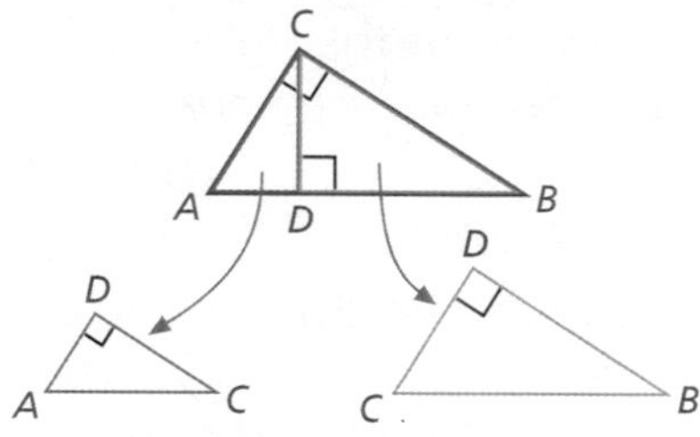

Proof Proof of Theorem 62

Given: Right $\triangle ABC$ with right $\angle ACB$ and altitude $\overline{CD}$

Prove: $\triangle ACD \sim \triangle ABC$, $\triangle CBD \sim \triangle ABC$, $\triangle ACD \sim \triangle CBD$

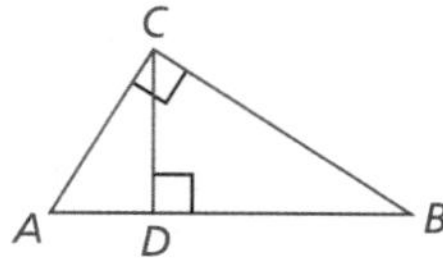

Statements	Reasons
1) $\angle ACB$ is a right angle.	1) Given
2) $\overline{CD}$ is an altitude.	2) Given
3) $\overline{CD} \perp \overline{AB}$	3) Definition of altitude
4) $\angle ADC$ and $\angle CDB$ are right angles.	4) Definition of $\perp$
5) $\angle ADC \cong \angle ACB$, $\angle CDB \cong \angle ACB$	5) All right ∠s are ≅.
6) $\angle A \cong \angle A$, $\angle B \cong \angle B$	6) Reflexive Property of ≅
7) $\triangle ACD \sim \triangle ABC$, $\triangle CBD \sim \triangle ABC$	7) AA ~ Postulate
8) $\angle ACD \cong \angle B$	8) Corresponding ∠s of ~ △s are ≅.
9) $\angle ADC \cong \angle CDB$	9) All right ∠s are ≅.
10) $\triangle ACD \sim \triangle CBD$	10) AA ~ Postulate

▼ DIGITAL

Problem 1 Identifying Similar Triangles

What similarity statement can you write relating the three triangles in the diagram?

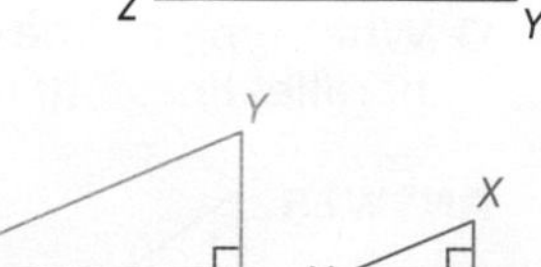

$\overline{YW}$ is the altitude to the hypotenuse of right $\triangle XYZ$, so you can use Theorem 7-3. There are three similar triangles.

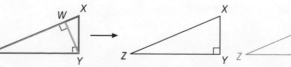

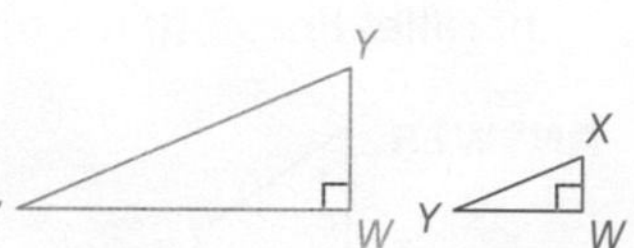

$\triangle XYZ \sim \triangle YWZ \sim \triangle XWY$

Got It?
Remind students to draw each triangle separately with the same orientation before they attempt to write a similarity statement or answer part (b).

ANSWERS

Got It? a. $\triangle PRQ \sim \triangle SPQ \sim \triangle SRP$ **b.** $\frac{SR}{SP} = \frac{SP}{SQ}, \frac{SR}{SP} = \frac{PR}{QP}$

Practice

1. Answers may vary. Sample: $\triangle KJL \sim \triangle NJK \sim \triangle NKL$
2. Answers may vary. Sample: $\triangle QPR \sim \triangle SPQ \sim \triangle SQR$

▼ STUDENT PAGES 370–371

Got It? a. What similarity statement can you write relating the three triangles in the diagram?

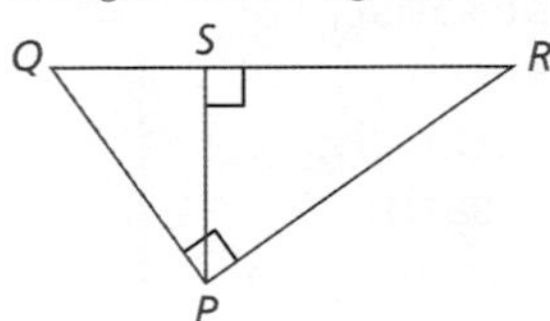

b. **Reasoning** From the similarity statement in part (a), write two different proportions using the ratio $\frac{SR}{SP}$.

Plan
What will help you see the corresponding vertices?

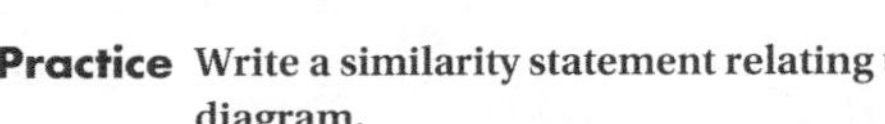

Practice Write a similarity statement relating the three triangles in each diagram.

1.
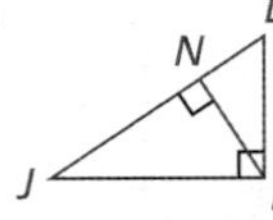

2.
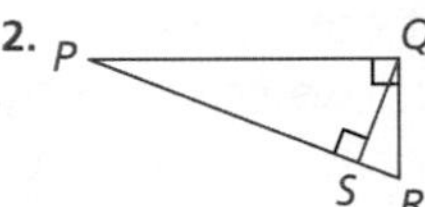

Problem 2 Finding the Geometric Mean

Q How would you state the definition of geometric mean in your own words? **[Answers will vary. Sample: The geometric mean of two numbers has the same ratio to the first number that the second number has to the mean.]**

Q How do you find the geometric mean of two numbers? **[Set up a proportion where the means are unknown and the given numbers are the extremes.]**

Got It SYNTHESIZING
Remind students to set up a proportion with the unknowns in the mean positions. Prompt students to extend the definition of geometric mean to include the geometric mean of three numbers. **[The geometric mean of three numbers is the cube root of the product of the numbers.]**

ANSWERS

Got It? $6\sqrt{2}$

Practice

3. 25
4. 14

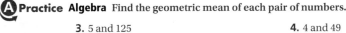

▼ STUDENT PAGE 371

Proportions in which the means are equal occur frequently in geometry. For any two positive numbers a and b, the **geometric mean** of a and b is the positive number x such that $\frac{a}{x} = \frac{x}{b}$.

▼ DIGITAL

Problem 2 Finding the Geometric Mean

Multiple Choice What is the geometric mean of 6 and 15?

Ⓐ 90 Ⓑ $3\sqrt{10}$ Ⓒ $9\sqrt{10}$ Ⓓ 30

$\frac{6}{x} = \frac{x}{15}$	Definition of geometric mean
$x^2 = 90$	Cross Products Property
$x = \sqrt{90}$	Take the positive square root of each side.
$x = 3\sqrt{10}$	Write in simplest radical form.

The geometric mean of 6 and 15 is $3\sqrt{10}$. The correct answer is B.

▼ STUDENT PAGE 371

Got It? What is the geometric mean of 4 and 18?

Plan
How do you use the definition of *geometric mean*?

Practice **Algebra** Find the geometric mean of each pair of numbers.

3. 5 and 125
4. 4 and 49

Problem 3 Using the Corollaries

Take Note

Corollary 1 to Theorem 62

Ask students to find a set of integers that satisfy Corollary 1 to Theorem 62. Have them sketch the triangle and label each segment accordingly. Then they should show that the numbers satisfy Corollary 1. Students could also use the corollary to find the numbers by finding equivalent ratios.

Take Note

Corollary 2 to Theorem 62

Have students compare and contrast the corollaries to Theorem 62. The first corollary relates the segments of the hypotenuse created by the altitude. The second corollary relates the entire hypotenuse to the length of a leg and the segment of the hypotenuse adjacent to that leg. Also, have students read the proportions using analogy language: "*AB* is to *AC* as *AC* is to *AD*."

In part (b) of the Got it for Problem 1, you used a pair of similar triangles to write a proportion with a geometric mean.

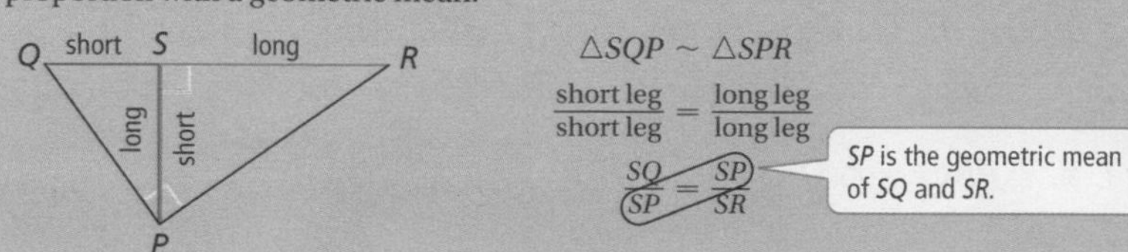

Q short S long R
long
short
P
△SQP ~ △SPR
short leg / short leg = long leg / long leg
SQ / SP = SP / SR
SP is the geometric mean of SQ and SR.

This illustrates the first of two important corollaries of Theorem 62.

Corollary 1 to Theorem 62

Corollary	If . . .	Then . . .
The length of the altitude to the hypotenuse of a right triangle is the geometric mean of the lengths of the segments of the hypotenuse.	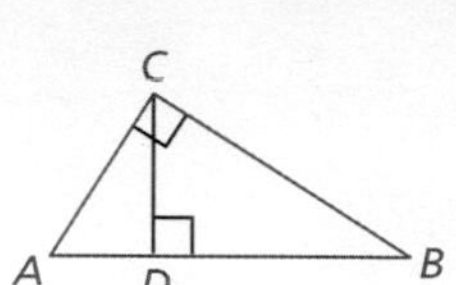	$\frac{AD}{CD} = \frac{CD}{DB}$

Example

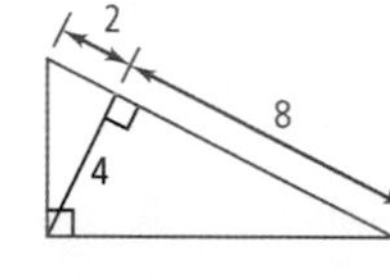

Segments of hypotenuse → $\frac{2}{4} = \frac{4}{8}$ ← Altitude to hypotenuse

You will prove Corollary 1 in Exercise 34.

Corollary 2 to Theorem 62

Corollary	If . . .	Then . . .
The altitude to the hypotenuse of a right triangle separates the hypotenuse so that the length of each leg of the triangle is the geometric mean of the length of the hypotenuse and the length of the segment of the hypotenuse adjacent to the leg.	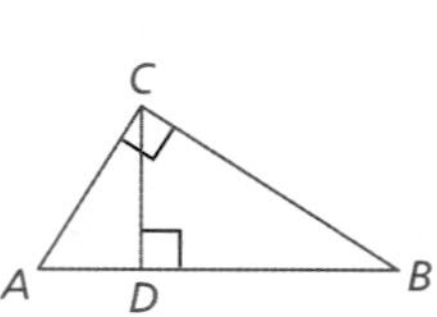	$\frac{AB}{AC} = \frac{AC}{AD}$ $\frac{AB}{CB} = \frac{CB}{DB}$

Example

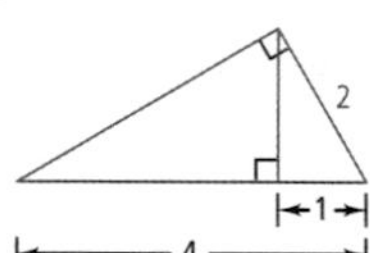

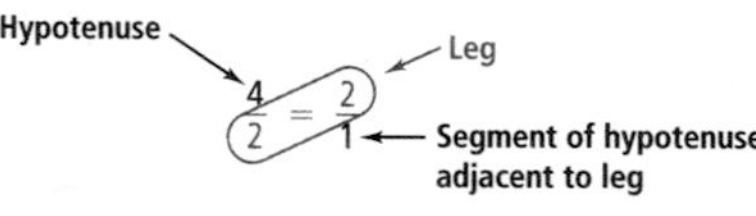

You will prove Corollary 2 in Exercise 35.

The corollaries to Theorem 62 give you ways to write proportions using lengths in right triangles without thinking through the similar triangles. To help remember these corollaries, consider the diagram and these properties.

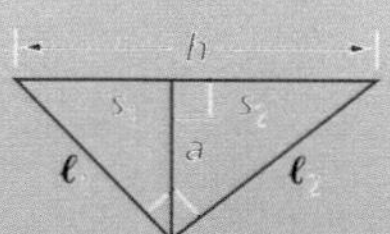

Corollary 1

$\frac{s_1}{a} = \frac{a}{s_2}$

Corollary 2

$\frac{h}{\ell_1} = \frac{\ell_1}{s_1}, \frac{h}{\ell_2} = \frac{\ell_2}{s_2}$

Problem 3

Have students redraw each triangle in the same orientation. This helps them to write proportions based on the similarity of the triangles.

Q Which corollary relates segments in the triangle to the segment marked x? Explain. **[The segment marked as x is a leg of the largest right triangle. Corollary 2 relates this segment to the entire hypotenuse and the adjacent segment of the hypotenuse.]**

Got It?

Q What proportion do you write to solve for x? Which corollary did you use? **[$\frac{4}{x} = \frac{x}{9}$; Corollary 2]**

Q What proportion do you write to solve for y? Which corollary did you use? **[$\frac{4}{y} = \frac{y}{5}$; Corollary 1]**

ANSWERS

Got It? $x = 6$, $y = 2\sqrt{5}$

Practice

5. $x = 6\sqrt{3}$, $y = 3\sqrt{3}$ **6.** $x = 20$, $y = 10\sqrt{5}$

▼ DIGITAL

Problem 3 Using the Corollaries

Algebra What are the values of x and y?

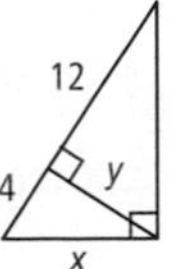

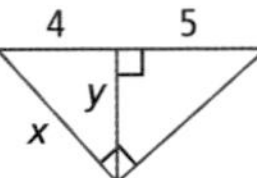
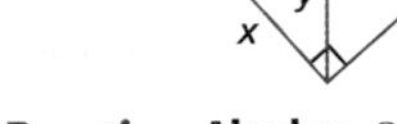

$\frac{4+12}{x} = \frac{x}{4}$	Write a proportion.	$\frac{4}{y} = \frac{y}{12}$	Use Corollary 1.
$x^2 = 64$	Cross Products Property	$y^2 = 48$	
$x = \sqrt{64}$	Take the positive square root.	$y = \sqrt{48}$	
$x = 8$	Simplify.	$y = 4\sqrt{3}$	

▼ STUDENT PAGE 373

Got It? What are the values of x and y?

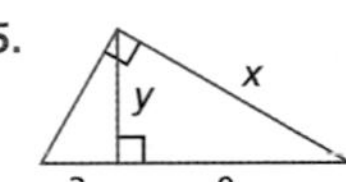

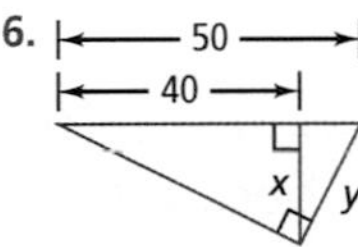

How do you decide which corollary to use?

A Practice Algebra Solve for x and y.

5.

6.

3 Lesson Check

Do you know HOW?

If students have difficulty with Exercises 9–12, then have them redraw the triangles so that they are oriented the same way.

Do you UNDERSTAND?

If students have difficulty with Exercise 14, then have them review Problem 3.

Close

Q How is the geometric mean used in right triangles? **[The altitude of a right triangle to the hypotenuse is the geometric mean of the segments of the hypotenuse it creates. A leg of a right triangle is the geometric mean of the hypotenuse and the segment of the hypotenuse created by the altitude, adjacent to the leg.]**

ANSWERS

7. 6 **8.** $\sqrt{48}$ or $4\sqrt{3}$

9. h **10.** g

11. j, h or h, j **12.** d, d

13. a. $\overline{RT}$

b. $\overline{RP}$, $\overline{PT}$

c. $\overline{PT}$

14. The length 8 is the entire hypotenuse, so the segments of the hypotenuse have lengths 3 and 5. The correct proportion is $\frac{3}{x} = \frac{x}{5}$.

▼ STUDENT PAGES 374–375

Lesson Check

Do you know HOW?

Find the geometric mean of each pair of numbers.

7. 4 and 9 **8.** 4 and 12

Use the figure to complete each proportion.

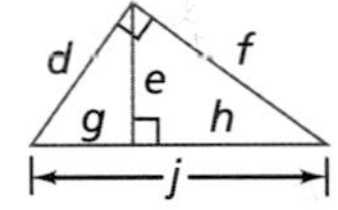

9. $\frac{g}{e} = \frac{e}{■}$

10. $\frac{j}{d} = \frac{d}{■}$

11. $\frac{■}{f} = \frac{f}{■}$

12. $\frac{j}{■} = \frac{■}{g}$

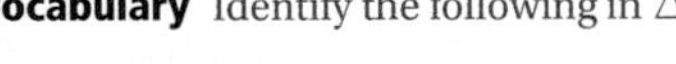
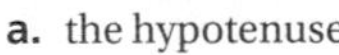

Do you UNDERSTAND?

MATHEMATICAL PRACTICES

13. Vocabulary Identify the following in $\triangle RST$.

a. the hypotenuse

b. the segments of the hypotenuse

c. the segment of the hypotenuse adjacent to leg $\overline{ST}$

14. Error Analysis A classmate wrote an incorrect proportion to find x. Explain and correct the error.

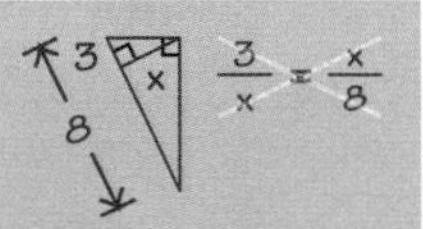

4 Practice

More Practice and Problem-Solving Exercises

ASSIGNMENT GUIDE
The assignments below are for the More Practice and Problem-Solving Exercises. You may also want to assign the A-Level Practice Exercises for homework if these are not used in class.
Average: 15–36
Advanced: 15–39

Mathematical Practices The exercises listed focus on the Standards for Mathematical Practices listed.
EX. 22: Make Sense of Problems (MP 1)
EX. 24: Construct Arguments (MP 3)
EX. 15c: Communicate (MP 3)
EX. 14, 21: Critique the Reasoning of Others (MP 3)
EX. 23: Model (MP 4)

EXERCISE 29: Use the **Think About a Plan** worksheet in the Online Teacher Resources to further support students' development in becoming independent learners.

HOMEWORK QUICK CHECK
To check students' understanding of key skills and concepts, go over Exercises 17, 22, 27, 29, and 33.

ANSWERS

15. a. 4 cm

b.

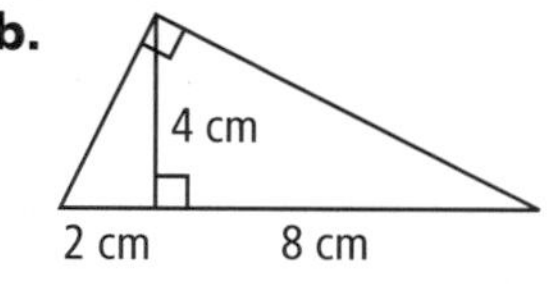

c. Answers may vary. Sample: Draw a 10-cm segment. Construct a $\perp$ of length 4 cm that is 2 cm from one endpoint; connect to form a $\triangle$.

16. $10\sqrt{10}$ **17.** 2.5
18. 2 **19.** 1
20. $\sqrt{14}$
21. Yes; the proportion $\frac{a}{\sqrt{ab}} = \frac{\sqrt{ab}}{b}$ is true by the Cross Products Prop. and satisfies the definition of the geometric mean.
22. $12\sqrt{2}$ units **23.** 8.50 m
24. They are equal. Sample explanation: Let $a =$ length of the altitude and $2x =$ the length of the hypotenuse. Then $\frac{a}{x} = \frac{x}{a}$, so $a = x$.
25. $\ell_1 = \sqrt{2}$, $\ell_2 = \sqrt{2}$, $a = 1$, $s_2 = 1$
26. $\ell_1 = 6\sqrt{2}$, $\ell_2 = 6\sqrt{2}$, $h = 12$, $s_2 = 6$
27. $\ell_1 = 3\sqrt{2}$; $\ell_2 = 3\sqrt{2}$; $a = 3$, $s_1 = 3$
28. $\ell_1 = 2\sqrt{2}$; $\ell_2 = 2\sqrt{2}$; $a = 2$, $s_2 = 2$
29. (2, 6), (6, 6)

▼ STUDENT PAGES 375–376

More Practice and Problem-Solving Exercises

B Apply

15. a. The altitude to the hypotenuse of a right triangle divides the hypotenuse into segments 2 cm and 8 cm long. Find the length of the altitude to the hypotenuse.

b. Use a ruler to make an accurate drawing of the right triangle in part (a).

c. Writing Describe how you drew the triangle in part (b).

Algebra **Find the geometric mean of each pair of numbers.**

16. 1 and 1000 **17.** 5 and 1.25 **18.** $\sqrt{8}$ and $\sqrt{2}$
19. $\frac{1}{2}$ and 2 **20.** $\sqrt{28}$ and $\sqrt{7}$

21. Reasoning A classmate says the following statement is true: The geometric mean of positive numbers a and b is $\sqrt{ab}$. Do you agree? Explain.

22. Think About a Plan The altitude to the hypotenuse of a right triangle divides the hypotenuse into segments with lengths in the ratio 1 : 2. The length of the altitude is 8. How long is the hypotenuse?
- How can you use the given ratio to help you draw a sketch of the triangle?
- How can you use the given ratio to write expressions for the lengths of the segments of the hypotenuse?
- Which corollary to Theorem 62 applies to this situation?

23. Archaeology To estimate the height of a stone figure, Anya holds a small square up to her eyes and walks backward from the figure. She stops when the bottom of the figure aligns with the bottom edge of the square and the top of the figure aligns with the top edge of the square. Her eye level is 1.84 m from the ground. She is 3.50 m from the figure. What is the height of the figure to the nearest hundredth of a meter?

24. Reasoning Suppose the altitude to the hypotenuse of a right triangle bisects the hypotenuse. How does the length of the altitude compare with the lengths of the segments of the hypotenuse? Explain.

The diagram shows the parts of a right triangle with an altitude to the hypotenuse. For the two given measures, find the other four. Use simplest radical form.

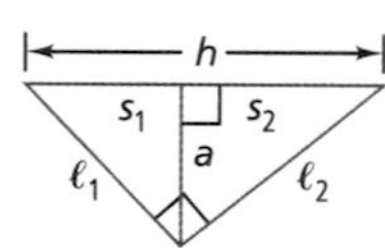

25. $h = 2$, $s_1 = 1$ **26.** $a = 6$, $s_1 = 6$ **27.** $h = 6$, $s_2 = 3$ **28.** $s_1 = 2$, $h = 4$

29. Coordinate Geometry $\overline{CD}$ is the altitude to the hypotenuse of right $\triangle ABC$. The coordinates of A, D, and B are (4, 2), (4, 6), and (4, 7), respectively. Find all possible coordinates of point C.

30. 6 **31.** 4

32. 8 **33.** 10

34. $\triangle ACD \sim \triangle CBD$ by Thm. 62, so $\frac{AD}{CD} = \frac{CD}{BD}$ because corresp. sides of ~ triangles are proportional.

35. $\triangle ABC \sim \triangle ACD$ and $\triangle ABC \sim \triangle CBD$ by Thm. 62. Then $\frac{AB}{AC} = \frac{AC}{AD}$ and $\frac{AB}{CB} = \frac{BC}{BD}$ because corresp. sides of ~ triangles are proportional.

36. Rt. $\triangle ABC$ with alt. to the hypotenuse $\overline{AB}$ (given); $\frac{a}{b} = \frac{b}{c}$ (Corollary 1 to Thm. 62); Slope of $\overleftrightarrow{AC} = \frac{b}{a}$ and slope of $\overleftrightarrow{BC} = -\frac{b}{c}$. Since $\frac{a}{b} = \frac{b}{c}$, $-\frac{a}{b} = -\frac{b}{c}$. Therefore the product of the slopes, $\frac{b}{a} \cdot -\frac{a}{b} = -1$.

37. a.

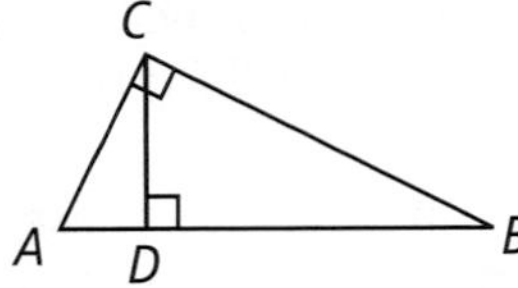

Given: $\overline{AC} \perp \overline{BC}$, $\overline{AB} \perp \overline{CD}$
Prove: $AC \cdot BC = AB \cdot CD$

b. The conjecture is true. You can express the area of $\triangle ABC$ as $\frac{1}{2}(AC)(BC)$ or as $\frac{1}{2}(AB)(CD)$, so $AC \cdot BC = AB \cdot CD$.

38. a. $\frac{x}{a} = \frac{a}{c}$, $\frac{y}{b} = \frac{b}{c}$

b. $c^2 = a^2 + b^2$

c. In a right triangle, the square of the hypotenuse equals the sum of the squares of the legs.

39. Answers may vary. Sample: $\triangle ABC \sim \triangle DEC$ (AA ~ Post.), so $\frac{AC}{DC} = \frac{BC}{EC}$ (Corr. sides of ~ triangles are in prop.). By the Subtraction Property of =, $\frac{AC - DC}{DC} = \frac{BC - EC}{EC}$, or $\frac{AD}{DC} = \frac{BE}{EC}$.

Algebra Find the value of x.

30.

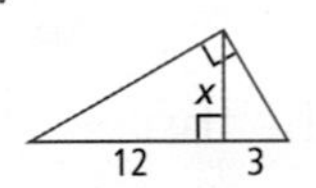

31.

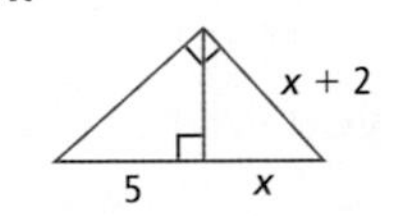

32.

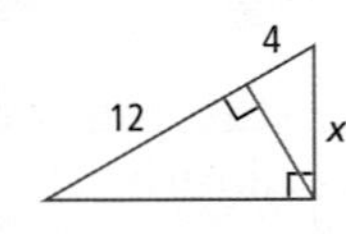

33.

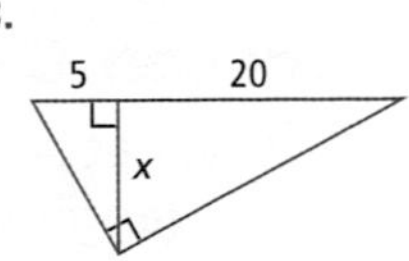

Use the figure at the right for Exercises 34 and 35.

34. Proof Prove Corollary 1 to Theorem 62.

Given: Right $\triangle ABC$ with altitude to the hypotenuse $\overline{CD}$
Prove: $\frac{AD}{CD} = \frac{CD}{DB}$

35. Proof Prove Corollary 2 to Theorem 62.

Given: Right $\triangle ABC$ with altitude to the hypotenuse $\overline{CD}$
Prove: $\frac{AB}{AC} = \frac{AC}{AD}, \frac{AB}{BC} = \frac{BC}{DB}$

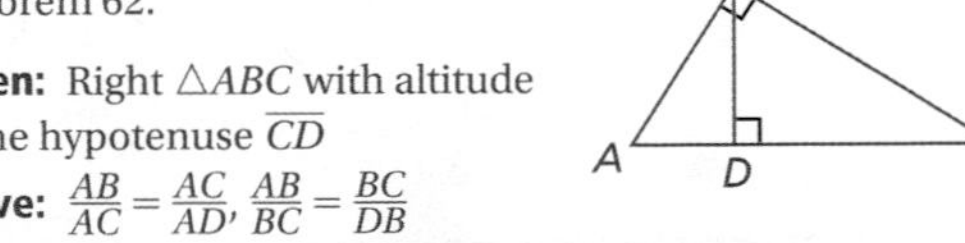

36. Proof **Given:** Right $\triangle ABC$ with altitude $\overline{CD}$ to the hypotenuse $\overline{AB}$.
Prove: The product of the slopes of perpendicular lines, where neither line is vertical is -1.

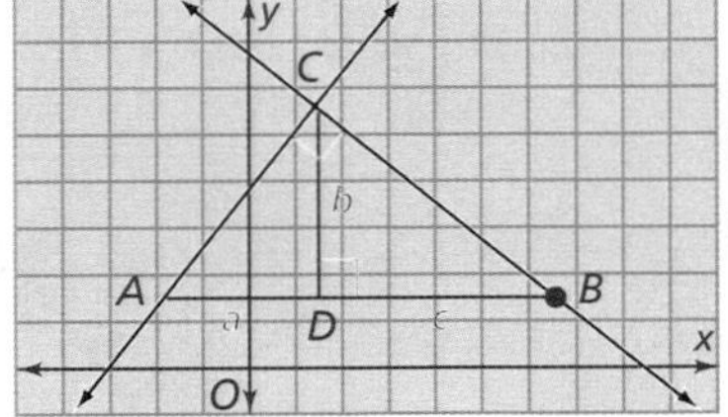

Challenge

37. a. Consider the following conjecture: The product of the lengths of the two legs of a right triangle is equal to the product of the lengths of the hypotenuse and the altitude to the hypotenuse. Draw a figure for the conjecture. Write the *Given* information and what you are to *Prove*.

b. Reasoning Is the conjecture true? Explain.

38. a. In the diagram, $c = x + y$. Use Corollary 2 to Theorem 62 to write two more equations involving a, b, c, x, and y.

b. The equations in part (a) form a system of three equations in five variables. Reduce the system to one equation in three variables by eliminating x and y.

c. State in words what the one resulting equation tells you.

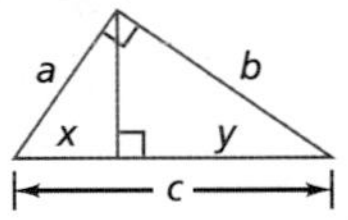

39. Proof **Given:** In right $\triangle ABC$, $\overline{BD} \perp \overline{AC}$, and $\overline{DE} \perp \overline{BC}$.
Prove: $\frac{AD}{DC} = \frac{BE}{EC}$

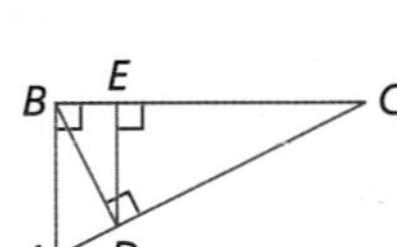

5 Assess and Remediate

Lesson Quiz

1. What similarity statement can you write relating the three triangles in the diagram?

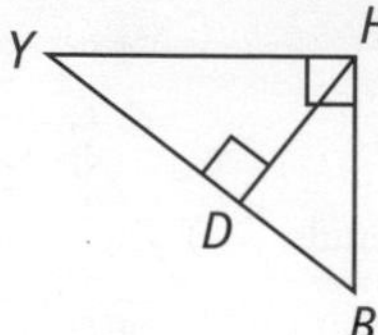

2. What is the geometric mean of 6 and 16?
3. **Do you UNDERSTAND?** What are the values of x and y?

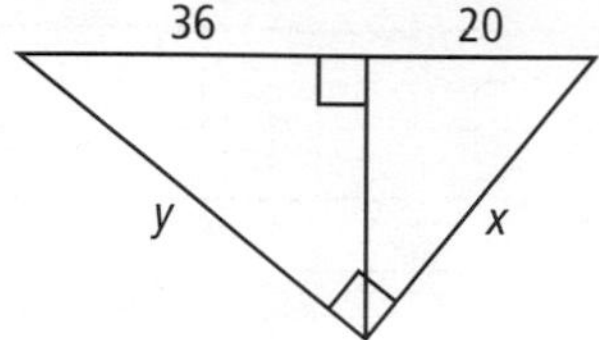

ANSWERS TO LESSON QUIZ

1. $\triangle YHB \sim \triangle YDH \sim \triangle HDB$
2. $4\sqrt{6}$
3. $x = 4\sqrt{70}$, $y = 12\sqrt{14}$

Prescription for Remediation

Use the student work on the Lesson Quiz to prescribe a differentiated assignment.

Points	Differentiated Remediation
0–1	Intervention
2	On-level
3	Extension

Online Assessment

Assign the Lesson Quiz in Success Tracker on **pearsonsuccessnet.com**. Success Tracker will automatically score the quiz and assign appropriate intervention or enrichment to each student based on the results. The compiled data appear in three different reports for instant analysis of whole class and individual student performance.

Differentiated Remediation

Intervention

- **RETEACHING** (2 pages) Provides reteaching and practice exercises for the key lesson concepts. Use with struggling students or absent students.
- **ENGLISH LANGUAGE LEARNER SUPPORT** Helps students develop and reinforce mathematical vocabulary and key concepts.

On-Level

- **PRACTICE** (2 pages) Provides extra practice for each lesson. For simpler practice exercises, use the Form K Practice pages found in the Online Teacher Resources.
- **THINK ABOUT A PLAN** Helps students develop specific problem-solving skills and strategies by providing scaffolded guiding questions.
- **STANDARDIZED TEST PREP** Focuses on all major exercises, all major question types, and helps students prepare for the high-stakes assessments.

Extension

- **ENRICHMENT** Provides students with interesting problems and activities that extend the concepts of the lesson.
- **ACTIVITIES, GAMES, AND PUZZLES** Worksheets that can be used for concept development, enrichment, and for fun!

TECHNOLOGY LAB

Use With Lesson 6-5

Exploring Proportions in Triangles

Common Core State Standards
G.CO.12 Make formal geometric constructions with a variety of tools and methods . . . **Also prepares for G.SRT.4**

Mathematical Practices

This Technology Lab supports students in becoming proficient in using appropriate tools, Mathematical Practice 5.

Guided Instruction

PURPOSE To use geometry software to investigate proportions in triangles

PROCESS Students will
- construct a triangle.
- construct a line parallel to a given side of a triangle.
- construct an angle bisector of an angle of a triangle.

DISCUSS Students make constructions using geometry software that will enable them to explore and make conjectures regarding proportions that exist within triangles.

Activity 1

In this Activity, students draw a triangle and construct a line parallel to one side of the triangle.

Q What do you notice about the ratios of the side lengths? **[They are equal.]**

Q What conjecture can be made about triangles *ABC* and *DBE*? **[They are similar.]**

Q If $BD = 8$, $DA = 12$, and $BE = 10$, what is *EC*? **[15]**

ANSWERS

1. Students' values for *BD*, *DA*, *BE*, and *EC* will vary, but $\frac{BD}{DA} = \frac{BE}{EC}$.
2. For each location of *D*, $\frac{BD}{DA} = \frac{BC}{EC}$.
3. The $\parallel$ line divides the sides into proportional segments.

Activity 2

In this Activity, students construct a triangle and partition it into two similar triangles.

Q What do you notice about the ratio of *AC* to *AE* and the ratio of *AB* to *AD*? **[The ratios are the same.]**

Q Is $\triangle ADE$ similar to $\triangle ABC$? Explain. **[Yes; the sides are proportional and the corresponding angles are congruent.]**

ANSWERS

4. $AD = 5$, $AE \approx 2.8$, $DE \approx 6.1$
5. Sample: You could partition each side of the triangle into thirds, and estimate the coordinates of a point at $\frac{2}{3}$ the length.
6. $B\left(\frac{1}{3}, 1\right)$; $C\left(4\frac{1}{3}, 1\frac{2}{3}\right)$

Exercises

ANSWERS

7. Answers may vary. Sample: If three $\parallel$ lines intersect two transversals, then the segments intercepted on the transversals are proportional.
8. Answers may vary. Sample: If four or more $\parallel$ lines intersect two transversals, then the segments intercepted on the transversals are proportional.

▼ STUDENT PAGES 378–380

Activity 1

MATHEMATICAL PRACTICES

Use geometry software to draw $\triangle ABC$. Construct point *D* on $\overline{AB}$. Next, construct a line through *D* parallel to $\overline{AC}$. Then construct the intersection *E* of the parallel line with $\overline{BC}$.

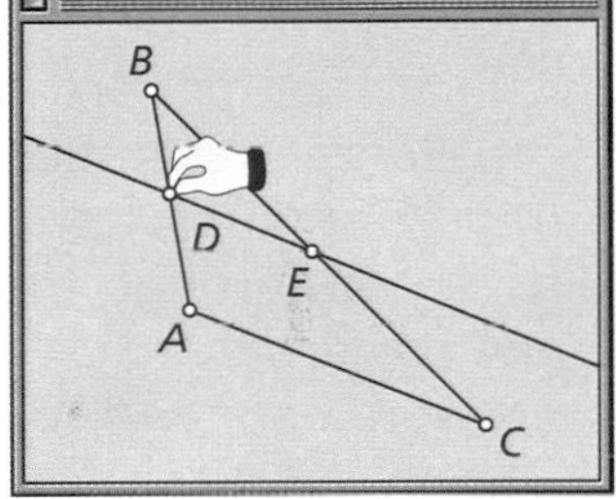

1. Measure $\overline{BD}$, $\overline{DA}$, $\overline{BE}$, and $\overline{EC}$. Calculate the ratios $\frac{BD}{DA}$ and $\frac{BE}{EC}$.
2. Manipulate $\triangle ABC$ and observe $\frac{BD}{DA}$ and $\frac{BE}{EC}$. What do you notice?
3. Make a conjecture about the four segments formed by a line parallel to one side of a triangle intersecting the other two sides.

Activity 2

Use geometry software to construct $\triangle ADE$ with vertices $A(3, 3)$, $D(-1, 0)$, and $E(5, 1)$.

4. Measure $\overline{AD}$, $\overline{AE}$, and $\overline{DE}$.
5. Suppose you draw $\overline{BC}$ so that it partitions $\triangle ADE$ and $AB = \frac{2}{3}AD$ and $CB \parallel DE$. Describe how you could approximate the coordinates of points *B* and *C*.
6. Now use the geometry software to draw $\overline{BC}$ and manipulate the segment to most closely find the points *B* and *C*. What are the coordinates of points *B* and *C*?

Exercises

7. Construct $\overleftrightarrow{AB} \parallel \overleftrightarrow{CD} \parallel \overleftrightarrow{EF}$. Then construct two transversals that intersect all three parallel lines. Measure $\overline{AC}$, $\overline{CE}$, $\overline{BD}$, and $\overline{DF}$. Calculate the ratios $\frac{AC}{CE}$ and $\frac{BD}{DF}$. Manipulate the locations of *A* and *B* and observe $\frac{AC}{CE}$ and $\frac{BD}{DF}$. Make a conjecture about the segments of the transversals formed by the three parallel lines intersecting two transversals.
8. Suppose four or more parallel lines intersect two transversals. Make a conjecture about the segments of the transversals.

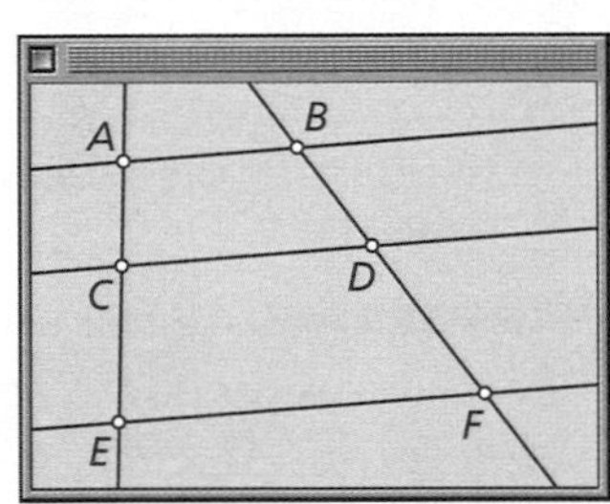

6-5 Proportions in Triangles

Common Core State Standard
G.SRT.4 Prove theorems about triangles . . . a line parallel to one side of a triangle divides the other two proportionally . . .

Preparing to Teach

BIG ideas Reasoning and Proof
Visualization
Proportionality

ESSENTIAL UNDERSTANDING

When two or more parallel lines intersect other lines, proportional segments are formed. The bisector of an angle of a triangle divides the opposite side into two segments with lengths proportional to the sides of the triangle that form the angle.

Math Background

Similar triangles are used to prove the theorems and corollaries presented in this chapter. Without an understanding of proportionality, students will not be able to reason through these theorems. The Side-Splitter Theorem and its corollary lead to solving problems with indirect measurement and splitting figures into similar figures.

ELL Support

USE GRAPHIC ORGANIZERS Ask: What is the central idea of Lessons 6-1 through 6-5? [Similar triangles or Similarity] Have groups of students make a graphic organizer. Say: Use the Essential Understandings from these lessons. Encourage the groups to use examples, illustrations, diagrams, and familiar words in their graphic organizer.

Assign each group one lesson. Have the group make a more detailed graphic organizer for that lesson. Say: Explain the lesson vocabulary words and each of the problems in your organizers. Have each group show their graphic organizers to the class.

Mathematical Practices

CONSTRUCT VIABLE ARGUMENTS AND CRITIQUE THE REASONING OF OTHERS. Students will use their knowledge of similarity in triangles to prove the Triangle-Angle-Bisector Theorem in Exercise 37.

1 Interactive Learning

Solve It!

PURPOSE To use similar triangles to show that parallel lines divide segments proportionally

PROCESS Students may prove that all triangles in the diagram are similar by AA~ or create proportions involving the side lengths of similar triangles to solve for the unknown.

Q Are there any similar triangles in the diagram? How do you know the triangles are similar? **[All the triangles that include the far right vertex and one lamppost as a side are similar.]**

Q How can you use these angles to make a statement about the triangles in the drawing? **[By AA~, all triangles in the diagram are similar.]**

ANSWER ≈ 0.48 in.; answers may vary. Sample: The $\parallel$ lines determine similar $\triangle$s so $\frac{1.25}{1.25 + 0.42} = \frac{1.42}{1.42 + x}$, which simplifies to $\frac{1.25}{1.67} = \frac{1.42}{1.42 + x}$. Then $1.25(1.42 + x) = 2.3714$ (Cross Products Prop.); $1.775 + 1.25x = 2.3714$ (Distr. Prop.); $1.25x = 0.5964$ (Subtr. Prop. of $=$); $x = 0.47712$ (Div. Prop. of Eq.); $x \approx 0.48$.

CONNECT THE MATH Students should recognize that the parallel lines (lampposts in the Solve It) separate one large triangle into smaller similar triangles. By the properties of similar triangles, the lengths of the sides are proportional. This leads to the Side-Splitter Theorem, which states that parallel lines divide segments proportionally.

▼ DIGITAL (STUDENT WORK SPACE PAGE 381)

Getting Ready!

An artist uses perspective to draw parallel lampposts along a city street, as shown in the diagram. What is the value of x? Justify your answer.

2 Guided Instruction

Problem 1 Using the Side-Splitter Theorem

Take Note

Have students draw each triangle separately. Then write proportions that relate the sides of the triangles.

Q How can you use the fact that $\overleftrightarrow{RS} \parallel \overleftrightarrow{XY}$ in the proof? **[Because the lines are parallel, the corresponding angles are congruent.]**

Q What two triangles are in the diagram? **[$\triangle XQY$ and $\triangle RQS$]**

Q How are the two triangles related? **[They are similar.]**

Q If the triangles are similar, what statement can you make about their side lengths? **[They are proportional.]**

Q How can you use the Segment Addition Postulate to write the side lengths? **[$XQ = XR + RQ$ and $YQ = YS + SQ$]**

Problem 1

Q What condition of the Side-Splitter Theorem is marked in the diagram? **[$\overline{KL}$ is parallel to $\overline{PN}$.]**

Q What conclusion can you draw using the Side-Splitter Theorem? **[The segments of the sides of the triangle are proportional.]**

Got It?

For part (b), have students create a diagram of the figure described. Have students substitute numbers for the lengths of segments that satisfy the conditions in the problem. Then, ask students to identify the type of special segment that $\overline{RS}$ represents.

ANSWERS

Got It? a. 8 **b.** $RS = \frac{1}{2}XY$ (Triangle Midsegment Thm.)

Practice

1. 10 **2.** 8

▼ STUDENT PAGES 381–382

The Solve It involves parallel lines cut by two transversals that intersect. In this lesson, you will learn how to use proportions to find lengths of segments formed by parallel lines that intersect two or more transversals.

Essential Understanding When two or more parallel lines intersect other lines, proportional segments are formed.

take note **Theorem 63 Side-Splitter Theorem**

Theorem	If . . .	Then . . .
If a line is parallel to one side of a triangle and intersects the other two sides, then it divides those sides proportionally.	$\overleftrightarrow{RS} \parallel \overleftrightarrow{XY}$  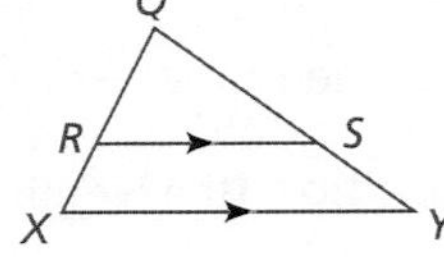	$\frac{XR}{RQ} = \frac{YS}{SQ}$

Proof Proof of Theorem 63: Side-Splitter Theorem

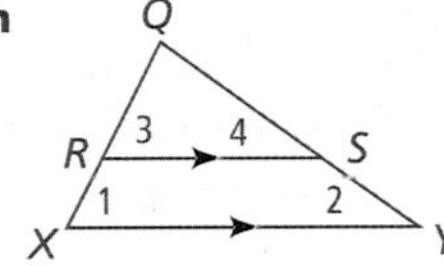

Given: $\triangle QXY$ with $\overleftrightarrow{RS} \parallel \overleftrightarrow{XY}$

Prove: $\frac{XR}{RQ} = \frac{YS}{SQ}$

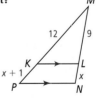

Statements	Reasons
1) $\overleftrightarrow{RS} \parallel \overleftrightarrow{XY}$	1) Given
2) $\angle 1 \cong \angle 3$, $\angle 2 \cong \angle 4$	2) If lines are $\parallel$, then corresponding $\angle$s are $\cong$.
3) $\triangle QXY \sim \triangle QRS$	3) AA ~ Postulate
4) $\frac{XQ}{RQ} = \frac{YQ}{SQ}$	4) Corresponding sides of ~ $\triangle$s are proportional.
5) $XQ = XR + RQ$, $YQ = YS + SQ$	5) Segment Addition Postulate
6) $\frac{XR + RQ}{RQ} = \frac{YS + SQ}{SQ}$	6) Substitution Property
7) $\frac{XR}{RQ} = \frac{YS}{SQ}$	7) Property of Proportions (3)

▼ DIGITAL

Problem 1 Using the Side-Splitter Theorem GRIDDED RESPONSE

What is the value of x in the diagram at the right?

$\frac{PK}{KM} = \frac{NL}{LM}$		Side-Splitter Theorem
$\frac{x+1}{12} = \frac{x}{9}$		Substitute.
$9x + 9 = 12x$		Cross Products Property
$9 = 3x$		Subtract 9x from each side.
$3 = x$		Divide each side by 3.

Grid in the number 3.

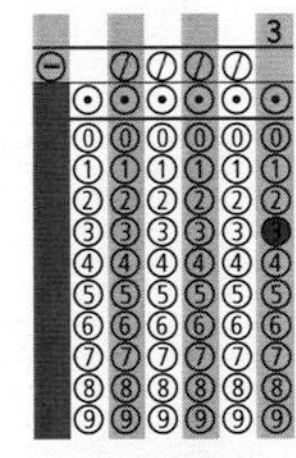

▼ STUDENT PAGES 382–383

Got It? **a.** What is the value of a in the diagram below?

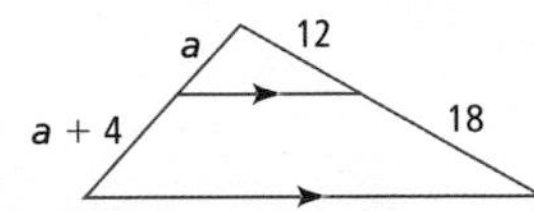

Plan How can you use the parallel lines in the diagram?

b. Reasoning In $\triangle XYZ$, $\overline{RS}$ joins $\overline{XY}$ and $\overline{YZ}$ with R on $\overline{XY}$ and S on $\overline{YZ}$, and $\overline{RS} \parallel \overline{XZ}$. If $\frac{YR}{RX} = \frac{YS}{SZ} = 1$, what must be true about RS? Justify your reasoning.

Practice **Algebra** Solve for x.

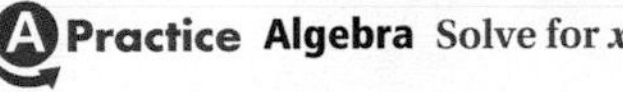

1.

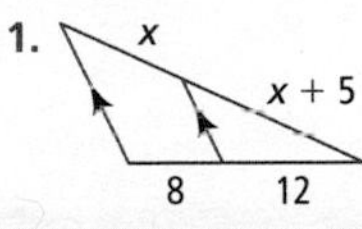

2.

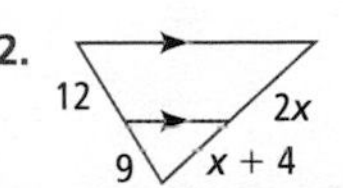

Problem 2 Finding a Length

Take Note

To see how the Corollary to the Side-Splitter Theorem connects to the theorem itself, continue the transversal lines until they intersect. Then students can identify similar triangles in the diagram and prove the corollary.

Problem 2

Q For which proportional sides have both measurements been given? **[Both sides of Site B have been given.]**

Q Which side should be labeled as the unknown? **[the length of Site A along the river]**

Q If the river side of Site B is in the numerator of the first ratio, what measurement should be in the denominator of the second ratio? **[the length of Site A along the road]**

Got It?

Remind students that the numerators of both ratios must be corresponding sides, and so must the two denominators.

ANSWERS

Got It? 5.76 yd

Practice

3. 8.25 mm **4.** $3\frac{5}{13}$

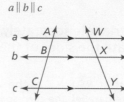

▼ STUDENT PAGE 383

take note

Corollary Corollary to the Side-Splitter Theorem

Corollary	If . . .	Then . . .
If three parallel lines intersect two transversals, then the segments intercepted on the transversals are proportional.	$a \parallel b \parallel c$	$\frac{AB}{BC} = \frac{WX}{XY}$

a A W
b B X
c C Y

You will prove the Corollary to Theorem 63 in Exercise 36.

▼ DIGITAL

Problem 2 Finding a Length

Camping Three campsites are shown in the diagram. What is the length of Site A along the river?

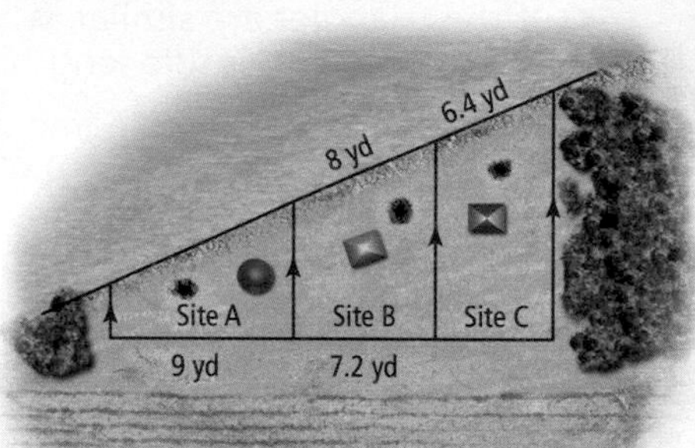

Let x be the length of Site A along the river.

$\frac{x}{8} = \frac{9}{7.2}$ Corollary to the Side-Splitter Theorem

$7.2x = 72$ Cross Products Property

$x = 10$ Divide each side by 7.2.

The length of Site A along the river is 10 yd.

▼ STUDENT PAGES 383–384

Got It? In the figure in Problem 2, what is the length of Site C along the road?

Plan

What information does the diagram give you?

A Practice **3. Marine Biology** Use the information shown on the auger shell. What is the value of y?

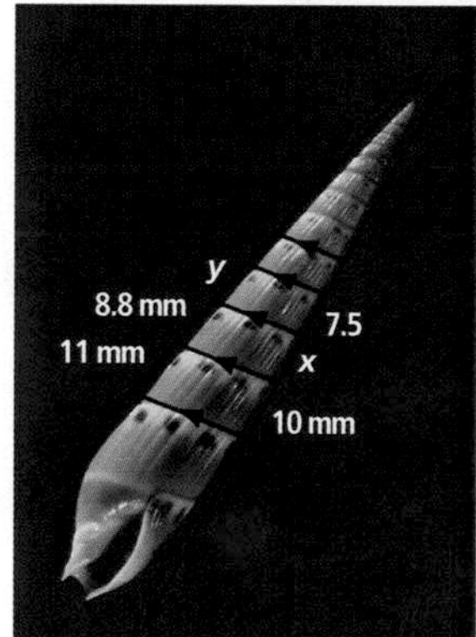

4. Algebra Solve for x.

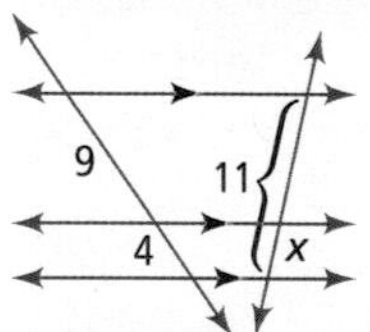

Problem 3 Using the Triangle-Angle-Bisector Theorem

Take Note

Have students redraw the triangles so that they have the same orientation. Then, ask students to make a similarity statement that shows how the two triangles and their sides are related.

Problem 3

Q What type of segment is drawn inside the triangle? How do you know? **[angle bisector; the angles it creates are congruent.]**

Q Using the properties of proportions, how can the proportion be rewritten so that the x is in a numerator? **[Property 1 of proportions allows the proportion to be written as $\frac{18}{10} = \frac{x}{12}$.]**

Got It?

If students struggle with this problem, have them label each point in the diagram and write the proportion based on the Triangle-Angle-Bisector Theorem. Then students can substitute values into the proportion.

ANSWERS

Got It? 14.4

Practice

5. 6

6. 5-cm side: 2.4 cm, 2.6 cm
12-cm side: $3\frac{1}{3}$ cm, $8\frac{2}{3}$ cm
13-cm side: about 3.8 cm, about 9.2 cm

▼ STUDENT PAGE 384

Essential Understanding The bisector of an angle of a triangle divides the opposite side into two segments with lengths proportional to the sides of the triangle that form the angle.

take note **Theorem 64** Triangle-Angle-Bisector Theorem

Theorem	If . . .	Then . . .
If a ray bisects an angle of a triangle, then it divides the opposite side into two segments that are proportional to the other two sides of the triangle.	$\overrightarrow{AD}$ bisects $\angle CAB$	$\frac{CD}{DB} = \frac{CA}{BA}$

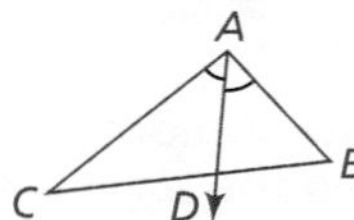

You will prove the Triangle-Angle-Bisector Theorem in Exercise 37.

▼ DIGITAL

Problem 3 Using the Triangle-Angle-Bisector Theorem

Algebra What is the value of x in the diagram at the right?

R 10 Q 18 S, 12, x, P

Think	Write
$\overline{PQ}$ bisects $\angle RPS$. Use the Triangle-Angle-Bisector Theorem to write a proportion.	$\frac{RQ}{QS} = \frac{PR}{PS}$
Substitute corresponding side lengths in the proportion.	$\frac{10}{18} = \frac{12}{x}$
Use the Cross Products Property.	$10x = 216$
Divide each side by 10.	$x = 21.6$

▼ STUDENT PAGE 385

Got It? What is the value of y?

A Practice 5. **Algebra** Solve for x.

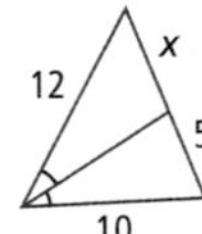

6. The lengths of the sides of a triangle are 5 cm, 12 cm, and 13 cm. Find the lengths, to the nearest tenth, of the segments into which the bisector of each angle divides the opposite side.

Lesson Check

Do you know HOW?

If students have difficulty with Exercises 7–9, then have them review Problem 2.

Do you UNDERSTAND?

If students have difficulty with Exercise 13, then have them review Problem 3.

Close

Q When parallel lines intersect two or more lines, what is the relationship between the segments formed? **[The segments formed between the parallel lines are proportional.]**

ANSWERS

7. *d* **8.** *c*

9. *d* **10.** 5

11. 15

12. Answers may vary. Sample: The Corollary to the Side-Splitter Thm. takes the same three (or more) ∥ lines as in Thm. 44, but instead of cutting off ≅ segments it allows the segments to be proportional.

13. Answers may vary. Sample: Alike: Both involve a △ and a seg. from one vertex to the opposite side of the △. Different: In Corollary 1 to Thm. 62, the △ is a rt. △ and the seg. is an alt., while in the △-∠-Bis. Thm. the △ does not have to be a rt. △ and the seg. is an ∠ bis.

14. The Side-Splitter Thm. involves only the segments formed on the two sides intersected by the ∥ line. (To find *x*, you can use a proportion involving the two ~ triangles.)

▼ STUDENT PAGES 386–387

Lesson Check

Do you know HOW?

Use the figure to complete each proportion.

7. $\frac{a}{b} = \frac{■}{e}$

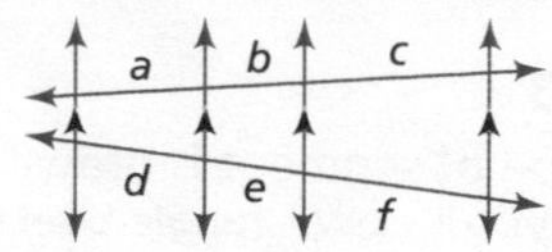

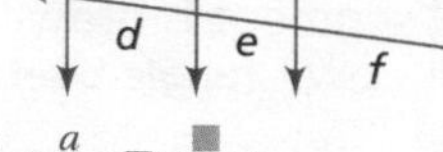

8. $\frac{b}{■} = \frac{e}{f}$

9. $\frac{a}{b+c} = \frac{■}{e+f}$

What is the value of *x* in each figure?

10.

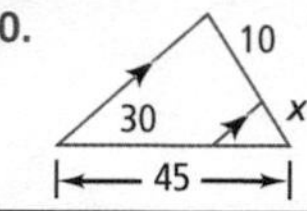

11.

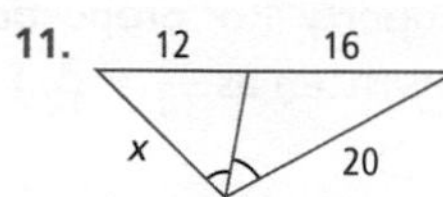

Do you UNDERSTAND?

12. Compare and Contrast How is the Corollary to the Side-Splitter Theorem related to Theorem 44: If three (or more) parallel lines cut off congruent segments on one transversal, then they cut off congruent segments on every transversal?

13. Compare and Contrast How are the Triangle-Angle-Bisector Theorem and Corollary 1 to Theorem 62 alike? How are they different?

14. Error Analysis A classmate says you can use the Side-Splitter Theorem to find both *x* and *y* in the diagram. Explain what is wrong with your classmate's statement.

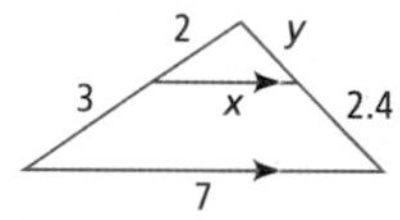

4 Practice

More Practice and Problem-Solving Exercises

ASSIGNMENT GUIDE

The assignments below are for the More Practice and Problem-Solving Exercises. You may also want to assign the A-Level Practice Exercises for homework if these are not used in class.

Average: 15–37

Advanced: 15–40

Mathematical Practices The exercises listed focus on the Standards for Mathematical Practices listed.

EX. 12, 13, 26: Make Sense of Problems (MP 1)

EX. 32, 33: Construct Arguments (MP 3)

EX. 14: Critique the Reasoning of Others (MP 3)

EX. 21, 22: Model (MP 4)

STEM exercises focus on science or engineering applications.

EXERCISE 31: Use the **Think About a Plan** worksheet in the Online Teacher Resources to further support students' development in becoming independent learners.

HOMEWORK QUICK CHECK

To check students' understanding of key skills and concepts, go over Exercises 16, 28, 31, 33, and 35.

ANSWERS

15. KS by the △ – ∠ -Bis. Thm.

16. SQ by the Side-Splitter Thm.

17. JP by the Side-Splitter Thm.

18. KP by the △ – ∠ -Bis. Thm.

19. KM by the △ – ∠ -Bis. Thm.

20. MP by the Side-Splitter Thm.

21. 575 ft **22.** 750 ft

23. 20 **24.** 2.5

25. 3 **26.** $x = 18$ m, $y = 12$ m

27. $\frac{XR}{RQ} = \frac{YS}{SQ}$ (Given); $\frac{XR + RQ}{RQ} = \frac{YS + SQ}{SQ}$ (Prop. of Proportions (3)); $XQ = XR + RQ$, $YQ = YS + SQ$ (Seg. Add. Post.); $\frac{XQ}{RQ} = \frac{YQ}{SQ}$ (Subst.); $\angle Q \cong \angle Q$ (Refl. Prop. of ≅); $\triangle XQY \sim \triangle RQS$ (SAS ~ Thm.); $\angle 1 \cong \angle 2$ (Corresp. ∡ of ~ ⧊ are ≅.); $\overline{RS} \parallel \overline{XY}$ (If corresp. ∡ are ≅, the lines are ∥.)

28. yes; $\frac{6}{10} = \frac{9}{15}$ (Converse of Side-Splitter Thm.)

29. no; $\frac{28}{12} \neq \frac{24}{10}$

30. yes; $\frac{15}{12} = \frac{20}{16}$ (Converse of Side-Splitter Thm.)

31. 12.5 cm or 4.5 cm

32. Answers may vary. Sample: 10 and 15, 8 and 12, or any two sides in the ratio 2 : 3 where the shorter side > 6 cm and < 15 cm.

33. Isosc.; $AC : BC$ is 1 : 1 by the △ – ∠ -Bis. Thm.

More Practice and Problem-Solving Exercises

B Apply

Use the figure at the right to complete each proportion. Justify your answer.

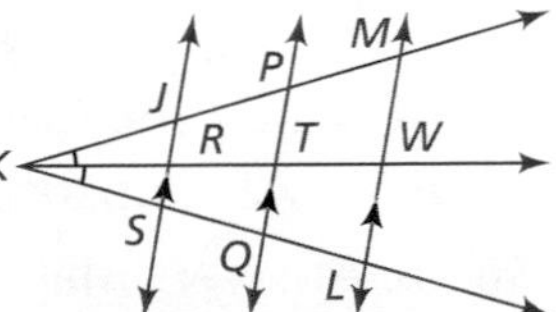

15. $\frac{RS}{■} = \frac{JR}{KJ}$

16. $\frac{KJ}{JP} = \frac{KS}{■}$

17. $\frac{QL}{PM} = \frac{SQ}{■}$

18. $\frac{PT}{■} = \frac{TQ}{KQ}$

19. $\frac{KL}{LW} = \frac{■}{MW}$

20. $\frac{■}{KP} = \frac{LQ}{KQ}$

STEM Urban Design In Washington, D.C., E. Capitol Street, Independence Avenue, C Street, and D Street are parallel streets that intersect Kentucky Avenue and 12th Street.

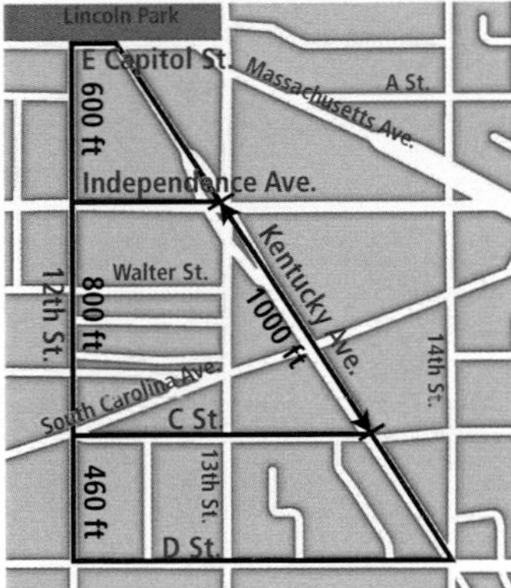

21. How long (to the nearest foot) is Kentucky Avenue between C Street and D Street?

22. How long (to the nearest foot) is Kentucky Avenue between E. Capitol Street and Independence Avenue?

Algebra Solve for x.

23.

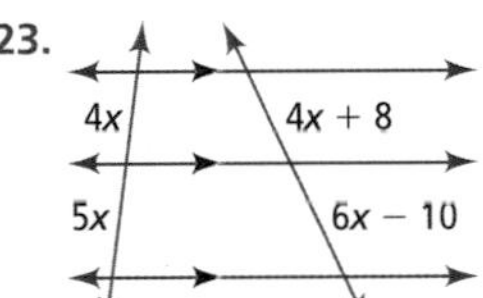

24.

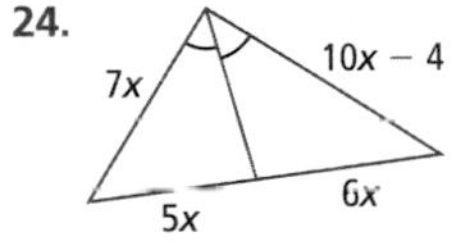

25.

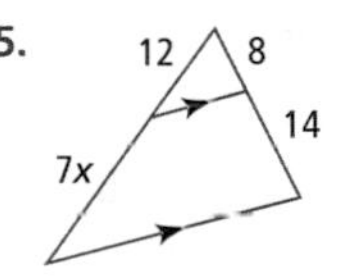

26. Think About a Plan The perimeter of the triangular lot at the right is 50 m. The surveyor's tape bisects an angle. Find the lengths x and y.

- How can you use the perimeter to write an equation in x and y?
- What other relationship do you know between x and y?

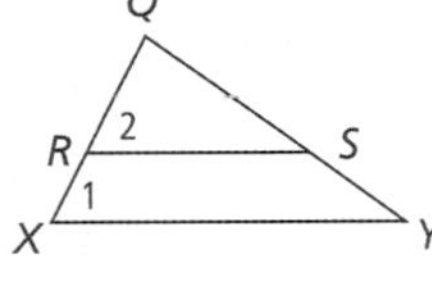

27. Prove the Converse of the Side-Splitter Theorem: If a line divides two sides of a triangle proportionally, then it is parallel to the third side.

Proof

Given: $\frac{XR}{RQ} = \frac{YS}{SQ}$

Prove: $\overline{RS} \parallel \overline{XY}$

Q, R, S, X, Y, 1, 2

Determine whether the red segments are parallel. Explain each answer. You can use the theorem proved in Exercise 27.

28.

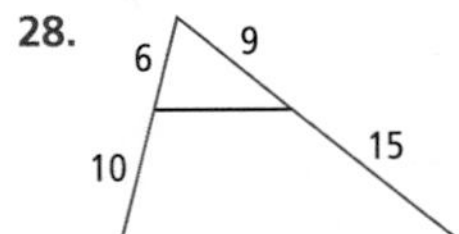

29.

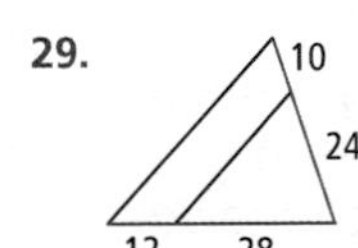

30.

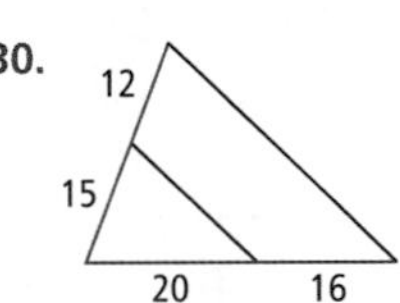

31. An angle bisector of a triangle divides the opposite side of the triangle into segments 5 cm and 3 cm long. A second side of the triangle is 7.5 cm long. Find all possible lengths for the third side of the triangle.

32. Open-Ended In a triangle, the bisector of an angle divides the opposite side into two segments with lengths 6 cm and 9 cm. How long could the other two sides of the triangle be? (*Hint:* Make sure the three sides satisfy the Triangle Inequality Theorem.)

33. Reasoning In $\triangle ABC$, the bisector of $\angle C$ bisects the opposite side. What type of triangle is $\triangle ABC$? Explain your reasoning.

More Practice and Problem-Solving Exercises *continued*

34. $\frac{10}{3}$

35. 5.2

36. $\frac{AB}{BC} = \frac{WP}{PC}$ by the Side-Splitter Thm., and $\frac{WP}{PC} = \frac{WX}{XY}$. Therefore $\frac{AB}{BC} = \frac{WX}{XY}$ by the Transitive Prop. of =.

37. By the Side-Splitter Thm., $\frac{CD}{BD} = \frac{CA}{AF}$. By the Corresp. ∠s Thm., $\angle 3 \cong \angle 1$. Since $\overrightarrow{AD}$ bisects $\angle CAB$, $\angle 1 \cong \angle 2$. By the Alt. Int. ∠s Thm., $\angle 2 \cong \angle 4$. So, $\angle 3 \cong \angle 4$ by the Trans. Prop. of ≅. By the Converse of the Isosc. △ Thm., $BA = AF$. Substituting BA for AF, $\frac{CD}{DB} = \frac{CA}{BA}$.

38. a. Answers may vary. Sample: A midsegment of a parallelogram connects the midpts. of two opposite sides of the parallelogram.

b.

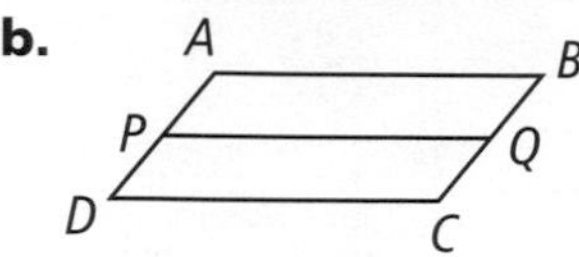

Given: $\overline{PQ}$ is a midsegment of parallelogram $ABCD$.

Prove: $\overline{PQ} \parallel \overline{AB}$, $\overline{PQ} \parallel \overline{DC}$

$\overline{AD} \cong \overline{BC}$ and $\overline{AD} \parallel \overline{BC}$ (properties of parallelograms), so $PD = \frac{1}{2}(AD) = \frac{1}{2}(BC) = QC$, and $PA = \frac{1}{2}(AD) = \frac{1}{2}(BC) = BQ$, both by the def. of midpt. Therefore, $ABQP$ and $PQCD$ are parallelograms because each has a pair of opposite sides that are ≅ and ∥. So $\overline{PQ} \parallel \overline{AB}$ and $\overline{PQ} \parallel \overline{DC}$ because opposite sides of a parallegorams are ∥.

c.

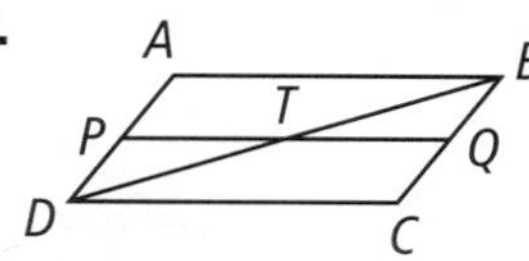

Given: Parallelogram $ABCD$ and midsegment $\overline{PQ}$

Prove: $\overline{PQ}$ bisects $\overline{BD}$.

From part (b) of this exercise, $\overline{AB} \parallel \overline{PQ} \parallel \overline{DC}$. Since $\overline{AP} \cong \overline{PD}$ by the def. of midsegment, $\overline{DT} \cong \overline{TB}$ because if ∥ lines cut off ≅ segments on one transversal, they cut off ≅ segments on every transversal (Thm. 44). Since $\overline{PQ}$ contains the midpt. of $\overline{BD}$, then $\overline{PQ}$ bisects $\overline{BD}$ by the def. of bisect. Also, point T is the midpt. of both diagonals (because the diagonals of a parallelogram have the same midpt.), so $\overline{PQ}$ bisects both diagonals of the parallelogram.

Algebra Solve for x.

34.

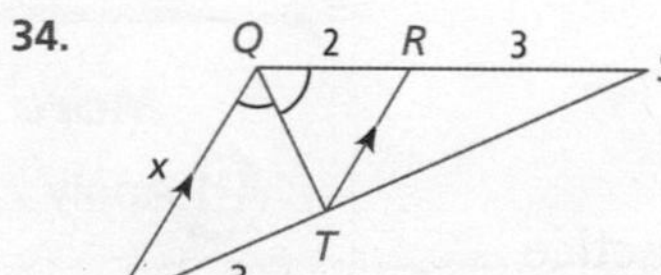

35.

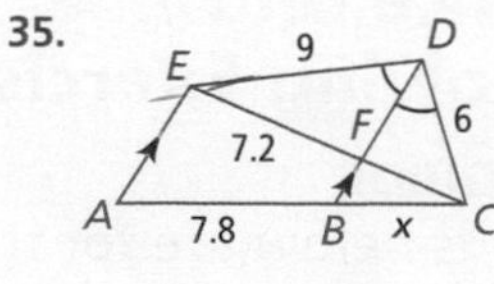

36. Prove the Corollary to the Side-Splitter Theorem. In the diagram from the statement of the theorem, draw the auxiliary line $\overleftrightarrow{CW}$ and label its intersection with b as point P.

Proof

Given: $a \parallel b \parallel c$

Prove: $\frac{AB}{BC} = \frac{WX}{XY}$

37. Prove the Triangle-Angle-Bisector Theorem. In the diagram from the statement of the theorem, draw the auxiliary line $\overleftrightarrow{BE}$ so that $\overleftrightarrow{BE} \parallel \overline{DA}$. Extend $\overline{CA}$ to meet $\overleftrightarrow{BE}$ at point F.

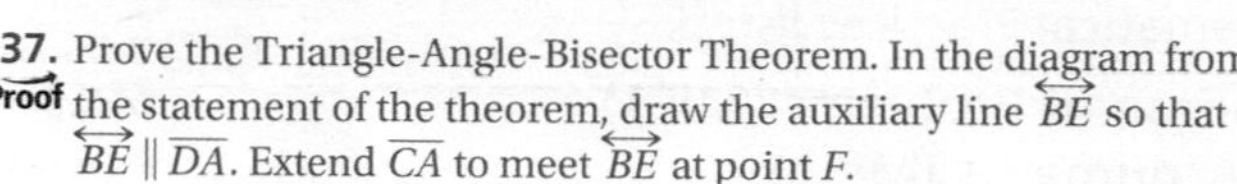

Proof

Given: $\overrightarrow{AD}$ bisects $\angle CAB$.

Prove: $\frac{CD}{DB} = \frac{CA}{BA}$

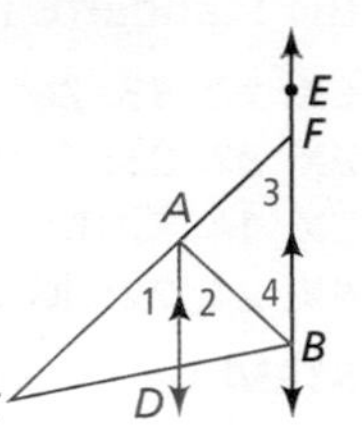

Challenge

38. Use the definition in part (a) to prove the statements in parts (b) and (c).

a. Write a definition for a midsegment of a parallelogram.

b. A parallelogram midsegment is parallel to two sides of the parallelogram.

c. A parallelogram midsegment bisects the diagonals of a parallelogram.

39. State the converse of the Triangle-Angle-Bisector Theorem. Give a convincing argument that the converse is true or a counterexample to prove that it is false.

40. In △ABC, the bisectors of $\angle A$, $\angle B$, and $\angle C$ cut the opposite sides into lengths a_1 and a_2, b_1 and b_2, and c_1 and c_2, respectively, labeled in order counterclockwise around △ABC. Find the perimeter of △ABC for each set of values.

a. $b_1 = 16, b_2 = 20, c_1 = 18$

b. $a_1 = \frac{5}{3}, a_2 = \frac{10}{3}, b_1 = \frac{15}{4}$

39. Use the diagram with Ex. 37, with $\overline{AD} \parallel \overline{EB}$. It is given that $\frac{CD}{DB} = \frac{CA}{BA}$, and you want to prove that $\angle 1 \cong \angle 2$. By the Side-Splitter Thm., $\frac{CA}{AF} = \frac{CD}{DB}$. So $\frac{CA}{BA} = \frac{CA}{AF}$ by the Transitive Prop. of =, and $BA = AF$. Therefore, $\angle 3 \cong \angle 4$ by the Isosc. △ Thm. Using properties of ∥ lines, $\angle 1 \cong \angle 3$ and $\angle 2 \cong \angle 4$. So $\angle 1 \cong \angle 2$ by the Transitive Prop. of ≅, and $\overline{AD}$ bisects $\angle CAB$ by the def. of ∠ bis.

40. a. 90 units

b. 14 units

Assess and Remediate

Lesson Quiz

1. What is the value of x in the diagram?

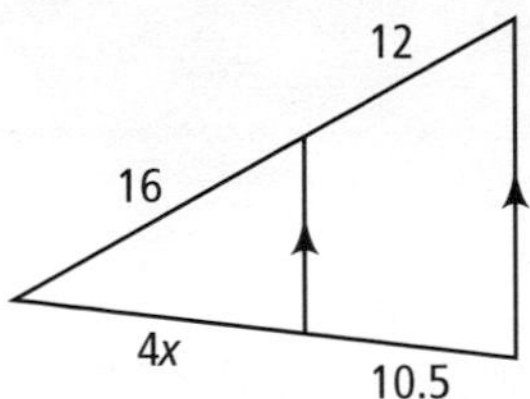

2. What is the value of x in the diagram?

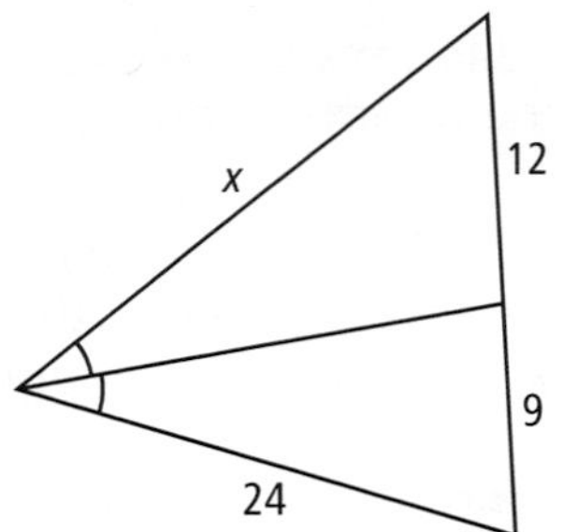

3. Do you UNDERSTAND? What is the length of Site A along $\overline{QZ}$?

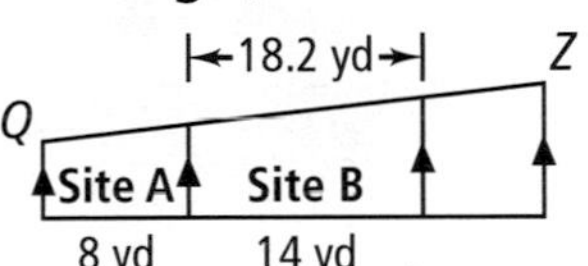

ANSWERS TO LESSON QUIZ

1. 3.5

2. 32

3. 10.4 yd

Prescription for Remediation

Use the student work on the Lesson Quiz to prescribe a differentiated assignment.

Points	Differentiated Remediation
0–1	Intervention
2	On-level
3	Extension

Online Assessment

Assign the Lesson Quiz in Success Tracker on **pearsonsuccessnet.com**. Success Tracker will automatically score the quiz and assign appropriate intervention or enrichment to each student based on the results. The compiled data appear in three different reports for instant analysis of whole class and individual student performance.

Differentiated Remediation

Intervention

- **RETEACHING** (2 pages) Provides reteaching and practice exercises for the key lesson concepts. Use with struggling students or absent students.
- **ENGLISH LANGUAGE LEARNER SUPPORT** Helps students develop and reinforce mathematical vocabulary and key concepts.

On-Level

- **PRACTICE** (2 pages) Provides extra practice for each lesson. For simpler practice exercises, use the Form K Practice pages found in the Online Teacher Resources.
- **THINK ABOUT A PLAN** Helps students develop specific problem-solving skills and strategies by providing scaffolded guiding questions.
- **STANDARDIZED TEST PREP** Focuses on all major exercises, all major question types, and helps students prepare for the high-stakes assessments.

Extension

- **ENRICHMENT** Provides students with interesting problems and activities that extend the concepts of the lesson.
- **ACTIVITIES, GAMES, AND PUZZLES** Worksheets that can be used for concept development, enrichment, and for fun!

ACTIVITY LAB

Use With Lesson 6-6

Exploring Dilations

Common Core State Standards
G.SRT.1.b The dilation of a line segment is . . . given by the scale factor. **Also G.SRT.1.a**

Mathematical Practices

This Activity Lab supports students in becoming proficient in using stated assumptions and definitions, Mathematical Practice 3.

Guided Instruction

PURPOSE To dilate segments and geometric figures and make conjectures about properties of dilations.

PROCESS Students will

- graph dilations of a segment with scale factors of 2 and $\frac{1}{2}$ and make conjectures about how dilations change the length of segments.
- graph a quadrilateral and one of its dilations and compare the shape, size, and orientation of the preimage and the image.

DISCUSS Students first graph dilations of a segment and make a conjecture about how the scale factor affects the length of the image. Then they graph a quadrilateral and its image after a dilation and make conjectures about the shape, size, and orientation of the image in relationship to the preimage.

Activity 1

In this Activity students dilate a segment on a coordinate plane.

Q Does a translation of a segment change its length? **[no]**

Q Does a rotation of a segment change its length? **[no]**

Q Does a reflection of a segment change its length? **[no]**

ANSWERS

1. $RS = \sqrt{(2-1)^2 + (-1-4)^2} = \sqrt{1 + 25} = \sqrt{26}$

2–4.

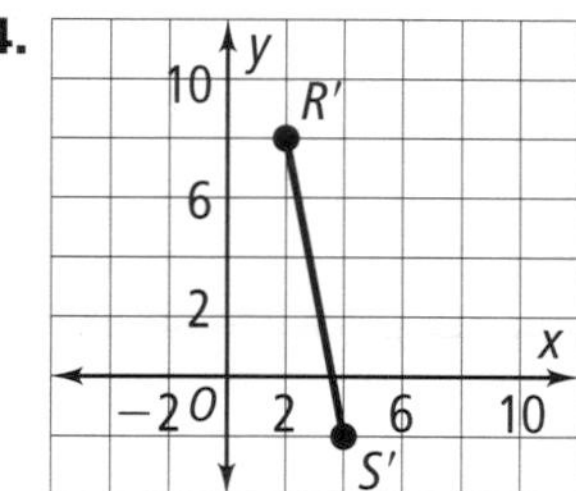

5. $R'S' = \sqrt{(4-2)^2 + (-2-8)^2} = \sqrt{4 + 100}$
$= \sqrt{104} = 2\sqrt{26}$

6. $R'S' = 2RS$

7.

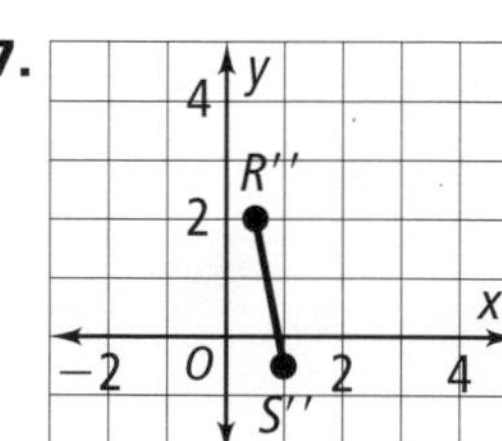

▼ STUDENT PAGES 390–391

In this activity, you will explore the properties of dilations. A dilation is defined by a center of dilation and a scale factor.

Activity 1

To dilate a segment by a scale factor n with center of dilation at the origin, you measure the distance from the origin to each point on the segment. The diagram at the right shows the dilation of $\overline{GH}$ by the scale factor 3 with center of dilation at the origin. To locate the dilation image of $\overline{GH}$, draw rays from the origin through points G and H. Then measure the distance from the origin to G. Next, find the point along the same ray that is 3 times that distance. Label the point G'. Now dilate the endpoint H similarly. Draw $\overline{G'H'}$.

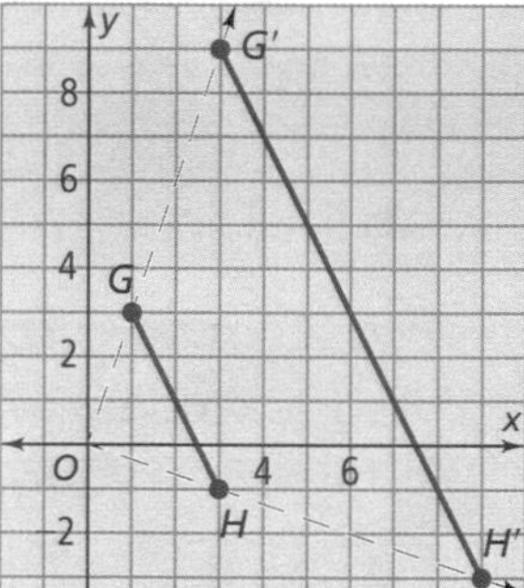

1. Graph $\overline{RS}$ with $R(1, 4)$ and $S(2, -1)$. What is the length of $\overline{RS}$?
2. Graph the dilations of the endpoints of $\overline{RS}$ by scale factor 2 and center of dilation at the origin. Label the dilated endpoints R' and S'.
3. What are the coordinates of R' and S'?
4. Graph $\overline{R'S'}$.
5. What is $R'S'$?
6. How do the lengths of $\overline{RS}$ and $\overline{R'S'}$ compare?
7. Graph the dilation of $\overline{RS}$ by scale factor $\frac{1}{2}$ with center of dilation at the origin. Label the dilation $\overline{R''S''}$.

8. $R''S'' = \sqrt{\left(1 - \frac{1}{2}\right)^2 + \left(-\frac{1}{2} - 2\right)^2}$

$= \sqrt{\frac{1}{4} + \frac{25}{4}} = \sqrt{\frac{26}{4}} = \frac{1}{2}\sqrt{26}$

9. $R''S'' = \frac{1}{2}RS$

10. Answers may vary. Sample: The length of the image segment after a dilation with scale factor n is equal to n times the length of the preimage segment.

Activity 2

In this Activity students dilate a quadrilateral on a coordinate plane.

Q If you use a copier to copy this page at a reduction of 75%, will everything on the copied page be the same shape as the original? **[yes]**

Q Will everything on this copied page be the same size as the original? **[no]**

Q Will everything on this copied page be in the same order as the original? **[yes]**

VISUAL LEARNERS

Encourage students to make dilations of other geometric figures on a coordinate plane. Ask them if their conjectures still seem valid.

ANSWERS

11. $L'(-15, 3)$, $M'(-3, 9)$, $N'(0, 3)$, $P'(-6, -3)$

12. The x- and y-coordinates of each vertex in the image are 3 times the x- and y-coordinates of the corresponding vertex in the preimage.

13. The image has the same shape and orientation as the preimage, but not the same size. Possible conjectures include: Dilations preserve angle measure, but not distance; When you dilate a polygon by a scale factor k, the side lengths change by a factor of k.

▼ STUDENT PAGES 391–392

8. What is $R''S''$?

9. How do the lengths of $\overline{R'S'}$ and $\overline{R''S''}$ compare?

10. What can you conjecture about the length of a line segment that has been dilated by scale factor n?

Activity 2

11. Graph $L'M'N'P'$, the dilation of $LMNP$ with scale factor 3 and center of dilation at the origin. What are the coordinates of L', M', N', and P'?

12. How are the coordinates of the vertices of $LMNP$ and $L'M'N'P'$ related?

13. Compare the shape, size, and orientation of the preimage $LMNP$ with the image $L'M'N'P'$. What conjecture can you make about the properties of dilations?

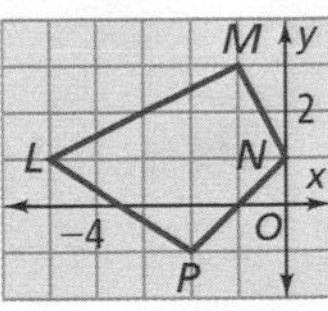

Dilations

Common Core State Standards
G.SRT.1.a A dilation takes a line not passing through the center of the dilation to a parallel line . . . **Also G.SRT.1.b**

Preparing to Teach

BIG ideas Transformations
Coordinate Geometry

ESSENTIAL UNDERSTANDING

A scale factor can be used to make a larger or smaller copy of a figure that is also similar to the original figure.

Math Background

A dilation is not a rigid motion because it does not preserve the size of the figure. A dilation produces a pair of similar figures whose corresponding side lengths are proportional. The scale factor related to a dilation is equal to the ratio of distances between pairs of corresponding points. Dilations are used in multiple real-world areas, such as science, technology, and photography. Students can connect the terms in this lesson with reducing and enlarging photos.

ELL Support

FOCUS ON LANGUAGE Use the following activity to familiarize students with the lesson vocabulary. Ask if students have ever heard of *shrink* or *growth rays*. Discuss how fictional *shrink rays* make an object smaller without changing its shape. Ask what real machine makes things larger or smaller. [a copy machine]

Next ask questions like the following:

- Does part of the word *enlargement* suggest its meaning? [*Large* suggests enlargement makes things bigger.]
- Does part of the word *reduction* suggest its meaning? [*Reduce* suggests reduction makes things smaller.]

Have students integrate the concepts from this activity by working in small groups to make graphic organizers for the lesson vocabulary.

Lesson Vocabulary

- dilation
- center of dilation
- scale factor of a dilation
- enlargement
- reduction

Mathematical Practices

LOOK FOR AND MAKE USE OF STRUCTURE. Students will build on their knowledge of scale factors in Lesson 6-2 to construct an understanding of dilations. They will also see dilations as being defined by a center and a scale factor.

Interactive Learning

Solve It!

PURPOSE To identify a dilation as a similarity transformation

PROCESS Students may extend their knowledge of similar figures to describe a dilation.

Q What is the definition of similar figures? **[Similar figures are figures of the same shape, but different sizes. They have the same angle measures and proportional sides.]**

Q How do circles fit into the definition of similar figures? **[All circles are the same shape, but can be different sizes. All circles are similar to each other.]**

Q Is each radius in the dilated pupil proportional to the corresponding radius in the dim light pupil? **[Yes]**

ANSWER The shape stays the same, but the size changes. In the other transformations, the size and the shape of the figure stays the same. In this case, only the shape stays the same.

CONNECT THE MATH Students review their understanding of similar figures to include circles and realize that similar figures can be reductions or enlargements of each other. In the lesson, students learn that a dilation is a transformation where the preimage and image are similar figures.

▼ DIGITAL (STUDENT WORK SPACE PAGE 393)

SOLVE IT!

Getting Ready!

The pupil is the opening in the iris that lets light into the eye. Depending on the amount of light available, the size of the pupil changes.

Normal Light	Dim Light
Iris	Pupil
12 mm	12 mm
Diameter of pupil = 2 mm	Diameter of pupil = 8 mm

Observe the size and shape of the iris in normal light and in dim light. What characteristics stay the same and what characteristics change? How do these observations compare to transformation of figures you have learned about earlier in the chapter?

2 Guided Instruction

Problem 1 Finding a Scale Factor

Take Note

Ask students to identify the scale factor between the image and the preimage. Be sure that students understand the difference between a reduction and an enlargement.

Problem 1

Q Which triangle is larger? **[$\triangle X'T'R'$]**

Q Which triangle is the preimage? **[$\triangle XTR$]**

Q Which side corresponds to $\overline{XT}$? **[$\overline{X'T'}$]**

Q What is the ratio of corresponding sides? **[$\frac{X'T'}{XT} = \frac{4+8}{4} = \frac{12}{4} = 3$]**

Got It?

Q Is the dilation a reduction or an enlargement? Justify your answer. **[It is a reduction because $J'K'L'M'$ is smaller than $JKLM$.]**

Q What is the advantage to having the figures on a coordinate grid? **[You can identify the ordered pairs of the vertices.]**

Q How can you find the lengths of corresponding sides? **[Use the Distance Formula.]**

ANSWERS

Got It? reduction; $n = \frac{1}{2}$

Practice

1. reduction; $\frac{1}{3}$
2. enlargement; $\frac{3}{2}$

▼ STUDENT PAGES 393–394

In the Solve It, you looked at how the pupil of an eye changes in size, or *dilates*. In this lesson, you will learn how to dilate geometric figures.

Essential Understanding You can use a scale factor to make a larger or smaller copy of a figure that is similar to the original figure.

take note

Key Concept Dilation

A **dilation** with **center of dilation** C and **scale factor** n, $n > 0$, can be written as $D_{(n, C)}$. A dilation is a transformation with the following properties.

- The image of C is itself (that is, $C' = C$).
- For any other point R, R' is on $\overrightarrow{CR}$ and $CR' = n \cdot CR$, or $n = \frac{CR'}{CR}$.
- Dilations preserve angle measure.

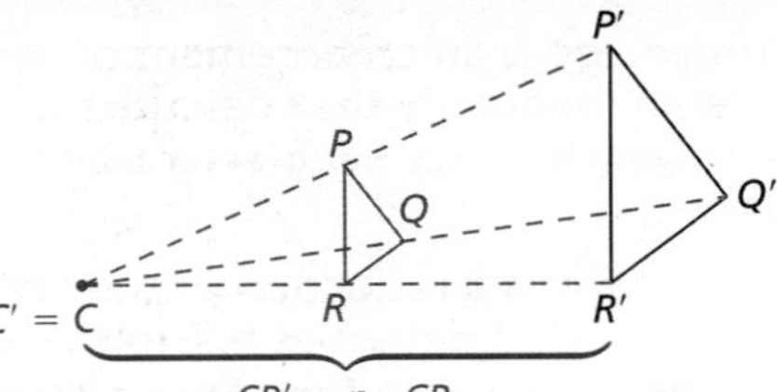

The scale factor n of a dilation is the ratio of a length of the image to the corresponding length in the preimage, with the image length always in the numerator. For the figure shown above, $n = \frac{CR'}{CR} = \frac{R'P'}{RP} = \frac{P'Q'}{PQ} = \frac{Q'R'}{QR}$.

A dilation is an **enlargement** if the scale factor n is greater than 1. The dilation is a **reduction** if the scale factor n is between 0 and 1.

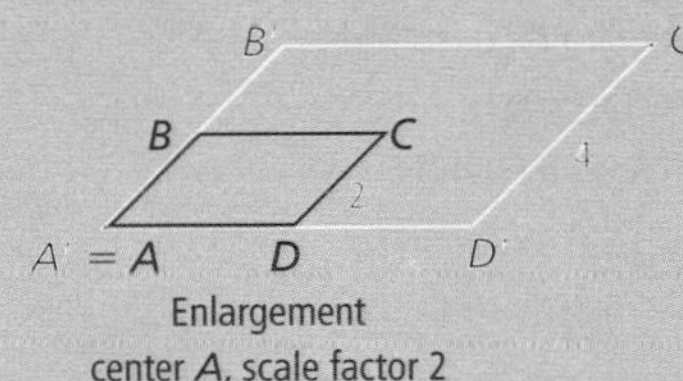

Enlargement
center A, scale factor 2

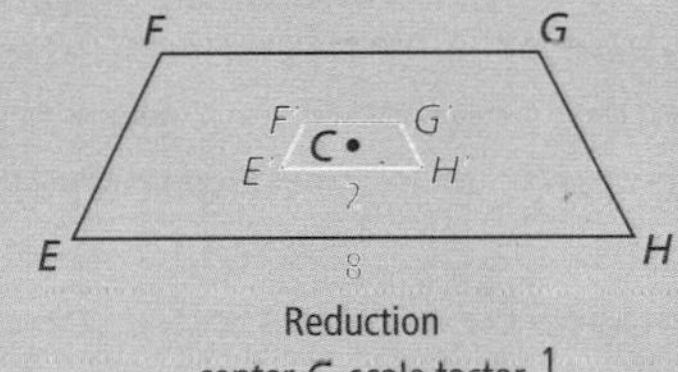

Reduction
center C, scale factor $\frac{1}{4}$

▼ DIGITAL

Problem 1 Finding a Scale Factor

Multiple Choice Is $D_{(n, X)}(\triangle XTR) = \triangle X'T'R'$ an enlargement or a reduction? What is the scale factor n of the dilation?

Ⓐ enlargement; $n = 2$ Ⓒ reduction; $n = \frac{1}{3}$

Ⓑ enlargement; $n = 3$ Ⓓ reduction; $n = 3$

The image is larger than the preimage, so the dilation is an enlargement.
Use the ratio of the lengths of corresponding sides to find the scale factor.

$$n = \frac{X'T'}{XT} = \frac{4+8}{4} = \frac{12}{4} = 3$$

$\triangle X'T'R'$ is an enlargement of $\triangle XTR$, with a scale factor of 3. The correct answer is B.

▼ STUDENT PAGE 394

Got It? Is $D_{(n, O)}(JKLM) = J'K'L'M'$ an enlargement or a reduction? What is the scale factor n of the dilation?

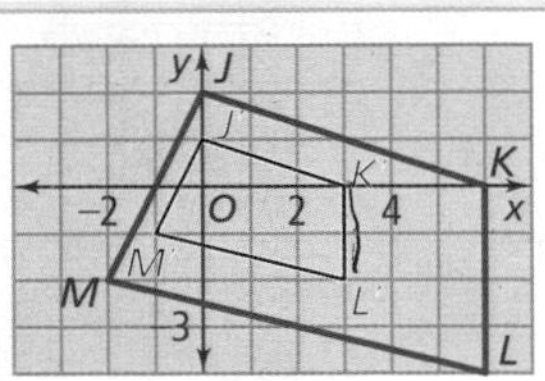

Practice The red figure is a dilation image of the blue figure. The labeled point is the center of dilation. Tell whether the dilation is an enlargement or a reduction. Then find the scale factor of the dilation.

1. 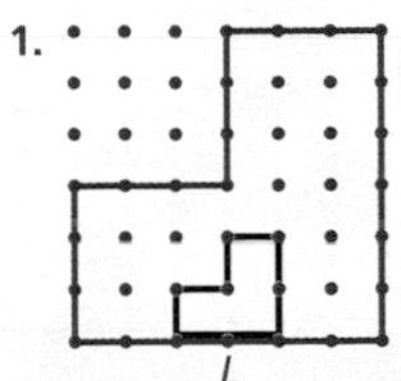

2. 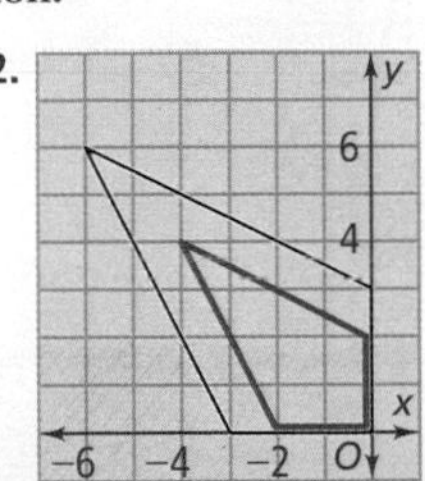

Problem 2 Finding a Dilation Image

Have students consider both a dilation that is a reduction of the preimage and an enlargement of the preimage when they read the statement about multiplying the coordinates of a point by the scale factor.

Q If the preimage and image are the same size, what would be the value of n? Explain. **[1; multiplying by 1 does not change a number.]**

Q If the image is an enlargement of the preimage, write an inequality that describes n? Explain. **[$n > 1$; multiplying by a number greater than 1 produces a greater number.]**

Q If the image is a reduction of the preimage, write an inequality that describes n. Explain. **[$n < 1$; multiplying by a number less than 1 produces a lesser number.]**

Problem 2

Q Is the dilation a reduction or an enlargement? Justify your answer. **[The dilation is an enlargement because the scale factor is greater than 1.]**

Q How do you find the coordinates of points of a dilation centered at the origin? **[Multiply each coordinate of ordered pairs of the preimage by the scale factor.]**

Got It?

ERROR PREVENTION

Have students identify the dilation as a reduction or an enlargement. Make sure that students show their work for calculating the new coordinates for each point. Students should multiply each x- and y-coordinate by the scale factor.

ANSWERS

Got It? a. $P'(1, -0.5)$, $Z'(-1, 0.5)$, $G'(0, -1)$.
b. Sample answer: $\overline{PZ}$ and $\overline{P'Z'}$ lie on the same line. $\overline{PG}$ and $\overline{P'G'}$ are parallel, and so are $\overline{GZ}$ and $\overline{G'Z'}$. Since $\overline{PZ}$ and $\overline{P'Z'}$ both pass through O, you can conjecture that lines that pass through the center of dilation have images that pass through the center of dilation, and that a dilation of a line that does not pass through the center of dilation is a line parallel to the preimage.

Practice

3. $P'(6, -3)$, $Q'(6, 12)$, $R'(12, -3)$

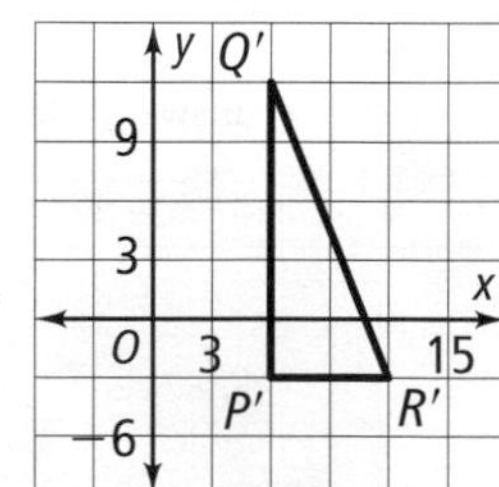

4. $P'\left(-\frac{9}{4}, 0\right)$, $Q'\left(0, \frac{9}{4}\right)$, $R'\left(\frac{3}{4}, -\frac{9}{4}\right)$

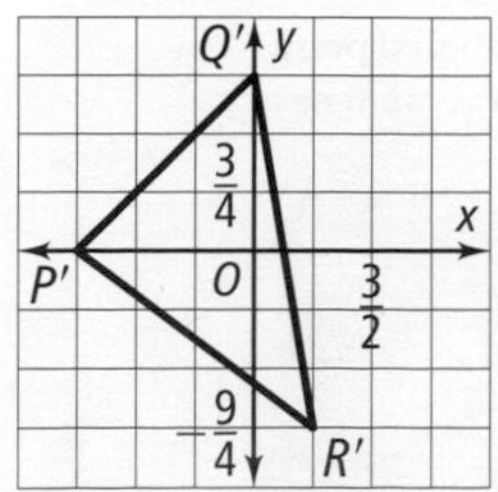

▼ STUDENT PAGE 395

In the Got It for Problem 1, you looked at a dilation of a figure drawn in the coordinate plane. In this book, all dilations of figures in the coordinate plane have the origin as the center of dilation. So you can find the dilation image of a point $P(x, y)$ by multiplying the coordinates of P by the scale factor n. A dilation of scale factor n with center of dilation at the origin can be written as

$D_n(x, y) = (nx, ny)$

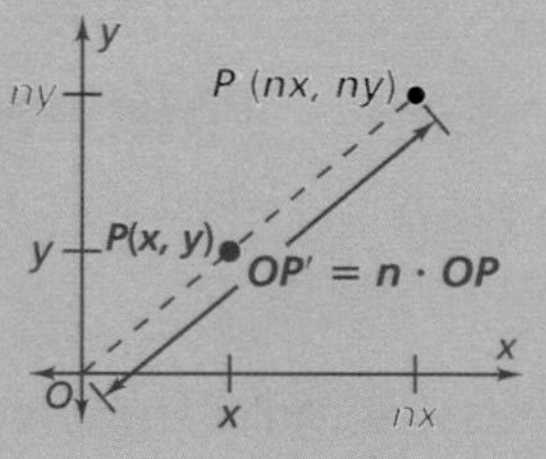

▼ DIGITAL

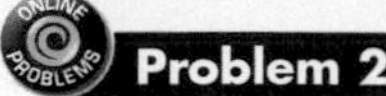

Problem 2 **Finding a Dilation Image**

What are the coordinates of the vertices of $D_2(\triangle PZG)$? Graph the image of $\triangle PZG$.

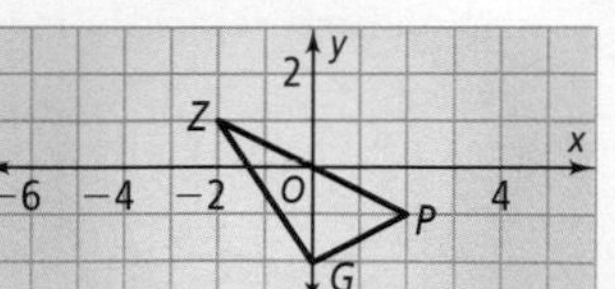

Identify the coordinates of each vertex. The center of dilation is the origin and the scale factor is 2, so use the dilation rule $D_2(x, y) = (2x, 2y)$.

$D_2(P) = (2 \cdot 2, 2 \cdot (-1))$, or $P'(4, -2)$.

$D_2(Z) = (2 \cdot (-2), 2 \cdot 1)$, or $Z'(-4, 2)$.

$D_2(G) = (2 \cdot 0, 2 \cdot (-2))$, or $G'(0, -4)$.

To graph the image of $\triangle PZG$, graph P', Z', and G'. Then draw $\triangle P'Z'G'$.

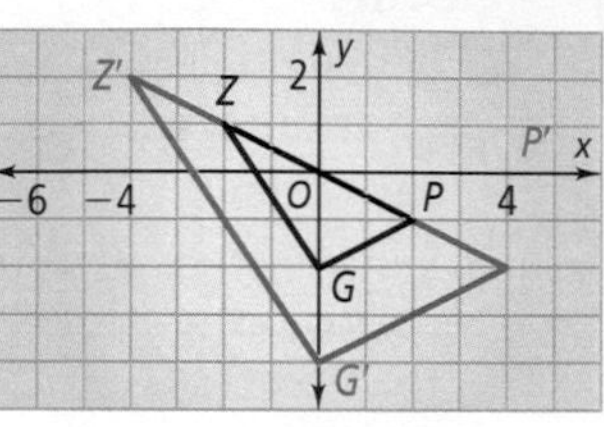

▼ STUDENT PAGES 395–396

Got It? **a.** What are the coordinates of the vertices of $D_{\frac{1}{2}}(\triangle PZG)$?

Think
Will the vertices of the triangle move closer to (0, 0) or farther from (0, 0)?

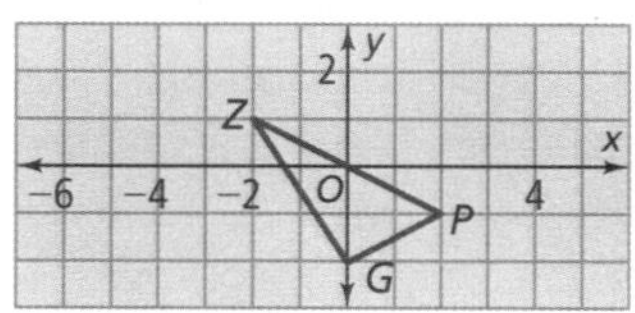

b. Reasoning How are $\overline{PZ}$ and $\overline{P'Z'}$ related? How are $\overline{PG}$ and $\overline{P'G'}$, and $\overline{GZ}$ and $\overline{G'Z'}$ related? Use these relationships to make a conjecture about the effects of dilations on lines.

A Practice **Find the images of the vertices of $\triangle PQR$ for each dilation. Graph the image.**

3. $D_3(\triangle PQR)$

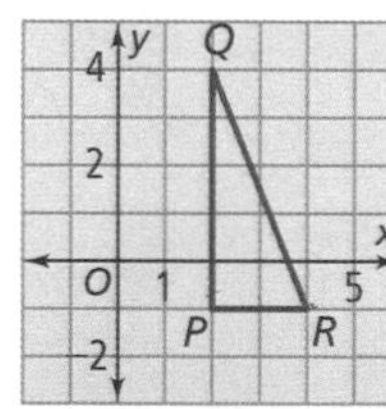

(2,4)Q
P(2,-1)
R(4,-1)

4. $D_{\frac{3}{4}}(\triangle PQR)$

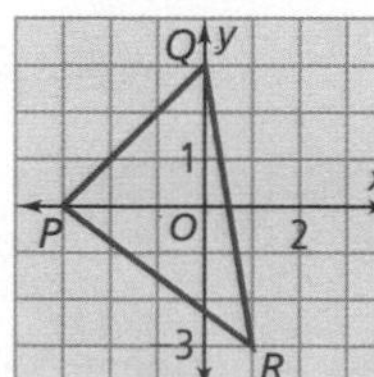

Q(0,3)
P(-3,0)
R(1,3)

Problem 3 Using a Scale Factor to Find a Length

Q Is the magnifying glass reducing or enlarging the image of the seed? **[enlarging]**

Q How can you find the actual length of the seed? **[Divide the length in the magnification by the magnification factor.]**

Got It? **ERROR PREVENTION**
Have students write a proportion that relates the corresponding heights of the documents and the scale factor. Use properties of proportions to solve for the new height.

ANSWERS

Got It? 5.1 cm

Practice

5. 0.2 cm **6.** 0.28 cm

▼ STUDENT PAGE 396

Dilations and scale factors help you understand real-world enlargements and reductions, such as images seen through a microscope or on a computer screen.

▼ DIGITAL

Problem 3 **Using a Scale Factor to Find a Length**

Biology **A magnifying glass shows you an image of an object that is 7 times the object's actual size. So the scale factor of the enlargement is 7. The photo shows an apple seed under this magnifying glass. What is the actual length of the apple seed?**

$1.75 = 7 \cdot p$ image length = scale factor · actual length

$0.25 = p$ Divide each side by 7.

The actual length of the apple seed is 0.25 in.

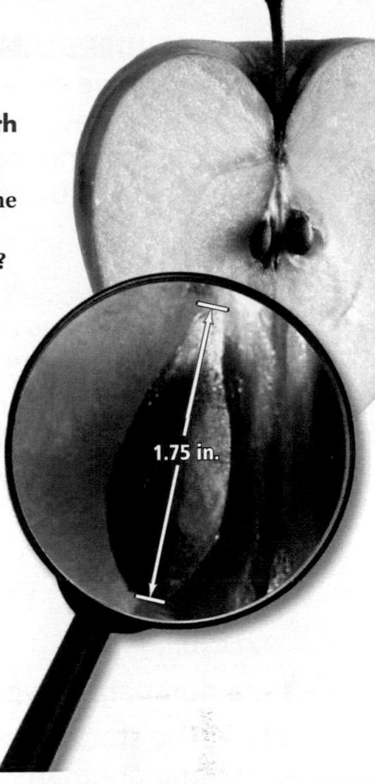

▼ STUDENT PAGES 396–397

Got It? The height of a document on your computer screen is 20.4 cm. When you change the zoom setting on your screen from 100% to 25%, the new image of your document is a dilation of the previous image with scale factor 0.25. What is the height of the new image?

Think
What does a scale factor of 0.25 tell you?

Practice **Magnification** **You look at each object described in Exercises 5 and 6 under a magnifying glass. Find the actual dimension of each object.**

5. The image of an ant is 7 times the ant's actual size and has a length of 1.4 cm.

6. The image of a capital letter N is 6 times the letter's actual size and has a height of 1.68 cm.

3 Lesson Check

Do you know HOW?
If students have difficulty with Exercises 8–10, then have them review Problem 2 to see which factors are to be multiplied.

Do you UNDERSTAND?
If students have difficulty with Exercise 12, then have them review Problem 1 to determine if the process is the same or the opposite of what is shown as the solution.

Close

Q How are the image and preimage related in a dilation? **[The ratio of corresponding side lengths in the two figures is equal to the scale factor of the dilation.]**

Q What is the difference between a reduction and an enlargement? **[An enlargement makes the figure bigger and has a scale factor greater than 1. A reduction makes the figure smaller and has a scale factor between 0 and 1.]**

ANSWERS

7. enlargement; 1.5
8. $D'(2, -10)$
9. $D'(0, 3)$
10. $D'(0, 0)$
11. a number between 0 and 1
12. **a.** The student used 6, instead of $2 + 6 = 8$, as the preimage length in the denominator; the correct scale factor is $n = \frac{2}{2+6} = \frac{1}{4}$.
b. The student did not write the scale factor with the image length in the numerator; the correct scale factor is $n = \frac{1}{4}$.

▼ STUDENT PAGES 397–398

Lesson Check

Do you know HOW?

7. The red figure is a dilation image of the blue figure with center of dilation C. Is the dilation an enlargement or a reduction? What is the scale factor of the dilation?

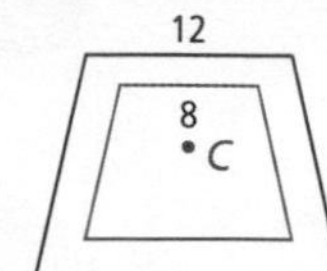

Find the image of each point.

8. $D_2(1, -5)$
9. $D_{\frac{1}{2}}(0, 6)$
10. $D_{10}(0, 0)$

Do you UNDERSTAND? MATHEMATICAL PRACTICES

11. Vocabulary Describe the scale factor of a reduction.

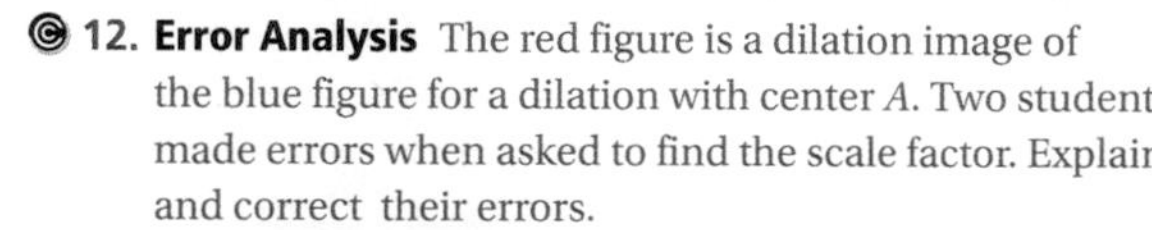

12. Error Analysis The red figure is a dilation image of the blue figure for a dilation with center A. Two students made errors when asked to find the scale factor. Explain and correct their errors.

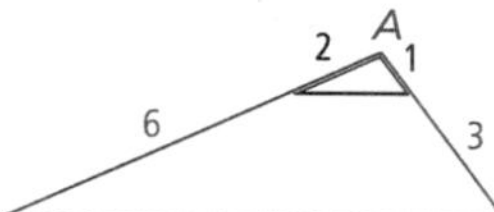

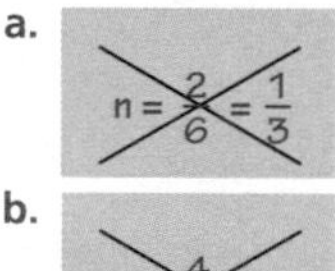

Practice

More Practice and Problem-Solving Exercises

ASSIGNMENT GUIDE
The assignments below are for the More Practice and Problem-Solving Exercises. You may also want to assign the A-Level Practice Exercises for homework if these are not used in class.
Average: 13–42
Advanced: 13–45

Mathematical Practices The exercises listed focus on the Standards for Mathematical Practices listed.

EX. 25: Make Sense of Problems (MP 1)
EX. 24, 26, 29: Communicate (MP 3)
EX. 38, 39–42: Construct Arguments (MP 3)
EX. 12: Critique the Reasoning of Others (MP 3)
EX. 30, 45: Model (MP 4)

EXERCISE 38: Use the **Think About a Plan** worksheet in the Online Teacher Resources to further support students' development in becoming independent learners.

HOMEWORK QUICK CHECK
To check students' understanding of key skills and concepts, go over Exercises 20, 24, 25, 32, and 38.

ANSWERS

13. $L'(-15, 0)$ **14.** $N'(-0.8, 1.4)$

15. $A'(-9, 3)$ **16.** $F'\left(1, -\frac{2}{3}\right)$

17. $B'\left(\frac{1}{8}, -\frac{3}{20}\right)$ **18.** $Q'\left(6\sqrt{6}, \frac{3\sqrt{2}}{2}\right)$

19. $Q'\left(-\frac{3}{4}, 1\right)$, $R'\left(-\frac{1}{2}, -\frac{1}{4}\right)$, $T'\left(\frac{3}{4}, \frac{1}{4}\right)$, $W'\left(\frac{3}{4}, \frac{5}{4}\right)$

20. $Q'(-1.8, 2.4)$, $R'(-1.2, -0.6)$, $T'(1.8, 0.6)$, $W'(1.8, 3)$

21. $Q'(-2.7, 3.6)$, $R'(-1.8, -0.9)$, $T'(2.7, 0.9)$, $W'(2.7, 4.5)$

22. $Q'(-30, 40)$, $R'(-20, -10)$, $T'(30, 10)$, $W'(30, 50)$

23. $Q'(-300, 400)$, $R'(-200, -100)$, $T'(300, 100)$, $W'(300, 500)$

24. Answers may vary. Sample: Each type of scale factor is a constant ratio of corresp. lengths. For a dilation, the scale factor is always the ratio of an image length to a corresp. preimage length, while for similar figures, the scale factor ratio can relate the two figures in either order. The scale factor of two similar figures is always the ratio of the lengths of two corresponding sides, while the scale factor of a dilation is also the ratio of the distances of corresponding points from the center of dilation. If the center is not on the preimage, then these distances are not lengths of corresponding sides of the image and preimage.

25. $x = 3$, $y = 60$; the image of a dilation is similar to the preimage, so $\triangle L'N'M' \sim \triangle LNM$. The ratio of the corresp. sides is the same as the scale factor of the dilation, which is 4 : 2, or 2 : 1. To find x, solve the proportion $\frac{x+3}{x} = \frac{2}{1}$. $y = 60$ because corresponding angles of ~ figures are ≅.

26. Answers may vary. Sample: The image is an equilateral triangle with sides 10 in. long. For two of the pairs of corresp. sides, the corresp. sides lie on the same line. The sides of the third pair of corresp. sides are ∥.

27.

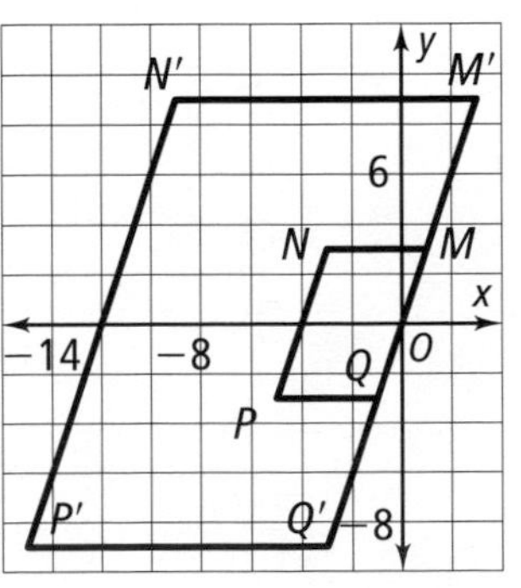

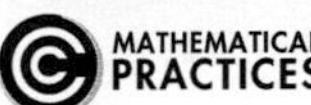

More Practice and Problem-Solving Exercises

B Apply

Find the image of each point for the given scale factor.

13. $L(-3, 0); D_5(L)$ **14.** $N(-4, 7); D_{0.2}(N)$ **15.** $A(-6, 2); D_{1.5}(A)$

16. $F(3, -2); D_{\frac{1}{3}}(F)$ **17.** $B\left(\frac{5}{4}, -\frac{3}{2}\right); D_{\frac{1}{10}}(B)$ **18.** $Q\left(6, \frac{\sqrt{3}}{2}\right); D_{\sqrt{6}}(Q)$

Use the graph at the right. Find the vertices of the image of $QRTW$ for a dilation with center (0, 0) and the given scale factor.

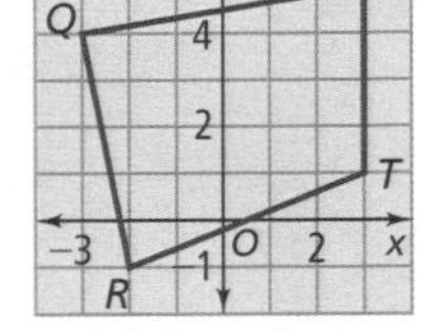

19. $\frac{1}{4}$ **20.** 0.6 **21.** 0.9 **22.** 10 **23.** 100

24. Compare and Contrast Compare the definition of scale factor of a dilation to the definition of scale factor of two similar polygons. How are they alike? How are they different?

25. Think About a Plan The diagram at the right shows $\triangle LMN$ and its image $\triangle L'M'N'$ for a dilation with center P. Find the values of x and y. Explain your reasoning.

- What is the relationship between $\triangle LMN$ and $\triangle L'M'N'$?
- What is the scale factor of the dilation?
- Which variable can you find using the scale factor?

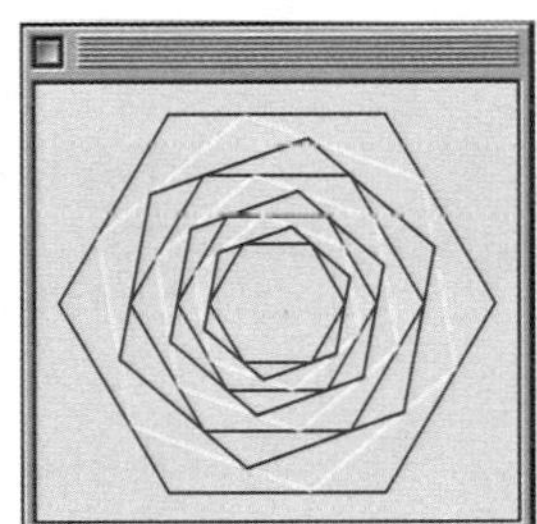

26. Writing An equilateral triangle has 4-in. sides. Describe its image for a dilation with center at one of the triangle's vertices and scale factor 2.5.

Coordinate Geometry Graph $MNPQ$ and its image $M'N'P'Q'$ for a dilation with center (0, 0) and the given scale factor.

27. $M(1, 3), N(-3, 3), P(-5, -3), Q(-1, -3); 3$

28. $M(2, 6), N(-4, 10), P(-4, -8), Q(-2, -12); \frac{1}{4}$

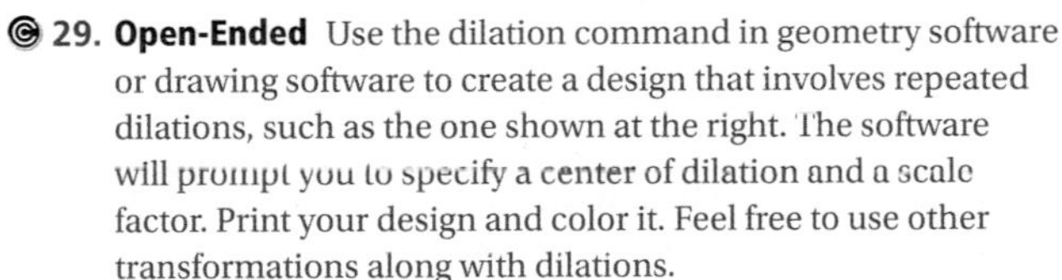

29. Open-Ended Use the dilation command in geometry software or drawing software to create a design that involves repeated dilations, such as the one shown at the right. The software will prompt you to specify a center of dilation and a scale factor. Print your design and color it. Feel free to use other transformations along with dilations.

30. Copy Reduction Your picture of your family crest is 4.5 in. wide. You need a reduced copy for the front page of the family newsletter. The copy must fit in a space 1.8 in. wide. What scale factor should you use on the copy machine to adjust the size of your picture of the crest?

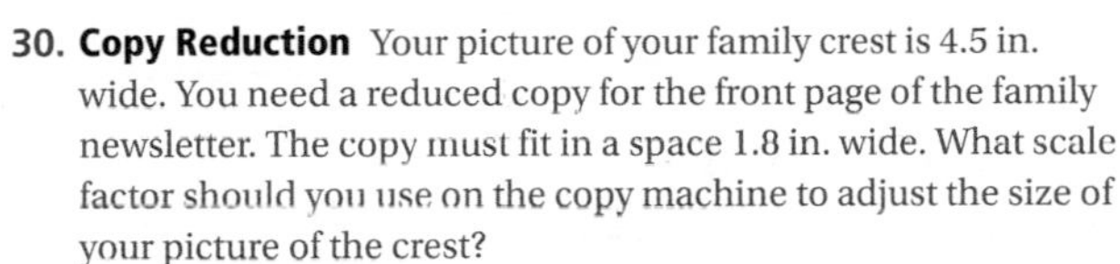

28.

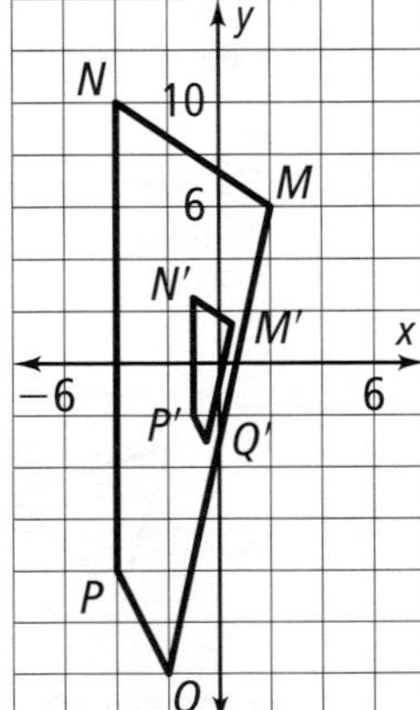

29. Check students' work.

30. 0.4

31. $I'J' = 10$ in.; $H'J' = 12$ in.

32. $HJ = 12$ cm; $I'J' = 5.25$ cm

33. $HI = 32$ ft; $I'J' = 7.5$ ft

34.

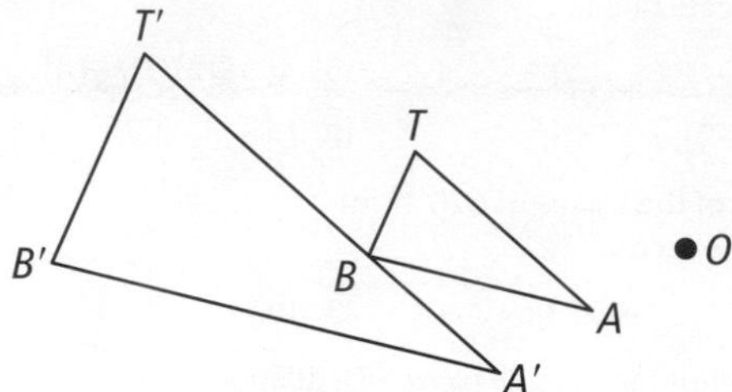

35.

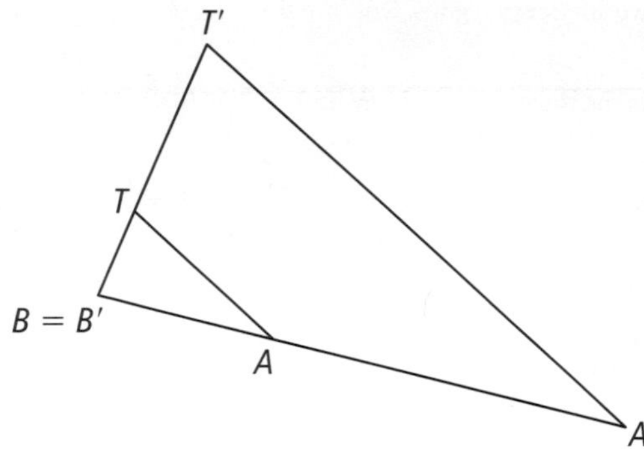

36.

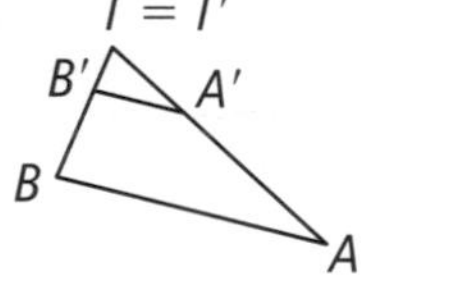

37.

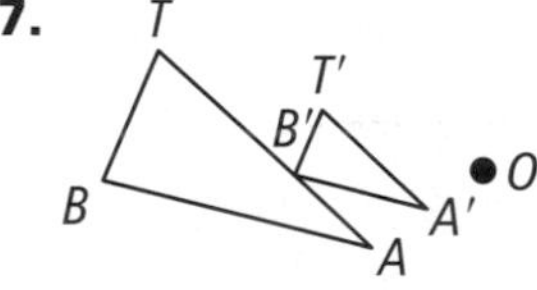

38. Connect corresp. points A and A', and B and B'. Extend $\overline{AA'}$ and $\overline{BB'}$ until they intersect. The intersection point is the center of dilation. The scale factor is the length of $\overline{A'B'}$ divided by the length of $\overline{AB}$.

39. False; a dilation does not map a segment to a ≅ segment unless the scale factor is 1.

40. False; a dilation with a scale factor greater than 1 is an enlargement.

41. True; the image and preimage are ~, so the corresp. angles are ≅.

42. False; for example, if the center of dilation is on the preimage, then it is also on the image.

43.

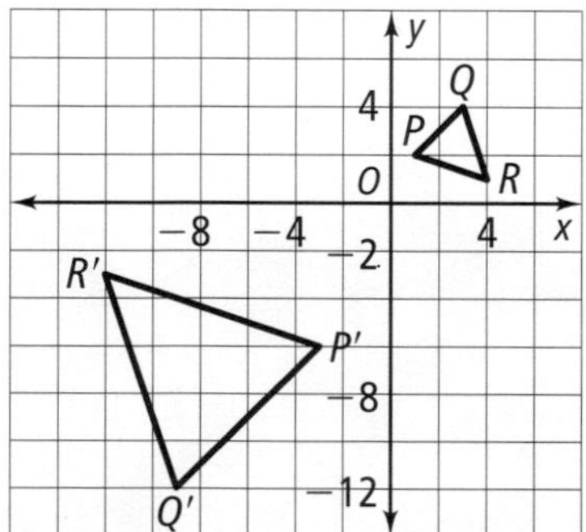

A dilation maps $\triangle HIJ$ onto $\triangle H'I'J'$. Find the missing values.

31.	$HI = 8$ in.	$H'I' = 16$ in.	**32.**	$HI = 7$ cm	$H'I' = 5.25$ cm	**33.**	$HI = ■$ ft	$H'I' = 8$ ft
	$IJ = 5$ in.	$I'J' = ■$ in.		$IJ = 7$ cm	$I'J' = ■$ cm		$IJ = 30$ ft	$I'J' = ■$ ft
	$HJ = 6$ in.	$H'J' = ■$ in.		$HJ = ■$ cm	$H'J' = 9$ cm		$HJ = 24$ ft	$H'J' = 6$ ft

Copy $\triangle TBA$ and point O for each of Exercises 34–37. Draw the dilation image $\triangle T'B'A'$.

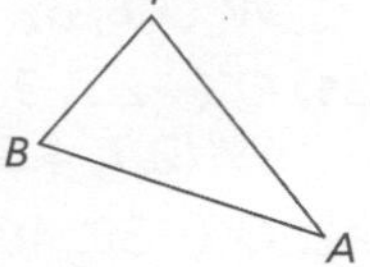

34. $D_{(2,\,O)}(\triangle TBA)$

35. $D_{(3,\,B)}(\triangle TBA)$

36. $D_{(\frac{1}{3},\,T)}(\triangle TBA)$

37. $D_{(\frac{1}{2},\,O)}(\triangle TBA)$

38. Reasoning You are given $\overline{AB}$ and its dilation image $\overline{A'B'}$ with A, B, A', and B' noncollinear. Explain how to find the center of dilation and scale factor.

Reasoning Write *true* or *false* for Exercises 39–42. Explain your answers.

39. A dilation is an isometry.

40. A dilation with a scale factor greater than 1 is a reduction.

41. For a dilation, corresponding angles of the image and preimage are congruent.

42. A dilation image cannot have any points in common with its preimage.

Challenge

Coordinate Geometry In the coordinate plane, you can extend dilations to include scale factors that are negative numbers. For Exercises 43 and 44, use $\triangle PQR$ with vertices $P(1, 2)$, $Q(3, 4)$, and $R(4, 1)$.

43. Graph $D_{-3}(\triangle PQR)$.

44. a. Graph $D_{-1}(\triangle PQR)$.

b. Explain why the dilation in part (a) may be called a *reflection through a point*. Extend your explanation to a new definition of point symmetry.

45. Shadows A flashlight projects an image of rectangle $ABCD$ on a wall so that each vertex of $ABCD$ is 3 ft away from the corresponding vertex of $A'B'C'D'$. The length of $\overline{AB}$ is 3 in. The length of $\overline{A'B'}$ is 1 ft. How far from each vertex of $ABCD$ is the light?

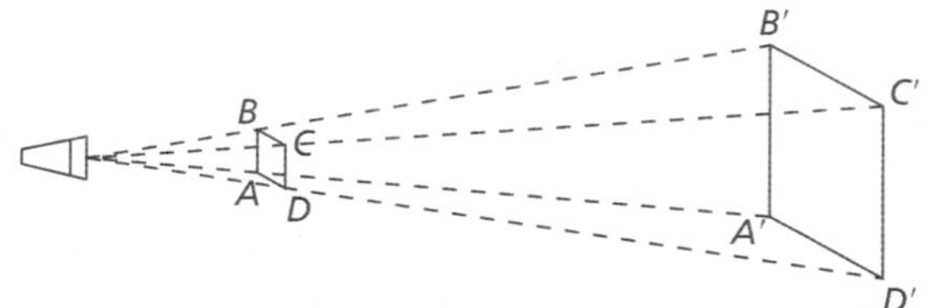

44. a.

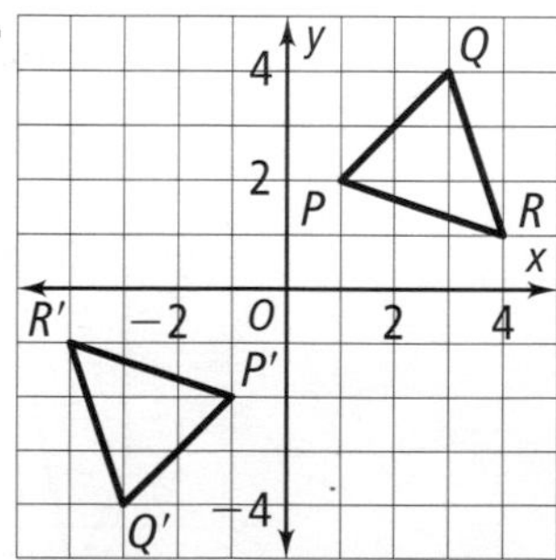

b. Answers may vary. Sample: The origin is the midpt. of each segment joining an image point to its preimage. A figure has point symmetry if there is a point P through which the figure reflects onto itself.

45. 1 ft

Assess and Remediate

Lesson Quiz

1. Is $D_n(\triangle DEF) = \triangle D'E'F'$ an enlargement or a reduction? What is the scale factor n of the dilation?

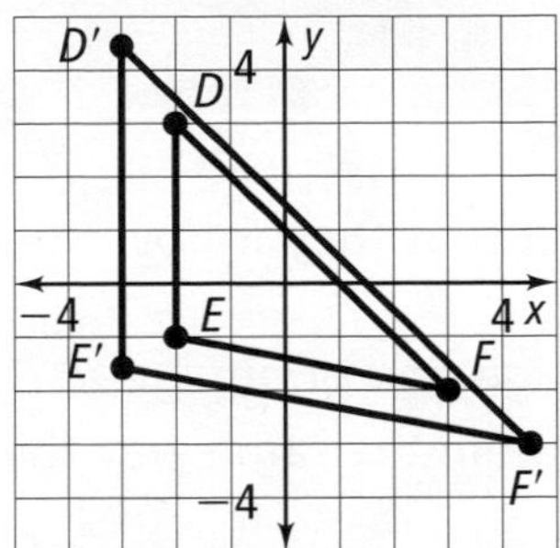

2. Do you UNDERSTAND? Quadrilateral $WXYZ$ has coordinates $W(-3, 2)$, $X(1, 3)$, $Y(2, -2)$, and $Z(-1, -2)$. What are the coordinates of the vertices of $D_2(WXYZ)$? Graph the preimage and image on a coordinate grid.

ANSWERS TO LESSON QUIZ

1. enlargement, 1.5

2. $W'(-6, 4)$, $X'(2, 6)$, $Y'(4, -4)$, and $Z'(-2, -4)$

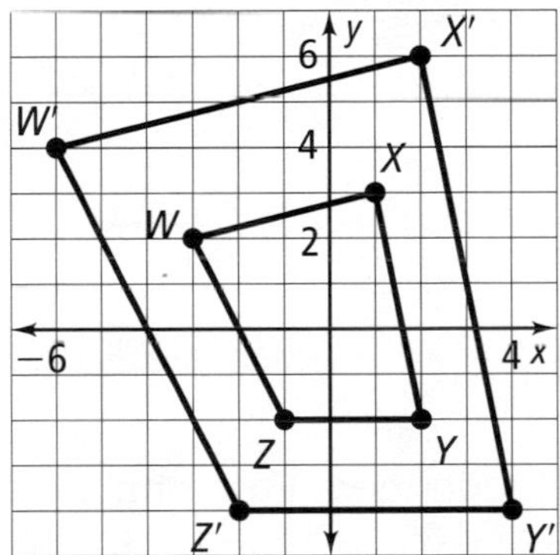

Prescription for Remediation

Use the student work on the Lesson Quiz to prescribe a differentiated assignment.

Points	Differentiated Remediation
0	Intervention
1	On-level
2	Extension

Online Assessment

Assign the Lesson Quiz in Success Tracker on **pearsonsuccessnet.com**. Success Tracker will automatically score the quiz and assign appropriate intervention or enrichment to each student based on the results. The compiled data appear in three different reports for instant analysis of whole class and individual student performance.

Differentiated Remediation

Intervention

- **RETEACHING** (2 pages) Provides reteaching and practice exercises for the key lesson concepts. Use with struggling students or absent students.
- **ENGLISH LANGUAGE LEARNER SUPPORT** Helps students develop and reinforce mathematical vocabulary and key concepts.

On-Level

- **PRACTICE** (2 pages) Provides extra practice for each lesson. For simpler practice exercises, use the Form K Practice pages found in the Online Teacher Resources.
- **THINK ABOUT A PLAN** Helps students develop specific problem-solving skills and strategies by providing scaffolded guiding questions.
- **STANDARDIZED TEST PREP** Focuses on all major exercises, all major question types, and helps students prepare for the high-stakes assessments.

Extension

- **ENRICHMENT** Provides students with interesting problems and activities that extend the concepts of the lesson.
- **ACTIVITIES, GAMES, AND PUZZLES** Worksheets that can be used for concept development, enrichment, and for fun!

6-7 Similarity Transformations

Common Core State Standards
G.SRT.2 Given two figures, use the definition of similarity in terms of similarity transformations to decide if they are similar . . . **Also G.SRT.3**

Preparing to Teach

BIG ideas Coordinate Geometry
Visualization

ESSENTIAL UNDERSTANDING

Compositions of rigid motions and dilations can be used to understand the properties of similarity. Two figures are similar if there is a similarity transformation that maps one to the other.

Math Background

In Lesson 3-8, students learned that a composition of rigid motions results in an image that is congruent to the preimage. In this lesson, students will learn that a composition of rigid motions and dilations results in an image that is similar to the preimage.

When a figure undergoes a composition of rigid motions and dilations, the corresponding angles of the image and preimage are congruent, and the ratios of corresponding sides are proportional.

So, two figures are similar if there is a composition of rigid motions and dilations that maps one figure to the other.

ELL Support

USE MANIPULATIVES To help students who have difficulty seeing how a preimage is transformed to create an image in a similarity transformation, suggest that they follow the steps below.

- Use tracing paper to trace the image and preimage.
- Cut the drawings out and orient them the same way they appear in your book.
- Manipulate the preimage using flips, slides, and turns until it is orientated the same way as the image and two corresponding vertices are intersecting.
- Align the figures at each pair of corresponding vertices to be sure all pairs of corresponding angles are congruent.

Instruct students to keep track of the rigid motions that they used to get the first two corresponding vertices to intersect. Then write the composition of rigid motions and include the appropriate dilation.

Lesson Vocabulary

- similarity transformation
- similar

Mathematical Practices

CONSTRUCT VIABLE ARGUMENTS. Students will use similarity transformations to verify the AA and SSS criteria for triangle similarity.

Interactive Learning

Solve It!

PURPOSE To describe the composition of transformations in a mapping of two triangles

PROCESS Students should recognize that because the image is larger than the preimage, a dilation is one of the transformations used.

Q Do the figures appear to have the same shape? Do they appear to have the same size? Explain. **[yes; no; The triangles appear to be similar.]**

ANSWER Sample answer: translation followed by a dilation; Translate $\triangle ABC$ until points B and B' coincide. Then dilate by the appropriate scale factor until the two triangles overlap.

CONNECT THE MATH In the Solve It, students describe how to map from one triangle to a similar triangle through a composition of transformations. In this lesson, students will learn that two figures are similar if and only if there is a similarity transformation that maps one figure onto the other.

▼ DIGITAL (STUDENT WORK SPACE PAGE 401)

SOLVE IT! **Getting Ready!**

Your friend says that she performed a composition of transformations to map $\triangle ABC$ to $\triangle A'B'C'$. Describe the composition of transformations.

2 Guided Instruction

Problem 1 Drawing Transformations

In this problem, students will draw the image of a similarity transformation.

Q Why is the reflection performed before the dilation? **[The transformation to the right of the ∘ symbol is always performed first.]**

Got It?

Q How would you write this composition using function notation? $[D_{0.5} \circ T_{<4, 2>}]$

ANSWERS

Got It? $L''(0, 2)$, $M''(0.5, -0.5)$, $N''(1.5, 1.5)$

Practice

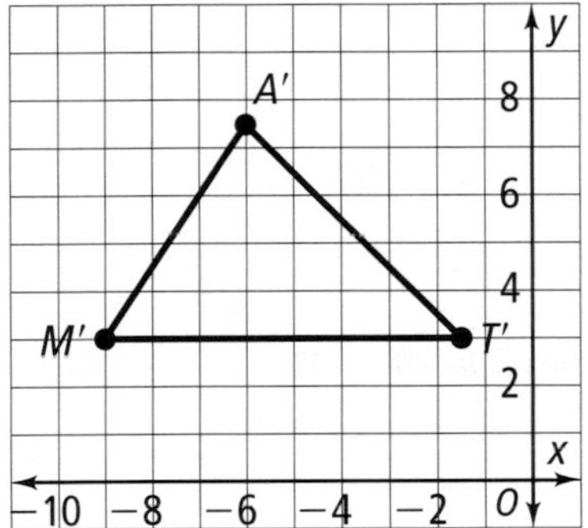

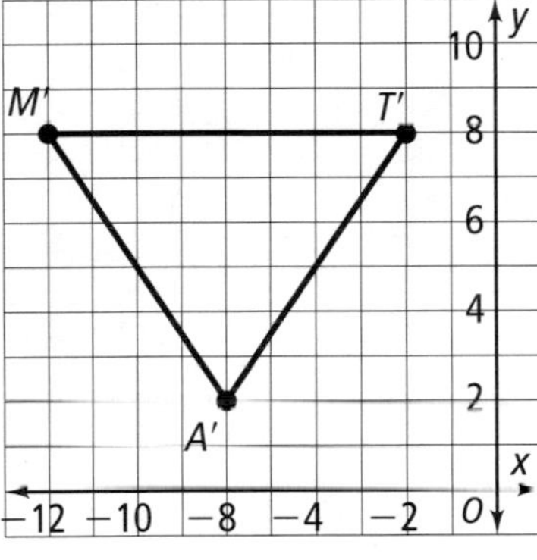

▼ STUDENT PAGE 401

In the Solve It, you used a composition of a rigid motion and a dilation to describe the mapping from $\triangle ABC$ to $\triangle A'B'C'$.

Essential Understanding You can use compositions of rigid motions and dilations to help you understand the properties of similarity.

▼ DIGITAL

Problem 1 **Drawing Transformations**

$\triangle DEF$ has vertices $D(2, 0)$, $E(1, 4)$, and $F(4, 2)$. What is the image of $\triangle DEF$ when you apply the composition $D_{1.5} \circ R_{y\text{-axis}}$?

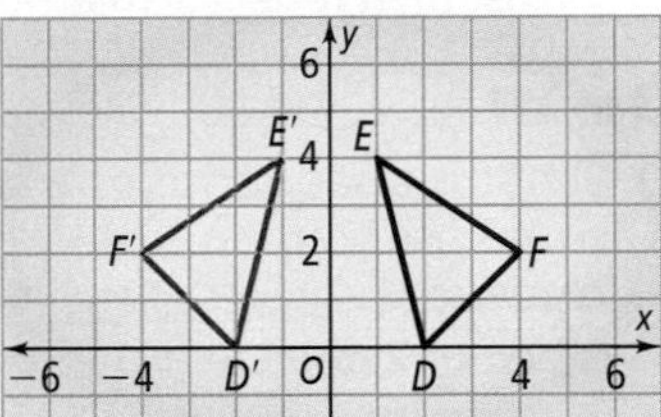

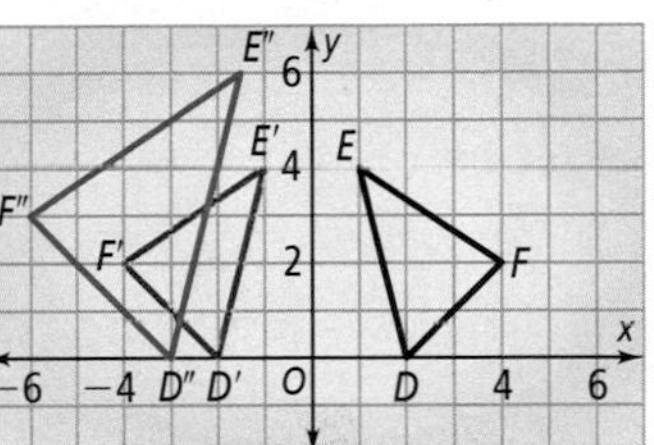

Step 1 Find the vertices of $R_{y\text{-axis}}(\triangle DEF)$. Then connect the vertices to draw the image.

$R_{y\text{-axis}}(D) = D'(-2, 0)$
$R_{y\text{-axis}}(E) = E'(-1, 4)$
$R_{y\text{-axis}}(F) = F'(-4, 2)$

Step 2 Find the vertices of the dilation of $\triangle D'E'F'$. Then connect the vertices to draw the image.

$D_{1.5}(D') - D''(-3, 0)$
$D_{1.5}(E') = E''(-1.5, 6)$
$D_{1.5}(F') = F''(-6, 3)$

The vertices of the image after the composition of transformations are $D''(-3, 0)$, $E''(-1.5, 6)$, and $F''(-6, 3)$.

▼ STUDENT PAGES 401–402

Got It? **Reasoning** $\triangle LMN$ has vertices $L(-4, 2)$, $M(-3, -3)$, and $N(-1, 1)$. Suppose the triangle is translated 4 units right and 2 units up and then dilated by a scale factor of 0.5 with center of dilation at the origin. Sketch the resulting image of the composition of transformations.

Practice **$\triangle MAT$ has vertices $M(6, -2)$, $A(4, -5)$, and $T(1, -2)$. For each of the following, sketch the image of the composition of transformations.**

1. rotation of 180° about the origin followed by a dilation by a scale factor of 1.5
2. translation 6 units up followed by a reflection across the y-axis and then a dilation by a scale factor of 2

Problem 2 Describing Transformations

In this problem, students identify a sequence of transformations that maps a preimage onto an image.

Q In looking at the figures, what is the one type of transformation that was certainly used? Explain. **[dilation; The figures are different sizes.]**

Q Do you think there is more than one composition of transformations from $\triangle RST$ to $\triangle PYZ$? If so, give an example. **[Yes. Sample answer: Reflect $\triangle RST$ across the y-axis, then reflect across the x-axis, then dilate.]**

Got It?

Q What is a sequence of transformations that you could use to map from trapezoid $MNHP$ back onto trapezoid $ABCD$? **[Sample answer: dilate by a scale factor of 2, then reflect across the y-axis.]**

ANSWERS

Got It? $D_{0.5} \circ R_{y\text{-axis}}$

Practice

3. Answers may vary. Sample: $D_{0.5} \circ r_{(90°, O)}$
4. Answers may vary. Sample: $D_{1.5} \circ R_{y\text{-axis}}$

▼ DIGITAL

Problem 2 Describing Transformations

What is a composition of rigid motions and a dilation that maps $\triangle RST$ to $\triangle PYZ$?

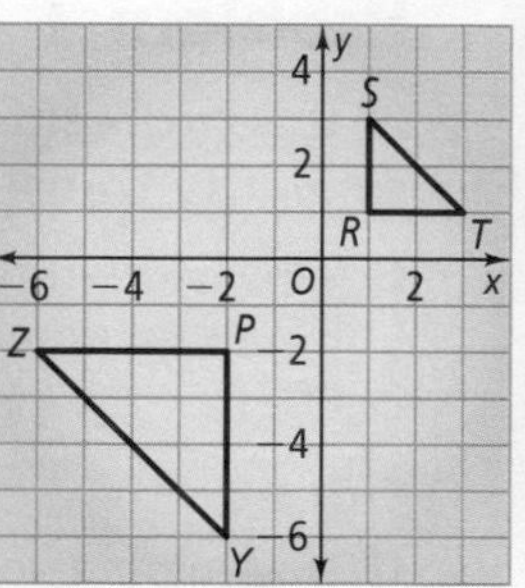

Know	Need	Plan
The vertices of the preimage and image	A composition of transformations that maps $\triangle RST$ to $\triangle PYZ$	Study the figures to determine how the image could have resulted from the preimage. Then use the vertices to verify the composition of transformations.

It appears that $\triangle RST$ was rotated and then enlarged to create $\triangle PYZ$. To verify the composition of transformations, begin by rotating the triangle 180° about the origin.

$r_{(180°, O)}(R) = R'(-1, -1)$ Use the rule $r_{(180°, O)}(x, y) = (-x, -y)$.

$r_{(180°, O)}(S) = S'(-1, -3)$

$r_{(180°, O)}(T) = T'(-3, -1)$

$\triangle PYZ$ appears to be about twice as large as $\triangle RST$. Scale the vertices of the intermediate image $R'S'T'$ to verify the composition.

$D_2(-1, -1) = P(-2, -2)$ Use the rule $D_2(x, y) = (2x, 2y)$.

$D_2(-1, -3) = Y(-2, -6)$

$D_2(-3, -1) = Z(-6, -2)$

The vertices of the dilation of $\triangle R'S'T'$ match the vertices of $\triangle PYZ$.

A rotation of 180° about the origin followed by a dilation with scale factor 2 maps $\triangle RST$ to $\triangle PYZ$.

▼ STUDENT PAGES 402–403

Got It? What is a composition of rigid motions and a dilation that maps trapezoid $ABCD$ to trapezoid $MNHP$?

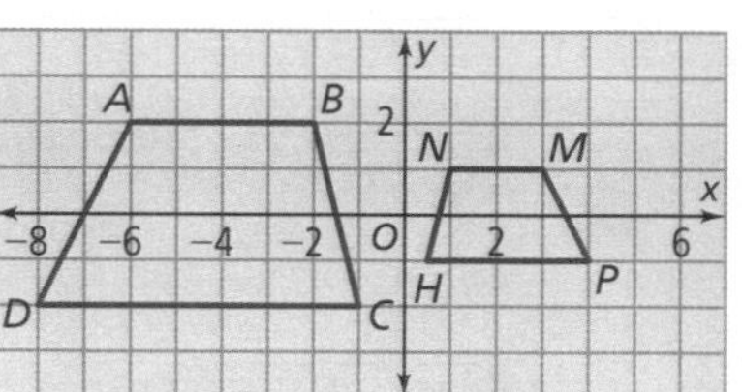

Practice For each graph, describe the composition of transformations that maps $\triangle FGH$ to $\triangle QRS$.

3. 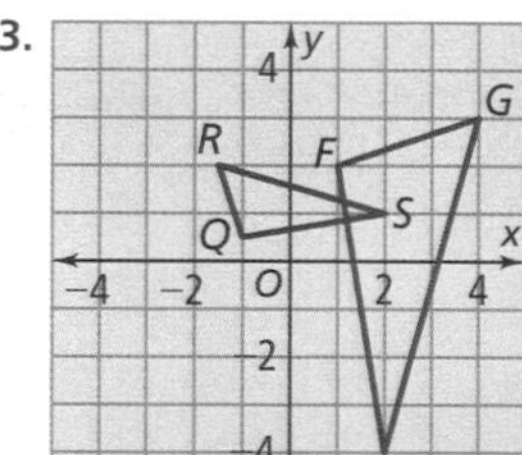

4. 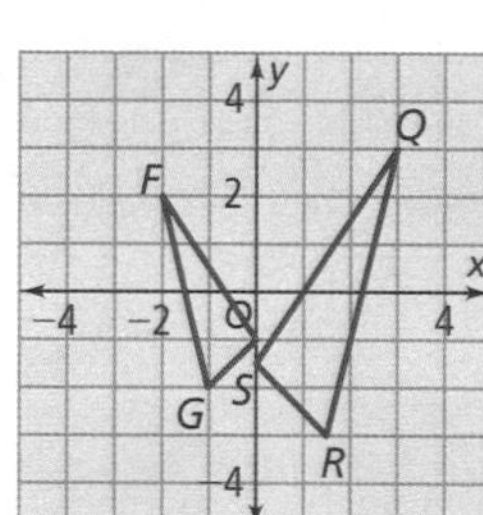

Problem 3 Finding Similarity Transformations

Take Note EXTENSION
Ask students what is needed in order to show that two figures are similar according to this Take Note definition.

Here's Why It Works
Students may have difficulty following the abstract algebraic proportions. Provide students with side lengths such as $PQ = 3$, $PR = 5$, $QR = 7$, $P'Q' = 6$, $P'R' = 10$, $Q'R' = 14$. Then have students calculate the scale factor k.

Problem 3 VISUAL LEARNERS
Some students may have difficulty seeing how a preimage was transformed to create the image. Have them simplify the process by only focusing on one pair of congruent angles or one pair of corresponding sides at a time.

Q $\overline{QA}$ corresponds to $\overline{ON}$. Which rigid motion(s) could have been performed to map $\overline{QA}$ to $\overline{ON}$? **[rotation and translation]**

Got It?
Pair students who have difficulty visualizing the similarity transformations with students who are more proficient to work together on the Got It problems. Ask them to share strategies on how to approach looking for similarity transformations.

ANSWERS

Got It? No, there is no similarity transformation that maps one triangle to the other. The side lengths are not all proportional.

Practice

5. Answers may vary. Sample answer: There is no similarity transformation. The figures are not similar because corresponding sides are not proportional.
6. Answers may vary. Sample answer: The similarity transformation is a rotation about point A followed by a dilation with center A. $\triangle SCA$ is similar to $\triangle ELA$.

▼ STUDENT PAGES 403–404

Notice that the figures in Problems 1 and 2 appear to have the same shape but different sizes. Compositions of rigid motions and dilations map preimages to similar images. For this reason, they are called **similarity transformations**. Similarity transformations give you another way to think about similarity.

take note **Key Concept** Similar Figures

Two figures are **similar** if and only if there is a similarity transformation that maps one figure onto the other.

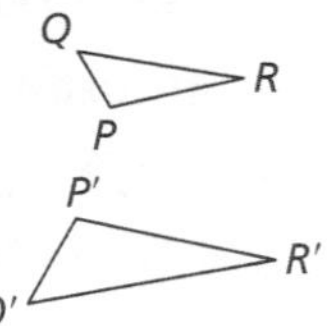

Here's Why It Works Consider the composition of a rigid motion and a dilation shown at the right.

Because rigid motions and dilations preserve angle measure, $m\angle P = m\angle P'$, $m\angle Q = m\angle Q'$, and $m\angle R = m\angle R'$. So corresponding angles are congruent.

Because there is a dilation, there is some scale factor k such that:

$P'Q' = kPQ$ $\quad Q'R' = kQR$ $\quad P'R' = kPR$

$k = \frac{P'Q'}{PQ}$ $\quad k = \frac{Q'R'}{QR}$ $\quad k = \frac{P'R'}{PR}$

So $\frac{P'Q'}{PQ} = \frac{Q'R'}{QR} = \frac{P'R'}{PR}$.

▼ DIGITAL

ONLINE PROBLEMS **Problem 3** Finding Similarity Transformations

Is there a similarity transformation that maps $\triangle PAQ$ to $\triangle TNO$? If so, identify the similarity transformation and write a similarity statement. If not, explain.

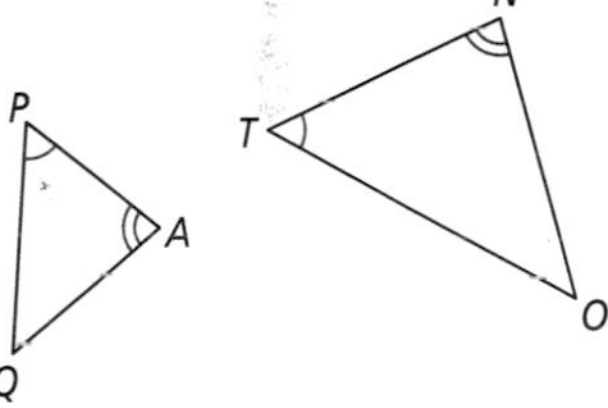

Although $PA \neq TN$, there is a scale factor k such that $k \cdot PA = TN$. Dilate $\triangle PAQ$ using this scale factor. Then $\overline{P'A'} \cong \overline{TN}$. Since dilations preserve angle measure, you also know that $\angle P' \cong \angle T$ and $\angle A' \cong \angle N$. Therefore, $\triangle P'A'Q' \cong \triangle TNO$ by ASA. This means that there is a sequence of rigid motions that maps $\triangle P'A'Q'$ onto $\triangle TNO$.

So, there is a dilation that maps $\triangle PAQ$ to $\triangle P'A'Q'$, and a sequence of rigid motions that maps $\triangle P'A'Q'$ to $\triangle TNO$. Therefore, there is a composition of a dilation and rigid motions that maps $\triangle PAQ$ onto $\triangle TNO$.

▼ STUDENT PAGES 404–405

Think Does it matter what the center of dilation is?

Got It? Is there a similarity transformation that maps $\triangle JKL$ to $\triangle RST$? If so, identify the similarity transformation and write a similarity statement. If not, explain.

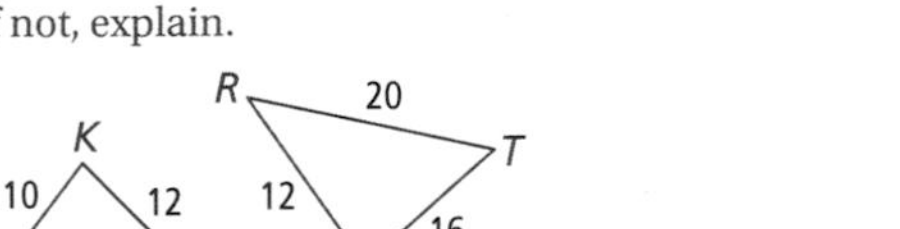

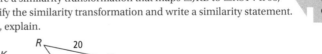

A Practice **For each pair of figures in Exercises 5 and 6, determine if there is a similarity transformation that maps one figure onto the other. If so, identify the similarity transformation and write a similarity statement. If not, explain.**

5.

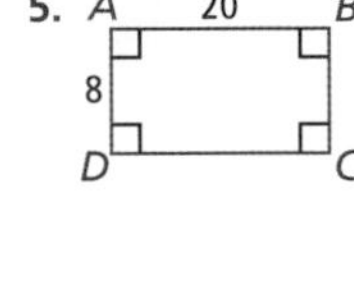

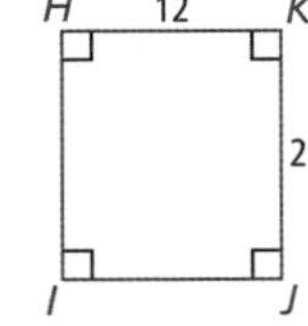

6.

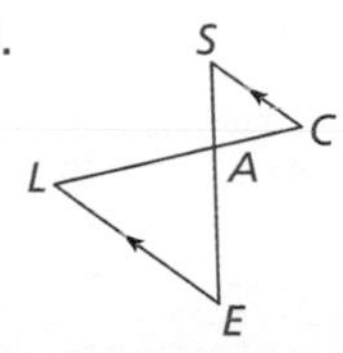

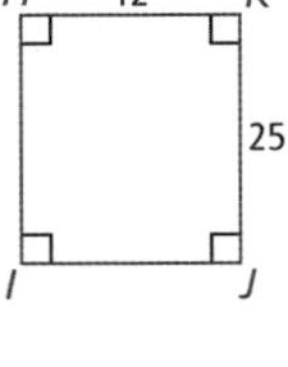

Problem 4 Determining Similarity

In this problem, students will determine if two figures are similar.

Q What do you know about the lengths of the segments used to create each lightning bolt? **[Corresponding segments are proportional.]**

Got It?

Q If you divide the height of the smaller face by the height of the larger face, what does the numerical result represent? **[the scale factor of the dilation]**

ANSWERS

Got It? Yes, there is a similarity transformation: rotation, translation, and then dilation.

Practice

7. Answers may vary. Sample answer: Yes, there is a similarity transformation between the two figures: a translation and a rotation followed by a dilation.
8. Answers may vary. Sample answer: Yes, there is a similarity transformation between the two figures: a translation and a rotation followed by a dilation.

▼ STUDENT PAGE 405

Similarity transformations provide a powerful general approach to similarity. In Problem 3, you used similarity transformations to verify the AA Postulate for triangle similarity. Another advantage to the transformational approach to similarity is that you can apply it to figures other than polygons.

▼ DIGITAL

Determining Similarity

A new company is using a computer program to design its logo. Are the two figures used in the logo so far similar?

If you can find a similarity transformation between two figures, then you know they are similar. The smaller lightning bolt can be translated so that the tips coincide. Then it can be enlarged by some scale factor so that the two bolts overlap.

The figures are similar because there is a similarity transformation that maps one figure onto the other. The transformation is a translation followed by a dilation.

▼ STUDENT PAGES 405–406

Got It? Are the figures below similar? Explain.

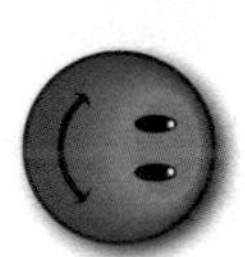

Think
How can you determine whether two figures are similar if you have no information about side lengths or angle measures?

Practice **For each pair of figures in Exercises 7 and 8, determine whether or not the figures are similar. Explain your reasoning.**

7.  

8. 

3 Lesson Check

Do you know HOW? **ERROR INTERVENTION**
If students have trouble solving Exercise 9, then ask them which angles appear to be congruent.

Do you UNDERSTAND?
In Exercise 11, ask students to share their examples with the rest of the class. Have students brainstorm different real-world applications of similarity transformations.

Close

Q What do you know about corresponding sides and corresponding angles of figures that are mapped using a composition of rigid motions and dilations? **[Corresponding angles are congruent; corresponding sides are proportional.]**

Q How can you show that two figures are similar? **[Find a composition of rigid motions and dilations that maps one figure onto the other.]**

ANSWERS

9. Answers may vary. Sample: $D_{1.5} \circ R_{y\text{-axis}}$

10. $R''\left(\frac{3}{4}, -\frac{1}{2}\right)$, $S''\left(\frac{1}{4}, -\frac{1}{4}\right)$, $T''\left(\frac{1}{2}, -1\right)$

11. Sample answer: The pupils of your eyes dilate when you go from dark to bright locations or from bright to dark. The pupils are reduced or enlarged proportionally to form similar pupils.

12. Answers may vary. Check students' work.

▼ STUDENT PAGES 406–407

Lesson Check

Do you know HOW?

Use the diagram at the right for Exercises 9 and 10.

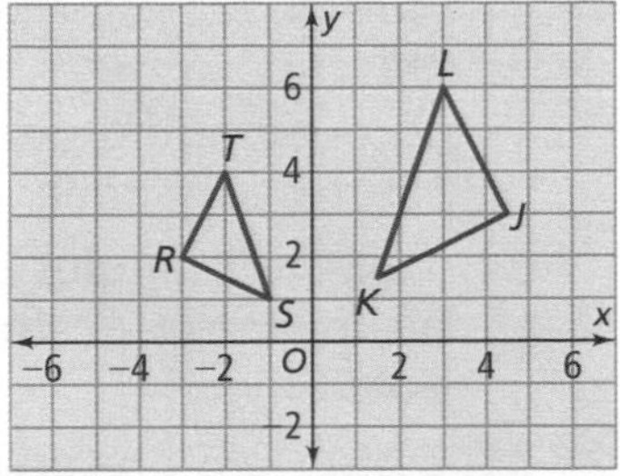

9. What is a similarity transformation that maps $\triangle RST$ to $\triangle JKL$?

10. What are the coordinates of $(D_{\frac{1}{4}} \circ r_{(180°, O)})(\triangle RST)$?

Do you UNDERSTAND?

11. Vocabulary Describe how the word *dilation* is used in areas outside of mathematics. How do these applications relate the mathematical definition?

12. Open-Ended For $\triangle TUV$ at the right, give the vertices of a similar triangle after a similarity transformation that uses at least 1 rigid motion.

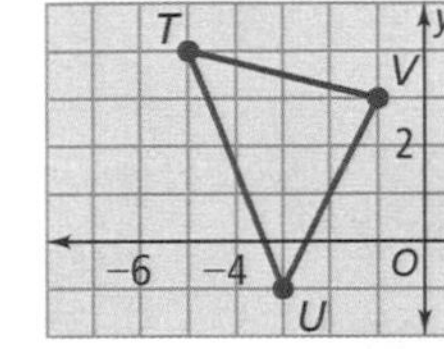

4 Practice

More Practice and Problem-Solving Exercises

ASSIGNMENT GUIDE
The assignments below are for the More Practice and Problem-Solving Exercises. You may also want to assign the A-Level Practice Exercises for homework if these are not used in class.
Average: 13–23
Advanced: 13–26

Mathematical Practices The exercises listed focus on the Standards for Mathematical Practices listed.

EX. 14: Make Sense of Problems (MP 1)
EX. 12: Reason Abstractly (MP 2)
EX. 22, 26: Construct Arguments (MP 3)
EX. 13, 15: Communicate (MP 3)
EX. 20, 21, 23: Model (MP 4)

EXERCISE 20: Use the **Think About a Plan** worksheet in the Online Teacher Resources to further support students' development in becoming independent learners.

HOMEWORK QUICK CHECK
To check students' understanding of key skills and concepts, go over Exercises 14, 16, 20, 21, and 23.

▼ STUDENT PAGE 407

More Practice and Problem-Solving Exercises

MATHEMATICAL PRACTICES

B Apply

13. Writing Your teacher used geometry software program to plot $\triangle ABC$ with vertices $A(2, 1)$, $B(6, 1)$, and $C(6, 4)$. Then he used a similarity transformation to plot $\triangle DEF$ with vertices $D(-4, -2)$, $E(-12, -2)$, and $F(-12, -8)$. The corresponding angles of the two triangles are congruent. How can the Distance Formula be used to verify that the lengths of the corresponding sides are proportional? Verify that the figures are similar.

14. Think About a Plan Suppose that $\triangle JKL$ is formed by connecting the midpoints of $\triangle ABC$. Is $\triangle AJL$ similar to $\triangle ABC$? Explain.

- How are the side lengths of $\triangle AJL$ related to the side lengths of $\triangle ABC$?
- Can you find a similarity transformation that maps $\triangle AJL$ to $\triangle ABC$? Explain.

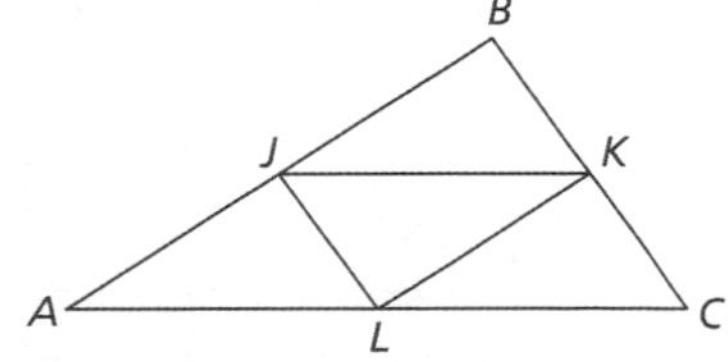

More Practice and Problem-Solving Exercises *continued*

ANSWERS

13. Answers may vary. Sample answer: Use the Distance Formula to find the lengths of the sides. Then verify that the ratios of corresponding sides are proportional. $AB = 4$, $BC = 3$, $AC = 5$, $DE = 8$, $EF = 6$, and $DF = 10$. Since $\frac{AB}{DE} = \frac{BC}{EF} = \frac{AC}{DF} = 0.5$, the ratios of corresponding sides are proportional, and the figures are similar.

14. Yes, the triangles are similar because there is a similarity transformation that maps $\triangle AJL$ to $\triangle ABC$.

15. Distance is preserved by rigid motions, but not by similarity transformations.

16. sometimes **17.** always

18. always **19.** never

20. a. Yes, the triangles are similar because there is a similarity transformation between them: You can map the smaller triangle to the larger triangle by a rotation of 180° around their shared vertex followed by a dilation with scale factor 2.5 and center at the shared vertex.

b. 330 m

21. No, the photos will not be similar. There is no similarity transformation that maps the smaller photo to the larger photo.

22. Answers may vary. Sample answer: Yes, a rigid motion is a similarity transformation with a scale factor of 1. The preimage and image of a rigid motion are congruent, so they are also similar.

23. a. 104 inches by 24 inches;

b. Enlarging the banner is a dilation, which is an example of a similarity transformation.

24. Answers may vary. Sample answer: No, there is not a similarity transformation. To create $\triangle NOP$, $\triangle ABC$ is reflected across the x-axis. Then the x-coordinates are scaled by a factor of 5 and the y-coordinates are scaled by a factor of 4. Because the reflected triangle is 5 times as wide as $\triangle ABC$ but only 4 times as tall, the figures are not similar. Therefore, there is no similarity transformation between them.

25. Yes, the image of the transparency is rotated in space and dilated. The image on the wall is similar to the preimage on the transparency.

26. a. true

b. true

c. false

15. Writing What properties are preserved by rigid motions but not by similarity transformations?

Determine whether each statement is *always, sometimes,* or *never* true.

16. There is a similarity transformation between two rectangles.

17. There is a similarity transformation between two squares.

18. There is a similarity transformation between two circles.

19. There is a similarity transformation between a right triangle and an equilateral triangle.

20. Indirect Measurement A surveyor wants to use similar triangles to determine the distance across a lake as shown at the right.

a. Are the two triangles in the figure similar? Justify your reasoning.

b. What is the distance d across the lake?

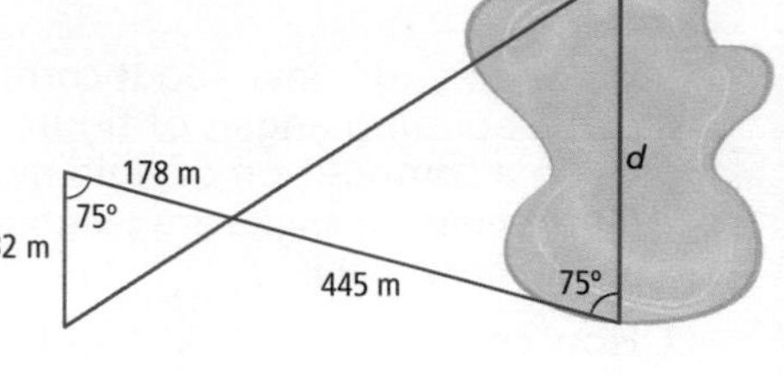

21. Photography A 4-in. by 6-in. rectangular photo is enlarged to fit an 8-in. by 10-in. frame. Are the two photographs similar? Explain.

22. Reasoning Is a rigid motion an example of a similarity transformation? Explain your reasoning and give an example.

23. Art A printing company enlarges a banner for a graduation party by a scale factor of 8.

a. What are the dimensions of the larger banner?

b. How can the printing company be sure that the enlarged banner is similar to the original?

Challenge

24. If $\triangle ABC$ has vertices given by $A(u, v)$, $B(w, x)$, and $C(y, z)$, and $\triangle NOP$ has vertices given by $N(5u, 24v)$, $O(5w, 24x)$, and $P(5y, 24z)$, is there a similarity transformation that maps $\triangle ABC$ to $\triangle NOP$? Explain.

25. Overhead Projector When Mrs. Sheldon places a transparency on the screen of the overhead projector, the projector shows an enlargement of the transparency on the wall. Does this situation represent a similarity transformation? Explain.

26. Reasoning Tell whether each statement below is *true* or *false*.

a. In order to show that two figures are similar, it is sufficient to show that there is a similarity transformation that maps one figure to the other.

b. If there is a similarity transformation that maps one figure to another figure, then the figures are similar.

c. If there is a similarity transformation that maps one figure to another figure, then the figures are congruent.

Assess and Remediate

Lesson Quiz

1. $\triangle BCD$ has vertices $B(-8, 3)$, $C(-4, 6)$, and $D(2, 0)$. If the triangle is reflected across the x-axis and dilated by a scale factor of 0.5 with respect to the origin, what are the coordinates of the vertices of $\triangle B''C''D''$?
2. **Do you UNDERSTAND?** What is a sequence of transformations that maps $\triangle RST$ to $\triangle LMN$?

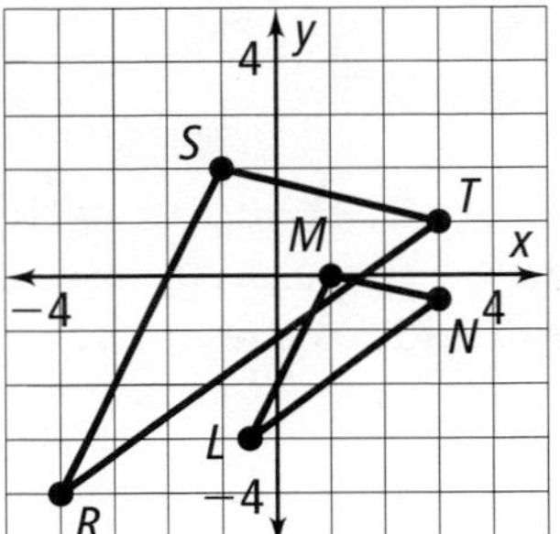

3. Are the figures below similar? Explain.

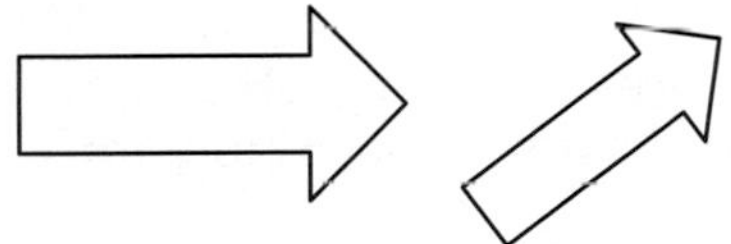

ANSWERS TO LESSON QUIZ

1. $B''(-4, -1.5)$, $C''(-2, -3)$, $D''(1, 0)$
2. $D_{0.5} \circ T_{<3, -2>}$
3. Yes, there is a similarity transformation: translation, rotation, then dilation.

Prescription for Remediation

Use the student work on the Lesson Quiz to prescribe a differentiated assignment.

Points	Differentiated Remediation
0–1	Intervention
2	On-level
3	Extension

Online Assessment

Assign the Lesson Quiz in Success Tracker on **pearsonsuccessnet.com**. Success Tracker will automatically score the quiz and assign appropriate intervention or enrichment to each student based on the results. The compiled data appear in three different reports for instant analysis of whole class and individual student performance.

Differentiated Remediation

Intervention

- **RETEACHING** (2 pages) Provides reteaching and practice exercises for the key lesson concepts. Use with struggling students or absent students.
- **ENGLISH LANGUAGE LEARNER SUPPORT** Helps students develop and reinforce mathematical vocabulary and key concepts.

On-Level

- **PRACTICE** (2 pages) Provides extra practice for each lesson. For simpler practice exercises, use the Form K Practice pages found in the Online Teacher Resources.
- **THINK ABOUT A PLAN** Helps students develop specific problem-solving skills and strategies by providing scaffolded guiding questions.
- **STANDARDIZED TEST PREP** Focuses on all major exercises, all major question types, and helps students prepare for the high-stakes assessments.

Extension

- **ENRICHMENT** Provides students with interesting problems and activities that extend the concepts of the lesson.
- **ACTIVITIES, GAMES, AND PUZZLES** Worksheets that can be used for concept development, enrichment, and for fun!

Chapter Review

Essential Questions

BIG idea Similarity

ESSENTIAL QUESTION How do you use proportions to find side lengths in similar polygons?

ANSWER You can set up and solve proportions using corresponding sides of similar polygons.

BIG idea Reasoning and Proof

ESSENTIAL QUESTION How do you show two triangles are similar?

ANSWER Two triangles are similar if certain relationships exist between two or three pairs of corresponding parts.

BIG idea Visualization

ESSENTIAL QUESTION How do you identify corresponding parts of similar triangles?

ANSWER Sketch and label triangles separately in the same orientation to see how the sides and vertices correspond.

Summative Questions

Use the following prompts as you review this chapter with your students. The prompts are designed to help you assess your students' understanding of the BIG Ideas they have studied.

- How do you form a proportion?
- How do you solve a proportion?
- What conditions must be true for two polygons to be similar?
- When a figure is made up of more than one polygon, how can you visualize the vertices and sides of each polygon?

6-1 Ratios and Proportions

ANSWERS

1. 1 : 116 or $\frac{1}{116}$
2. 36
3. 6
4. $\frac{55}{4}$ or $13\frac{3}{4}$
5. 6
6. 7

▼ STUDENT PAGE 409

6-1 Ratios and Proportions

Quick Review

A **ratio** is a comparison of two quantities by division. A **proportion** is a statement that two ratios are equal. The **Cross Products Property** states that if $\frac{a}{b} = \frac{c}{d}$, where $b \neq 0$ and $d \neq 0$, then $ad = bc$.

Example

What is the solution of $\frac{x}{x+3} = \frac{4}{6}$?

$6x = 4(x + 3)$	Cross Products Property
$6x = 4x + 12$	Distributive Property
$2x = 12$	Subtract 4x from each side.
$x = 6$	Divide each side by 2.

Exercises

1. A high school has 16 math teachers for 1856 math students. What is the ratio of math teachers to math students?
2. The measures of two complementary angles are in the ratio 2 : 3. What is the measure of the smaller angle?

Algebra Solve each proportion.

3. $\frac{x}{7} = \frac{18}{21}$
4. $\frac{6}{11} = \frac{15}{2x}$
5. $\frac{x}{3} = \frac{x+4}{5}$
6. $\frac{8}{x+9} = \frac{2}{x-3}$

6-2 and 6-3 Similar Polygons and Proving Triangles Similar

ANSWERS

7. *JEHN* ~ *JKLP*; 3 : 4

8. $\triangle PQR \sim \triangle XYZ$; 3 : 2

9. 120 ft

10. 45 ft

11. The ratio of each pair of corresp. sides is 2 : 1, so $\triangle AMY \sim \triangle ECD$ by SSS ~.

12. If lines are ∥, then corresp. angles are ≅, so $\triangle RPT \sim \triangle SGT$ by AA ~.

▼ STUDENT PAGE 409

6-2 and 6-3 Similar Polygons and Proving Triangles Similar

Quick Review

Similar polygons have congruent corresponding angles and proportional corresponding sides. You can prove triangles similar with limited information about congruent corresponding angles and proportional corresponding sides.

Postulate or Theorem	What You Need
Angle-Angle (AA ~)	two pairs of ≅ angles
Side-Angle-Side (SAS ~)	two pairs of proportional sides and the included angles ≅
Side-Side-Side (SSS ~)	three pairs of proportional sides

Example

Is $\triangle ABC$ similar to $\triangle RQP$? How do you know?

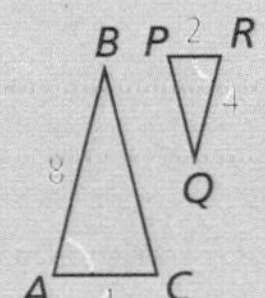

You know that $\angle A \cong \angle R$. $\frac{AB}{RQ} = \frac{AC}{RP} = \frac{2}{1}$, so the triangles are similar by the SAS ~ Theorem.

Exercises

The polygons are similar. Write a similarity statement and give the scale factor.

7.

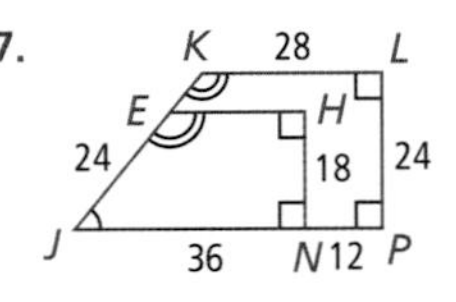

8.

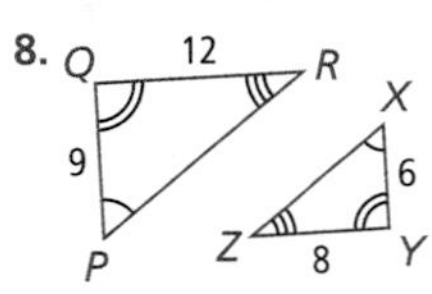

9. City Planning The length of a rectangular playground in a scale drawing is 12 in. If the scale is 1 in. = 10 ft, what is the actual length?

10. Indirect Measurement A 3-ft vertical post casts a 24-in. shadow at the same time a pine tree casts a 30-ft shadow. How tall is the pine tree?

Are the triangles similar? How do you know?

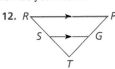

11.

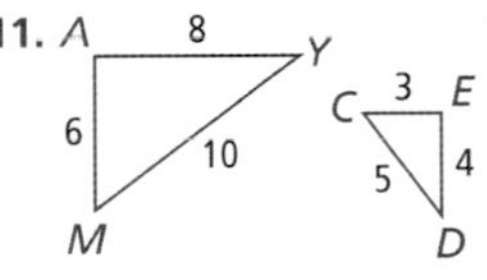

12.

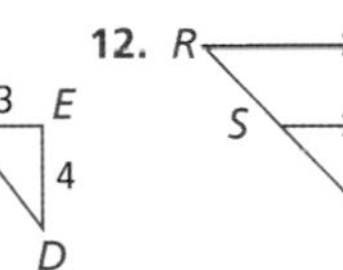

6-4 Similarity in Right Triangles

ANSWERS

13. 12

14. $2\sqrt{15}$

15. $x = 6\sqrt{2}$, $y = 6\sqrt{6}$

16. $\sqrt{35}$

17. $x = 2\sqrt{21}$, $y = 4\sqrt{3}$

18. $x = 12$, $y = 4\sqrt{5}$

▼ STUDENT PAGE 410

6-4 Similarity in Right Triangles

Quick Review

$\overline{CD}$ is the altitude to the hypotenuse of right $\triangle ABC$.

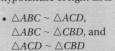

- $\triangle ABC \sim \triangle ACD$, $\triangle ABC \sim \triangle CBD$, and $\triangle ACD \sim \triangle CBD$

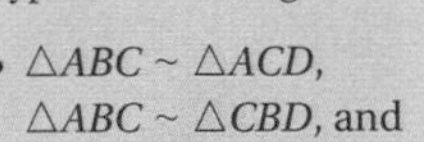

- $\frac{AD}{CD} = \frac{CD}{DB}$, $\frac{AB}{AC} = \frac{AC}{AD}$, and $\frac{AB}{CB} = \frac{CB}{DB}$

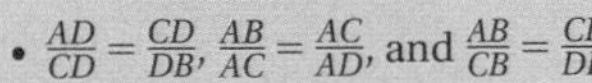

Example

What is the value of x?

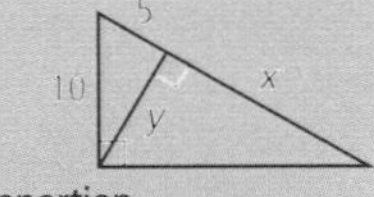

$\frac{5+x}{10} = \frac{10}{5}$	Write a proportion.
$5(5+x) = 100$	Cross Products Property
$25 + 5x = 100$	Distributive Property
$5x = 75$	Subtract 25 from each side.
$x = 15$	Divide each side by 5.

Exercises

Find the geometric mean of each pair of numbers.

13. 9 and 16

14. 5 and 12

Algebra Find the value of each variable. Write your answer in simplest radical form.

15.

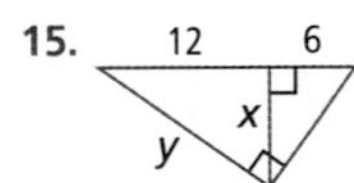

16.

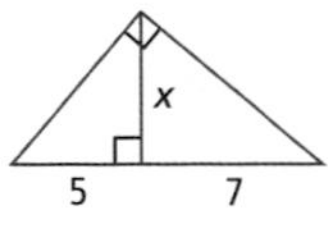

17.

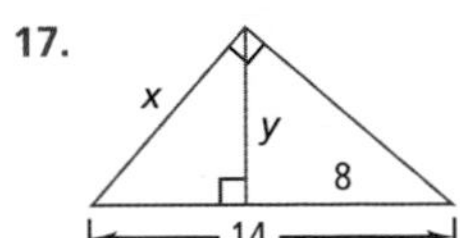

18.

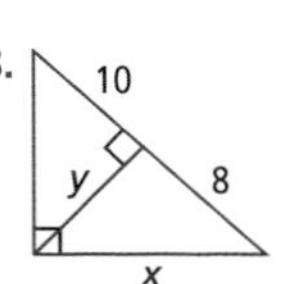

Chapter Review *(continued)*

6-5 Proportions in Triangles

ANSWERS

19. 7.5

20. 3.6

21. 22.5

22. 12

23. 17.5

24. 77

▼ STUDENT PAGE 410

6-5 Proportions in Triangles

Quick Review

Side-Splitter Theorem and Corollary

If a line parallel to one side of a triangle intersects the other two sides, then it divides those sides proportionally. If three parallel lines intersect two transversals, then the segments intercepted on the transversals are proportional.

Triangle-Angle-Bisector Theorem

If a ray bisects an angle of a triangle, then it divides the opposite side into two segments that are proportional to the other two sides of the triangle.

Example

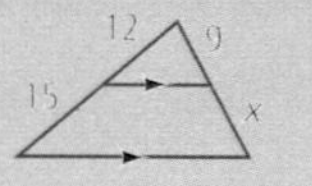

What is the value of x?

$\frac{12}{15} = \frac{9}{x}$	Write a proportion.
$12x = 135$	Cross Products Property
$x = 11.25$	Divide each side by 12.

Exercises

Algebra Find the value of x.

19.

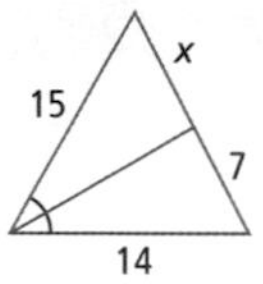

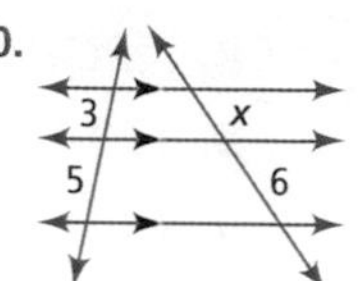

20.

21.

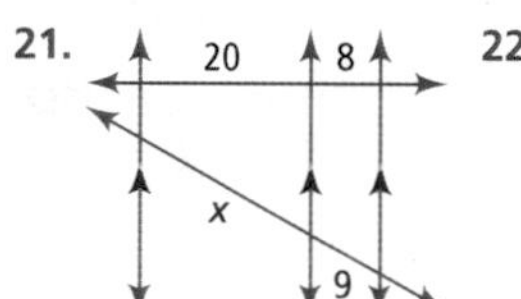

22.

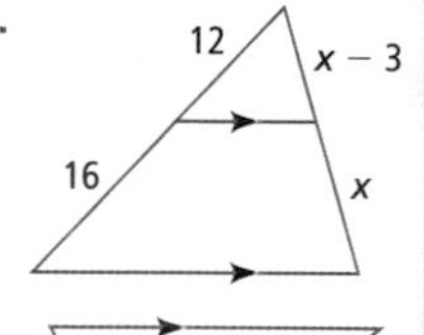

23.

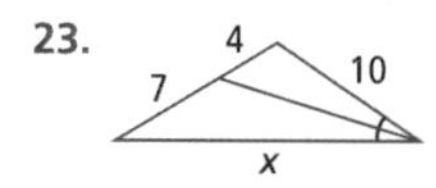

24.

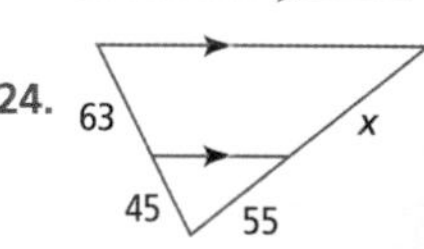

6-6 Dilations

ANSWERS

25. enlargement; 2

26. $M'(-15, 20)$, $A'(-30, -5)$, $T'(0, 0)$, $H'(15, 10)$; check students' graphs.

27.

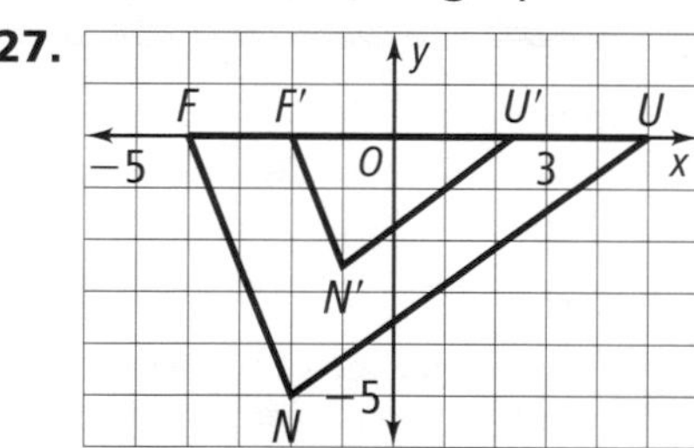

28. $L'N' = 6.5$ ft, $M'N' = 11.25$ ft

▼ STUDENT PAGE 411

6-6 Dilations

Quick Review

The diagram shows a **dilation** with center C and scale factor n. The preimage and image are similar.

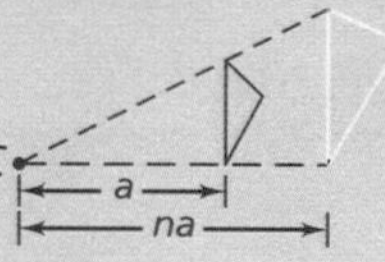

Example

The blue figure is a dilation image of the black figure. The center of dilation is A. Is the dilation an enlargement or a reduction? What is the scale factor?

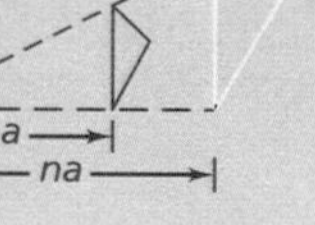

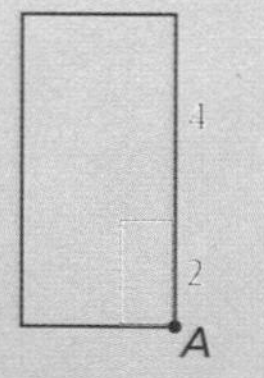

The image is smaller than the preimage, so the dilation is a reduction. The scale factor is $\frac{\text{image length}}{\text{original length}} = \frac{2}{2+4} = \frac{2}{6}$, or $\frac{1}{3}$.

Exercises

25. The red figure is a dilation image of the blue figure. The center of dilation is O. Tell whether the dilation is an enlargement or a reduction. Then find the scale factor.

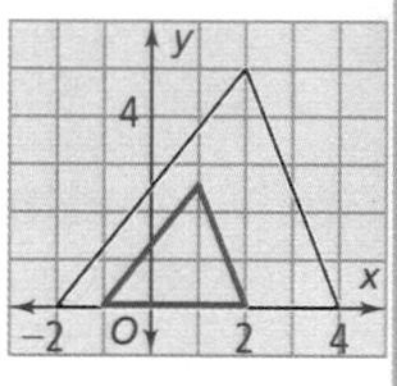

Graph the polygon with the given vertices. Then graph its image for a dilation with center (0, 0) and the given scale factor.

26. $M(-3, 4)$, $A(-6, -1)$, $T(0, 0)$, $H(3, 2)$; scale factor 5

27. $F(-4, 0)$, $U(5, 0)$, $N(-2, -5)$; scale factor $\frac{1}{2}$

28. A dilation maps $\triangle LMN$ onto $\triangle L'M'N'$. $LM = 36$ ft, $LN = 26$ ft, $MN = 45$ ft, and $L'M' = 9$ ft. Find $L'N'$ and $M'N'$.

6-7 Similarity Transformations

ANSWERS

29.

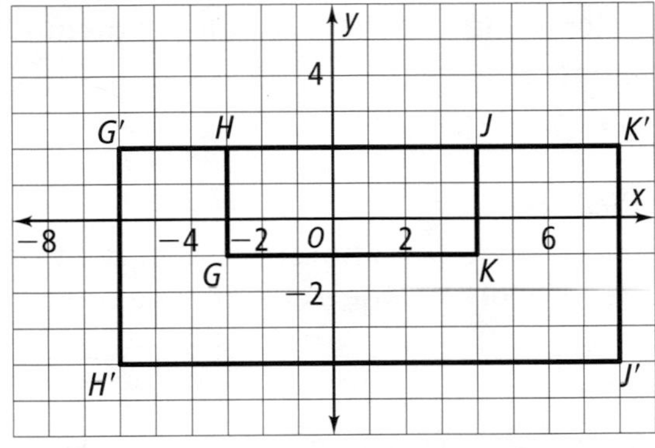

30. No. The side lengths are not proportional.

31. No, because all of the dimensions of the airplane must dilate by the same scale factor for the figures to be similar.

32. Answers may vary. Sample answer: The figures are similar because a composition of a translation, rotation, and a dilation maps *p* to *d*.

▼ STUDENT PAGE 411

Lesson 6-7 Similarity Transformations

Quick Review

Two figures are similar if and only if there is a similarity transformation that maps one figure onto the other. When a figure is transformed by a composition of rigid motions and dilations, the corresponding angles of the image and preimage are congruent, and the ratios of corresponding sides are proportional.

Example

Is $\triangle JKL$ similar to $\triangle DCX$? If so, write a similarity transformation rule. If not, explain why not.

$\triangle JKL$ can be rotated and then translated so that J and D coincide and $\overline{JK}$ and $\overline{CD}$ are collinear. Then if $\triangle JKL$ is dilated by scale factor $\frac{4}{5}$, then $\triangle JKL$ will coincide with $\triangle DCX$. So $\triangle JKL$ is similar to $\triangle DCX$, and the similarity transformation is a rotation, followed by a translation, followed by a dilation of scale factor $\frac{4}{5}$.

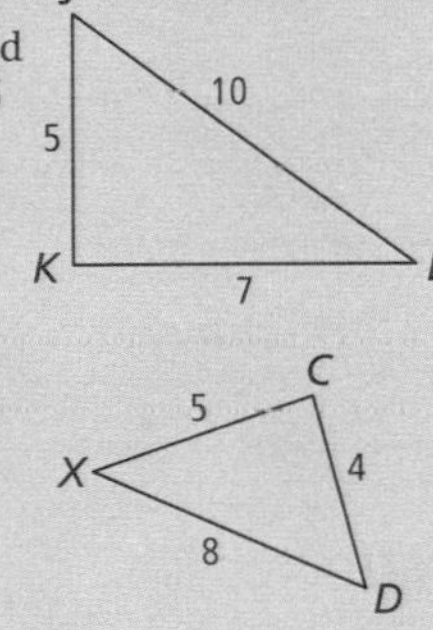

Exercises

29. $\square GHJK$ has vertices $G(-3, -1)$, $H(-3, 2)$ $J(4, 2)$, and $K(4, -1)$. Draw $\square GHJK$ and its image when you apply the composition $D_2 \circ R_{x\text{-axis}}$.

30. Writing Suppose that you have an 8-in. by 12-in. photo of your friends and a 2-in. by 6-in. copy of the same picture. Are the two photos similar figures? How do you know?

31. Reasoning A model airplane has an overall length that is $\frac{1}{20}$ the actual plane's length, and an overall height that is $\frac{1}{18}$ the actual plane's height. Are the model airplane and the actual airplane similar figures? Explain.

32. Determine whether the figures at the right are similar. If so, write the similarity transformation rule. If not, explain.

p

Pull It All Together

Common Core State Standard
G.SRT.5 Use . . . similarity criteria . . . to solve problems.

Using Performance Tasks

Understanding by Design® principles support using performance tasks to assess students' progress toward mastering content standards and developing proficiency with the Mathematical Practices.

Mathematical Practices

- Make sense of problems and persevere in solving them.
- Model with mathematics.
- Use appropriate tools strategically.

Assessing Performance

See the Implementation Guide for a holistic scoring rubric to use in assessing students' work on the performance task.

Guiding Questions

Q Why don't the lines on Lillian's calculator screen appear perpendicular?

Q Why might a ruler help to solve this problem?

Q What is true about the ratios of the length and width of similar rectangles?

Solution Outline

Using a centimeter ruler, you can determine that the graphing calculator screen has a width of 5.1 cm and a height of 3.4 cm. The ratio of the width to the height is $\frac{3}{2}$.

The length of the portion of the y-axis shown is 20 units, since Ymin = −10 and Ymax = 10. If the dimensions of the WINDOW form a rectangle that is similar to the graphing calculator screen, then the graph of the lines will not be skewed. Let x represent the length of the portion of the x-axis to be shown on the screen. Write and solve a proportion:

$$\frac{3}{2} = \frac{x}{20}$$
$$60 = 2x$$
$$x = 30$$

The length of the portion of the x-axis shown should be 30 units. Since the graph is centered at the origin, use Xmin = −15 and Xmax = 15.

▼ STUDENT PAGE 412

Adjusting a Graphing Calculator Window

ASSESSMENT

Lillian graphs the functions $y = 2x + 3$ and $y = -\frac{1}{2}x + 1$ on her graphing calculator. She knows the lines are perpendicular, but they do not appear to be on the screen.

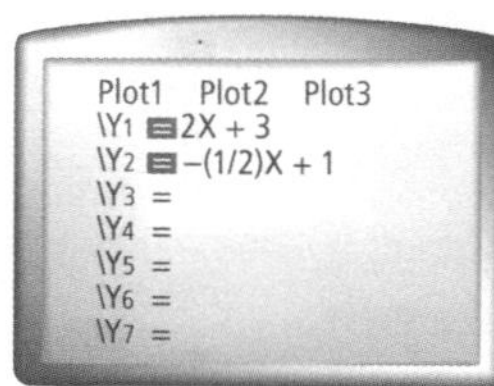

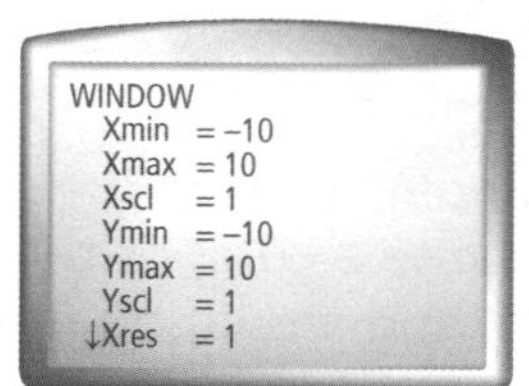

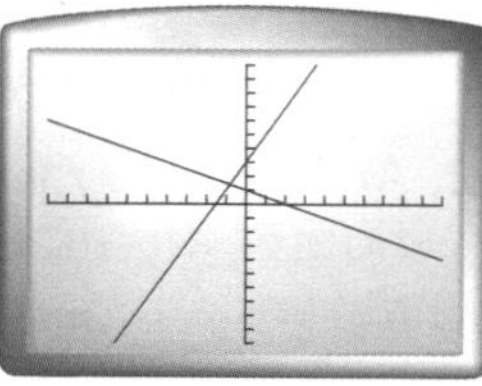

The screens above are the same shape as Lillian's graphing calculator screen. The **window** screen shows the interval of the x-axis (from **Xmin** to **Xmax**) and the y-axis (from **Ymin** to **Ymax**) for the viewing screen.

Lillian wants to adjust the values of **Xmin** and **Xmax** so that the graph of the lines is not skewed.

Task Description

Determine the values of Xmin and Xmax that Lillian should use for the viewing screen.

- What are the dimensions of the calculator screen in centimeters?
- How can similar figures help you solve the problem?

Get Ready!

Using This Diagnostic Assessment

Assign this diagnostic assessment to determine if students have the prerequisite skills for Chapter 7.

Lesson	Skill
6-1	Solving Proportions
6-3	Proving Triangles Similar
6-4	Similarity in Right Triangles

To remediate students, select from these resources (available for every lesson).

- Online Problems (pearsonsuccessnet.com)
- Reteaching (Online Teacher Resources)
- Practice (Online Teacher Resources)

Why Students Need These Skills

SOLVING PROPORTIONS Students will use proportions in conjunction with trigonometric ratios to make indirect measurements.

PROVING TRIANGLES SIMILAR Students will use relationships of similar triangles when solving problems related to right triangle trigonometry.

SIMILARITY IN RIGHT TRIANGLES Concepts of similar right triangles will help students understand properties of special right triangles.

Looking Ahead Vocabulary

ANGLE OF ELEVATION Have students identify objects in the classroom that they are using an angle of elevation to view.

TRIGONOMETRIC RATIO Have students name other words that use the prefix *tri-*.

ANSWERS

1. 4.648
2. 40.970
3. 6149.090
4. −5
5. AA~
6. SSS~
7. SAS~
8. 12
9. 8
10. $2\sqrt{13}$
11. 15
12. Answers may vary. Sample: When something is "elevated" you look up to see it, so an ∠ of elevation is formed by a horizontal line and the line of sight.
13. Answers may vary. Sample: The prefix *tri-* means 3; triangles are associated with trigonometric ratios.

▼ STUDENT PAGE 413

Solving Proportions

Algebra Solve for x. If necessary, round answers to the nearest thousandth.

1. $0.2734 = \frac{x}{17}$
2. $0.5858 = \frac{24}{x}$
3. $0.8572 = \frac{5271}{x}$
4. $0.5 = \frac{x}{3x + 5}$

Proving Triangles Similar

Name the postulate or theorem that proves each pair of triangles similar.

5. $\overline{CD} \parallel \overline{AB}$

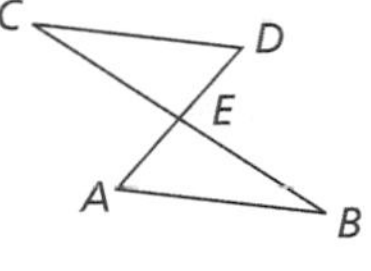

6.

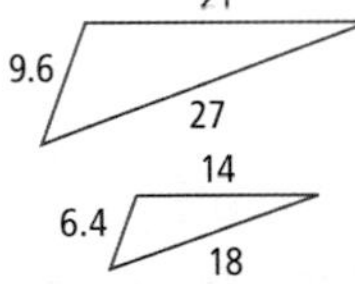

7. $\overline{JK} \perp \overline{ML}$

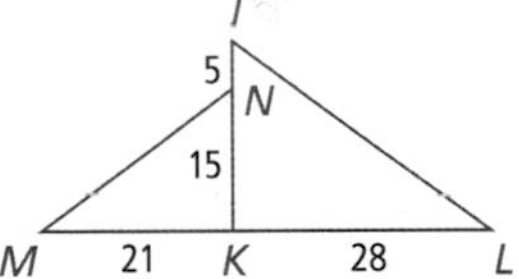

Similarity in Right Triangles

Algebra Find the value of x in $\triangle ABC$ with right $\angle C$ and altitude $\overline{CD}$.

8.

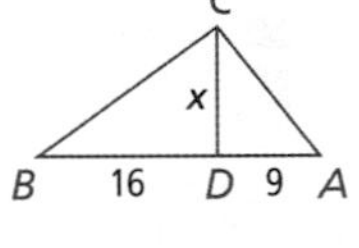

9.

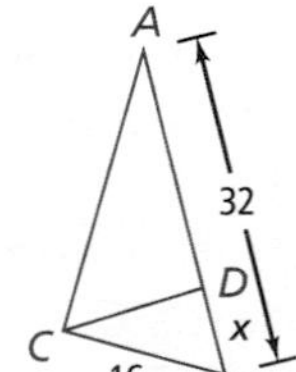

10.

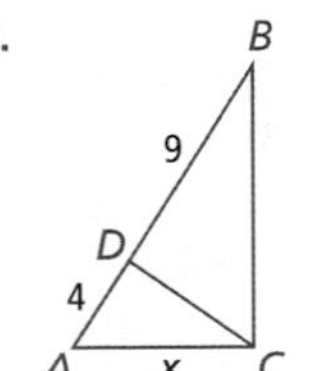

11.

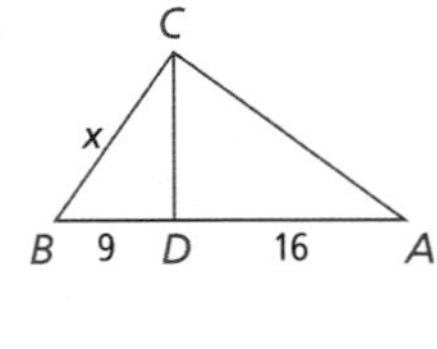

Looking Ahead Vocabulary

12. People often describe the height of a mountain as its *elevation*. How might you describe an *angle of elevation* in geometry?
13. You see the prefix *tri-* in many words, such as *triad, triathlon, trilogy,* and *trimester*. What does the prefix indicate in these words? What geometric figure do you think is associated with the phrase *trigonometric ratio*? Explain.

CHAPTER
7

RIGHT TRIANGLES AND TRIGONOMETRY

Chapter 7 Overview

Interactive Digital Path
Log in to pearsonsuccessnet.com and click on Interactive Digital Path to access the Solve Its and animated Problems.

In Chapter 7 students explore concepts related to right triangles, including trigonometry. Students will develop the answers to the Essential Questions posed below as they learn the bulleted concepts and skills.

BIG idea Measurement

ESSENTIAL QUESTION How do you find a side length or angle measure in a right triangle?

- Students will use the Pythagorean Theorem.
- Students will use concepts of 30°-60°-90° and 45°-45°-90° triangles.
- Students will use trigonometric ratios to form proportions.

BIG idea Similarity

ESSENTIAL QUESTION How do trigonometric ratios relate to similar right triangles?

- Students will examine the sine ratio.
- Students will examine the cosine ratio.
- Students will examine the tangent ratio.

Chapter Preview

DYNAMIC ACTIVITIES

Dynamic Activity

Use the Dynamic Activity, an interactive math tool with guided instruction, to have students explore concepts visually and support the development of the Standards for Mathematical Practice.

Content Standards

Following are the key standards covered in this chapter.

Conceptual Category Geometry

DOMAIN Congruence G.CO

CLUSTER Make geometric constructions (Standard G.CO.13) **LESSON** 7-5

DOMAIN Similarity, Right Triangles, and Trigonometry G.SRT

CLUSTER Prove theorems involving similarity (Standard G.SRT.4) **LESSON** 7-1

CLUSTER Define trigonometric ratios and solve problems involving right triangles (Standards G.SRT.6, G.SRT.7, G.SRT.8) **LESSONS** 7-1, 7-2, TL 7-3, 7-3, 7-4

VOCABULARY

Vocabulary

English/Spanish Vocabulary Audio Online:

English	Spanish
angle of depression, *p. 447**	ángulo de depresión
angle of elevation, *p. 447*	ángulo de elevación
apothem, *p. 454*	apotema
cosine, *p. 438*	coseno
Pythagorean triple, *p. 416*	tripleta de Pitágoras
radius of a regular polygon, *p. 454*	radio de un polígono regular
sine, *p. 438*	seno
tangent, *p. 438*	tangente

**All page numbers refer to the Student Edition.*

RIGHT TRIANGLES AND TRIGONOMETRY

Math Background

Understanding by Design® principles were central to the development of the Big Ideas and the Essential Understandings. These will help your students build a structure on which to make connections to prior learning.*

Measurement

BIG idea Some attributes of geometric figures, such as length, area, volume, and angle measure, are measurable. Units are used to describe these attributes.

ESSENTIAL UNDERSTANDINGS

7-1 If the lengths of any two sides of a right triangle are known, the length of the third side can be found by using the Pythagorean Theorem.

7-2 Certain right triangles have properties that allow their side lengths to be determined without using the Pythagorean Theorem.

7-3 If certain combinations of side lengths and angle measures of a right triangle are known, ratios can be used to find other side lengths and angle measures.

7-5 The area of a regular polygon is a function of the distance from the center to a side and the perimeter.

Similarity

BIG idea Two geometric figures are similar when corresponding lengths are proportional and corresponding angles are congruent.

ESSENTIAL UNDERSTANDINGS

7-3 Ratios can be used to find side lengths and angle measures of a right triangle when certain combinations of side lengths and angles measures are known.

7-4 The angles of elevation and depression are the acute angles of right triangles formed by a horizontal distance and a vertical height.

*UNDERSTANDING BY DESIGN® and UbD™ are trademarks of ASCD, and are used under license.

Pythagorean Theorem

The Pythagorean Theorem states that the square of the hypotenuse of a right triangle is equal to the sum of the squares of the other two sides.

In algebraic notation, $a^2 + b^2 = c^2$, where c is the hypotenuse, and a and b are the legs.

The hypotenuse c is the longest side of the triangle.

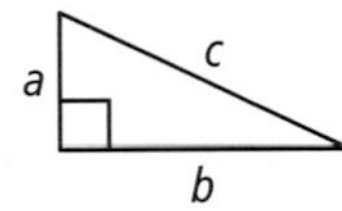

The sets of nonzero whole numbers that satisfy the Pythagorean Theorem are known as Pythagorean triples. One example is the lengths 3, 4, and 5.

The Pythagorean Theorem can also be used to determine if a triangle is acute, right, or obtuse.

If $a^2 + b^2 > c^2$, then the triangle is acute.

If $a^2 + b^2 = c^2$, then the triangle is right.

If $a^2 + b^2 < c^2$, then the triangle is obtuse.

Common Errors With Pythagorean Theorem

When using the Pythagorean Theorem to classify a triangle as right, obtuse, or acute, conditions for obtuse and acute can be confused because they seem to be counterintuitive.

For example:

A triangle has side lengths 7, 15, and 18. Is it acute, obtuse, or right?

$18^2 \overset{?}{>} 7^2 + 15^2$

$324 \overset{?}{>} 49 + 225$

$324 > 274$

The student might conclude that the triangle is acute instead of obtuse.

Mathematical Practices

Construct viable arguments and critique the reasoning of others. Students explore a famous result, the Pythagorean Theorem, and discover not only Pythagorean triples but their multiples (6-8-10 is mathematically similar to 3-4-5).

Look for and make use of structure. The proof in Lesson 7-1 Exercise 33 builds on work from Chapter 6 on altitudes in right triangles.

Math Background *(continued)*

30°-60°-90° and 45°-45°-90° Triangles

You can use the ratios of the side lengths of 30°-60°-90° and 45°-45°-90° triangles to set up proportions and solve for unknown side lengths.

45°-45°-90° 30°-60°-90°

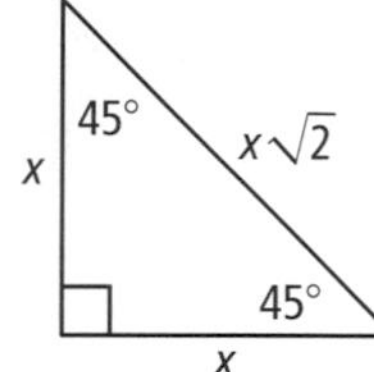

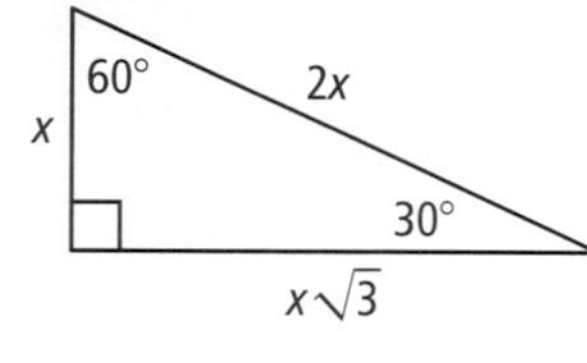

To find the unknown length in a 45°-45°-90° triangle:

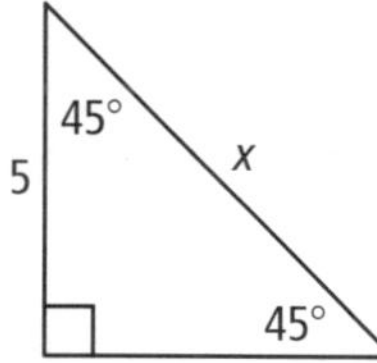

$$\frac{x}{5} = \frac{\sqrt{2}}{1}$$
$$x = 5\sqrt{2}$$

To find the unknown length in a 30°-60°-90° triangle:

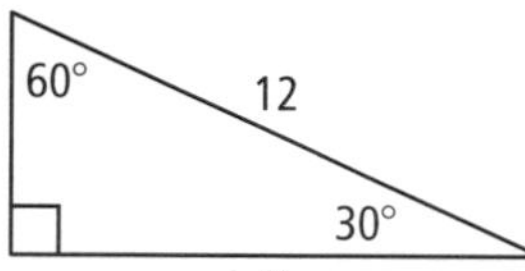

$$\frac{y}{12} = \frac{\sqrt{3}}{2}$$
$$2y = 12\sqrt{3}$$
$$y = 6\sqrt{3}$$

Common Errors With 30°-60°-90° and 45°-45°-90° Triangles

Often students are unsure of how to solve for a side length when they are not given the length of the shortest side in a 30°-60°-90° triangle. Instruct students to set up an equation with x and solve.

For example:

$$6 = x\sqrt{3}$$
$$\frac{6}{\sqrt{3}} = \frac{x\sqrt{3}}{\sqrt{3}}$$
$$\frac{\sqrt{3}}{\sqrt{3}} \cdot \frac{6}{\sqrt{3}} = x$$
$$x = 2\sqrt{3}$$

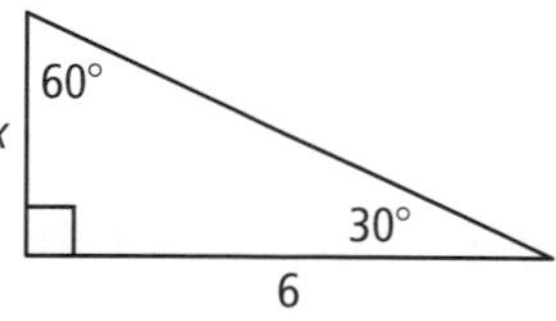

Mathematical Practices

Model with Mathematics Students combine algebraic and geometric thinking to develop the special triangles and their side ratios. They see patterns in the lengths of sides and can solve for nonintegral as well as integral sides in figures.

Look for and express regularity in repeated reasoning. They apply these ideas to figures other than right triangles in the exercises and look at some applied cases where these triangles might be used.

Trigonometric Ratios

With respect to $\angle A$, there are six trigonometric ratios:

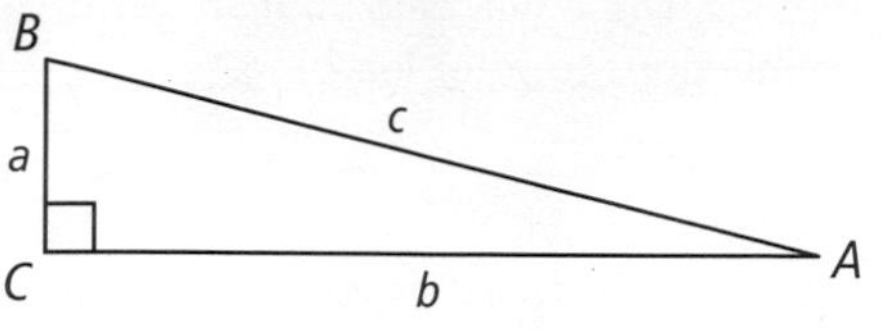

$\sin A = \frac{a}{c} = \frac{\text{opposite}}{\text{hypotenuse}}$ $\csc A = \frac{c}{a} = \frac{\text{hypotenuse}}{\text{opposite}}$

$\cos A = \frac{b}{c} = \frac{\text{adjacent}}{\text{hypotenuse}}$ $\sec A = \frac{c}{b} = \frac{\text{hypotenuse}}{\text{adjacent}}$

$\tan A = \frac{a}{b} = \frac{\text{opposite}}{\text{adjacent}}$ $\cot A = \frac{b}{a} = \frac{\text{adjacent}}{\text{opposite}}$

Trigonometric ratios provide the tools needed to find unknown right triangle measurements when certain combinations of side lengths and angle measures are given. When finding an unknown side length, use the direct ratio. When finding an unknown angle measure, use the inverse trigonometric function.

Example 1: $a = 8$, $A = 43$

$$\sin A = \frac{a}{c} = \frac{\text{opposite}}{\text{hypotenuse}}$$
$$\sin 43 = \frac{8}{c}$$
$$c = \frac{8}{\sin 43} \approx 11.7$$

Example 2: $b = 6$, $c = 8$

$$\cos A = \frac{b}{c} = \frac{\text{adjacent}}{\text{hypotenuse}}$$
$$\cos A = \frac{6}{8} = \frac{3}{4}$$
$$\cos^{-1}(\cos A) = \cos^{-1}\left(\frac{3}{4}\right)$$
$$A = \cos^{-1}\left(\frac{3}{4}\right) \approx 41.4$$

Common Errors With Trigonometric Ratios Students may get confused about when to use the trigonometric functions and when to use the inverse trigonometric functions. Instruct students always to write the equations setting the trigonometric term equal to a ratio. Then they will see if they need to use the inverse.

Mathematical Practices

Make sense of problems and persevere in solving them. Students learn trigonometric ratios and apply them to specific situations.

Model with Mathematics They decontextualize a problem, which they represent with a trigonometric equation, and then contextualize it, to make sense of the results.

Reason abstractly and quantitatively. They look at exercises that build on these skills, first considering simpler cases and then working up to the more complex problem at hand.

7-1 The Pythagorean Theorem and Its Converse

Common Core State Standards
G.SRT.8 Use . . . the Pythagorean Theorem to solve right triangles in applied problems. **Also G.SRT.4**

Preparing to Teach

BIG ideas Measurement
Reasoning and Proof

ESSENTIAL UNDERSTANDING

If the lengths of any two sides of a right triangle are known, the length of the third side can be found using the Pythagorean Theorem. If the lengths of all sides of a triangle are known, it can be determined whether the triangle is acute, right, or obtuse.

Math Background

The Pythagorean Theorem was one of the first theorems used by mathematicians in ancient civilizations. Although named after and credited to the Greek mathematician Pythagoras because of his proof of the theorem, the notion of the theorem actually dates back to a millennium earlier, when it was first used by the Babylonians. The distance formula, used in coordinate geometry, is a derivative of the Pythagorean Theorem and is the foundation on which much of trigonometry is based.

There are numerous proofs of the Pythagorean Theorem. As an extension of this lesson, have students research various examples of proofs of the theorem and present their findings to the class.

ELL Support

USE GRAPHIC ORGANIZERS Have students make an organizer to organize the lesson concepts. At the top, have them draw a right triangle. Do the same on the board. Trace the legs and hypotenuse as you say their name. Label the legs *a* and *b* and the hypotenuse *c*. Write the Pythagorean Theorem and the following underneath:
$(\text{leg})^2 + (\text{leg})^2 = (\text{hypotenuse})^2$.

Ask: If you have two side lengths of a right triangle, how can you use the Pythagorean Theorem to find an unknown length? Then draw two lines to two examples: one that asks how to find the hypotenuse and one that asks how to find a missing leg measure.

Then ask: How can you use the Pythagorean Theorem to prove this triangle is a right triangle? Complete the organizer after the lesson.

Lesson Vocabulary

- Pythagorean triple

Mathematical Practices

MAKE SENSE OF PROBLEMS AND PERSEVERE IN SOLVING THEM. Students will analyze the relationship between sides in a right triangle through the Pythagorean Theorem.

1 Interactive Learning

Solve It!

PURPOSE To explore Pythagorean triples

PROCESS Students may

- use the formula for the area of a square.
- use trial and error to write the equations.
- use algebraic properties.

Q How do you determine the area of a square? **[Square the side length.]**

Q Which property states that you can multiply each side of an equation by the same number and create an equivalent equation? **[the Multiplication Property of Equality]**

ANSWER $3^2 + 4^2 = 5^2$, $6^2 + 8^2 = 10^2$, $1.5^2 + 2^2 = 2.5^2$; answers may vary. Sample: The numbers 6, 8, and 10 result from multiplying 3, 4, and 5 by 2. The numbers 3, 4, and 5 result from multiplying 1.5, 2, and 2.5 by 2.

▼ DIGITAL (STUDENT WORK SPACE PAGE 415)

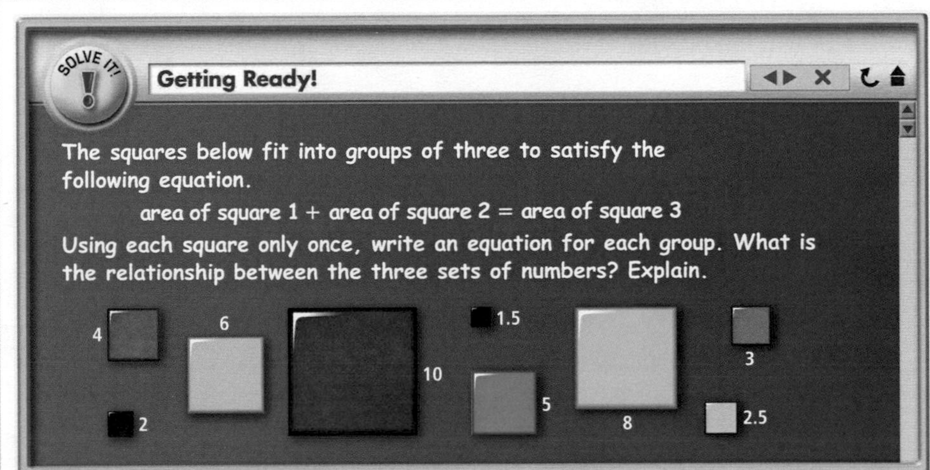

CONNECT THE MATH In the Solve It, students discover the relationship known as the Pythagorean Theorem. In the lesson, students learn the Pythagorean Theorem and how to use it to find unknown side lengths in a right triangle.

2 Guided Instruction

Problem 1 Finding the Length of the Hypotenuse

Take Note

Use properties of real numbers to change the form of the Pythagorean Theorem so that it is solved for a^2 and then for b^2.

Problem 1

Q What are the lengths of the legs in the right triangle? **[20 and 21]**

Q Does it matter which of these side lengths is assigned to *a* and which to *b*? Explain. **[No, addition is commutative, so the squared values can be added in any order.]**

Q Why is only the principal (positive) square root found when solving the equation $c^2 = 841$? **[The length of a side cannot be negative.]**

Got It? VISUAL LEARNERS

Even though the problem can be solved by substituting the given values into the formula and solving for *c*, students benefit from drawing a sketch of the triangle. This action reinforces identifying the legs and the hypotenuse.

ANSWERS

Got It? a. 26 **b.** Yes; 10, 24, and 26 are whole numbers that satisfy $a^2 + b^2 = c^2$.

Practice

1. 17

2. $4^2 + 5^2 \neq 6^2$

▼ STUDENT PAGES 415–416

The equations in the Solve It demonstrate an important relationship in right triangles called the Pythagorean Theorem. This theorem is named for Pythagoras, a Greek mathematician who lived in the 500s B.C. We now know that the Babylonians, Egyptians, and Chinese were aware of this relationship before its discovery by Pythagoras. There are many proofs of the Pythagorean Theorem. You will see one proof in this lesson and others later in the book.

Essential Understanding If you know the lengths of any two sides of a right triangle, you can find the length of the third side by using the Pythagorean Theorem.

take note

Theorem 65 Pythagorean Theorem

Theorem	If . . .	Then . . .
If a triangle is a right triangle, then the sum of the squares of the lengths of the legs is equal to the square of the length of the hypotenuse.	$\triangle ABC$ is a right triangle	$(\text{leg}_1)^2 + (\text{leg}_2)^2 = (\text{hypotenuse})^2$ $a^2 + b^2 = c^2$

You will prove Theorem 65 in Exercise 33.

A **Pythagorean triple** is a set of nonzero whole numbers *a*, *b*, and *c* that satisfy the equation $a^2 + b^2 = c^2$. Below are some common Pythagorean triples.

3, 4, 5   5, 12, 13   8, 15, 17   7, 24, 25

If you multiply each number in a Pythagorean triple by the same whole number, the three numbers that result also form a Pythagorean triple. For example, the Pythagorean triples 6, 8, 10, and 9, 12, 15 each result from multiplying the numbers in the triple 3, 4, 5 by a whole number.

▼ DIGITAL

Problem 1 Finding the Length of the Hypotenuse

What is the length of the hypotenuse of $\triangle ABC$? Do the side lengths of $\triangle ABC$ form a Pythagorean triple? Explain.

$(\text{leg}_1)^2 + (\text{leg}_2)^2 = (\text{hypotenuse})^2$ Pythagorean Theorem

$a^2 + b^2 = c^2$

$21^2 + 20^2 = c^2$ Substitute 21 for *a* and 20 for *b*.

$441 + 400 = c^2$ Simplify.

$841 = c^2$

$c = 29$ Take the positive square root.

The length of the hypotenuse is 29. The side lengths 20, 21, and 29 form a Pythagorean triple because they are whole numbers that satisfy $a^2 + b^2 = c^2$.

▼ STUDENT PAGES 416–417

Got It? a. The legs of a right triangle have lengths 10 and 24. What is the length of the hypotenuse?

b. Do the side lengths in part (a) form a Pythagorean triple? Explain.

Practice 1. **Algebra** Find the value of *x*.

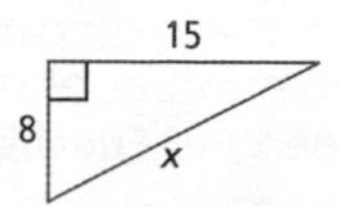

2. Do the numbers 4, 5, 6 form a Pythagorean triple? Explain.

Problem 2 Finding the Length of a Leg

Q How can you decide which side of the triangle is the hypotenuse? **[The hypotenuse is the side opposite the right angle.]**

Q What are the lengths of the legs of the right triangle? **[x and 8]**

Got It?

Q What are the lengths of the legs of the right triangle? **[6 units and x units]**

Q What is the length of the hypotenuse? **[12 units]**

ANSWERS

Got It? $6\sqrt{3}$

Practice

3. $\sqrt{33}$

4. $3\sqrt{2}$

▼ DIGITAL

Problem 2 Finding the Length of a Leg

Algebra **What is the value of x? Express your answer in simplest radical form.**

$a^2 + b^2 = c^2$	Pythagorean Theorem
$8^2 + x^2 = 20^2$	Substitute.
$64 + x^2 = 400$	Simplify.
$x^2 = 336$	Subtract 64 from each side.
$x = \sqrt{336}$	Take the positive square root.
$x = \sqrt{16(21)}$	Factor out a perfect square.
$x = 4\sqrt{21}$	Simplify.

▼ STUDENT PAGE 417

Got It? The hypotenuse of a right triangle has length 12. One leg has length 6. What is the length of the other leg? Express your answer in simplest radical form.

Practice **Algebra** Find the value of x. Express your answer in simplest radical form.

3.

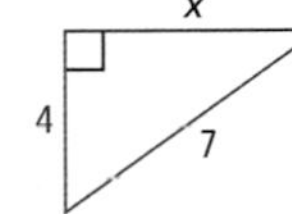

4.

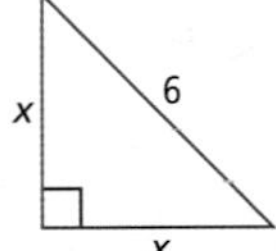

Problem 3 Finding Distance

Q What formula can be used to find the distance between two points? **[$d = \sqrt{(x_2 - x_1)^2 + (y_2 - y_1)^2}$]**

Q Can you use the distance formula to complete this problem? Why or why not? **[Answers may vary. Sample: No, because the diagram is not in the coordinate plane.]**

Q Which side of the right triangle is unknown? **[a leg]**

Q Is the square of 24.8997992 exactly 620? Explain. **[No, it is an approximation of 620.]**

Got It? **VISUAL LEARNERS**

Encourage students to make a sketch of the computer monitor and label its parts prior to completing the problem.

ANSWERS

Got It? 15.5 in.

Practice

5. 14.1 ft

6. 17 m

▼ DIGITAL

Problem 3 Finding Distance

Dog Agility **Dog agility courses often contain a seesaw obstacle, as shown below. To the nearest inch, how far above the ground are the dog's paws when the seesaw is parallel to the ground?**

$a^2 + b^2 = c^2$	Pythagorean Theorem
$26^2 + b^2 = 36^2$	Substitute.
$676 + b^2 = 1296$	Simplify.
$b^2 = 620$	Subtract 676 from each side.
$b \approx 24.8997992$	Use a calculator to take the positive square root.

The dog's paws are 25 in. above the ground.

▼ STUDENT PAGE 418

Got It? The size of a computer monitor is the length of its diagonal. You want to buy a 19-in. monitor that has a height of 11 in. What is the width of the monitor? Round to the nearest tenth of an inch.

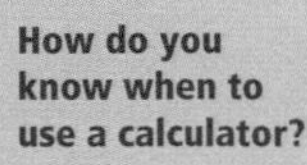

Think
How do you know when to use a calculator?

Practice

5. Home Maintenance A painter leans a 15-ft ladder against a house. The base of the ladder is 5 ft from the house. To the nearest tenth of a foot, how high on the house does the ladder reach?

6. A walkway forms one diagonal of a square playground. The walkway is 24 m long. To the nearest meter, how long is a side of the playground?

Problem 4 Identifying a Right Triangle

Take Note

Because this theorem is the converse of Theorem 65, the Pythagorean Theorem can be written as a biconditional statement. Ask students to write such a statement.

Problem 4

Q How would the third line of the solution differ if you assigned the side length 84 to a? **[The left side of the equation would be 7056 + 169.]**

Q Are the numbers 13, 84, and 85 a Pythagorean triple? Explain. **[Yes; all three lengths are nonzero whole numbers, and $13^2 + 84^2 = 85^2$.]**

Got It? ERROR PREVENTION

If students are unsure of the answer for part (b), encourage them to experiment with the numbers in part (a) as a way to check.

ANSWERS

Got It? a. No; $16^2 + 48^2 \neq 50^2$

b. No; $a^2 + b^2 = b^2 + a^2$ for any values of a and b.

Practice

7. No; $19^2 + 20^2 \neq 28^2$

8. Yes; $33^2 + 56^2 = 65^2$

▼ STUDENT PAGE 419

You can use the Converse of the Pythagorean Theorem to determine whether a triangle is a right triangle.

take note

Theorem 66 Converse of the Pythagorean Theorem

Theorem	If . . .	Then . . .
If the sum of the squares of the lengths of two sides of a triangle is equal to the square of the length of the third side, then the triangle is a right triangle.	$a^2 + b^2 = c^2$	$\triangle ABC$ is a right triangle

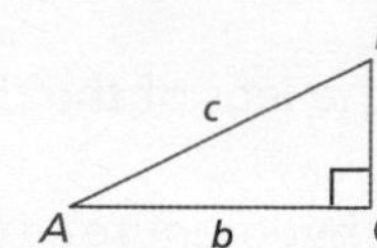

You will prove Theorem 66 in Exercise 36.

▼ DIGITAL

Problem 4 Identifying a Right Triangle

A triangle has side lengths 85, 84, and 13. Is the triangle a right triangle? Explain.

$a^2 + b^2 \stackrel{?}{=} c^2$	Pythagorean Theorem
$13^2 + 84^2 \stackrel{?}{=} 85^2$	Substitute 13 for a, 84 for b, and 85 for c.
$169 + 7056 \stackrel{?}{=} 7225$	Simplify.
$7225 = 7225$ ✓	

Yes, the triangle is a right triangle because $13^2 + 84^2 = 85^2$.

▼ STUDENT PAGES 419–420

Got It? a. A triangle has side lengths 16, 48, and 50. Is the triangle a right triangle? Explain.

Plan How do you know where each of the side lengths goes in the equation?

b. **Reasoning** Once you know which length represents the hypotenuse, does it matter which length you substitute for a and which length you substitute for b? Explain.

Practice Is the triangle a right triangle? Explain.

7. 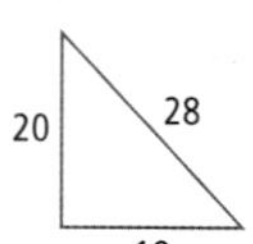

8. 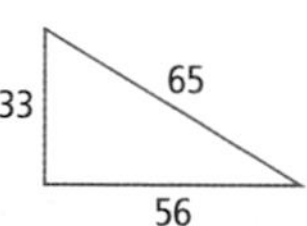

Problem 5 Classifying a Triangle

Take Note

Students can use geometry software to explore these two theorems. They can begin by constructing a right triangle with sides *a*, *b*, and *c*, and recording the values of $a^2 + b^2$ and c^2. Next, students can manipulate the measure of angle *C*, the right angle, so that the triangle becomes acute and then obtuse. Students should record the angle measures of each triangle for classification reasons as well as the values of $a^2 + b^2$ and c^2.

Problem 5

Q Which of the given numbers do you know are the side lengths *a* and *b*? Why? **[6 and 11 because 14 is the longest side.]**

Q What is the square of the longest side? **[196]**

Q What sentence describes the relationship between the sum of the squares of the lengths of the two shorter sides and the square of the length of the longest side? **[The sum of the squares of the lengths of the two shorter sides is less than the square of the length of the longest side.]**

Got It? ERROR PREVENTION

Q What is the sum of the squares of the lengths of the shorter sides? **[113]**

Q What is the square of the length of the longest side? **[81]**

ANSWERS

Got It? acute

Practice

9. obtuse

10. acute

▼ STUDENT PAGE 420

The theorems below allow you to determine whether a triangle is acute or obtuse. These theorems relate to the Hinge Theorem, which states that the longer side is opposite the larger angle and the shorter side is opposite the smaller angle.

take note **Theorem 67**

Theorem	If . . .	Then . . .
If the square of the length of the longest side of a triangle is greater than the sum of the squares of the lengths of the other two sides, then the triangle is obtuse.	$c^2 > a^2 + b^2$ 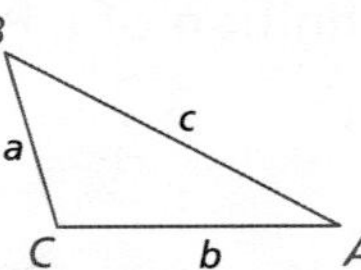	$\triangle ABC$ is obtuse

You will prove Theorem 67 in Exercise 37.

take note **Theorem 68**

Theorem	If . . .	Then . . .
If the square of the length of the longest side of a triangle is less than the sum of the squares of the lengths of the other two sides, then the triangle is acute.	$c^2 < a^2 + b^2$ 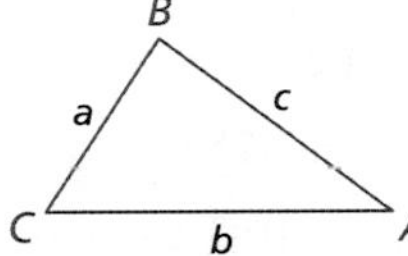	$\triangle ABC$ is acute

You will prove Theorem 68 in Exercise 38.

▼ DIGITAL

Problem 5 **Classifying a Triangle**

A triangle has side lengths 6, 11, and 14. Is it *acute, obtuse,* or *right*?

$c^2 \blacksquare a^2 + b^2$ Compare c^2 to $a^2 + b^2$.

$14^2 \blacksquare 6^2 + 11^2$ Substitute the greatest value for c.

$196 \blacksquare 36 + 121$ Simplify.

$196 > 157$

Since $c^2 > a^2 + b^2$, the triangle is obtuse.

▼ STUDENT PAGE 421

Got It? Is a triangle with side lengths 7, 8, and 9 *acute, obtuse,* or *right*?

Plan What information do you need?

A Practice **The lengths of the sides of a triangle are given. Classify each triangle as *acute, obtuse,* or *right.***

9. 0.3, 0.4, 0.6

10. $\sqrt{11}$, $\sqrt{7}$, 4

Lesson Check

Do you know HOW?
If students have difficulty with Exercise 13, then have them decide if the *x* is substituted into the side of the equation that contains addition.

Do you UNDERSTAND?
If students have difficulty with Exercise 15, then have them review the definition of a Pythagorean triple on page 416.

Close

Q What is the difference between how the Pythagorean Theorem and its converse are used? **[The Pythagorean Theorem is used to determine the length of the third side of a right triangle given two of the sides. The converse is used to determine if three given side lengths form a right triangle.]**

ANSWERS

11. 37 **12.** $\sqrt{130}$

13. 4 **14.** $4\sqrt{3}$

15. The three numbers *a*, *b*, and *c* must be whole numbers that satisfy $a^2 + b^2 = c^2$.

16. The longest side is 34, so the student should have tested $16^2 + 30^2 \stackrel{?}{=} 34^2$.

▼ STUDENT PAGES 422–423

Lesson Check

Do you know HOW?

What is the value of *x* in simplest radical form?

11.

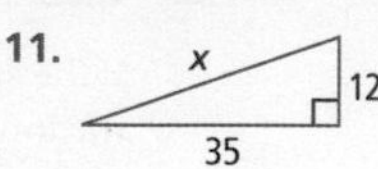

12.

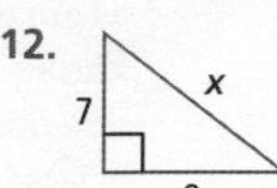

13.

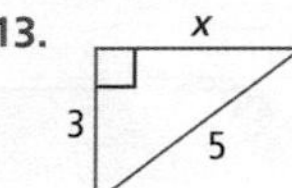

14.

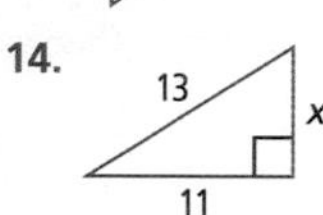

Do you UNDERSTAND?

15. Vocabulary Describe the conditions that a set of three numbers must meet in order to form a Pythagorean triple.

16. Error Analysis A triangle has side lengths 16, 34, and 30. Your friend says it is not a right triangle. Look at your friend's work and describe the error.

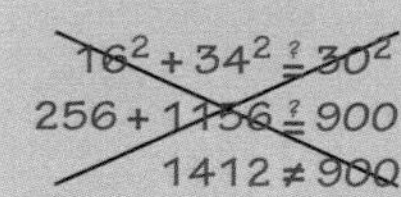

4 Practice

More Practice and Problem-Solving Exercises

ASSIGNMENT GUIDE

The assignments below are for the More Practice and Problem-Solving Exercises. You may also want to assign the A-Level Practice Exercises for homework if these are not used in class.

Average: 17–35

Advanced: 17–38

Mathematical Practices The exercises listed focus on the Standards for Mathematical Practices listed.

EX. 17: Make Sense of Problems (MP 1)

EX. 16: Critique the Reasoning of Others (MP 3)

EX. 34: Model (MP 4)

EX. 27–32: Repeated Reasoning (MP 8)

STEM exercises focus on science or engineering applications.

EXERCISE 34: Use the **Think About a Plan** worksheet in the Online Teacher Resources to further support students' development in becoming independent learners.

HOMEWORK QUICK CHECK

To check students' understanding of key skills and concepts, go over Exercises 17, 21, 25, 27, and 34.

ANSWERS

17. 4.2 in.

18. Yes; $7^2 + 24^2 = 25^2$, so $\angle S$ is a rt. $\angle$.

19. a. $|x_2 - x_1|$; $|y_2 - y_1|$

b. $PQ^2 = (x_2 - x_1)^2 + (y_2 - y_1)^2$

c. $PQ = \sqrt{(x_2 - x_1)^2 + (y_2 - y_1)^2}$

20. 10 **21.** $8\sqrt{5}$

22. $2\sqrt{2}$ **23.** 29

24. 50 **25.** 84

26. 35

27–32. Answers may vary. Samples are given.

27. a. 6 **b.** 7 **28. a.** 4 **b.** 5

29. a. 8 **b.** 11 **30. a.** 11 **b.** 12

31. a. 8 **b.** 10 **32. a.** 14 **b.** 16

33. $\frac{q}{b} = \frac{b}{c}$ and $\frac{r}{a} = \frac{a}{c}$ because each leg is the geometric mean of the adj. hypotenuse segment and the hypotenuse. By the Cross Products Property, $b^2 = qc$ and $a^2 = rc$. Then $a^2 + b^2 = qc + rc = c(q + r)$. Substituting c for $q + r$ gives $a^2 + b^2 = c^2$.

▼ STUDENT PAGES 423–424

More Practice and Problem-Solving Exercises

MATHEMATICAL PRACTICES

B Apply

17. Think About a Plan You want to embroider a square design. You have an embroidery hoop with a 6 in. diameter. Find the largest value of x so that the entire square will fit in the hoop. Round to the nearest tenth.

- What does the diameter of the circle represent in the square?
- What do you know about the sides of a square?
- How do the side lengths of the square relate to the length of the diameter?

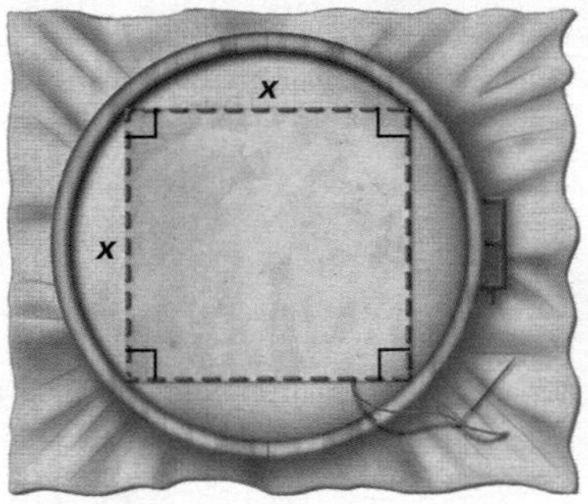

18. In parallelogram $RSTW$, $RS = 7$, $ST = 24$, and $RT = 25$. Is $RSTW$ a rectangle? Explain.

Proof **19. Coordinate Geometry** You can use the Pythagorean Theorem to prove the Distance Formula. Let points $P(x_1, y_1)$ and $Q(x_2, y_2)$ be the endpoints of the hypotenuse of a right triangle.

a. Write an algebraic expression to complete each of the following: $PR = \underline{?}$ and $QR = \underline{?}$.

b. By the Pythagorean Theorem, $PQ^2 = PR^2 + QR^2$. Rewrite this statement by substituting the algebraic expressions you found for PR and QR in part (a).

c. Complete the proof by taking the square root of each side of the equation that you wrote in part (b).

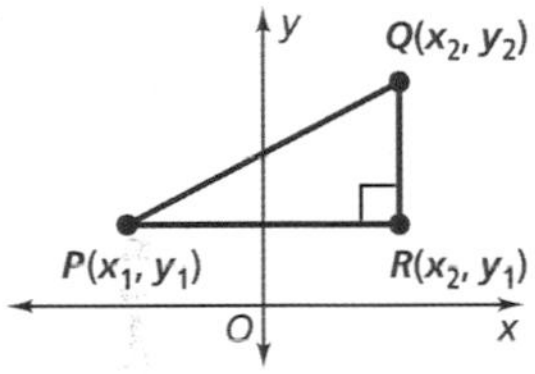

Algebra Find the value of x. If your answer is not an integer, express it in simplest radical form.

20.
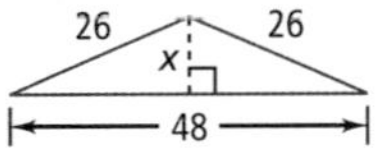

21.
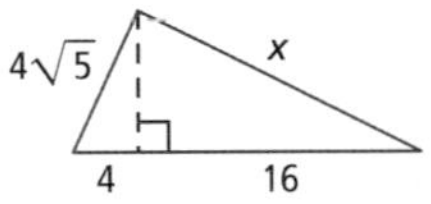

22.
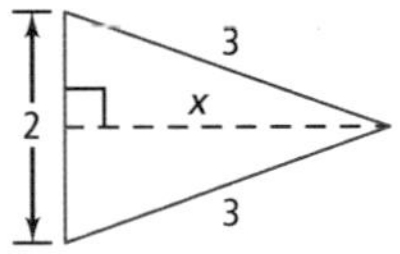

For each pair of numbers, find a third whole number such that the three numbers form a Pythagorean triple.

23. 20, 21 **24.** 14, 48 **25.** 13, 85 **26.** 12, 37

Open-Ended Find integers j and k such that (a) the two given integers and j represent the side lengths of an acute triangle and (b) the two given integers and k represent the side lengths of an obtuse triangle.

27. 4, 5 **28.** 2, 4 **29.** 6, 9

30. 5, 10 **31.** 6, 7 **32.** 9, 12

Proof **33.** Prove the Pythagorean Theorem.

Given: $\triangle ABC$ is a right triangle.

Prove: $a^2 + b^2 = c^2$

(*Hint:* Begin with proportions suggested by Theorem 62 or its corollaries.)

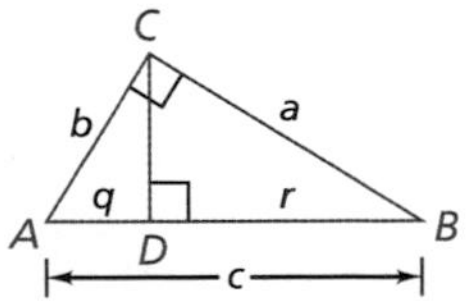

More Practice and Problem-Solving Exercises *continued*

34. 2830 km

35. a. Horiz. lines have slope 0, and vert. lines have undef. slope. Neither could be mult. to get -1.

b. Assume the lines do not intersect. Then they have the same slope m. Then $m \cdot m = m^2 = -1$, which is impossible. So the lines must intersect.

c. Let ℓ_1 be $y = \frac{b}{a}x$ and ℓ_2 be $y = -\frac{a}{b}x$. Define $C(a, b)$, $A(0, 0)$, and $B(a, -\frac{a^2}{b})$.

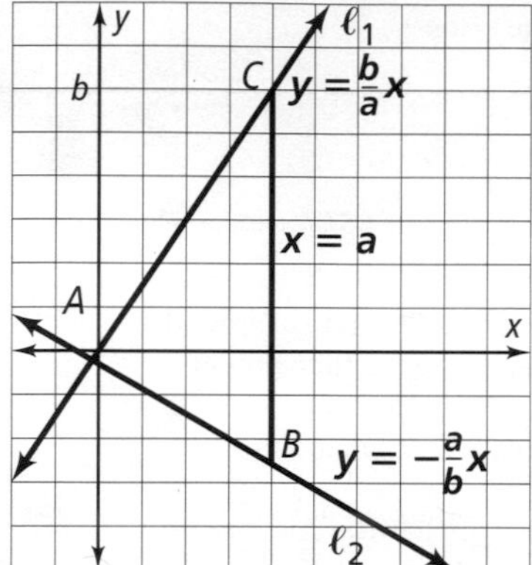

Using the Distance Formula, $AC = \sqrt{a^2 + b^2}$, $BA = \sqrt{a^2 + \frac{a^4}{b^2}}$, and $CB = b + \frac{a^2}{b}$. Then $AC^2 + BA^2 = CB^2$ and $m\angle A = 90$ by the Conv. of the Pythagorean Thm. So $\ell_1 \perp \ell_2$.

Note: the choice of the coordinates of B is challenging.

36. Draw right $\triangle FDE$ with legs $\overline{DE}$ of length a and $\overline{EF}$ of length b, and hypotenuse of length x. Then $a^2 + b^2 = x^2$ by the Pythagorean Thm. You are given $\triangle ABC$ with sides of length a, b, and c, and $a^2 + b^2 = c^2$. By subst., $c^2 = x^2$, so $c = x$. Since all side lengths of $\triangle ABC$ and $\triangle FDE$ are the same, $\triangle ABC \cong \triangle FDE$ by SSS. $\angle C \cong \angle E$ because corresp. parts of $\cong$ ▵s are $\cong$, so $m\angle C = 90$. Therefore, $\triangle ABC$ is a right $\triangle$.

37. Draw right $\triangle FDE$ with legs $\overline{DE}$ of length a and $\overline{EF}$ of length b, and hypotenuse of length x. By the Pythagorean Thm., $a^2 + b^2 = x^2$. $\triangle ABC$ has sides of length a, b, and c, where $c^2 > a^2 + b^2$. $c^2 > x^2$ and $c > x$ by Prop. of Inequalities. If $c > x$, then $m\angle C > m\angle E$ by the Converse of the Hinge Thm. An angle with measure > 90 is obtuse, so $\triangle ABC$ is an obtuse $\triangle$.

38. Draw right $\triangle FDE$ with legs $\overline{DE}$ of length a and $\overline{EF}$ of length b, and hypotenuse of length x. By the Pythagorean Thm., $a^2 + b^2 = x^2$. $\triangle ABC$ has sides of length a, b, and c, where $c^2 < a^2 + b^2$. $c^2 < x^2$ and $c < x$ by Prop. of Inequalities. If $c < x$, then $m\angle C < m\angle E$ by the Converse of the Hinge Thm. An angle with measure < 90 is acute, so $\triangle ABC$ is an acute $\triangle$.

STEM **34. Astronomy** The Hubble Space Telescope orbits 600 km above Earth's surface. Earth's radius is about 6370 km. Use the Pythagorean Theorem to find the distance x from the telescope to Earth's horizon. Round your answer to the nearest ten kilometers. (Diagram is not to scale.)

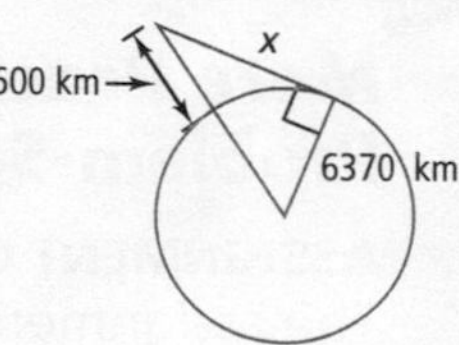

35. Prove that if the slopes of two lines ℓ_1 and ℓ_2 have product -1, then the lines are perpendicular. Use parts (a)–(c) to write a coordinate proof.

a. First, argue that neither line can be horizontal nor vertical.

b. Then, tell why the lines must intersect. (*Hint:* Use indirect reasoning.)

c. Place the lines in the coordinate plane. Choose a point on ℓ_1 and find a related point on ℓ_2. Complete the proof.

Proof 36. Use the plan and write a proof of Theorem 66 (Converse of the Pythagorean Theorem).

Given: $\triangle ABC$ with sides of length a, b, and c, where $a^2 + b^2 = c^2$
Prove: $\triangle ABC$ is a right triangle.
Plan: Draw a right triangle (not $\triangle ABC$) with legs of lengths a and b. Label the hypotenuse x. By the Pythagorean Theorem, $a^2 + b^2 = x^2$. Use substitution to compare the lengths of the sides of your triangle and $\triangle ABC$. Then prove the triangles congruent.

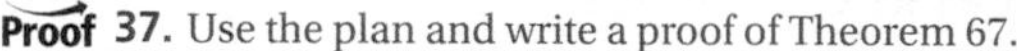

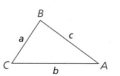

Proof 37. Use the plan and write a proof of Theorem 67.

Given: $\triangle ABC$ with sides of length a, b, and c, where $c^2 > a^2 + b^2$
Prove: $\triangle ABC$ is an obtuse triangle.
Plan: Draw a right triangle (not $\triangle ABC$) with legs of lengths a and b. Label the hypotenuse x. By the Pythagorean Theorem, $a^2 + b^2 = x^2$. Use substitution to compare lengths c and x. Then use the Converse of the Hinge Theorem to compare $\angle C$ to the right angle.

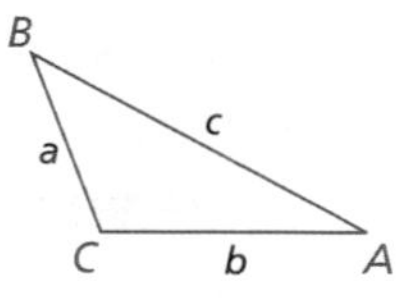

Proof 38. Prove Theorem 68.

Given: $\triangle ABC$ with sides of length a, b, and c, where $c^2 < a^2 + b^2$
Prove: $\triangle ABC$ is an acute triangle.

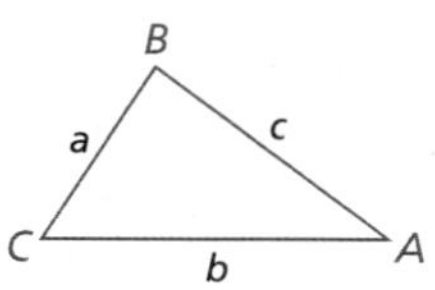

Assess and Remediate

Lesson Quiz

1. What is the length of the hypotenuse of $\triangle RST$? Do the side lengths of $\triangle RST$ form a Pythagorean triple? Explain.

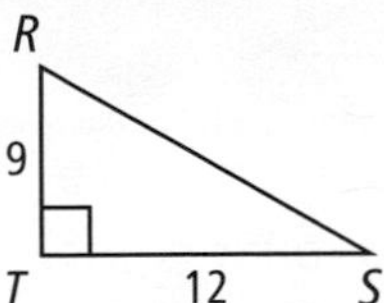

2. Cassie's computer monitor is in the shape of a rectangle. The screen on the monitor is 11.5 in. high and 18.5 in. wide. What is the length of the diagonal? Round to the nearest tenth of an inch.
3. A triangle has side lengths 24, 32, and 42. Is it a right triangle? Explain.
4. A triangle has side lengths 9, 10, and 12. Is it acute, obtuse, or right? Explain.
5. **Do you UNDERSTAND?** Can three segments with lengths 4 cm, 6 cm, and 11 cm be assembled to form an acute triangle, a right triangle, or an obtuse triangle? Explain.

ANSWERS TO LESSON QUIZ

1. 15; Yes, because all three side lengths are whole numbers.
2. 21.8 in.
3. No; $24^2 + 32^2 \neq 42^2$.
4. Acute; $9^2 + 10^2 = 181$ and $12^2 = 144$, so the triangle is acute by Theorem 68.
5. Because $4 + 6 < 11$, the three lengths are not the side lengths of a triangle of any kind.

Prescription for Remediation

Use the student work on the Lesson Quiz to prescribe a differentiated assignment.

Points	Differentiated Remediation
0–2	Intervention
3–4	On-level
5	Extension

Online Assessment

Assign the Lesson Quiz in Success Tracker on **pearsonsuccessnet.com**. Success Tracker will automatically score the quiz and assign appropriate intervention or enrichment to each student based on the results. The compiled data appear in three different reports for instant analysis of whole class and individual student performance.

Differentiated Remediation

Intervention

- **RETEACHING** (2 pages) Provides reteaching and practice exercises for the key lesson concepts. Use with struggling students or absent students.
- **ENGLISH LANGUAGE LEARNER SUPPORT** Helps students develop and reinforce mathematical vocabulary and key concepts.

On-Level

- **PRACTICE** (2 pages) Provides extra practice for each lesson. For simpler practice exercises, use the Form K Practice pages found in the Online Teacher Resources.
- **THINK ABOUT A PLAN** Helps students develop specific problem-solving skills and strategies by providing scaffolded guiding questions.
- **STANDARDIZED TEST PREP** Focuses on all major exercises, all major question types, and helps students prepare for the high-stakes assessments.

Extension

- **ENRICHMENT** Provides students with interesting problems and activities that extend the concepts of the lesson.
- **ACTIVITIES, GAMES, AND PUZZLES** Worksheets that can be used for concept development, enrichment, and for fun!

7-2 Special Right Triangles

Common Core State Standard
G.SRT.8 Use . . . the Pythagorean Theorem to solve right triangles in applied problems.

Preparing to Teach

BIG ideas Measurement
Reasoning and Proof

ESSENTIAL UNDERSTANDING

Certain right triangles have properties that allow their side lengths to be determined without using the Pythagorean Theorem.

Math Background

The study of the relationship of the lengths of the sides of the special right triangles provides a bridge between the study of the Pythagorean Theorem and the study of trigonometry. The properties of right triangles and isosceles triangles, along with the Pythagorean Theorem, can be easily used to determine the ratios of the sides of triangles that contain acute angles of 45° and 45° or of 30° and 60°. It is helpful to students to present these triangles in different orientations so that students can internalize the importance of the relative positions within the triangles. Students should memorize the ratios of the sides in the special triangles because they provide shortcuts for finding lengths of sides.

In coming lessons, student will learn that all similar right triangles have constant ratios of side lengths which are referred to as trigonometric functions.

ELL Support

USE MANIPULATIVES Have students work in small groups. On graph paper, have each group of students draw a square of a different size with a diagonal. Ask them to cut out the square and fold it along the diagonal. Ask: How would you classify this triangle? Then have them measure the two acute angles and the length of each leg. Ask: How can you find the length of the hypotenuse without measuring? Have them multiply the length of one leg by $\sqrt{2}$. Students should compare their results with one another and make a conjecture.

Mathematical Practices

MAKE SENSE OF PROBLEMS AND PERSEVERE IN SOLVING THEM. Students will compute the ratios of side lengths in right triangles in the special cases of 45°-45°-90° and 30°-60°-90° right triangles.

Interactive Learning

Solve It!

PURPOSE To use the Pythagorean Theorem to explore the lengths of the sides of 45°-45°-90° triangles

PROCESS Students may use congruent triangle theorems, the Pythagorean Theorem, or algebraic properties.

Q What is the distance from the dining hall to the library? Explain. **[150 yd, because of congruent triangles]**

Q What is the length of each side of the quad? Explain. **[300 yd by the Segment Addition Postulate]**

Q What is the distance from the dorm to the science lab? Explain. **[Using the Pythagorean Theorem, it is about 424.3 yd.]**

Q What is the distance from the dining hall to the intersection of the diagonals of the quad? **[Answers may vary. Sample: using the definition of an isosceles triangle, it is 150 yd.]**

ANSWER 1960.7 yd;
$150 + 150 + 150\sqrt{2} + 300\sqrt{2} + 300 + 300\sqrt{2} + 300$
Total: $900 + 750\sqrt{2} \approx 1960.7$ yd

▼ DIGITAL (STUDENT WORK SPACE PAGE 426)

SOLVE IT! **Getting Ready!**

This map of part of a college campus shows a square "quad" area with walking paths. The distance from the dorm to the dining hall is 150 yd.

Suppose you go from your dorm to the dining hall, to the science lab, to your dorm, to the student center, to the library, and finally back to your dorm. To the nearest tenth, how far do you walk? Justify your answer. (Assume you always take the most direct routes and stay on the paths.)

Student Center
Dorm
Dining Hall
Science Lab
Library

CONNECT THE MATH Students use elements on a diagram to form a right triangle. In this lesson, students learn about a special right triangle with angles measuring 45°, 45°, and 90°.

2 Guided Instruction

Problem 1 Finding the Length of the Hypotenuse

Take Note

Using algebraic properties and rules for simplifying radicals, show students how to solve the equation so that the length of the leg is given in terms of the length of the hypotenuse.

Problem 1

Q How do you simplify the expression $2\sqrt{2} \cdot \sqrt{2}$? **[$2\sqrt{2} \cdot \sqrt{2} = 2 \cdot 2 = 4$]**

Q Can you use the Pythagorean Theorem to determine the length of the hypotenuse in 1A? Explain. **[Yes; because it is an isosceles triangle, you know the lengths of both legs.]**

Q How can you use the Pythagorean Theorem to check your work? **[You can substitute the lengths of all three sides into the Pythagorean Theorem.]**

Got It?

Q According to Theorem 69, what product gives the length of the hypotenuse? **[$5\sqrt{3}(\sqrt{2})$]**

Q How do you multiply terms that contain radicals? **[Multiply the whole numbers together and multiply the radicals by finding the product of the numbers under the radicals signs.]**

ANSWERS

Got It? $5\sqrt{6}$

Practice

1. $60\sqrt{2}$
2. $\sqrt{10}$

▼ STUDENT PAGE 426

The Solve It involves triangles with angles 45°, 45°, and 90°.

Essential Understanding Certain right triangles have properties that allow you to use shortcuts to determine side lengths without using the Pythagorean Theorem.

The acute angles of a right isosceles triangle are both 45° angles. Another name for an isosceles right triangle is a 45°-45°-90° triangle. If each leg has length x and the hypotenuse has length y, you can solve for y in terms of x.

$x^2 + x^2 = y^2$ Use the Pythagorean Theorem.

$2x^2 = y^2$ Simplify.

$x\sqrt{2} = y$ Take the positive square root of each side.

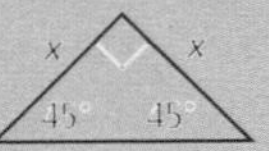

You have just proved the following theorem.

take note **Theorem 69 45°-45°-90° Triangle Theorem**

In a 45°-45°-90° triangle, both legs are congruent and the length of the hypotenuse is $\sqrt{2}$ times the length of a leg.

hypotenuse $= \sqrt{2} \cdot$ leg

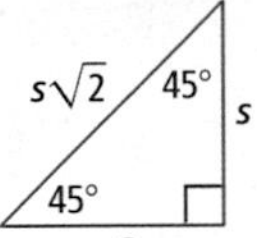

▼ DIGITAL

Problem 1 **Finding the Length of the Hypotenuse**

What is the value of each variable?

A

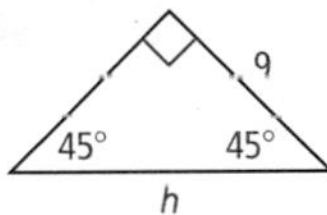

hypotenuse $= \sqrt{2} \cdot$ leg   45°-45°-90° △ Theorem

$h = \sqrt{2} \cdot 9$ Substitute.

$h = 9\sqrt{2}$ Simplify.

B

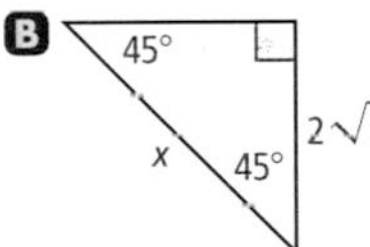

hypotenuse $= \sqrt{2} \cdot$ leg

$x = \sqrt{2} \cdot 2\sqrt{2}$

$x = 4$

▼ STUDENT PAGE 427

Got It? What is the length of the hypotenuse of a 45°-45°-90° triangle with leg length $5\sqrt{3}$?

Practice **Find the value of each variable. If your answer is not an integer, express it in simplest radical form.**

1. 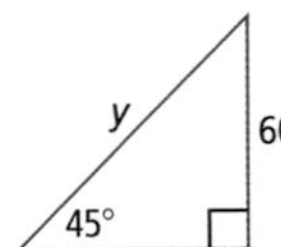

2. 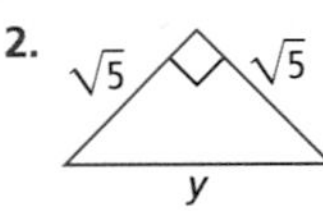

Problem 2 Finding the Length of a Leg

Q Why is the expression $\frac{6}{\sqrt{2}}$ not in simplified form? **[In simplest form, you cannot have a radical in the denominator of a fraction.]**

Q What does it mean to rationalize a denominator? **[to change the form of the fraction so that it does not have a radical in the denominator]**

Q How can you work backward to solve this problem? **[You can multiply each answer choice by $\sqrt{2}$ to see if you get 6.]**

Got It?

Encourage students to check that the leg length is accurate by multiplying it by $\sqrt{2}$ to make sure that they get the length of the hypotenuse.

ANSWERS

Got It? a. $8\sqrt{2}$; **b.** $\frac{\sqrt{2}}{\sqrt{2}} = 1$, so multiplying by $\frac{\sqrt{2}}{\sqrt{2}}$ is the same as multiplying by 1.

Practice

3. $x = 15$, $y = 15$ **4.** $5\sqrt{2}$

▼ DIGITAL

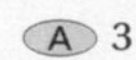

Problem 2 Finding the Length of a Leg

Multiple Choice What is the value of x?

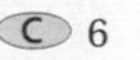

Ⓐ 3 Ⓑ $3\sqrt{2}$ Ⓒ 6 Ⓓ $6\sqrt{2}$

hypotenuse $= \sqrt{2} \cdot$ leg	45°-45°-90° Triangle Theorem
$6 = \sqrt{2} \cdot x$	Substitute.
$x = \frac{6}{\sqrt{2}}$	Divide each side by $\sqrt{2}$.
$x = \frac{6}{\sqrt{2}} \cdot \frac{\sqrt{2}}{\sqrt{2}}$	Multiply by a form of 1 to rationalize the denominator.
$x = \frac{6\sqrt{2}}{2}$	Simplify.
$x = 3\sqrt{2}$	Simplify.

The correct answer is B.

▼ STUDENT PAGE 428

Got It? a. The length of the hypotenuse of a 45°-45°-90° triangle is 16. What is the length of one leg?

b. Reasoning In Problem 2, why can you multiply $\frac{6}{\sqrt{2}}$ by $\frac{\sqrt{2}}{\sqrt{2}}$?

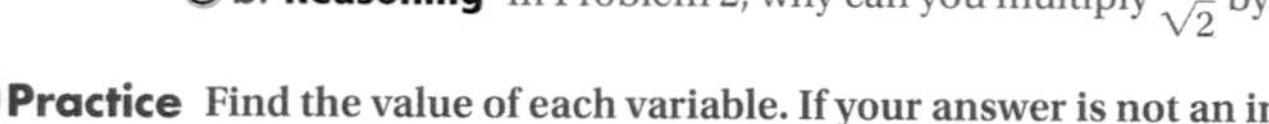

Practice Find the value of each variable. If your answer is not an integer, express it in simplest radical form.

3.
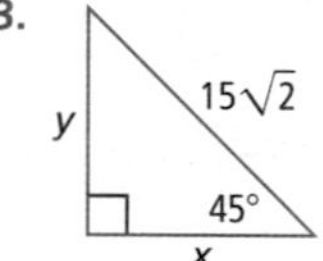

4.
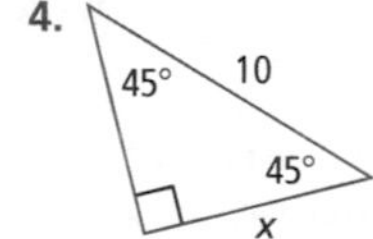

Problem 3 Finding Distance

Q How do you know that the triangles formed in the square are 45°-45°-90° triangles? **[Answers may vary. Sample: Diagonals bisect the angles of a square, and each angle of a square is a right angle.]**

Q What part of the right triangle does the 60 ft measurement represent? **[leg, because the hypotenuse is opposite the right angle]**

Q Is 85 ft the longest throwing distance from one player to another when both players are in the infield of the softball diamond? Explain. **[Yes, the diagonal of the square is the longest distance between the vertices.]**

Got It? VISUAL LEARNERS

Q Can you use Theorem 69 to determine the length of the diagonal of a rectangular garden that is not a square? Explain. **[No; because the diagonal and two sides of the garden would not form a 45°-45°-90° triangle.]**

ANSWERS

Got It? 141 ft

Practice

5. 14.1 cm **6.** 25.5 ft

▼ STUDENT PAGE 429

When you apply the 45°-45°-90° Triangle Theorem to a real-life example, you can use a calculator to evaluate square roots.

▼ DIGITAL

Problem 3 Finding Distance

Softball A high school softball diamond is a square. The distance from base to base is 60 ft. To the nearest foot, how far does a catcher throw the ball from home plate to second base?

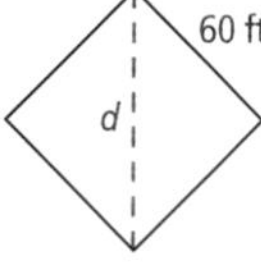

The distance d is the length of the hypotenuse of a 45°-45°-90° triangle.

$d = 60\sqrt{2}$	hypotenuse $= \sqrt{2} \cdot$ leg
$d \approx 84.85281374$	Use a calculator.

The catcher throws the ball about 85 ft from home plate to second base.

▼ STUDENT PAGE 429

Got It? You plan to build a path along one diagonal of a 100 ft-by-100 ft square garden. To the nearest foot, how long will the path be?

Practice **5. Dinnerware Design** What is the side length of the smallest square plate on which a 20-cm chopstick can fit along a diagonal without any overhang? Round your answer to the nearest tenth of a centimeter.

6. Aviation The four blades of a helicopter meet at right angles and are all the same length. The distance between the tips of two adjacent blades is 36 ft. How long is each blade? Round your answer to the nearest tenth of a foot.

Problem 4 Using the Length of One Side

Take Note
Ask students to determine the coordinates of point C in the following diagram such that $AC = AB = BC$. Students will need to set up an equation using the distance formula in order to determine the y-coordinate.

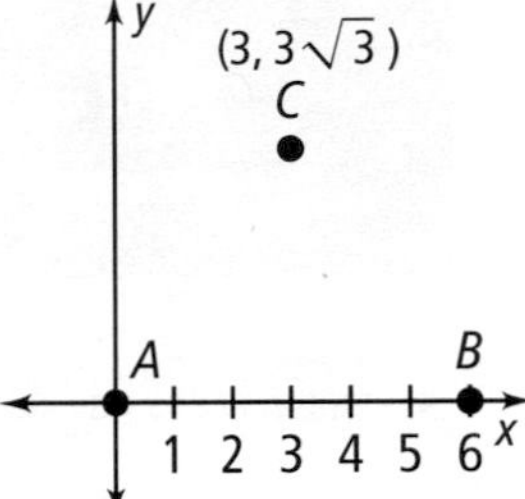

Problem 4

Q Is the leg whose length is given the shorter leg, the longer leg, or the hypotenuse? How can you tell? **[longer leg; it is across from the 60° angle.]**

Q How is the length of the shorter leg of a 30°-60°-90° triangle related to the length of the longer leg? **[The longer leg is $\sqrt{3}$ times as long as the shorter leg.]**

Got It? **ERROR PREVENTION**

Q How is the length of the hypotenuse of a 30°-60°-90° triangle related to the length of the shorter leg? **[The hypotenuse is twice the length of the shorter leg.]**

ANSWERS

Got It? $\frac{10\sqrt{3}}{3}$

Practice

7. $x = 20$, $y = 20\sqrt{3}$

8. $x = 4$, $y = 2$

▼ STUDENT PAGE 430

Another type of special right triangle is a 30°-60°-90° triangle.

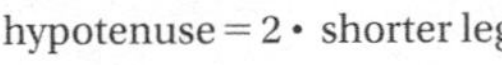

take note **Theorem 70 30°-60°-90° Triangle Theorem**

In a 30°-60°-90° triangle, the length of the hypotenuse is twice the length of the shorter leg. The length of the longer leg is $\sqrt{3}$ times the length of the shorter leg.

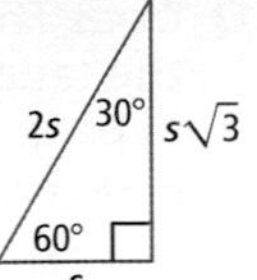

hypotenuse $= 2 \cdot$ shorter leg

longer leg $= \sqrt{3} \cdot$ shorter leg

Proof of Theorem 70: 30°-60°-90° Triangle Theorem

For equilateral $\triangle WXZ$, altitude $\overline{WY}$ bisects $\angle W$ and is the perpendicular bisector of $\overline{XZ}$. So, $\overline{WY}$ divides $\triangle WXZ$ into two congruent 30°-60°-90° triangles.

Thus, $XY = \frac{1}{2}XZ = \frac{1}{2}XW$, or $XW = 2XY = 2s$.

$XY^2 + YW^2 = XW^2$	Use the Pythagorean Theorem.
$s^2 + YW^2 = (2s)^2$	Substitute s for XY and $2s$ for XW.
$YW^2 = 4s^2 - s^2$	Subtract s^2 from each side.
$YW^2 = 3s^2$	Simplify.
$YW = s\sqrt{3}$	Take the positive square root of each side.

You can also use the 30°-60°-90° Triangle Theorem to find side lengths.

▼ DIGITAL

Problem 4 **Using the Length of One Side**

Algebra **What is the value of d in simplest radical form?**

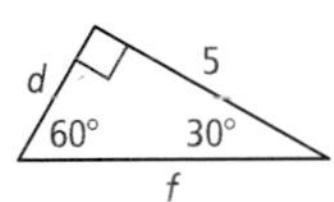

Think	Write
In a 30°-60°-90° triangle, the leg opposite the 60° angle is the longer leg. So d represents the length of the shorter leg. Write an equation relating the legs.	longer leg $= \sqrt{3} \cdot$ shorter leg $5 = d\sqrt{3}$
Divide each side by $\sqrt{3}$ to solve for d.	$d = \frac{5}{\sqrt{3}}$
The value of d is not in simplest radical form because there is a radical in the denominator. Multiply d by a form of 1.	$\frac{5}{\sqrt{3}} \cdot \frac{\sqrt{3}}{\sqrt{3}} = \frac{5\sqrt{3}}{3}$ So $d = \frac{5\sqrt{3}}{3}$.

▼ STUDENT PAGES 430–431

Got It? What is the value of f in simplest radical form?

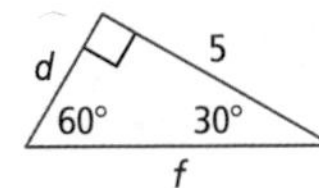

Think
How can you write an equation that relates the longer leg to the hypotenuse?

Practice **Algebra** In Exercises 7–8, find the value of each variable. If your answer is not an integer, express it in simplest radical form.

7.

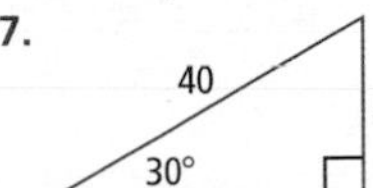

8.

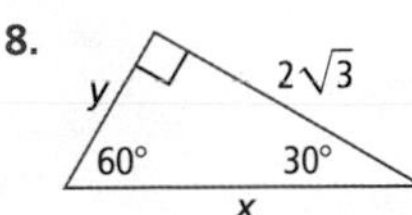

Problem 5 Applying the 30°-60°-90° Triangle Theorem

Q Is the leg whose length is given the shorter leg, the longer leg, or the hypotenuse? How can you tell? **[Longer leg; it is across from the 60°angle.]**

Q Does Theorem 70 express a relationship between the length of the longer leg and the length of the hypotenuse? Explain. **[No, the length of the hypotenuse is expressed in terms of the length of the shorter leg.]**

Q How could you solve this problem using two steps? **[Determine the length of the shorter leg, and then double the length to get the length of the hypotenuse.]**

Got It?

Q How does this problem differ from Problem 5? **[You are given the length of the hypotenuse of a 30°-60°-90° triangle instead of the length of the longer leg.]**

ANSWERS

Got It? 15.6 mm

Practice

9. 50 ft

10. 300 ft

▼ DIGITAL

Problem 5 Applying the 30°-60°-90° Triangle Theorem

Jewelry Making An artisan makes pendants in the shape of equilateral triangles. The height of each pendant is 18 mm. What is the length *s* of each side of a pendant to the nearest tenth of a millimeter?

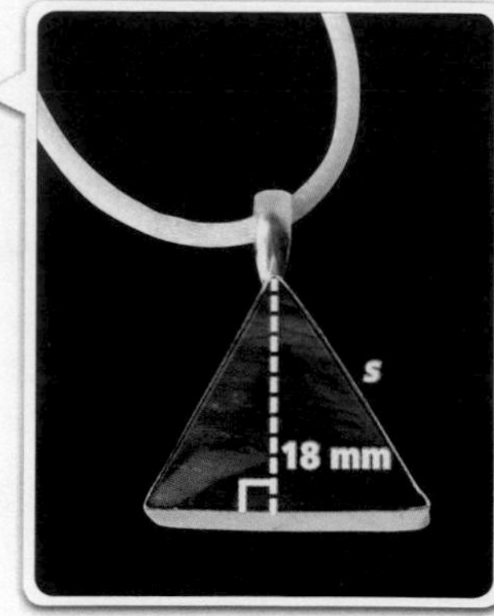

The hypotenuse of each 30°-60°-90° triangle is *s*. The shorter leg is $\frac{1}{2}s$.

$18 = \sqrt{3}\left(\frac{1}{2}s\right)$	longer leg $= \sqrt{3} \cdot$ shorter leg
$18 = \frac{\sqrt{3}}{2}s$	Simplify.
$\frac{2}{\sqrt{3}} \cdot 18 = s$	Multiply each side by $\frac{2}{\sqrt{3}}$.
$s \approx 20.78460969$	Use a calculator.

Each side of a pendant is about 20.8 mm long.

▼ STUDENT PAGES 431–432

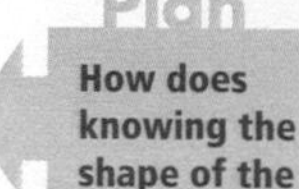

Got It? Suppose the sides of the pendant, from Problem 5, are 18 mm long. What is the height of the pendant to the nearest tenth of a millimeter?

How does knowing the shape of the pendant help?

A Practice

STEM **9. Architecture** An escalator lifts people to the second floor of a building, 25 ft above the first floor. The escalator rises at a 30° angle. To the nearest foot, how far does a person travel from the bottom to the top of the escalator?

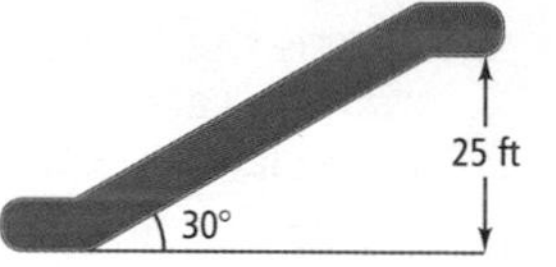

STEM **10. City Planning** A rectangular park has a walkway that joins opposite corners. A triangle formed from two sides of the park and the walkway is a 30°-60°-90° triangle. If the shorter side of the park measures 150 feet, what is the length of the walkway?

Lesson Check

Do you know HOW?

If students have difficulty with Exercise 13, then have them review Problem 2 to understand how to rationalize a denominator.

Do you UNDERSTAND?

If students have difficulty with Exercise 15, then remind them that 30°-60°-90° triangles are a subset of right triangles, and that satisfying the Pythagorean Theorem alone does not guarantee that it is a 30°-60°-90° triangle.

Close

Q What are special right triangles? **[They are 30°-60°-90° triangles and 45°-45°-90° triangles. They are studied because their special properties can be used as shortcuts for finding the lengths of the sides of these triangles.]**

ANSWERS

11. $7\sqrt{2}$ **12.** 3

13. $4\sqrt{2}$ **14.** $6\sqrt{3}$

15. Rika; 5 should be opposite the 30°∠ and $5\sqrt{3}$ should be opposite the 60°∠.

16. Answers may vary. Sample: The triangle is isosc. The legs have equal lengths. Use the Pythagorean Thm. to find the hypotenuse; 6, $6\sqrt{2}$.

▼ STUDENT PAGES 432–433

Lesson Check

Do you know HOW?

What is the value of x? If your answer is not an integer, express it in simplest radical form.

11. 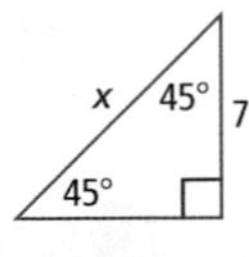

12. 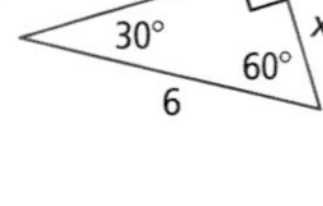

13. 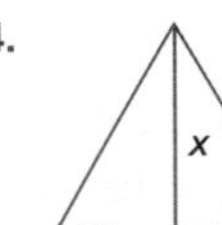

14.
x
12
60°
60°

Do you UNDERSTAND?

MATHEMATICAL PRACTICES

15. Error Analysis Sandra drew the triangle at the right. Rika said that the labeled lengths are not possible. With which student do you agree? Explain.

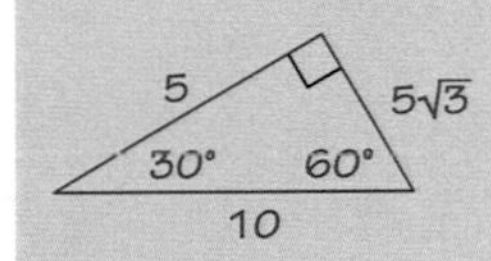

16. Reasoning A test question asks you to find two side lengths of a 45°-45°-90° triangle. You know that the length of one leg is 6, but you forgot the special formula for 45°-45°-90° triangles. Explain how you can still determine the other side lengths. What are they?

4 Practice

More Practice and Problem-Solving Exercises

ASSIGNMENT GUIDE

The assignments below are for the More Practice and Problem-Solving Exercises. You may also want to assign the A-Level Practice Exercises for homework if these are not used in class.

Average: 17–26

Advanced: 17–27

Mathematical Practices The exercises listed focus on the Standards for Mathematical Practices listed.

EX. 23: Make Sense of Problems (MP 1)

EX. 16: Construct Arguments (MP 3)

EX. 15: Critique the Reasoning of Others (MP 3)

EX. 23, 25: Model with Mathematics (MP 4)

STEM exercises focus on science or engineering applications.

EXERCISE 24: Use the **Think About a Plan** worksheet in the Online Teacher Resources to further support students' development in becoming independent learners.

HOMEWORK QUICK CHECK

To check students' understanding of key skills and concepts, go over Exercises 17, 21, 23, 24, and 25.

▼ STUDENT PAGES 433–434

More Practice and Problem-Solving Exercises

MATHEMATICAL PRACTICES

B Apply

Algebra Find the value of each variable. If your answer is not an integer, express it in simplest radical form.

17. 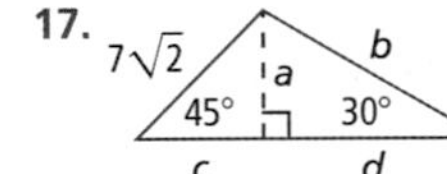

18.
4√3
a
b
60°
45°
c
d

19. 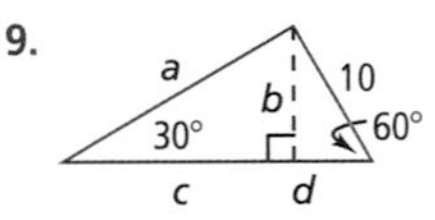

20.
6
60°
2√3
a
b

21. 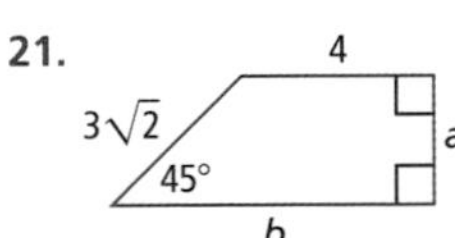

22. 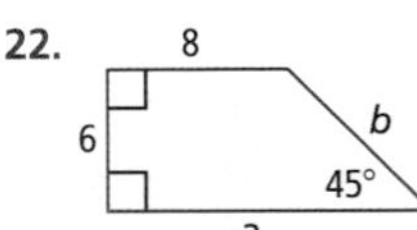

23. Think About a Plan A farmer's conveyor belt carries bales of hay from the ground to the barn loft. The conveyor belt moves at 100 ft/min. How many seconds does it take for a bale of hay to go from the ground to the barn loft?

- Which part of a right triangle does the conveyor belt represent?
- You know the speed. What other information do you need to find time?
- How are minutes and seconds related?

More Practice and Problem-Solving Exercises *continued*

ANSWERS

17. $a = 7$, $b = 14$, $c = 7$, $d = 7\sqrt{3}$

18. $a = 6$, $b = 6\sqrt{2}$, $c = 2\sqrt{3}$, $d = 6$

19. $a = 10\sqrt{3}$, $b = 5\sqrt{3}$, $c = 15$, $d = 5$

20. $a = 4$, $b = 4$

21. $a = 3$, $b = 7$

22. $a = 14$, $b = 6\sqrt{2}$

23. 14.4 s

24. **a.** 8.5 m
b. 3.1 m

25. Answers may vary. Sample: A ramp up to a door is 12 ft long. The ramp forms a 30°∠ with the ground. How high off the ground is the door? 6 ft

26. Answers may vary. Samples using the following segment are given.

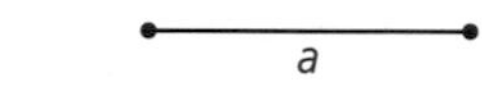

a.

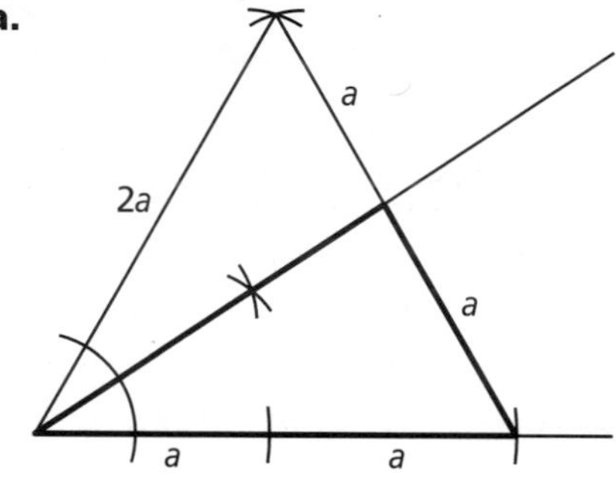

b.

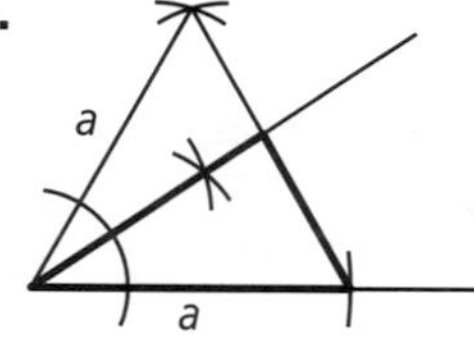

c.

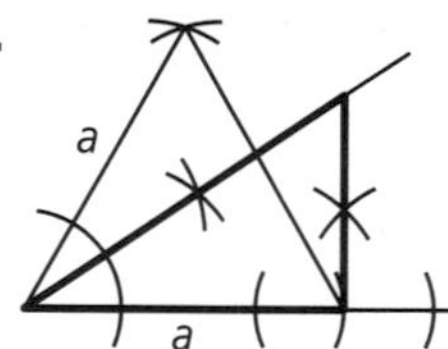

27. **a.** $\sqrt{3}$ units
b. $2\sqrt{3}$ units
c. $s\sqrt{3}$ units

▼ STUDENT PAGE 434

24. House Repair After heavy winds damaged a house, workers placed a 6-m brace against its side at a 45° angle. Then, at the same spot on the ground, they placed a second, longer brace to make a 30° angle with the side of the house.
a. How long is the longer brace? Round to the nearest tenth of a meter.
b. About how much higher does the longer brace reach than the shorter brace?

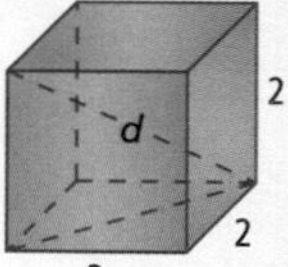

25. Open-Ended Write a real-life problem that you can solve using a 30°-60°-90° triangle with a 12-ft hypotenuse. Show your solution.

26. Constructions Construct a 30°-60°-90° triangle using a segment that is the given side.
a. the shorter leg **b.** the hypotenuse **c.** the longer leg

27. Geometry in 3 Dimensions Find the length d, in simplest radical form, of the diagonal of a cube with edges of the given length.
a. 1 unit **b.** 2 units **c.** s units

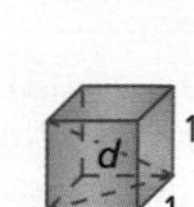

5 Assess and Remediate

Lesson Quiz

1. What is the value of h?

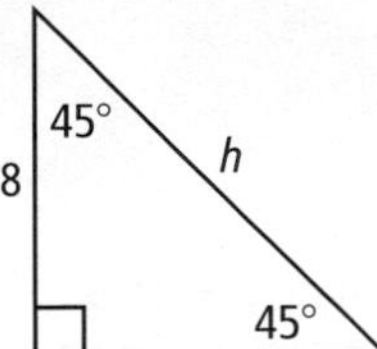

2. What is the value of x?

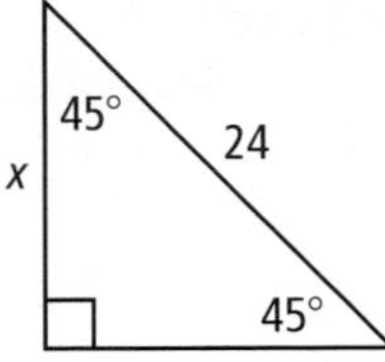

3. Do you UNDERSTAND? A company logo is shaped like an equilateral triangle with 2-in.-long sides. What is the height of the logo? Round to the nearest tenth.

4. What is the value of a?

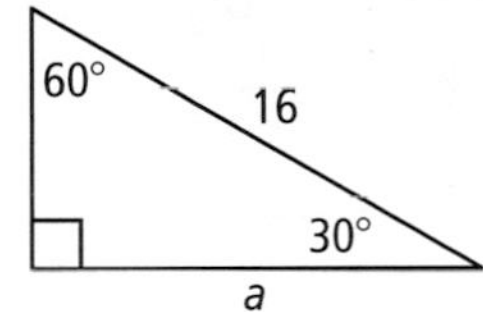

ANSWERS TO LESSON QUIZ

1. $8\sqrt{2}$

2. $12\sqrt{2}$

3. 1.7 in.

4. $8\sqrt{3}$

Prescription for Remediation

Use the student work on the Lesson Quiz to prescribe a differentiated assignment.

Points	Differentiated Remediation
0–2	Intervention
3	On-level
4	Extension

Online Assessment

Assign the Lesson Quiz in Success Tracker on **pearsonsuccessnet.com**. Success Tracker will automatically score the quiz and assign appropriate intervention or enrichment to each student based on the results. The compiled data appear in three different reports for instant analysis of whole class and individual student performance.

Differentiated Remediation

Intervention

- **RETEACHING** (2 pages) Provides reteaching and practice exercises for the key lesson concepts. Use with struggling students or absent students.
- **ENGLISH LANGUAGE LEARNER SUPPORT** Helps students develop and reinforce mathematical vocabulary and key concepts.

On-Level

- **PRACTICE** (2 pages) Provides extra practice for each lesson. For simpler practice exercises, use the Form K Practice pages found in the Online Teacher Resources.
- **THINK ABOUT A PLAN** Helps students develop specific problem-solving skills and strategies by providing scaffolded guiding questions.
- **STANDARDIZED TEST PREP** Focuses on all major exercises, all major question types, and helps students prepare for the high-stakes assessments.

Extension

- **ENRICHMENT** Provides students with interesting problems and activities that extend the concepts of the lesson.
- **ACTIVITIES, GAMES, AND PUZZLES** Worksheets that can be used for concept development, enrichment, and for fun!

TECHNOLOGY LAB

Use With Lesson 7-3

Exploring Trigonometric Ratios

Common Core State Standard
G.SRT.6 Understand that by similarity, side ratios in right triangles are properties of the angles in the triangle, . . .

Mathematical Practices

This Technology Lab supports students in becoming proficient in using appropriate tools, Mathematical Practice 5.

Guided Instruction

PURPOSE To use geometry software to explore the trigonometric ratios of sine, cosine, and tangent

PROCESS Students will construct a triangle using geometry software. They will manipulate a point on the triangle to see how moving the point impacts the three trigonometric ratios.

DISCUSS Students have not yet been introduced to the trigonometric ratios; in this activity they are exploring ratios of side lengths to one another.

Exercises

The exercises allow students to see how the ratio of side lengths of a right triangle changes as an acute angle in the triangle gets larger or smaller.

Q Why is the ratio $\frac{ED}{AE}$ a function of $m\angle A$? **[The lengths of $\overline{ED}$ and $\overline{AE}$ change as $m\angle A$ changes.]**

Q For what angle measure is the ratio $\frac{\text{leg opposite } \angle A}{\text{hypotenuse}}$ equal to 1? **[90°]**

Q For what angle measure is the ratio $\frac{\text{leg adjacent to } \angle A}{\text{hypotenuse}}$ equal to 1? **[0°]**

Q For what angle measure is the ratio $\frac{\text{leg opposite } \angle A}{\text{leg adjacent to } \angle A}$ equal to 1? **[45°]**

Exercises and Extend

ANSWERS

1. The ratio does not change.
2. **a.** The ratio becomes larger as the measure of $\angle A$ increases.
   b. 0; 1
3. yes; sine
4. It does not change; the ratio becomes smaller as $m\angle A$ increases; 1, 0; yes; cosine; it does not change; the ratio becomes larger as $\angle A$ increases; 0; very large; yes; tangent
5. Sample: When the ratios are equal, the angles are complements.

▼ STUDENT PAGES 435–437

Construct

Use geometry software to construct $\overrightarrow{AB}$ and $\overrightarrow{AC}$ so that $\angle A$ is acute. Through a point D on $\overrightarrow{AB}$, construct a line perpendicular to $\overrightarrow{AB}$ that intersects $\overrightarrow{AC}$ in point E.

Moving point D changes the size of $\triangle ADE$.
Moving point C changes the size of $\angle A$.

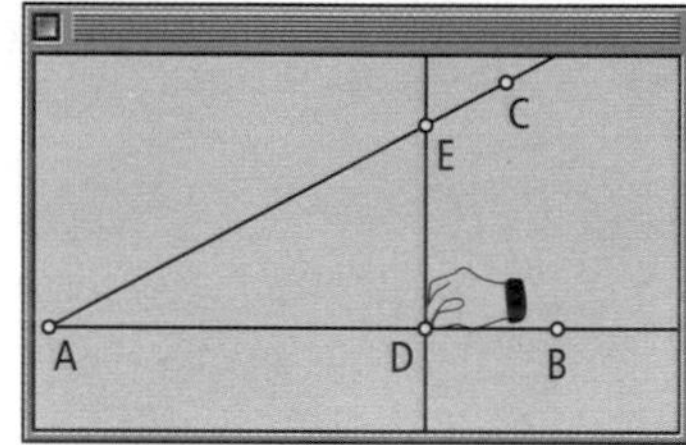

Exercises

1. • Measure $\angle A$ and find the lengths of the sides of $\triangle ADE$.
   • Calculate the ratio $\frac{\text{leg opposite } \angle A}{\text{hypotenuse}}$, which is $\frac{ED}{AE}$.
   • Move point D to change the size of $\triangle ADE$ without changing $m\angle A$.

   What do you observe about the ratio as the size of $\triangle ADE$ changes?

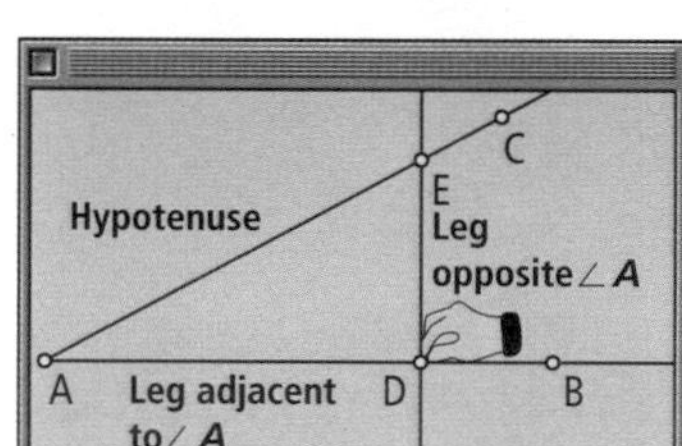

2. • Move point C to change $m\angle A$.
   a. What do you observe about the ratio as $m\angle A$ changes?
   b. What value does the ratio approach as $m\angle A$ approaches 0? As $m\angle A$ approaches 90?
3. • Make a table that shows values for $m\angle A$ and the ratio $\frac{\text{leg opposite } \angle A}{\text{hypotenuse}}$. In your table, include 10, 20, 30, . . ., 80 for $m\angle A$.
   • Compare your table with a table of trigonometric ratios.

   Do your values for $\frac{\text{leg opposite } \angle A}{\text{hypotenuse}}$ match the values in one of the columns of the table? What is the name of this ratio in the table?

Extend

4. Repeat Exercises 1–3 for $\frac{\text{leg adjacent to } \angle A}{\text{hypotenuse}}$, which is $\frac{AD}{AE}$, and $\frac{\text{leg opposite } \angle A}{\text{leg adjacent to } \angle A}$, which is $\frac{ED}{AD}$.
5. • Choose a measure for $\angle A$ and determine the ratio $r = \frac{\text{leg opposite } \angle A}{\text{hypotenuse}}$. Record $m\angle A$ and this ratio.
   • Manipulate the triangle so that $\frac{\text{leg adjacent to } \angle A}{\text{hypotenuse}}$ has the same value r. Record this $m\angle A$ and compare it with your first value of $m\angle A$.
   • Repeat this procedure several times. Look for a pattern in the two measures of $\angle A$ that you found for different values of r.

   Make a conjecture.

7-3 Trigonometry

Common Core State Standards
G.SRT.8 Use trigonometric ratios . . . to solve right triangles in applied problems. **Also G.SRT.7, F.TF.8**

Preparing to Teach

BIG ideas Reasoning and Proof
Measurement

ESSENTIAL UNDERSTANDING

If certain combinations of side lengths and angle measures of a right triangle are known, ratios can be used to find other side lengths and angle measures.

Math Background

From the study of similar triangles and right triangles, students learn that the lengths of corresponding sides in similar right triangles have equal ratios.

Right triangles and special right triangles lead to the study of right triangle trigonometry. Right triangle trigonometry is the foundation for the study of unit circle trigonometry. When using right triangles, as in this lesson, only the ratios of angles measuring between 0 and 90 degrees can be considered. Once unit circle trigonometry is introduced, ratios of angles with any real number measure can be considered.

Three additional right triangle trigonometric ratios exist but are not covered in this lesson. Those ratios are cotangent (the reciprocal of the tangent ratio), secant (the reciprocal of the cosine ratio), and cosecant (the reciprocal of the sine ratio).

ELL Support

FOCUS ON LANGUAGE Display a word wall with vocabulary words and other key words and pictures. For example, write *isosceles, right triangle,* and *ratio*, with their definitions from the chapter and a picture of each.

USE MANIPULATIVES A bike ramp has a height of 30 in. and a base length of 48 in. Draw a picture to model the situation. Calculate the angle of elevation of the ramp.

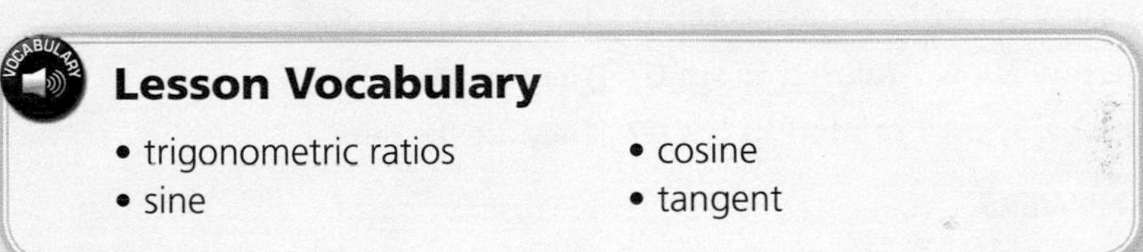

VOCABULARY
Lesson Vocabulary
• trigonometric ratios
• sine
• cosine
• tangent

Mathematical Practices

ATTEND TO PRECISION. Students will define sine, cosine, and tangent, as well as compute their values in right triangles.

1 Interactive Learning

Solve It!

PURPOSE To make a conjecture about the ratios of the lengths of the corresponding sides of similar triangles

PROCESS Students may use similar triangle postulates, the Pythagorean Theorem, or logical reasoning.

Q What is *DF*? Explain. **[*DF* = 1; △*ADF*; is similar to △*AEG*.]**

Q What is the length of the hypotenuse of △*AEG*? **[$4\sqrt{5}$]**

Q What is the ratio of the length of the shortest leg of △*AEG* to the length of the hypotenuse of △*AEG*? **[The ratio is $\frac{\sqrt{5}}{5}$.]**

ANSWER $\frac{\sqrt{5}}{5}, \frac{\sqrt{5}}{5}, \frac{\sqrt{5}}{5}$; the ratio does not change for similar triangles.

CONNECT THE MATH In the Solve It, students find the ratio of the short leg to the hypotenuse in three triangles. In this lesson, students learn the ratios of the side lengths to the hypotenuse and to each other.

▼ DIGITAL (STUDENT WORK SPACE PAGE 438)

SOLVE IT! Getting Ready!

What is the ratio of the length of the shorter leg to the length of the hypotenuse for each of △ADF, △AEG, and △ABC? Make a conjecture based on your results.

A, D, E, B, F, G, C; 2, 6, 4, 4

2 Guided Instruction

Problem 1 Writing Trigonometric Ratios

Take Note
Some students have difficulty correctly identifying the opposite and adjacent sides for a given angle. Provide practice for students by drawing right triangles in different orientations and using different combinations of variables to represent the length of each side.

Problem 1

Q How can you identify the hypotenuse of a right triangle? **[It is the side opposite the right angle.]**

Q How can you identify the adjacent leg of an angle? **[It is one of the two sides of the triangle that forms the given angle, but is not the hypotenuse.]**

Q If in a second right triangle $\triangle ABC$, $\sin A = \frac{8}{17}$, what do you know about $\triangle ABC$ and $\triangle TGR$? **[They are similar triangles.]**

Got It? **ERROR PREVENTION**

Q How is tan T related to tan G? **[They are reciprocals.]**

Q How is cos T related to sin G? **[They are the same.]**

Q How is sin T related to cos G? **[They are the same.]**

ANSWERS

Got It? $\frac{15}{17}$; $\frac{8}{17}$; $\frac{15}{8}$

Practice

1. $\frac{7}{25}$; $\frac{24}{25}$; $\frac{7}{24}$ **2.** $\frac{\sqrt{3}}{2}$; $\frac{1}{2}$; $\sqrt{3}$

▼ STUDENT PAGE 438

Essential Understanding If you know certain combinations of side lengths and angle measures of a right triangle, you can use ratios to find other side lengths and angle measures.

Any two right triangles that have a pair of congruent acute angles are similar by the AA Similarity Postulate. Similar right triangles have equivalent ratios for their corresponding sides called **trigonometric ratios**.

take note **Key Concept** Trigonometric Ratios

sine of $\angle A = \frac{\text{length of leg opposite } \angle A}{\text{length of hypotenuse}} = \frac{a}{c}$

cosine of $\angle A = \frac{\text{length of leg adjacent to } \angle A}{\text{length of hypotenuse}} = \frac{b}{c}$

tangent of $\angle A = \frac{\text{length of leg opposite } \angle A}{\text{length of leg adjacent to } \angle A} = \frac{a}{b}$

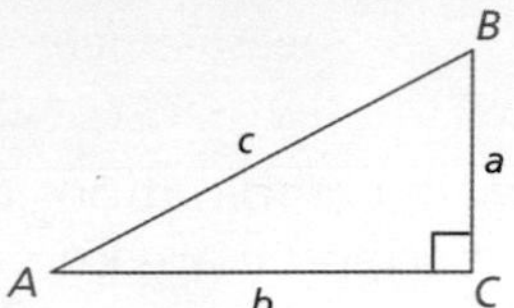

You can abbreviate the ratios as

$\sin A = \frac{\text{opposite}}{\text{hypotenuse}}$, $\cos A = \frac{\text{adjacent}}{\text{hypotenuse}}$, and $\tan A = \frac{\text{opposite}}{\text{adjacent}}$.

▼ DIGITAL

Problem 1 Writing Trigonometric Ratios

What are the sine, cosine, and tangent ratios for $\angle T$?

$\sin T = \frac{\text{opposite}}{\text{hypotenuse}} = \frac{8}{17}$

$\cos T = \frac{\text{adjacent}}{\text{hypotenuse}} = \frac{15}{17}$

$\tan T = \frac{\text{opposite}}{\text{adjacent}} = \frac{8}{15}$

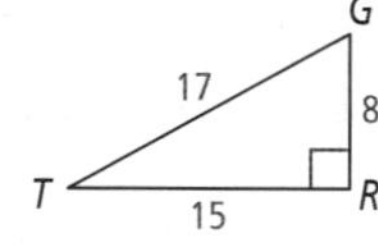

▼ STUDENT PAGE 439

Think
How do the sides relate to $\angle G$?

Got It? What are the sine, cosine, and tangent ratios for $\angle G$?

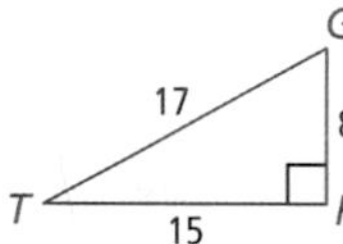

Practice Write the ratios for sin M, cos M, and tan M.

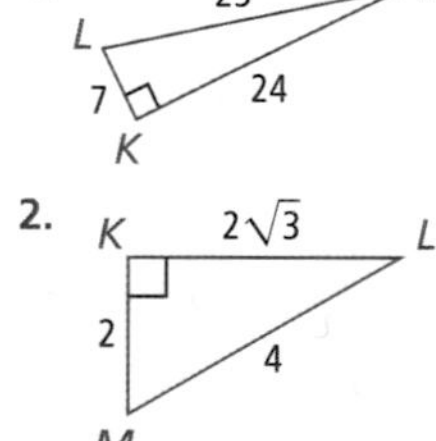

Problem 2 Using a Trigonometric Ratio to Find Distance

Q In relation to the 5° angle, what do the sides in the diagram represent? **[The side representing the 150-ft drop is the adjacent leg and the side representing the distance from the base of the tower is the opposite leg.]**

Q Which trigonometric ratio involves the lengths of the adjacent and opposite legs? **[tan]**

Q What is the measure of the angle formed by the ground and the tower? Explain. **[85; 180 − 90 − 5 = 85]**

Q What trigonometric ratio of the 85° angle could you use to determine *x*? **[tan]**

Got It? **VISUAL LEARNERS**
Encourage students to sketch a diagram of part (d) before solving the problem. Make sure that they label the hypotenuse of the triangle 150 ft.

ANSWERS

Got It? a. 13.8 **b.** 1.9 **c.** 3.8 **d.** 44 ft

Practice

3. 8.3 **4.** 1085 ft

▼ STUDENT PAGE 440

In Chapter 6, you used similar triangles to measure distances indirectly. You can also use trigonometry for indirect measurement.

▼ DIGITAL

Problem 2 Using a Trigonometric Ratio to Find Distance

Landmarks **In 1990, the Leaning Tower of Pisa was closed to the public due to safety concerns. The tower reopened in 2001 after a 10-year project to reduce its tilt from vertical. Engineers' efforts were successful and resulted in a tilt of 5°, reduced from 5.5°. Suppose someone drops an object from the tower at a height of 150 ft. How far from the base of the tower will the object land? Round to the nearest foot.**

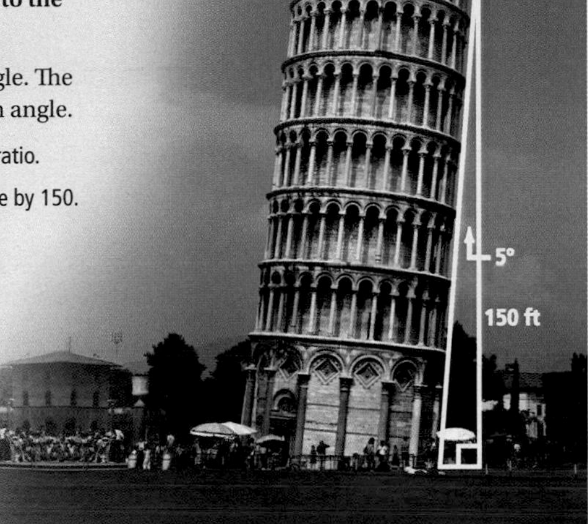

The given side is adjacent to the given angle. The side you want to find is opposite the given angle.

$\tan 5^\circ = \frac{x}{150}$ Use the tangent ratio.

$x = 150(\tan 5^\circ)$ Multiply each side by 150.

150 tan 5 enter Use a calculator.

$x \approx 13.12329953$

The object will land about 13 ft from the base of the tower.

▼ STUDENT PAGES 440–441

Got It? For parts (a)–(c), find the value of w to the nearest tenth.

a. 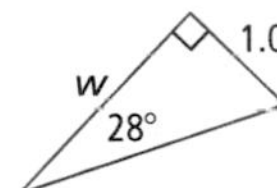

b. 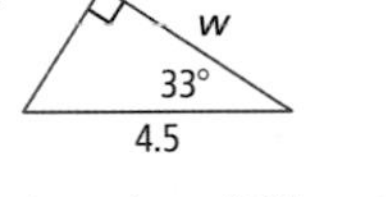

c. 

d. A section of Filbert Street in San Francisco rises at an angle of about 17°. If you walk 150 ft up this section, what is your vertical rise? Round to the nearest foot.

Practice

3. Find the value of x. Round to the nearest tenth.

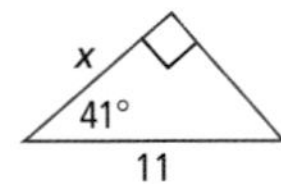

4. Public Transportation An escalator in the subway station has a vertical rise of 195 ft 9.5 in., and rises at an angle of 10.4°. How long is the escalator? Round to the nearest foot.

Problem 3 Using Inverses

Q How could you use the tangent ratio to determine $m\angle X$? **[You could first determine the third side of the triangle using the Pythagorean Theorem. Then you can compute the tangent ratio.]**

Q How could you use $\angle H$ to determine $m\angle X$? **[You could first determine $m\angle H$ using the cosine ratio, and then use the Triangle Angle-Sum Theorem to determine $m\angle X$.]**

Got It? **ERROR PREVENTION**

If students do not get the correct angle measures using their calculators, make certain that their calculators are in degree mode rather than in radian mode. Explain to students that radians are another unit used to measure angles.

ANSWERS

Got It? a. 68 **b.** No; you can use any of the three trigonometric ratios as long as you identify the appropriate leg that is opp. or adj. to each acute $\angle$.

Practice

5. 58 **6.** 46

▼ STUDENT PAGE 441

If you know the sine, cosine, or tangent ratio for an angle, you can use an inverse ($\sin^{-1}$, $\cos^{-1}$, or $\tan^{-1}$) to find the measure of the angle.

▼ DIGITAL

Problem 3 **Using Inverses**

What is $m\angle X$ to the nearest degree?

A

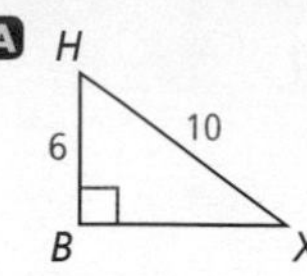

You know the lengths of the hypotenuse and the side opposite $\angle X$.

Use the sine ratio.

$\sin X = \frac{6}{10}$ Write the ratio.

$m\angle X = \sin^{-1}\left(\frac{6}{10}\right)$ Use the inverse.

sin-1 6 ÷ 10 enter Use a calculator.

$m\angle X \approx 36.86989765$

≈ 37

B

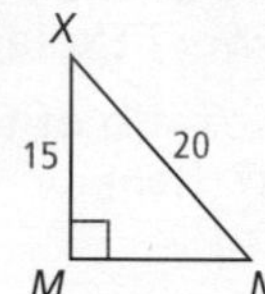

You know the lengths of the hypotenuse and the side adjacent to $\angle X$.

Use the cosine ratio.

$\cos X = \frac{15}{20}$

$m\angle X = \cos^{-1}\left(\frac{15}{20}\right)$

cos-1 15 ÷ 20 enter

$m\angle X \approx 41.40962211$

≈ 41

▼ STUDENT PAGES 441–442

Think

When should you use an inverse?

Got It? **a.** Use the figure below. What is $m\angle Y$ to the nearest degree?

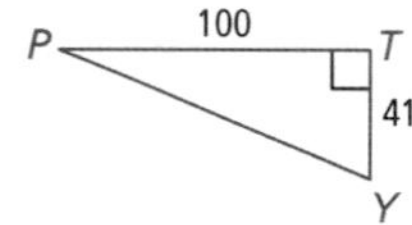

b. Reasoning Suppose you know the lengths of all three sides of a right triangle. Does it matter which trigonometric ratio you use to find the measure of any of the three angles? Explain.

Practice **Find the value of x. Round to the nearest degree.**

5.

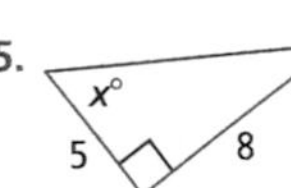

6.

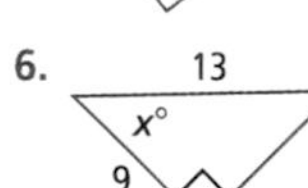

Lesson Check

Do you know HOW?

If students have difficulty with Exercises 7–12, then have them review Problem 1. They should write the ratio using the words *opposite*, *adjacent*, and *hypotenuse* for each before substituting the values for *a*, *b*, and *c*.

Do you UNDERSTAND?

If students have difficulty with Exercise 16, then have them refer to the triangles used in the Solve It.

Close

Q How could you determine the value of sin 35° without using a calculator? **[Draw a right triangle with an acute angle of 35°. Measure the length of the opposite side and the hypotenuse. Then find the ratio of the length of the opposite side to the length of the hypotenuse.]**

ANSWERS

7. $\frac{8}{10}$ or $\frac{4}{5}$

8. $\frac{6}{10}$ or $\frac{3}{5}$

9. $\frac{8}{6}$ or $\frac{4}{3}$

10. $\frac{6}{10}$ or $\frac{3}{5}$

11. $\frac{8}{10}$ or $\frac{4}{5}$

12. $\frac{6}{8}$ or $\frac{3}{4}$

13. 12.1

14. 57.5

15. The word is made up of the first letters of each ratio: $S = \frac{O}{H}$, $C = \frac{A}{H}$, $T = \frac{O}{A}$

16. $\sin X = \frac{YZ}{YX}$, $\sin A = \frac{BC}{BA}$, and $\triangle XYZ \sim \triangle ABC$ by AA $\sim$ so $\frac{YZ}{YX} = \frac{BC}{BA}$ because corresp. sides of $\sim$ triangles are proportional. Therefore, $\sin X = \sin A$.

▼ STUDENT PAGES 442–443

Lesson Check

Do you know HOW?

Write each ratio.

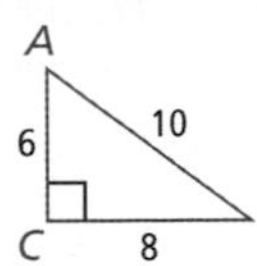

7. sin *A**

8. cos *A*

9. tan *A*

10. sin *B*

11. cos *B*

12. tan *B*

What is the value of *x*? Round to the nearest tenth.

13.

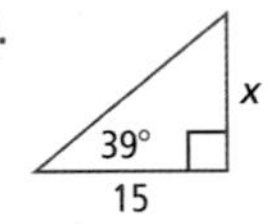

14.

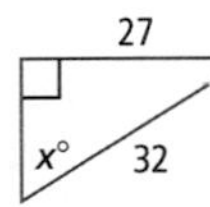

Do you UNDERSTAND?

15. Vocabulary Some people use SOH-CAH-TOA to remember the trigonometric ratios for sine, cosine, and tangent. Why do you think that word might help? (*Hint:* Think of the first letters of the ratios.)

16. Error Analysis A student states that $\sin A > \sin X$ because the lengths of the sides of $\triangle ABC$ are greater than the lengths of the sides of $\triangle XYZ$. What is the student's error? Explain.

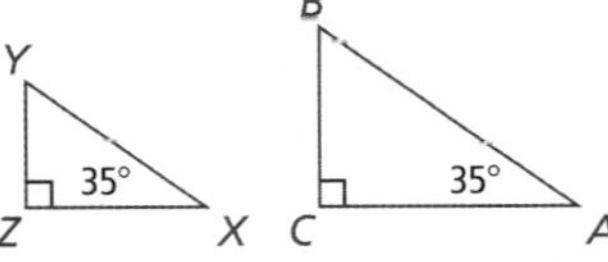

4 Practice

More Practice and Problem-Solving Exercises

ASSIGNMENT GUIDE
The assignments below are for the More Practice and Problem-Solving Exercises. You may also want to assign the A-Level Practice Exercises for homework if these are not used in class.
Average: 17–36
Advanced: 17–45

Mathematical Practices The exercises listed focus on the Standards for Mathematical Practices listed.
EX. 18: Make Sense of Problems (MP 1)
EX. 36: Construct Arguments (MP 3)
EX. 26b, 28: Communicate (MP 3)
EX. 16: Critique the Reasoning of Others (MP 3)
EX. 25: Model (MP 4)

STEM exercises focus on science or engineering applications.

EXERCISE 24: Use the **Think About a Plan** worksheet in the Online Teacher Resources to further support students' development in becoming independent learners.

HOMEWORK QUICK CHECK
To check students' understanding of key skills and concepts, go over Exercises 18, 24, 28, 33, and 36.

ANSWERS

17. 44 and 136 **18.** about 17 ft 8 in.

19. $\frac{\sin X}{\cos X} = \sin X \cdot \frac{1}{\cos X} = \frac{\text{opposite}}{\text{hypotenuse}} \cdot \frac{\text{hypotenuse}}{\text{adjacent}} = \frac{\text{opposite}}{\text{adjacent}} = \tan X$

20. $\cos X \cdot \tan X = \frac{\text{adjacent}}{\text{hypotenuse}} \cdot \frac{\text{opposite}}{\text{adjacent}} = \frac{\text{opposite}}{\text{hypotenuse}} = \sin X$

21. $\sin X \cdot \frac{1}{\tan X} = \frac{\text{opposite}}{\text{hypotenuse}} \cdot \frac{\text{adjacent}}{\text{opposite}} = \frac{\text{adjacent}}{\text{hypotenuse}} = \cos X$

22. $w = 3$, $x \approx 41$ **23.** $w \approx 6.7$, $x \approx 8.1$

24. $w \approx 68.3$, $x \approx 151.6$ **25.** 52 m

26. a. They are equal; yes; sine and cosine of compl. angles are =.
b. $\angle B$; $\angle A$
c. Sample: The cosine is the complement's sine.

27. a. $\sin A = \frac{\text{opposite}}{\text{hypotenuse}}$, and the hypotenuse of a right triangle is always the longest side, so $\sin A$ is a proper fraction, and $\sin A < 1$.
b. $\cos A = \frac{\text{adjacent}}{\text{hypotenuse}}$, and the hypotenuse of a rt. triangle is always the longest side, so $\cos A$ is a proper fraction, and $\cos A < 1$.

▼ STUDENT PAGES 444–445

More Practice and Problem-Solving Exercises

Apply

17. The lengths of the diagonals of a rhombus are 2 in. and 5 in. Find the measures of the angles of the rhombus to the nearest degree.

18. Think About a Plan Carlos plans to build a grain bin with a radius of 15 ft. The recommended slant of the roof is 25°. He wants the roof to overhang the edge of the bin by 1 ft. What should the length x be? Give your answer in feet and inches.
- What is the position of the side of length x in relation to the given angle?
- What information do you need to find a side length of a right triangle?
- Which trigonometric ratio could you use?

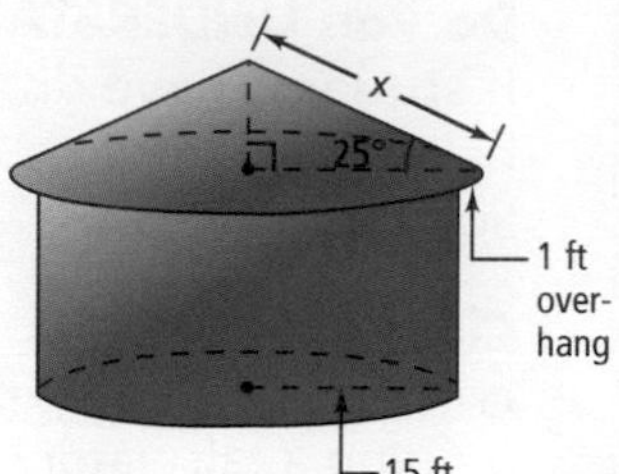

An *identity* is an equation that is true for all the allowed values of the variable. Use what you know about trigonometric ratios to show that each equation is an identity.

19. $\tan X = \frac{\sin X}{\cos X}$ **20.** $\sin X = \cos X \cdot \tan X$ **21.** $\cos X = \frac{\sin X}{\tan X}$

Find the values of w and then x. Round lengths to the nearest tenth and angle measures to the nearest degree.

22.
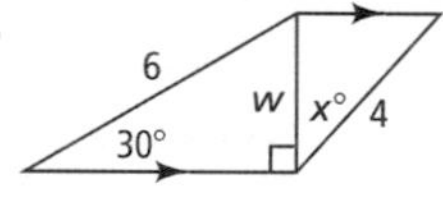

23.
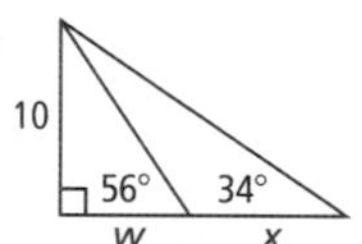

24.
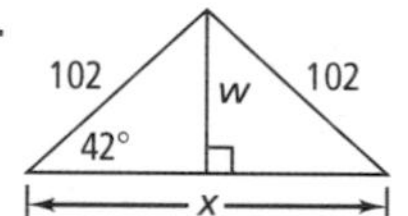

STEM **25. Pyramids** All but two of the pyramids built by the ancient Egyptians have faces inclined at 52° angles. Suppose an archaeologist discovers the ruins of a pyramid. Most of the pyramid has eroded, but the archaeologist is able to determine that the length of a side of the square base is 82 m. How tall was the pyramid, assuming its faces were inclined at 52°? Round your answer to the nearest meter.

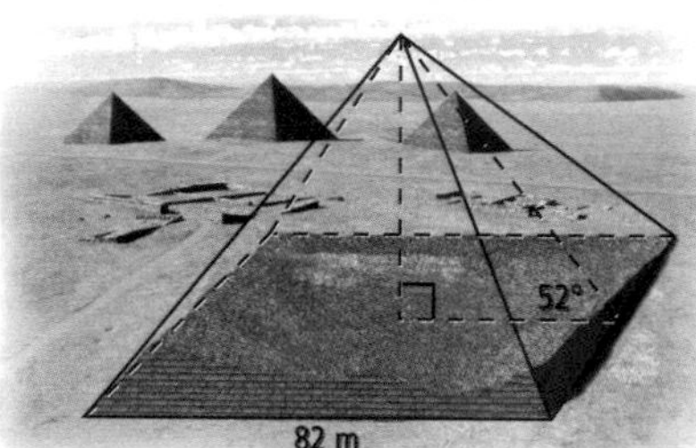

26. a. In $\triangle ABC$ at the right, how does $\sin A$ compare to $\cos B$? Is this true for the acute angles of other right triangles?
b. Reading Math The word *cosine* is derived from the words *complement's sine*. Which angle in $\triangle ABC$ is the complement of $\angle A$? Of $\angle B$?
c. Explain why the derivation of the word *cosine* makes sense.

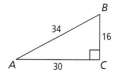

(Figure: right triangle ABC with AB = 34, BC = 16, AC = 30, right angle at C)

Proof **27.** For right $\triangle ABC$ with right $\angle C$, prove each of the following.
a. $\sin A < 1$ **b.** $\cos A < 1$

28. a. Writing Explain why $\tan 60° = \sqrt{3}$. Include a diagram with your explanation.
b. Make a Conjecture How are the sine and cosine of a 60° angle related? Explain.

28. a.
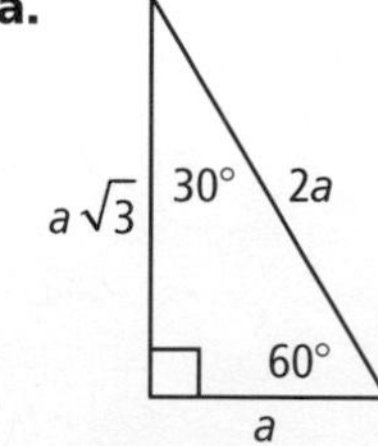

Using the ratio of sides $1 : \sqrt{3} : 2$ for a 30°-60°-90° triangle, $\tan 60° = \frac{\sqrt{3}}{1} = \sqrt{3}$.

b. Answers may vary. Sample: $\sin 60° = \sqrt{3} \cdot \cos 60°$

29. $\frac{15}{12}$ or $\frac{5}{4}$

30. $\frac{15}{9}$ or $\frac{5}{3}$

31. $\frac{9}{12}$ or $\frac{3}{4}$

32. $\frac{15}{9}$ or $\frac{5}{3}$

33. $\frac{15}{12}$ or $\frac{5}{4}$

34. $\frac{12}{9}$ or $\frac{4}{3}$

35. **a.** 0.99985
    b. 1
    c. 1; 89.9; yes, $\sin X = 1$ and is not < 1.
    d. For angles with measures that approach 90, the opposite side and hypotenuse are almost the same length, and $\sin X$ approaches 1.

36. **a.** No; answers may vary. Sample: $\tan 45^\circ + \tan 30^\circ = 1 + \frac{\sqrt{3}}{3} \approx 1.6$, but $\tan 75^\circ \approx 3.7$.
    b. No; assume $\tan A - \tan B = \tan(A - B)$; $\tan A = \tan B + \tan(A - B)$ by the Add. Prop. of =; let $A = B + C$, then $\tan(B + C) = \tan B + \tan C$ by the Subst. Prop.; part (a) proved this false; this contradicts the assumption, so $\tan A - \tan B \neq \tan(A - B)$.

37. $$(\sin A)^2 + (\cos A)^2 = \left(\frac{a}{c}\right)^2 + \left(\frac{b}{c}\right)^2 = \frac{a^2}{c^2} + \frac{b^2}{c^2} = \frac{a^2 + b^2}{c^2} = \frac{c^2}{c^2} = 1$$

38. $$(\sin B)^2 + (\cos B)^2 = \left(\frac{b}{c}\right)^2 + \left(\frac{a}{c}\right)^2 = \frac{b^2}{c^2} + \frac{a^2}{c^2} = \frac{b^2 + a^2}{c^2} = \frac{c^2}{c^2} = 1$$

39. $$\frac{1}{(\cos A)^2} - (\tan A)^2 = \left(1 \div \frac{b^2}{c^2}\right) - \frac{a^2}{b^2} = \frac{c^2}{b^2} - \frac{a^2}{b^2} = \frac{c^2 - a^2}{b^2} = \frac{b^2}{b^2} = 1$$

40. $$\frac{1}{(\sin A)^2} - \frac{1}{(\tan A)^2} = \frac{1}{\left(\frac{a}{c}\right)^2} - \frac{1}{\left(\frac{a}{b}\right)^2} = \frac{c^2}{a^2} - \frac{b^2}{a^2} = \frac{c^2 - b^2}{a^2} = \frac{a^2}{a^2} = 1$$

41. $\frac{5}{13}$

42. $\frac{\sqrt{7}}{4}$

43. $\frac{3}{4}$

44. $$(\tan A)^2 - (\sin A)^2 = \left(\frac{a}{b}\right)^2 - \left(\frac{a}{c}\right)^2 = \frac{a^2}{b^2} - \frac{a^2}{c^2} = \frac{a^2c^2}{b^2c^2} - \frac{a^2b^2}{b^2c^2} = \frac{a^2c^2 - a^2b^2}{b^2c^2} = \frac{a^2(c^2 - b^2)}{b^2c^2} = \frac{a^2 \cdot a^2}{b^2c^2} = \left(\frac{a}{b}\right)^2\left(\frac{a}{c}\right)^2 = (\tan A)^2(\sin A)^2$$

45. **a.** about 1.5 AU
    b. about 5.2 AU

The sine, cosine, and tangent ratios each have a reciprocal ratio. The reciprocal ratios are cosecant (csc), secant (sec), and cotangent (cot). Use $\triangle ABC$ and the definitions below to write each ratio.

$\csc X = \frac{1}{\sin X}$ $\sec X = \frac{1}{\cos X}$ $\cot X = \frac{1}{\tan X}$

29. $\csc A$ **30.** $\sec A$ **31.** $\cot A$

32. $\csc B$ **33.** $\sec B$ **34.** $\cot B$

35. Graphing Calculator Use the table feature of your graphing calculator to study $\sin X$ as X gets close to (but not equal to) 90. In the y= screen, enter $Y1 = \sin X$.
a. Use the tblset feature so that X starts at 80 and changes by 1. Access the table. From the table, what is $\sin X$ for $X = 89$?
b. Perform a "numerical zoom-in." Use the tblset feature, so that X starts with 89 and changes by 0.1. What is $\sin X$ for $X = 89.9$?
c. Continue to zoom in numerically on values close to 90. What is the greatest value you can get for $\sin X$ on your calculator? How close is X to 90? Does your result contradict what you are asked to prove in Exercise 27a?
d. Use right triangles to explain the behavior of $\sin X$ found above.

36. **a. Reasoning** Does $\tan A + \tan B = \tan(A + B)$ when $A + B < 90$? Explain.
b. Does $\tan A - \tan B = \tan(A - B)$ when $A - B > 0$? Use part (a) and indirect reasoning to explain.

Challenge

Verify that each equation is an identity by showing that each expression on the left simplifies to 1.

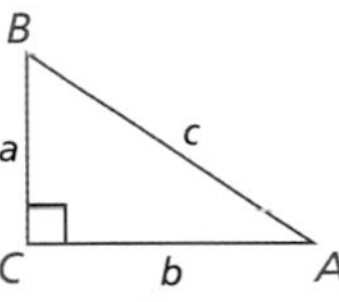

37. $(\sin A)^2 + (\cos A)^2 = 1$ **38.** $(\sin B)^2 + (\cos B)^2 = 1$

39. $\frac{1}{(\cos A)^2} - (\tan A)^2 = 1$ **40.** $\frac{1}{(\sin A)^2} - \frac{1}{(\tan A)^2} = 1$

In Exercises 41–43, the value of one trigonometric ratio is given. Find the value of the other trigonometric ratio using the identities from Exercises 19 and 37.

41. $\sin x = \frac{12}{13}$; $\cos x$ **42.** $\cos x = \frac{3}{4}$; $\sin x$ **43.** $\sin x = \frac{3}{5}$; $\tan x$

44. Show that $(\tan A)^2 - (\sin A)^2 = (\tan A)^2 \cdot (\sin A)^2$ is an identity.

STEM **45. Astronomy** The Polish astronomer Nicolaus Copernicus devised a method for determining the sizes of the orbits of planets farther from the sun than Earth. His method involved noting the number of days between the times that a planet was in the positions labeled A and B in the diagram. Using this time and the number of days in each planet's year, he calculated c and d.
a. For Mars, $c = 55.2$ and $d = 103.8$. How far is Mars from the sun in astronomical units (AU)? One astronomical unit is defined as the average distance from Earth to the center of the sun, about 93 million miles.
b. For Jupiter, $c = 21.9$ and $d = 100.8$. How far is Jupiter from the sun in astronomical units?

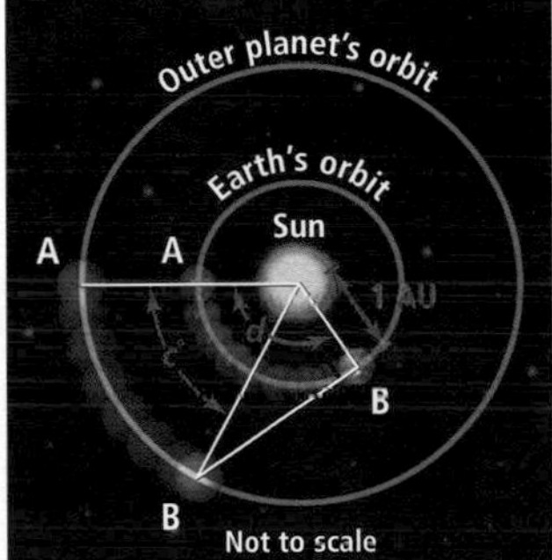

5 Assess and Remediate

Lesson Quiz

1. What are the sine, cosine, and tangent ratios for $\angle B$?

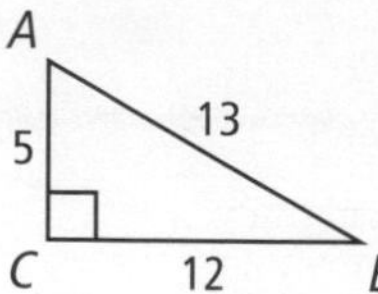

2. What is the value of x? Round to the nearest tenth.

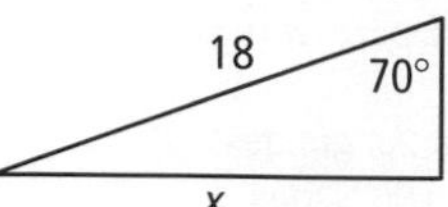

3. What is $m\angle X$ to the nearest degree?

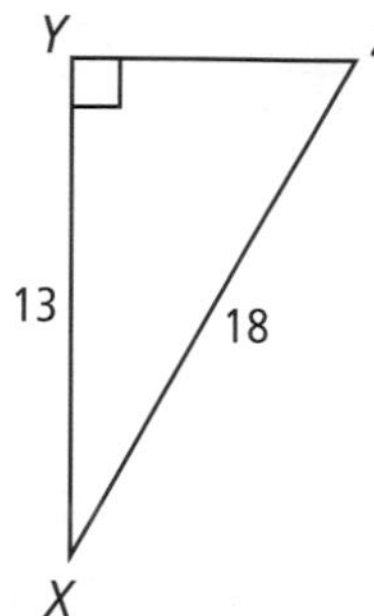

4. Do you UNDERSTAND? Can a sine be greater than 1? Explain.

ANSWERS TO LESSON QUIZ

1. $\sin B = \frac{5}{13}$, $\cos B = \frac{12}{13}$, $\tan B = \frac{5}{12}$

2. 16.9

3. 44

4. No; a leg of a right triangle cannot be longer than the hypotenuse.

Prescription for Remediation

Use the student work on the Lesson Quiz to prescribe a differentiated assignment.

Points	Differentiated Remediation
0–2	Intervention
3	On-level
4	Extension

Online Assessment

Assign the Lesson Quiz in Success Tracker on **pearsonsuccessnet.com**. Success Tracker will automatically score the quiz and assign appropriate intervention or enrichment to each student based on the results. The compiled data appear in three different reports for instant analysis of whole class and individual student performance.

Differentiated Remediation

Intervention

- **RETEACHING** (2 pages) Provides reteaching and practice exercises for the key lesson concepts. Use with struggling students or absent students.
- **ENGLISH LANGUAGE LEARNER SUPPORT** Helps students develop and reinforce mathematical vocabulary and key concepts.

On-Level

- **PRACTICE** (2 pages) Provides extra practice for each lesson. For simpler practice exercises, use the Form K Practice pages found in the Online Teacher Resources.
- **THINK ABOUT A PLAN** Helps students develop specific problem-solving skills and strategies by providing scaffolded guiding questions.
- **STANDARDIZED TEST PREP** Focuses on all major exercises, all major question types, and helps students prepare for the high-stakes assessments.

Extension

- **ENRICHMENT** Provides students with interesting problems and activities that extend the concepts of the lesson.
- **ACTIVITIES, GAMES, AND PUZZLES** Worksheets that can be used for concept development, enrichment, and for fun!

7-4 Angles of Elevation and Depression

Common Core State Standard
G.SRT.8 Use trigonometric ratios . . . to solve right triangles in applied problems.

Preparing to Teach

BIG ideas Reasoning and Proof
Coordinate Geometry

ESSENTIAL UNDERSTANDING

The angles of elevation and depression are the acute angles of right triangles formed by a horizontal distance and a vertical height.

Math Background

Many practical applications of trigonometry in surveying, construction, aeronautics, and other fields involve indirect measurement. Indirect measurement is a technique used to find the measure of something when the use of a measuring device is either impractical or impossible.

In order to see an object above your eye level, you must raise your line of sight. The angle formed from the horizontal at your eye level to the raised or elevated line of sight is called the angle of elevation. An angle of elevation is measured from a horizontal below an object to the line of sight of an object. Similarly, an angle of depression describes the angle from a horizontal at eye level to the line of sight below.

ELL Support

FOCUS ON LANGUAGE Focus on elevation and depression. What are synonyms and antonyms of elevation and depression? [Synonyms of *elevation* may include *altitude, mountain*, or *roof*. Synonyms of *depression* may include *sag*, *crater*, or *dent*. *Elevation* and *depression* are antonyms.]

USE MULTIPLE REPRESENTATION Read through the examples of elevation and depression in this lesson, such as the balloon, geography, and windmill problems. Draw pictures on the board and trace the angles of elevation and depression. Divide students into heterogeneous pairs. Invite students to think of their own examples with angles of elevation and depression. Students can draw their ideas on the board to share with the class.

Lesson Vocabulary

- angle of elevation
- angle of depression

Mathematical Practices

ATTEND TO PRECISION. Students will make explicit use of the terms "angle of elevation" and "angle of depression" and will solve for them.

Interactive Learning

Solve It!

PURPOSE To determine an angle of depression using inverse trigonometric ratios and geometric reasoning

PROCESS Students may use trigonometric ratios, knowledge of complementary angles, or properties of parallel lines.

Q What is the measure of the angle at the upper vertex of the triangle formed by the lead, spotlight B, and the vertical line from the spotlight to the ground? Explain. **[≈ 22°, $\tan^{-1}\left(\frac{10}{25}\right) = 21.801$]**

Q What is the measure of the angle in the upper vertex of the triangle formed by the lead, spotlight A, and the vertical line from the spotlight to the ground? Explain. **[≈ 22°, the triangles are congruent.]**

Q How are the acute angles in the lower vertices of the triangles related to the angles below the horizontal that the lamps are set at? **[They are congruent, because they are alternate interior angles.]**

ANSWER Lamp A: 68°; Lamp B: 68°; The measure of the angle of Lamp A decreases, and the measure of the angle of Lamp B increases.

CONNECT THE MATH The Solve It situation illustrates an angle of depression in context. In the lesson, students distinguish between angles of elevation and depression and how to calculate the measure of these angles.

▼ DIGITAL (STUDENT WORK SPACE PAGE 447)

Getting Ready!

You are on the lighting crew for the school musical. You hang a set of lights 25 ft above the stage. For one song, the female lead is on stage alone and you want all the lights on her. If she stands in the middle of the stage as shown, at what angle from horizontal should you set lamps A and B? Round to the nearest degree. Describe how each angle changes if you set the lamps for her to stand a few feet closer to the tree. (Diagram is not to scale.)

A B
10 ft 10 ft

2 Guided Instruction

Problem 1 Identifying Angles of Elevation and Depression

Q How is ∠1 related to ∠2? Explain. **[They are alternate interior angles formed by parallel lines, so they are congruent.]**

Q Using the diagram, can you determine the angle of elevation from the base of the mountain to the bird? **[No, there is not enough information.]**

Got It? **VISUAL LEARNERS**

Q What are the two pairs of congruent angles shown in the diagram in Problem 1? **[∠1 and ∠2; ∠3 and ∠4]**

ANSWERS

Got It? a. ∠ of elevation from the person in the hot-air balloon to bird **b.** ∠ of depression from the person in the hot-air balloon to base of mountain

Practice

1. ∠ of depression from boat to sub
2. ∠ of elevation from Max to top of waterfall

▼ STUDENT PAGE 447

The angles in the Solve It are formed below the horizontal black pipe. Angles formed above and below a horizontal line have specific names.

Suppose a person on the ground sees a hang glider at a 38° angle above a horizontal line. This angle is the **angle of elevation.**

At the same time, the person in the hang glider sees the person on the ground at a 38° angle below a horizontal line. This angle is the **angle of depression.**

Notice that the angle of elevation is congruent to the angle of depression because they are alternate interior angles.

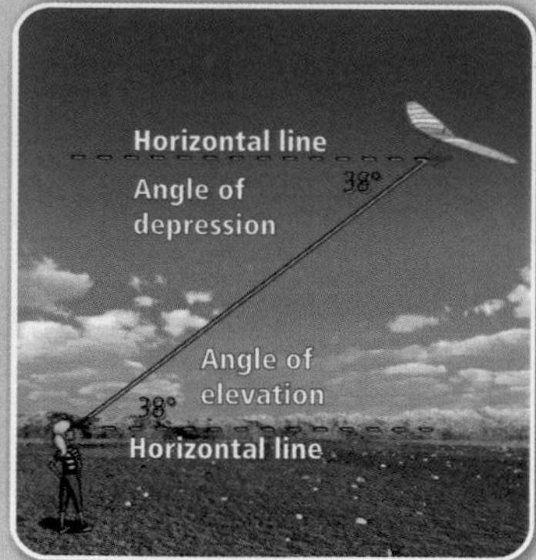

Essential Understanding You can use the angles of elevation and depression as the acute angles of right triangles formed by a horizontal distance and a vertical height.

▼ DIGITAL

Problem 1 **Identifying Angles of Elevation and Depression**

What is a description of the angle as it relates to the situation shown?

A ∠1

∠1 is the angle of depression from the bird to the person in the hot-air balloon.

B ∠4

∠4 is the angle of elevation from the base of the mountain to the person in the hot-air balloon.

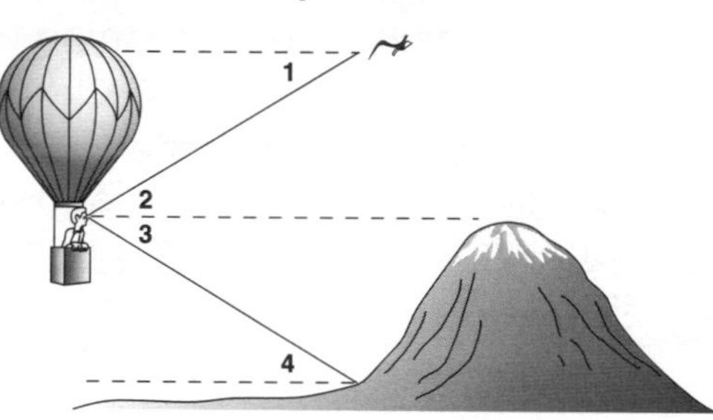

▼ STUDENT PAGE 448

Got It? Use the diagram in Problem 1. What is a description of the angle as it relates to the situation shown?

a. ∠2 b. ∠3

Plan

How can you tell if it is an angle of elevation or depression?

Practice **Describe each angle as it relates to the situation in the diagram.**

1. ∠2

2. ∠5

Problem 2 Using the Angle of Elevation

Q In relation to the angle of elevation in the diagram, which two sides of the triangle are labeled? **[The opposite side is x, and the adjacent side is 53 ft.]**

Q Which trigonometric ratio involves the lengths of the adjacent and opposite sides? **[tangent]**

Q What are the measures of the other two angles in the triangle? Explain. **[90°, since it is a right angle and 33.5°, since 180 − 90 − 56.5 = 33.5.]**

Q What trigonometric ratio of the 33.5° angle could you use to determine x? **[tangent]**

Got It?

Ask students to identify the angle of depression from the line of sight from the climber to the person on the ground. Make certain that students answer 32° rather than 58°.

ANSWERS

Got It? about 631 ft

Practice

3. 34.2 ft

4. 986 m

▼ DIGITAL

Problem 2 Using the Angle of Elevation

Wind Farm **Suppose you stand 53 ft from a wind farm turbine. Your angle of elevation to the hub of the turbine is 56.5°. Your eye level is 5.5 ft above the ground. Approximately how tall is the turbine from the ground to its hub?**

$\tan 56.5^\circ = \frac{x}{53}$ Use the tangent ratio.

$x = 53(\tan 56.5^\circ)$ Solve for x.

53 [tan] 56.5 [enter] Use a calculator.

80.07426526

So $x \approx 80$, which is the height from your eye level to the hub of the turbine. To find the total height of the turbine, add the height from the ground to your eyes. Since $80 + 5.5 = 85.5$, the wind turbine is about 85.5 ft tall from the ground to its hub.

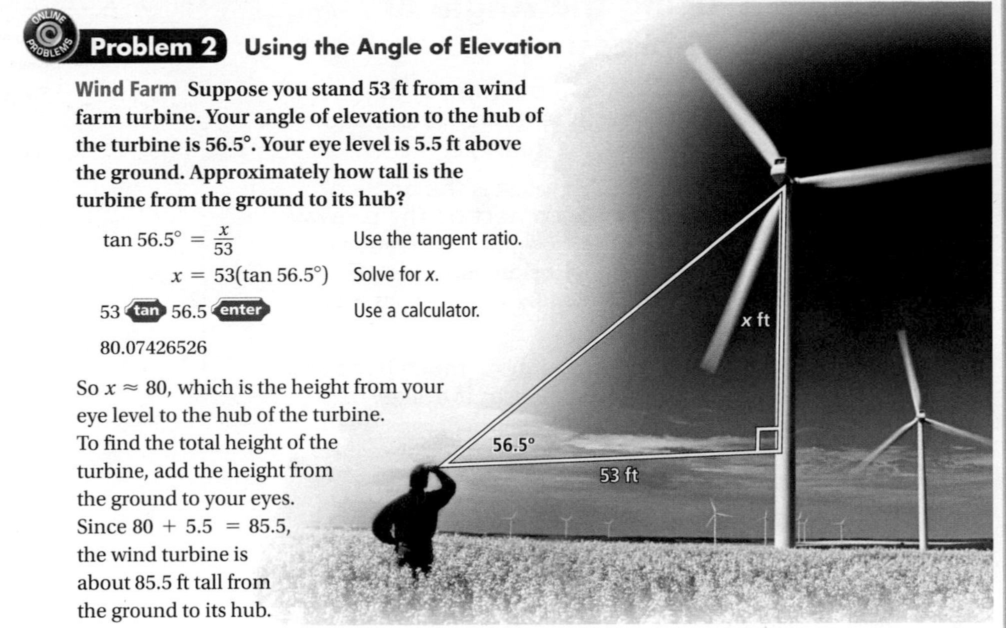

▼ STUDENT PAGE 449

Got It? You sight a rock climber on a cliff at a 32° angle of elevation. Your eye level is 6 ft above the ground and you are 1000 ft from the base of the cliff. What is the approximate height of the rock climber from the ground?

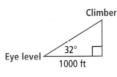

Climber

Eye level 32° 1000 ft

Think Why does your eye level matter here?

Practice Find the value of x. Round to the nearest tenth of a unit.

3. 100 ft, 20°, x

STEM **4. Meteorology** A meteorologist measures the angle of elevation of a weather balloon as 41°. A radio signal from the balloon indicates that it is 1503 m from his location. To the nearest meter, how high above the ground is the balloon?

Problem 3 Using the Angle of Depression

Q Is the airplane 2714 ft above the runway as it begins its descent? Explain. **[No, 2714 ft is its altitude above sea level, not its altitude above the runway.]**

Q If the angle of descent is 3°, what is the angle of elevation from the point of contact on the runway to the airplane? Explain. **[The angle of elevation is congruent to the angle of depression because they are alternate interior angles formed by parallel lines, so it is also 3°.]**

Q To the nearest tenth of a mile, how much horizontal distance does the airplane cover as it makes its descent? **[6.2 mi]**

Got It?

It is implied that the life raft is at sea level and therefore has an altitude of zero.

ANSWERS

Got It? about 6.2 km

Practice

5. 263.3 yd **6.** 769 ft

▼ DIGITAL

Problem 3 Using the Angle of Depression

To approach runway 17 of the Ponca City Municipal Airport in Oklahoma, the pilot must begin a 3° descent starting from a height of 2714 ft above sea level. The airport is 1007 ft above sea level. To the nearest tenth of a mile, how far from the runway is the airplane at the start of this approach?

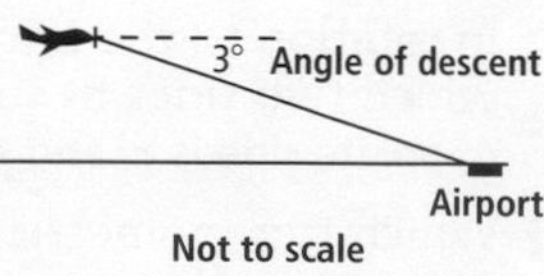

The airplane is 2714 − 1007, or 1707 ft, above the level of the airport.

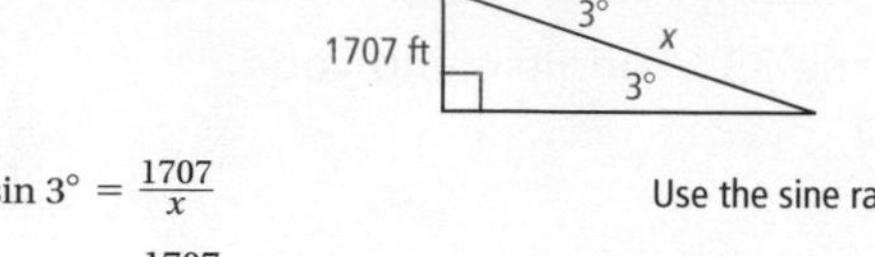

$\sin 3° = \frac{1707}{x}$ Use the sine ratio.

$x = \frac{1707}{\sin 3°}$ Solve for x.

1707 ÷ sin 3 enter 32616.19969 Use a calculator.

÷ 5280 enter 6.177310548 Divide by 5280 to convert feet to miles.

The airplane is about 6.2 mi from the runway.

▼ STUDENT PAGE 450

Got It? An airplane pilot sights a life raft at a 26° angle of depression. The airplane's altitude is 3 km. What is the airplane's horizontal distance d from the raft?

Practice Find the value of x. Round to the nearest tenth of a unit.

5.

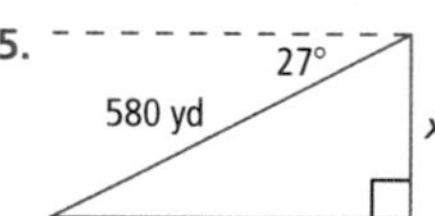

6. **Indirect Measurement** A tourist looks out from the crown of the Statue of Liberty, approximately 250 ft above the ground. The tourist sees a ship coming into the harbor and measures the angle of depression as 18°. Find the distance from the base of the statue to the ship to the nearest foot.

3 Lesson Check

Do you know HOW?

If students have difficulty with Exercises 7–11, then have them review Problem 1.

Do you UNDERSTAND?

If students have difficulty with Exercise 14, then remind them that an angle of depression is the angle below a horizontal line.

Close

Q If two buildings are 30 ft apart and the angle of elevation from the top of the first to the top of the second is 19°, what is the angle of depression from the top of the second to the top of the first? What is the difference in their heights to the nearest tenth of a foot? **[19°; 10.3 ft]**

ANSWERS

7. $\angle$ of elevation from *C* to *A*
8. $\angle$ of depression from *A* to *C*
9. $\angle$ of elevation from *A* to *D*
10. $\angle$ of elevation from *A* to *B*
11. $\angle$ of depression from *B* to *A*
12. $\angle 1 \cong \angle 2$ (alt. int. angles); $\angle 4 \cong \angle 5$ (alt. int. angles)
13. Answers may vary. Sample: An $\angle$ of elevation is formed by two rays with a common endpoint when one ray is horizontal and the other ray is above the horizontal ray.
14. Answers may vary. Sample: The $\angle$ labeled in the sketch is the complement of the $\angle$ of depression.

▼ STUDENT PAGES 451–452

Lesson Check

Do you know HOW?

What is a description of each angle as it relates to the diagram?

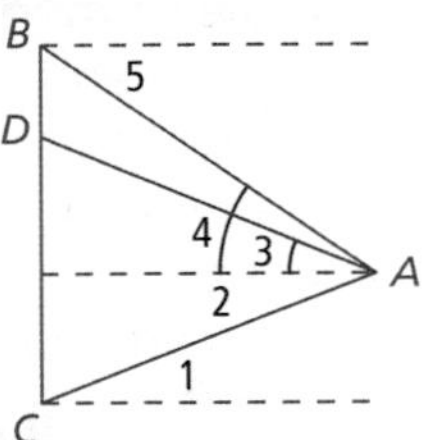

7. $\angle 1$
8. $\angle 2$
9. $\angle 3$
10. $\angle 4$
11. $\angle 5$
12. What are two pairs of congruent angles in the diagram? Explain why they are congruent.

Do you UNDERSTAND?

13. **Vocabulary** How is an angle of elevation formed?
14. **Error Analysis** A homework question says that the angle of depression from the bottom of a house window to a ball on the ground is 20°. At the right is your friend's sketch of the situation. Describe your friend's error.

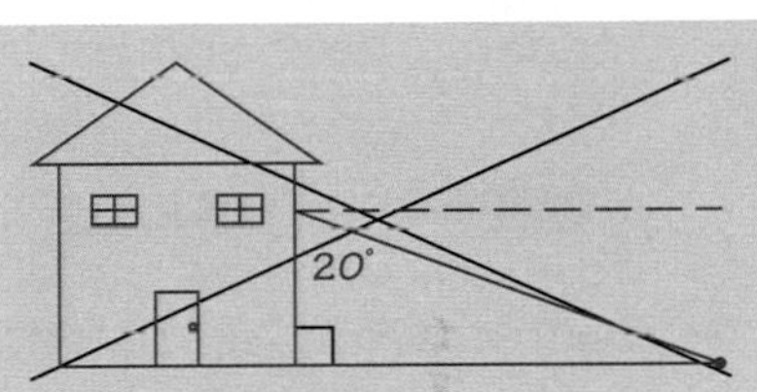

Practice

More Practice and Problem-Solving Exercises

ASSIGNMENT GUIDE
The assignments below are for the More Practice and Problem-Solving Exercises. You may also want to assign the A-Level Practice Exercises for homework if these are not used in class.
Average: 15–25
Advanced: 15–27

Mathematical Practices The exercises listed focus on the Standards for Mathematical Practices listed.
EX. 16: Make Sense of Problems (MP 1)
EX. 21: Communicate (MP 3)
EX. 14: Critique the Reasoning of Others (MP 3)
EX. 15, 22–27: Model (MP 4)

EXERCISE 15: Use the **Think About a Plan** worksheet in the Online Teacher Resources to further support students' development in becoming independent learners.

HOMEWORK QUICK CHECK
To check students' understanding of key skills and concepts, go over Exercises 15, 16, 19, 21, and 24.

ANSWERS

15. 64°
16. 193 m
17. 72, 72
18. 46, 46
19. 27, 27
20. 20, 20
21. a. length of any guy wire = distance on the ground from the tower to the guy wire divided by the cosine of the ∠ formed by the guy wire and the ground
b. height of attachment = distance on the ground from the tower to the guy wire times the tangent of the ∠ formed by the guy wire and the ground
22. 5
23. about 2.8
24. 0.5; about 85
25. 3300 m
26. about 27.7 ft
27. Check students' work.

More Practice and Problem-Solving Exercises

B Apply

15. Flagpole The world's tallest unsupported flagpole is a 282-ft-tall steel pole in Surrey, British Columbia. The shortest shadow cast by the pole during the year is 137 ft long. To the nearest degree, what is the angle of elevation of the sun when the flagpole casts its shortest shadow?

16. Think About a Plan Two office buildings are 51 m apart. The height of the taller building is 207 m. The angle of depression from the top of the taller building to the top of the shorter building is 15°. Find the height of the shorter building to the nearest meter.
- How can a diagram help you?
- How does the angle of depression from the top of the taller building relate to the angle of elevation from the top of the shorter building?

Algebra The angle of elevation e from A to B and the angle of depression d from B to A are given. Find the measure of each angle.

17. e: $(7x - 5)°$, d: $4(x + 7)°$
18. e: $(3x + 1)°$, d: $2(x + 8)°$
19. e: $(x + 21)°$, d: $3(x + 3)°$
20. e: $5(x - 2)°$, d: $(x + 14)°$

21. Writing A communications tower is located on a plot of flat land. The tower is supported by several guy wires. Assume that you are able to measure distances along the ground, as well as angles formed by the guy wires and the ground. Explain how you could estimate each of the following measurements.
a. the length of any guy wire
b. how high on the tower each wire is attached

Tower
Guy wires

Flying An airplane at a constant altitude a flies a horizontal distance d toward you at velocity v. You observe for time t and measure its angles of elevation $\angle E_1$ and $\angle E_2$ at the start and end of your observation. Find the missing information.

22. $a = ■$ mi, $v = 5$ mi/min, $t = 1$ min, $m\angle E_1 = 45$, $m\angle E_2 = 90$
23. $a = 2$ mi, $v = ■$ mi/min, $t = 15$ s, $m\angle E_1 = 40$, $m\angle E_2 = 50$
24. $a = 4$ mi, $d = 3$ mi, $v = 6$ mi/min, $t = ■$ min, $m\angle E_1 = 50$, $m\angle E_2 = ■$

25. Aerial Television A blimp provides aerial television views of a football game. The television camera sights the stadium at a 7° angle of depression. The altitude of the blimp is 400 m. What is the line-of-sight distance from the television camera to the base of the stadium? Round to the nearest hundred meters.

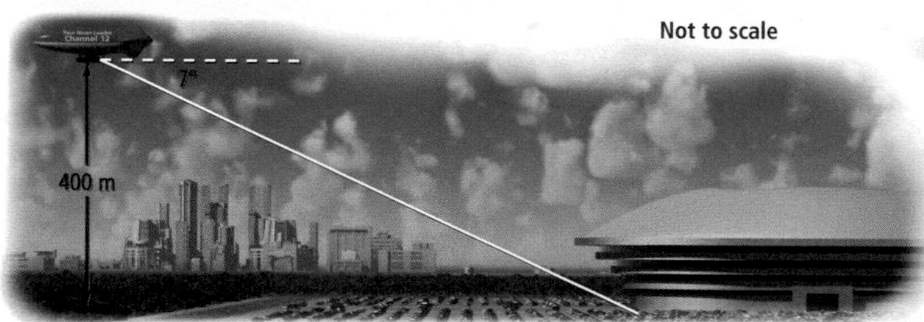

C Challenge

26. Firefighting A firefighter on the ground sees fire break through a window near the top of the building. The angle of elevation to the windowsill is 28°. The angle of elevation to the top of the building is 42°. The firefighter is 75 ft from the building and her eyes are 5 ft above the ground. What roof-to-windowsill distance can she report by radio to firefighters on the roof?

27. Geography For locations in the United States, the relationship between the latitude ℓ and the greatest angle of elevation a of the sun at noon on the first day of summer is $a = 90° - \ell + 23.5°$. Find the latitude of your town. Then determine the greatest angle of elevation of the sun for your town on the first day of summer.

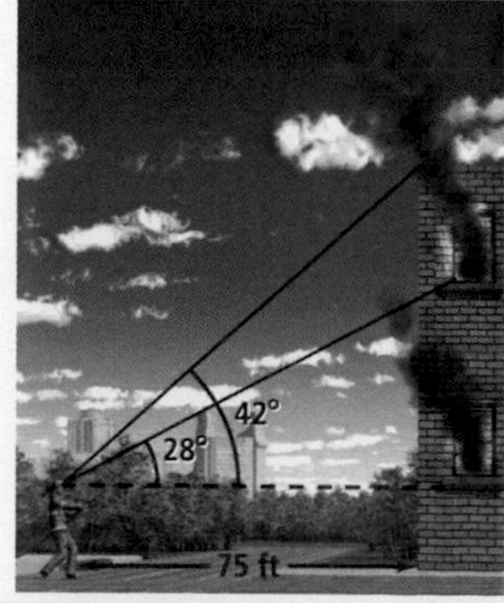

5 Assess and Remediate

Lesson Quiz

1. Missy stands at a horizontal distance of 45 ft from the base of a building. The angle of elevation from eye level to the top of the building is 48°. Missy's height to eye level is 5 ft. What is the height of the building to the nearest foot?

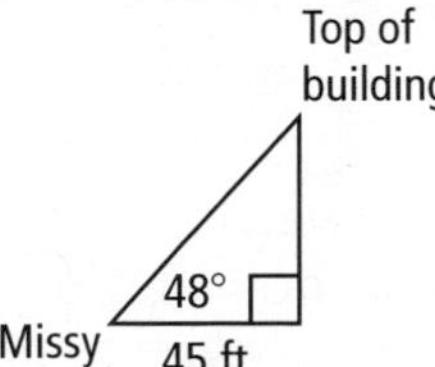

2. The flagpole in Terry's schoolyard is 42 ft tall. On a sunny day, the flagpole casts a shadow 20 ft long. What is the angle of elevation of the sun at that moment? Round to the nearest tenth of a degree.
3. Kurt leans a 20-ft-long ladder against the side of his house. The ladder reaches to a height of 18.9 feet up the side of the house. What is the angle of elevation of the ladder to the nearest tenth of a degree?
4. **Do you UNDERSTAND?** You sight the top of a 50-ft tree from a point on the ground 50 ft from the base of the tree. What is the angle of elevation to the top of the tree?

ANSWERS TO LESSON QUIZ

1. 55 ft **2.** 64.5°

3. 70.9° **4.** 45°

Prescription for Remediation

Use the student work on the Lesson Quiz to prescribe a differentiated assignment.

Points	Differentiated Remediation
0–2	Intervention
3	On-level
4	Extension

Online Assessment

Assign the Lesson Quiz in Success Tracker on **pearsonsuccessnet.com**. Success Tracker will automatically score the quiz and assign appropriate intervention or enrichment to each student based on the results. The compiled data appear in three different reports for instant analysis of whole class and individual student performance.

Differentiated Remediation

Intervention

- **RETEACHING** (2 pages) Provides reteaching and practice exercises for the key lesson concepts. Use with struggling students or absent students.
- **ENGLISH LANGUAGE LEARNER SUPPORT** Helps students develop and reinforce mathematical vocabulary and key concepts.

On-Level

- **PRACTICE** (2 pages) Provides extra practice for each lesson. For simpler practice exercises, use the Form K Practice pages found in the Online Teacher Resources.
- **THINK ABOUT A PLAN** Helps students develop specific problem-solving skills and strategies by providing scaffolded guiding questions.
- **STANDARDIZED TEST PREP** Focuses on all major exercises, all major question types, and helps students prepare for the high-stakes assessments.

Extension

- **ENRICHMENT** Provides students with interesting problems and activities that extend the concepts of the lesson.
- **ACTIVITIES, GAMES, AND PUZZLES** Worksheets that can be used for concept development, enrichment, and for fun!

7-5 Areas of Regular Polygons

Common Core State Standards
G.CO.13 Construct . . . a regular hexagon inscribed in a circle. **Also A.SSE.1.b**

Preparing to Teach

BIG idea Measurement

ESSENTIAL UNDERSTANDING

The area of a regular polygon is a function of the distance from the center to a side and the perimeter.

Math Background

The area of polygons can be found using the length of the apothem. The apothem is the perpendicular segment that connects the center of the polygon to the side. The apothem and radius create a right triangle within a polygon. Students will use their knowledge of special right triangles to solve for unknown side lengths in polygons. Note that students can find the area of a square in an easier way. Request that they use the new formula here and use previous knowledge to check their results.

Students often have difficulty understanding the relationship between a regular polygon and its inscribed and circumscribed circle. The relationship is critical to understanding how to determine the length of the apothem and the radius of the regular polygon.

ELL Support

FOCUS ON LANGUAGE Place the lesson on an overhead projector. Read aloud as students read along, pointing to each word as you read. As you come across vocabulary words or other key words such as *circumscribe*, *regular*, and *apothem*, think aloud as you determine their meanings. Invite students to rephrase sentences in their own words.

Write key words on the board while reading the lesson. Ask students for synonyms, or words with the same meaning. For example, a synonym for *apothem* may be *inscribed radius*. A synonym for *perpendicular* may be *upright*.

Lesson Vocabulary

- radius of a regular polygon
- apothem

Mathematical Practices

LOOK FOR AND MAKE USE OF STRUCTURE. In finding the area of a regular polygon, students will find a polygon of *n* sides to be composed of *n* congruent triangles and find the areas of those triangles. As a result, they will determine a formula for the area of a regular polygon.

1 Interactive Learning

Solve It!

PURPOSE To realize that increasing the number of sides in a regular polygon increases its area

PROCESS Students may guess and check by drawing diagrams of the figures and calculate the area or solve a simpler problem by constructing regular polygons with fewer sides.

Q Can you form a regular triangle with the pieces? If so, what is its area? **[Yes, the area is approximately 62.35 ft^2.]**

Q Can you form a regular quadrilateral with the pieces? If so, what is its area? **[Yes, the area is 81 ft^2.]**

Q Can you form a regular hexagon? If so, what is its area? (*Hint*: Use composite figures.) **[Yes, the area is approximately 93.53 ft^2.]**

ANSWER The shape should be a regular polygon with 12 sides (dodecagon), where each side is 3 ft long. Explanations may vary. Sample: A regular dodecagon has a larger area than an equilateral triangle, a square, or any other polygon that can be formed using the 12 pieces of wood and its shape is closer to the shape of a circle, which has the largest area for the fixed perimeter 36 ft.

▼ DIGITAL (STUDENT WORK SPACE PAGE 454)

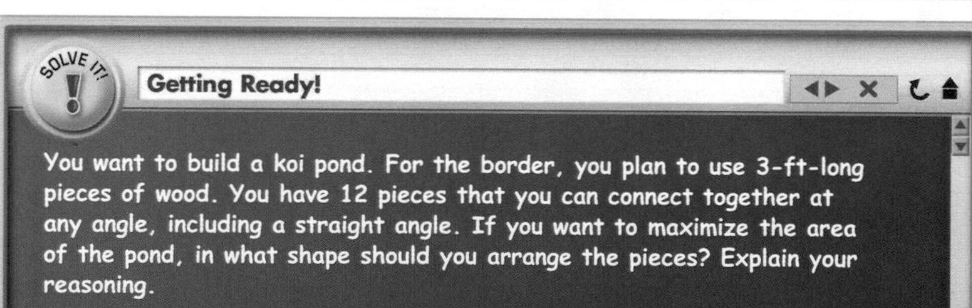

SOLVE IT!
Getting Ready!
You want to build a koi pond. For the border, you plan to use 3-ft-long pieces of wood. You have 12 pieces that you can connect together at any angle, including a straight angle. If you want to maximize the area of the pond, in what shape should you arrange the pieces? Explain your reasoning.

CONNECT THE MATH In the Solve It, students experiment with different regular polygons and investigate their areas. In the lesson, students learn that a regular *n*-gon contains the maximum area of any polygon with the same perimeter and number of sides.

2 Guided Instruction

Problem 1 Finding Angle Measures

Q If the apothem and radius of the polygon form two legs of a triangle, and the third leg connects them, what type of triangle is formed? **[a right triangle]**

Got It? **VISUAL LEARNERS**
Have students draw a diagram of the right triangle and label each angle as they find its measure.

ANSWERS

Got It? $m\angle 1 = 45$, $m\angle 2 = 22.5$, $m\angle 3 = 67.5$

Practice

1. $m\angle 1 = 120$, $m\angle 2 = 60$, $m\angle 3 = 30$
2. $m\angle 4 = 90$, $m\angle 5 = 45$, $m\angle 6 = 45$

▼ STUDENT PAGE 454

The Solve It involves the area of a polygon. You can use trigonometric ratios and special right triangles to investigate properties of regular polygons.

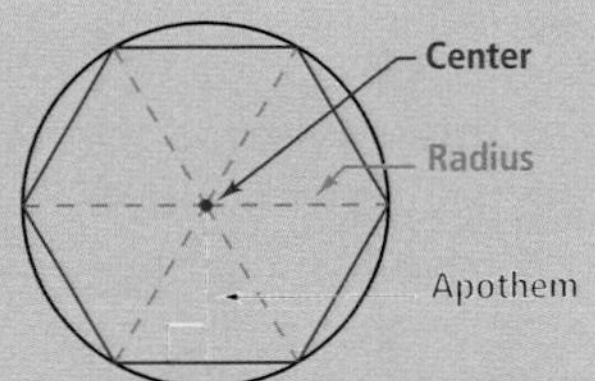

Essential Understanding The area of a regular polygon is related to the distance from the center to a side.

You can circumscribe a circle about any regular polygon. The center of a regular polygon is the center of the circumscribed circle. The **radius of a regular polygon** is the distance from the center to a vertex. The **apothem** is the perpendicular distance from the center to a side.

▼ DIGITAL

Problem 1 Finding Angle Measures

The figure at the right is a regular pentagon with radii and an apothem drawn. What is the measure of each numbered angle?

$m\angle 1 = \frac{360}{5} = 72$ Divide 360 by the number of sides.

$m\angle 2 = \frac{1}{2}m\angle 1$ The apothem bisects the vertex angle of the isosceles triangle formed by the radii.

$= \frac{1}{2}(72) = 36$

$90 + 36 + m\angle 3 = 180$ The sum of the measures of the angles of a triangle is 180.

$m\angle 3 = 54$

$m\angle 1 = 72$, $m\angle 2 = 36$, and $m\angle 3 = 54$.

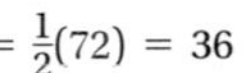

▼ STUDENT PAGES 454–455

Think
How do you know the radii make isosceles triangles?

Got It? Below, a portion of a regular octagon has radii and an apothem drawn. What is the measure of each numbered angle?

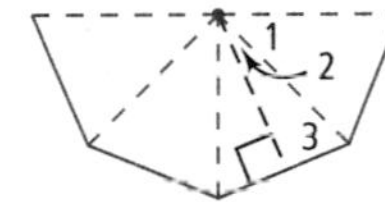

A Practice **Each regular polygon has radii and apothem as shown. Find the measure of each numbered angle.**

1.
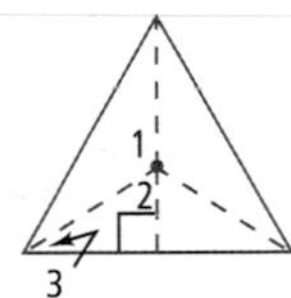

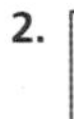

2.
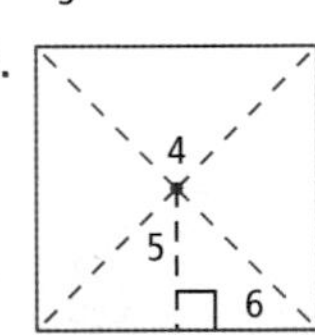

Problem 2 Finding the Area of a Regular Polygon

Take Note

Postulate 18
Have students derive the formula for the area of a regular polygon by drawing a diagram. Lead them through the logic of adding the areas of all the isosceles triangles contained by the polygon.

Take Note

Theorem 71
Apothem may be a new vocabulary word for many students. Draw several diagrams on the board and verify that students can identify the apothems.

Problem 2

Q What values do you need to find the area of the polygon? **[the perimeter and the apothem length]**

Q How can you find the perimeter of the polygon? **[Find the sum of the side lengths or the product of the number of sides and the side length.]**

Got It? **ERROR PREVENTION**
Have students draw a diagram of the pentagon and label the known segment lengths. Be sure that students perform both steps as in Problem 2. In part (b), use the perimeter formula, $n \cdot s$, to find the larger perimeter. Have students substitute $\frac{1}{2}s$ into the formula. Ask them to compare the results.

ANSWERS

Got It? a. 232 cm^2 **b.** It is reduced by half; explanations may vary. Sample: The perimeter of the original polygon is $n \cdot s$. If the side is reduced to half its length, the new perimeter is $n \cdot \frac{1}{2}s$, or $\frac{1}{2}ns$.

Practice

3. 2852 ft^2 **4.** 2475 in.^{2}

▼ STUDENT PAGE 455

take note

Postulate 18

If two figures are congruent, then their areas are equal.

Suppose you have a regular n-gon with side s. The radii divide the figure into n congruent isosceles triangles. By Postulate 17, the areas of the isosceles triangles are equal. Each triangle has a height of a and a base of length s, so the area of each triangle is $\frac{1}{2}as$.

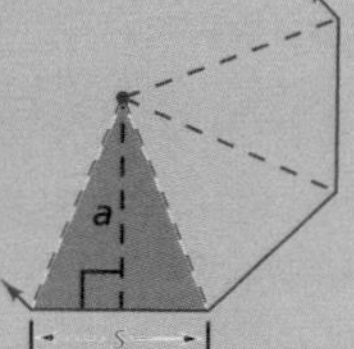

Since there are n congruent triangles, the area of the n-gon is $A = n \cdot \frac{1}{2}as$. The perimeter p of the n-gon is the number of sides n times the length of a side s, or ns. By substitution, the area can be expressed as $A = \frac{1}{2}ap$.

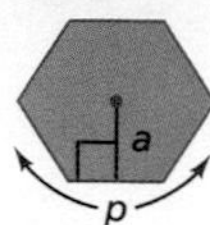

Theorem 71 Area of a Regular Polygon

The area of a regular polygon is half the product of the apothem and the perimeter.

$A = \frac{1}{2}ap$

▼ DIGITAL

Problem 2 Finding the Area of a Regular Polygon

What is the area of the regular decagon at the right?

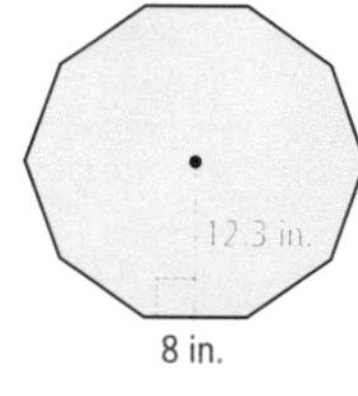

Step 1 Find the perimeter of the regular decagon.

$p = ns$ Use the formula for the perimeter of an n-gon.

$= 10(8)$ Substitute 10 for n and 8 for s.

$= 80$ in.

Step 2 Find the area of the regular decagon.

$A = \frac{1}{2}ap$ Use the formula for the area of a regular polygon.

$= \frac{1}{2}(12.3)(80)$ Substitute 12.3 for a and 80 for p.

$= 492$

The regular decagon has an area of 492 in.^{2}.

▼ STUDENT PAGE 456

Got It? **a.** What is the area of a regular pentagon with an 8-cm apothem and 11.6-cm sides?

Plan
What do you know about the regular pentagon?

b. Reasoning If the side of a regular polygon is reduced to half its length, how does the perimeter of the polygon change? Explain.

Practice **Find the area of each regular polygon with the given apothem a and side length s. Round to the nearest square unit.**

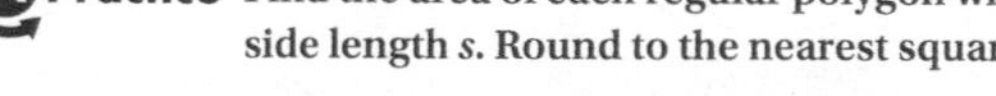

3. 7-gon, $a = 29.1$ ft, $s = 28$ ft

4. nonagon, $a = 27.5$ in., $s = 20$ in.

Problem 3 Using Special Triangles to Find Area

Q What type of triangle is created by half of a side of the hexagon, its apothem, and its radius? **[a 30°-60°-90° triangle]**

Q How can you find the length of the apothem of the hexagon? **[The apothem is the longer leg of the 30°-60°-90° triangle. Its length is $\sqrt{3}$ times the length of the shorter side.]**

Got It?

Have students draw a diagram and label the side length. They can draw the 30°-60°-90° triangle and determine the length of the apothem as in Problem 3.

ANSWERS

Got It? 665 ft^2

Practice

5. 210 in.^{2} **6.** $75\sqrt{3}$ m^2

▼ DIGITAL

Problem 3 Using Special Triangles to Find Area STEM

Zoology A honeycomb is made up of regular hexagonal cells. The length of a side of a cell is 3 mm. What is the area of a cell?

Know	Need	Plan
You know the length of a side, which you can use to find the perimeter.	The apothem	*Draw a diagram* to help find the apothem. Then use the area formula for a regular polygon.

Step 1 Find the apothem.

The radii form six 60° angles at the center, so you can use a 30°-60°-90° triangle to find the apothem.

$a = 1.5\sqrt{3}$ longer leg $= \sqrt{3} \cdot$ shorter leg

Step 2 Find the perimeter.

$p = ns$ Use the formula for the perimeter of an n-gon.

$= 6(3)$ Substitute 6 for n and 3 for s.

$= 18$ mm

Step 3 Find the area.

$A = \frac{1}{2}ap$ Use the formula for the area of a regular polygon.

$= \frac{1}{2}(1.5\sqrt{3})(18)$ Substitute $1.5\sqrt{3}$ for a and 18 for p.

≈ 23.3826859 Use a calculator.

The area is about 23 mm^2.

▼ STUDENT PAGE 457

Got It? The side of a regular hexagon is 16 ft. What is the area of the hexagon? Round your answer to the nearest square foot.

Practice **5. Art** You are painting a mural of colored equilateral triangles. The radius of each triangle is 12.7 in. What is the area of each triangle to the nearest square inch?

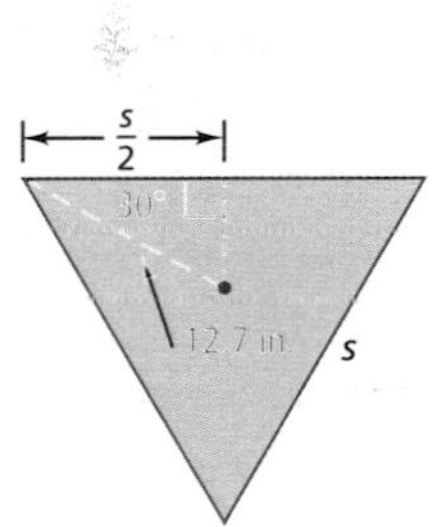

6. Find the area of the equilateral triangle. Leave your answer in simplest radical form.

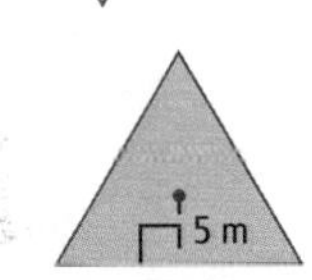

3 Lesson Check

Do you know HOW?

If students have difficulty with Exercise 7, then have them draw the right triangle created by the radius.

Do you UNDERSTAND?

If students have difficulty with Exercise 12, then have them review Problem 3 and Exercise 7. Students can draw a diagram of each figure named and label side length and apothem for easier comparisons.

Close

Q What is the formula for the area of a regular polygon? What does each variable represent? **[$A = \frac{1}{2}ap$, where a is the length of the apothem and p is the perimeter of the polygon.]**

▼ STUDENT PAGE 458

Lesson Check

Do you know HOW?

What is the area of each regular polygon? Round your answer to the nearest tenth.

7.

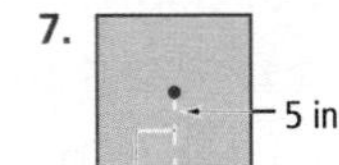

8.

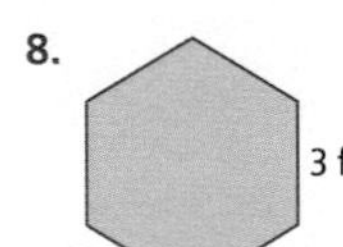

9. 2 m

10.

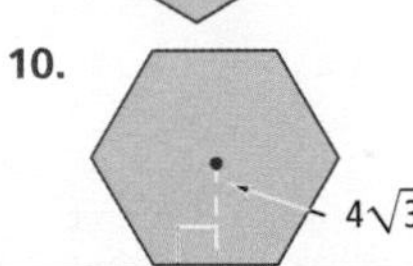

Lesson Check *continued*

ANSWERS

7. 100.0 $in.^2$ **8.** 23.4 ft^2

9. 5.2 m^2 **10.** 166.3 $units^2$

11. A radius is the distance from the center to a vertex, while the apothem is the perpendicular distance from the center to a side.

12. a. $s = 2a$

b. $s = \frac{2\sqrt{3}}{3}a$

c. $s = 2\sqrt{3}a$

13. Special triangles have angles of 30°, 60°, 90° or 45°, 45°, 90° and are found in equilateral triangles, squares, and regular hexagons, but not in all regular polygons.

▼ STUDENT PAGE 459

Do you UNDERSTAND?

11. Vocabulary What is the difference between a radius and an apothem?

12. What is the relationship between the side length and the apothem in each figure?

a. a square

b. a regular hexagon

c. an equilateral triangle

13. Error Analysis Your friend says you can use special triangles to find the apothem of any regular polygon. What is your friend's error? Explain.

4 Practice

More Practice and Problem-Solving Exercises

ASSIGNMENT GUIDE

The assignments below are for the More Practice and Problem-Solving Exercises. You may also want to assign the A-Level Practice Exercises for homework if these are not used in class.

Average: 14–29

Advanced: 14–31

Mathematical Practices The exercises listed focus on the Standards for Mathematical Practices listed.

EX. 19, 24d: Make Sense of Problems (MP 1)

EX. 23: Construct Arguments (MP 3)

EX. 13: Critique the Reasoning of Others (MP 3)

EX. 19: Model with Mathematics (MP 4)

EX. 21d: Look for Patterns (MP 7)

STEM exercises focus on science or engineering applications.

EXERCISE 20: Use the **Think About a Plan** worksheet in the Online Teacher Resources to further support students' development in becoming independent learners.

HOMEWORK QUICK CHECK

To check students' understanding of key skills and concepts, go over Exercises 16, 19, 20, 23, and 27.

ANSWERS

14. a. 72

b. 54

15. a. 45

b. 67.5

16. a. 40

b. 70

17. a. 30

b. 75

▼ STUDENT PAGE 460

More Practice and Problem-Solving Exercises

B Apply

Find the measures of the angles formed by (a) two consecutive radii and (b) a radius and a side of the given regular polygon.

14. pentagon **15.** octagon **16.** nonagon **17.** dodecagon

STEM **18. Satellites** One of the smallest space satellites ever developed has the shape of a pyramid. Each of the four faces of the pyramid is an equilateral triangle with sides about 13 cm long. What is the area of one equilateral triangular face of the satellite? Round your answer to the nearest whole number.

19. Think About a Plan The gazebo in the photo is built in the shape of a regular octagon. Each side is 8 ft long, and the enclosed area is about 309 ft^2. What is the length of the apothem?

- How can you *draw a diagram* to help you solve the problem?
- How can you use the area of a regular polygon formula?

20. A regular hexagon has perimeter 120 m. Find its area.

21. The area of a regular polygon is 36 $in.^2$. Find the length of a side if the polygon has the given number of sides. Round your answer to the nearest tenth.

a. 3 **b.** 4 **c.** 6

d. Estimation Suppose the polygon is a pentagon. What would you expect the length of a side to be? Explain.

18. 73 cm^2

19. about 9.7 ft

20. $600\sqrt{3}$ m^2 or about 1039.2 m^2

21. a. 9.1 in.

b. 6 in.

c. 3.7 in.

d. Answers may vary. Sample: About 4 in.; the length of a side of a pentagon should be between 3.7 in. and 6 in.

22. $m\angle 1 = 36$, $m\angle 2 = 18$, $m\angle 3 = 72$

23. The apothem is one leg of a rt. triangle that has the radius as the hypotenuse.

24. a–c.

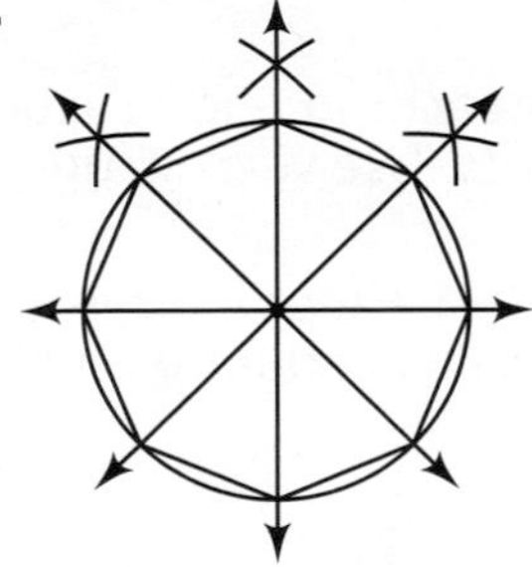

regular octagon

d. Construct a 60° angle with the vertex at the center of the circle.

25. 17.0; 18

26. 30; 43.3

27. 19.0; 26.0

28. a. $b = s$, $h = \frac{\sqrt{3}}{2}s$; $A = \frac{1}{2}bh = \frac{1}{2}s \cdot \frac{\sqrt{3}}{2}s = \frac{s^2\sqrt{3}}{4}$

b. $a = \frac{s\sqrt{3}}{6}$; $A = \frac{1}{2}ap = \frac{1}{2}\left(\frac{s\sqrt{3}}{6}\right)(3s) = \frac{s^2\sqrt{3}}{4}$

29. The apothem is ⊥ to a side of the pentagon. Two right triangles are formed with the radii of the pentagon. The triangles are ≅ by HL. So, the angles formed by the apothem and radii are ≅ because corresp. parts of ≅ triangles are ≅. Therefore, the apothem bisects the vertex ∠.

30. For regular *n*-gon *ABCDE* . . . , let *P* be the intersection of the bisectors of ∠*ABC* and ∠*BCD*. $\overline{BC} \cong \overline{DC}$, ∠*BCP* ≅ ∠*DCP*, and $\overline{CP} \cong \overline{CP}$, so △*BCP* ≅ △*DCP*, and ∠*CBP* ≅ ∠*CDP* because corresp. parts of ≅ triangles are ≅. Since ∠*BCP* is half the size of ∠*ABC* and ∠*ABC* ≅ ∠*CDE*, then ∠*CDP* is half the size of ∠*CDE*. By a similar argument, *P* is on the bisector of each ∠ around the polygon. The smaller angles formed by each of the ∠ bisectors are all ≅. By the Converse of the Isosc. Triangle Thm., each of △*APB*, △*BPC*, △*CPD*, etc., are isosc. with $\overline{AP} \cong \overline{BP} \cong \overline{CP}$, etc. Thus, *P* is equidistant from the polygon's vertices. So *P* is the center of the polygon and the ∠ bisectors are radii.

31. a. (2.8, 2.8)

b. 5.6 units^2

c. 45 units^2

---

22. A portion of a regular decagon has radii and an apothem drawn. Find the measure of each numbered angle.

23. Writing Explain why the radius of a regular polygon is greater than the apothem.

24. Constructions Use a compass to draw a circle.

a. Construct two perpendicular diameters of the circle.
b. Construct diameters that bisect each of the four right angles.
c. Connect the consecutive points where the diameters intersect the circle. What regular polygon have you constructed?
d. Use your construction to construct a square inscribed in a circle.

Find the perimeter and area of each regular polygon. Round to the nearest tenth, as necessary.

25. a square with vertices at (−1, 0), (2, 3), (5, 0) and(2, −3)

26. an equilateral triangle with two vertices at (−4, 1) and (4, 7)

27. a hexagon with two adjacent vertices at (−2, 1) and (1, 2)

28. To find the area of an equilateral triangle, you can use the formula $A = \frac{1}{2}bh$ or $A = \frac{1}{2}ap$. A third way to find the area of an equilateral triangle is to use the formula $A = \frac{1}{4}s^2\sqrt{3}$. Verify the formula $A = \frac{1}{4}s^2\sqrt{3}$ in two ways as follows:

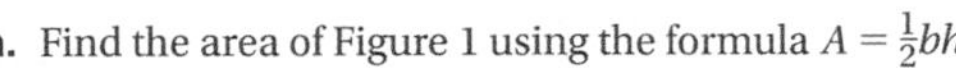
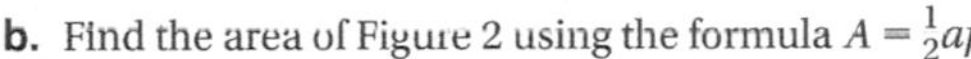
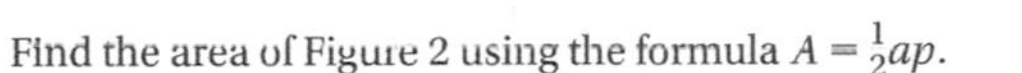

a. Find the area of Figure 1 using the formula $A = \frac{1}{2}bh$.
b. Find the area of Figure 2 using the formula $A = \frac{1}{2}ap$.

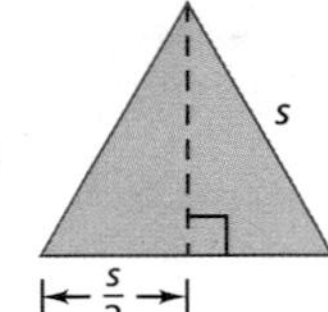
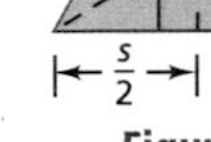

Figure 1 Figure 2

Proof 29. For Problem 1 in this lesson, write a proof that the apothem bisects the vertex angle of an isosceles triangle formed by two radii.

Challenge

Proof 30. Prove that the bisectors of the angles of a regular polygon are concurrent and that they are, in fact, radii of the polygon. (*Hint*: For regular *n*-gon *ABCDE*. . ., let *P* be the intersection of the bisectors of ∠*ABC* and ∠*BCD*. Show that $\overline{DP}$ must be the bisector of ∠*CDE*.)

31. Coordinate Geometry A regular octagon with center at the origin and radius 4 is graphed in the coordinate plane.

a. Since V_2 lies on the line $y = x$, its *x*- and *y*-coordinates are equal. Use the Distance Formula to find the coordinates of V_2 to the nearest tenth.
b. Use the coordinates of V_2 and the formula $A = \frac{1}{2}bh$ to find the area of $\triangle V_1OV_2$ to the nearest tenth.
c. Use your answer to part (b) to find the area of the octagon to the nearest whole number.

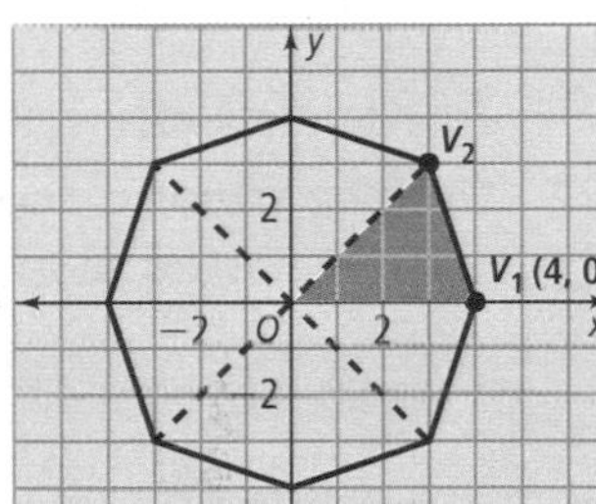

5 Assess and Remediate

Lesson Quiz

1. What is the area of the regular pentagon below?

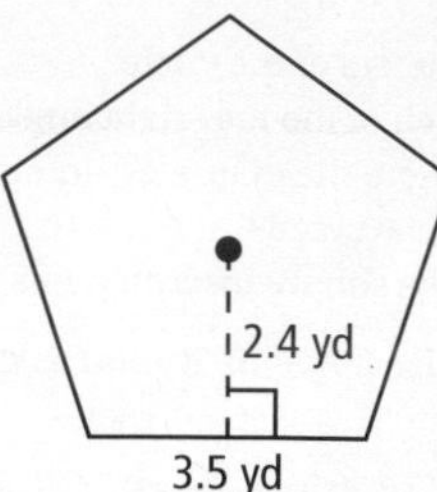

2. What is the length of the apothem of a regular hexagon with 10-cm sides? Round to the nearest tenth if necessary.

3. Do you UNDERSTAND? Geoff uses hexagonal tiles to create a tessellation pattern in his garden. What is the area of each tile? Round to the nearest whole number.

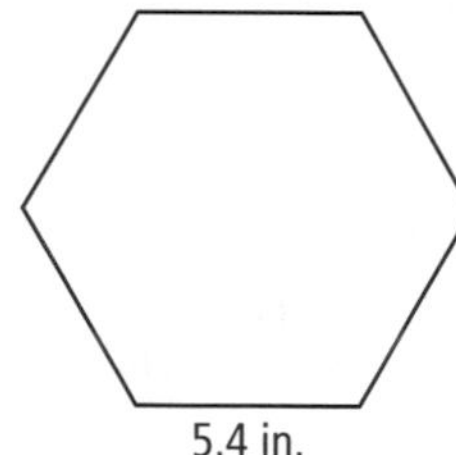

ANSWERS TO LESSON QUIZ

1. 21 yd^2

2. about 8.7 cm

3. about 76 $in.^2$

Prescription for Remediation

Use the student work on the Lesson Quiz to prescribe a differentiated assignment.

Points	Differentiated Remediation
0–1	Intervention
2	On-level
3	Extension

Online Assessment

Assign the Lesson Quiz in Success Tracker on **pearsonsuccessnet.com**. Success Tracker will automatically score the quiz and assign appropriate intervention or enrichment to each student based on the results. The compiled data appear in three different reports for instant analysis of whole class and individual student performance.

Differentiated Remediation

Intervention

- **RETEACHING** (2 pages) Provides reteaching and practice exercises for the key lesson concepts. Use with struggling students or absent students.
- **ENGLISH LANGUAGE LEARNER SUPPORT** Helps students develop and reinforce mathematical vocabulary and key concepts.

On-Level

- **PRACTICE** (2 pages) Provides extra practice for each lesson. For simpler practice exercises, use the Form K Practice pages found in the Online Teacher Resources.
- **THINK ABOUT A PLAN** Helps students develop specific problem-solving skills and strategies by providing scaffolded guiding questions.
- **STANDARDIZED TEST PREP** Focuses on all major exercises, all major question types, and helps students prepare for the high-stakes assessments.

Extension

- **ENRICHMENT** Provides students with interesting problems and activities that extend the concepts of the lesson.
- **ACTIVITIES, GAMES, AND PUZZLES** Worksheets that can be used for concept development, enrichment, and for fun!

Chapter Review

Essential Questions

BIG idea Measurement

ESSENTIAL QUESTION How do you find a side length or angle measure in a right triangle?

ANSWER Use the Pythagorean Theorem or trigonometric ratios to find a side length or angle measure of a right triangle.

BIG idea Similarity

ESSENTIAL QUESTION How do trigonometric ratios relate to similar right triangles?

ANSWER A trigonometric ratio compares the lengths of two sides of a right triangle. The ratios remain constant within a group of similar right triangles.

Summative Questions

Use the following prompts as you review this chapter with your students. The prompts are designed to help you assess your students' understanding of the BIG Ideas they have studied.

- What is the Pythagorean Theorem? When is it used?
- What are the trigonometric ratios? What are they used for?

7-1 The Pythagorean Theorem and Its Converse

ANSWERS

1. $2\sqrt{113}$
2. 17
3. $12\sqrt{2}$
4. $9\sqrt{3}$

▼ STUDENT PAGE 462

7-1 The Pythagorean Theorem and Its Converse

Quick Review

The **Pythagorean Theorem** holds true for any right triangle.

$(\text{leg}_1)^2 + (\text{leg}_2)^2 = (\text{hypotenuse})^2$

$a^2 + b^2 = c^2$

The Converse of the Pythagorean Theorem states that if $a^2 + b^2 = c^2$, where c is the greatest side length of a triangle, then the triangle is a right triangle.

Example

What is the value of x?

$a^2 + b^2 = c^2$	Pythagorean Theorem
$x^2 + 12^2 = 20^2$	Substitute.
$x^2 = 256$	Simplify.
$x = 16$	Take the positive square root.

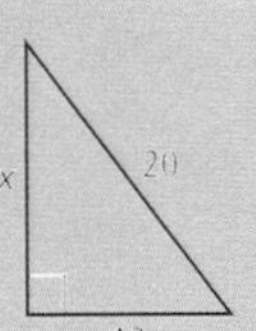

Exercises

Find the value of x. If your answer is not an integer, express it in simplest radical form.

1. 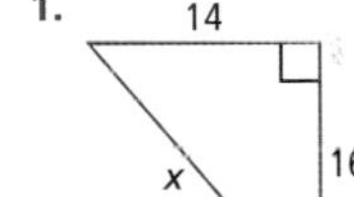

2. 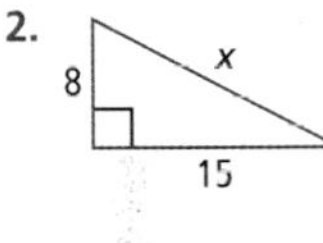

3. 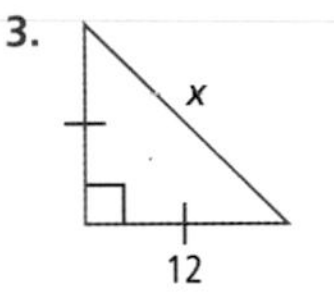

4. 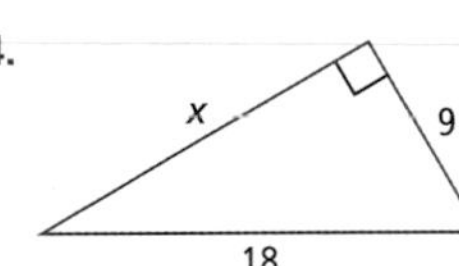

Chapter Review *(continued)*

7-2 Special Right Triangles

ANSWERS

5. $x = 7,\ y = 7\sqrt{2}$

6. $x = 5\sqrt{2}$

7. $x = 6\sqrt{3},\ y = 12$

8. $x = 7,\ y = 7\sqrt{3}$

9. 70.7 ft

▼ STUDENT PAGE 462

7-2 Special Right Triangles

Quick Review

45°-45°-90° Triangle

hypotenuse = $\sqrt{2}$ • leg

30°-60°-90° Triangle

hypotenuse = 2 • shorter leg

longer leg = $\sqrt{3}$ • shorter leg

Example

What is the value of *x*?

The triangle is a 30°-60°-90° triangle, and *x* represents the length of the longer leg.

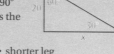

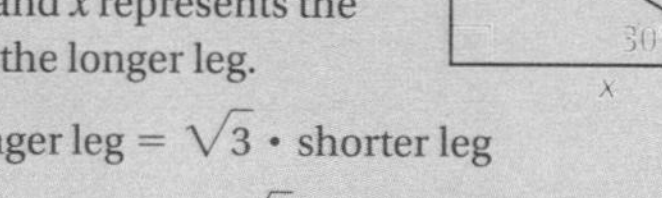

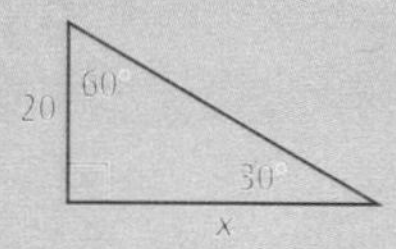

longer leg = $\sqrt{3}$ • shorter leg

$x = 20\sqrt{3}$

Exercises

Find the value of each variable. If your answer is not an integer, express it in simplest radical form.

5.

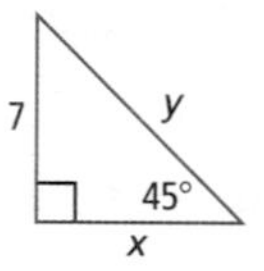

6.

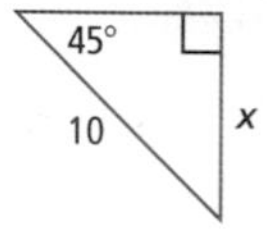

45°
10
x

7.

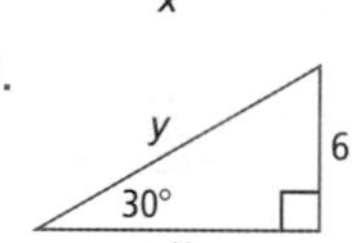

8.

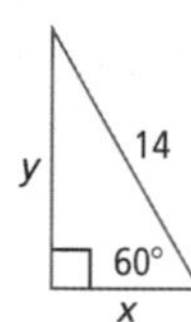

9. A square garden has sides 50 ft long. You stretch a hose from one corner of the garden to another corner along the garden's diagonal. To the nearest tenth, how long is the hose?

7-3 and 7-4 Trigonometry and Angles of Elevation and Depression

ANSWERS

10. $\frac{2\sqrt{19}}{20}$ or $\frac{\sqrt{19}}{10}$; $\frac{18}{20}$ or $\frac{9}{10}$; $\frac{2\sqrt{19}}{18}$ or $\frac{\sqrt{19}}{9}$

11. $\frac{16}{20}$ or $\frac{4}{5}$; $\frac{12}{20}$ or $\frac{3}{5}$; $\frac{16}{12}$ or $\frac{4}{3}$

12. 16.5

13. 33.1

14. 38.2 ft

▼ STUDENT PAGE 463

7-3 and 7-4 Trigonometry and Angles of Elevation and Depression

Quick Review

In right △*ABC*, *C* is the right angle.

$\sin A = \frac{\text{leg opposite } \angle A}{\text{hypotenuse}}$

$\cos A = \frac{\text{leg adjacent to } \angle A}{\text{hypotenuse}}$

$\tan A = \frac{\text{leg opposite } \angle A}{\text{leg adjacent to } \angle A}$

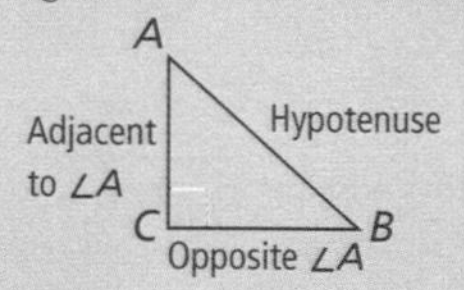

A
Adjacent to ∠A
Hypotenuse
C
B
Opposite ∠A

Example

What is *FE* to the nearest tenth?

You know the length of the hypotenuse, and $\overline{FE}$ is the side adjacent to ∠*E*.

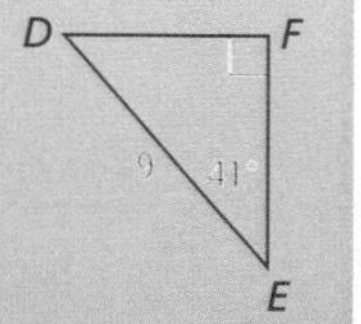

D
F
9
41°
E

$\cos 41° = \frac{FE}{9}$ Use cosine.

$FE = 9(\cos 41°)$ Multiply each side by 9.

$FE \approx 6.8$ Use a calculator.

Exercises

Express sin *A*, cos *A*, and tan *A* as ratios.

10.

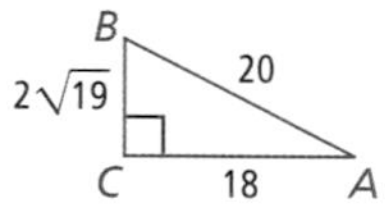

B
$2\sqrt{19}$
20
C
18
A

11.

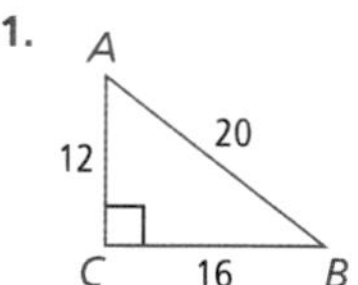

Find the value of *x* to the nearest tenth.

12.

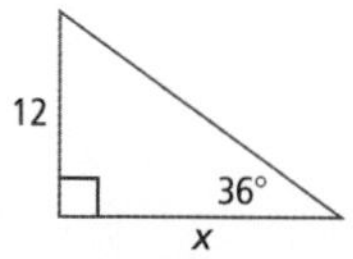

12
36°
x

13.

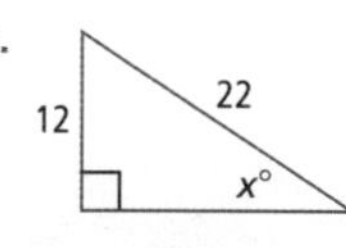

14. While flying a kite, Linda lets out 45 ft of string and anchors it to the ground. She determines that the angle of elevation of the kite is 58°. What is the height of the kite from the ground? Round to the nearest tenth.

7-5 Areas of Regular Polygons

ANSWERS

15. $9\sqrt{3}$ in.^{2}

16. 28 m^2

17. $2400\sqrt{3}$ cm^2

18. 112.5 m^2

19.

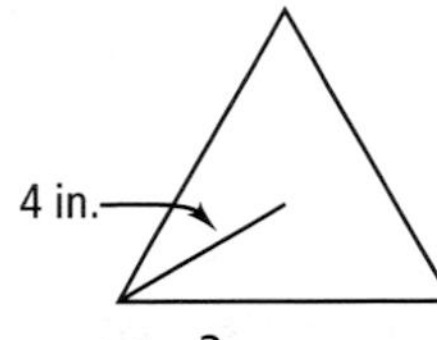

20.8 in.^{2}

20.

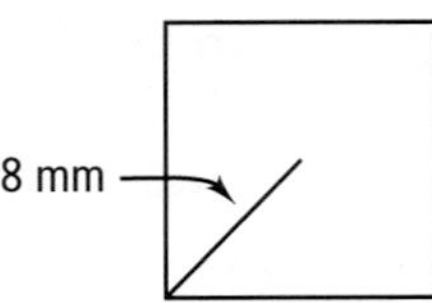

128 mm^2

21.

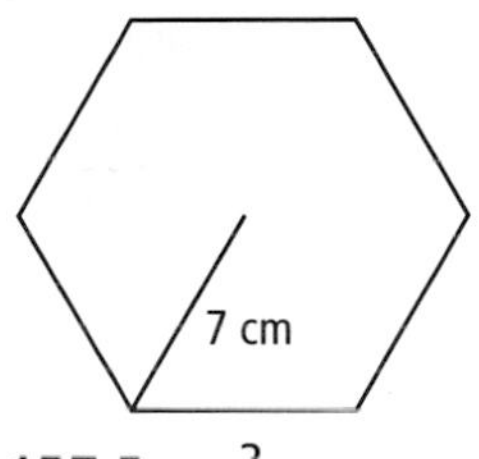

127.3 cm^2

▼ STUDENT PAGE 463

7-5 Areas of Regular Polygons

Quick Review

The **center of a regular polygon** C is the center of its circumscribed circle. The **radius** r is the distance from the center to a vertex. The **apothem** a is the perpendicular distance from the center to a side. The area of a regular polygon with apothem a and perimeter p is $A = \frac{1}{2}ap$.

Example

What is the area of a regular hexagon with apothem 17.3 mm and perimeter 120 mm?

$A = \frac{1}{2}ap$ Use the area formula.

$= \frac{1}{2}(17.3)(120) = 1038$ Substitute and simplify.

The area of the hexagon is 1038 mm^2.

Exercises

Find the area of each regular polygon. If your answer is not an integer, leave it in simplest radical form.

15.

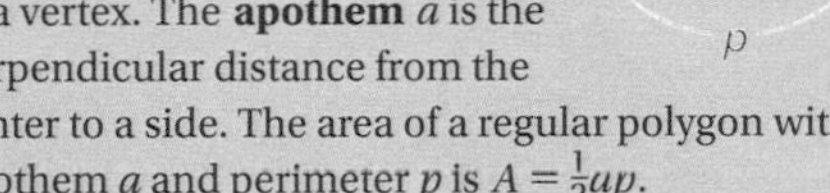

16.

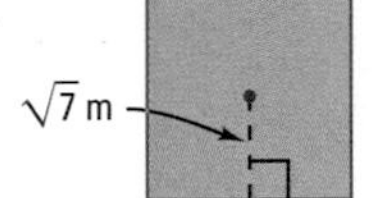

17. What is the area of a regular hexagon with a perimeter of 240 cm?

18. What is the area of a square with radius 7.5 m?

Sketch each regular polygon with the given radius. Then find its area to the nearest tenth.

19. triangle; radius 4 in.

20. square; radius 8 mm

21. hexagon; radius 7 cm

Pull It All Together

Common Core State Standards
G.SRT.8 Use trigonometric ratios . . . to solve right triangles in applied problems. Also G.SRT.6

Using Performance Tasks

Understanding by Design® principles support using performance tasks to assess students' progress toward mastering content standards and developing proficiency with the Mathematical Practices.

Mathematical Practices

- Make sense of problems and persevere in solving them.
- Model with mathematics.
- Reason abstractly and quantitatively.

Assessing Performance

See the Implementation Guide for a holistic scoring rubric to use in assessing students' work on the performance task.

Guiding Questions

Q If one part of the distance between the towers is x, what expression represents the other part of the distance?

Q What type of special right triangle is in the diagram? What are the ratios of its side lengths?

Q What ratio in the diagram is equal to tan 54°?

Solution Outline

Let x represent the length of one part of the distance between the towers, so that $2000 - x$ represents the length of the other part. The triangle on the right side of the figure is a 30°-60°-90° triangle. The dashed line is the shorter of the two legs of the triangle, so an expression for the length of the dashed line is $\frac{2000 - x}{\sqrt{3}}$.

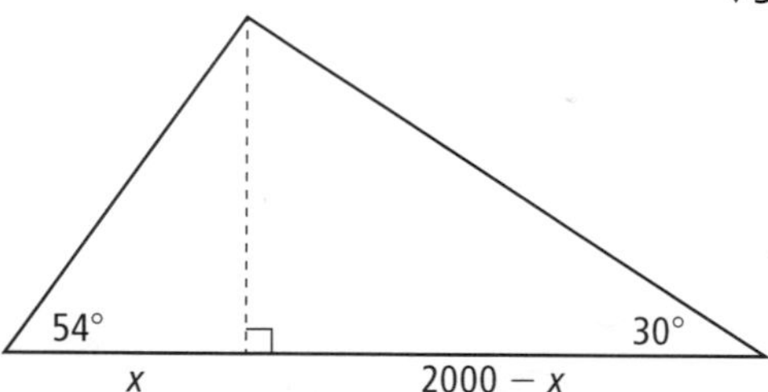

Use the tangent ratio to solve for x.

$\tan 54° = \frac{2000 - x}{\sqrt{3}} \div x = \frac{2000 - x}{x\sqrt{3}}$

$x\sqrt{3} \tan 54° = 2000 - x$

$x\sqrt{3} \tan 54° + x = 2000$

$x = \frac{2000}{\sqrt{3} \tan 54° + 1} \approx 591.02$

$2000 - x \approx 1408.98$

The length of the dashed line is $\frac{1408.98}{\sqrt{3}} \approx 813.47$.

Use the Pythagorean Theorem to calculate the distance from each tower to the fire:

▼ STUDENT PAGE 464

Locating a Forest Fire

Rangers in the two lookout towers at a state forest notice a plume of smoke, as shown in the diagram. The towers are 2000 ft apart. One ranger observes the smoke at an angle of 54°. The other ranger observes it an angle of 30°. Both angles are measured from the line that connects the two towers. When the rangers call to report the fire, they must give the fire department the approximate distance from their lookout tower to the fire.

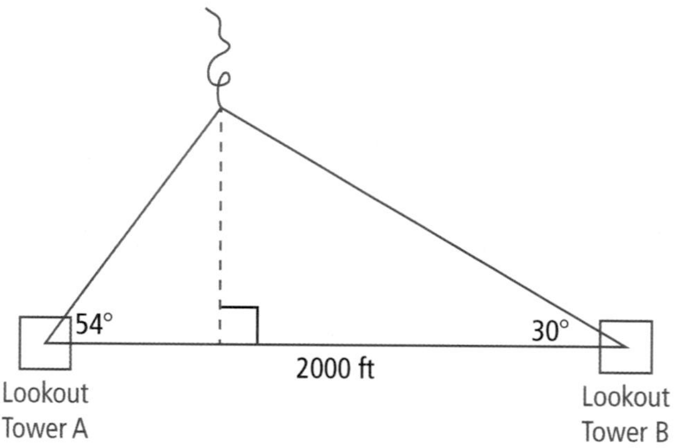

Task Description

Find the distance from each lookout tower to the fire.

- The dashed vertical line segment divides the distance between the lookout towers into two parts. What expressions can you use to represent the lengths of the parts?
- What expression represents the length of the dashed vertical line segment?

Distance (Tower A): $\sqrt{813.47^2 + 591.02^2} \approx 1005.50$

Distance (Tower B): $\sqrt{813.47^2 + 1408.98^2} \approx 1626.95$

Tower A is about 1006 ft from the fire. Tower B is about 1627 ft from the fire.

Get Ready!

Using This Diagnostic Assessment

Assign this diagnostic assessment to determine if students have the prerequisite skills for Chapter 8.

Lesson	Skill
Previous Course	Solving Equations
3-5	Isosceles and Equilateral Triangles
7-1	The Pythagorean Theorem

To remediate students, select from these resources (available for every lesson).

- Online Problems (pearsonsuccessnet.com)
- Reteaching (Online Teacher Resources)
- Practice (Online Teacher Resources)

Why Students Need These Skills

SOLVING EQUATIONS Students will solve equations to find unknown quantities in circles and the special segments related to circles.

ISOSCELES AND EQUILATERAL TRIANGLES Students will use triangles created by tangent lines, secant lines, and chords to solve for unknown measures.

THE PYTHAGOREAN THEOREM Right triangles are formed when a radius of a circle intersects a tangent line. Students will use the Pythagorean Theorem to solve for unknown side lengths in these right triangles.

Looking Ahead Vocabulary

TANGENT Discuss what it means to "go off on a tangent."

INSCRIBED Draw an image of a polygon inscribed in a circle.

INTERCEPTED Have students give other examples of objects that may be intercepted.

ANSWERS

1. 82
2. $6\frac{2}{3}$
3. 15
4. 18
5. 24
6. 45
7. 60
8. $4\sqrt{2}$
9. 13
10. $\sqrt{10}$
11. 6
12. Answers may vary. Sample: A tangent touches a circle at one point.
13. Answers may vary. Sample: An inscribed ∠ has its vertex on a circle and its sides are inside the circle.
14. Answers may vary. Sample: An intercepted arc is the part of a circle that lies in the interior of an ∠.

▼ STUDENT PAGE 465

Solving Equations

Algebra Solve for x.

1. $\frac{1}{2}(x + 42) = 62$ **2.** $(5 + 3)8 = (4 + x)6$ **3.** $(9 + x)2 = (12 + 4)3$

Isosceles and Equilateral Triangles

Algebra Find the value of x.

4. 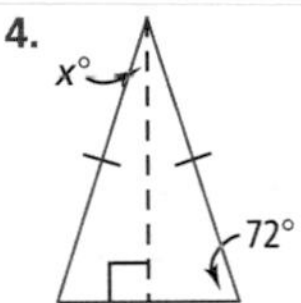

5. 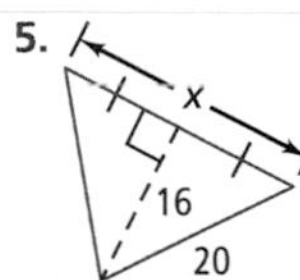

6. 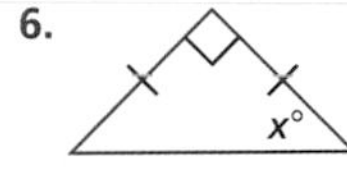

7. 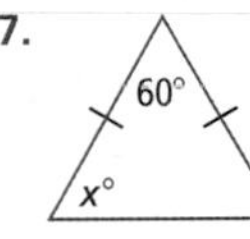

The Pythagorean Theorem

Algebra Find the value of x. Leave your answer in simplest radical form.

8. **9.** **10.** 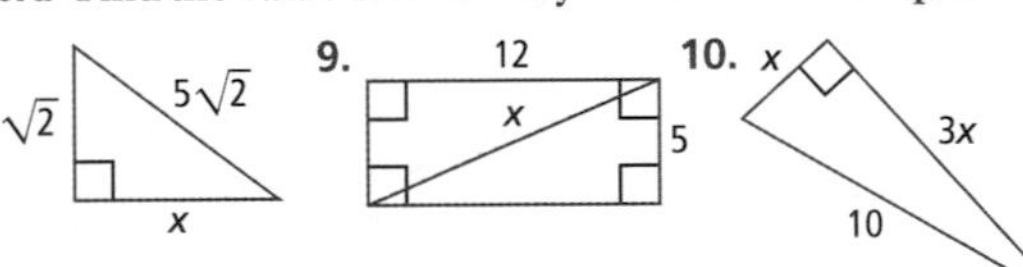

11. 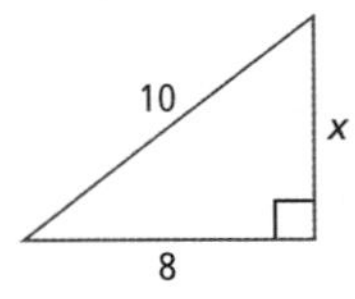

Looking Ahead Vocabulary

12. When you are in a conversation and you go off on a *tangent*, you are leading the conversation away from the main topic. What do you think a line that is *tangent* to a circle might look like?

13. You learned how to *inscribe* a triangle in a circle in Chapter 4. What do you think an *inscribed* angle is?

14. A defensive player *intercepts* a pass when he catches the football before it reaches the intended receiver. On a circle, what might an *intercepted* arc of an angle be?

CHAPTER
8

CIRCLES

Chapter 8 Overview

Interactive Digital Path
Log in to pearsonsuccessnet.com and click on Interactive Digital Path to access the Solve Its and animated Problems.

In Chapter 8 students explore concepts related to circles. Students will develop the answers to the Essential Questions posed below as they learn the bulleted concepts and skills.

BIG idea Reasoning and Proof

ESSENTIAL QUESTION How can you prove relationships between angles and arcs in a circle?

- Students will examine angles formed by lines that intersect inside and outside a circle.
- Students will relate arcs and angles.

BIG idea Measurement

ESSENTIAL QUESTION When lines intersect outside, on, or within a circle, how do you find the measures of the resulting angles, arcs, and segments?

- Students will use properties of tangent lines.
- Students will use the relationships among chords, arcs, and central angles.
- Students will solve problems with angles formed by secants and tangents.

Chapter Preview

8-1 Circles and Arcs
8-2 Areas of Circles and Sectors
8-3 Tangent Lines
8-4 Chords and Arcs
8-5 Inscribed Angles
8-6 Angle Measures and Segment Lengths

DYNAMIC ACTIVITIES

Dynamic Activity

Use the Dynamic Activity, an interactive math tool with guided instruction, to have students explore concepts visually and support the development of the Standards for Mathematical Practice.

Content Standards

Following are the key standards covered in this chapter.

Conceptual Category Geometry

DOMAIN Circles G.C

CLUSTER Understand and apply theorems about circles (Standards G.C.1, G.C.2, G.C.3, G.C.4)
LESSONS 8-1, 8-3, 8-4, 8-5, 8-6

CLUSTER Find arc lengths and areas of sectors of circles (Standard G.C.5)
LESSONS 8-2, AL 8-2

VOCABULARY

Vocabulary

English/Spanish Vocabulary Audio Online:

English	Spanish
central angle, *p. 467**	ángulo central
chord, *p. 498*	cuerda
concentric circles, *p. 470*	círculos concéntricos
diameter, *p. 467*	diámetro
inscribed angle, *p. 509*	ángulo inscrito
intercepted arc, *p. 509*	arco interceptor
major arc, *p. 467*	arco mayor
minor arc, *p. 467*	arco menor
secant, *p. 519*	secante
sector of a circle, *p. 479*	sector de un círculo
segment of a circle, *p. 480*	segmento de un círculo
tangent to a circle, *p. 488*	tagente de un círculo

**All page numbers refer to the Student Edition.*

CIRCLES

Math Background

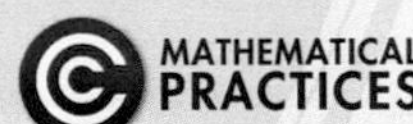

Understanding by Design® principles were central to the development of the Big Ideas and the Essential Understandings. These will help your students build a structure on which to make connections to prior learning.*

Reasoning and Proof

BIG idea Definitions establish meanings and remove possible misunderstanding. Other truths are more complex and difficult to see. It is often possible to verify complex truths by reasoning from simpler ones by using deductive reasoning.

ESSENTIAL UNDERSTANDINGS

8-3 A radius of a circle and the tangent that intersects the endpoint of the radius on the circle have a special relationship.

8-4 Information about congruent parts of a circle (or congruent circles) can be used to find information about other parts of the circle (or circles).

Measurement

BIG idea Some attributes of geometric figures, such as length, area, volume, and angle measure, are measurable. Units are used to describe these attributes.

ESSENTIAL UNDERSTANDINGS

8-1 The length of part of a circle's circumference can be found by relating it to an angle in the circle.

8-2 The area of parts of a circle formed by radii and arcs can be found when the circle's radius is known.

8-5 to 8-6 Angles formed by intersecting lines have a special relationship to the arcs the intersecting lines intercept. This includes (1) arcs formed by chords determined by inscribed angles, (2) angles and arcs formed by lines intersecting either within a circle or outside a circle, and (3) intersecting chords, intersecting secants, or a secant that intersects a tangent.

*UNDERSTANDING BY DESIGN® and UbD™ are trademarks of ASCD, and are used under license.

Segments Related to Circles

A radius is a segment that connects the center of a circle to a point on the circle. A diameter connects two points on the circle and passes through the center of the circle.

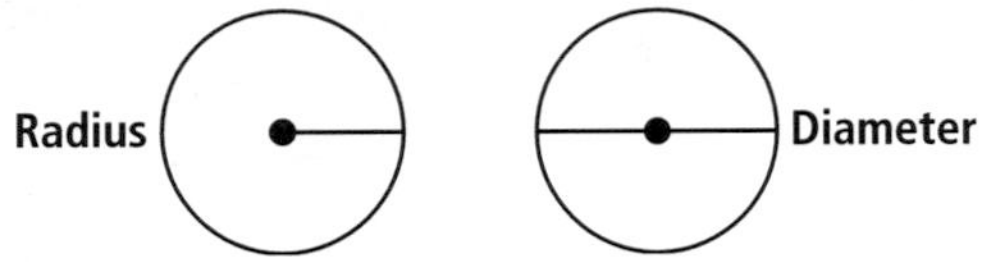

A tangent touches a circle at exactly one point. A chord connects two points on a circle.

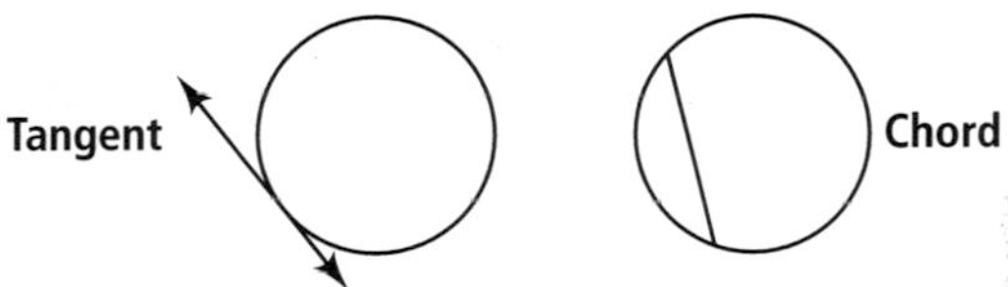

Tangents to a circle are congruent if they share a common endpoint outside of the circle.

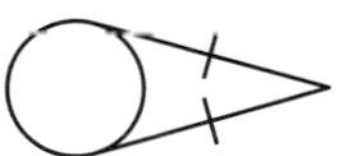

Chords in a circle are congruent if:

- The central angles that create them are congruent.
- Their arcs are congruent.
- They are the same distance from the center.

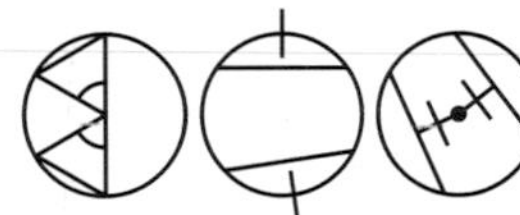

Common Errors With Segments Related to Circles

Students sometimes get confused identifying segments of a circle. Have students create a vocabulary sheet that includes definitions and diagrams of each type of segment. Discuss the relationship between the segments as well. For example, is a diameter a chord? [Yes, but a chord is not necessarily a diameter.]

Mathematical Practices

Attend to Precision. Students acquire a large collection of terms relating to circles and must be precise in differentiating between them.

Math Background *(continued)*

Angles Formed by Special Segments of Circles

The measure of angles formed by chords, tangents, and secants can be determined from arc lengths.

Using two chords that intersect on a circle:

$m\angle B = \frac{1}{2}m\widehat{AC}$

A chord and a tangent:

$m\angle C = \frac{1}{2}m\widehat{BDC}$

Two secants:

$m\angle ACE = \frac{1}{2}(m\widehat{AE} - m\widehat{BD})$

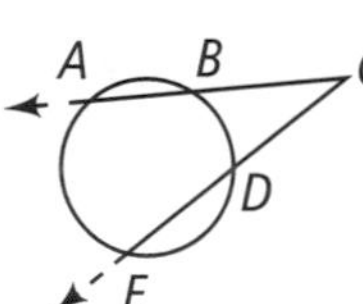

Two chords or secants that intersect inside a circle:

$m\angle ABC = \frac{1}{2}(m\widehat{AC} + m\widehat{DE})$

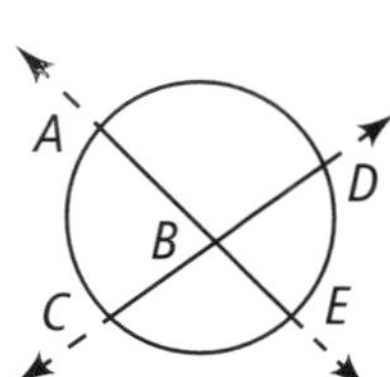

Common Errors With Angles Formed by Special Segments of Circles

Students might try to apply the Inscribed Angle Theorem, $m\angle B = \frac{1}{2}m\widehat{AC}$, when the vertex is not on the circle.

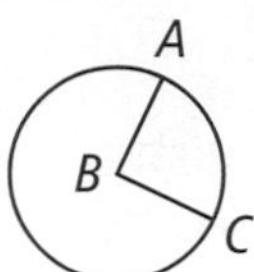

$m\angle B \neq \frac{1}{2}m\widehat{AC}$

Mathematical Practices

Construct viable arguments and critique the reasoning of others. Students develop relationships between angles in and around circles by building on exterior angles, using isosceles triangles, and algebraic substitution. They use inscribed angles to expand their knowledge of angle-arc relationships.

8-1 Circles and Arcs

Common Core State Standards
G.C.1 Prove . . . all circles are similar. **Also G.C.2, G.C.5**

Preparing to Teach

BIG idea Measurement

ESSENTIAL UNDERSTANDING

The length of part of a circle's circumference can be found by relating it to a central angle in the circle.

Math Background

In this lesson, students will learn important vocabulary related to circles. They will learn to identify major and minor arcs and their measures. An arc is measured by the central angle that defines it. Students will learn how to find the circumference of a circle. The ratio of the central angle of an arc to 360° can be used to find the length of the arc. Students will learn how to find distances along circular paths using circumference and arc length.

In 2002, Japanese mathematicians used a supercomputer to calculate the value of π to more than 1 trillion decimal places. In 1874, William Shanks set the record of 707 decimal places for the paper-and-pencil calculation of π. Today when a calculator is not available, most students use $\frac{22}{7}$ or 3.14 as an approximation for π. Estimates for π date back as far as 240 B.C.

ELL Support

USE GRAPHIC ORGANIZERS Students can work in mixed pairs or small groups. Have students construct then cut out a circle to use as an organizer for key vocabulary. Have them draw and label the parts of a circle on their circle organizer using the vocabulary list from the lesson. Encourage students to use multiple colors to differentiate between parts. Ask students to add related words to the labels on their organizers.

Lesson Vocabulary

- circle
- center
- diameter
- radius
- congruent circles
- central angle
- semicircle
- minor arc
- major arc
- adjacent arcs
- circumference
- pi
- concentric circles
- arc length

Mathematical Practices

ATTEND TO PRECISION. Students will use clear definitions of both arc measure and arc length and compute both quantities.

1 Interactive Learning

Solve It!

PURPOSE To find the portion of the circumference represented by an arc

PROCESS Students may

- find the percentage of the circumference represented by the 120° angle.
- use a proportion to find the portion of the circumference represented by the 120° angle.

Q What does the distance of one complete rotation represent? **[The distance represents the circumference of the wheel.]**

Q Will the wheel complete a full rotation? What does this mean in terms of the distance it travels? **[No, the wheel will not rotate completely around so it will not travel the full distance.]**

Q What portion of a rotation will the wheel complete? **[The wheel will complete $\frac{120}{360} = \frac{1}{3}$ of a rotation.]**

ANSWER 21 in.; explanations may vary. Sample: 120° is one third of a complete revolution, so the wheel will travel $\frac{1}{3} \cdot 63 = 21$ in. for a rotation of 120°.

▼ DIGITAL (STUDENT WORK SPACE PAGE 467)

Getting Ready!

The bicycle wheel shown at the right travels 63 in. in one complete rotation. If the wheel rotates only 120° about the center, how far does it travel? Justify your reasoning.

CONNECT THE MATH In Solve It, students should see how an arc is related to its central angle. The lesson presents instruction about arc measurements, arc addition, and circumference.

2 Guided Instruction

Problem 1 Naming Arcs

Have students make a manipulative with diagrams of the vocabulary. Allow them to refer to this manipulative throughout the lesson to reinforce definitions.

Problem 1

Q How can you tell a minor arc in a circle? **[It is smaller than a semicircle.]**

Q How can you indicate which direction you want the arc to go? **[List more than two points on the circle.]**

Q What are major arcs? **[They are larger than a semicircle.]**

Got It? **ERROR PREVENTION**
Students may benefit from tracing the figures with colored pencils. Have them redraw the circle three times and use four different colors on each part.

ANSWERS

Got It? a. $\overset{\frown}{SP}$, $\overset{\frown}{PQ}$, $\overset{\frown}{SQ}$, $\overset{\frown}{QR}$, $\overset{\frown}{RS}$
b. $\overset{\frown}{RSP}$, $\overset{\frown}{RQP}$ **c.** $\overset{\frown}{PQS}$, $\overset{\frown}{PSQ}$, $\overset{\frown}{SPR}$, $\overset{\frown}{QRS}$, $\overset{\frown}{RSQ}$

Practice

1. $\overset{\frown}{BDF}$, $\overset{\frown}{CDB}$, $\overset{\frown}{DEB}$, $\overset{\frown}{EFC}$, $\overset{\frown}{EFD}$, $\overset{\frown}{FBD}$, $\overset{\frown}{FBE}$, $\overset{\frown}{CFD}$
2. $\overset{\frown}{BCE}$, $\overset{\frown}{BFE}$, $\overset{\frown}{CBF}$, $\overset{\frown}{CDF}$

▼ STUDENT PAGE 467

In a plane, a **circle** is the set of all points equidistant from a given point called the **center**. You name a circle by its center. Circle P ($\odot P$) is shown below.

A **diameter** is a segment that contains the center of a circle and has both endpoints on the circle. A **radius** is a segment that has one endpoint at the center and the other endpoint on the circle. **Congruent circles** have congruent radii. A **central angle** is an angle whose vertex is the center of the circle.

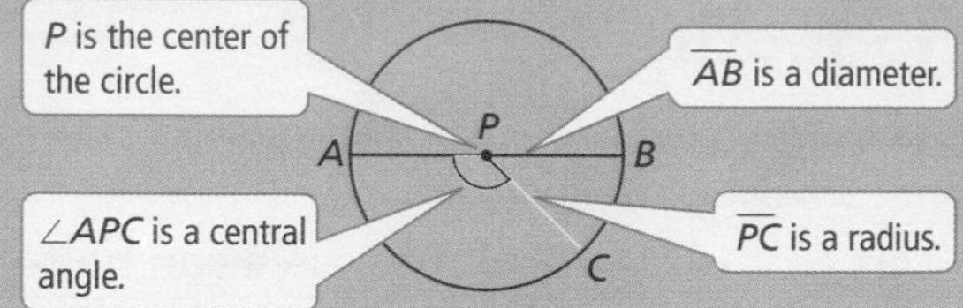

Essential Understanding You can find the length of part of a circle's circumference by relating it to an angle in the circle.

An arc is a part of a circle. One type of arc, a **semicircle**, is half of a circle. A **minor arc** is smaller than a semicircle. A **major arc** is larger than a semicircle. You name a minor arc by its endpoints and a major arc or a semicircle by its endpoints and another point on the arc.

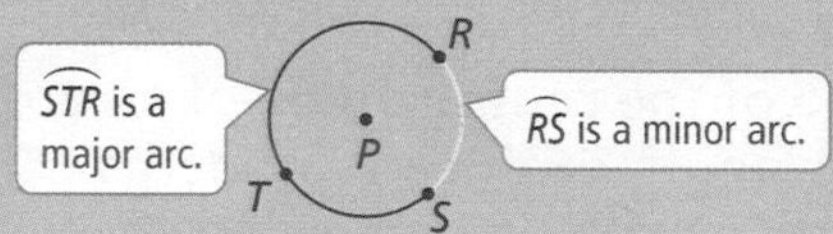

▼ DIGITAL

Problem 1 Naming Arcs

A **What are the minor arcs of $\odot O$?**

The minor arcs are $\overset{\frown}{AD}$, $\overset{\frown}{CE}$, $\overset{\frown}{AC}$, and $\overset{\frown}{DE}$.

B **What are the semicircles of $\odot O$?**

The semicircles are $\overset{\frown}{ACE}$, $\overset{\frown}{CED}$, $\overset{\frown}{EDA}$, and $\overset{\frown}{DAC}$.

C **What are the major arcs of $\odot O$ that contain point A?**

The major arcs that contain point A are $\overset{\frown}{ACD}$, $\overset{\frown}{CEA}$, $\overset{\frown}{EDC}$, and $\overset{\frown}{DAE}$.

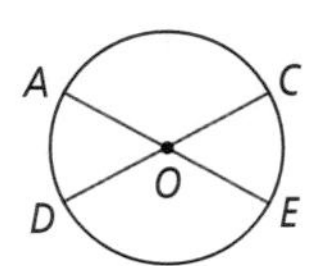

▼ STUDENT PAGE 468

Got It? a. What are the minor arcs of $\odot A$?

b. What are the semicircles of $\odot A$?

c. What are the major arcs of $\odot A$ that contain point Q?

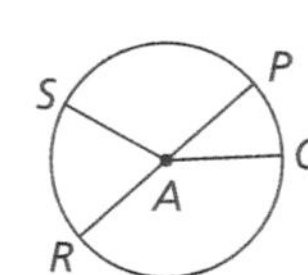

Think How can you identify the minor arcs?

A Practice Name the following in $\odot O$.

1. the major arcs

2. the semicircles

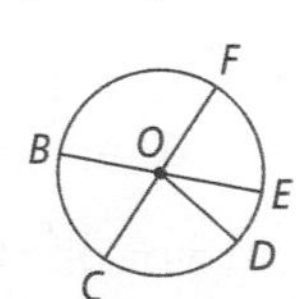

Problem 2 Finding the Measures of Arcs

Take Note

Arc Measure
Have students practice finding the measure of related arcs in a circle. Call out an arc measure and have them give the related measure.

Take Note

Arc Addition Postulate
Discuss the similarities between Postulate 19 and the Segment and Angle Addition Postulates. Emphasize that they are called postulates because they are taken as self-evident.

Problem 2

Q How is the measure of an arc related to the measure of its central angle? **[The measures are the same.]**

Q How can you write $m\overset{\frown}{BD}$ as a sum of two other arc measures? **[$m\overset{\frown}{BC} + m\overset{\frown}{CD}$]**

Q How can you classify $\overset{\frown}{ABC}$? [It is a semicircle.]

Q What is $m\overset{\frown}{AB}$? **[$m\overset{\frown}{AB} = 180 - m\overset{\frown}{BC} = 180 - 32 = 148$]**

Got It?

ERROR PREVENTION
Have students calculate and label each central angle in the diagram.

ANSWERS

Got It? a. 77 **b.** 103 **c.** 208 **d.** 283

Practice

3. 308 **4.** 270

▼ STUDENT PAGE 468

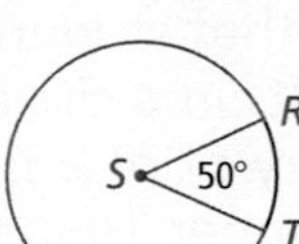

Key Concept Arc Measure

Arc Measure

The measure of a minor arc is equal to the measure of its corresponding central angle.

The measure of a major arc is the measure of the related minor arc subtracted from 360.

The measure of a semicircle is 180.

Example

$m\overset{\frown}{RT} = m\angle RST = 50$

$m\overset{\frown}{TQR} = 360 - m\overset{\frown}{RT}$

$= 310$

Adjacent arcs are arcs of the same circle that have exactly one point in common. You can add the measures of adjacent arcs just as you can add the measures of adjacent angles.

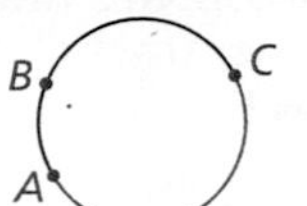

Postulate 19 Arc Addition Postulate

The measure of the arc formed by two adjacent arcs is the sum of the measures of the two arcs.

$m\overset{\frown}{ABC} = m\overset{\frown}{AB} + m\overset{\frown}{BC}$

▼ DIGITAL

Problem 2 Finding the Measures of Arcs

What is the measure of each arc in ⊙O?

A $\overset{\frown}{BC}$ $m\overset{\frown}{BC} = m\angle BOC = 32$

B $\overset{\frown}{BD}$ $m\overset{\frown}{BD} = m\overset{\frown}{BC} + m\overset{\frown}{CD}$

$m\overset{\frown}{BD} = 32 + 58 = 90$

C $\overset{\frown}{ABC}$ $\overset{\frown}{ABC}$ is a semicircle.

$m\overset{\frown}{ABC} = 180$

D $\overset{\frown}{AB}$ $m\overset{\frown}{AB} = 180 - 32 = 148$

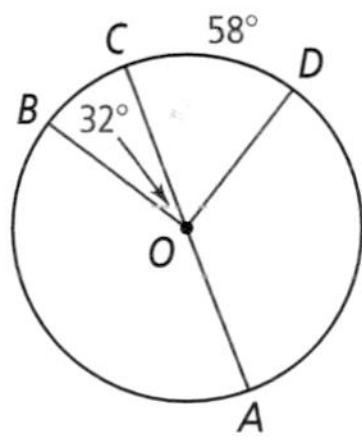

▼ STUDENT PAGE 469

Got It? What is the measure of each arc in ⊙C?

a. $m\overset{\frown}{PR}$

b. $m\overset{\frown}{RS}$

c. $m\overset{\frown}{PRQ}$

d. $m\overset{\frown}{PQR}$

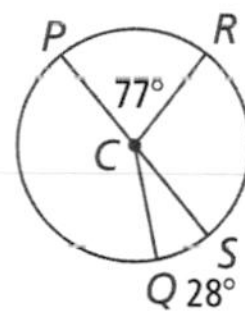

Practice Find the measure of each arc in ⊙P.

3. $\overset{\frown}{CBD}$

4. $\overset{\frown}{BCD}$

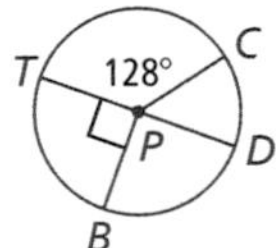

Problem 3 Finding a Distance

Take Note

Review the relationship between radius and diameter. Be sure that students can identify both measurements in a circle. Have students research the history of pi (π). Emphasize that pi is an irrational number. Help students locate and understand how to use the pi (π) button on their calculators.

EXTENSION

Have students investigate the relationship between scale factor and circumference using several circles with different radii.

Problem 3

Q How can you find the distance traveled by wheels on the two tracks? **[Calculate the circumference of the two circles.]**

Q What is the radius of the outer circle? **[8 ft + 2 ft = 10 ft]**

Q How do you know that a wheel on the outer edge travels farther than a wheel on the inner edge? **[The radius of the outer edge is greater, so the circumference is greater.]**

Q How can you find the difference in the distances traveled? **[Calculate the difference between the two circumferences.]**

▼ STUDENT PAGE 470

The **circumference** of a circle is the distance around the circle. The number **pi** (π) is the ratio of the circumference of a circle to its diameter.

take note

Theorem 72 Circumference of a Circle

The circumference of a circle is π times the diameter.

$C = \pi d$ or $C = 2\pi r$

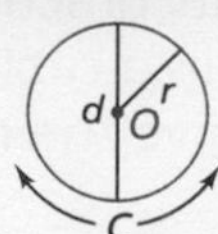

The number π is irrational, so you cannot write it as a terminating or repeating decimal. To approximate π, you can use 3.14, $\frac{22}{7}$, or the π key on your calculator.

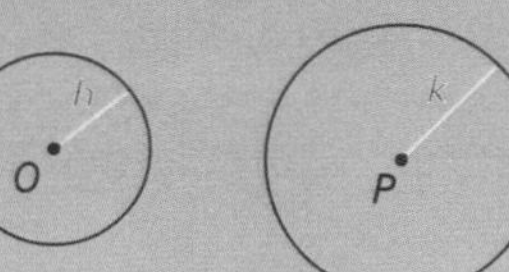

Many properties of circles deal with ratios that stay the same no matter what size the circle is. This is because all circles are similar to each other. To see this, consider the circles at the right. There is a translation that maps circle O so that it shares the same center with circle P.

There also exists a dilation with scale factor $\frac{k}{h}$ that maps circle O to circle P. A translation followed by a dilation is a similarity transformation. Because a similarity transformation maps circle O to circle P, the two circles are similar.

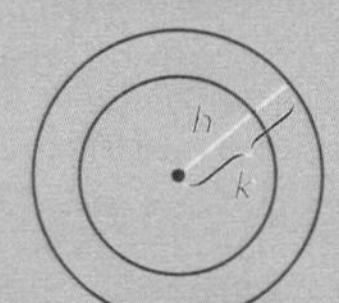

Concentric circles

Coplanar circles that have the same center are called **concentric circles**.

▼ DIGITAL

Problem 3 Finding a Distance

Film **A 2-ft-wide circular track for a camera dolly is set up for a movie scene. The two rails of the track form concentric circles. The radius of the inner circle is 8 ft. How much farther does a wheel on the outer rail travel than a wheel on the inner rail of the track in one turn?**

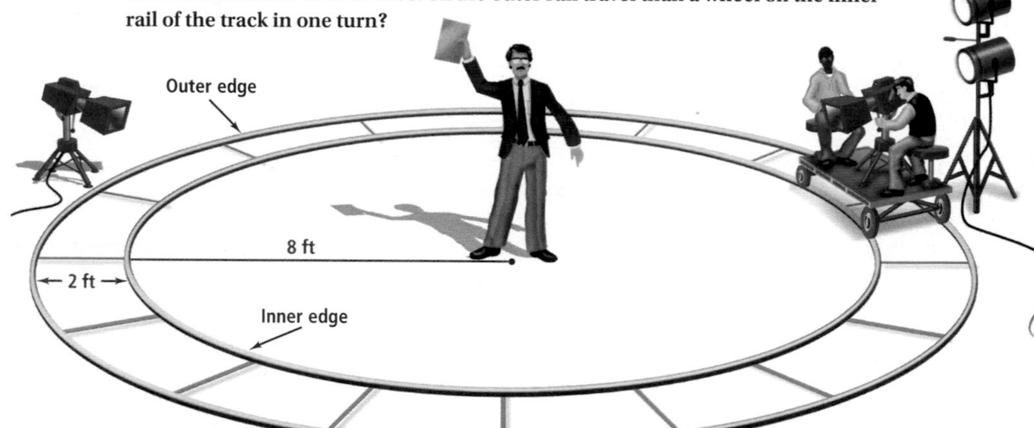

circumference of inner circle $= 2\pi r$ Use the formula for the circumference of a circle.

$= 2\pi(8)$ Substitute 8 for r.

$= 16\pi$ Simplify.

The radius of the outer circle is the radius of the inner circle plus the width of the track.

radius of the outer circle $= 8 + 2 = 10$

circumference of outer circle $= 2\pi r$ Use the formula for the circumference of a circle.

$= 2\pi(10)$ Substitute 10 for r.

$= 20\pi$ Simplify.

The difference in the two distances traveled is $20\pi - 16\pi$, or 4π ft.

$4\pi \approx 12.56637061$ Use a calculator.

A wheel on the outer edge of the track travels about 13 ft farther than a wheel on the inner edge of the track.

Got It?
Be sure that students find the radius of the entire outer circle. They should draw and label a diagram of the situation on their papers. In part (b), have students calculate the circumference of each circle using a common variable to relate the two radii. Have students write a ratio of the circumferences and simplify.

ANSWERS

Got It? a. about 29.5 ft **b.** 2 : 1; if the radius of circle A is r, then its circumference is $2\pi r$. Circle B will have a circumference of πr. The ratio of their circumferences is $\frac{2\pi r}{\pi r} = \frac{2}{1}$, or 2 : 1.

Practice

5. 8.4π m **6.** 19 in.

▼ STUDENT PAGES 470–471

Got It? **a.** A car has a circular turning radius of 16.1 ft. The distance between the two front tires is 4.7 ft. How much farther does a tire on the outside of the turn travel than a tire on the inside?

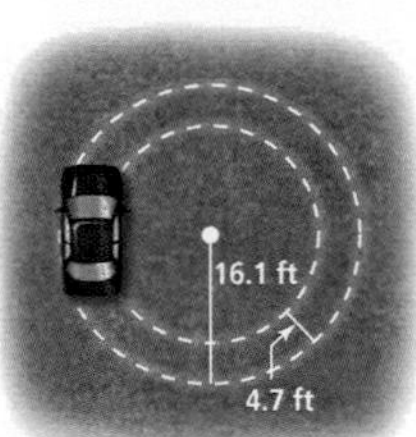

Plan
What do you need to find?

b. Reasoning Suppose the radius of $\odot A$ is equal to the diameter of $\odot B$. What is the ratio of the circumference of $\odot A$ to the circumference of $\odot B$? Explain.

Practice **5.** Find the circumference of this circle. Leave your answer in terms of π.

6. The wheel of a compact car has a 25-in. diameter. The wheel of a pickup truck has a 31-in. diameter. To the nearest inch, how much farther does the pickup truck wheel travel in one revolution than the compact car wheel?

Problem 4 Finding Arc Length

ERROR PREVENTION

Discuss the difference between arc measure and arc length. Arc measure is a degree measure similar to the measure of angles and is denoted by $m\widehat{AB}$. Arc length is the distance around the curve and is similar to the length of a line segment. Show students that it is possible for two arcs of different circles to have the same measure but different lengths. Similarly, it is possible for two arcs of different circles to have the same length but different measures.

Take Note
Students should begin to see that an arc is related to a circle by the central angle that defines it. Have them review their work in the Solve It. The ratio of the central angle to the total number of degrees in a circle will appear again when discussing the area of a sector. Be sure that students understand its significance.

Problem 4

Q In 4A, what fraction of the circle is represented by the central angle that created the arc? [$\frac{1}{4}$]

Q What fraction of the circle is represented by the highlighted arc in 4B? [$\frac{2}{3}$]

▼ STUDENT PAGES 471–472

The measure of an arc is in degrees, while the **arc length** is a fraction of the circumference.

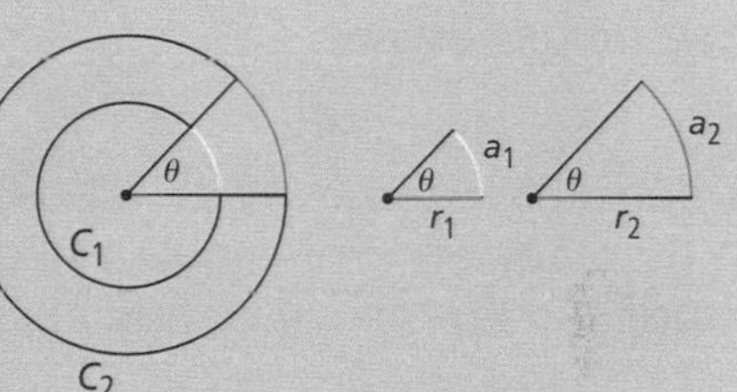

Consider the arcs shown at the right. Since the circles are concentric, there is a dilation that maps C_1 to C_2. The same dilation maps the slice of the small circle to the slice of the large circle. Since corresponding lengths of similar figures are proportional,

$$\frac{r_1}{r_2} = \frac{a_1}{a_2}$$
$$r_1 a_2 = r_2 a_1$$
$$a_1 = r_1 \cdot \frac{a_2}{r_2}$$

This means that the arc length a_1 is equal to the radius r_1 times some number. So for a given central angle, the length of the arc it intercepts depends only on the radius.

An arc of 60° represents $\frac{60}{360}$, or $\frac{1}{6}$, of the circle. So its arc length is $\frac{1}{6}$ of the circumference. This observation suggests the following theorem.

take note **Theorem 73 Arc Length**

The length of an arc of a circle is the product of the ratio $\frac{\text{measure of the arc}}{360}$ and the circumference of the circle.

$$\text{length of } \widehat{AB} = \frac{m\widehat{AB}}{360} \cdot 2\pi r = \frac{m\widehat{AB}}{360} \cdot \pi d$$

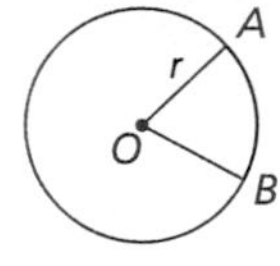

▼ DIGITAL

Problem 4 Finding Arc Length

What is the length of each arc shown in red? Leave your answer in terms of π.

A

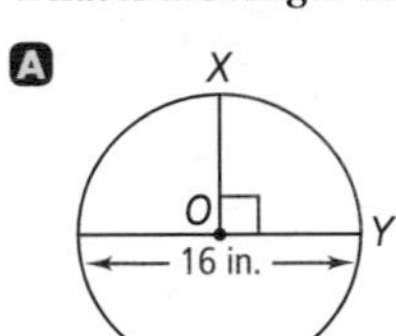

length of $\widehat{XY} = \frac{m\widehat{XY}}{360} \cdot \pi d$ Use a formula for arc length.

$= \frac{90}{360} \cdot \pi(16)$ Substitute.

$= 4\pi$ in. Simplify.

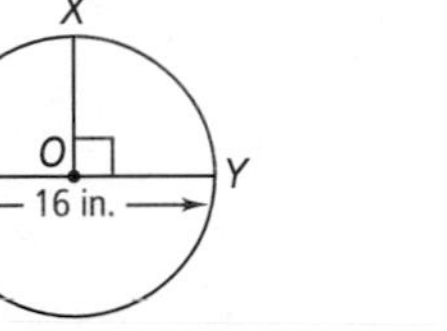

B

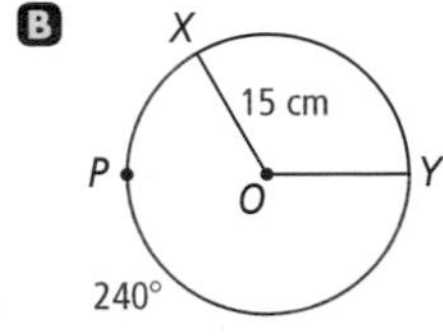

length of $\widehat{XPY} = \frac{m\widehat{XPY}}{360} \cdot 2\pi r$

$= \frac{240}{360} \cdot 2\pi(15)$

$= 20\pi$ cm

Problem 4 *continued*

Got It?

Ask students to define a semicircle. They should be able to identify the fraction of a circle represented by a semicircle without first identifying the measure of its associated central angle.

ANSWERS

Got It? 1.3π m

Practice

7. 8π ft **8.** $\frac{5\pi}{4}$ m

▼ STUDENT PAGE 472

Got It? What is the length of a semicircle with radius 1.3 m? Leave your answer in terms of π.

Practice Find the length of each arc shown in red. Leave your answer in terms of π.

7.

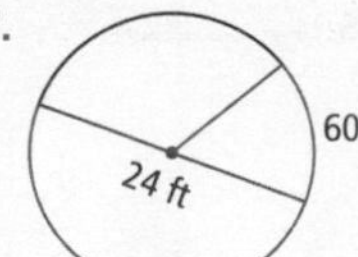

8.

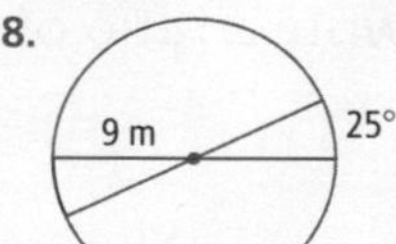

3 Lesson Check

Do you know HOW?

If students have difficulty with Exercise 13, then have them review Theorem 72 to state the formula for the circumference.

Do you UNDERSTAND?

If students have difficulty with Exercise 15, then have them review Problem 2 to find an arc measure and Problem 4 to find an arc length.

Close

Q What is the measure of an arc? **[It is equal to the measure of the central angle that defines it.]**

Q How do you find the circumference of a circle? **[Multiply 2π by the radius of the circle or multiply π by the diameter of the circle.]**

Q How can you find the length of an arc? **[Multiply the ratio of the arc measure to 360° by the circumference of the circle.]**

ANSWERS

9–11. Answers may vary. Samples are given.

9. $\overparen{AB}$ **10.** $\overparen{DAB}$

11. $\overparen{CAB}$ **12.** 81

13. 18π cm **14.** $\frac{23\pi}{4}$ cm

15. The measure of an arc corresponds to the measure of a central angle; an arc length is a fraction of the circle's circumference.

16. The student substituted the diameter into the formula that requires the radius.

▼ STUDENT PAGES 473–474

Lesson Check

Do you know HOW?

Use $\odot P$ at the right to answer each question. For Exercises 13 and 14, leave your answers in terms of π.

9. What is the name of a minor arc?

10. What is the name of a major arc?

11. What is the name of a semicircle?

12. What is $m\overparen{AB}$?

13. What is the circumference of $\odot P$?

14. What is the length of $\overparen{BD}$?

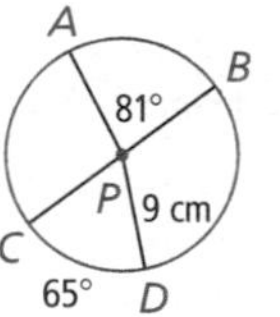

Do you UNDERSTAND?

15. Vocabulary What is the difference between the measure of an arc and arc length? Explain.

16. Error Analysis Your class must find the length of $\overparen{AB}$. A classmate submits the following solution. What is the error?

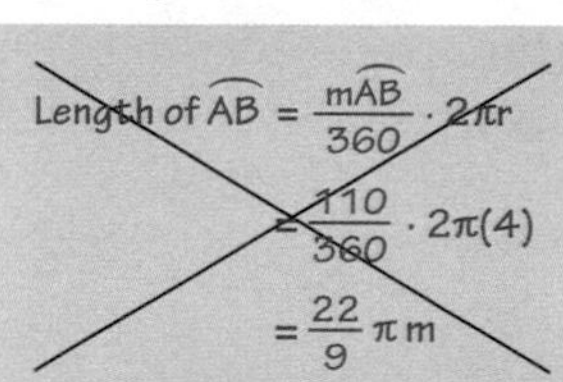

$$\text{Length of } \overparen{AB} = \frac{m\overparen{AB}}{360} \cdot 2\pi r$$
$$= \frac{110}{360} \cdot 2\pi(4)$$
$$= \frac{22}{9}\pi \text{ m}$$

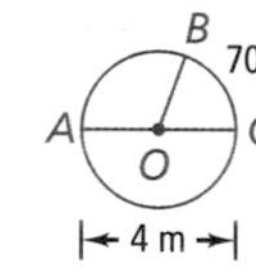

4 Practice

More Practice and Problem-Solving Exercises

ASSIGNMENT GUIDE

The assignments below are for the More Practice and Problem-Solving Exercises. You may also want to assign the A-Level Practice Exercises for homework if these are not used in class.
Average: 17–37
Advanced: 17–40

Mathematical Practices The exercises listed focus on the Standards for Mathematical Practices listed.

EX. 17: Make Sense of Problems (MP 1)
EX. 31: Construct Arguments (MP 3)
EX. 16: Critique the Reasoning of Others (MP 3)
EX. 24, 25, 27, 30, and 40: Model (MP 4)
EX. 26: Repeated Reasoning (MP 8)

STEM exercises focus on science or engineering applications.

EXERCISE 27: Use the **Think About a Plan** worksheet in the Online Teacher Resources to further support students' development in becoming independent learners.

HOMEWORK QUICK CHECK

To check students' understanding of key skills and concepts, go over Exercises 17, 20, 27, 31, and 35.

ANSWERS

17. 99 ft
18. 70
19. 180
20. 110
21. 55
22. 235
23. 290
24. about 183.3 ft
25. B
26. Find the measure of the major arc, then use Thm. 73; or find the length of the minor arc using Thm. 73, then subtract that length from the circumference of the circle.
27. a. 6
b. 30
c. 120
28. 38
29. 40
30. 31 m
31. The circumference is doubled; explanations may vary. Sample: Since $C = 2\pi r$, doubling the radius results in $2\pi(2r) = 2(2\pi r) = 2C$.
32. 3 : 4
33. 5.125π ft
34. 2.6π in.
35. 3π m
36. 7.9 units
37. 18 cm

More Practice and Problem-Solving Exercises

B Apply

17. Think About a Plan Nina designed a semicircular arch made of wrought iron for the top of a mall entrance. The nine segments between the two concentric semicircles are each 3 ft long. What is the total length of wrought iron used to make this structure? Round your answer to the nearest foot.
- What do you know from the diagram?
- What formula should you use to find the amount of wrought iron used in the semicircular arches?

Find each indicated measure for $\odot O$.

18. $m\angle EOF$ **19.** $m\widehat{EJH}$ **20.** $m\widehat{FH}$
21. $m\angle FOG$ **22.** $m\widehat{JEG}$ **23.** $m\widehat{HFJ}$

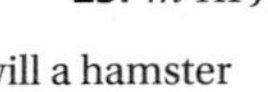
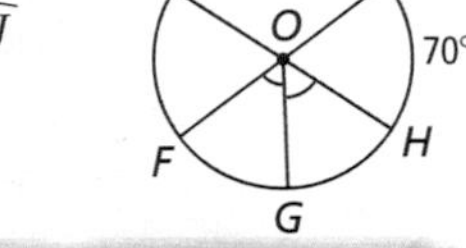

24. Pets A hamster wheel has a 7-in. diameter. How many feet will a hamster travel in 100 revolutions of the wheel?

STEM 25. Traffic Five streets come together at a traffic circle, as shown at the right. The diameter of the circle traveled by a car is 200 ft. If traffic travels counterclockwise, what is the approximate distance from East St. to Neponset St.?

Ⓐ 227 ft Ⓒ 454 ft
Ⓑ 244 ft Ⓓ 488 ft

26. Writing Describe two ways to find the arc length of a major arc if you are given the measure of the corresponding minor arc and the radius of the circle.

27. Time Hands of a clock suggest an angle whose measure is continually changing. How many degrees does a minute hand move through during each time interval?
a. 1 min **b.** 5 min **c.** 20 min

Algebra Find the value of each variable.

28.

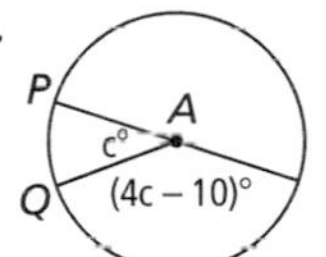

29.

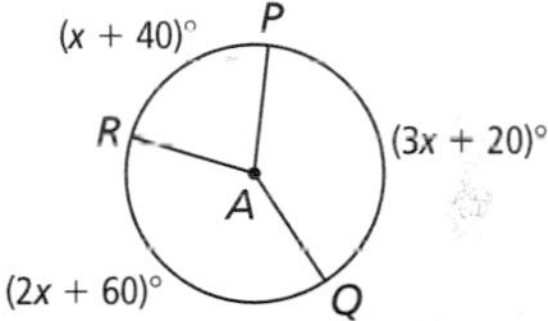

30. Landscape Design A landscape architect is constructing a curved path through a rectangular yard. The curved path consists of two 90° arcs. He plans to edge the two sides of the path with plastic edging. What is the total length of plastic edging he will need? Round your answer to the nearest meter.

31. Reasoning Suppose the radius of a circle is doubled. How does this affect the circumference of the circle? Explain.

32. A 60° arc of $\odot A$ has the same length as a 45° arc of $\odot B$. What is the ratio of the radius of $\odot A$ to the radius of $\odot B$?

Find the length of each arc shown in red. Leave your answer in terms of π.

33.

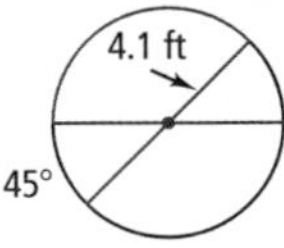

34.

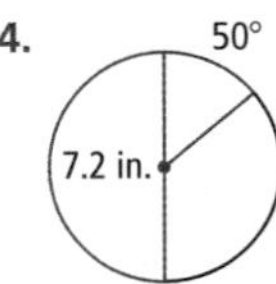

35.

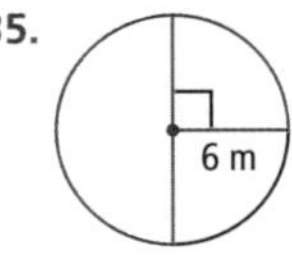

36. Coordinate Geometry Find the length of a semicircle with endpoints (1, 3) and (4, 7). Round your answer to the nearest tenth.

37. In $\odot O$, the length of $\widehat{AB}$ is 6π cm and $m\widehat{AB}$ is 120. What is the diameter of $\odot O$?

More Practice and Problem-Solving Exercises *continued*

38. Since $\overline{AR} \cong \overline{RW}$ and $AR + RW = AW$ by the Seg. Add. Post., $AW = 2 \cdot AR$. So the radius of the outer circle is twice the radius of the inner circle. Because $\angle QAR$ and $\angle SAU$ are vertical ⦣s, and $m\angle SAT = \frac{1}{2} m\angle SAU$, $m\angle QAR = 2 \cdot m\angle SAT$. The length of $\widehat{ST} = \frac{m\angle SAT}{360} \cdot 2\pi(2 \cdot AR) = \frac{m\angle SAT}{90} \cdot \pi(AR)$ and the length of $\widehat{QR} = \frac{m\angle QAR}{360} \cdot 2\pi(AR) = \frac{2 \cdot m\angle SAT}{360} \cdot 2\pi(AR) = \frac{m\angle SAT}{90} \cdot \pi(AR)$. Therefore the length of $\widehat{ST}$ = the length of $\widehat{QR}$ by the Trans. Prop. of Eq.

39. $\overline{AP} \cong \overline{BP}$ (Radii of a circle are $\cong$.); $\triangle APB$ is isosc. (def. of an isosc. $\triangle$); $\angle A \cong \angle B$ (Isosc. $\triangle$ Thm.); $\overline{AB} \parallel \overline{PC}$ (Given); $\angle B \cong \angle BPC$ (Alt. Int. ⦣ Thm.); $\angle A \cong \angle CPD$ (Corresp. ⦣ Post.); $\angle BPC \cong \angle CPD$ (Trans. Prop. of $\cong$); $m\angle BPC = m\widehat{BC}$ and $m\angle CPD = m\widehat{CD}$ (The measure of a minor arc is = to the measure of its corresp. central $\angle$.); $m\widehat{BC} = m\widehat{CD}$ (Trans. Prop. of =).

40. 325.7 yd, 333.5 yd, 341.4 yd, 349.2 yd, 357.1 yd, 364.9 yd, 372.8 yd, 380.6 yd

▼ STUDENT PAGE 476

Challenge

38. The diagram below shows two concentric circles. $\overline{AR} \cong \overline{RW}$. Show that the length of $\widehat{ST}$ is equal to the length of $\widehat{QR}$.

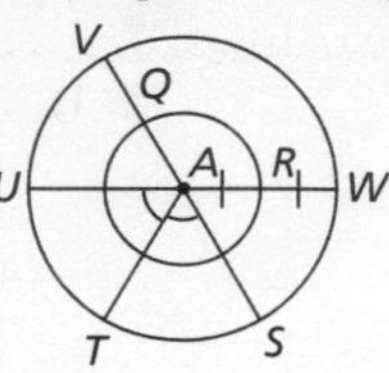

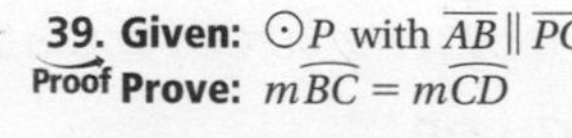

39. Given: $\odot P$ with $\overline{AB} \parallel \overline{PC}$

Proof Prove: $m\widehat{BC} = m\widehat{CD}$

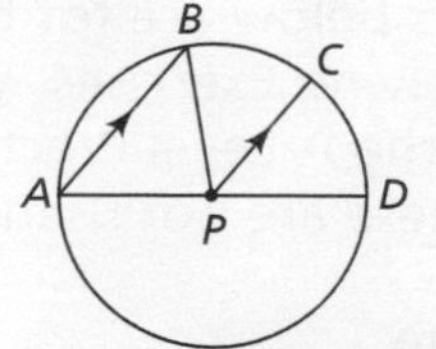

40. Sports An athletic field is a 100 yd-by-40 yd rectangle, with a semicircle at each of the short sides. A running track 10 yd wide surrounds the field. If the track is divided into eight lanes of equal width, what is the distance around the track along the inside edge of each lane?

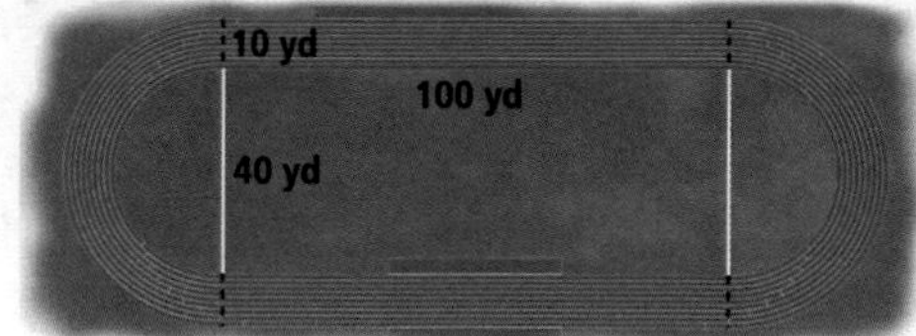

Problem 2 Finding the Area of a Sector of a Circle

Take Note

Review the formula for finding the length of an arc from Lesson 8-1. Focus on the ratio of the central angle and 360°. Connect this to the formula for finding the area of a sector. Be sure that students understand that a sector, arc, and central angle are connected by the portion of the circle they represent.

Problem 2

Q What portion of the circle is represented by the shaded sector? [$\frac{72}{360} = \frac{1}{5}$]

Q How can you find the area of the sector? **[Multiply $\frac{1}{5}$ by the area of the circle.]**

Got It?

Have students sketch a diagram of the circle and sector. They should label each known measurement.

ANSWERS

Got It? 2π in.^{2}

Practice

3. 12π in.^{2}

4. 24π in.^{2}

▼ STUDENT PAGE 479

A **sector of a circle** is a region bounded by an arc of the circle and the two radii to the arc's endpoints. You name a sector using one arc endpoint, the center of the circle, and the other arc endpoint.

The area of a sector is a fractional part of the area of a circle. The area of a sector formed by a 60° arc is $\frac{60}{360}$, or $\frac{1}{6}$, of the area of the circle.

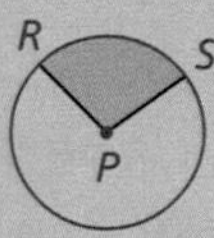

Sector *RPS*

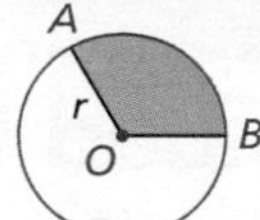

Theorem 75 Area of a Sector of a Circle

The area of a sector of a circle is the product of the ratio $\frac{\text{measure of the arc}}{360}$ and the area of the circle.

Area of sector $AOB = \frac{m\widehat{AB}}{360} \cdot \pi r^2$

▼ DIGITAL

Problem 2 Finding the Area of a Sector of a Circle

What is the area of sector *GPH*? Leave your answer in terms of π.

area of sector $GPH = \frac{m\widehat{GH}}{360} \cdot \pi r^2$

$= \frac{72}{360} \cdot \pi(15)^2$ Substitute 72 for $m\widehat{GH}$ and 15 for r.

$= 45\pi$ Simplify.

The area of sector *GPH* is 45π cm^2.

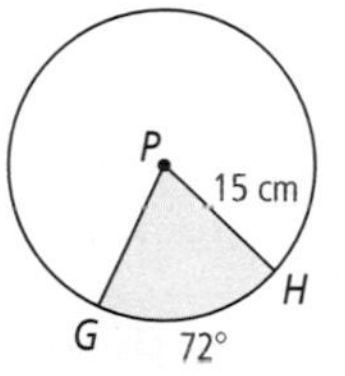

▼ STUDENT PAGE 479

Got It? A circle has a radius of 4 in. What is the area of a sector bounded by a 45° minor arc? Leave your answer in terms of π.

Think
What fraction of a circle's area is the area of a sector formed by a 45° arc?

Practice 3. Find the area of each shaded sector of the circle. Leave your answer in terms of π.

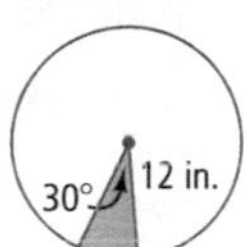

4. Find the area of sector *TOP* in $\odot O$ using the given information. Leave your answer in terms of π.

$d = 16$ in., $m\widehat{PT} = 135$

ANSWER 20-gon: 6.25737…; 3.09016…; 50-gon: 6.27905…; 3.13333…; 100-gon: 6.28215…; 3.13952…; 1000-gon: 6.28317…; 3.14157…

About 6.28, or 2π units; about 3.14, or π units^2; explanations may vary. Sample: As the number of sides of a regular polygon with radius 1 increases, its shape gets closer and closer to the circumscribed circle of radius 1. The table shows that as the perimeter gets closer to 6.28, which $\approx 2\pi$, the area gets closer to 3.14, which $\approx \pi$.

CONNECT THE MATH In the Solve It, students see that the area of a unit circle is π and the circumference is 2π. The lesson presents more instruction about circles, specifically about sectors and segments.

2 Guided Instruction

Problem 1 Finding the Area of a Circle

Take Note

Have students describe what they know about the value of π. Help students locate and use the pi key on their calculators. Discuss as a class the differences in answers when the π key is used on a calculator in place of one of the common estimates, 3.14 or $\frac{22}{7}$.

Problem 1

Q What measurement is given on the wrestling mat? **[the diameter of the wrestling region]**

Got It? ERROR PREVENTION

For part (b), be sure that students verify their answer by substituting the expression for the radius $\frac{1}{2}r$ into the formula for the area of a circle and simplifying. Most students will think the area will be halved instead of quartered.

ANSWERS

Got It? a. about 1385 ft^2 **b.** The area is $\frac{1}{4}$ the original area; explanations may vary. Sample: half the radius is $\frac{r}{2}$. So, if $A = \pi r^2$, then $\pi\left(\frac{r}{2}\right)^2 = \frac{1}{4}\pi r^2 = \frac{1}{4}A$.

Practice

1. $\frac{\pi}{9}$ in.^{2} **2.** about 282,743 ft^2

▼ STUDENT PAGE 477

In the Solve It, you explored the area of a circle.

Essential Understanding You can find the area of a circle when you know its radius. You can use the area of a circle to find the area of part of a circle formed by two radii and the arc the radii form when they intersect with the circle.

take note **Theorem 74 Area of a Circle**

The area of a circle is the product of π and the square of the radius.

$A = \pi r^2$

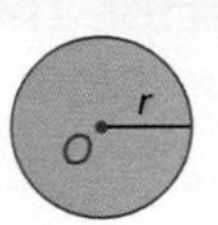

▼ DIGITAL

Problem 1 Finding the Area of a Circle

Sports What is the area of the circular region on the wrestling mat?

Since the diameter of the region is 32 ft, the radius is $\frac{32}{2}$, or 16 ft.

$A = \pi r^2$	Use the area formula.
$= \pi(16)^2$	Substitute 16 for r.
$= 256\pi$	Simplify.
≈ 804.2477193	Use a calculator.

The area of the wrestling region is about 804 ft^2.

▼ STUDENT PAGE 478

Got It? a. What is the area of a circular wrestling region with a 42-ft diameter?

Think What do you need in order to use the area formula?

b. Reasoning If the radius of a circle is halved, how does its area change? Explain.

Practice Find the area of the circle. Leave your answer in terms of π.

1.

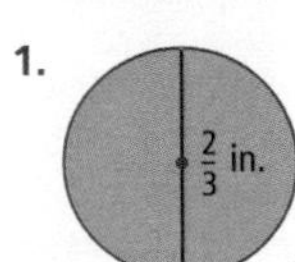

STEM **2. Agriculture** Some farmers use a circular irrigation method. An irrigation arm acts as the radius of an irrigation circle. How much land is covered with an irrigation arm of 300 ft?

Problem 3 Finding the Area of a Segment of a Circle

Take Note

Have students identify the type of triangle in the second diagram. They should recognize the isosceles triangle formed by the radii and the segment of the circle. Remind students of the trigonometry they used to find the length of an apothem in regular polygons. They will be using the same methods to find the height of the triangle in the circle.

Problem 3

Q What two areas must you find to get the area of the shaded segment in the diagram? **[the area of the sector and the area of the isosceles triangle]**

Q What measurement must you find in order to find the area of the triangle? **[the height]**

Q What type of triangle is formed by the altitude of the isosceles triangle? **[30°-60°-90° triangle]**

Q What is the height of the triangle? **[$9\sqrt{3}$]**

Q How can you find the area of the shaded segment? **[Subtract the area of the triangle from the area of the sector.]**

Got It? ERROR PREVENTION

Be sure that students complete each step carefully. Students should model Problem 3 in the book closely.

ANSWERS

Got It? 4.6 m^2

Practice

5. 22.1 cm^2 **6.** 18.3 ft^2

▼ STUDENT PAGE 480

A part of a circle bounded by an arc and the segment joining its endpoints is a **segment of a circle**.

To find the area of a segment for a minor arc, draw radii to form a sector. The area of the segment equals the area of the sector minus the area of the triangle formed.

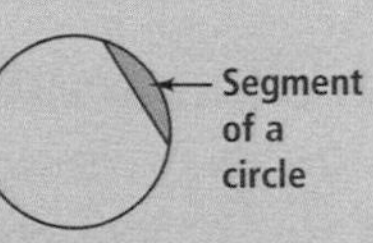

take note **Key Concept** Area of a Segment

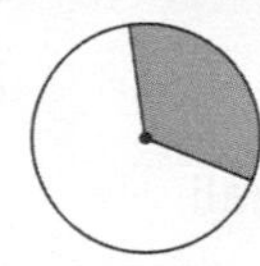 − 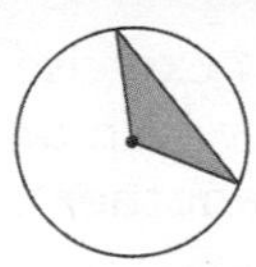 = 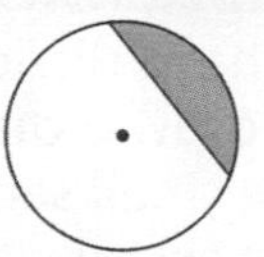

Area of sector − Area of triangle = Area of segment

▼ DIGITAL

Problem 3 Finding the Area of a Segment of a Circle

What is the area of the shaded segment shown at the right? Round your answer to the nearest tenth.

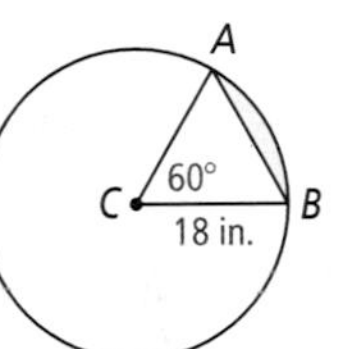

Know	Need	Plan
• The radius and $m\widehat{AB}$ • $\overline{CA} \cong \overline{CB}$ and $m\angle ACB$	The area of sector ACB and the area of $\triangle ACB$	Subtract the area of $\triangle ACB$ from the area of sector ACB.

area of sector $ACB = \frac{m\widehat{AB}}{360} \cdot \pi r^2$ Use the formula for area of a sector.

$= \frac{60}{360} \cdot \pi(18)^2$ Substitute 60 for $m\widehat{AB}$ and 18 for r.

$= 54\pi$ Simplify.

$\triangle ACB$ is equilateral. The altitude forms a 30°-60°-90° triangle.

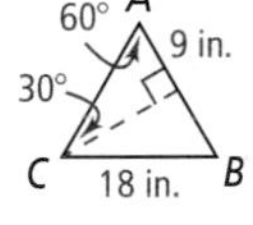

area of $\triangle ACB = \frac{1}{2}bh$ Use the formula for area of a triangle.

$= \frac{1}{2}(18)(9\sqrt{3})$ Substitute 18 for b and $9\sqrt{3}$ for h.

$= 81\sqrt{3}$ Simplify.

area of shaded segment $=$ area of sector ACB $-$ area of $\triangle ACB$

$= 54\pi - 81\sqrt{3}$ Substitute.

≈ 29.34988788 Use a calculator.

The area of the shaded segment is about 29.3 in.^{2}.

▼ STUDENT PAGE 480

Got It? What is the area of the shaded segment shown at the right? Round your answer to the nearest tenth.

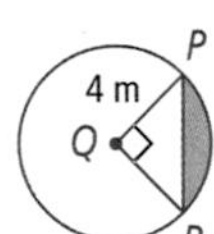

A Practice **Find the area of each shaded segment. Round your answer to the nearest tenth.**

5. 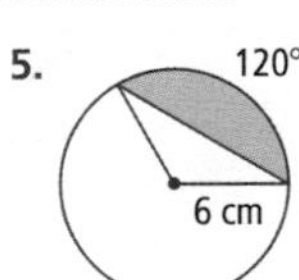

6. 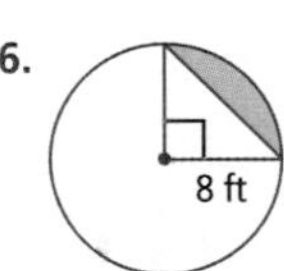

Lesson Check

Do you know HOW?
If students have difficulty with Exercise 7, then have them review Problem 1 to write the formula for area and know how to find the value of r to substitute into the formula.

Do you UNDERSTAND?
If students have difficulty with Exercise 11, then have them draw a diagram in which one circle is large with a small sector and another circle is small with a large sector.

Close

Q How do you find the area of a sector? **[Multiply the ratio of the arc measure and 360° by the area of the circle.]**

Q What is a segment of a circle? **[A segment of a circle is a region bounded by an arc and the line segment joining the endpoints of two radii in a circle.]**

ANSWERS

7. 64π in.^{2}
8. $\frac{135}{8}\pi$ in.^{2}, or 16.875π in.^{2}
9. $\left(\frac{4}{3}\pi - \sqrt{3}\right)$m^2
10. A sector of a circle is a region bounded by an arc and the two radii to the endpoints of the arc. A segment is a part of a circle bounded by an arc and the seg. joining the arc's endpoints.
11. No; the central angles corresponding to the arcs and the radii of the circles may be different. Circles with different radii do not have the same area.
12. 6^2 was incorrectly evaluated as $6 \cdot 2$.

▼ STUDENT PAGES 481–482

Lesson Check

Do you know HOW?

7. What is the area of a circle with diameter 16 in.? Leave your answer in terms of π.

Find the area of the shaded region of the circle. Leave your answer in terms of π.

8.
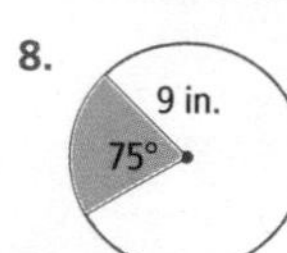

9.
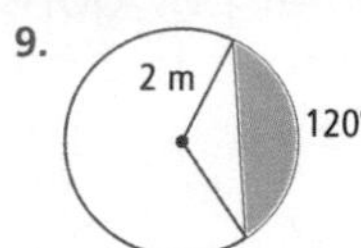

Do you UNDERSTAND?

10. **Vocabulary** What is the difference between a sector of a circle and a segment of a circle?

11. **Reasoning** Suppose a sector of $\odot P$ has the same area as a sector of $\odot O$. Can you conclude that $\odot P$ and $\odot O$ have the same area? Explain.

12. **Error Analysis** Your class must find the area of a sector of a circle determined by a 150° arc. The radius of the circle is 6 cm. What is your classmate's error? Explain.

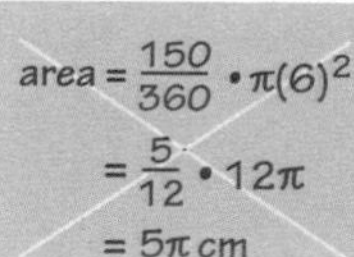

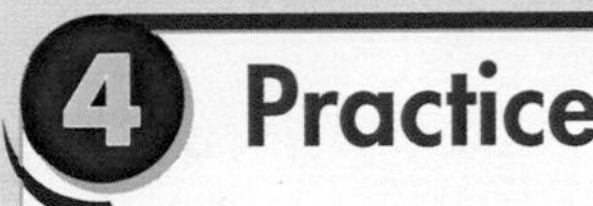

Practice

▼ STUDENT PAGES 482–483

More Practice and Problem-Solving Exercises

ASSIGNMENT GUIDE
The assignments below are for the More Practice and Problem-Solving Exercises. You may also want to assign the A-Level Practice Exercises for homework if these are not used in class.
Average: 13–31
Advanced: 13–37

Mathematical Practices The exercises listed focus on the Standards for Mathematical Practices listed.

EX. 21: Make Sense of Problems (MP 1)
EX. 11, 23: Construct Arguments (MP 3)
EX. 12: Critique the Reasoning of Others (MP 3)
EX. 19, 20, 22, 35: Model (MP 4)
EX. 27: Attend to Precision (MP 6)
EX. 28a: Repeated Reasoning (MP 8)

STEM exercises focus on science or engineering applications.

EXERCISE 22: Use the **Think About a Plan** worksheet in the Online Teacher Resources to further support students' development in becoming independent learners.

HOMEWORK QUICK CHECK
To check students' understanding of key skills and concepts, go over Exercises 19, 20, 22, 23, and 31.

ANSWERS

13. $(243\pi + 162)$ ft^2
14. $(54\pi + 20.25\sqrt{3})$ cm^2
15. $(120\pi + 36\sqrt{3})$ m^2
16. $(4 - \pi)$ ft^2
17. $(64 - 16\pi)$ ft^2
18. $(784 - 196\pi)$ in.^{2}
19. 12.6 mi^2
20. 314 ft^2
21. 112π in.^{2} or about 351.9 in.^{2}
22. 116 mm^2
23. Yes; $\angle AOC \cong \angle BOD$ (Vertical ∠s are ≅.), so the two sectors are ≅ and will have = areas.
24. 22.6 mm^2
25. 169π in.^{2}
26. 12 in.
27. Check students' work.
28. a. Answers may vary. Sample: Subtract the minor arc segment from the area of the circle; or add the areas of the major sector and the triangle that is part of the minor arc sector.
b. $(25\pi - 50)$ units^2; $(75\pi + 50)$ units^2

More Practice and Problem-Solving Exercises

B Apply

Find the area of the shaded region. Leave your answer in terms of π and in simplest radical form.

13. 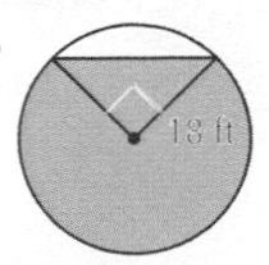

14. 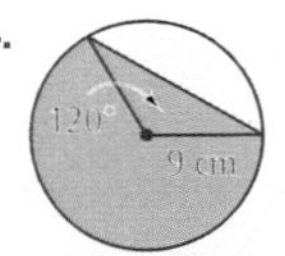

15. 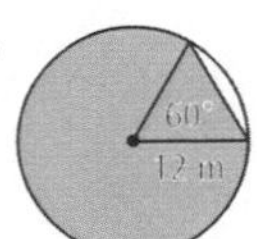

16. 2 ft

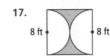

17. 8 ft 8 ft

18. 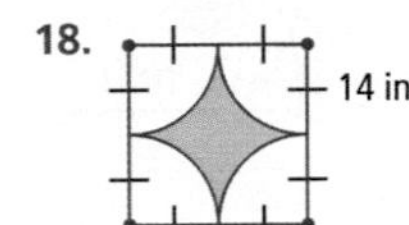

19. **Transportation** A town provides bus transportation to students living beyond 2 mi of the high school. What area of the town does *not* have the bus service? Round to the nearest tenth.

20. **Design** A homeowner wants to build a circular patio. If the diameter of the patio is 20 ft, what is its area to the nearest whole number?

21. **Think About a Plan** A circular mirror is 24 in. wide and has a 4-in. frame around it. What is the area of the frame?
- How can you *draw a diagram* to help solve the problem?
- What part of a circle is the width?
- Is there more than one area to consider?

STEM 22. **Industrial Design** Refer to the diagram of the regular hexagonal nut. What is the area of the hexagonal face to the nearest millimeter?

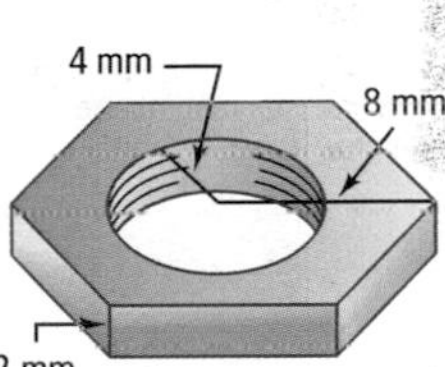

23. **Reasoning** $\overline{AB}$ and $\overline{CD}$ are diameters of ⊙O. Is the area of sector AOC equal to the area of sector BOD? Explain.

24. A circle with radius 12 mm is divided into 20 sectors of equal area. What is the area of one sector to the nearest tenth?

25. The circumference of a circle is 26π in. What is its area? Leave your answer in terms of π.

26. In a circle, a 90° sector has area 36π in.^{2}. What is the radius of the circle?

27. **Open-Ended** Draw a circle and a sector so that the area of the sector is 16π cm^2. Give the radius of the circle and the measure of the sector's arc.

28. A method for finding the area of a segment determined by a minor arc is described in this lesson.
   a. **Writing** Describe two ways to find the area of a segment determined by a major arc.
   b. If $m\widehat{AB} = 90$ in a circle of radius 10 in., find the areas of the two segments determined by $\widehat{AB}$.

More Practice and Problem-Solving Exercises *continued*

29. 23.1 ft^2

30. 4.4 m^2

31. 39.3 $in.^2$

32. $\left[\frac{5\pi}{6} - 4(\sin 37.5°)(\cos 37.5°)\right]$

33. $(49\pi - 73.5\sqrt{3})\ m^2$

34. $(200 - 50\pi)\ m^2$

35. a.

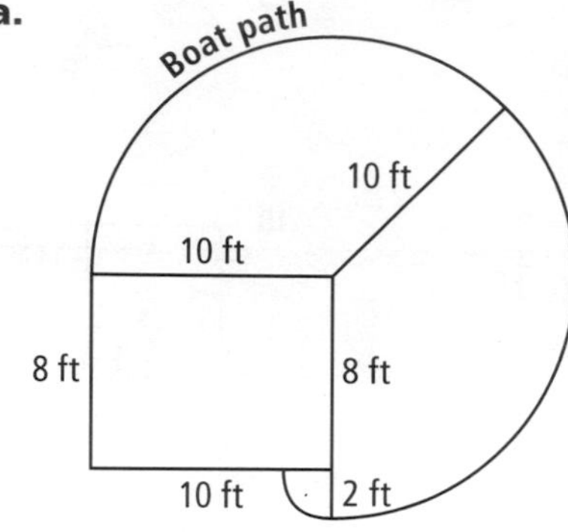

b. 239 ft^2

36. Blue region: Let $AB = 2$. Area of blue $= 4 - \pi$; area of red $= \pi - 2$, and $4 - \pi < \pi - 2$.

37. $\left(\frac{200\pi}{3} - 50\sqrt{3}\right)$ $units^2$

▼ STUDENT PAGES 483–484

Find the area of the shaded segment to the nearest tenth.

29. 9 ft, 45°

30.

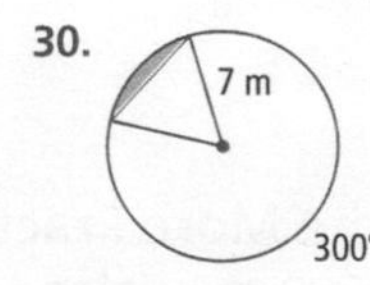

31.

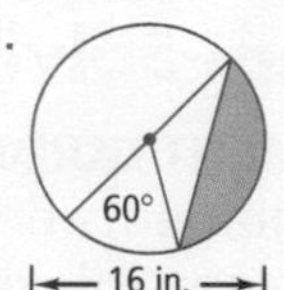

Find the area of the shaded region. Leave your answer in terms of π.

32.

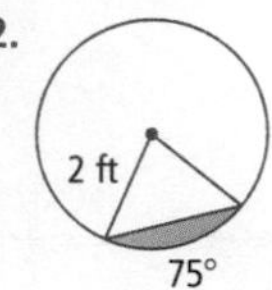

33.

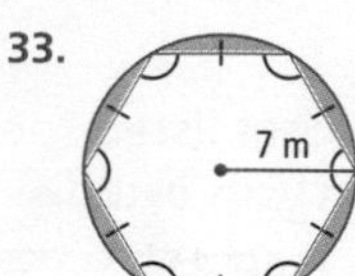

34.

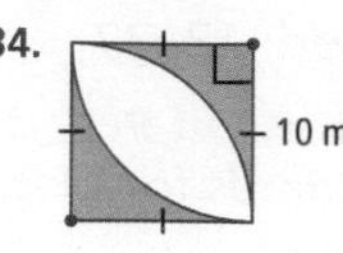

35. Recreation An 8 ft-by-10 ft floating dock is anchored in the middle of a pond. The bow of a canoe is tied to a corner of the dock with a 10-ft rope, as shown in the picture below.

a. Sketch a diagram of the region in which the bow of the canoe can travel.

b. What is the area of that region? Round your answer to the nearest square foot.

36. $\odot O$ at the right is inscribed in square $ABCD$ and circumscribed about square $PQRS$. Which is smaller, the blue region or the red region? Explain.

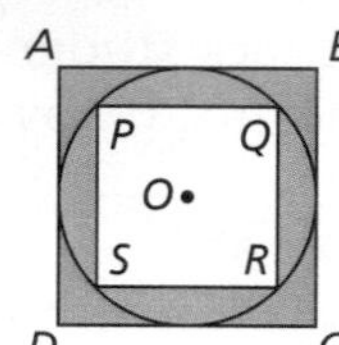

37. Circles T and U each have radius 10, and $TU = 10$. Find the area of the region that is contained inside both circles. (*Hint:* Think about where T and U must lie in a diagram of $\odot T$ and $\odot U$.)

Assess and Remediate

Lesson Quiz

1. **Do you UNDERSTAND?** Suppose the landing pad for a helicopter is shaped like a circle with a 35-ft diameter. What is the area of the landing pad?

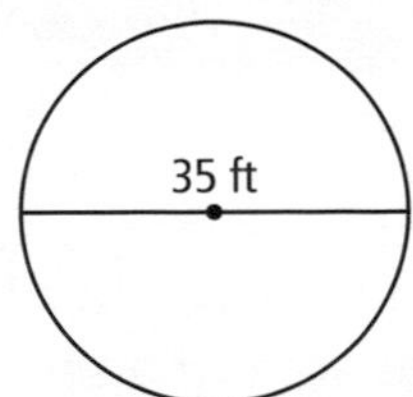

2. What is the area of sector XYZ? Leave your answer in terms of π.

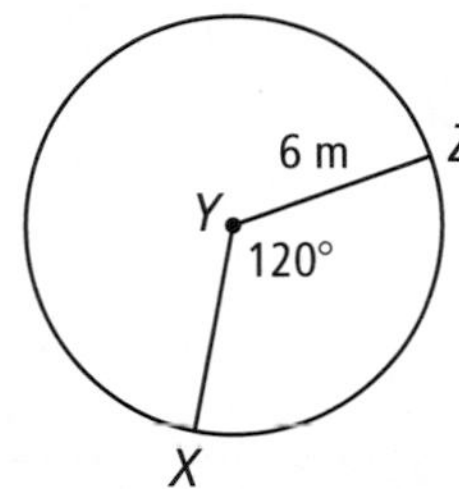

3. Suppose $\overline{XZ}$ is drawn in the circle from Question 2 above. What is the area of the segment between $\overline{XZ}$ and $\overset{\frown}{XZ}$ to the nearest tenth?

ANSWERS TO LESSON QUIZ

1. about 962 ft^2
2. 12π m^2
3. 22.1 m^2

Prescription for Remediation

Use the student work on the Lesson Quiz to prescribe a differentiated assignment.

Points	Differentiated Remediation
0–1	Intervention
2	On-level
3	Extension

Online Assessment

Assign the Lesson Quiz in Success Tracker on **pearsonsuccessnet.com**. Success Tracker will automatically score the quiz and assign appropriate intervention or enrichment to each student based on the results. The compiled data appear in three different reports for instant analysis of whole class and individual student performance.

Differentiated Remediation

Intervention

- **RETEACHING** (2 pages) Provides reteaching and practice exercises for the key lesson concepts. Use with struggling students or absent students.
- **ENGLISH LANGUAGE LEARNER SUPPORT** Helps students develop and reinforce mathematical vocabulary and key concepts.

On-Level

- **PRACTICE** (2 pages) Provides extra practice for each lesson. For simpler practice exercises, use the Form K Practice pages found in the Online Teacher Resources.
- **THINK ABOUT A PLAN** Helps students develop specific problem-solving skills and strategies by providing scaffolded guiding questions.
- **STANDARDIZED TEST PREP** Focuses on all major exercises, all major question types, and helps students prepare for the high-stakes assessments.

Extension

- **ENRICHMENT** Provides students with interesting problems and activities that extend the concepts of the lesson.
- **ACTIVITIES, GAMES, AND PUZZLES** Worksheets that can be used for concept development, enrichment, and for fun!

ACTIVITY LAB

Use With Lesson 8-2

Circles and Radians

Common Core State Standard

G.C.5 Derive using similarity the fact that the length of the arc intercepted by an angle is proportional to the radius . . . derive the formula for the area of a sector.

Mathematical Practices

This Activity Lab supports students in becoming proficient in reasoning abstractly and quantitatively, Mathematical Practice 2.

Guided Instruction

PURPOSE To explore radian measure and find the areas of sectors.

PROCESS Students will

- find the radian measure of an angle as the ratio of the intercepted arc length to the radius of the circle.
- derive a formula for the area of a sector when a central angle is given in radians.

DISCUSS Talk to students about how degree measure is essentially an arbitrary scale. There are 360 degrees in a full circle, but you could just as easily use a division into 100 units, or 10, or any other convenient number. But there is a unit of angle measure that arises naturally from the properties of a circle, namely, radian measure.

Activity 1

In this Activity, students learn that the radian measure of a central angle is the ratio of the arc length to the radius of the circle.

Q What is the relationship between the length of an intercepted arc and the circumference of the circle? **[The ratio of the arc length to the circumference is equal to the ratio of the measure of the central angle (in degrees) to 360°.]**

Q Will the radian measure of the 90° angle change if the radius is increased or decreased? Explain. **[Sample answer: No, the radian measure will remain the same. The radius cancels out in the ratio of arc length to radius.]**

Q What would the radian measure be for a central angle of 180°? What would the radian measure be for a central angle of 270°? **[π radians; $\frac{3\pi}{2}$ radians]**

EXTENSION

Have students draw a circle and mark the degree measures at 30°, 45°, 60°, 90°, 120°, 135°, 150°, 180°, 210°, 225°, 240°, 270°, 300°, 315°, 330°, and 360°. Then mark the same angles using radians. They can use the radian measures below to help them.

$30^\circ = \frac{\pi}{6}$, $45^\circ = \frac{\pi}{4}$, $60^\circ = \frac{\pi}{3}$, $90^\circ = \frac{\pi}{2}$

ANSWERS

1. 6π cm
2. $\frac{\pi}{2}$ radians

▼ STUDENT PAGE 485

Angles can be measured in degrees or *radians*. Radians are measures based on arc length.

Activity 1

Circle O has a radius of 12 cm and $m\angle POQ = 90$.

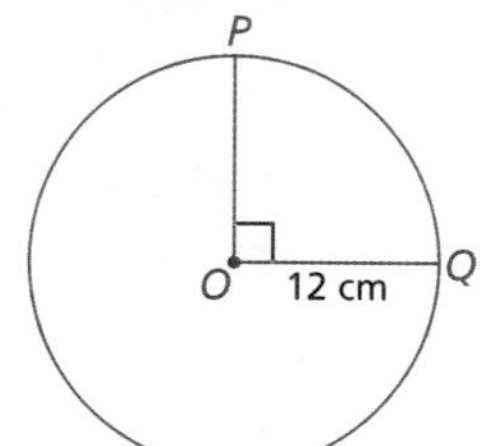

1. Find the length of $\widehat{PQ}$. Write your answer in terms of π.

2. Find the ratio of the arc length to the radius of circle P. This is the radian measure of $\angle POQ$.

The **radian measure** of a central angle of a circle is the ratio of the arc length of the intercepted arc to the radius of the circle.

$$\text{radian measure} = \frac{\text{arc length}}{\text{radius}}$$

One radian is equal to the measure of the central angle whose intercepted arc has a length equal to the radius of the circle.

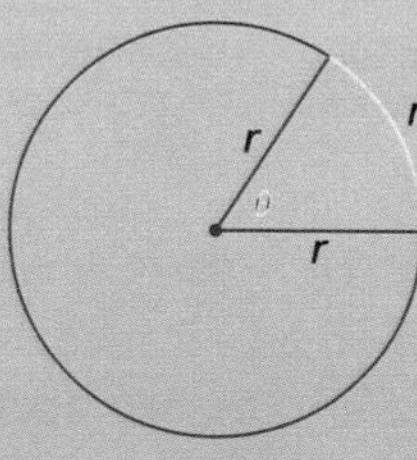

$\theta = 1$ radian

Activity 2

In this Activity, students derive the formula for the area of a sector when the central angle of the sector is given in radians.

Q What is the relationship between the area of a sector and the area of the circle? **[The ratio of the area of the sector to the area of the circle is equal to the ratio of the measure of the central angle (in degrees) to 360°.]**

Q What is an advantage of working with central angles measured in radians as opposed to degrees when finding the areas of sectors? **[Sample answer: The computations for finding the areas of sectors do not involve π, so they may be more straightforward and rounding may not be necessary.]**

ANSWERS

3. πr^2
4. 2π radians
5. $\frac{\theta}{2\pi}$
6. $\frac{\theta}{2\pi} = \frac{x}{\pi r^2}$; $x = \frac{\theta}{2}r^2$

Exercises

ANSWERS

7. 36.5 in.^2
8. 16.2 ft^2
9. 225 mm^2
10. **a.** 360°
    b. π radians
    c. To convert from degrees to radians, multiply the number of degrees by $\frac{\pi}{180}$. To convert from radians to degrees, multiply the number of radians by $\frac{180}{\pi}$.

In Lesson 8-2, you learned how to find the area of the sector of a circle using proportions and the area of the circle. In Activity 2, you will derive a formula for the area of a sector when the central angle is given in radians.

Activity 2

Consider the circle below with a central angle of θ radians and radius r.

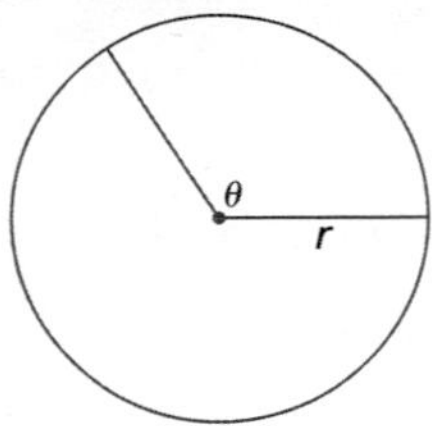

3. Write an expression for the area of the circle.

4. What is the angle measure, in radians, of a 360° central angle of the circle?

5. Write an expression for the ratio of θ to the radian measure of a 360° central angle.

6. The ratio of the area of the sector, x, to the area of the circle is equal to the ratio of the measure of the central angle θ to 2π radians. Write an equation that shows this proportional relationship. Then solve for x, the area of the sector.

Exercises

In Exercises 7–9, find the area of each sector with given radius and central angle. Round to the nearest tenth.

7. $r = 9$ in., $m\angle\theta = 0.9$ radian

8. $r = 4.5$ ft, $m\angle\theta = 1.6$ radians

9. $r = 15$ mm, $m\angle\theta = 2$ radians

10. a. How many degrees are in 2π radians?

b. How many radians are in 180 degrees?

c. Reasoning How can you convert angle measures from degrees to radians? How can you convert angle measures from radians to degrees?

8-3 Tangent Lines

Common Core State Standards
G.C.2 Identify and describe relationships among inscribed angles, radii, and chords . . . the radius of a circle is perpendicular to the tangent where the radius intersects the circle. **Also G.C.4**

Preparing to Teach

BIG ideas Reasoning and Proof
Measurement

ESSENTIAL UNDERSTANDING

A radius of a circle and the tangent that intersects the endpoint of the radius on the circle have a special relationship. A circle has a special relationship to a triangle whose sides are tangent to the circle.

Math Background

Students will use their understanding of congruent triangles to prove statements about tangent lines. Tangent lines have two important characteristics: they only touch the circle at one point, and they are perpendicular to the radius at the point of tangency. These characteristics are illustrated by real-world relationships between the Earth and lines of sight. Students can determine characteristics of circumscribed figures using characteristics of tangent lines.

Have students imagine and describe twirling and then releasing a ball attached to a string. The released ball will follow a path (easy to see because of the string) influenced by gravity, but its direction at the point of release is along the line tangent to its original orbit at the point of release. Point out that the law of physics that the ball obeys is related to the geometry theorems in this lesson.

In future lessons, students will learn about other special segments in circles. Tangent lines will be used again in the study of the slope of a nonlinear function.

ELL Support

FOCUS ON LANGUAGE Project the lesson on the board and read Theorem 76 as you point to each word. Invite students to define key words such as *tangent* and *perpendicular*. Model an example of a line that is tangent to a circle. Trace the tangent line, the point of tangency, and the angles formed by the perpendicular lines as you restate the theorem and identify each part. Now have students rewrite the theorem in their own words and draw their own examples. Invite students to share their work. Repeat with Theorem 77.

Lesson Vocabulary

- tangent to a circle
- point of tangency

Mathematical Practices

MAKE SENSE OF PROBLEMS AND PERSEVERE IN SOLVING THEM. Students will draw diagrams of circles and tangent lines and identify important relationships, such as segment lengths and angle measurements.

1 Interactive Learning

Solve It!

PURPOSE To discover characteristics of tangent segments

PROCESS Students measure the lengths of tangent segments with a common endpoint and use inductive reasoning to make a conjecture.

FACILITATE

As students draw circles with different tangent segments, be sure that they are drawing them correctly. Model the process on the board. They should align a straight edge so that it touches the circle in only one point.

Q Label the points of intersection of the lines with the circle *B* and *C*. What triangles could be formed? **[$\triangle ABO$, $\triangle ACO$, $\triangle ABC$, and $\triangle BCO$]**

Q How can you classify the segments $\overline{BO}$ and $\overline{CO}$? **[They are radii of the circle.]**

Q What is the relationship between $\triangle ABO$ and $\triangle ACO$? Justify your answer. **[They are congruent by SSS.]**

ANSWER The two segments have the same length.

▼ DIGITAL (STUDENT WORK SPACE PAGE 488)

Getting Ready!

Draw a diagram like the one at the right. Each ray from Point *A* touches the circle in only one place no matter how far it extends. Measure $\overline{AB}$ and $\overline{AC}$. Repeat the procedure with a point farther away from the circle. Consider any two rays with a common endpoint outside the circle. Make a conjecture about the lengths of the two segments formed when the rays touch the circle.

CONNECT THE MATH Students should see that two tangent segments drawn from the same point to a circle are congruent. In the lesson, students will examine this relationship and others regarding tangent lines and circles.

2 Guided Instruction

Problem 1 Finding Angle Measures

Take Note
Have students identify the hypothesis and conclusion of Theorem 76. Ask them to name the right angles in the diagram.

Proof
Students may need to review the definition of circles to understand how Theorem 76 proves that K and P must both be on the circle. Because $\overline{OK} \cong \overline{OP}$, K and P are equidistant from O. Students may benefit from working backwards to prove the theorem. Ask them to identify the statement that contradicts the given information. They must use the definition of a tangent.

Problem 1

Q How can you classify $\overline{LO}$ and $\overline{NO}$? **[They are radii of the circle.]**

Q What is $m\angle L$ and $m\angle N$? **[90]**

Q What type of geometric figure do the tangents and radii form? **[a quadrilateral]**

Q How can you find the missing angle measure in the quadrilateral? **[Subtract the known angle measures from 360.]**

▼ STUDENT PAGES 488–489

In the Solve It, you drew lines that touch a circle at only one point. These lines are called tangents. This use of the word *tangent* is related to, but different from, the tangent ratio in right triangles that you studied in Chapter 7.

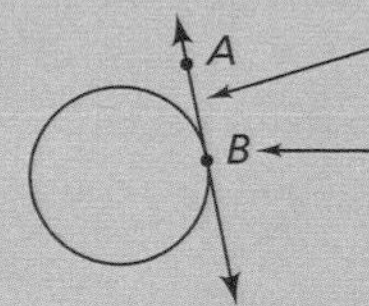

A **tangent to a circle** is a line in the plane of the circle that intersects the circle in exactly one point.

The point where a circle and a tangent intersect is the **point of tangency.**

$\overrightarrow{BA}$ is a tangent ray and $\overline{BA}$ is a tangent segment.

Essential Understanding A radius of a circle and the tangent that intersects the endpoint of the radius on the circle have a special relationship.

take note **Theorem 76**

Theorem	If . . .	Then . . .
If a line is tangent to a circle, then the line is perpendicular to the radius at the point of tangency.	$\overleftrightarrow{AB}$ is tangent to $\odot O$ at P 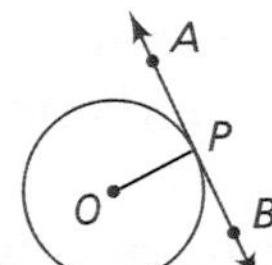	$\overleftrightarrow{AB} \perp \overline{OP}$ 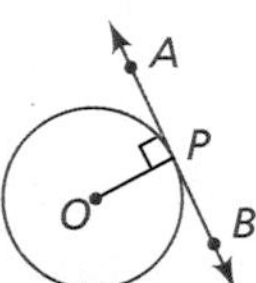

Proof Indirect Proof of Theorem 76

Given: n is tangent to $\odot O$ at P.
Prove: $n \perp \overline{OP}$

Step 1 Assume that n is not perpendicular to $\overline{OP}$.

Step 2 If line n is not perpendicular to $\overline{OP}$, then, for some other point L on n, $\overline{OL}$ must be perpendicular to n. Also there is a point K on n such that $\overline{LK} \cong \overline{LP}$ because perpendicular lines form congruent adjacent angles. $\overline{OL} = \overline{OL}$. So, $\triangle OLK \cong \triangle OLP$ by SAS.

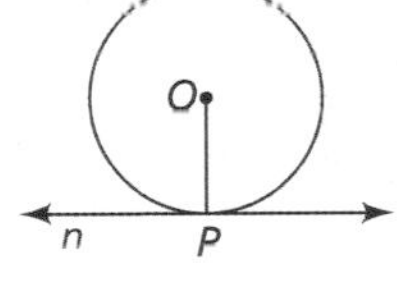

Since corresponding parts of congruent triangles are congruent, $\overline{OK} \cong \overline{OP}$. So K and P are both on $\odot O$ by the definition of a circle. For two points on n to also be on $\odot O$ contradicts the given fact that n is tangent to $\odot O$ at P. So the assumption that n is not perpendicular to $\overline{OP}$ must be false.

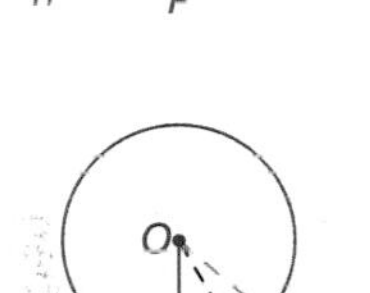

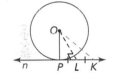

Step 3 Therefore, $n \perp \overline{OP}$ must be true.

▼ DIGITAL

Problem 1 Finding Angle Measures

Multiple Choice $\overline{ML}$ **and** $\overline{MN}$ **are tangent to** $\odot O$**. What is the value of** x**?**

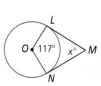

Ⓐ 58 Ⓒ 90
Ⓑ 63 Ⓓ 117

L, O, 117°, x°, M, N

Since $\overline{ML}$ and $\overline{MN}$ are tangent to $\odot O$, $\angle L$ and $\angle N$ are right angles. $LMNO$ is a quadrilateral. So the sum of the angle measures is 360.

$$m\angle L + m\angle M + m\angle N + m\angle O = 360$$
$$90 + m\angle M + 90 + 117 = 360 \quad \text{Substitute.}$$
$$297 + m\angle M = 360 \quad \text{Simplify.}$$
$$m\angle M = 63 \quad \text{Solve.}$$

The correct answer is B.

Problem 1 *continued*

Got It? **ERROR PREVENTION**

Have students label the known angle measures in the diagram. Emphasize that the third angle, call it $\angle F$, is not 90 because $\overline{EF}$ is not tangent to the circle. Ask them to write an equation using the angle measures.

Students may need to be reminded that the angles of a triangle have a sum of 180.

ANSWERS

Got It? a. 52 **b.** $x = 180 - c$

Practice

1. 120 **2.** 30

▼ STUDENT PAGES 489–490

Got It? a. $\overline{ED}$ is tangent to $\odot O$. What is the value of x?

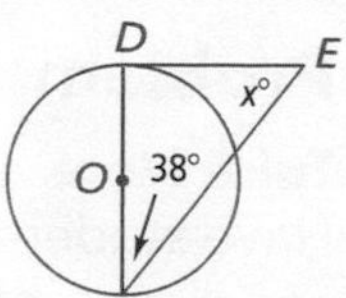

b. Reasoning Consider a quadrilateral like the one in Problem 1. Write a formula you could use to find the measure of any angle x formed by two tangents when you know the measure of the central angle c whose radii intersect the tangents.

Practice **Algebra** **Lines that appear to be tangent are tangent. *O* is the center of each circle. What is the value of *x*?**

1.

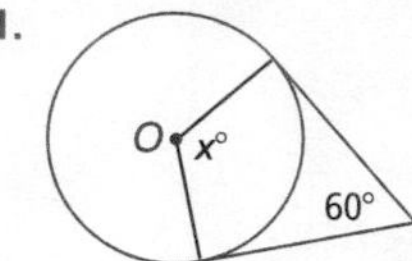

2.

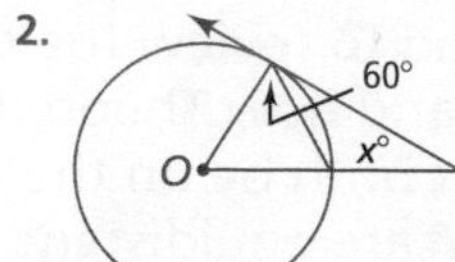

Problem 2 Finding Distance

Encourage students to draw a diagram of the situation. Discuss which segments and angles can be labeled with their measurements.

Q How can you classify the line that represents the line of sight from the top of the tower? **[The line of sight is tangent to the Earth.]**

Q What does the horizon represent in relation to the circle that is Earth? **[The horizon is the point of tangency of the line of sight.]**

Q What type of angle do the line of sight and the radius of the Earth form? **[a right angle]**

Q How can you find the distance between the top of the tower and the center of the Earth? **[Add the height of the tower and the radius of the Earth.]**

Got It? **VISUAL LEARNERS**

Have students draw a diagram of the situation. Ask them to identify the tangent line and point of tangency. Have them label the known lengths.

ANSWERS

Got It? about 127 mi

Practice

3. 113.1 km **4.** 178.9 km

▼ DIGITAL

Problem 2 **Finding Distance** STEM

Earth Science **The CN Tower in Toronto, Canada, has an observation deck 447 m above ground level. About how far is it from the observation deck to the horizon? Earth's radius is about 6400 km.**

447 m

Step 1 Make a sketch. The length 447 m is about 0.45 km.

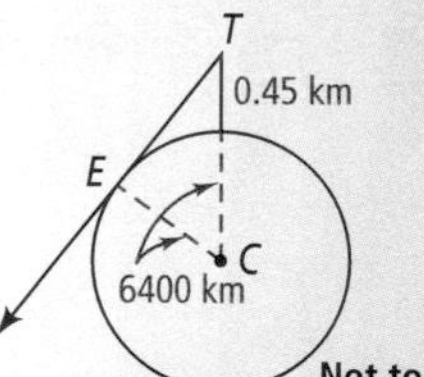

Step 2 Use the Pythagorean Theorem.

$CT^2 = TE^2 + CE^2$	
$(6400 + 0.45)^2 = TE^2 + 6400^2$	Substitute.
$(6400.45)^2 = TE^2 + 6400^2$	Simplify.
$40{,}965{,}760.2025 = TE^2 + 40{,}960{,}000$	Use a calculator.
$5760.2025 = TE^2$	Subtract 40,960,000 from each side.
$76 \approx TE$	Take the positive square root of each side.

The distance from the CN Tower to the horizon is about 76 km.

▼ STUDENT PAGES 490–491

Got It? What is the distance to the horizon that a person can see on a clear day from an airplane 2 mi above Earth? Earth's radius is about 4000 mi.

Practice STEM **Earth Science** **The circle at the right represents Earth. The radius of Earth is about 6400 km. Find the distance *d* to the horizon that a person can see on a clear day from each of the following heights *h* above Earth. Round your answer to the nearest tenth of a kilometer.**

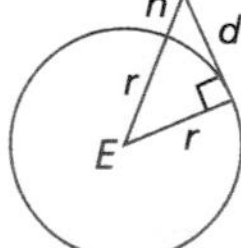

3. 1 km

4. 2500 m

Problem 3 Finding a Radius

Take Note

Be sure that students can identify Theorems 76 and 77 as converses. Have them identify the hypothesis and conclusion of each theorem. Then ask students to combine the two theorems to form a biconditional statement.

Problem 3

Q Which segment is tangent to the circle? **[$\overline{AB}$]**

Q What is the length of the hypotenuse in the right triangle? **[$x + 8$]**

Q How can you check your answer? **[Verify that the side lengths satisfy the Pythagorean Theorem.]**

Got It? VISUAL LEARNERS

Have students label each side of the right triangle *a*, *b*, or *c*, making sure that *c* is the hypotenuse. Have them write out the Pythagorean Theorem and substitute the values given for *a*, *b*, and *c*.

ANSWERS

Got It? 6.6

Practice

5. 4.8 **6.** 8 in.

▼ STUDENT PAGE 491

Theorem 77 is the converse of Theorem 76. You can use it to prove that a line or segment is tangent to a circle. You can also use it to construct a tangent to a circle.

take note **Theorem 77**

Theorem	If . . .	Then . . .
If a line in the plane of a circle is perpendicular to a radius at its endpoint on the circle, then the line is tangent to the circle.	$\overleftrightarrow{AB} \perp \overline{OP}$ at P	$\overleftrightarrow{AB}$ is tangent to $\odot O$

You will prove Theorem 77 in Exercise 26.

▼ DIGITAL

Problem 3 Finding a Radius

What is the radius of $\odot C$?

$AC^2 = AB^2 + BC^2$	Pythagorean Theorem
$(x + 8)^2 = 12^2 + x^2$	Substitute.
$x^2 + 16x + 64 = 144 + x^2$	Simplify.
$16x = 80$	Subtract x^2 and 64 from each side.
$x = 5$	Divide each side by 16.

The radius is 5.

▼ STUDENT PAGE 492

Got It? What is the radius of $\odot O$?

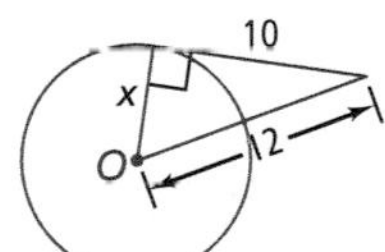

Think: Why does the value *x* appear on each side of the equation?

A Practice **Algebra** In each circle, what is the value of *x*, to the nearest tenth?

5.

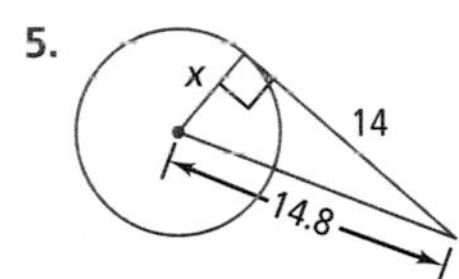

6. P 15 in. Q x O 17

Problem 4 Identifying a Tangent

Q If $\overline{ML}$ is tangent to the circle, then what type of triangle is $\triangle LMN$? **[a right triangle]**

Q Which segment is the hypotenuse of $\triangle LMN$? **[$\overline{MN}$]**

Q How can you verify that $\triangle LMN$ is a right triangle? **[Verify that the side lengths satisfy the Pythagorean Theorem.]**

Got It? ERROR PREVENTION

Ask students to write an equation to relate the lengths of the segments using the Pythagorean Theorem. Once they have come to a conclusion about $\overline{ML}$, have them write an indirect proof to justify their answer.

ANSWERS

Got It? no; $4^2 + 7^2 = 65 \neq 8^2$

Practice

7. no; $5^2 + 15^2 \neq 16^2$ **8.** yes; $2.5^2 + 6^2 = 6.5^2$

▼ DIGITAL

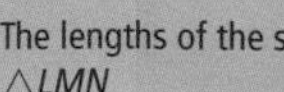

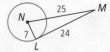

Problem 4 Identifying a Tangent

Is $\overline{ML}$ tangent to $\odot N$ at L? Explain.

Know

The lengths of the sides of $\triangle LMN$

Need

To determine whether $\overline{ML}$ is tangent to $\odot O$

Plan

$\overline{ML}$ is a tangent if $\overline{ML} \perp \overline{NL}$. Use the Converse of the Pythagorean Theorem to determine whether $\triangle LMN$ is a right triangle.

$NL^2 + ML^2 \stackrel{?}{=} NM^2$

$7^2 + 24^2 \stackrel{?}{=} 25^2$ Substitute.

$625 = 625$ Simplify.

By the Converse of the Pythagorean Theorem, $\triangle LMN$ is a right triangle with $\overline{ML} \perp \overline{NL}$. So $\overline{ML}$ is tangent to $\odot N$ at L because it is perpendicular to the radius at the point of tangency (Theorem 77).

▼ STUDENT PAGE 493

Got It? Is $\overline{ML}$ tangent to $\odot N$ at L? Explain.

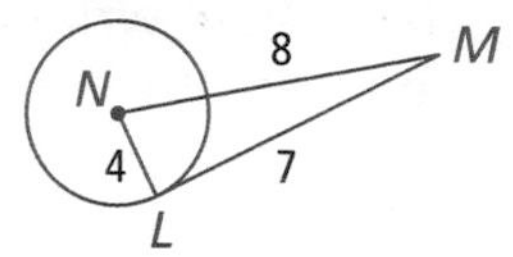

Practice Determine whether a tangent is shown in each diagram. Explain.

7.

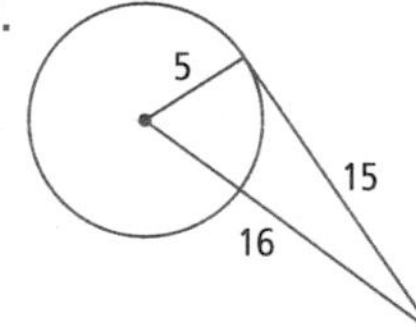

8.

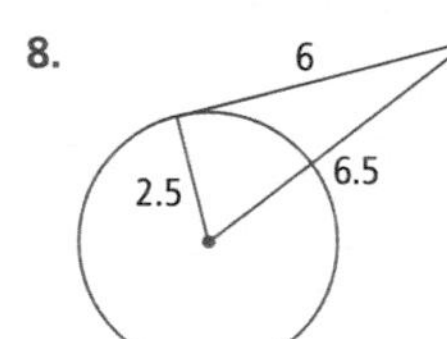

Problem 5 Circles Inscribed in Polygons

Q How can you classify the sides of the triangle? Justify your answer. **[Because the circle is inscribed in the triangle, the sides are tangent to the circle.]**

Q Which pairs of segments are congruent in $\triangle ABC$? **[$\overline{AD} \cong \overline{AF}$, $\overline{BD} \cong \overline{BE}$, and $\overline{CE} \cong \overline{CF}$]**

▼ STUDENT PAGES 493–494

In the Solve It, you made a conjecture about the lengths of two tangents from a common endpoint outside a circle. Your conjecture may be confirmed by the following theorem.

take note **Theorem 78**

Theorem	If . . .	Then . . .
If two tangent segments to a circle share a common endpoint outside the circle, then the two segments are congruent.	$\overline{BA}$ and $\overline{BC}$ are tangent to $\odot O$ 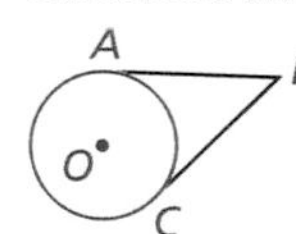	$\overline{BA} \cong \overline{BC}$

You will prove Theorem 78 in Exercise 19.

In the figure at the right, the sides of the triangle are tangent to the circle. The circle is *inscribed* in the triangle. The triangle is *circumscribed about* the circle.

▼ DIGITAL

Problem 5 Circles Inscribed in Polygons

$\odot O$ is inscribed in $\triangle ABC$. What is the perimeter of $\triangle ABC$?

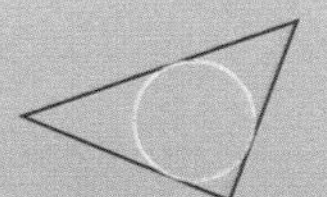

$AD = AF = 10$ cm
$BD = BE = 15$ cm
$CF = CE = 8$ cm

Two segments tangent to a circle from a point outside the circle are congruent, so they have the same length.

$p = AB + BC + CA$ Definition of perimeter p

$= AD + DB + BE + EC + CF + FA$ Segment Addition Postulate

$= 10 + 15 + 15 + 8 + 8 + 10$ Substitute.

$= 66$

The perimeter is 66 cm.

Got It?
Have students write an equation relating the segment lengths to the perimeter of the triangle.

ANSWERS

Got It? 12 cm

Practice

9. 78 cm **10.** 14.2 in.

▼ STUDENT PAGE 494

Plan

How does knowing the pairs of congruent segments help?

Got It? $\odot O$ is inscribed in $\triangle PQR$, which has a perimeter of 88 cm. What is the length of $\overline{QY}$?

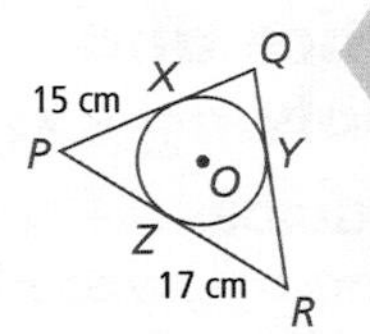

A Practice **Each polygon circumscribes a circle. What is the perimeter of each polygon?**

9.

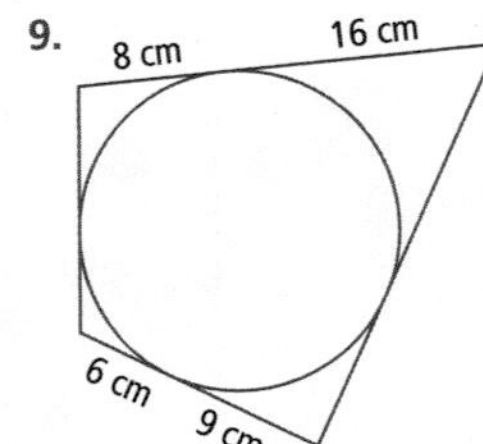

10.

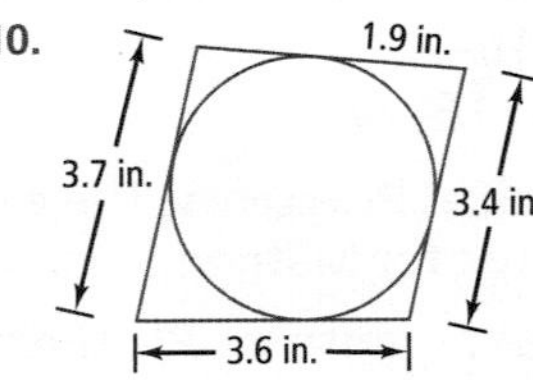

3 Lesson Check

Do you know HOW?
If students have difficulty with Exercise 11, then remind them that the measures of the angles of a triangle have a sum of 180°.

If students have difficulty with Exercise 12, then point out that there are two radius lengths in the diagram.

Do you UNDERSTAND?
If students have difficulty with Exercise 15, then ask them if a triangle can have more than one right angle. Then review Theorem 76.

Close

Q What type of angle is formed at the intersection of a tangent and the radius of a circle? **[a right angle]**

Q What is the relationship between two segments drawn from the same point, tangent to a circle? **[The segments are congruent.]**

ANSWERS

11. 32 **12.** 6 units

13. $\sqrt{63} \approx 7.94$ units

14. Answers may vary. Sample: *Tangent ratio* refers to a ratio of the lengths of two sides of a rt. triangle, while *tangent to a circle* refers to a line or a part of a line that is in the plane of a circle and touches the circle in exactly one point.

15. If $\overline{DF}$ is tangent to $\odot E$, then $\overline{DF} \perp \overline{EF}$. That would mean that $\triangle DEF$ contains two rt. $\triangle$s, which is impossible. So $\overline{DF}$ is not a tangent to $\odot E$.

▼ STUDENT PAGES 495–496

Lesson Check

Do you know HOW?

Use the figure at the right for Exercises 11–13.

11. If $m\angle A = 58$, what is $m\angle ACB$?

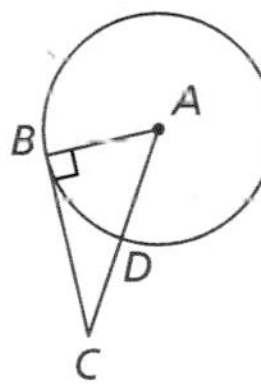

12. If $AC = 10$ and $BC = 8$, what is the radius?

13. If $AC = 12$ and $BC = 9$, what is the radius?

Do you UNDERSTAND?

14. Vocabulary How are the phrases *tangent ratio* and *tangent of a circle* used differently?

15. Error Analysis A classmate insists that $\overline{DF}$ is a tangent to $\odot E$. Explain how to show that your classmate is wrong.

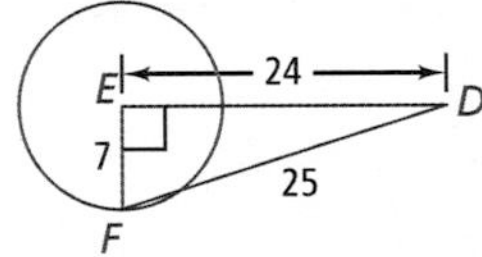

Practice

More Practice and Problem-Solving Exercises

ASSIGNMENT GUIDE
The assignments below are for the More Practice and Problem-Solving Exercises. You may also want to assign the A-Level Practice Exercises for homework if these are not used in class.
Average: 16–25
Advanced: 16–27

Mathematical Practices The exercises listed focus on the Standards for Mathematical Practices listed.

EX. 18: Make Sense of Problems (MP 1)
EX. 17: Construct Arguments (MP 3)
EX. 15: Critique the Reasoning of Others (MP 3)
EX. 16: Model (MP 4)

STEM exercises focus on science or engineering applications.

EXERCISE 22: Use the **Think About a Plan** worksheet in the Online Teacher Resources to further support students' development in becoming independent learners.

HOMEWORK QUICK CHECK
To check students' understanding of key skills and concepts, go over Exercises 16, 17, 18, 22, and 25.

ANSWERS

16. **a.** external
b. external
c. internal
d. blue segments; orange segments

17. All 4 are ≅; the two tangents to each coin from A are ≅, so by the Transitive Prop. of ≅, all the tangents are ≅.

18. Answers may vary. Sample: One square is inscribed in the circle and the other square circumscribes the circle. If the circle has radius a, each side of the smaller square has length $a\sqrt{2}$ and the area of the square is $2a^2$. Each side of the larger square has length $2a$ and the area of the square is $4a^2$. So the larger square has double the area of the smaller square.

19. 1. $\overline{BA}$ and $\overline{BC}$ are tangent to $\odot O$ at A and C. (Given) 2. $\overline{AB} \perp \overline{OA}$ and $\overline{BC} \perp \overline{OC}$ (If a line is tan. to a ⊙, it is ⊥ to the radius at the point of tangency.) 3. $\triangle BAO$ and $\triangle BCO$ are rt. ⊿s. (Def. of rt. △) 4. $\overline{AO} \cong \overline{OC}$ (Radii of a circle are ≅.) 5. $\overline{BO} \cong \overline{BO}$ (Refl. Prop. of ≅) 6. $\triangle BAO \cong \triangle BCO$ (HL) 7. $\overline{BA} \cong \overline{BC}$ (Corresp. parts of ≅ ⊿s are ≅.)

▼ STUDENT PAGES 496–497

More Practice and Problem-Solving Exercises

B Apply

STEM **16. Solar Eclipse** Common tangents to two circles may be *internal* or *external*. If you draw a segment joining the centers of the circles, a common internal tangent will intersect the segment. A common external tangent will not. For this cross-sectional diagram of the sun, moon, and Earth during a solar eclipse, use the terms above to describe the types of tangents of each color.

a. red **b.** blue **c.** orange
d. Which tangents show the extent on Earth's surface of total eclipse? Of partial eclipse?

17. Reasoning A nickel, a dime, and a quarter are touching as shown. Tangents are drawn from point A to both sides of each coin. What can you conclude about the four tangent segments? Explain.

18. Think About a Plan Leonardo da Vinci wrote, "When each of two squares touch the same circle at four points, one is double the other." Explain why the statement is true.
- How will drawing a sketch help?
- Are both squares inside the circle?

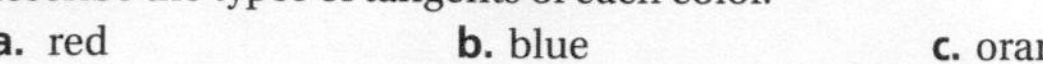

Proof **19.** Prove Theorem 78.
Given: $\overline{BA}$ and $\overline{BC}$ are tangent to $\odot O$ at A and C, respectively.
Prove: $\overline{BA} \cong \overline{BC}$

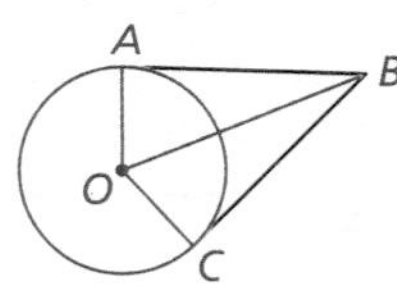

20. 1. $\overline{BC}$ is tangent to $\odot A$ at D. (Given) 2. $\overline{DB} \cong \overline{DC}$ (Given) 3. $\overline{AD} \perp \overline{BC}$ (If a line is tan. to a $\odot$, it is $\perp$ to the radius at the point of tangency.) 4. $\angle ADB$ and $\angle ADC$ are rt. $\angle$s (Def. of $\perp$) 5. $\angle ADB \cong \angle ADC$ (Rt. $\angle$s are $\cong$.) 6. $\overline{AD} \cong \overline{AD}$ (Refl. Prop. of $\cong$) 7. $\triangle ADB \cong \triangle ADC$ (SAS) 8. $\overline{AB} \cong \overline{AC}$ (Corresp. parts of $\cong$ $\triangle$s are $\cong$.)

21. 1. $\odot A$ and $\odot B$ with common tangents $\overline{DF}$ and $\overline{CE}$ (Given) 2. $GD \cong GC$ and $GE \cong GF$ (Two tan. segments from a pt. to a $\odot$ are $\cong$.) 3. $\frac{GD}{GC} = 1$, $\frac{GF}{GE} = 1$ (Div. Prop. of =) 4. $\frac{GD}{GC} = \frac{GF}{GE}$ (Trans. Prop. of =) 5. $\angle DGC \cong \angle EGF$ (Vert. $\angle$s are $\cong$.) 6. $\triangle GDC \sim \triangle GFE$ (SAS $\sim$ Thm.)

22. **a.** Rectangle; $\overline{AB}$ is tangent to $\odot D$ and $\odot E$; $\overline{DB} \perp \overline{AB}$ and $\overline{AE} \perp \overline{AB}$ (A line tangent to a $\odot$ is $\perp$ to the radius.); $\overline{BC} \parallel \overline{AE}$ (Two coplanar lines $\perp$ to the same line are $\parallel$.) So, $ABCE$ is a $\square$ with two rt. $\angle$s. Therefore, $ABCE$ is a rectangle.

b. 35 in.

c. 35.5 in.

23. 57.5

24.

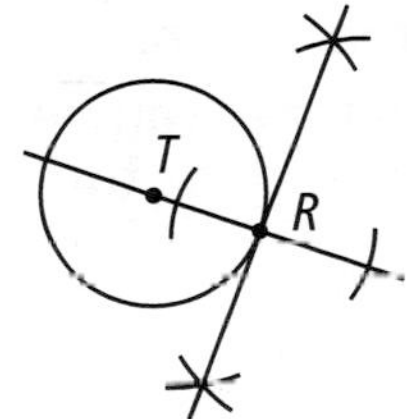

25.

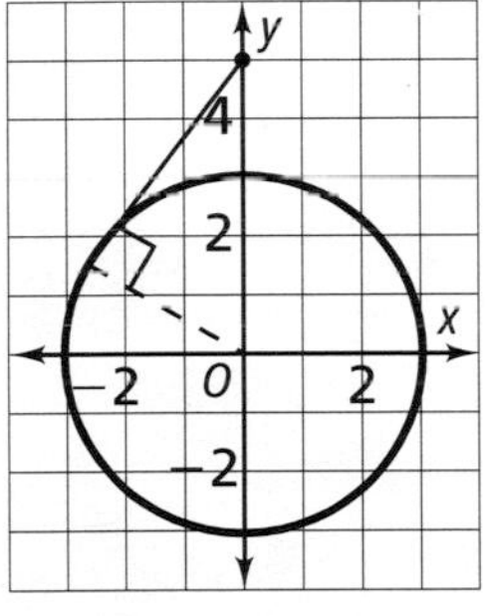

4 units

26. Assume $\overleftrightarrow{AB}$ is not tangent to $\odot O$. Then either $\overleftrightarrow{AB}$ does not intersect $\odot O$ or $\overleftrightarrow{AB}$ intersects $\odot O$ at two pts. If $\overleftrightarrow{AB}$ does not intersect $\odot O$, then P is not on $\odot O$, which contradicts $\overline{OP}$ being a radius. If $\overleftrightarrow{AB}$ intersects $\odot O$ at two pts., P and Q, then $\overline{OP} \cong \overline{OQ}$ ($\cong$ radii), $\triangle OPQ$ is isosc., and $\angle OPQ \cong \angle OQP$. But $\angle OPQ$ is a rt. $\angle$ since $\overleftrightarrow{AB} \perp \overline{OP}$, and $\triangle OPQ$ has two rt. $\angle$s. This is a contradiction also, so $\overleftrightarrow{AB}$ is tangent to $\odot O$.

27. At each vertex, let the radius of a circle be the distance from the vertex to either point of tangency of the inscribed circle.

▼ STUDENT PAGE 497

Proof **20. Given:** $\overline{BC}$ is tangent to $\odot A$ at D. $\overline{DB} \cong \overline{DC}$
Prove: $\overline{AB} \cong \overline{AC}$

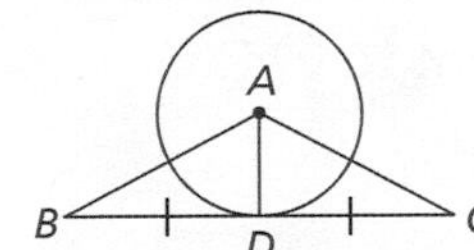

Proof **21. Given:** $\odot A$ and $\odot B$ with common tangents $\overline{DF}$ and $\overline{CE}$
Prove: $\triangle GDC \sim \triangle GFE$

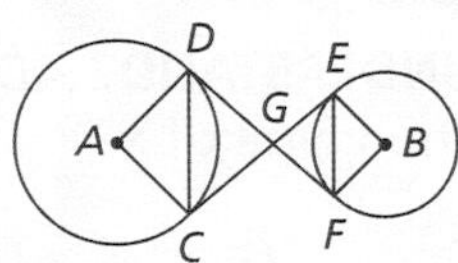

22. **a.** A belt fits snugly around the two circular pulleys. $\overline{CE}$ is an auxiliary line from E to $\overline{BD}$, and $\overline{CE} \parallel \overline{BA}$. What type of quadrilateral is $ABCE$? Explain.
b. What is the length of $\overline{CE}$?
c. What is the distance between the centers of the pulleys to the nearest tenth?

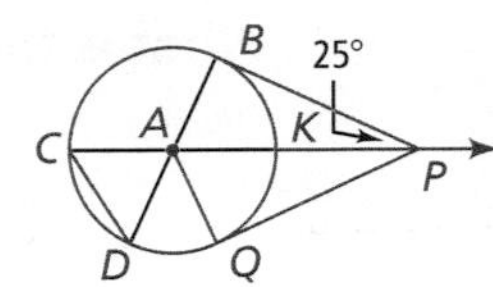

23. $\overline{BD}$ and $\overline{CK}$ at the right are diameters of $\odot A$. $\overline{BP}$ and $\overline{QP}$ are tangents to $\odot A$. What is $m\angle CDA$?

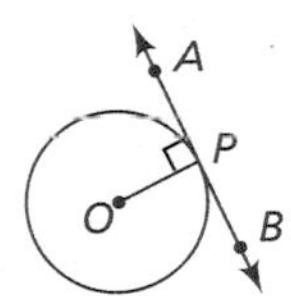

24. Constructions Draw a circle. Label the center T. Locate a point on the circle and label it R. Construct a tangent to $\odot T$ at R.

25. Coordinate Geometry Graph the equation $x^2 + y^2 = 9$. Then draw a segment from (0, 5) tangent to the circle. Find the length of the segment.

Challenge

Proof **26.** Write an indirect proof of Theorem 77.
Given: $\overleftrightarrow{AB} \perp \overline{OP}$ at P.
Prove: $\overleftrightarrow{AB}$ is tangent to $\odot O$.

27. Two circles that have one point in common are *tangent circles.* Given any triangle, explain how to draw three circles that are centered at each vertex of the triangle and are tangent to each other.

5 Assess and Remediate

Lesson Quiz

1. **Do you UNDERSTAND?** $\overline{AD}$ and $\overline{AB}$ are tangent to $\odot C$. What is the value of x?

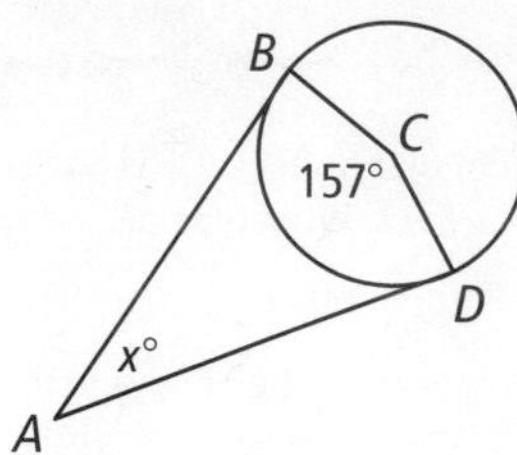

2. What is the radius of $\odot F$?

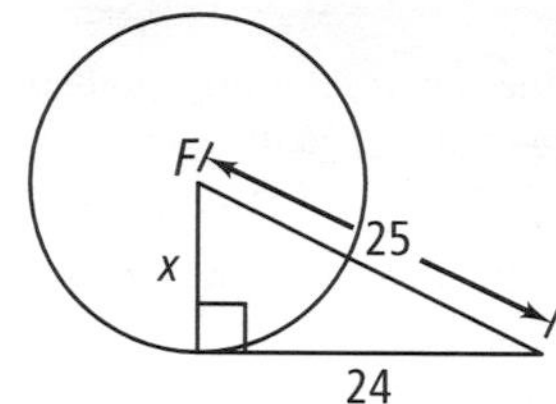

3. $\overline{FT}$ is tangent to $\odot P$ at T. What is PT?

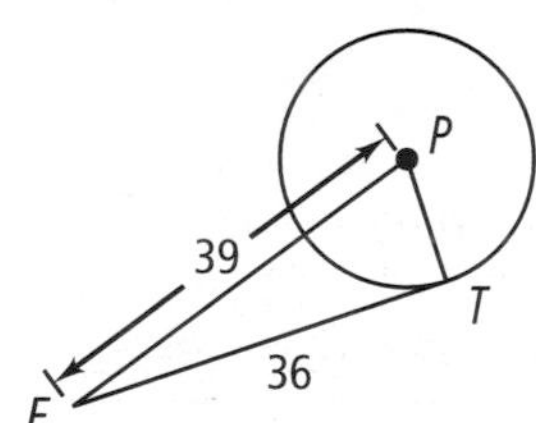

ANSWERS TO LESSON QUIZ

1. 23
2. 7
3. 15

Prescription for Remediation

Use the student work on the Lesson Quiz to prescribe a differentiated assignment.

Points	Differentiated Remediation
0–1	Intervention
2	On-level
3	Extension

Online Assessment

Assign the Lesson Quiz in Success Tracker on **pearsonsuccessnet.com**. Success Tracker will automatically score the quiz and assign appropriate intervention or enrichment to each student based on the results. The compiled data appear in three different reports for instant analysis of whole class and individual student performance.

Differentiated Remediation

Intervention

- **RETEACHING** (2 pages) Provides reteaching and practice exercises for the key lesson concepts. Use with struggling students or absent students.
- **ENGLISH LANGUAGE LEARNER SUPPORT** Helps students develop and reinforce mathematical vocabulary and key concepts.

On-Level

- **PRACTICE** (2 pages) Provides extra practice for each lesson. For simpler practice exercises, use the Form K Practice pages found in the Online Teacher Resources.
- **THINK ABOUT A PLAN** Helps students develop specific problem-solving skills and strategies by providing scaffolded guiding questions.
- **STANDARDIZED TEST PREP** Focuses on all major exercises, all major question types, and helps students prepare for the high-stakes assessments.

Extension

- **ENRICHMENT** Provides students with interesting problems and activities that extend the concepts of the lesson.
- **ACTIVITIES, GAMES, AND PUZZLES** Worksheets that can be used for concept development, enrichment, and for fun!

8-4 Chords and Arcs

Common Core State Standard
G.C.2 Identify and describe relationships among inscribed angles, radii, and chords . . .

Preparing to Teach

BIG ideas Reasoning and Proof
Measurement

ESSENTIAL UNDERSTANDING

Information about congruent parts of a circle (or congruent circles) can be used to find information about other parts of the circle (or circles).

Math Background

In this lesson, students will broaden their understanding of special segments in circles. They will learn that congruent chords and arcs are formed by congruent central angles. Congruent chords are also equidistant from the center of the circle. Additionally, students will learn that a diameter that is perpendicular to a chord bisects the chord and its related arc. These properties of segments in circles can be used to determine characteristics of circles.

Paper folding activities offer students a good way to develop key concepts related to central angles, chords, and arcs.

ELL Support

USE MANIPULATIVES Have students work in pairs. Hand out different sizes of circles that have been cut from construction paper. Tell students to use a protractor and a ruler to draw the center and two congruent chords on one circle, and two congruent central angles on the other. Students can trade their circles and prove the chords and central angles are congruent. Discuss the results.

ASSESS UNDERSTANDING Draw three different-sized circles on the board, each with a central angle of the same measure. Ask whether the central angles are congruent and whether the arcs are congruent. Ask students to explain what is different and the same.

Lesson Vocabulary

- chord

Mathematical Practices

CONSTRUCT VIABLE ARGUMENTS AND CRITIQUE THE REASONING OF OTHERS. With a knowledge of proving triangles congruent, students will prove that chords that are equidistant from the center of a circle are congruent.

Interactive Learning

Solve It!

PURPOSE To show that in congruent circles chords formed by congruent central angles are congruent

PROCESS Students use congruent triangles to show that the chords are congruent.

Q What does it mean for two circles to be congruent? **[Their radii are equal.]**

Q Which four segments in the diagram are congruent? **[$\overline{AB} \cong \overline{AC} \cong \overline{DE} \cong \overline{DF}$]**

Q How can you prove $\triangle ABC \cong \triangle DEF$? **[The triangles are congruent by SAS.]**

Q What theorem allows you to conclude that $\overline{BC} \cong \overline{EF}$? **[Corresponding Parts of Congruent Triangles]**

ANSWER 15; $\triangle ABC \cong \triangle DEF$ by SAS, so $\overline{EF} \cong \overline{BC}$ because corresp. parts of ≅ triangles are ≅.

CONNECT THE MATH In the Solve It, students explored congruent circles and segments to prove triangles were congruent. In the lesson, students will use congruent triangles to identify congruent chords.

▼ DIGITAL (STUDENT WORK SPACE PAGE 498)

SOLVE IT! Getting Ready!

$\odot A \cong \odot D$, and $\angle A \cong \angle D$. If $BC = 15$, what is the length of EF? How do you know?

A B C D E F

2 Guided Instruction

Problem 1 Using Congruent Chords

Take Note

Theorem 79 and Its Converse
Have students list the congruent parts in the diagram. They should list congruent radii, central angles, and arcs.

Take Note

Theorem 80 and Its Converse, Theorem 81 and Its Converse
Discuss and summarize the information in Theorems 80 and 81. Review the definition of a central angle and arc. Be sure that students can explain the connection between the measures of these figures.

Problem 1

Q Which arcs are related to $\overline{BC}$ and $\overline{DF}$? **[$\overset{\frown}{BC}$ and $\overset{\frown}{DF}$]**

Q Which central angles are related to $\overline{BC}$ and $\overline{DF}$? **[$\angle O$ and $\angle P$]**

▼ STUDENT PAGES 498–499

In the Solve It, you found the length of a **chord**, which is a segment whose endpoints are on a circle. The diagram shows the chord $\overline{PQ}$ and its related arc, $\overset{\frown}{PQ}$.

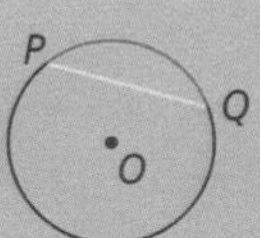

Essential Understanding You can use information about congruent parts of a circle (or congruent circles) to find information about other parts of the circle (or circles).

The following theorems and their converses confirm that if you know that chords, arcs, or central angles in a circle are congruent, then you know the other two parts are congruent.

take note

Theorem 79 and Its Converse

Theorem

Within a circle or in congruent circles, congruent central angles have congruent arcs.

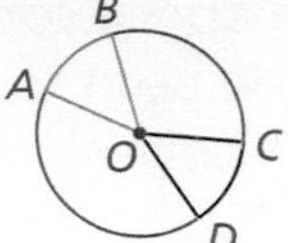

Converse

Within a circle or in congruent circles, congruent arcs have congruent central angles.

If $\angle AOB \cong \angle COD$, then $\overset{\frown}{AB} \cong \overset{\frown}{CD}$.
If $\overset{\frown}{AB} \cong \overset{\frown}{CD}$, then $\angle AOB \cong \angle COD$.

You will prove Theorem 79 and its converse in Exercises 17 and 33.

take note

Theorem 80 and Its Converse

Theorem

Within a circle or in congruent circles, congruent central angles have congruent chords.

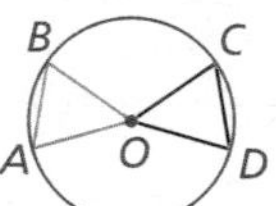

Converse

Within a circle or in congruent circles, congruent chords have congruent central angles.

If $\angle AOB \cong \angle COD$, then $\overline{AB} \cong \overline{CD}$.
If $\overline{AB} \cong \overline{CD}$, then $\angle AOB \cong \angle COD$.

You will prove Theorem 80 and its converse in Exercises 18 and 34.

Theorem 81 and Its Converse

Theorem

Within a circle or in congruent circles, congruent chords have congruent arcs.

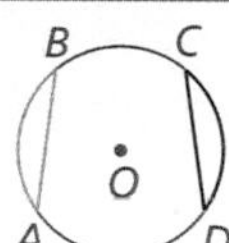

Converse

Within a circle or in congruent circles, congruent arcs have congruent chords.

If $\overline{AB} \cong \overline{CD}$, then $\overset{\frown}{AB} \cong \overset{\frown}{CD}$.
If $\overset{\frown}{AB} \cong \overset{\frown}{CD}$, then $\overline{AB} \cong \overline{CD}$.

You will prove Theorem 81 and its converse in Exercises 19 and 35.

▼ DIGITAL

Problem 1 Using Congruent Chords

In the diagram, $\odot O \cong \odot P$. Given that $\overline{BC} \cong \overline{DF}$, what can you conclude?

$\angle O \cong \angle P$ because, within congruent circles, congruent chords have congruent central angles (conv. of Thm. 80). $\overset{\frown}{BC} \cong \overset{\frown}{DF}$ because, within congruent circles, congruent chords have congruent arcs (Thm. 81).

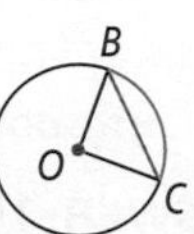

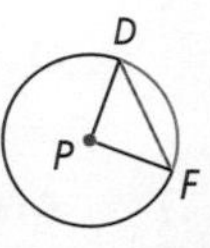

Got It? **ERROR PREVENTION**

Have students identify the central angles and chords that are related to the given arcs. Challenge students to prove the chords and angles congruent using congruent triangles instead of the theorems.

ANSWERS

Got It? Since the circles are ≅, their radii are ≅ and ⊿s BOC and DPF are isosceles. So $\overline{OB} \cong \overline{OC} \cong \overline{PD} \cong \overline{PF}$. Since $\angle B \cong \angle D$ and the ⊿s are isosceles, $\angle B \cong \angle C \cong \angle D \cong \angle F$. So $\triangle BOC \cong \triangle DPF$ by AAS. So $\angle O \cong \angle P$. Therefore, $\overline{BC} \cong \overline{DF}$ (either by corresp. parts of ≅ ⊿s are ≅ or by within ≅ circles, ≅ central ⦣s have ≅ chords) and $\overset{\frown}{BC} \cong \overset{\frown}{DF}$ (within ≅ circles, ≅ central ⦣s have ≅ arcs).

Practice

1. $\overset{\frown}{BC} \cong \overset{\frown}{YZ}$, $\overline{BC} \cong \overline{YZ}$
2. Answers may vary. Sample:
   $\overset{\frown}{ET} \cong \overset{\frown}{GH} \cong \overset{\frown}{JN} \cong \overset{\frown}{ML}$;
   $\overline{ET} \cong \overline{GH} \cong \overline{JN} \cong \overline{ML}$;
   $\angle TFE \cong \angle HFG$; $\angle JKN \cong \angle MKL$

▼ STUDENT PAGES 499–500

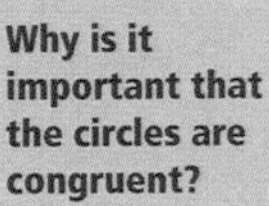

Think
Why is it important that the circles are congruent?

Got It? **Reasoning** Use the diagram in Problem 1, shown below. Suppose you are given $\odot O \cong \odot P$ and $\angle OBC \cong \angle PDF$. How can you show $\angle O \cong \angle P$? From this, what else can you conclude?

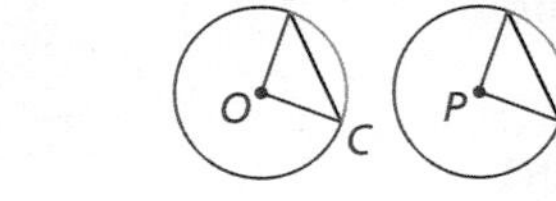

A Practice In Exercises 1 and 2, the circles are congruent. What can you conclude?

1. 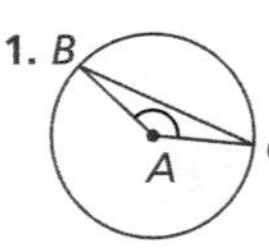 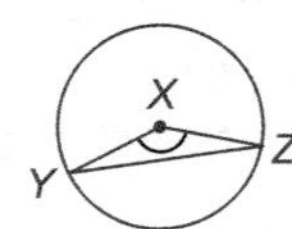

2. 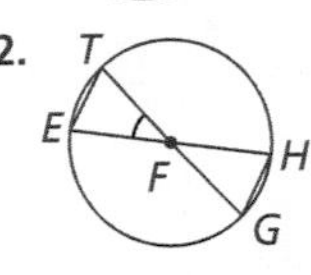 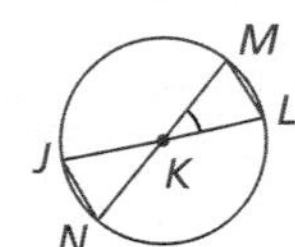

Problem 2 Finding the Length of a Chord

Take Note

Review the definition of the distance from a point to a line. Emphasize that the segments that represent the distances must be perpendicular to the chords.

It may benefit students to work backwards through the proof. Ask them to identify a theorem that will help them show the chords are congruent. [Converse of Theorem 80]

Using the converse of Theorem 80, students can identify triangles that they need to prove congruent to show the central angles are congruent.

▼ STUDENT PAGES 500–501

take note **Theorem 82 and Its Converse**

Theorem

Within a circle or in congruent circles, chords equidistant from the center or centers are congruent.

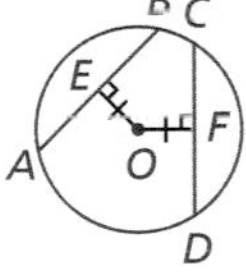

Converse

Within a circle or in congruent circles, congruent chords are equidistant from the center (or centers).

If $OE = OF$, then $\overline{AB} \cong \overline{CD}$.
If $\overline{AB} \cong \overline{CD}$, then $OE = OF$.

You will prove the converse of Theorem 82 in Exercise 36.

Proof **Proof of Theorem 82**

Given: $\odot O$, $\overline{OE} \cong \overline{OF}$, $\overline{OE} \perp \overline{AB}$, $\overline{OF} \perp \overline{CD}$
Prove: $\overline{AB} \cong \overline{CD}$

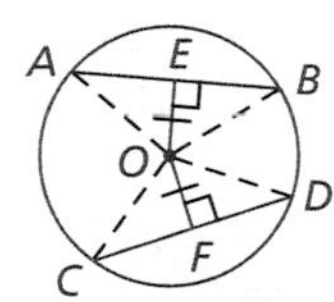

Statements	Reasons
1) $\overline{OA} \cong \overline{OB} \cong \overline{OC} \cong \overline{OD}$	1) Radii of a circle are congruent.
2) $\overline{OE} \cong \overline{OF}$, $\overline{OE} \perp \overline{AB}$, $\overline{OF} \perp \overline{CD}$	2) Given
3) $\angle AEO$ and $\angle CFO$ are right angles.	3) Def. of perpendicular segments
4) $\triangle AEO \cong \triangle CFO$	4) HL Theorem
5) $\angle A \cong \angle C$	5) Corres. parts of ≅ ⊿s are ≅.
6) $\angle B \cong \angle A$, $\angle C \cong \angle D$	6) Isosceles Triangle Theorem
7) $\angle B \cong \angle D$	7) Transitive Property of Congruence
8) $\angle AOB \cong \angle COD$	8) If two ⦣s of a △ are ≅ to two ⦣s of another △, then the third ⦣s are ≅.
9) $\overline{AB} \cong \overline{CD}$	9) ≅ central angles have ≅ chords.

Problem 2 *continued*

Q What type of segment is $\overline{OQ}$? **[It is the perpendicular bisector of $\overline{PR}$]**

Q How is PQ related to PR? **[$PQ + QR = PR$ or $2PQ = PR$]**

Q How are the chords in the circle related? Justify your answer. **[They are congruent because they are equidistant from the center of the circle.]**

Got It? VISUAL LEARNERS

Ask students to describe the relationship between the chords in the circle. Have them identify the theorem that allows them to determine the distance from the center of the circle to the chord.

ANSWERS

Got It? 16; ≅ chords are equidistant from the center.

Practice

3. 14

4. 8

▼ DIGITAL

Problem 2 **Finding the Length of a Chord** GRIDDED RESPONSE

What is the length of $\overline{RS}$ in $\odot O$?

Know
The diagram indicates that $PQ = QR = 12.5$ and $\overline{PR}$ and $\overline{RS}$ are both 9 units from the center.

Need
The length of chord $\overline{RS}$

Plan
$\overline{PR} \cong \overline{RS}$, since they are the same distance from the center of the circle. So finding PR gives the length of $\overline{RS}$.

$PQ = QR = 12.5$	Given in the diagram
$PQ + QR = PR$	Segment Addition Postulate
$12.5 + 12.5 = PR$	Substitute.
$25 = PR$	Add.
$RS = PR$	Chords equidistant from the center of a circle are congruent.
$RS = 25$	Substitute.

▼ STUDENT PAGES 501–502

Got It? What is the value of x? Justify your answer.

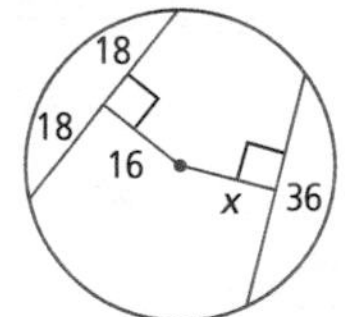

Plan
What information can you gather from the chords?

A Practice Find the value of x.

3.

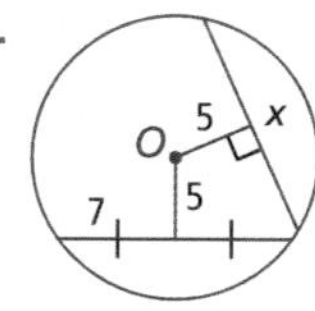

4.

Problem 3 Using Diameters and Chords

Take Note

Review the logic of these theorems with students. They should identify the congruent triangles created by the endpoints of the chord, the center of the circle, and the midpoint of the segment.

For Theorem 83: $\triangle OCD$ is an isosceles triangle, so $\angle C \cong \angle D$. $\triangle COE \cong \triangle DOE$ by AAS. $\overline{CE} \cong \overline{DE}$ because they are corresponding parts. $\angle COE \cong \angle DOE$ because they are corresponding parts. Arcs AC and AD are congruent because they are formed by congruent central angles.

For Theorem 84: $\triangle COE \cong \triangle DOE$ by SAS. $\overline{CE} \cong \overline{DE}$ because they are corresponding parts. $\angle COE \cong \angle DOE$ because they are corresponding parts. Arcs AC and AD are congruent because they are formed by congruent central angles.

▼ STUDENT PAGE 502

The Converse of the Perpendicular Bisector Theorem from Lesson 4-2 has special applications to a circle and its diameters, chords, and arcs.

take note

Theorem 83

Theorem	If . . .	Then . . .
In a circle, if a diameter is perpendicular to a chord, then it bisects the chord and its arc.	$\overline{AB}$ is a diameter and $\overline{AB} \perp \overline{CD}$	$\overline{CE} \cong \overline{ED}$ and $\overset{\frown}{CA} \cong \overset{\frown}{AD}$

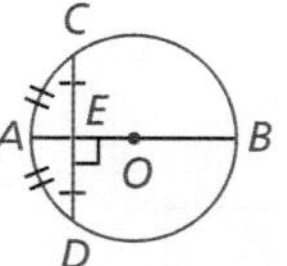

You will prove Theorem 83 in Exercise 20.

Theorem 84

Theorem	If . . .	Then . . .
In a circle, if a diameter bisects a chord (that is not a diameter), then it is perpendicular to the chord.	$\overline{AB}$ is a diameter and $\overline{CE} \cong \overline{ED}$	$\overline{AB} \perp \overline{CD}$

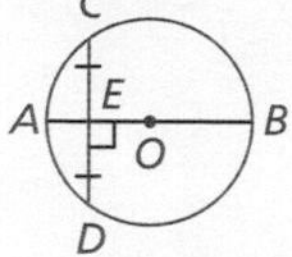

For Theorem 85: Review the properties of perpendicular bisectors and lines. Have students connect the definitions to classify $\overline{AB}$.

Problem 3

Q How is the perpendicular bisector of a chord related to a circle? **[It contains a diameter of the circle.]**

Q How many diameters do you need to draw to locate the center of a circle? **[at least two]**

Q How can you find the perpendicular bisectors of chords? **[Construct perpendicular bisectors using a compass and straightedge.]**

Got It? **VISUAL LEARNERS**

Review the steps involved in constructing the perpendicular bisector of a segment. Be sure that students are constructing perpendicular bisectors correctly before they measure the radius of the circle.

ANSWERS

Got It? Check students' work.

Practice

5. The center is at the intersection of $\overline{GH}$ and $\overline{KM}$, because if a chord is the ⊥ bis. of another chord, then the first chord is a diameter; two diameters intersect at the center of a circle.
6. $CE = ED$, $\widehat{BC} \cong \widehat{BD}$

▼ STUDENT PAGE 503

take note

Theorem 85

Theorem	If . . .	Then . . .
In a circle, the perpendicular bisector of a chord contains the center of the circle.	$\overline{AB}$ is the perpendicular bisector of chord $\overline{CD}$	$\overline{AB}$ contains the center of $\odot O$

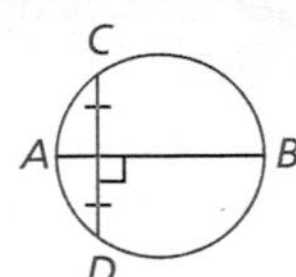

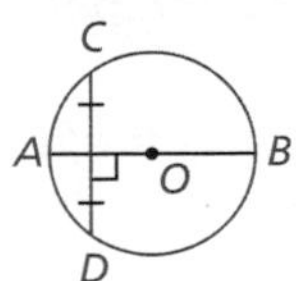

You will prove Theorem 85 in Exercise 31.

Proof Proof of Theorem 84

Given: $\odot O$ with diameter $\overline{AB}$ bisecting $\overline{CD}$ at E

Prove: $\overline{AB} \perp \overline{CD}$

Proof: $OC = OD$ because the radii of a circle are congruent. $CE = ED$ by the definition of *bisect*. Thus, O and E are both equidistant from C and D. By the Converse of the Perpendicular Bisector Theorem, both O and E are on the perpendicular bisector of $\overline{CD}$. Two points determine one line or segment, so $\overline{OE}$ is the perpendicular bisector of $\overline{CD}$. Since $\overline{OE}$ is part of $\overline{AB}$, $\overline{AB} \perp \overline{CD}$.

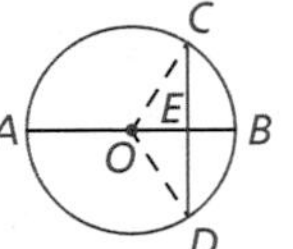

▼ DIGITAL

ONLINE PROBLEMS **Problem 3** **Using Diameters and Chords**

Archaeology **An archaeologist found pieces of a jar. She wants to find the radius of the rim of the jar to help guide her as she reassembles the pieces. What is the radius of the rim?**

Step 1 Trace a piece of the rim. Draw two chords and construct perpendicular bisectors.

Step 2 The center is the intersection of the perpendicular bisectors. Use the center to find the radius.

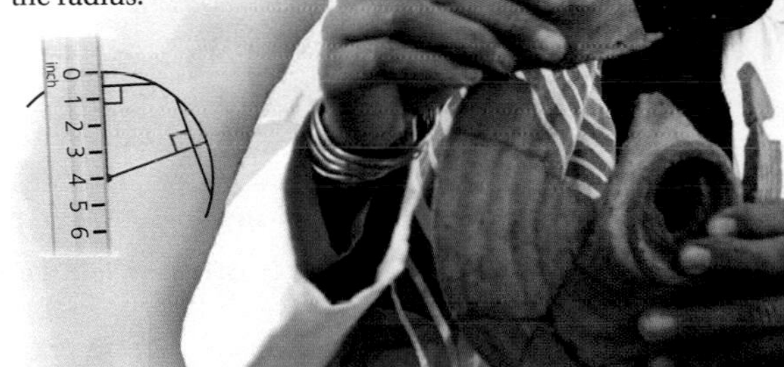

The radius is 4 in.

▼ STUDENT PAGES 503–504

Got It? Trace a coin. What is its radius?

A Practice

5. In the diagram at the right, $\overline{GH}$ and $\overline{KM}$ are perpendicular bisectors of the chords they intersect. What can you conclude about the center of the circle? Justify your answer.

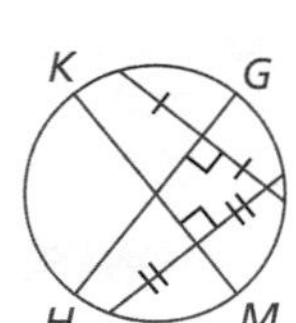

6. In $\odot O$, $\overline{AB}$ is a diameter of the circle and $\overline{AB} \perp \overline{CD}$. What conclusions can you make?

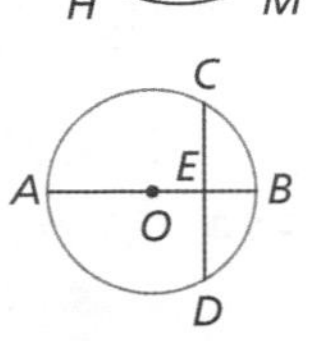

Problem 4 Finding Measures in a Circle

Q In 4A, what is the relationship between $\overline{KN}$ and $\overline{LM}$? **[They are perpendicular, so $\overline{KN}$ bisects $\overline{LM}$ by Theorem 83.]**

Q What type of triangle is formed by the chord, the radius, and the perpendicular bisector? **[a right triangle]**

Q In 4B, what is the relationship between $\overline{BC}$ and $\overline{AF}$? **[$\overline{BC}$ bisects $\overline{AF}$, so they are perpendicular by Theorem 84.]**

Q How are $\overline{BA}$ and $\overline{BE}$ related? **[They are radii of the same circle, so they are congruent.]**

Got It? **ERROR PREVENTION**

Review the definition of an auxiliary line. Ask students why the segment is called auxiliary.

ANSWERS

Got it? $\overline{BA}$ is the hypotenuse of rt. $\triangle BAC$, so the Pythagorean Theorem can be used.

Practice

7. 6 **8.** 5.4

▼ DIGITAL

Problem 4 **Finding Measures in a Circle**

Algebra **What is the value of each variable to the nearest tenth?**

A

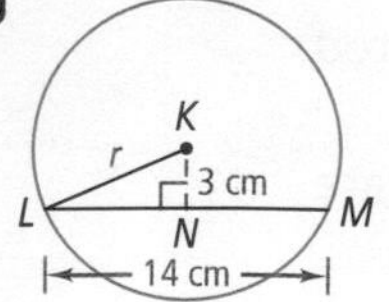

$LN = \frac{1}{2}(14) = 7$ A diameter ⊥ to a chord bisects the chord.

$r^2 = 3^2 + 7^2$ Use the Pythagorean Theorem.

$r \approx 7.6$ Find the positive square root of each side.

B

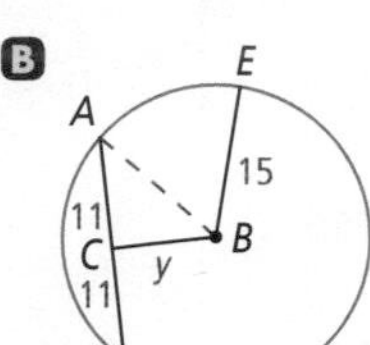

$\overline{BC} \perp \overline{AF}$ A diameter that bisects a chord that is not a diameter is ⊥ to the chord.

$BA = BE = 15$ Draw an auxiliary $\overline{BA}$. The auxiliary $\overline{BA} \cong \overline{BE}$ because they are radii of the same circle.

$y^2 + 11^2 = 15^2$ Use the Pythagorean Theorem.

$y^2 = 104$ Solve for y^2.

$y \approx 10.2$ Find the positive square root of each side.

▼ STUDENT PAGES 504–505

Got It? **Reasoning** In part (B) of Problem 4, how does the auxiliary $\overline{BA}$ make it simpler to solve for y?

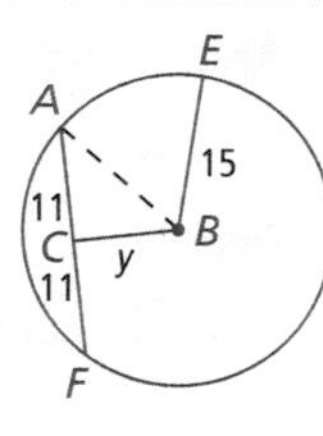

Practice **Algebra** Find the value of x to the nearest tenth.

7.

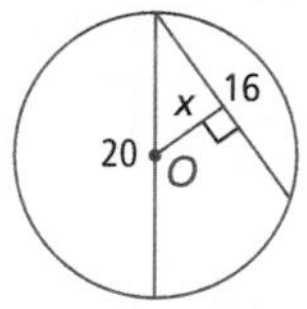

8.

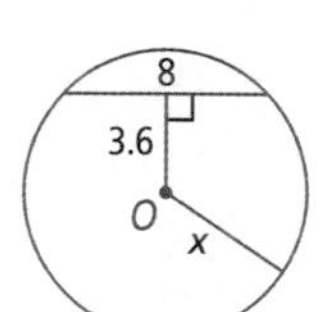

3 Lesson Check

Do you know HOW?

If students have difficulty with Exercise 9, then have them classify $\angle AOB$ and $\angle COD$.

Do you UNDERSTAND?

If students have difficulty with Exercise 13, then have them review the diagram in Problem 2.

Close

Q If two central angles are congruent, what can you say about the arcs and chords that they create? **[The arcs are congruent, and so are the chords.]**

Q What is true about two congruent chords in a circle? **[They are equidistant from the center of the circle.]**

Q If a diameter is perpendicular to a chord, what is true about the chord and its related arc? **[The diameter bisects the chord and arc.]**

ANSWERS

9. 50; $\angle COD \cong \angle AOB$ (Vert. ∠s are ≅), so $\overset{\frown}{CD} \cong \overset{\frown}{AB}$ because ≅ central ∠s have ≅ arcs. Therefore, $m\overset{\frown}{CD} = m\overset{\frown}{AB}$.

10. $\overset{\frown}{CA} \cong \overset{\frown}{BD}$ because in a circle ≅ chords have ≅ arcs.

11. The distances are equal because in a circle ≅ chords are equidistant from the center.

12. A radius is *not* a chord because one of its endpoints is not on the circle. A diameter *is* a chord because both of its endpoints are on the circle.

13. If chords $\overline{SR}$ and $\overline{QP}$ are equidistant from the center, then their lengths must be equal.

▼ STUDENT PAGES 505–506

Lesson Check

Do you know HOW?

In ⊙O, $m\overset{\frown}{CD} = 50$ and $\overline{CA} \cong \overline{BD}$.

9. What is $m\overset{\frown}{AB}$? How do you know?

10. What is true of $\overset{\frown}{CA}$ and $\overset{\frown}{BD}$? Why?

11. Since $CA = BD$, what do you know about the distance of $\overline{CA}$ and $\overline{BD}$ from the center of ⊙O?

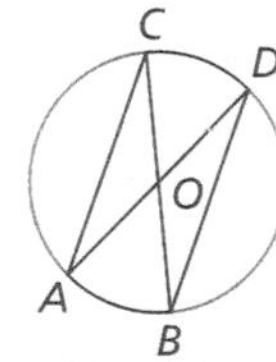

Do you UNDERSTAND?

12. Vocabulary Is a radius a chord? Is a diameter a chord? Explain your answers.

13. Error Analysis What is the error in the diagram?

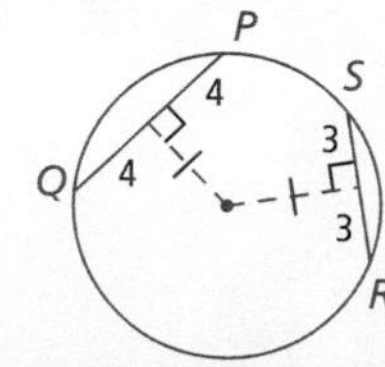

4 Practice

More Practice and Problem-Solving Exercises

ASSIGNMENT GUIDE

The assignments below are for the More Practice and Problem-Solving Exercises. You may also want to assign the A-Level Practice Exercises for homework if these are not used in class.

Average: 14–32

Advanced: 14–37

Mathematical Practices The exercises listed focus on the Standards for Mathematical Practices listed.

EX. 16: Make Sense of Problems (MP 1)

EX. 27: Communicate (MP 3)

EX. 13: Critique the Reasoning of Others (MP 3)

EXERCISE 21: Use the **Think About a Plan** worksheet in the Online Teacher Resources to further support students' development in becoming independent learners.

HOMEWORK QUICK CHECK

To check students' understanding of key skills and concepts, go over Exercises 16, 21, 27, 30, and 32.

ANSWERS

14. 12 cm

15. 6 in.

16. 13.9 cm

17. Since $\angle AOB \cong \angle COD$, it follows that $m\angle AOB = m\angle COD$. Now $m\angle AOB = m\overset{\frown}{AB}$ and $m\angle COD = m\overset{\frown}{CD}$ (definition of arc measure). So $m\overset{\frown}{AB} = m\overset{\frown}{CD}$ (Substitution). Therefore, $\overset{\frown}{AB} \cong \overset{\frown}{CD}$ (definition of $\cong$ arcs).

18. $\odot O$ with $\angle AOB \cong \angle COD$ (given); $\overline{AO} \cong \overline{BO} \cong \overline{CO} \cong \overline{DO}$ (all radii of a $\odot$ are $\cong$). $\triangle AOB \cong \triangle COD$ (SAS); $\overline{AB} \cong \overline{CD}$ (corresp. parts of $\cong$ ▲s are $\cong$).

19. $\odot O$ with $\overset{\frown}{AB} \cong \overset{\frown}{CD}$ (given); $\overline{AO} \cong \overline{BO} \cong \overline{CO} \cong \overline{DO}$ (all radii of a $\odot$ are $\cong$); $\triangle AOB \cong \triangle COD$ (SSS); $\angle AOB \cong \angle COD$ (corresp. parts of $\cong$ ▲s are $\cong$); $\overset{\frown}{AB} \cong \overset{\frown}{CD}$ ($\cong$ central ∠s have $\cong$ arcs).

20. $\odot O$ with diameter $\overline{ED} \perp \overline{AB}$ at C (given). Draw $\overline{OA}$ and $\overline{OB}$ (2 pts. determine a line). $\angle ACO$ and $\angle BCO$ are rt. ∠s ($\perp$ lines form rt. ∠s). $\triangle ACO$ and $\triangle BCO$ are rt. ▲s (Def. of a rt. $\triangle$) $\overline{OA} \cong \overline{OB}$ (all radii of a $\odot$ are $\cong$); $\overline{OC} \cong \overline{OC}$ (Refl. Prop. of $\cong$); $\triangle ACO \cong \triangle BCO$ (HL); $\overline{AC} \cong \overline{BC}$ (corresp. parts of $\cong$ ▲s are $\cong$); $\angle AOC \cong \angle BOC$ (corresp. parts of $\cong$ ▲s are $\cong$); $\overset{\frown}{AD} \cong \overset{\frown}{BD}$ ($\cong$ central ∠s have $\cong$ arcs).

21. 5 in.

22. 10 cm

23. 10 ft

▼ STUDENT PAGES 506–507

More Practice and Problem-Solving Exercises

B Apply

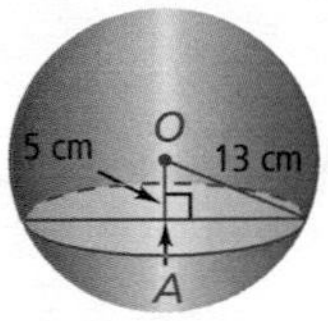

14. Geometry in 3 Dimensions In the figure at the right, sphere O with radius 13 cm is intersected by a plane 5 cm from center O. Find the radius of the cross section $\odot A$.

15. Geometry in 3 Dimensions A plane intersects a sphere that has radius 10 in., forming the cross section $\odot B$ with radius 8 in. How far is the plane from the center of the sphere?

16. Think About a Plan Two concentric circles have radii of 4 cm and 8 cm. A segment tangent to the smaller circle is a chord of the larger circle. What is the length of the segment to the nearest tenth?

- How will you start the diagram?
- Where is the best place to position the radius of each circle?

Proof **17.** Prove Theorem 79.

Given: $\odot O$ with $\angle AOB \cong \angle COD$

Prove: $\overset{\frown}{AB} \cong \overset{\frown}{CD}$

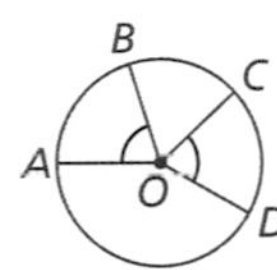

Proof **18.** Prove Theorem 80.

Given: $\odot O$ with $\angle AOB \cong \angle COD$

Prove: $\overline{AB} \cong \overline{CD}$

Proof **19.** Prove Theorem 81.

Given: $\odot O$ with $\overline{AB} \cong \overline{CD}$

Prove: $\overset{\frown}{AB} \cong \overset{\frown}{CD}$

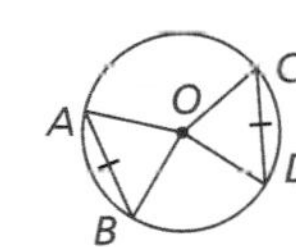

Proof **20.** Prove Theorem 83.

Given: $\odot O$ with diameter $\overline{ED} \perp \overline{AB}$ at C

Prove: $\overline{AC} \cong \overline{BC}$, $\overset{\frown}{AD} \cong \overset{\frown}{BD}$

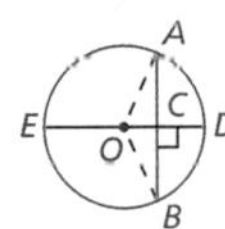

$\odot A$ and $\odot B$ are congruent. $\overline{CD}$ is a chord of both circles.

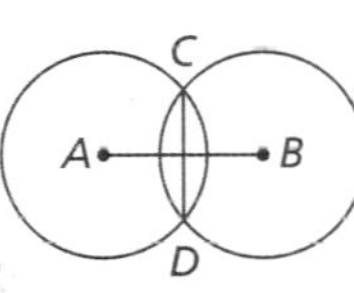

21. If $AB = 8$ in. and $CD = 6$ in., how long is a radius?

22. If $AB = 24$ cm and a radius $= 13$ cm, how long is $\overline{CD}$?

23. If a radius $= 13$ ft and $CD = 24$ ft, how long is $\overline{AB}$?

More Practice and Problem-Solving Exercises *continued*

24.

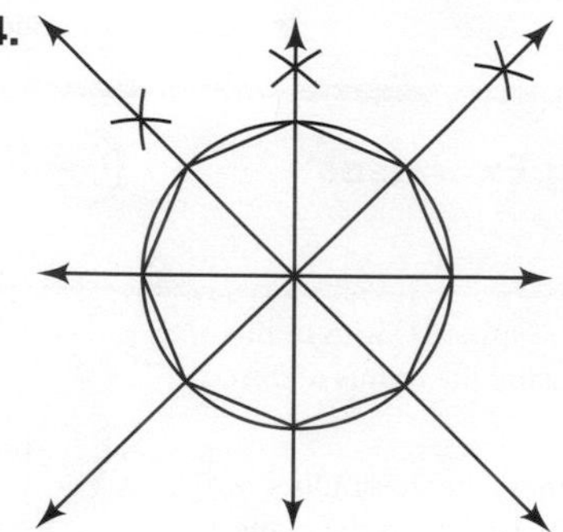

25. 9.2 units

26.

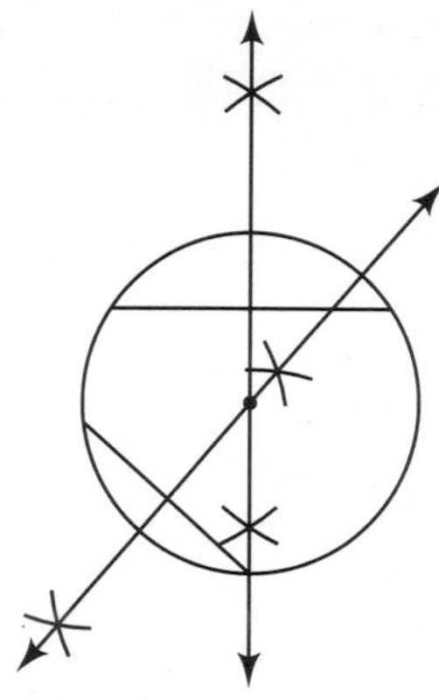

27. The length of a chord or an arc is determined not only by the measure of the central angles, but also by the radius of the circle.

28. 108

29. 90

30. about 123.9

31. $\overline{XW} \cong \overline{XY}$ (all radii of a circle are $\cong$); X is on the $\perp$ bis. of $\overline{WY}$ (Converse of $\perp$ Bis. Thm.); ℓ is the $\perp$ bis. of $\overline{WY}$ (given); X is on ℓ (Subst. Prop.), so ℓ contains the center of $\odot X$.

32. $\odot A$ with $\overline{CE} \perp \overline{BD}$ (given); $\overline{CF} \cong \overline{CF}$ (Refl. Prop. of $\cong$); $\overline{BF} \cong \overline{DF}$ (a diameter $\perp$ to a chord bisects the chord); $\angle BFC$ and $\angle DFC$ are rt. $\angle$s ($\perp$ lines form rt. $\angle$s); $\angle BFC \cong \angle DFC$ (Rt. $\angle$s are $\cong$); $\triangle BFC \cong \triangle DFC$ (SAS); $\overline{BC} \cong \overline{CD}$ (corresp. parts of $\cong$ $\triangle$s are $\cong$); $\widehat{BC} \cong \widehat{DC}$ ($\cong$ chords have $\cong$ arcs).

33.

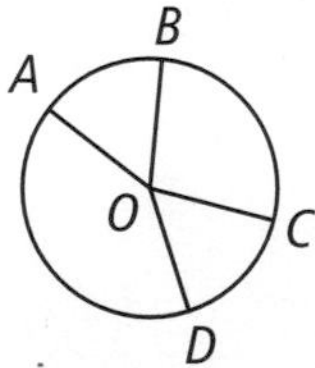

Given: $\odot O$ with $\widehat{AB} \cong \widehat{CD}$
Prove: $\angle AOB \cong \angle COD$
Proof: $m\angle AOB = m\widehat{AB}$ and $m\angle COD = m\widehat{CD}$ (definition of arc measure) $\widehat{AB} \cong \widehat{CD}$ (given), so $m\widehat{AB} = m\widehat{CD}$ (Def. of $\cong$ arcs). Therefore, $m\angle AOB = m\angle COD$ (Substitution). Hence $\angle AOB \cong \angle COD$ (Def. of $\cong$ $\angle$s).

▼ STUDENT PAGES 507–508

24. Construction Use Theorem 80 to construct a regular octagon.

25. In the diagram at the right, the endpoints of the chord are the points where the line $x = 2$ intersects the circle $x^2 + y^2 = 25$. What is the length of the chord? Round your answer to the nearest tenth.

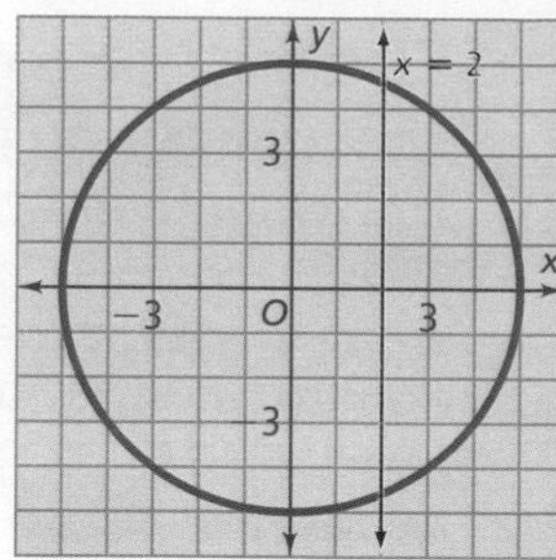

26. Construction Use a circular object such as a can or a saucer to draw a circle. Construct the center of the circle.

27. Writing Theorems 79 and 80 both begin with the phrase "within a circle or in congruent circles." Explain why the word *congruent* is essential for both theorems.

Find $m\widehat{AB}$. (*Hint:* You will need to use trigonometry in Exercise 30.)

28.

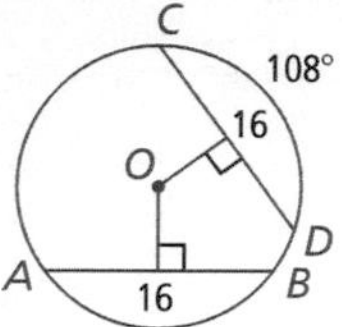

29.

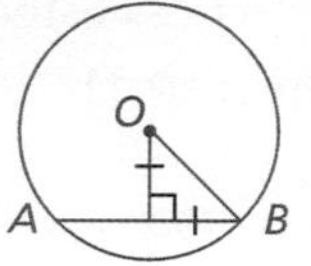

30.

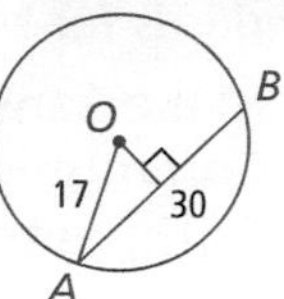

Proof **31.** Prove Theorem 85.

Given: ℓ is the $\perp$ bisector of $\overline{WY}$.
Prove: ℓ contains the center of $\odot X$.

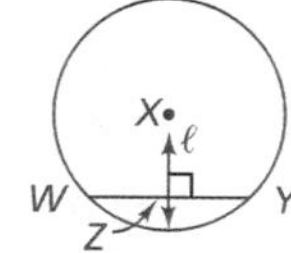

Proof **32. Given:** $\odot A$ with $\overline{CE} \perp \overline{BD}$
Prove: $\widehat{BC} \cong \widehat{DC}$

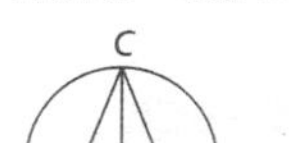

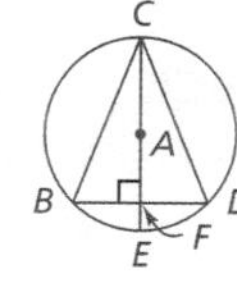

Challenge

Proof **Prove each of the following.**

33. Converse of Theorem 79: Within a circle or in congruent circles, congruent arcs have congruent central angles.

34. Converse of Theorem 80: Within a circle or in congruent circles, congruent chords have congruent central angles.

35. Converse of Theorem 81: Within a circle or in congruent circles, congruent arcs have congruent chords.

36. Converse of Theorem 82: Within a circle or congruent circles, congruent chords are equidistant from the center (or centers).

Proof 37. If two circles are concentric and a chord of the larger circle is tangent to the smaller circle, prove that the point of tangency is the midpoint of the chord.

34.

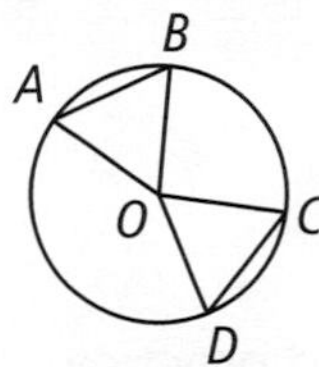

Given: $\odot O$ with $\overline{AB} \cong \overline{CD}$
Prove: $\angle AOB \cong \angle COD$
Proof: In circle O, $AO \cong BO \cong CO \cong DO$ (radii of a $\odot$ are $\cong$) and $\overline{AB} \cong \overline{CD}$ (given). So $\triangle AOB \cong \triangle COD$ (SSS) and $\angle AOB \cong \angle COD$ (corresp. parts of $\cong$ △s are $\cong$).

35.

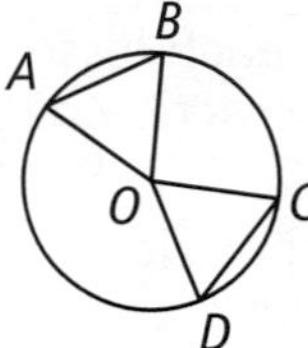

Given: $\odot O$ with $\overset{\frown}{AB} \cong \overset{\frown}{CD}$
Prove: $\overline{AB} \cong \overline{CD}$
Proof: It is given that $\overset{\frown}{AB} \cong \overset{\frown}{CD}$, so $\angle AOB \cong \angle COD$ (if arcs are $\cong$ then their central ∠s are $\cong$). Also, $AO \cong BO \cong CO \cong DO$ (radii of a $\odot$ are $\cong$), so $\triangle AOB \cong \triangle COD$ (SAS), and $\overline{AB} \cong \overline{CD}$ (corresp. parts of $\cong$ △s are $\cong$).

36.

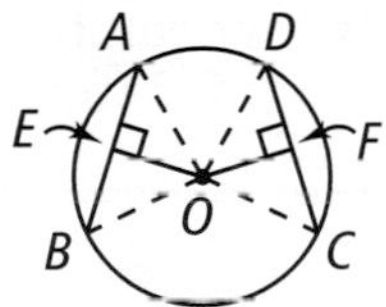

Given: $\odot O$ with $\overline{AB} \cong \overline{CD}$, $\overline{OE} \perp \overline{AB}$, $\overline{OF} \perp \overline{CD}$
Prove: $\overline{OE} \cong \overline{OF}$
Proof: All radii of $\odot O$ are $\cong$ and it is given that $\overline{AB} \cong \overline{CD}$, so $\triangle AOB \cong \triangle COD$ by SSS. $\angle A \cong \angle C$ (corresp. parts of $\cong$ △s are $\cong$). $\angle OEA$ and $\angle OFC$ are rt. ∠s ($\perp$ lines form rt. ∠s). So, $\angle OEA \cong \angle OFC$ (Rt. ∠s are $\cong$). Thus, $\triangle OEA \cong \triangle OFC$ by AAS, and $\overline{OE} \cong \overline{OF}$ (corresp. parts of $\cong$ △s are $\cong$).

37.

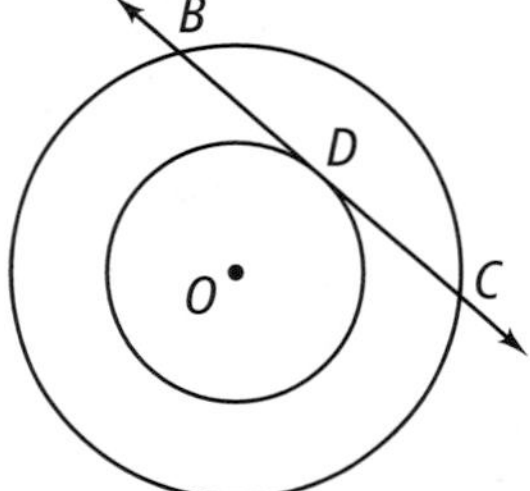

Given: Concentric circles, $\overline{BC}$ is tangent to the smaller circle at D
Prove: D is the midpt. of $\overline{BC}$
Proof: It is given that $\overline{BC}$ is tangent to the smaller circle, so $\overline{BC} \perp \overline{OD}$ (a tangent is $\perp$ to a radius at the point of tangency). $\overline{OD}$ is part of a diameter of the larger circle, so $\overline{BD} \cong \overline{CD}$ (if a diameter is $\perp$ to a chord, it bisects the chord). D is the midpt. of $\overline{BC}$ (Def. of midpt.)

5 Assess and Remediate

Lesson Quiz

1. **Do you UNDERSTAND?** In the diagram, $\angle GHF \cong \angle KHJ$. What can you conclude?

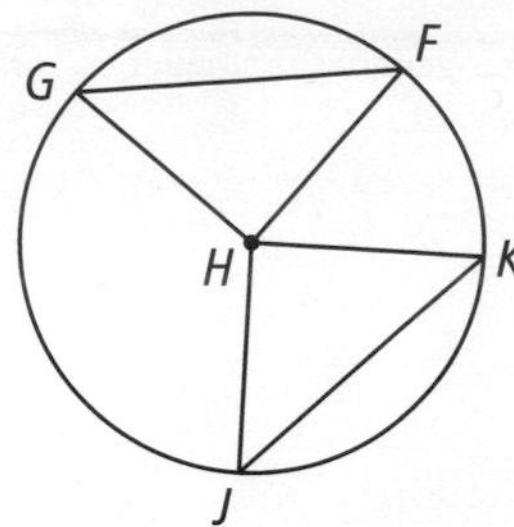

2. In the above diagram, $JK = 8$. The perimeter of $\triangle JHK = 18$. What is HK?
3. What is the missing length?

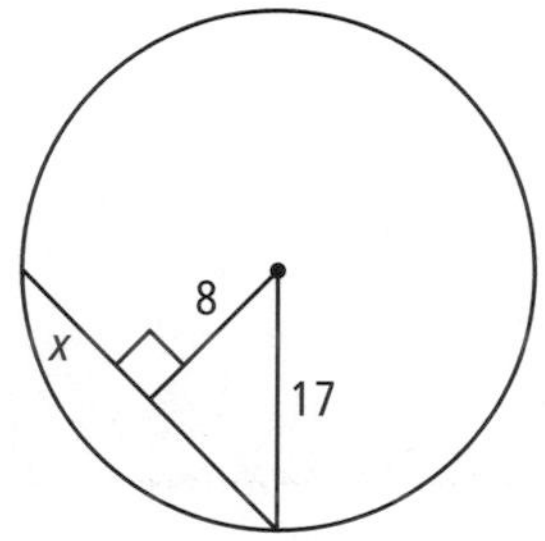

ANSWERS TO LESSON QUIZ

1. $\overline{GF} \cong \overline{KJ}$, $\overset{\frown}{GF} \cong \overset{\frown}{KJ}$
2. 5
3. 15

Prescription for Remediation

Use the student work on the Lesson Quiz to prescribe a differentiated assignment.

Points	Differentiated Remediation
0–1	Intervention
2	On-level
3	Extension

Online Assessment

Assign the Lesson Quiz in Success Tracker on **pearsonsuccessnet.com**. Success Tracker will automatically score the quiz and assign appropriate intervention or enrichment to each student based on the results. The compiled data appear in three different reports for instant analysis of whole class and individual student performance.

Differentiated Remediation

Intervention

- **RETEACHING** (2 pages) Provides reteaching and practice exercises for the key lesson concepts. Use with struggling students or absent students.
- **ENGLISH LANGUAGE LEARNER SUPPORT** Helps students develop and reinforce mathematical vocabulary and key concepts.

On-Level

- **PRACTICE** (2 pages) Provides extra practice for each lesson. For simpler practice exercises, use the Form K Practice pages found in the Online Teacher Resources.
- **THINK ABOUT A PLAN** Helps students develop specific problem-solving skills and strategies by providing scaffolded guiding questions.
- **STANDARDIZED TEST PREP** Focuses on all major exercises, all major question types, and helps students prepare for the high-stakes assessments.

Extension

- **ENRICHMENT** Provides students with interesting problems and activities that extend the concepts of the lesson.
- **ACTIVITIES, GAMES, AND PUZZLES** Worksheets that can be used for concept development, enrichment, and for fun!

8-5 Inscribed Angles

Common Core State Standards
G.C.2 Identify and describe relationships among inscribed angles, radii, and chords . . . **Also G.C.3, G.C.4**

Preparing to Teach

BIG ideas Reasoning and Proof
Measurement

ESSENTIAL UNDERSTANDING

Angles formed by intersecting lines have a special relationship to the arcs the intersecting lines intercept. Specifically, arcs intercepted by chords that form inscribed angles are related to the inscribed angles.

Math Background

Similar to the relationship between a central angle and the arc it intercepts, an inscribed angle is related to its intercepted arc. Students will learn how to calculate the measure of either the inscribed angle or intercepted arc based on the known measure. Corollaries from this theorem lead to observations about congruent inscribed angles, right angles within circles, and the angles of an inscribed quadrilateral.

The proof of the Inscribed Angle Theorem uses a divide-and-conquer strategy. The proof is important for students to see, because it illustrates how a complex situation can be broken into simpler situations that are easier to prove.

ELL Support

USE ROLE PLAYING Arrange students into heterogeneous groups of four. Assign a student to act as the instructor. Have a student from each group form a temporary group with one student from each of the other groups. Assign each group a concept: Case I, II, or III from Theorem 86 or Theorem 87. Students in the temporary groups will thoroughly learn about their concepts and be prepared to provide an oral explanation, a drawn example, and a demonstration of how to solve a problem. The problems students can model should be from the lesson, or ones you have specifically assigned. Students will rejoin their groups and peer-teach their concept to the rest of their group members.

Lesson Vocabulary

- inscribed angle
- intercepted arc

Mathematical Practices

ATTEND TO PRECISION. Students will examine the mathematical argument posed by Theorem 87 and will use a series of graphical representations to discover its truth.

1 Interactive Learning

Solve It!

PURPOSE To discover that inscribed angles that intercept the same arc are congruent

PROCESS Students may measure the angles using a protractor and draw a conclusion based on their findings.

Q For each player, where does the angle of shots intersect with the circle? **[Each angle intersects the sides of the goal.]**

Q How are the measures of the angles related? **[They are the same.]**

Q Which player has the widest angle in which to shoot? **[They all have the same angle.]**

ANSWER No. Note to teacher: Through some method, students must determine that all three angles are ≅.

CONNECT THE MATH In the Solve It, students should realize that inscribed angles that intersect congruent arcs are congruent. In this lesson, students will learn theorems related to inscribed angles.

▼ DIGITAL (STUDENT WORK SPACE PAGE 509)

SOLVE IT! **Getting Ready!**

Three high-school soccer players practice kicking goals from the points shown in the diagram. All three points are along an arc of a circle. Player A says she is in the best position because the angle of her kicks toward the goal is wider than the angle of the other players' kicks. Do you agree? Explain.

Player B
Player A
Player C

2 Guided Instruction

Problem 1 Using the Inscribed Angle Theorem

Take Note

Have students practice finding the measure of $\overset{\frown}{AC}$ or $\angle B$. Give them the measurement of one figure and have them determine the measurement of the other. Ask students to identify the length of an arc that would be intercepted by a 90° angle.

Have students compare the three cases. Ask them why each case must be considered separately. Emphasize to students that properties of equality must be used to show that two quantities are equal.

Problem 1

Q Which arc is related to $\angle PQT$? **[$\overset{\frown}{PT}$]**

Q How can you find the measure of the arc? **[Multiply the measure of the inscribed angle by 2.]**

Q Which angle is related to $\overset{\frown}{PS}$? **[$\angle PRS$]**

Q How can you find the measure of the angle? **[Divide the associated arc measure by 2.]**

▼ STUDENT PAGES 509–510

An angle whose vertex is on the circle and whose sides are chords of the circle is an **inscribed angle**. An arc with endpoints on the sides of an inscribed angle, and its other points in the interior of the angle, is an **intercepted arc**. In the diagram, inscribed $\angle C$ intercepts $\overset{\frown}{AB}$.

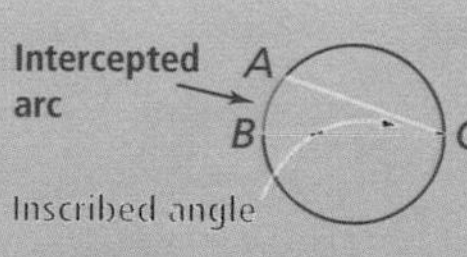

Essential Understanding Angles formed by intersecting lines have a special relationship to the arcs the intersecting lines intercept. In this lesson, you will study arcs formed by inscribed angles.

take note

Theorem 86 Inscribed Angle Theorem

The measure of an inscribed angle is half the measure of its intercepted arc.

$$m\angle B = \frac{1}{2}m\overset{\frown}{AC}$$

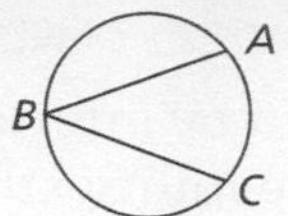

To prove Theorem 86, there are three cases to consider.

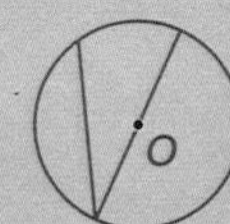

I: The center is on a side of the angle.

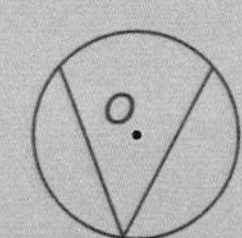

II: The center is inside the angle.

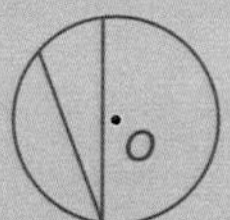

III: The center is outside the angle.

The following is a proof of Case I. You will prove Case II and Case III in Exercises 19 and 20.

Proof **Proof of Theorem 86, Case I**

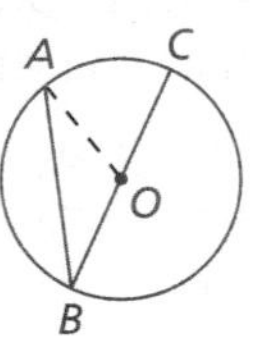

Given: $\odot O$ with inscribed $\angle B$ and diameter $\overline{BC}$

Prove: $m\angle B = \frac{1}{2}m\overset{\frown}{AC}$

Draw radius $\overline{OA}$ to form isosceles $\triangle AOB$ with $OA = OB$ and, hence, $m\angle A = m\angle B$ (Isosceles Triangle Theorem).

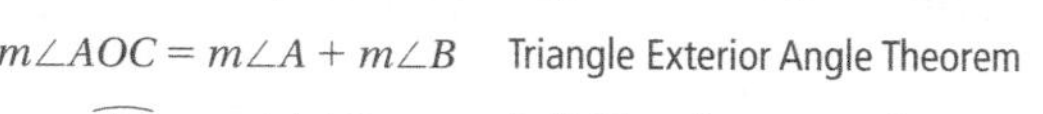

$m\angle AOC = m\angle A + m\angle B$	Triangle Exterior Angle Theorem
$m\overset{\frown}{AC} = m\angle AOC$	Definition of measure of an arc
$m\overset{\frown}{AC} = m\angle A + m\angle B$	Substitute.
$m\overset{\frown}{AC} = 2m\angle B$	Substitute and simplify.
$\frac{1}{2}m\overset{\frown}{AC} = m\angle B$	Divide each side by 2.

▼ DIGITAL

Problem 1 **Using the Inscribed Angle Theorem**

What are the values of *a* and *b*?

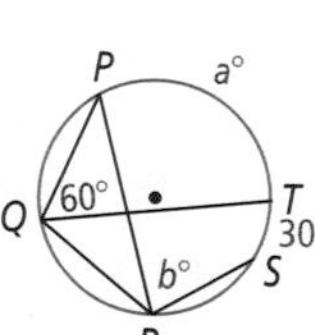

$m\angle PQT = \frac{1}{2}m\overset{\frown}{PT}$	Inscribed Angle Theorem
$60 = \frac{1}{2}a$	Substitute.
$120 = a$	Multiply each side by 2.
$m\angle PRS = \frac{1}{2}m\overset{\frown}{PS}$	Inscribed Angle Theorem
$m\angle PRS = \frac{1}{2}(m\overset{\frown}{PT} + m\overset{\frown}{TS})$	Arc Addition Postulate
$b = \frac{1}{2}(120 + 30)$	Substitute.
$b = 75$	Simplify.

Got It? **ERROR PREVENTION**

Have students identify the arc that is intercepted by the angle. They must find the sum of the smaller arcs to find the measure of the associated arc.

ANSWERS

Got It? a. 90 **b.** $m\angle A = 95$, $m\angle B = 77$, $m\angle C = 85$, and $m\angle D = 103$ **c.** The sum of the measures of opposite angles is 180.

Practice

1. $a = 218$, $b = 109$
2. $a = 54$, $b = 30$, $c = 96$

▼ STUDENT PAGES 510–511

Got It? a. In $\odot O$, what is $m\angle A$?

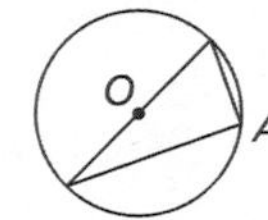

b. What are $m\angle A$, $m\angle B$, $m\angle C$, and $m\angle D$?

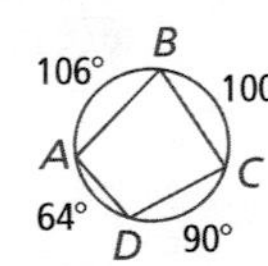

c. What do you notice about the sums of the measures of the opposite angles in the quadrilateral in part (b)?

Plan
What is the intercepted arc of each angle?

A Practice Find the value of each variable. For each circle, the dot represents the center.

1.

2.
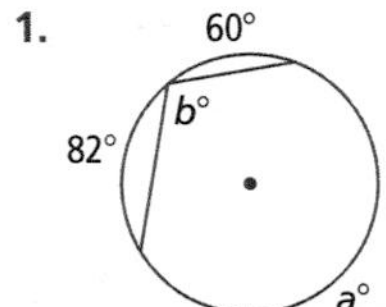

Problem 2 Using Corollaries to Find Angle Measures

Take Note

Have students review their answers for the Solve It at the beginning of this lesson. Then, challenge students to explain the logic of each corollary. They should use Theorem 86 for each corollary. For Corollary 3, ask students to write each angle measure as an expression involving its corresponding arc measure.

Problem 2

Q In 2A, what information do you not need? **[the measure of the small arcs]**

Q What type of arc does $\angle 1$ intercept? **[a semicircle]**

Q In 2B, which arc does $\angle 2$ intercept? **[the same arc as the angle marked 38°]**

▼ STUDENT PAGE 511

You will use three corollaries to the Inscribed Angle Theorem to find measures of angles in circles. The first corollary may confirm an observation you made in the Solve It.

take note **Corollaries to Theorem 86** The Inscribed Angle Theorem

Corollary 1

Two inscribed angles that intercept the same arc are congruent.

Corollary 2

An angle inscribed in a semicircle is a right angle.

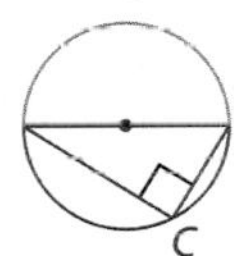

Corollary 3

The opposite angles of a quadrilateral inscribed in a circle are supplementary.

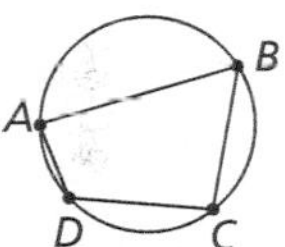

You will prove these corollaries in Exercises 24–26.

▼ DIGITAL

Problem 2 Using Corollaries to Find Angle Measures

What is the measure of each numbered angle?

A

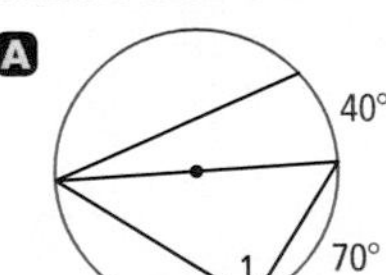

$\angle 1$ is inscribed in a semicircle. By Corollary 2, $\angle 1$ is a right angle, so $m\angle 1 = 90$.

B

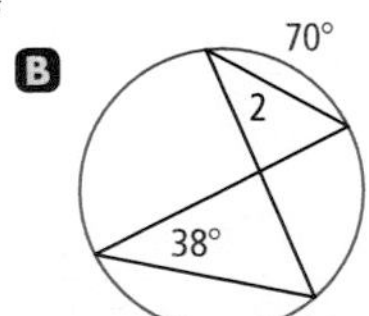

$\angle 2$ and the 38° angle intercept the same arc. By Corollary 1, the angles are congruent, so $m\angle 2 = 38$.

Problem 2 *continued*

Got It? **VISUAL LEARNERS**

Students may benefit from drawing each inscribed angle separately. Once students identify the measure of each angle, have them identify the theorem or corollary that justifies their answers.

ANSWERS

Got It? $m\angle 1 = 90$, $m\angle 2 = 110$, $m\angle 3 = 90$, $m\angle 4 = 70$

Practice

3. $x = 36$, $y = 36$
4. $a = 50$, $b = 90$, $c = 90$

▼ STUDENT PAGE 512

Got It? In the diagram at the right, what is the measure of each numbered angle?

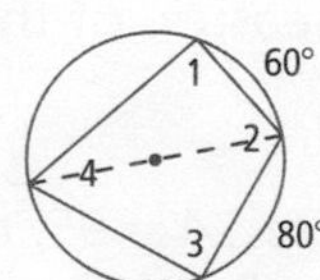

Think

What does the auxiliary line represent in the diagram?

A Practice Find the value of each variable. For each circle, the dot represents the center.

3.

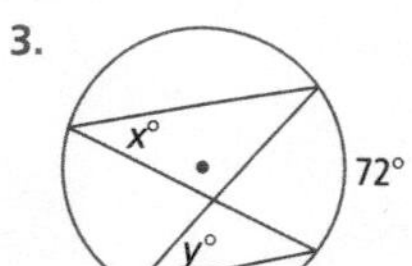

4.

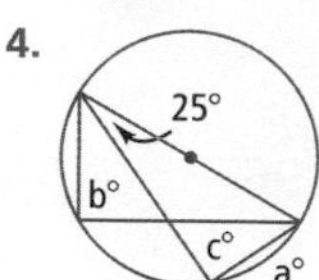

Problem 3 Using Arc Measure

Take Note

Ask students to identify the tangent and the chord in the diagram. Be sure that students connect this theorem with Theorem 86.

Problem 3

Q What angle is related to $\overparen{PMQ}$? **[$\angle PQS$]**

Q How is $\angle PQS$ related to $\angle PQR$? **[They are supplementary.]**

Q How can you find the measure of this angle? **[Subtract the measure of $\angle PQS$ from 180°.]**

▼ STUDENT PAGES 512–513

The following diagram shows point A moving along the circle until a tangent is formed. From the Inscribed Angle Theorem, you know that in the first three diagrams $m\angle A$ is $\frac{1}{2}m\,\overparen{BC}$. As the last diagram suggests, this is also true when A and C coincide.

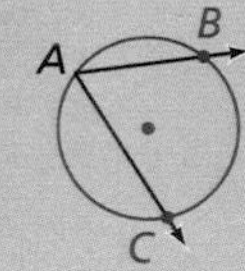

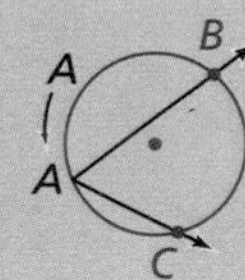

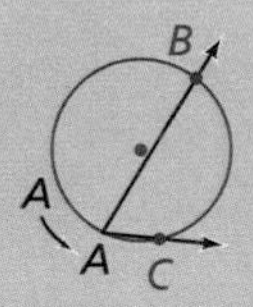

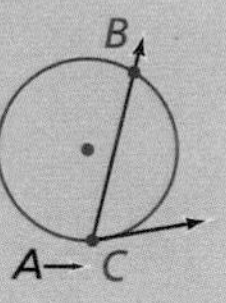

take note

Theorem 87

The measure of an angle formed by a tangent and a chord is half the measure of the intercepted arc.

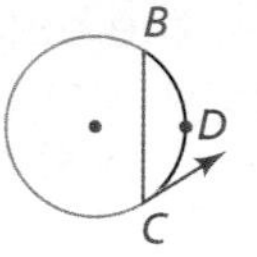

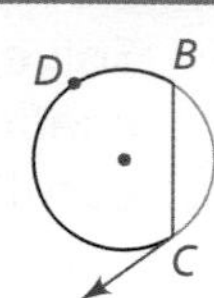

$m\angle C = \frac{1}{2}m\,\overparen{BDC}$

You will prove Theorem 87 in Exercise 27.

▼ DIGITAL

Problem 3 **Using Arc Measure**

In the diagram, $\overleftrightarrow{SR}$ is a tangent to the circle at Q. If $m\overparen{PMQ} = 212$, what is $m\angle PQR$?

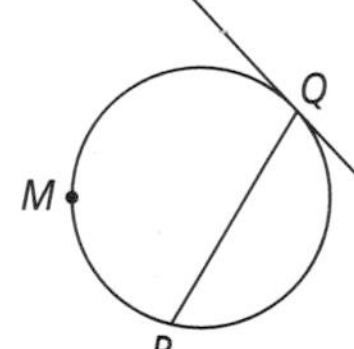

Know

- $\overleftrightarrow{SR}$ is tangent to the circle at Q
- $m\overparen{PMQ} = 212$

Need

$m\angle PQR$

Plan

$m\angle PQS + m\angle PQR = 180$. So first find $m\angle PQS$ using $\overparen{PMQ}$.

$\frac{1}{2}m\overparen{PMQ} = m\angle PQS$	The measure of an $\angle$ formed by a tangent and a chord is $\frac{1}{2}$ the measure of the intercepted arc.
$\frac{1}{2}(212) = m\angle PQS$	Substitute.
$106 = m\angle PQS$	Simplify.
$m\angle PQS + m\angle PQR = 180$	Linear Pair Postulate
$106 + m\angle PQR = 180$	Substitute.
$m\angle PQR = 74$	Simplify.

Got It?

VISUAL LEARNERS

Q What type of triangle is $\triangle JLQ$? Justify your answer. **[$\triangle JLQ$ is a right triangle because $\angle LJQ$ is an inscribed angle that intercepts a semicircle.]**

Q How can you find y? **[Subtract 35 from 90.]**

Q What arc does $\angle KJL$ intercept? **[$\overset{\frown}{JL}$]**

Q Which other inscribed angle intercepts the same arc? **[$\angle JQL$]**

ANSWERS

Got It? a. $x = 35$, $y = 55$ **b.** An inscribed $\angle$, and an $\angle$ formed by a tangent and chord, are both equal to half the measure of the intercepted arc. Since the angles intercept the same arc, their measures are = and they are ≅.

Practice

5. $x = 65$, $y = 130$ **6.** $e = 65$, $f = 130$

▼ STUDENT PAGES 513–514

Got It? **a.** In the diagram at the right, $\overline{KJ}$ is tangent to $\odot O$. What are the values of x and y?

b. Reasoning In part (a), an inscribed angle ($\angle Q$) and an angle formed by a tangent and chord ($\angle KJL$) intercept the same arc. What is always true of these angles? Explain.

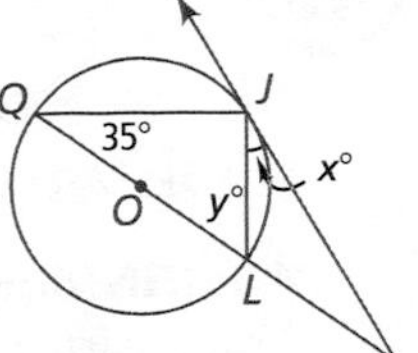

A Practice In Exercises 5 and 6, find the value of each variable. Lines that appear to be tangent are tangent.

5.

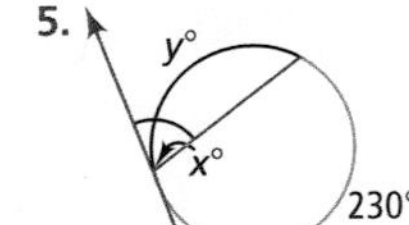

6.

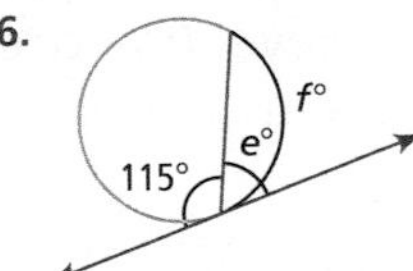

3 Lesson Check

Do you know HOW?
If students have difficulty with Exercise 7, then have them draw the angle separately.

Do you UNDERSTAND?
If students have difficulty with Exercise 11, then have them review Problem 2 and compare the drawings.

Close

Q How can you find the measure of an inscribed angle? **[Divide the measure of its intercepted arc by 2.]**

Q What is the relationship between an angle formed by a tangent and a chord and the arc it intercepts? **[The measure of the angle is half the measure of the intercepted arc.]**

ANSWERS

7. $\overset{\frown}{BCD}$ **8.** $\angle D$

9. $\angle A$ and $\angle C$ are suppl., and $\angle B$ and $\angle D$ are suppl.

10. Sample answer: For inscribed $\angle ABC$, B is the vertex and A, B, and C are points on the circle. The intercepted arc of $\angle ABC$ consists of points A, C, and all the points on the circle in the interior of $\angle ABC$.

11. $\angle A$ is not inscribed in a semicircle.

▼ STUDENT PAGES 514–515

Lesson Check

Do you know HOW?

Use the diagram for Exercises 7–9.

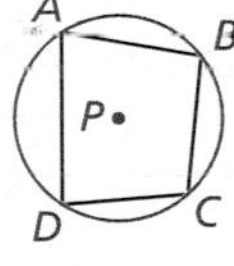

7. Which arc does $\angle A$ intercept?

8. Which angle intercepts $\overset{\frown}{ABC}$?

9. Which angles of quadrilateral $ABCD$ are supplementary?

Do you UNDERSTAND? MATHEMATICAL PRACTICES

10. Vocabulary What is the relationship between an inscribed angle and its intercepted arc?

11. Error Analysis A classmate says that $m\angle A = 90$. What is your classmate's error?

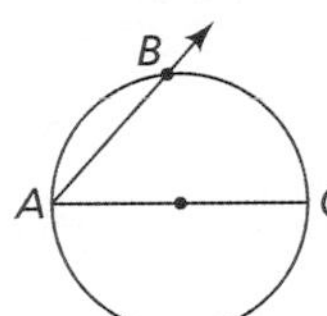

Practice

▼ STUDENT PAGES 515–516

More Practice and Problem-Solving Exercises

ASSIGNMENT GUIDE

The assignments below are for the More Practice and Problem-Solving Exercises. You may also want to assign the A-Level Practice Exercises for homework if these are not used in class.

Average: 12–27

Advanced: 12–31

Mathematical Practices The exercises listed focus on the Standards for Mathematical Practices listed.

EX. 15: Persevere in Solving Problems (MP 1)

EX. 21b, 22, 28, 29: Construct Arguments (MP 3)

EX. 11: Critique the Reasoning of Others (MP 3)

EX. 21: Model (MP 4)

EXERCISE 17: Use the **Think About a Plan** worksheet in the Online Teacher Resources to further support students' development in becoming independent learners.

HOMEWORK QUICK CHECK

To check students' understanding of key skills and concepts, go over Exercises 13, 15, 17, 22, and 27.

ANSWERS

12. Rectangle; opposite ∠s are ≅ (because figure is ▱) and suppl. (because opp. ∠s intercept arcs whose measures sum to 360). ≅ suppl. ∠s are rt. ∠s, so the inscribed ▱ must be a rectangle.

13. **a.** 96
b. 55
c. 77
d. 154

14. **a.** 40
b. 50
c. 40
d. 40
e. 65

15. Isosc. trapezoid; answers may vary. Sample: For inscribed trapezoid *ABCD*, ∠*A* must be suppl. to ∠*C* (Corollary 3 to Thm. 86), and ∠*C* must be suppl. to ∠*B* (same-side int. angles of parallel lines are suppl.). So ∠*A* ≅ ∠*B*, and the trapezoid must be isosc.

16. $a = 26$, $b = 64$, $c = 42$

17. $a = 22$, $b = 78$, $c = 156$

18. $a = 30$, $b = 60$, $c = 62$, $d = 124$, $e = 60$

More Practice and Problem-Solving Exercises

12. Writing A parallelogram inscribed in a circle must be what kind of parallelogram? Explain.

Find each indicated measure for ⊙*O*.

13. **a.** $m\widehat{BC}$
b. $m\angle B$
c. $m\angle C$
d. $m\widehat{AB}$

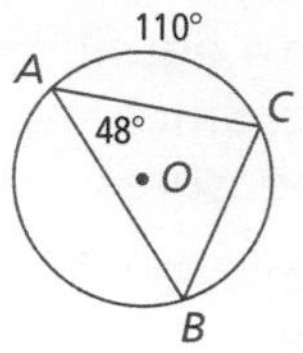

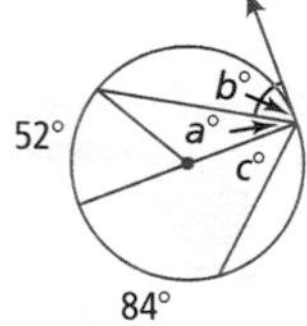

14. **a.** $m\angle A$
b. $m\widehat{CE}$
c. $m\angle C$
d. $m\angle D$
e. $m\angle ABE$

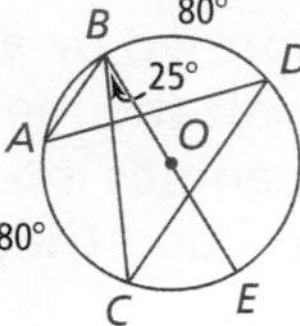

15. Think About a Plan What kind of trapezoid can be inscribed in a circle? Justify your response.

- Draw several diagrams to make a conjecture.
- How can parallel lines help?

Find the value of each variable. For each circle, the dot represents the center.

16.

17.

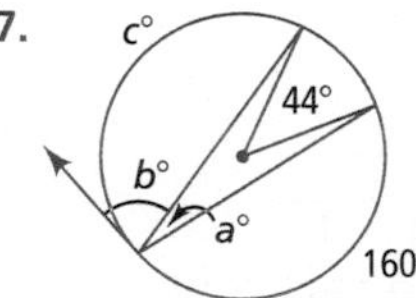

18.

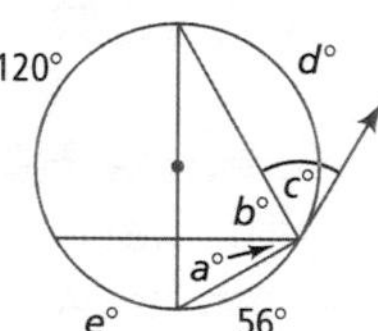

19. $\odot O$ with inscribed $\angle ABC$ (given); $m\angle ABO = \frac{1}{2}m\widehat{AP}$ and $m\angle OBC = \frac{1}{2}m\widehat{PC}$ (Inscribed $\angle$ Thm., Case I); $m\angle ABO + m\angle OBC = m\angle ABC$ ($\angle$ Add. Post.); $\frac{1}{2}m\widehat{AP} + \frac{1}{2}m\widehat{PC} = m\angle ABC$ (Subst. Prop.); $\frac{1}{2}(m\widehat{AP} + m\widehat{PC}) = m\angle ABC$ (Distr. Prop.); $\frac{1}{2}m\widehat{AC} = m\angle ABC$ (Arc Add. Post.)

20. $\odot S$ with inscribed $\angle PQR$ (given); $m\angle PQT = \frac{1}{2}m\widehat{PT}$ (Inscribed $\angle$Thm., Case I); $m\angle RQT = \frac{1}{2}m\widehat{RT}$ (Inscribed $\angle$Thm., Case I); $m\widehat{PR} = m\widehat{PT} - m\widehat{RT}$ (Arc Add. Post.); $m\angle PQR = m\angle PQT - m\angle RQT$ ($\angle$ Add. Post.); $m\angle PQR = \frac{1}{2}m\widehat{PT} - \frac{1}{2}m\widehat{RT}$ (Subst. Prop.); $m\angle PQR = \frac{1}{2}m\widehat{PR}$ (Subst. Prop.)

21. Answers may vary. Sample:

a. If the cameras' lenses open at ≅ angles, then in the positions shown they share the same arc of the scene.

b. No; the distances from each position of the scene to each camera affect the look of the scene.

22. No; since opposite angles of a quadrilateral inscribed in a circle must be supplementary, the only rhombus that meets the criteria is a square.

23. $\angle ACB$ is a rt. $\angle$ because it is inscribed in semicircle $\widehat{ACB}$, so $\overline{AC} \perp \overleftrightarrow{BC}$. If a line is ⊥ to a radius at its endpoint, it is tangent to the circle.

24. $\odot O$, $\angle A$ intercepts $\widehat{BC}$, and $\angle D$ intercepts $\widehat{BC}$ (Given); $m\angle A = \frac{1}{2}m\widehat{BC}$ and $m\angle D = \frac{1}{2}m\widehat{BC}$ (Inscribed $\angle$ Thm.); $m\angle A = m\angle D$ (Subst. Prop.); $\angle A \cong \angle D$ (Def. of ≅ ∠s).

25. $\odot O$ with $\angle CAB$ inscribed in a semicircle (Given); $m\angle CAB = \frac{1}{2}m\widehat{BDC}$ (Inscribed $\angle$ Thm.); $m\widehat{BDC} = 180$ (A semicircle has a measure of 180.); $m\angle CAB = 90$ (Subst. Prop.); $\angle CAB$ is a rt. $\angle$ (Def. of rt. $\angle$).

Write a proof for Exercises 19 and 20.

Proof **19.** Inscribed Angle Theorem, Case II

Given: $\odot O$ with inscribed $\angle ABC$

Prove: $m\angle ABC = \frac{1}{2}m\widehat{AC}$

(*Hint:* Use the Inscribed Angle Theorem, Case I.)

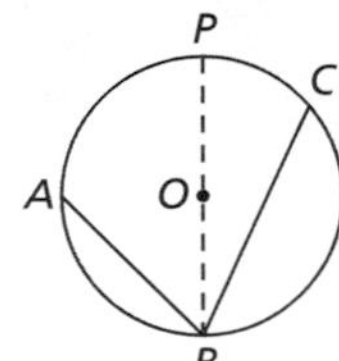

Proof **20.** Inscribed Angle Theorem, Case III

Given: $\odot S$ with inscribed $\angle PQR$

Prove: $m\angle PQR = \frac{1}{2}m\widehat{PR}$

(*Hint:* Use the Inscribed Angle Theorem, Case I.)

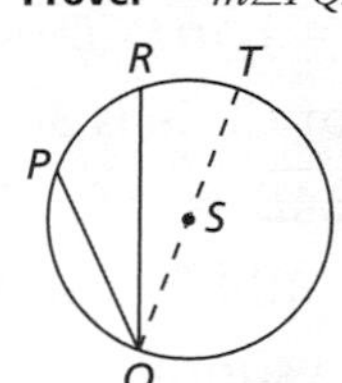

21. Television The director of a telecast wants the option of showing the same scene from three different views.

a. Explain why cameras in the positions shown in the diagram will transmit the same scene.

b. Reasoning Will the scenes look the same when the director views them on the control room monitors? Explain.

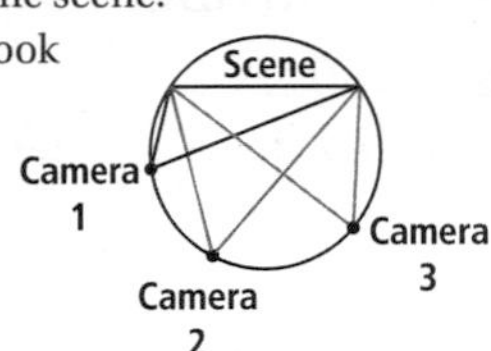

22. Reasoning Can a rhombus that is not a square be inscribed in a circle? Justify your answer.

23. Constructions The diagrams below show the construction of a tangent to a circle from a point outside the circle. Explain why $\overleftrightarrow{BC}$ must be tangent to $\odot A$. (*Hint:* Copy the third diagram and draw $\overline{AC}$.)

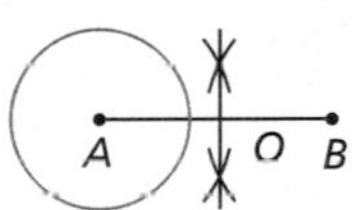

Given: ⊙A and point B Construct the midpoint of $\overline{AB}$. Label the point O.

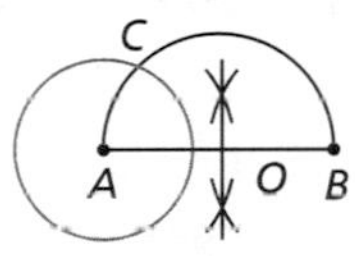

Construct a semicircle with radius OA and center O. Label its intersection with ⊙A as C.

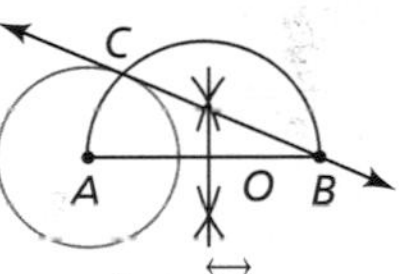

Draw $\overleftrightarrow{BC}$.

Write a proof for Exercises 24–27.

Proof **24.** Inscribed Angle Theorem, Corollary 1

Given: $\odot O$, $\angle A$ intercepts $\widehat{BC}$, $\angle D$ intercepts $\widehat{BC}$.

Prove: $\angle A \cong \angle D$

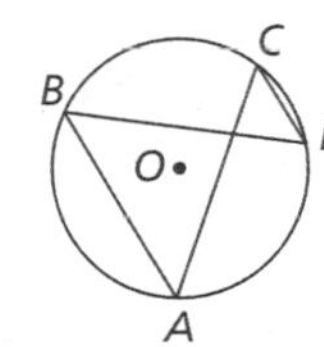

Proof **25.** Inscribed Angle Theorem, Corollary 2

Given: $\odot O$ with $\angle CAB$ inscribed in a semicircle

Prove: $\angle CAB$ is a right angle.

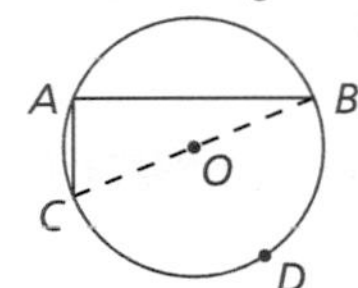

More Practice and Problem-Solving Exercises *continued*

26. Quadrilateral $ABCD$ inscribed in $\odot O$ (Given); $m\angle A = \frac{1}{2}m\widehat{BCD}$ and $m\angle C = \frac{1}{2}m\widehat{BAD}$ (Inscribed $\angle$ Thm.); $m\angle A + m\angle C = \frac{1}{2}m\widehat{BCD} + \frac{1}{2}m\widehat{BAD}$ (Add. Prop. of =); $m\widehat{BCD} + m\widehat{BAD} = 360$ (Arc measure of circle is 360.); $\frac{1}{2}m\widehat{BCD} + \frac{1}{2}m\widehat{BAD} = 180$ (Mult. Prop. of =) $m\angle A + m\angle C = 180$ (Subst. Prop. of =); $\angle A$ and $\angle C$ are suppl. (Def. of suppl. A); $m\angle B = \frac{1}{2}m\widehat{ADC}$ and $m\angle D = \frac{1}{2}m\widehat{ABC}$ (Inscribed $\angle$ Thm.); $m\angle B + m\angle D = \frac{1}{2}m\widehat{ADC} + \frac{1}{2}m\widehat{ABC}$ (Add. Prop. of =); $m\widehat{ADC} + m\widehat{ABC} = 360$ (Arc measure of circle is 360.); $\frac{1}{2}m\widehat{ADC} + \frac{1}{2}m\widehat{ABC} = 180$ (Mult. Prop. of =) $m\angle B + m\angle D = 180$ (Subst. Prop. of =); $\angle B$ and $\angle D$ are suppl. (Def. of suppl. ∠s).

27. $\overline{GH}$ and tangent ℓ intersecting $\odot E$ at H (Given); draw $\overleftrightarrow{HE}$ intersecting $\odot E$ at D so $\overline{HD}$ is a diameter (2 pts. determine a line.); $\angle DHI$ is a rt. $\angle$ (A tangent line is $\perp$ to radius at pt. of tangency.); $m\angle DHI = 90$ (Def. of rt. $\angle$); $m\widehat{DGH} = 180$ (A semicircle has a measure of 180.); $m\angle DHG + m\angle GHI = m\angle DHI$ ($\angle$ Add. Post.); $m\widehat{DG} + m\widehat{GFH} = m\widehat{DGH}$ (Arc Add. Post.); $m\angle DHG + m\angle GHI = 90$ (Subst. Prop. of =); $m\widehat{DG} + m\widehat{GFH} = 180$ (Subst. Prop. of =); $\frac{1}{2}(m\widehat{DG} + m\widehat{GFH}) = 90$ (Mult. Prop. of =); $m\angle DHG + m\angle GHI = \frac{1}{2}(m\widehat{DG} + m\widehat{GFH})$ (Subst. Prop.); $m\angle DHG = \frac{1}{2}m\widehat{DG}$ (Inscribed $\angle$ Thm.); $\frac{1}{2}m\widehat{DG} + m\angle GHI = \frac{1}{2}m\widehat{DG} + \frac{1}{2}m\widehat{GFH}$ (Subst. Prop. and Distr. Prop.); $m\angle GHI = \frac{1}{2}m\widehat{GFH}$ (Subtr. Prop. of =).

28. false

29. True; the measure of the intercepted arc must be 2 • 90 or 180, so the intercepted arc is a semicircle.

▼ STUDENT PAGE 517

Proof **26.** Inscribed Angle Theorem, Corollary 3

Given: Quadrilateral $ABCD$ inscribed in $\odot O$

Prove: $\angle A$ and $\angle C$ are supplementary. $\angle B$ and $\angle D$ are supplementary.

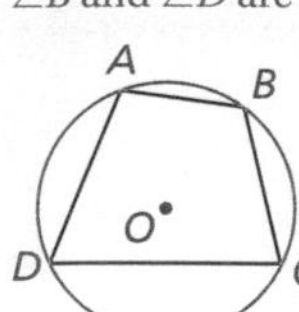

Proof **27.** Theorem 87

Given: $\overline{GH}$ and tangent ℓ intersecting $\odot E$ at H

Prove: $m\angle GHI = \frac{1}{2}m\widehat{GFH}$

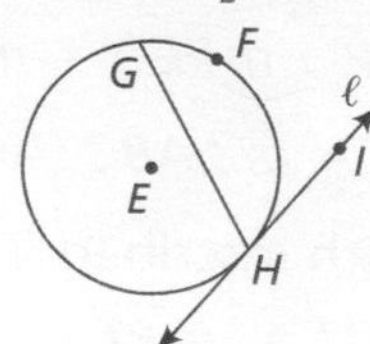

Challenge

Reasoning Is the statement *true* or *false*? If it is true, give a convincing argument. If it is false, give a counterexample.

28. If two angles inscribed in a circle are congruent, then they intercept the same arc.

29. If an inscribed angle is a right angle, then it is inscribed in a semicircle.

Proof **30.** Prove that if two arcs of a circle are included between parallel chords, then the arcs are congruent.

31. Constructions Draw two segments. Label their lengths x and y. Construct the geometric mean of x and y. (*Hint:* Recall a theorem about a geometric mean.)

30.

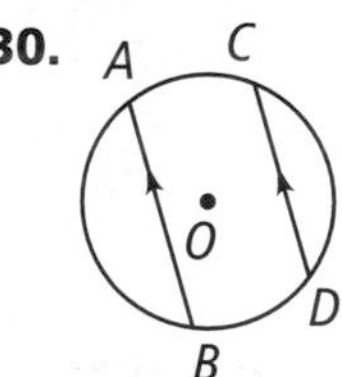

Given: $\overline{AB} \parallel \overline{CD}$
Prove: $\widehat{AC} \cong \widehat{BD}$
Proof: $\odot O$ with $\overline{AB} \parallel \overline{CD}$ (given); draw $\overline{AD}$ (2 pts. determine a line); $\angle CDA \cong \angle DAB$ (∥ lines have ≅ alt. int. ∠s); $\widehat{AC} \cong \widehat{BD}$ (≅ inscribed ∠s intercept ≅ arcs).

31.

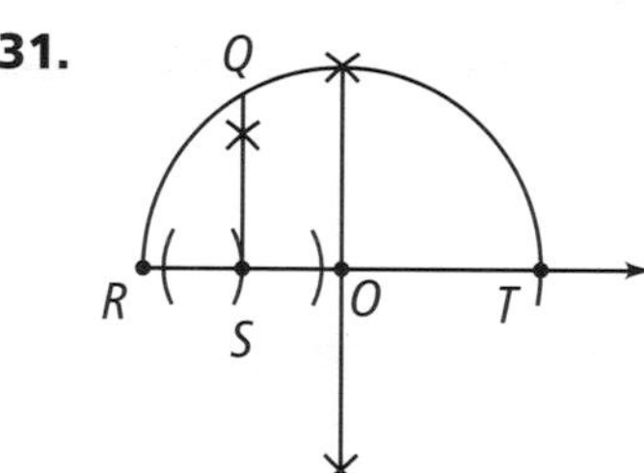

Construct $\overline{RT}$ so $RS = x$ and $ST = y$. Find O, the midpt. of $\overline{RT}$, and draw a semicircle with diameter $\overline{RT}$. Construct $\overline{SQ} \perp \overline{RT}$. Then $\triangle RQT$ is a rt. $\triangle$ and QS is the geometric mean of RS and ST.

5 Assess and Remediate

Lesson Quiz

1. What are the values of x and b?

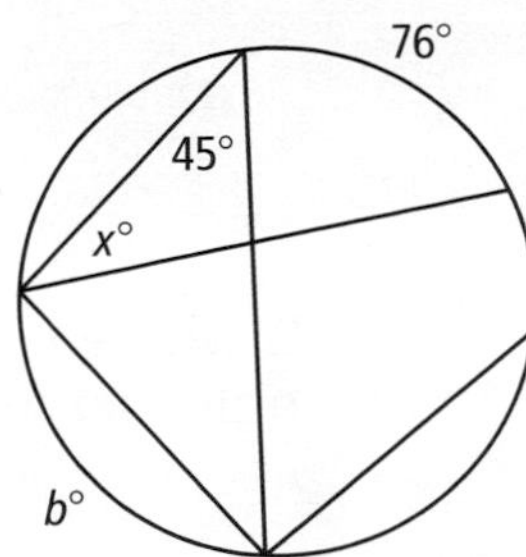

2. Do you UNDERSTAND? In the diagram, $\overleftrightarrow{RT}$ is tangent to the circle at S. If the measure of $\widehat{SVU}$ is 138°, what is $m\angle TSU$?

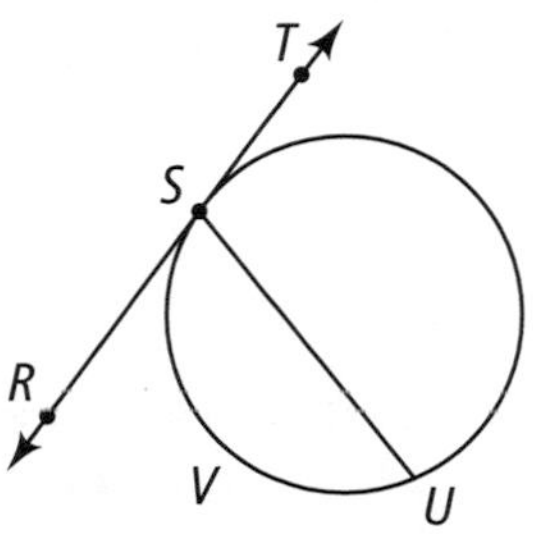

3. What is $m\angle C$?

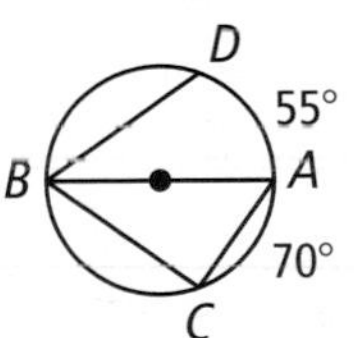

ANSWERS TO LESSON QUIZ

1. $x = 38$, $b = 90$

2. 111

3. 90

Prescription for Remediation

Use the student work on the Lesson Quiz to prescribe a differentiated assignment.

Points	Differentiated Remediation
0–1	Intervention
2	On-level
3	Extension

Online Assessment

Assign the Lesson Quiz in Success Tracker on **pearsonsuccessnet.com**. Success Tracker will automatically score the quiz and assign appropriate intervention or enrichment to each student based on the results. The compiled data appear in three different reports for instant analysis of whole class and individual student performance.

Differentiated Remediation

Intervention

- **RETEACHING** (2 pages) Provides reteaching and practice exercises for the key lesson concepts. Use with struggling students or absent students.
- **ENGLISH LANGUAGE LEARNER SUPPORT** Helps students develop and reinforce mathematical vocabulary and key concepts.

On-Level

- **PRACTICE** (2 pages) Provides extra practice for each lesson. For simpler practice exercises, use the Form K Practice pages found in the Online Teacher Resources.
- **THINK ABOUT A PLAN** Helps students develop specific problem-solving skills and strategies by providing scaffolded guiding questions.
- **STANDARDIZED TEST PREP** Focuses on all major exercises, all major question types, and helps students prepare for the high-stakes assessments.

Extension

- **ENRICHMENT** Provides students with interesting problems and activities that extend the concepts of the lesson.
- **ACTIVITIES, GAMES, AND PUZZLES** Worksheets that can be used for concept development, enrichment, and for fun!

8-6 Angle Measures and Segment Lengths

Common Core State Standard
G.C.2 Identify and describe relationships among inscribed angles, radii, and chords . . .

Preparing to Teach

BIG ideas Reasoning and Proof
Measurement

ESSENTIAL UNDERSTANDING

Angles formed by intersecting lines have a special relationship to the arcs the intersecting lines intercept. Arcs formed by lines intersecting either within a circle or outside a circle are related to the angles formed by the lines. There are special relationships between intersecting chords, intersecting secants, or a secant and tangent that intersect.

Math Background

Students will learn about the relationship between the angle formed by two segments that intersect a circle and the intercepted arcs. They will also learn that the segment lengths created by intersecting lines are proportional. Students may benefit from creating a table that contains a summary of all the information they have learned about circles so far.

Have them organize the information by the figures involved. Students should have a section for arc length, inscribed angles, tangents, and chords. Some information may appear in more than one section. Help students to organize all the theorems that they have learned about circles.

Dynamic geometry software can provide students with an excellent tool to investigate conjectures about angle measures and segment lengths related to circles.

ELL Support

FOCUS ON LANGUAGE Place students in small groups. Students can write the vocabulary words from the chapter on one side of individual index cards. Invite students to discuss the meaning of the word and restate a definition in their own words. Students can write the definition on the back of the card, along with sketches or examples. Have students use the cards to quiz each other and then keep the cards for later review.

USE MULTIPLE REPRESENTATION Have other texts and workbooks of different instructional levels that explore tangents, secants, chords, angles, and the other chapter concepts.

Lesson Vocabulary

- secant

Mathematical Practices

MODEL WITH MATHEMATICS. In Problem 2, students will apply their knowledge of circles and tangent lines to model the view from a satellite in orbit.

1 Interactive Learning

Solve It!

PURPOSE To discover the measure of an angle formed by two chords in a circle

PROCESS Students must use their knowledge of inscribed angles and exterior angles of triangles to write an equation for $m\angle 1$.

Q How is $\angle 1$ related to the triangles formed by the chords? **[It is an exterior angle of the triangles.]**

Q What do you know about an exterior angle of a triangle? **[Its measure is equal to the sum of the remote interior angles.]**

Q What is $m\angle C$ and $m\angle D$? **[$m\angle C = \frac{1}{2}m\widehat{AD}$, $m\angle D = \frac{1}{2}m\widehat{BC}$]**

ANSWER $m\angle 1 = \frac{1}{2}(m\widehat{AD} + m\widehat{BC})$. Sample explanation: $m\angle 1 = 100$ (Exterior $\angle$ Thm.); $m\angle B = \frac{1}{2}m\widehat{AD}$, so $m\widehat{AD} = 2m\angle B = 140$; $m\angle A = \frac{1}{2}m\widehat{BC}$, so $m\widehat{BC} = 2m\angle A = 60$; $m\widehat{AD} + m\widehat{BC} = 140 + 60 = 200$; $m\angle 1 = \frac{1}{2}(m\widehat{AD} + m\widehat{BC})$

▼ DIGITAL (STUDENT WORK SPACE PAGE 518)

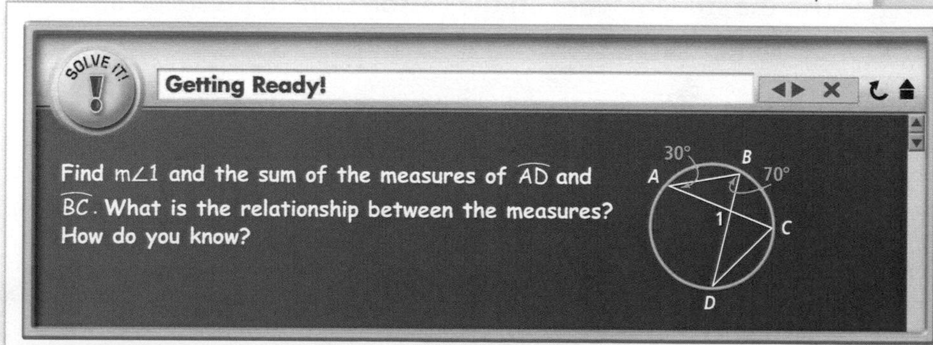

SOLVE IT!
Getting Ready!
Find m∠1 and the sum of the measures of AD and BC. What is the relationship between the measures? How do you know?
30°
A
B
70°
1
C
D

CONNECT THE MATH In the Solve It, students determine the relationship of an angle inside a circle formed by two chords and the measures of the arcs that the chords form. In this lesson, students use inscribed angles to see that the measure of an interior angle is equal to half the sum of the intercepted arcs.

2 Guided Instruction

Problem 1 Finding Angle Measures

Take Note
Have students compare and contrast the theorems presented in the Take Note. They should see that the theorems discuss intersecting lines. Inside a circle, the sum of the intercepted arcs is used. Outside, the difference is used.

Students should be able to produce this proof given their work in the Solve It. Ask them to identify which segment needs to be drawn to create a triangle within the circle. Then, students can use the same argument they developed in the Solve It.

Problem 1

Q In 1A, does the vertex of the angle lie inside or outside the circle? **[inside]**

Q Should you use the sum or difference of the arc measures to calculate the measure of the angle? **[the sum]**

Q In 1B, what measure is unknown? **[one of the intercepted arcs]**

Q Should you use addition or subtraction to calculate the measure of the arc? Why? **[Use the difference because the vertex of the angle is outside the circle.]**

Got It? **ERROR PREVENTION**
Have students describe the process for finding each type of figure. In part (a), the measure of an arc is unknown so there will be a variable in the equation. In part (b), students should be able to write an expression that can be simplified to find the value of y.

▼ STUDENT PAGES 518–519

Essential Understanding Angles formed by intersecting lines have a special relationship to the related arcs formed when the lines intersect a circle. In this lesson, you will study angles and arcs formed by lines intersecting either within a circle or outside a circle.

take note

Theorem 88

The measure of an angle formed by two lines that intersect inside a circle is half the sum of the measures of the intercepted arcs.

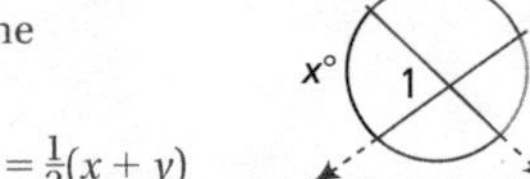

$m\angle 1 = \frac{1}{2}(x + y)$

Theorem 89

The measure of an angle formed by two lines that intersect outside a circle is half the difference of the measures of the intercepted arcs.

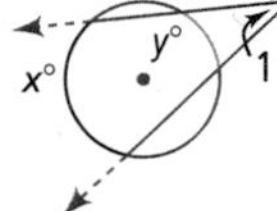

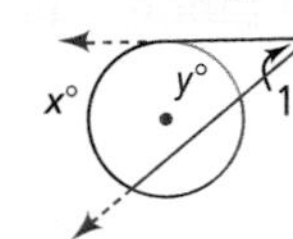

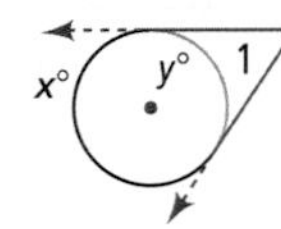

$m\angle 1 = \frac{1}{2}(x - y)$

You will prove Theorem 89 In Exercises 28 and 29.

In Theorem 88, the lines from a point outside the circle going through the circle are called secants. A **secant** is a line that intersects a circle at two points. $\overleftrightarrow{AB}$ is a secant, $\overrightarrow{AB}$ is a secant ray, and $\overline{AB}$ is a secant segment. A chord is part of a secant.

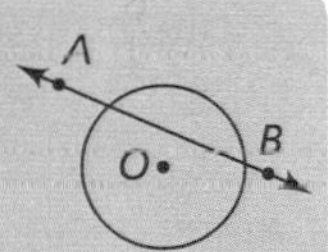

Proof Proof of Theorem 88

Given: $\odot O$ with intersecting chords $\overline{AC}$ and $\overline{BD}$

Prove: $m\angle 1 = \frac{1}{2}(m\widehat{AB} + m\widehat{CD})$

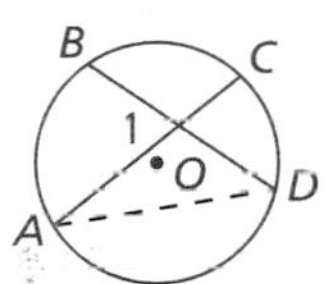

Begin by drawing auxiliary $\overline{AD}$ as shown in the diagram.

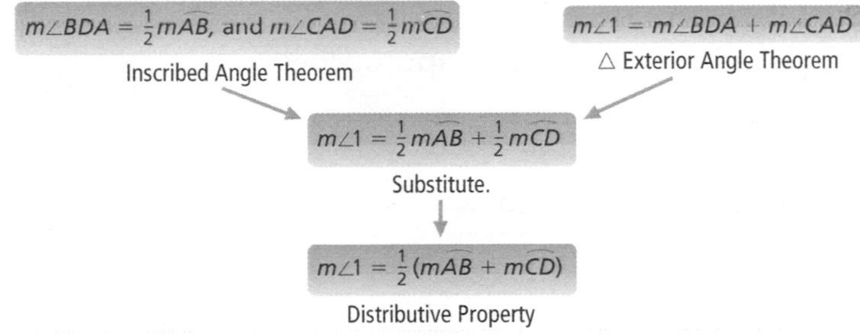

$m\angle BDA = \frac{1}{2}m\widehat{AB}$, and $m\angle CAD = \frac{1}{2}m\widehat{CD}$
Inscribed Angle Theorem
$m\angle 1 = m\angle BDA + m\angle CAD$
△ Exterior Angle Theorem
$m\angle 1 = \frac{1}{2}m\widehat{AB} + \frac{1}{2}m\widehat{CD}$
Substitute.
$m\angle 1 = \frac{1}{2}(m\widehat{AB} + m\widehat{CD})$
Distributive Property

▼ DIGITAL

Problem 1 **Finding Angle Measures**

Algebra What is the value of each variable?

A

$x = \frac{1}{2}(46 + 90)$ Theorem 88

$x = 68$ Simplify.

B

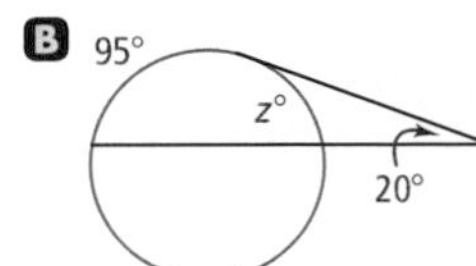

$20 = \frac{1}{2}(95 - z)$ Theorem 89

$40 = 95 - z$ Multiply each side by 2.

$z = 55$ Solve for z.

Problem 1 *continued*

ANSWERS

Got It? **a.** 250 **b.** 40 **c.** 40

Practice

1. 50 **2.** $x = 60$, $y = 70$

▼ STUDENT PAGES 519–520

Got It? What is the value of each variable?

a. 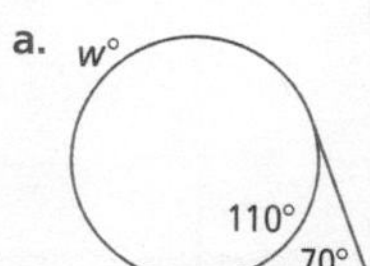

b. 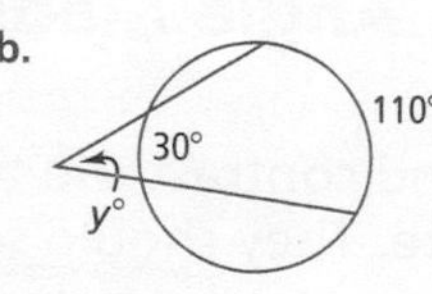

c. 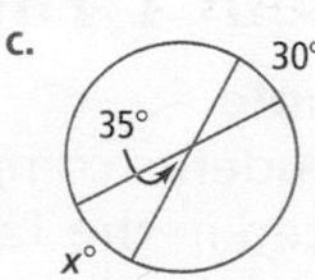

Practice **Algebra** Find the value of each variable.

1. 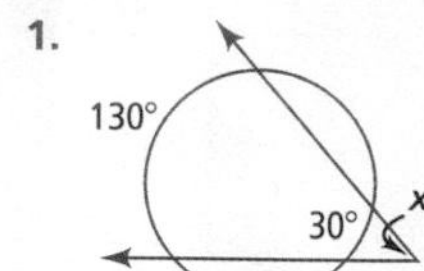

2. 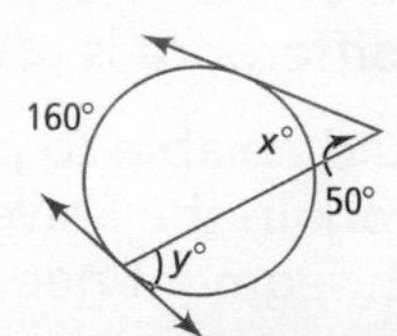

Problem 2 Finding an Arc Measure

Q What arcs are intercepted by the tangent lines? **[$\widehat{AB}$ and $\widehat{AEB}$]**

Q What is the relationship between the intercepted arcs? **[They form the entire circle, so their sum is 360°.]**

Q Which theorem can you use to find the measure of the arcs? **[Theorem 89]**

Got It? **VISUAL LEARNERS**

For part (a), have students draw a diagram with the new angle measure. The equation they write should be similar to the one in Problem 2. For part (b), have students act out the problem. They can hold their arms in an angle and view the chalkboard. Ask whether moving closer to the chalkboard increases or decreases the area of the chalkboard they can see between their arms.

ANSWERS

Got It? **a.** 160 **b.** The probe is closer; as an observer moves away from Earth, the viewing angle decreases and the measure of the arc of Earth that is viewed gets larger and approaches 180°.

Practice

3. $x = 115$, $y = 74$ **4.** 140

▼ DIGITAL

Problem 2 **Finding an Arc Measure**

Satellite **A satellite in a geostationary orbit above Earth's equator has a viewing angle of Earth formed by the two tangents to the equator. The viewing angle is about 17.5°. What is the measure of the arc of Earth that is viewed from the satellite?**

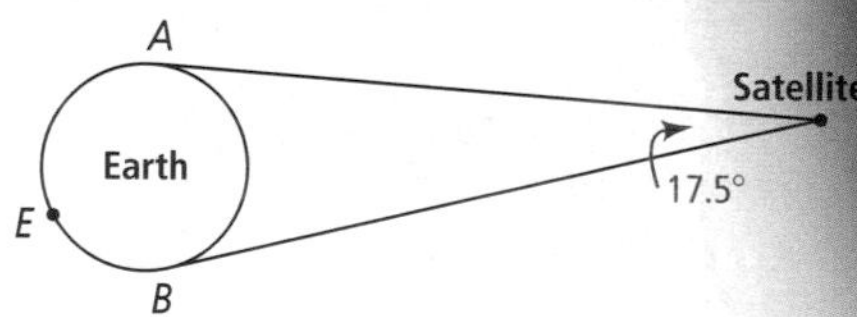

Let $m\widehat{AB} = x$.

Then $m\widehat{AEB} = 360 - x$.

$17.5 = \frac{1}{2}(m\widehat{AEB} - m\widehat{AB})$	Theorem 89
$17.5 = \frac{1}{2}[(360 - x) - x]$	Substitute.
$17.5 = \frac{1}{2}(360 - 2x)$	Simplify.
$17.5 = 180 - x$	Distributive Property
$x = 162.5$	Solve for x.

A 162.5° arc can be viewed from the satellite.

▼ STUDENT PAGES 520–521

Got It? a. A departing space probe sends back a picture of Earth as it crosses Earth's equator. The angle formed by the two tangents to the equator is 20°. What is the measure of the arc of the equator that is visible to the space probe?

Think How can you represent the measures of the arcs?

b. Reasoning Is the probe or the geostationary satellite in Problem 2 closer to Earth? Explain.

Practice **3. Algebra** Find the value of each variable.

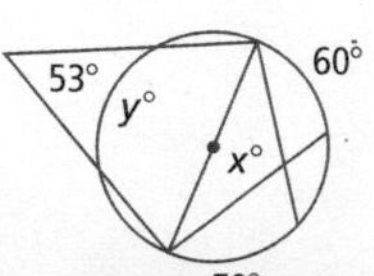

4. Photography You focus your camera on a circular fountain. Your camera is at the vertex of the angle formed by tangents to the fountain. You estimate that this angle is 40°. What is the measure of the arc of the circular basin of the fountain that will be in the photograph?

Problem 3 Finding Segment Lengths

Have students draw a diagram similar to the one at the bottom of the page. They can use a ruler to measure the segments created and find the product of those lengths. Have students write a conjecture about why they think the product remains constant.

Take Note

Emphasize that the products must use the entire segment length. Ask students to explain how this is shown in Case II and Case III.

Q What type of equation can lead to a set of equal products? **[a proportion]**

Q What type of triangles uses proportions? **[similar triangles]**

Problem 3

Q Which case of Theorem 90 is represented in 3A? **[Case II]**

Q What segment lengths should you use in the equation? **[6, 14, 7, and 7 + *y*]**

Q Which case of Theorem 90 is represented in 3B? **[Case III]**

Q Which segment length will be repeated in the equation? **[8]**

▼ STUDENT PAGES 521–522

Essential Understanding There is a special relationship between two intersecting chords, two intersecting secants, or a secant that intersects a tangent. This relationship allows you to find the lengths of unknown segments.

From a given point P, you can draw two segments to a circle along infinitely many lines. For example, $\overline{PA_1}$ and $\overline{PB_1}$ lie along one such line. Theorem 90 states the surprising result that no matter which line you use, the product of the lengths $PA \cdot PB$ remains constant.

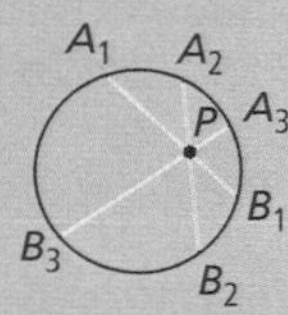

take note

Theorem 90

For a given point and circle, the product of the lengths of the two segments from the point to the circle is constant along any line through the point and circle.

I.

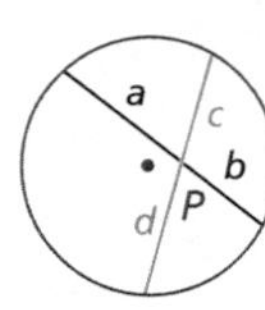

$a \cdot b = c \cdot d$

II.

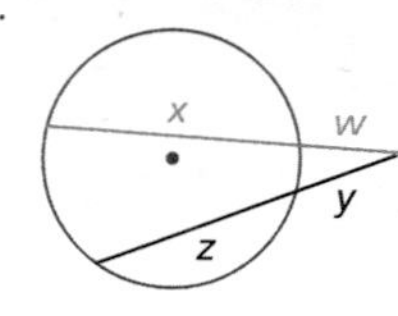

$(w + x)w = (y + z)y$

III.

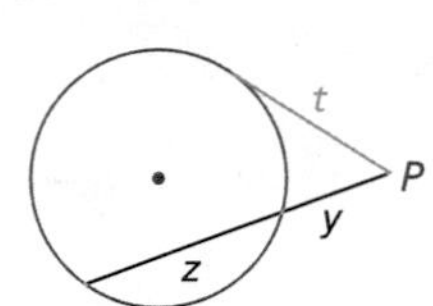

$(y + z)y = t^2$

As you use Theorem 90, remember the following.

- **Case I:** The products of the chord segments are equal.
- **Case II:** The products of the secants and their outer segments are equal.
- **Case III:** The product of a secant and its outer segment equals the square of the tangent.

Here is a proof for Case I. You will prove Case II and Case III in Exercises 30 and 31.

Proof of Theorem 90, Case I

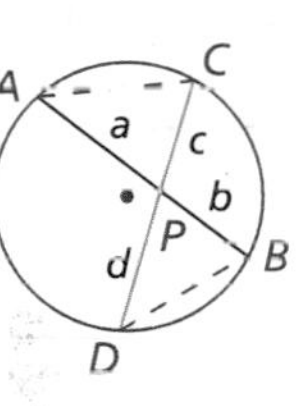

Given: A circle with chords $\overline{AB}$ and $\overline{CD}$ intersecting at P

Prove: $a \cdot b = c \cdot d$

Draw $\overline{AC}$ and $\overline{BD}$. $\angle A \cong \angle D$ and $\angle C \cong \angle B$ because each pair intercepts the same arc, and angles that intercept the same arc are congruent. $\triangle APC \sim \triangle DPB$ by the Angle-Angle Similarity Postulate. The lengths of corresponding sides of similar triangles are proportional, so $\frac{a}{d} = \frac{c}{b}$. Therefore, $a \cdot b = c \cdot d$.

▼ DIGITAL

ONLINE PROBLEMS

Problem 3 Finding Segment Lengths

Algebra Find the value of the variable in $\odot N$.

A

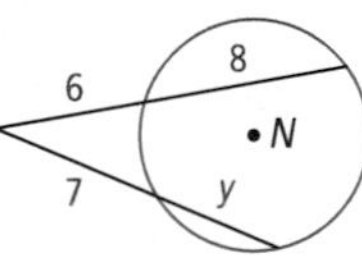

$(6 + 8)6 = (7 + y)7$	Thm. 90, Case II	
$84 = 49 + 7y$	Distributive Property	
$35 = 7y$		
$5 = y$	Solve for *y*.	

B

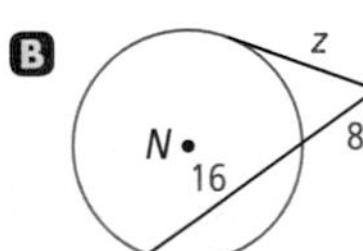

$(8 + 16)8 = z^2$	Thm. 90, Case III
$192 = z^2$	Simplify.
$13.9 \approx z$	Solve for *z*.

Problem 3 *continued*

Got It? VISUAL LEARNERS

Have students visually identify the case of Theorem 90 that is represented in each part. Make sure that students are using the sum of segment lengths to write their equations for part (a).

ANSWERS

Got It? a. 13.8 **b.** 3.2

Practice

5. $x = 25.8$, $y \approx 12.4$ **6.** $x \approx 5.3$, $y \approx 2.9$

▼ STUDENT PAGES 522–523

Plan

How can you identify the segments needed to use Theorem 90?

Got It? What is the value of the variable to the nearest tenth?

a.

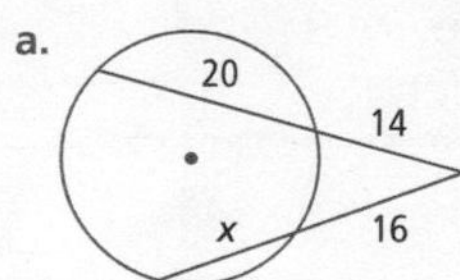

b.

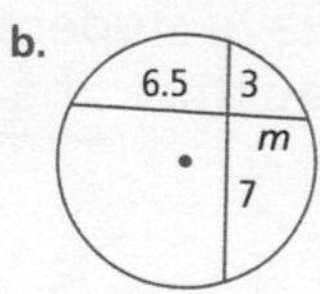

Practice **Algebra** Find the value of each variable using the given chord, secant, and tangent lengths. If the answer is not a whole number, round to the nearest tenth.

5.

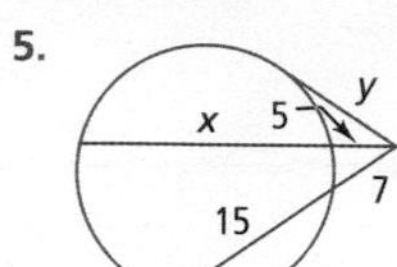

6.

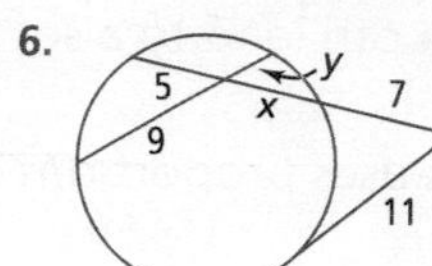

3 Lesson Check

Do you know HOW?

If students have difficulty with Exercise 8, then have them review Problem 1 and write an equation for this diagram.

Do you UNDERSTAND?

If students have difficulty with Exercise 13, then have them review Problem 3 and write an equation that models the one written for 3B.

Close

Q When two lines intersect inside a circle, how is the angle measure related to the measure of the intercepted arcs? **[The angle measure is equal to half the sum of the intercepted arcs.]**

Q When two lines intersect inside a circle, how are the segment lengths related? **[The products of the lengths of the segments from the intersection to the circle are equal.]**

ANSWERS

7. 5.4 **8.** 65

9. 11.2 **10.** 100, 260

11. A secant is a line that intersects a circle at two points; a tangent is a line that intersects a circle at one point.

12. No; we can find the sum of the measures of the two arcs (in this situation, that sum is 230), but there is not enough information to find the measure of each arc.

13. The student forgot to multiply by the length of the entire secant seg.; the equation should be $(13.5)(6) = x^2$.

▼ STUDENT PAGES 523–524

Lesson Check

Do you know HOW?

7. What is the value of x?

8. What is the value of y?

9. What is the value of z, to the nearest tenth?

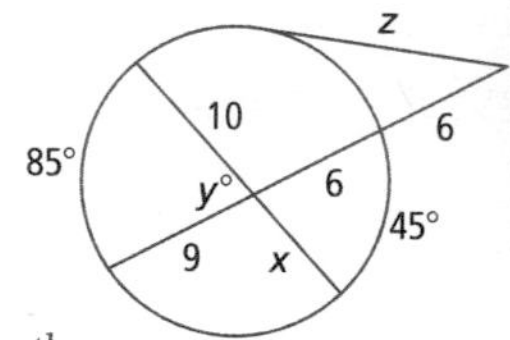

10. The measure of the angle formed by two tangents to a circle is 80. What are the measures of the intercepted arcs?

Do you UNDERSTAND?

11. Vocabulary Describe the difference between a *secant* and a *tangent*.

12. In the diagram for Exercises 7–9, is it possible to find the measures of the unmarked arcs? Explain.

13. Error Analysis To find the value of x, a student wrote the equation $(7.5)6 = x^2$. What error did the student make?

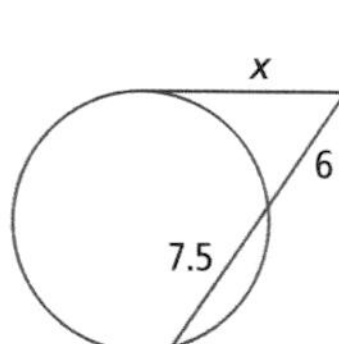

4 Practice

More Practice and Problem-Solving Exercises

ASSIGNMENT GUIDE

The assignments below are for the More Practice and Problem-Solving Exercises. You may also want to assign the A-Level Practice Exercises for homework if these are not used in class.
Average: 14–32
Advanced: 14–36

Mathematical Practices The exercises listed focus on the Standards for Mathematical Practices listed.

EX. 22, 24: Make Sense of Problems (MP 1)
EX. 21b: Construct Arguments (MP 3)
EX. 13: Critique the Reasoning of Others (MP 3)
EX. 21: Model (MP 4)

STEM exercises focus on science or engineering applications.

EXERCISE 20: Use the **Think About a Plan** worksheet in the Online Teacher Resources to further support students' development in becoming independent learners.

HOMEWORK QUICK CHECK

To check students' understanding of key skills and concepts, go over Exercises 14, 20, 22, 24, and 31.

ANSWERS

14. $360 - x$ **15.** $180 - x$
16. $180 \quad y$ **17.** 26.7
18. 16.7 **19.** 14.1
20. 95, 104, 86, 75
21. a. $(8 - 4\sqrt{3})$ in.
b. $\frac{4}{2+\sqrt{3}}$ in.;
$\frac{4}{2+\sqrt{3}} \cdot \frac{2-\sqrt{3}}{2-\sqrt{3}} = \frac{8-4\sqrt{3}}{4-3} = 8 - 4\sqrt{3}$
22. $c = b - a$
23. $m\widehat{PQ} = 120$, $m\widehat{QR} = 140$, $m\widehat{PR} = 100$

▼ STUDENT PAGE 525

More Practice and Problem-Solving Exercises

B Apply

Algebra $\overline{CA}$ and $\overline{CB}$ are tangents to $\odot O$. Write an expression for each arc or angle in terms of the given variable.

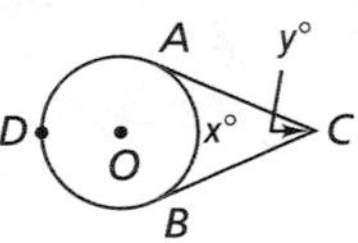

14. $m\widehat{ADB}$ using x **15.** $m\angle C$ using x **16.** $m\widehat{AB}$ using y

Find the diameter of $\odot O$. A line that appears to be tangent is tangent. If your answer is not a whole number, round it to the nearest tenth.

17.

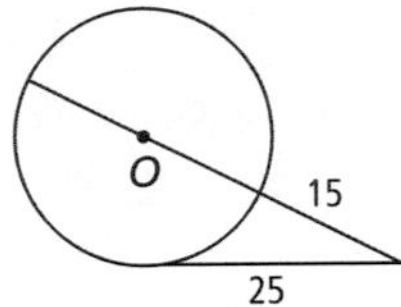

18.

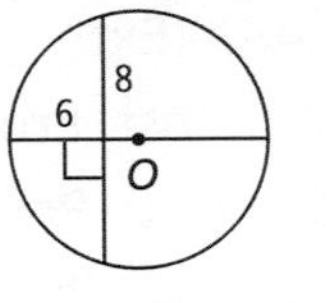

19.

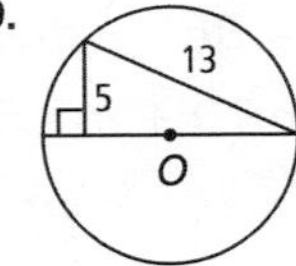
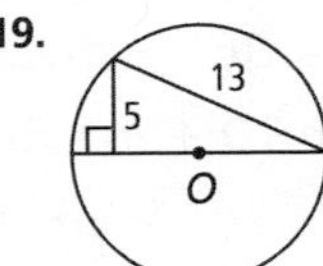

20. A circle is inscribed in a quadrilateral whose four angles have measures 85, 76, 94, and 105. Find the measures of the four arcs between consecutive points of tangency.

Wankel engine

STEM 21. Engineering The basis for the design of the Wankel rotary engine is an equilateral triangle. Each side of the triangle is a chord to an arc of a circle. The opposite vertex of the triangle is the center of the circle that forms the arc. In the diagram below, each side of the equilateral triangle is 8 in. long.

a. Use what you know about equilateral triangles and find the value of x.

b. Reasoning Copy the diagram and complete the circle with the given center. Then use Theorem 90 to find the value of x. Show that your answers to parts (a) and (b) are equal.

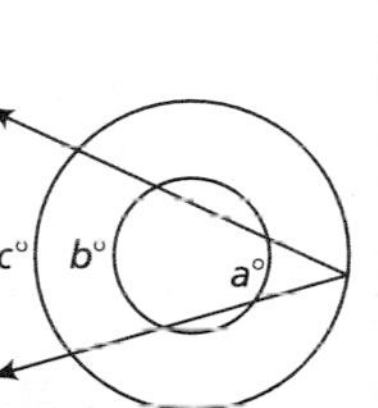

22. Think About a Plan In the diagram, the circles are concentric. What is a formula you could use to find the value of c in terms of a and b?
- How can you use the inscribed angle to find the value of c?
- What is the relationship of the inscribed angle to a and b?

23. $\triangle PQR$ is inscribed in a circle with $m\angle P = 70$, $m\angle Q = 50$, and $m\angle R = 60$. What are the measures of $\widehat{PQ}$, $\widehat{QR}$, and $\widehat{PR}$?

More Practice and Problem-Solving Exercises *continued*

24. $\angle 1$ is a central $\angle$, so $m\angle 1 = x$; $\angle 2$ is an inscribed $\angle$, so $m\angle 2 = \frac{1}{2}x$; $\angle 3$ is formed by the secants, so $m\angle 3 = \frac{1}{2}(x - y)$.

25. $x \approx 10.7$, $y = 10$

26. $x \approx 8.9$, $y = 2$

27. $x \approx 10.9$, $y \approx 2.3$

28. 1. $\odot O$ with secants $\overline{CA}$ and $\overline{CE}$. (Given)
2. Draw $\overline{BE}$ (2 pts. determine a line.)
3. $m\angle BEC = \frac{1}{2}m\widehat{BD}$ and $m\angle ABE = \frac{1}{2}m\widehat{AE}$ (The measure of an inscribed $\angle$ is half the measure of its intercepted arc.)
4. $m\angle BEC + m\angle BCE = m\angle ABE$ (Ext. $\angle$ Thm.)
5. $\frac{1}{2}m\widehat{BD} + m\angle BCE = \frac{1}{2}m\widehat{AE}$ (Subst. Prop. of =)
6. $m\angle BCE = \frac{1}{2}m\widehat{AE} - \frac{1}{2}m\widehat{BD}$ (Subtr. Prop. of =)
7. $m\angle BCE = \frac{1}{2}(m\widehat{AE} - m\widehat{BD})$ (Distr. Prop.)
8. $\angle BCE \cong \angle ACE$ (Refl. Prop. of $\cong$)
9. $m\angle ACE = \frac{1}{2}(m\widehat{AE} - m\widehat{BD})$ (Subst. Prop. of =)

29.

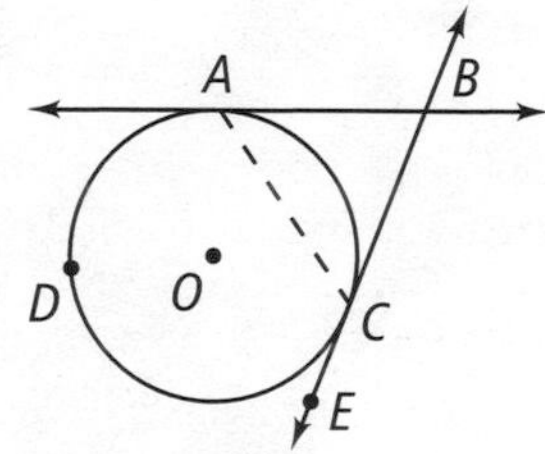

Given: $\overleftrightarrow{BA}$ is tangent to $\odot O$ at A, $\overleftrightarrow{BC}$ is tangent to $\odot O$ at C
Prove: $m\angle ABC = \frac{1}{2}(m\widehat{ADC} - m\widehat{AC})$
Proof: 1. Draw $\overline{AC}$ (2 pts. determine a line.)
2. $m\angle ACE = \frac{1}{2}m\widehat{ADC}$ (The measure of an $\angle$ formed by a tangent and a chord is half the measure of the intercepted arc.)
3. $m\angle ACE = m\angle ABC + m\angle BAC$ (Ext. $\angle$ Thm.)
4. $m\angle BAC = \frac{1}{2}m\widehat{AC}$ (The measure of an $\angle$ formed by a tangent and a chord is half the measure of the intercepted arc.)
5. $\frac{1}{2}m\widehat{ADC} = m\angle ABC + m\angle BAC$ (Subst. Prop. of =) 6. $\frac{1}{2}m\widehat{ADC} = m\angle ABC + \frac{1}{2}m\widehat{AC}$ (Subst. Prop. of =) 7. $m\angle ABC = \frac{1}{2}m\widehat{ADC} - \frac{1}{2}m\widehat{AC}$ (Subtr. Prop. of =)
8. $m\angle ABC = \frac{1}{2}(m\widehat{ADC} - m\widehat{AC})$ (Distr. Prop.)

▼ STUDENT PAGE 526

24. Reasoning Use the diagram at the right. If you know the values of x and y, how can you find the measure of each numbered angle?

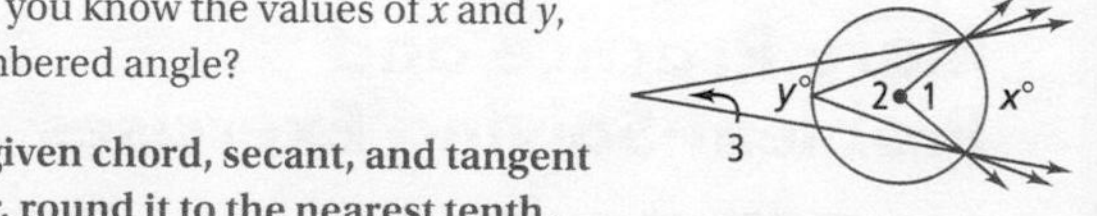

Algebra Find the values of x and y using the given chord, secant, and tangent lengths. If your answer is not a whole number, round it to the nearest tenth.

25.

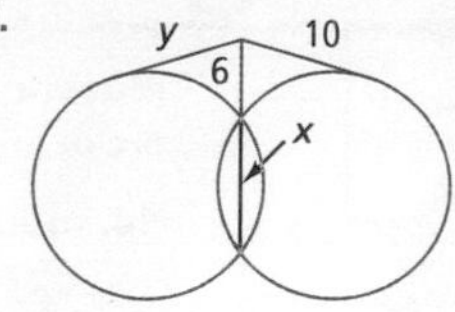

26.

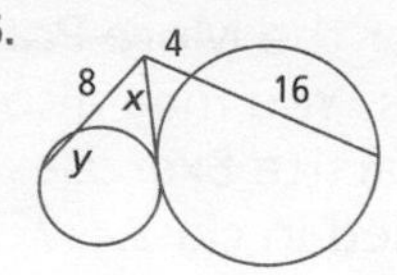

27.

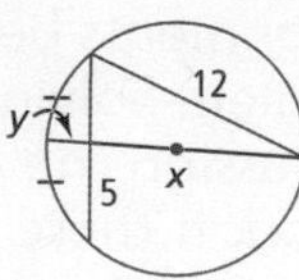

Proof 28. Prove Theorem 89 as it applies to two secants that intersect outside a circle.

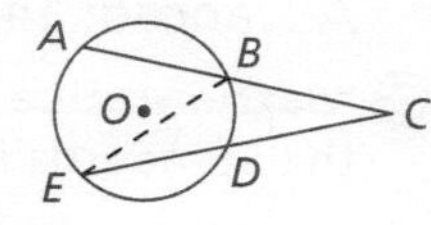

Given: $\odot O$ with secants $\overline{CA}$ and $\overline{CE}$
Prove: $m\angle ACE = \frac{1}{2}(m\widehat{AE} - m\widehat{BD})$

Proof 29. Prove the other two cases of Theorem 89. (See Exercise 28.)

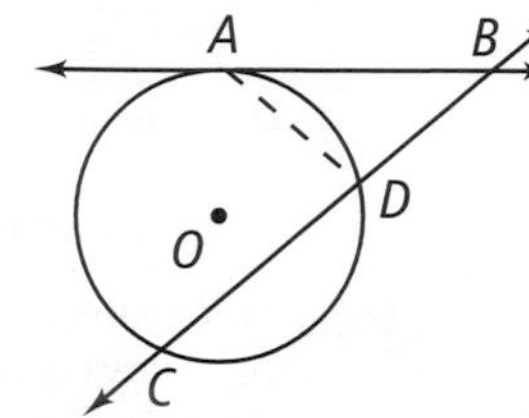

Given: $\odot O$ with tangent $\overleftrightarrow{BA}$ and secant $\overleftrightarrow{BC}$
Prove: $m\angle ABC = \frac{1}{2}(m\widehat{AC} - m\widehat{DA})$
Proof: 1. Draw $\overline{AD}$. (2 pts. determine a line.)
2. $m\angle DAB = \frac{1}{2}m\widehat{AD}$ (The measure of an $\angle$ formed by a tangent and a chord is half the measure of the intercepted arc.) 3. $m\angle ADC = \frac{1}{2}m\widehat{AC}$ (The measure of an inscribed $\angle$ is half the measure of its intercepted arc.)
4. $m\angle ABC = m\angle ADC - m\angle DAB$ (Subtr. Prop. of = and Ext. $\angle$Thm.) 5. $m\angle ABC = \frac{1}{2}m\widehat{AC} - \frac{1}{2}m\widehat{AD}$ (Subst. Prop. of =) 6. $m\angle B = \frac{1}{2}(m\widehat{AC} - m\widehat{AD})$ (Distr. Prop.)

30.

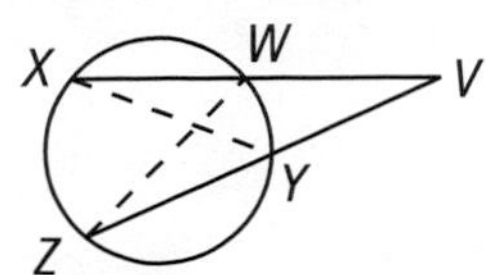

Given: A ⊙ with secant segments $\overline{XV}$ amd $\overline{ZV}$

Prove: $XV \cdot WV = ZV \cdot YV$.

Proof: Draw $\overline{XY}$ and $\overline{ZW}$. (2 pts. determine a line.); $\angle XVY \cong \angle ZVW$ (Refl. Prop of ≅); $\angle VXY \cong \angle WZV$(2 inscribed ∠s that intercept the same arc are ≅.); $\triangle XVY \sim \triangle ZVW$ (AA~); $\frac{XV}{ZV} = \frac{YV}{WV}$ (In similar figures, corresp. sides are proportional.); $XV \cdot WV = ZV \cdot YV$ (Prop. of Proportion).

31.

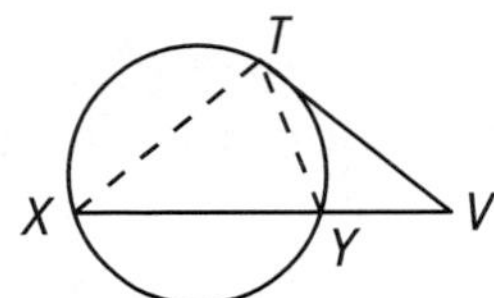

Given: A circle with tangent $\overline{TV}$ and secant $\overline{XV}$

Prove: $XV \cdot YV = (TV)^2$.

Proof: 1. Draw $\overline{TX}$ and $\overline{TY}$. (2 Pts. determine a line.) 2. $m\angle TXV = \frac{1}{2}m\widehat{TY}$ (The measure of an inscribed ∠ is half the measure of the intercepted arc.) 3. $m\angle VTY = \frac{1}{2}m\widehat{TY}$ (The measure of an ∠ formed by a chord and a tangent is half the measure of the intercepted arc.) 4. $m\angle TXV = m\angle VTY$ (Trans. Prop. of =) 5. $\angle TVY \cong \angle TVX$ (Reflexive Prop. of ≅) 6. $\triangle TVY \sim \triangle XVT$ (AA~) 7. $\frac{YV}{TV} = \frac{TV}{XV}$ (In similar figures, corresp. sides are proportional.) 8. $XV \cdot YV = (TV)^2$ (Prop. of Proportion)

32. **a.** $\triangle ACD$

b. $\tan A = \frac{DC}{AC} = \frac{DC}{1} = DC$, length of tangent seg.

c. $\text{secant } A = \frac{AD}{AC} = \frac{AD}{1} = AD$, length of secant seg.

33. $m\angle 1 = \frac{1}{2}m\widehat{QRP} - \frac{1}{2}m\widehat{PQ}$ (vertex outside ⊙, $m\angle = \frac{1}{2}$ difference of intercepted arcs); $m\angle 1 + m\widehat{PQ} = \frac{1}{2}m\widehat{QRP} + \frac{1}{2}m\widehat{PQ}$ (Add. Prop. of =); $m\angle 1 + m\widehat{PQ} = \frac{1}{2}\left(m\widehat{QRP} + m\widehat{PQ}\right)$ (Distr. Prop.); $m\angle 1 + m\widehat{PQ} = \frac{1}{2}(360)$ (arc measure of ⊙ is 360); $m\angle 1 + m\widehat{PQ} = 180$ (Simplify.)

34. $m\angle 1 = \frac{1}{2}m\widehat{QRP} - \frac{1}{2}m\widehat{PQ}$ and $m\angle 2 = \frac{1}{2}m\widehat{RQP} - \frac{1}{2}m\widehat{RP}$ (vertex outside ⊙, $m\angle =$ half difference of intercepted arcs); $m\angle 1 + m\angle 2 = \frac{1}{2}m\widehat{QRP} + \frac{1}{2}m\widehat{RQP} - \frac{1}{2}m\widehat{PQ} - \frac{1}{2}m\widehat{RP}$ (Subst. Prop. of =); $m\angle 1 + m\angle 2 = \frac{1}{2}m\widehat{QR} + \frac{1}{2}m\widehat{RP} + \frac{1}{2}m\widehat{QR} + \frac{1}{2}m\widehat{PQ} - \frac{1}{2}m\widehat{PQ} - \frac{1}{2}m\widehat{RP}$ (Arc Add. Postulate and Distr. Prop.); $m\angle 1 + m\angle 2 = m\widehat{QR}$ (Distr. Prop.).

For Exercises 30 and 31, write proofs that use similar triangles.

Proof **30.** Prove Theorem 90, Case II.

Proof **31.** Prove Theorem 90, Case III.

32. The diagram at the right shows a *unit circle*, a circle with radius 1.

a. What triangle is similar to $\triangle ABE$?

b. Describe the connection between the ratio for the tangent of $\angle A$ and the segment that is tangent to $\odot A$.

c. The secant ratio is $\frac{\text{hypotenuse}}{\text{length of leg adjacent to an angle}}$. Describe the connection between the ratio for the secant of $\angle A$ and the segment that is the secant in the unit circle.

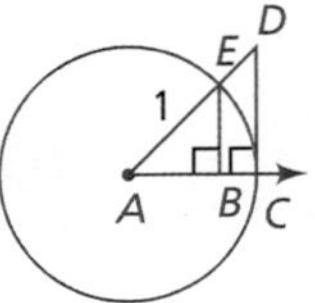

Challenge

For Exercises 33 and 34, use the diagram at the right. Prove each statement.

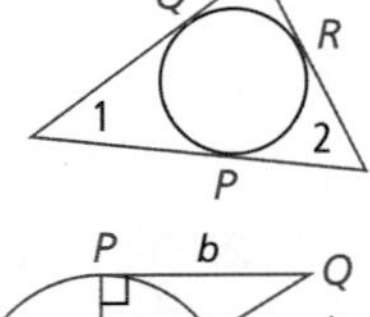

Proof **33.** $m\angle 1 + m\widehat{PQ} = 180$

Proof **34.** $m\angle 1 + m\angle 2 = m\widehat{QR}$

Proof **35.** Use the diagram at the right and the theorems of this lesson to prove the Pythagorean Theorem.

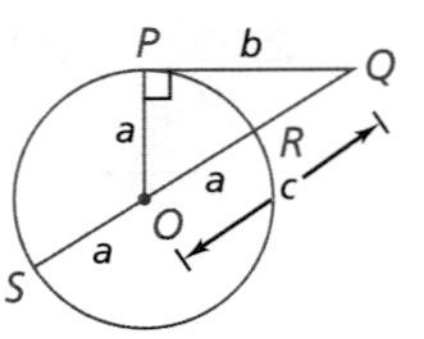

Proof **36.** If an equilateral triangle is inscribed in a circle, prove that the tangents to the circle at the vertices form an equilateral triangle.

35. 1. $(PQ)^2 = (QS)(QR)$ (Square of the tangent equals the product of the secant times the external segment.)

2. $b^2 = (c + a)(c - a)$ (Substitution)

3. $b^2 = c^2 - a^2$ (Distributive Prop.)

4. $b^2 + a^2 = c^2$ (Addition Prop. of Equality)

36.

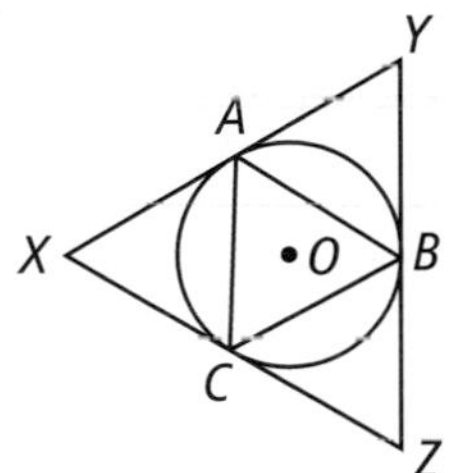

Given: Equilateral $\triangle ABC$ is inscribed in $\odot O$; XY, $\overline{YZ}$, and $\overline{XZ}$ are tangents to $\odot O$

Prove: $\triangle XYZ$ is equilateral.

Proof: $m\widehat{AB} = m\widehat{BC} = m\widehat{AC} = 120$, since chords $\overline{AB}$, $\overline{BC}$, and $\overline{CA}$ are all ≅. So the measures of $\angle X$, $\angle Y$, and $\angle Z$ are $\frac{1}{2}(240 - 120) = 60$, and $\triangle XYZ$ is equiangular, so it is also equilateral.

5 Assess and Remediate

Lesson Quiz

1. What is the value of the variable?

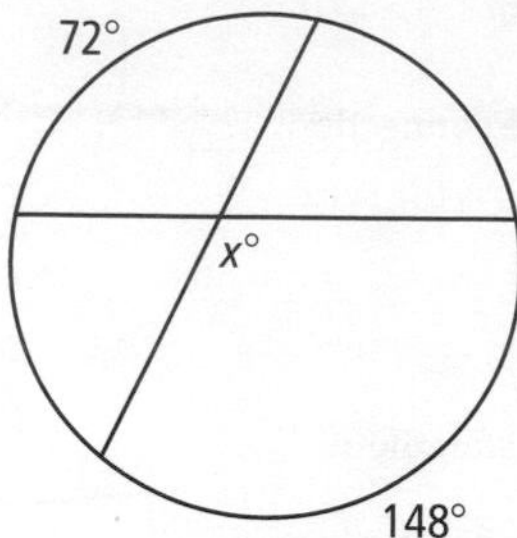

2. **Do you UNDERSTAND?** Find the value of the variable. If the answer is not a whole number, round to the nearest tenth.

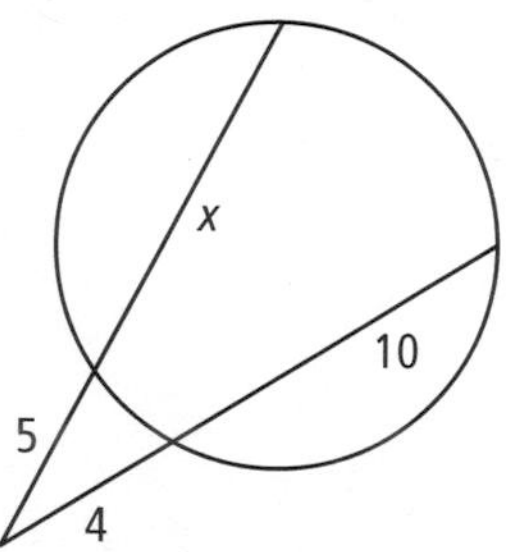

3. What is the value of g?

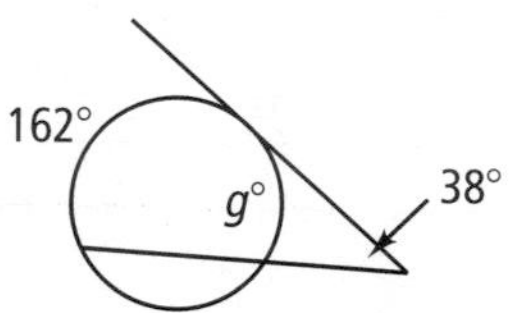

ANSWERS TO LESSON QUIZ

1. 110
2. 6.2
3. 86

Prescription for Remediation

Use the student work on the Lesson Quiz to prescribe a differentiated assignment.

Points	Differentiated Remediation
0–1	Intervention
2	On-level
3	Extension

Online Assessment

Assign the Lesson Quiz in Success Tracker on **pearsonsuccessnet.com**. Success Tracker will automatically score the quiz and assign appropriate intervention or enrichment to each student based on the results. The compiled data appear in three different reports for instant analysis of whole class and individual student performance.

Differentiated Remediation

Intervention

- **RETEACHING** (2 pages) Provides reteaching and practice exercises for the key lesson concepts. Use with struggling students or absent students.
- **ENGLISH LANGUAGE LEARNER SUPPORT** Helps students develop and reinforce mathematical vocabulary and key concepts.

On-Level

- **PRACTICE** (2 pages) Provides extra practice for each lesson. For simpler practice exercises, use the Form K Practice pages found in the Online Teacher Resources.
- **THINK ABOUT A PLAN** Helps students develop specific problem-solving skills and strategies by providing scaffolded guiding questions.
- **STANDARDIZED TEST PREP** Focuses on all major exercises, all major question types, and helps students prepare for the high-stakes assessments.

Extension

- **ENRICHMENT** Provides students with interesting problems and activities that extend the concepts of the lesson.
- **ACTIVITIES, GAMES, AND PUZZLES** Worksheets that can be used for concept development, enrichment, and for fun!

8 Chapter Review

Essential Questions

BIG idea Reasoning and Proof

ESSENTIAL QUESTION How can you prove relationships between angles and arcs in a circle?

ANSWER The measure of an arc equals the measure of its central angle. You can use this angle and arc to prove relationships of other angles and arcs.

BIG idea Measurement

ESSENTIAL QUESTION When lines intersect a circle or within a circle, how do you find the measures of resulting angles, arcs, and segments?

ANSWER Segments intersecting circles form angles and intercepted arcs. You can find some missing measures using given information and appropriate formulas.

Summative Questions

Use the following prompts as you review this chapter with your students. The prompts are designed to help you assess your students' understanding of the BIG Ideas they have studied.

- How is arc length related to circumference of a circle?
- What is a tangent?
- What is a segment of a circle?
- How can you find the measure of an angle formed in the interior of a circle?
- How can you find the measure of an angle formed in the exterior of a circle?

8-1 Circles and Arcs

ANSWERS

1. 30
2. 120
3. 330
4. 120
5. $\frac{22\pi}{9}$ in.
6. π mm
7. $\frac{25\pi}{9}$ m
8. 4π m

▼ STUDENT PAGE 527

8-1 Circles and Arcs

Quick Review

A **circle** is the set of all points in a plane equidistant from a point called the **center**. The **circumference** of a circle is $C = \pi d$ or $C = 2\pi r$. **Arc length** is a fraction of a circle's circumference. The length of $\overset{\frown}{AB} = \frac{m\overset{\frown}{AB}}{360} \cdot 2\pi r$.

Semicircle
A
Minor arc
Diameter
O
Radius
B
Central angle
C
$\overset{\frown}{ACB}$ is a major arc.

Example

A circle has a radius of 5 cm. What is the length of an arc measuring 80°?

length of $\overset{\frown}{AB} = \frac{m\overset{\frown}{AB}}{360} \cdot 2\pi r$ Use the arc length formula.

$= \frac{80}{360} \cdot 2\pi(5)$ Substitute.

$= \frac{20}{9}\pi$ Simplify.

The length of the arc is $\frac{20}{9}\pi$ cm.

Exercises

Find each measure.

1. $m\angle APD$
2. $m\overset{\frown}{AC}$
3. $m\overset{\frown}{ABD}$
4. $m\angle CPA$

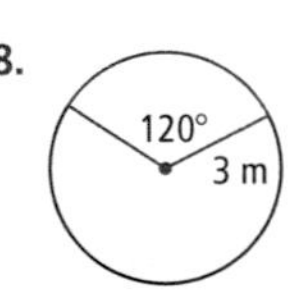

Find the length of each arc shown in red. Leave your answer in terms of π.

5. 110°, 4 in.
6. 3 mm, 120°
7. 50°, 10 m
8. 120°, 3 m

Chapter Review *(continued)*

8-2 Areas of Circles and Sectors

ANSWERS

9. 144π in.^{2}
10. $\frac{49\pi}{4}$ ft^2
11. 41.0 cm^2
12. 18.3 cm^2
13. 36.2 cm^2

▼ STUDENT PAGE 527

8-2 Areas of Circles and Sectors

Quick Review

The area of a circle is $A = \pi r^2$. A **sector of a circle** is a region bounded by two radii and their intercepted arc. The area of sector $APB = \frac{m\overset{\frown}{AB}}{360} \cdot \pi r^2$. A **segment of a circle** is the part bounded by an arc and the segment joining its endpoints.

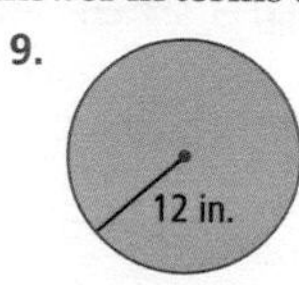

Example

What is the area of the shaded region?

$$\text{Area} = \frac{m\overset{\frown}{AB}}{360} \cdot \pi r^2 \quad \text{Use the area formula.}$$

$$= \frac{120}{360} \cdot \pi(4)^2 \quad \text{Substitute.}$$

$$= \frac{16\pi}{3} \quad \text{Simplify.}$$

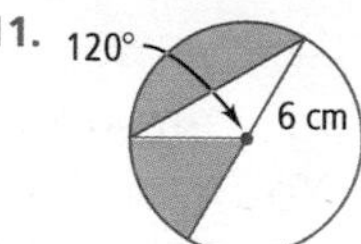

The area of the shaded region is $\frac{16\pi}{3}$ ft².

Exercises

What is the area of each circle? Leave your answer in terms of π.

9. 12 in.

10. 7 ft

Find the area of each shaded region. Round your answer to the nearest tenth.

11. 120°, 6 cm

12. 8 cm

13. A circle has a radius of 20 cm. What is the area of the smaller segment of the circle formed by a 60° arc? Round to the nearest tenth.

8-3 Tangent Lines

ANSWERS

14. 20
15. $\sqrt{3}$
16. 120

▼ STUDENT PAGE 528

8-3 Tangent Lines

Quick Review

A **tangent** to a circle is a line that intersects the circle at exactly one point. The radius to that point is perpendicular to the tangent. From any point outside a circle, you can draw two segments tangent to a circle. Those segments are congruent.

Example

$\overrightarrow{PA}$ and $\overrightarrow{PB}$ are tangents. Find x.

The radii are perpendicular to the tangents. Add the angle measures of the quadrilateral:

$$x + 90 + 90 + 40 = 360$$
$$x + 220 = 360$$
$$x = 140$$

Exercises

Use $\odot O$ for Exercises 14–16.

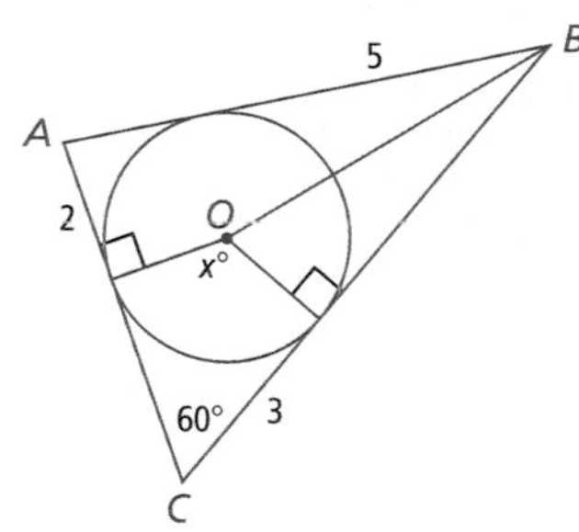

14. What is the perimeter of $\triangle ABC$?

15. $OB = \sqrt{28}$. What is the radius?

16. What is the value of x?

8-4 Chords and Arcs

ANSWERS

17. 90

18. 2 : 1 or $\frac{2}{1}$

19. $\overline{AB}$ is a diameter of the circle.

20. 4.5

21. $\frac{\sqrt{181}}{2} \approx 6.7$

▼ STUDENT PAGE 528

8-4 Chords and Arcs

Quick Review

A **chord** is a segment whose endpoints are on a circle. Congruent chords are equidistant from the center. A diameter that bisects a chord that is not a diameter is perpendicular to the chord. The perpendicular bisector of a chord contains the center of the circle.

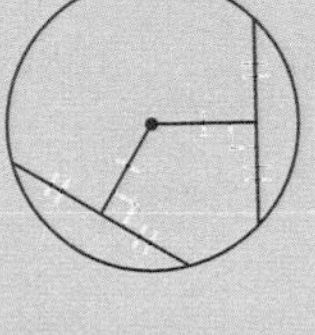

Example

Since the chord is bisected, $m\angle ACB = 90$. The radius is 13 units. So an auxiliary segment from A to B is 13 units. Use the Pythagorean Theorem.

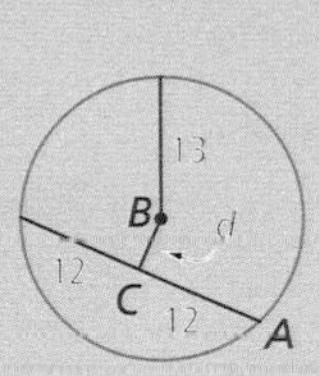

$$d^2 + 12^2 = 13^2$$
$$d^2 = 25$$
$$d = 5$$

Exercises

Use the figure below for Exercises 17–19.

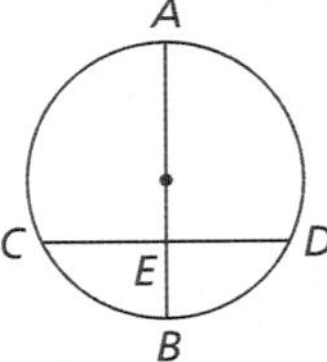

17. If $\overline{AB}$ is a diameter and $CE = ED$, then $m\angle AEC =$ __?__.

18. If $\overline{AB}$ is a diameter and is at right angles to $\overline{CD}$, what is the ratio of CD to DE?

19. If $CE = \frac{1}{2}CD$ and $m\angle DEB = 90$, what is true of $\overline{AB}$?

Use the circle below for Exercises 20 and 21.

20. What is the value of x?

21. What is the value of y?

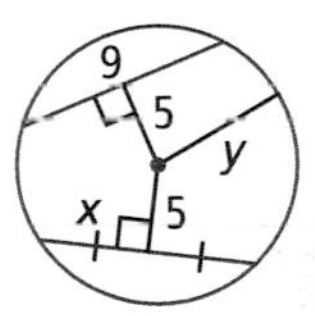

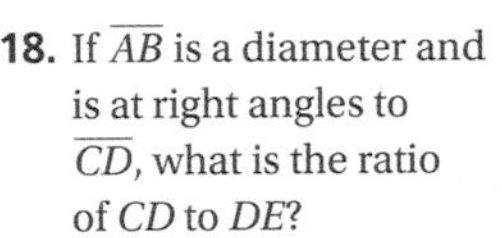

8-5 Inscribed Angles

ANSWERS

22. $a = 80$, $b = 40$, $c = 40$, $d = 100$

23. $a = 40$, $b = 140$, $c = 90$

24. $a = 118$, $b = 49$, $c = 144$, $d = 98$

25. $a = 90$, $b = 90$, $c = 70$, $d = 65$

▼ STUDENT PAGE 529

8-5 Inscribed Angles

Quick Review

An **inscribed angle** has its vertex on a circle and its sides are chords. An **intercepted arc** has its endpoints on the sides of an inscribed angle, and its other points in the interior of the angle. The measure of an inscribed angle is half the measure of its intercepted arc.

Intercepted arc — A, B, C — Inscribed angle

Example

What is $m\widehat{PS}$? What is $m\angle R$?

The $m\angle Q = 60$ is half of m, so $m\widehat{PS} = 120$. $\angle R$ intercepts the same arc as $\angle Q$, so $m\angle R = 60$.

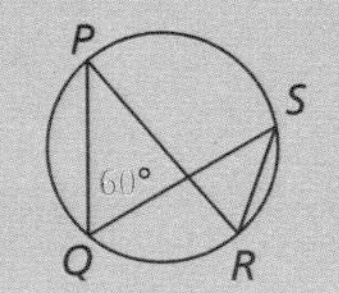

Exercises

Find the value of each variable. Line ℓ is a tangent.

22.

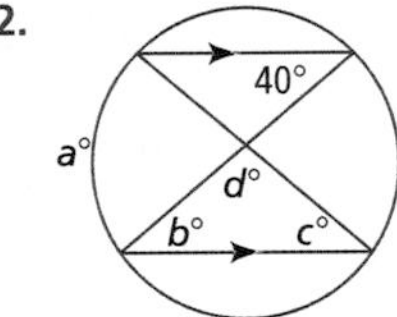

23.

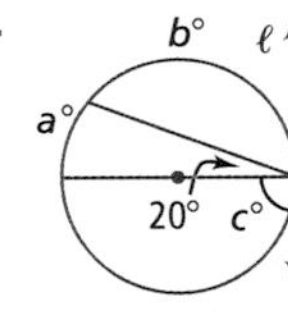

24. 59°, 72°, $a°$, $b°$, $c°$, $d°$

25.

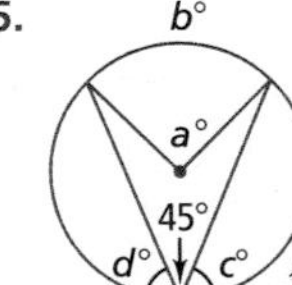

Chapter Review *(continued)*

8-6 Angle Measures and Segment Lengths

ANSWERS

26. 37

27. $a = 95$, $b = 85$

28. 6.5

29. 4

▼ STUDENT PAGE 529

8-6 Angle Measures and Segment Lengths

Quick Review

A **secant** is a line that intersects a circle at two points. The following relationships are true:

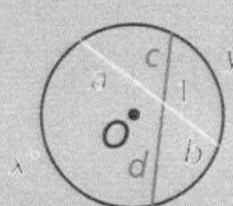

$a \cdot b = c \cdot d$

$m\angle 1 = \frac{1}{2}(x + y)$

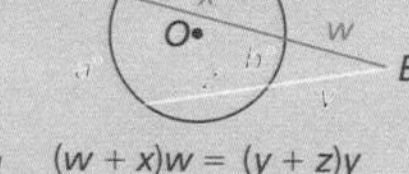

$(w + x)w = (y + z)y$

$m\angle B = \frac{1}{2}(a - b)$

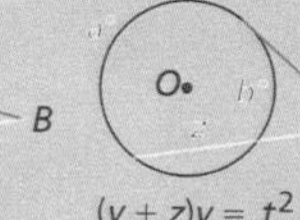

$(y + z)y = t^2$

$m\angle B = \frac{1}{2}(a - b)$

Example

What is the value of x?

$(x + 10)10 = (19 + 9)9$

$10x + 100 = 252$

$x = 15.2$

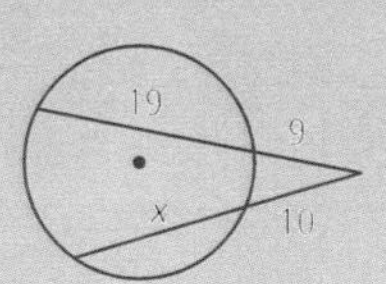

Exercises

Find the value of each variable.

26. **27.**

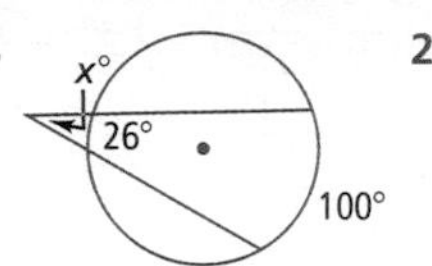

28. **29.**

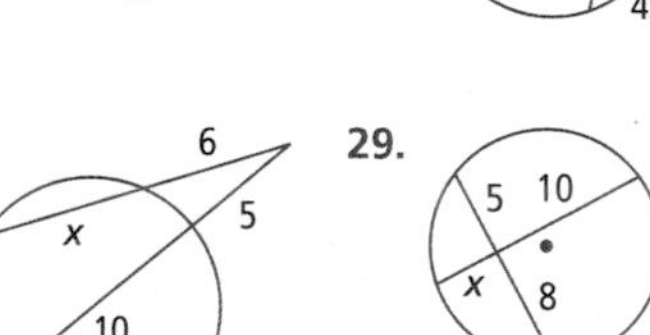

Pull It All Together

Common Core State Standards
G.C.2 Identify and describe relationships among inscribed angles, radii, and chords . . . Also G.SRT.8

Using Performance Tasks

Understanding by Design® principles support using performance tasks to assess students' progress toward mastering content standards and developing proficiency with the Mathematical Practices.

Mathematical Practices

- Make sense of problems and persevere in solving them.
- Model with mathematics.
- Construct viable arguments.

Assessing Performance

See the Implementation Guide for a holistic scoring rubric to use in assessing students' work on the performance task.

Guiding Questions

Q Which segments in the diagram can be used to determine the vertical distance from the bottom of the slot to the highest point on the top disk?

Q What theorem do you think you can apply to find some of the unknown lengths?

Q How can the base length of the slot and the radius of a disk help determine the length of the shorter leg in one of the right triangles?

Solution Outline

To determine the length of the shorter leg of a right triangle, look at the diagram below.

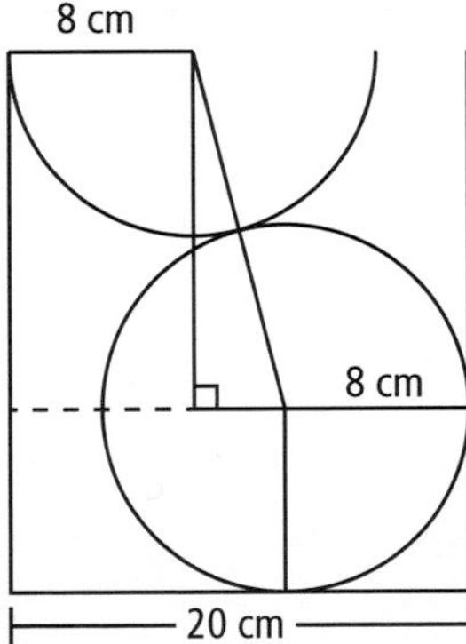

The distance across the slot is represented by the dashed line, the shorter leg, and the radius. Note that the dashed line aligns with the radius of the disk above, and therefore the dashed line is also 8 cm long. So the length of the shorter leg is $20 - 2(8) = 4$ cm. Also, the hypotenuse of the right triangle consists of two radii, so its length is $2(8) = 16$ cm.

▼ STUDENT PAGE 530

Designing a Game

A new game on a television show will involve flat circular disks falling into slots. The diagram shows the radius of a disk and the dimensions of a slot. The disks always fall in such a way that each one rests against a side of the slot, first on one side and then on the opposite side, as shown below.

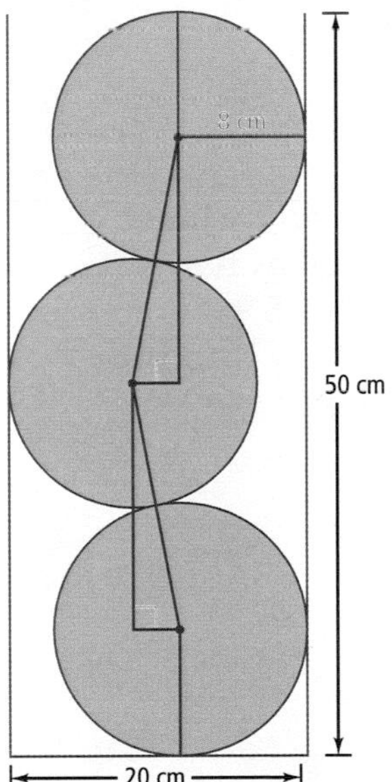

The game designer must verify that three disks will fit into a slot, without the top disk protruding from the top of the slot.

Task Description

Show that the vertical distance from the bottom of the slot to the highest point on the top disk is less than 50 cm.

- How would knowing the length of the longer leg of the right triangles in the diagram help you solve the problem?
- What are the lengths of the hypotenuse and shorter leg of the right triangles? How can you use these measurements to find the length of the longer leg?

8 *Pull It* **All Together** *(continued)*

Look at the diagram below. Using the Pythagorean Theorem, the length of the longer leg of the right triangle is $\sqrt{16^2 - 4^2} = \sqrt{240} = 4\sqrt{15}$ cm.

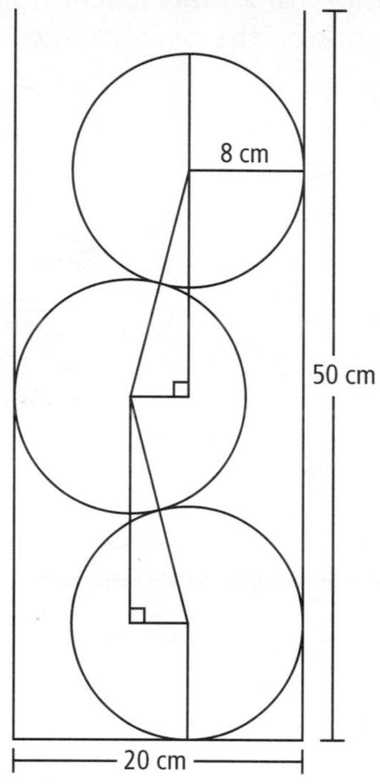

The total vertical distance of the disks includes two legs of length $4\sqrt{15}$ cm, as well as two radii. The vertical distance is $8 + 4\sqrt{15} + 4\sqrt{15} + 8 \approx 46.98$ cm, which is less than 50 cm. The top disk will not protrude from the top of the slot.

Postulates and Theorems

Postulates

Postulate 1
Through any two points there is exactly one line.

Postulate 2
If two distinct lines intersect, then they intersect in exactly one point.

Postulate 3
If two distinct planes intersect, then they intersect in exactly one line.

Postulate 4
Through any three noncollinear points there is exactly on plane.

Postulate 5
Ruler Postulate
Every point on a line can be paired with a real number. This makes a one-to-one correspondence between the points on the line and the real numbers.

Postulate 6
Segment Addition Postulate
If three points A, B, and C are collinear and B is between A and C, then $AB + BC = AC$.

Postulate 7
Protractor Postulate
Consider $\overrightarrow{OB}$ and a point A on one side of $\overrightarrow{OB}$. Every ray of the form $\overrightarrow{OA}$ can be paired one to one with a real number from 0 to 180.

Postulate 8
Angle Addition Postulate
If point B is in the interior of $\angle AOC$, then $m\angle AOB + m\angle BOC = m\angle AOC$.

Postulate 9
Linear Pair Postulate
If two angles form a linear pair, then they are supplementary.

Postulate 10
Area Addition Postulate
The area of a region is the sum of the area of its nonoverlapping parts.

Postulate 11
Same-Side Interior Angles Postulate
If a transversal intersects two parallel lines, then same-side interior angles are supplementary.

Postulate 12
Parallel Postulate
Through a point not on a line, there is one and only one line parallel to the given line.

Postulate 13
Perpendicular Postulate
Through a point not on a line, there is one and only one line perpendicular to the given line.

Postulate 14
Side-Side-Side (SSS) Postulate
If three sides of one triangle are congruent to the three sides of another triangle, then the two triangles are congruent.

Postulate 15
Side-Angle-Side (SAS) Postulate
If two sides and the included angle of one triangle are congruent to two sides and the included angle of another triangles, then the two triangles are congruent.

Postulate 16
Angle-Side-Angle (ASA) Postulate
If two angles and the included side of one triangle are congruent to two angles and the included side of another triangle, then the two triangles are congruent.

Theorems

Theorem 1
Vertical Angles Theorem
Vertical angles are congruent.

Theorem 2
Congruent Supplements Theorem
If two angles are supplements of the same angle (or of two congruent angles), then the two angles are congruent.

Theorem 3
Congruent Complements Theorem
If two angles are complements of the same angle (or of two congruent angles), then the two angles are congruent.

Theorem 4
All right angles are congruent.

Theorem 5
If two angles are congruent and supplementary, then each is a right angle.

Postulates • Theorems

Theorem 6
Alternate Interior Angles Theorem
If a transversal intersects two parallel lines, the alternate interior angles are congruent.

Theorem 7
Corresponding Angles Theorem
If a transversal intersects two parallel lines, then corresponding angles are congruent.

Theorem 8
Alternate Exterior Angles Theorem
If a transversal intersects two parallel lines, then alternate exterior angles are congruent.

Theorem 9
Converse of the Corresponding Angles Theorem
If two lines and a transversal form corresponding angles that are congruent, then the two lines are parallel.

Theorem 10
Converse of the Alternate Interior Angles Theorem
If two lines and a transversal form alternate interior angles that are congruent, then the two lines are parallel.

Theorem 11
Converse of the Same-Side Interior Angles Postulate
If two lines and a transversal form same-side interior angles that are congruent, then the two lines are parallel.

Theorem 12
Converse of the Alternate Exterior Angles Theorem
If two lines and a transversal form alternate exterior angles that are congruent, then the two lines are parallel.

Theorem 13
If two lines are parallel to the same line, then they are parallel to each other.

Theorem 14
In a plane, if two lines are perpendicular to the same line, then they are parallel to each other.

Theorem 15
Perpendicular Transversal Theorem
In a plane, if a line is perpendicular to one of two parallel lines, then it is perpendicular to the other.

Theorem 16
Triangle Angle-Sum Theorem
The sum of the measures of the angles of a triangle is 180.

Theorem 17
Triangle Exterior Angle Theorem
The measure of each exterior angle of a triangle equals the sum of the measure of its two remote interior angles.

Corollary
The measure of an exterior angle of a triangle is greater than the measure of each of its remote interior angles.

Theorem 18
Third Angles Theorem
If two angles of one triangle are congruent to two angles of another triangle, than the third angles are congruent.

Theorem 19
Angle-Angle-Side (AAS) Theorem
If two angles and a nonincluded side of one triangle are congruent to two angles and a nonincluded side of another triangle, then the two triangles are congruent.

Theorem 20
Isosceles Triangle Theorem
If two sides of a triangle are congruent, then the angles opposite those sides are congruent.

Corollary
If a triangle is equilateral, then the triangle is equiangular.

Theorem 21
Converse of the Isosceles Triangle Theorem
If two angles of a triangle are congruent, then the sides opposite the angles are congruent.

Corollary
If a triangle is equiangular, then it is equilateral.

Theorem 22
If a line bisects the vertex angle of an isosceles triangle, then the line is also the perpendicular bisector of the base.

Theorem 23
Hypotenuse-Leg (HL) Theorem
If the hypotenuse and a leg of one right triangle are congruent to the hypotenuse and a leg of another right triangle, then the triangles are congruent.

Theorem 24
Triangle Midsegment Theorem
If a line segment joins the midpoints of two sides of a triangle, then the segment is parallel to the third side and is half as long.

Postulates • Theorems

Theorem 25
Perpendicular Bisector Theorem
If a point is on the perpendicular bisector of a line segment, then it is equidistant from the endpoints of the segment.

Theorem 26
Converse of the Perpendicular Bisector Theorem
If a point is equidistant from the endpoints of a line segment, then it is on the perpendicular bisector of the segment.

Theorem 27
Angle Bisector Theorem
If a point is on the bisector of an angle, then the point is equidistant from the sides of the angle.

Theorem 28
Converse of the Angle Bisector Theorem
If a point in the interior of an angle is equidistant from the sides of the angle, then the point is on the angle bisector

Theorem 29
Concurrency of Perpendicular Bisectors Theorem
The perpendicular bisectors of the sides of a triangle are concurrent at a point equidistant from the vertices.

Theorem 30
Concurrency of Angle Bisectors Theorem
The bisectors of the angles of a triangle are concurrent at a point equidistant from the sides of the triangle.

Theorem 31
Concurrency of Medians Theorem
The medians of a triangle are concurrent at a point that is two-thirds the distance from each vertex to the midpoint of the opposite side.

Theorem 32
Concurrency of Altitudes Theorem
The lines that contain the altitudes of a triangle are concurrent.

Theorem 33
If two sides of a triangle are not congruent, then the larger angle lies opposite the longer side.

Theorem 34
If two angles of a triangle are not congruent, then the longer side lies opposite the larger angle.

Theorem 35
Triangle Inequality Theorem
The sum of the lengths of any two sides of a triangle is greater than the length of the third side.

Theorem 36
The Hinge Theorem (SAS Inequality Theorem)
If two sides of one triangle are congruent to two sides of another triangle and the included angles are not congruent, then the longer third side is opposite the larger included angle.

Theorem 37
Converse of the Hinge Theorem (SSS Inequality)
If two sides of one triangle are congruent to two sides of another triangle and the third sides are not congruent, then the larger included angle is opposite the longer third side.

Theorem 38
Polygon Angle-Sum Theorem
The sum of the measures of the angles of an n-gon is $(n - 2)180$.

Corollary
The measure of each angle of a regular n-gon is $\frac{(n-2)180}{n}$.

Theorem 39
The sum of the measures of the exterior angles of a polygon, one at each vertex, is 360.

Theorem 40
If a quadrilateral is a parallelogram, then its opposite sides are congruent.

Theorem 41
If a quadrilateral is a parallelogram, then its consecutive angles are supplementary.

Theorem 42
If a quadrilateral is a parallelogram, then its opposite angles are congruent.

Theorem 43
If a quadrilateral is a parallelogram, then its diagonals bisect each other.

Theorem 44
If three (or more) parallel lines cut off congruent segments on one transversal, then they cut off congruent segments on every transversal.

Theorem 45
If both pairs of opposite sides of a quadrilateral are congruent, then the quadrilateral is a parallelogram.

Theorem 46
If an angle of a quadrilateral is supplementary to both of its consecutive angles, then the quadrilateral is a parallelogram.

Theorem 47
If both pairs of opposite angles of a quadrilateral are congruent, then the quadrilateral is a parallelogram.

Theorem 48
If the diagonals of a quadrilateral bisect each other, then the quadrilateral is a parallelogram.

Theorem 49
If one pair of opposite sides of a quadrilateral is both congruent and parallel, then the quadrilateral is a parallelogram.

Theorem 50
If a parallelogram is a rhombus, then its diagonals are perpendicular.

Theorem 51
If a parallelogram is a rhombus, then each diagonal bisects a pair of opposite angles.

Theorem 52
If a parallelogram is a rectangle, then its diagonals are congruent.

Theorem 53
If the diagonals of a parallelogram are perpendicular, then the parallelogram is a rhombus.

Theorem 54
If one diagonal of a parallelogram bisects a pair of opposite angles, then the parallelogram is a rhombus.

Theorem 55
If the diagonals of a parallelogram are congruent, then the parallelogram is a rectangle.

Theorem 56
If a quadrilateral is an isosceles trapezoid, then each pair of base angles is congruent.

Theorem 57
If a quadrilateral is an isosceles trapezoid, then its diagonals are congruent.

Theorem 58
Trapezoid Midsegment Theorem
If a quadrilateral is a trapezoid, then

(1) the midsegment is parallel to the bases,and

(2) the length of the midsegment is half the sum of the lengths of the bases.

Theorem 59
If a quadrilateral is a kite, then its diagonals are perpendicular.

Theorem 60
Side-Angle-Side Similarity (SAS ~) Theorem
If an angle of one triangle is congruent to an angle of a second triangle, and the sides that include the two angles are proportional, then the triangles are similar.

Theorem 61
Side-Side-Side Similarity (SSS ~) Theorem
If the corresponding sides of two triangles are proportional, then the triangles are similar.

Theorem 62
The altitude to the hypotenuse of a right triangle divides the triangle into two triangles that are similar to the original triangle and to each other.

Corollary 1
The length of the altitude to the hypotenuse of a right triangle is the geometric mean of the lengths of the segments of the hypotenuse.

Corollary 2
The altitude to the hypotenuse of a right triangle separates the hypotenuse so that the length of each leg of the triangle is the geometric mean of the length of the hypotenuse and the length of the segment of the hypotenuse adjacent to the leg.

Theorem 63
Side-Splitter Theorem
If a line is parallel to one side of a triangle and intersects the other two sides, then it divides those sides proportionally.

Converse
If a line divides two sides of a triangle proportionally, then it is parallel to the third side.

Corollary
If three parallel lines intersect two transversals, then the segments intercepted on the transversals are proportional.

Theorem 64
Triangle-Angle-Bisector Theorem
If a ray bisects an angle of a triangle, then it divides the opposite side into two segments that are proportional to the other two sides of the triangle.

Theorem 65
Pythagorean Theorem
If a triangle is a right triangle, then the sum of the squares of the lengths of the legs is equal to the square of the length of the hypotenuse.

Theorem 66
Converse of the Pythagorean Theorem
If the sum of the squares of the lengths of two sides of a triangle is equal to the square of the length of the third side, then the triangle is a right triangle.

Theorem 67
If the square of the length of the longest side of a triangle is greater than the sum of the squares of the lengths of the other two sides, then the triangle is obtuse.

Theorem 68
If the square of the length of the longest side of a triangle is less than the sum of the squares of the lengths of the other two sides, then the triangle is acute.

Theorem 69
45°-45°-90° Triangle Theorem
In a 45°-45°-90° triangle, both legs are congruent and the length of the hypotenuse is $\sqrt{2}$ times the length of a leg.

Theorem 70
30°-60°-90° Triangle Theorem
In a 30°-60°-90° triangle, the length of the hypotenuse is twice the length of the shorter leg. The length of the longer leg is $\sqrt{3}$ times the length of the shorter leg.

hypotenuse = 2 • shorter leg longer leg 5 $\sqrt{3}$ • shorter leg.

Theorem 71
Area of a Regular Polygon
The area of a regular polygon is half the product of the apothem and the perimeter.

Theorem 72
Circumference of a Circle
The circumference of a circle is π times the diameter.

$C = \pi d$ or $C = 2\pi r$

Theorem 73
Arc Length
The length of an arc of a circle is the product of the ratio $\frac{\text{measure of the arc}}{360}$ and the circumference of the circle.

length of $\widehat{AB} = \frac{m\widehat{AB}}{360} \cdot 2\pi r$ or

length of $\widehat{AB} = \frac{m\widehat{AB}}{360} \cdot \pi d$

Theorem 74
Area of a Circle
The area of a circle is the product of π and the square of the radius.

$A = \pi r^2$

Theorem 75
Area of a Sector of a Circle
The area of a sector of a circle is the product of the ratio $\frac{\text{measure of the arc}}{360}$ and the area of the circle.
Area of sector $AOB = \frac{m\widehat{AB}}{360} \cdot \pi r^2$

Theorem 76
If a line is tangent to a circle, then the line is perpendicular to the radius at the point of tangency.

Theorem 77
If a line in the plane of a circle is perpendicular to a radius at its endpoint on the circle, then the line is tangent to the circle.

Theorem 78
If two segments are tangent to a circle from a point outside the circle, then the two segments are congruent.

Theorem 79
Within a circle or in congruent circles, congruent central angles have congruent arcs.

Converse
Within a circle or in congruent circles, congruent arcs have congruent central angles.

Theorem 80
Within a circle or in congruent circles, congruent central angles have congruent chords.

Converse
Within a circle or in congruent circles, congruent chords have congruent central angles.

Theorem 81
Within a circle or in congruent circles, congruent chords have congruent arcs.

Converse
Within a circle or in congruent circles, congruent arcs have congruent chords.

Theorem 82
Within a circle or in congruent circles, chords equidistant from the center (or centers) are congruent.

Converse
Within a circle or in congruent circles, congruent chords are equidistant from the center (or centers).

Theorem 83
In a circle, if a diameter is perpendicular to a chord, it bisects the chord and its arc.

Theorem 84
In a circle, if a diameter bisects a chord (that is not a diameter), it is perpendicular to the chord.

Theorem 85
In a circle, the perpendicular bisector of a chord contains the center of the circle.

Theorem 86
Inscribed Angle Theorem
The measure of an inscribed angle is half the measure of its intercepted arc.

Corollary 1
Two inscribed angles that intercept the same arc are congruent.

Corollary 2
An angle inscribed in a semicircle is a right angle.

Corollary 3
The opposite angles of a quadrilateral inscribed in a circle are supplementary.

Theorem 87
The measure of an angle formed by a tangent and a chord is half the measure of the intercepted arc.

Theorem 88
The measure of an angle formed by two lines that intersect inside a circle is half the sum of the measures of the intercepted arcs.

Theorem 89
The measure of an angle formed by two lines that intersect outside a circle is half the difference of the measures of the intercepted arcs.

Theorem 90
For a given point and circle, the product of the lengths of the two segments from the point to the circle is constant along any line through the point and circle.

Theorem 91
Lateral and Surface Areas of a Prism
The lateral area of a right prism is the product of the perimeter of the base and the height of the prism.

L.A. $= ph$

The surface area of a right prism is the sum of the lateral area and the areas of the two bases.

S.A. = L.A. $+ 2B$

Theorem 92
Lateral and Surface Areas of a Cylinder
The lateral area of a right cylinder is the product of the circumference of the base and the height of the cylinder.

L.A. $= 2\pi rh$, or L.A. $= \pi dh$

The surface area of a right cylinder is the sum of the lateral area and areas of the two bases.

S.A. = L.A. $+ 2B$, or S.A. $= \pi rh + 2\pi r^2$

Theorem 93
Lateral and Surface Areas of a Pyramid
The lateral area of a regular pyramid is half the product of the perimeter p of the base and the slant height ℓ of the pyramid.

L.A. $= \frac{1}{2}p\ell$

The surface area of a regular pyramid is the sum of the lateral area and the area B of the base.

S.A. = L.A. $+ B$

Theorem 94
Lateral and Surface Areas of a Cone
The lateral area of a right cone is half the product of the circumference of the base and the slant height of the cone.

L.A. $= \frac{1}{2} \cdot 2\pi r\ell$ or L.A. $= \pi r\ell$

The surface area of a right cone is the sum of the lateral area and the area of the base.

S.A. = L.A. $+ B$

Theorem 95
Cavalieri's Principle
If two space figures have the same height and the same cross-sectional area at every level, then they have the same volume.

Theorem 96
Volume of a Prism
The volume of a prism is the product of the area of the base and the height of the prism.

$V = Bh$

Theorem 97
Volume of a Cylinder
The volume of a cylinder is the product of the area of the base and the height of the cylinder.

$V = Bh$, or $V = \pi r^2 h$

Theorem 98
Volume of a Pyramid
The volume of a pyramid is one third the product of the area of the base and the height of the pyramid.

$V = \frac{1}{3}Bh$

Theorem 99
Volume of a Cone
The volume of a cone is one third the product of the area of the base and the height of the cone.

$V = \frac{1}{3}Bh$ or $V = \frac{1}{3}\pi r^2 h$

Theorem 100
Surface Area of a Sphere
The surface area of a sphere is four times the product of π and the square of the radius of the sphere.

$V = 4\pi r^2$

Theorem 101
Volume of a Sphere
The volume of a sphere is four thirds the product of π and the cube of the radius of the sphere.

$V = \frac{4}{3}\pi r^3$

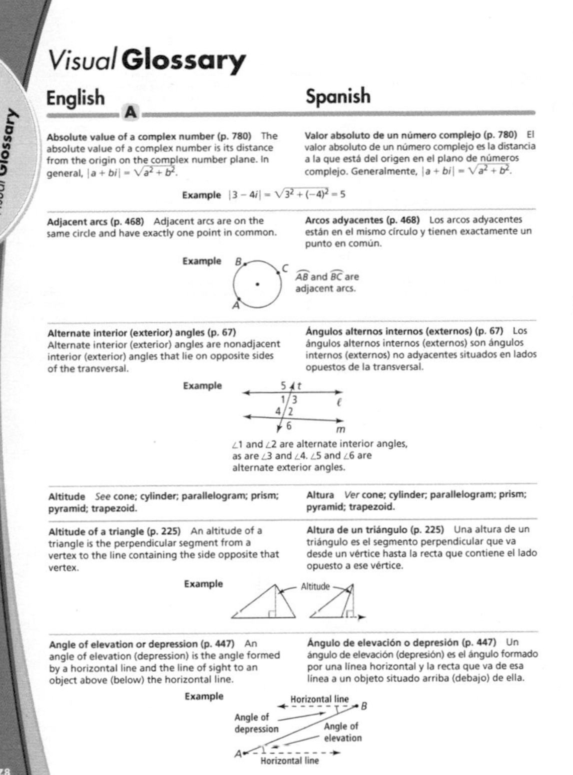

Visual Glossary

English | **Spanish**

A

Absolute value of a complex number (p. 780) The absolute value of a complex number is its distance from the origin on the complex number plane. In general, $|a + bi| = \sqrt{a^2 + b^2}$.

Valor absoluto de un número complejo (p. 780) El valor absoluto de un número complejo es la distancia a la que está del origen en el plano de números complejo. Generalmente, $|a + bi| = \sqrt{a^2 + b^2}$.

Example $|3 - 4i| = \sqrt{3^2 + (-4)^2} = 5$

Adjacent arcs (p. 468) Adjacent arcs are on the same circle and have exactly one point in common.

Arcos adyacentes (p. 468) Los arcos adyacentes están en el mismo círculo y tienen exactamente un punto en común.

Example $\widehat{AB}$ and $\widehat{BC}$ are adjacent arcs.

Alternate interior (exterior) angles (p. 67) Alternate interior (exterior) angles are nonadjacent interior (exterior) angles that lie on opposite sides of the transversal.

Ángulos alternos internos (externos) (p. 67) Los ángulos alternos internos (externos) son ángulos internos (externos) no adyacentes situados en lados opuestos de la transversal.

Example ∠1 and ∠2 are alternate interior angles, as are ∠3 and ∠4. ∠5 and ∠6 are alternate exterior angles.

Altitude *See* **cone; cylinder; parallelogram; prism; pyramid; trapezoid.**

Altura *Ver* **cone; cylinder; parallelogram; prism; pyramid; trapezoid.**

Altitude of a triangle (p. 225) An altitude of a triangle is the perpendicular segment from a vertex to the line containing the side opposite that vertex.

Altura de un triángulo (p. 225) Una altura de un triángulo es el segmento perpendicular que va desde un vértice hasta la recta que contiene el lado opuesto a ese vértice.

Example

Angle of elevation or depression (p. 447) An angle of elevation (depression) is the angle formed by a horizontal line and the line of sight to an object above (below) the horizontal line.

Ángulo de elevación o depresión (p. 447) Un ángulo de elevación (depresión) es el ángulo formado por una línea horizontal y la recta que va de esa línea a un objeto situado arriba (debajo) de ella.

Example

Z8

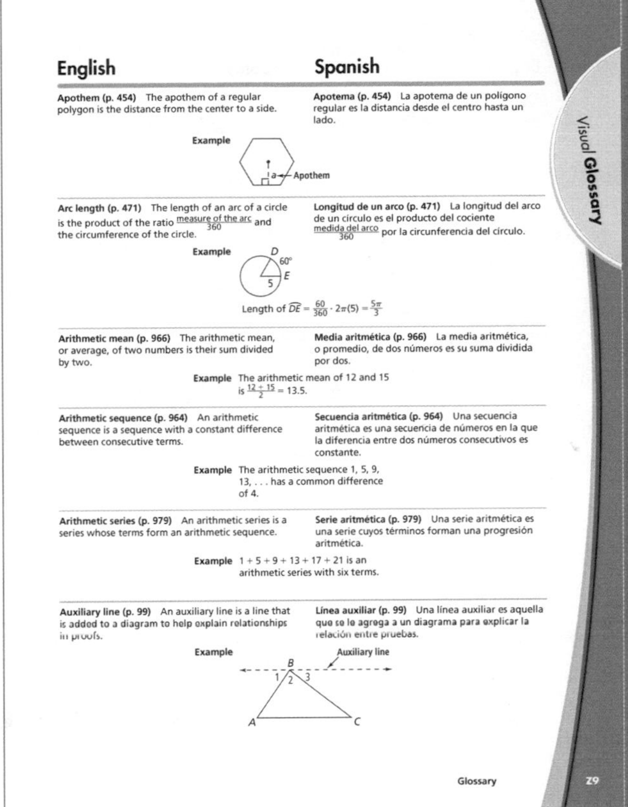

English | **Spanish**

Apothem (p. 454) The apothem of a regular polygon is the distance from the center to a side.

Apotema (p. 454) La apotema de un polígono regular es la distancia desde el centro hasta un lado.

Example

Arc length (p. 471) The length of an arc of a circle is the product of the ratio $\frac{\text{measure of the arc}}{360}$ and the circumference of the circle.

Longitud de un arco (p. 471) La longitud del arco de un círculo es el producto del cociente $\frac{\text{medida del arco}}{360}$ por la circunferencia del círculo.

Example Length of $\widehat{DE} = \frac{60}{360} \cdot 2\pi(5) = \frac{5\pi}{3}$

Arithmetic mean (p. 966) The arithmetic mean, or average, of two numbers is their sum divided by two.

Media aritmética (p. 966) La media aritmética, o promedio, de dos números es su suma dividida por dos.

Example The arithmetic mean of 12 and 15 is $\frac{12 + 15}{2} = 13.5$.

Arithmetic sequence (p. 964) An arithmetic sequence is a sequence with a constant difference between consecutive terms.

Secuencia aritmética (p. 964) Una secuencia aritmética es una secuencia de números en la que la diferencia entre dos números consecutivos es constante.

Example The arithmetic sequence 1, 5, 9, 13, . . . has a common difference of 4.

Arithmetic series (p. 979) An arithmetic series is a series whose terms form an arithmetic sequence.

Serie aritmética (p. 979) Una serie aritmética es una serie cuyos términos forman una progresión aritmética.

Example $1 + 5 + 9 + 13 + 17 + 21$ is an arithmetic series with six terms.

Auxiliary line (p. 99) An auxiliary line is a line that is added to a diagram to help explain relationships in proofs.

Línea auxiliar (p. 99) Una línea auxiliar es aquella que se le agrega a un diagrama para explicar la relación entre pruebas.

Example

Glossary Z9

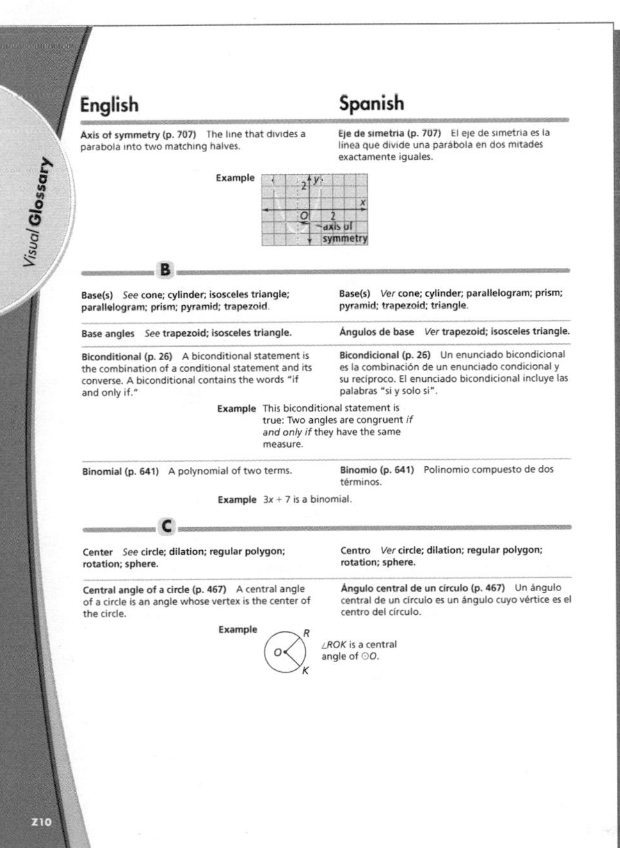

English | **Spanish**

Axis of symmetry (p. 707) The line that divides a parabola into two matching halves.

Eje de simetría (p. 707) El eje de simetría es la línea que divide una parábola en dos mitades exactamente iguales.

Example

B

Base(s) *See* **cone; cylinder; isosceles triangle; parallelogram; prism; pyramid; trapezoid.**

Base(s) *Ver* **cone; cylinder; parallelogram; prism; pyramid; trapezoid; triangle.**

Base angles *See* **trapezoid; isosceles triangle.**

Ángulos de base *Ver* **trapezoid; isosceles triangle.**

Biconditional (p. 26) A biconditional statement is the combination of a conditional statement and its converse. A biconditional contains the words "if and only if."

Bicondicional (p. 26) Un enunciado bicondicional es la combinación de un enunciado condicional y su recíproco. El enunciado bicondicional incluye las palabras "si y solo si".

Example This biconditional statement is true: Two angles are congruent *if and only if* they have the same measure.

Binomial (p. 641) A polynomial of two terms.

Binomio (p. 641) Polinomio compuesto de dos términos.

Example $3x + 7$ is a binomial.

C

Center *See* **circle; dilation; regular polygon; rotation; sphere.**

Centro *Ver* **circle; dilation; regular polygon; rotation; sphere.**

Central angle of a circle (p. 467) A central angle of a circle is an angle whose vertex is the center of the circle.

Ángulo central de un círculo (p. 467) Un ángulo central de un círculo es un ángulo cuyo vértice es el centro del círculo.

Example ∠*ROK* is a central angle of ⊙*O*.

Z10

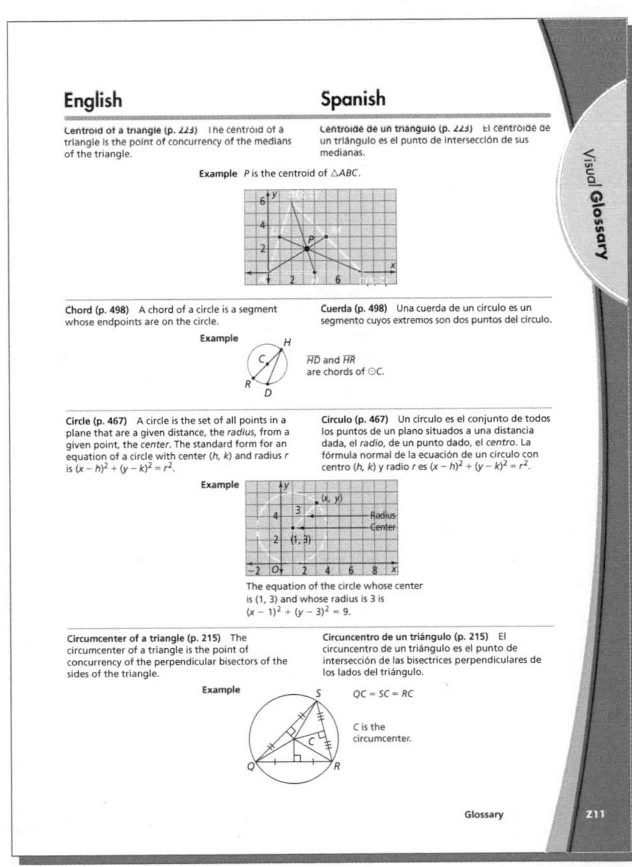

English | **Spanish**

Centroid of a triangle (p. 223) The centroid of a triangle is the point of concurrency of the medians of the triangle.

Centroide de un triángulo (p. 223) El centroide de un triángulo es el punto de intersección de sus medianas.

Example *P* is the centroid of △*ABC*.

Chord (p. 498) A chord of a circle is a segment whose endpoints are on the circle.

Cuerda (p. 498) Una cuerda de un círculo es un segmento cuyos extremos son dos puntos del círculo.

Example $\overline{HD}$ and $\overline{HR}$ are chords of ⊙*C*.

Circle (p. 467) A circle is the set of all points in a plane that are a given distance, the *radius*, from a given point, the *center*. The standard form for an equation of a circle with center (h, k) and radius r is $(x - h)^2 + (y - k)^2 = r^2$.

Círculo (p. 467) Un círculo es el conjunto de todos los puntos de un plano situados a una distancia dada, el *radio*, de un punto dado, el *centro*. La fórmula normal de la ecuación de un círculo con centro (h, k) y radio r es $(x - h)^2 + (y - k)^2 = r^2$.

Example

The equation of the circle whose center is (1, 3) and whose radius is 3 is $(x - 1)^2 + (y - 3)^2 = 9$.

Circumcenter of a triangle (p. 215) The circumcenter of a triangle is the point of concurrency of the perpendicular bisectors of the sides of the triangle.

Circuncentro de un triángulo (p. 215) El circuncentro de un triángulo es el punto de intersección de las bisectrices perpendiculares de los lados del triángulo.

Example $QC = SC = RC$

C is the circumcenter.

Glossary Z11

Visual **Glossary**

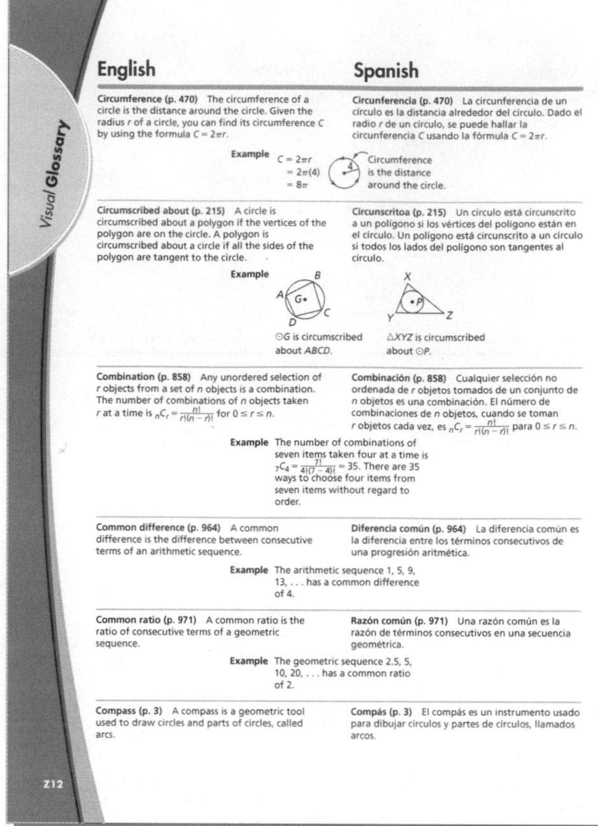
Visual **Glossary**

English | **Spanish**

Circumference (p. 470) The circumference of a circle is the distance around the circle. Given the radius r of a circle, you can find its circumference C by using the formula $C = 2\pi r$.

Circunferencia (p. 470) La circunferencia de un círculo es la distancia alrededor del círculo. Dado el radio r de un círculo, se puede hallar la circunferencia C usando la fórmula $C = 2\pi r$.

Example $C = 2\pi r = 2\pi(4) = 8\pi$ Circumference is the distance around the circle.

Circumscribed about (p. 215) A circle is circumscribed about a polygon if the vertices of the polygon are on the circle. A polygon is circumscribed about a circle if all the sides of the polygon are tangent to the circle.

Circunscritoa (p. 215) Un círculo está circunscrito a un polígono si los vértices del polígono están en el círculo. Un polígono está circunscrito a un círculo si todos los lados del polígono son tangentes al círculo.

Example ⊙G is circumscribed about $ABCD$. △XYZ is circumscribed about ⊙P.

Combination (p. 858) Any unordered selection of r objects from a set of n objects is a combination. The number of combinations of n objects taken r at a time is ${}_nC_r = \frac{n!}{r!(n-r)!}$ for $0 \le r \le n$.

Combinación (p. 858) Cualquier selección no ordenada de r objetos tomados de un conjunto de n objetos es una combinación. El número de combinaciones de n objetos, cuando se toman r objetos cada vez, es ${}_nC_r = \frac{n!}{r!(n-r)!}$ para $0 \le r \le n$.

Example The number of combinations of seven items taken four at a time is ${}_7C_4 = \frac{7!}{4!(7-4)!} = 35$. There are 35 ways to choose four items from seven items without regard to order.

Common difference (p. 964) A common difference is the difference between consecutive terms of an arithmetic sequence.

Diferencia común (p. 964) La diferencia común es la diferencia entre los términos consecutivos de una progresión aritmética.

Example The arithmetic sequence 1, 5, 9, 13, . . . has a common difference of 4.

Common ratio (p. 971) A common ratio is the ratio of consecutive terms of a geometric sequence.

Razón común (p. 971) Una razón común es la razón de términos consecutivos en una secuencia geométrica.

Example The geometric sequence 2.5, 5, 10, 20, . . . has a common ratio of 2.

Compass (p. 3) A compass is a geometric tool used to draw circles and parts of circles, called arcs.

Compás (p. 3) El compás es un instrumento usado para dibujar círculos y partes de círculos, llamados arcos.

Z12

English | **Spanish**

Complement of an event (p. 844) All possible outcomes that are not in the event. $P(\text{complement of event}) = 1 - P(\text{event})$

Complemento de un suceso (p. 844) Todos los resultados posibles que no se dan en el suceso. $P(\text{complemento de un suceso}) = 1 - P(\text{suceso})$

Example The complement of rolling a 1 or a 2 on a standard number cube is rolling a 3, 4, 5, or 6.

Completing the square (p. 760) A method of solving quadratic equations. Completing the square turns every quadratic equation into the form $x^2 = c$.

Completar el cuadrado (p. 760) Método para solucionar ecuaciones cuadráticas. Cuando se completa el cuadrado, se transforma la ecuación cuadática a la formula $x^2 = c$.

Example $x^2 + 6x - 7 = 9$ is rewritten as $(x + 3)^2 = 25$ by completing the square.

Complex conjugates (p. 784) Number pairs of the form $a + bi$ and $a - bi$ are complex conjugates.

Conjugados complejos (p. 784) Los pares de números de la forma $a + bi$ y $a - bi$ son conjugados complejos.

Example The complex number $2 - 3i$ and $2 + 3i$ are complex conjugates.

Complex number (p. 780) Complex numbers are the real numbers and the imaginary numbers.

Número complejo (p. 780) Los números complejos son los números reales y los números imaginarios.

Example $6 + i$, 7, $2i$

Complex number plane (p. 780) The complex number plane is identical to the coordinate plane except each ordered pair (a, b) represents the complex number $a + bi$. The horizontal axis is the Real axis. The vertical axis is the Imaginary axis.

Plano de números complejos (p. 780) El plano de los números complejos es idéntico al plano de coordenadas, a excepción de que cada par ordenado (a, b) representa el número complejo $a + bi$. El eje horizontal es el eje real. El eje vertical es el eje imaginario.

Example Imaginary axis; Real axis; $4i$, $2i$, $-2i$, $-4i$; -4, -2, O, 2, 4; $-4i$

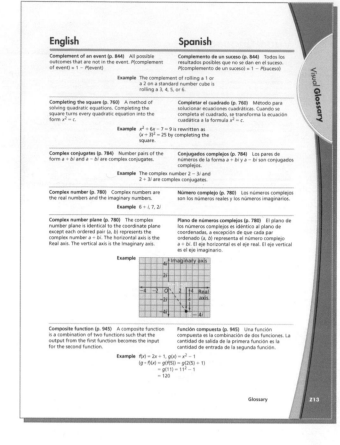

Composite function (p. 945) A composite function is a combination of two functions such that the output from the first function becomes the input for the second function.

Función compuesta (p. 945) Una función compuesta es la combinación de dos funciones. La cantidad de salida de la primera función es la cantidad de entrada de la segunda función.

Example $f(x) = 2x + 1$, $g(x) = x^2 - 1$
$(g \circ f)(x) = g(f(5)) = g(2(5) + 1) = g(11) = 11^2 - 1 = 120$

Glossary Z13

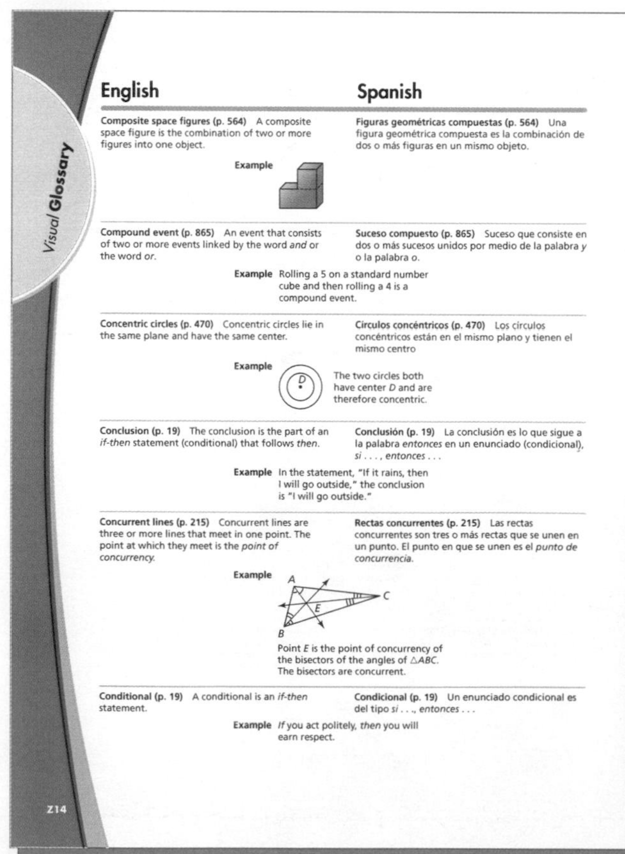
Visual **Glossary**

English | **Spanish**

Composite space figures (p. 564) A composite space figure is the combination of two or more figures into one object.

Figuras geométricas compuestas (p. 564) Una figura geométrica compuesta es la combinación de dos o más figuras en un mismo objeto.

Example

Compound event (p. 865) An event that consists of two or more events linked by the word *and* or the word *or*.

Suceso compuesto (p. 865) Suceso que consiste en dos o más sucesos unidos por medio de la palabra *y* o la palabra *o*.

Example Rolling a 5 on a standard number cube and then rolling a 4 is a compound event.

Concentric circles (p. 470) Concentric circles lie in the same plane and have the same center.

Círculos concéntricos (p. 470) Los círculos concéntricos están en el mismo plano y tienen el mismo centro

Example The two circles both have center D and are therefore concentric.

Conclusion (p. 19) The conclusion is the part of an *if-then* statement (conditional) that follows *then*.

Conclusión (p. 19) La conclusión es lo que sigue a la palabra *entonces* en un enunciado (condicional), *si . . . , entonces . . .*

Example In the statement, "If it rains, then I will go outside," the conclusion is "I will go outside."

Concurrent lines (p. 215) Concurrent lines are three or more lines that meet in one point. The point at which they meet is the *point of concurrency*.

Rectas concurrentes (p. 215) Las rectas concurrentes son tres o más rectas que se unen en un punto. El punto en que se unen es el *punto de concurrencia*.

Example Point E is the point of concurrency of the bisectors of the angles of △ABC. The bisectors are concurrent.

Conditional (p. 19) A conditional is an *if-then* statement.

Condicional (p. 19) Un enunciado condicional es del tipo *si . . ., entonces . . .*

Example *If* you act politely, *then* you will earn respect.

Z14

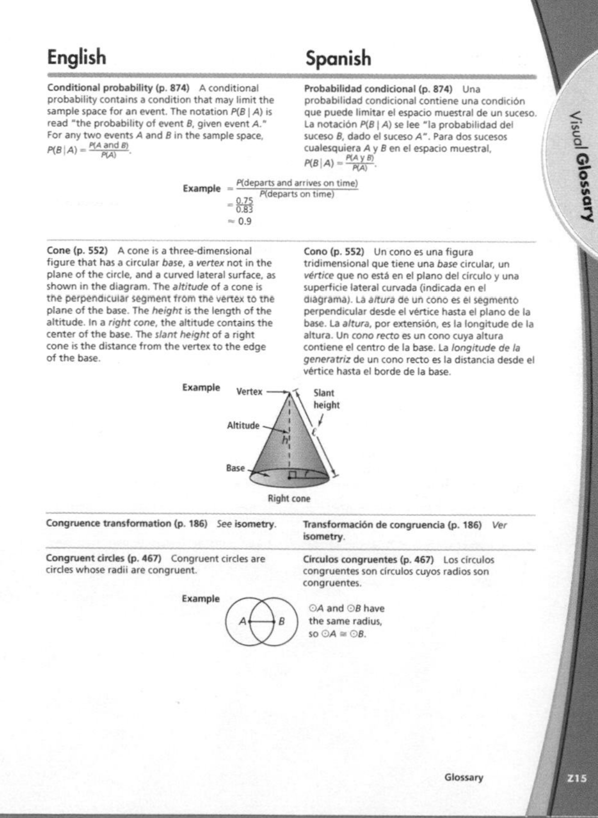
Visual **Glossary**

English | **Spanish**

Conditional probability (p. 874) A conditional probability contains a condition that may limit the sample space for an event. The notation $P(B \mid A)$ is read "the probability of event B, given event A." For any two events A and B in the sample space, $P(B \mid A) = \frac{P(A \text{ and } B)}{P(A)}$.

Probabilidad condicional (p. 874) Una probabilidad condicional contiene una condición que puede limitar el espacio muestral de un suceso. La notación $P(B \mid A)$ se lee "la probabilidad del suceso B, dado el suceso A". Para dos sucesos cualesquiera A y B en el espacio muestral, $P(B \mid A) = \frac{P(A \text{ y } B)}{P(A)}$.

Example $= \frac{P(\text{departs and arrives on time})}{P(\text{departs on time})} = \frac{0.75}{0.83} \approx 0.9$

Cone (p. 552) A cone is a three-dimensional figure that has a circular *base*, a *vertex* not in the plane of the circle, and a curved lateral surface, as shown in the diagram. The *altitude* of a cone is the perpendicular segment from the vertex to the plane of the base. The *height* is the length of the altitude. In a *right cone*, the altitude contains the center of the base. The *slant height* of a right cone is the distance from the vertex to the edge of the base.

Cono (p. 552) Un cono es una figura tridimensional que tiene una *base* circular, un *vértice* que no está en el plano del círculo y una superficie lateral curvada (indicada en el diagrama). La *altura* de un cono es el segmento perpendicular desde el vértice hasta el plano de la base. La *altura*, por extensión, es la longitude de la altura. Un *cono recto* es un cono cuya altura contiene el centro de la base. La *longitude de la generatriz* de un cono recto es la distancia desde el vértice hasta el borde de la base.

Example Vertex; Slant height; Altitude; Base; h; ℓ; r

Right cone

Congruence transformation (p. 186) *See* **isometry**.

Transformación de congruencia (p. 186) *Ver* **isometry**.

Congruent circles (p. 467) Congruent circles are circles whose radii are congruent.

Círculos congruentes (p. 467) Los círculos congruentes son círculos cuyos radios son congruentes.

Example ⊙A and ⊙B have the same radius, so ⊙$A \cong$ ⊙B.

Glossary Z15

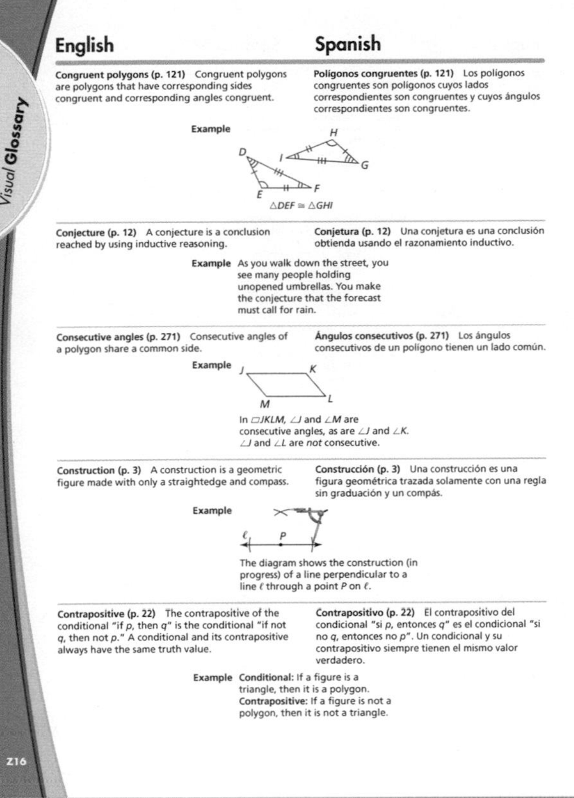

Visual Glossary

English / Spanish

Congruent polygons (p. 121) Congruent polygons are polygons that have corresponding sides congruent and corresponding angles congruent.

Polígonos congruentes (p. 121) Los polígonos congruentes son polígonos cuyos lados correspondientes son congruentes y cuyos ángulos correspondientes son congruentes.

Example $\triangle DEF \cong \triangle GHI$

Conjecture (p. 12) A conjecture is a conclusion reached by using inductive reasoning.

Conjetura (p. 12) Una conjetura es una conclusión obtienda usando el razonamiento inductivo.

Example As you walk down the street, you see many people holding unopened umbrellas. You make the conjecture that the forecast must call for rain.

Consecutive angles (p. 271) Consecutive angles of a polygon share a common side.

Ángulos consecutivos (p. 271) Los ángulos consecutivos de un polígono tienen un lado común.

Example In ▱$JKLM$, $\angle J$ and $\angle M$ are consecutive angles, as are $\angle J$ and $\angle K$. $\angle J$ and $\angle L$ are *not* consecutive.

Construction (p. 3) A construction is a geometric figure made with only a straightedge and compass.

Construcción (p. 3) Una construcción es una figura geométrica trazada solamente con una regla sin graduación y un compás.

Example The diagram shows the construction (in progress) of a line perpendicular to a line ℓ through a point P on ℓ.

Contrapositive (p. 22) The contrapositive of the conditional "if p, then q" is the conditional "if not q, then not p." A conditional and its contrapositive always have the same truth value.

Contrapositivo (p. 22) El contrapositivo del condicional "si p, entonces q" es el condicional "si no q, entonces no p". Un condicional y su contrapositivo siempre tienen el mismo valor verdadero.

Example **Conditional:** If a figure is a triangle, then it is a polygon. **Contrapositive:** If a figure is not a polygon, then it is not a triangle.

Z16

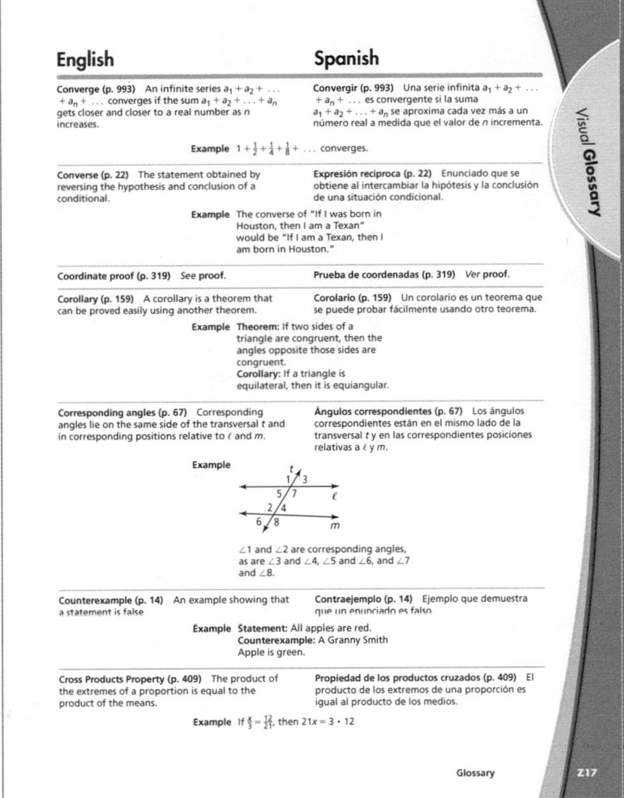

English / Spanish

Converge (p. 993) An infinite series $a_1 + a_2 + \ldots + a_n + \ldots$ converges if the sum $a_1 + a_2 + \ldots + a_n$ gets closer and closer to a real number as n increases.

Convergir (p. 993) Una serie infinita $a_1 + a_2 + \ldots + a_n + \ldots$ es convergente si la suma $a_1 + a_2 + \ldots + a_n$ se aproxima cada vez más a un número real a medida que el valor de n incrementa.

Example $1 + \frac{1}{2} + \frac{1}{4} + \frac{1}{8} + \ldots$ converges.

Converse (p. 22) The statement obtained by reversing the hypothesis and conclusion of a conditional.

Expresión recíproca (p. 22) Enunciado que se obtiene al intercambiar la hipótesis y la conclusión de una situación condicional.

Example The converse of "If I was born in Houston, then I am a Texan" would be "If I am a Texan, then I am born in Houston."

Coordinate proof (p. 319) *See* proof.

Prueba de coordenadas (p. 319) *Ver* proof.

Corollary (p. 159) A corollary is a theorem that can be proved easily using another theorem.

Corolario (p. 159) Un corolario es un teorema que se puede probar fácilmente usando otro teorema.

Example **Theorem:** If two sides of a triangle are congruent, then the angles opposite those sides are congruent. **Corollary:** If a triangle is equilateral, then it is equiangular.

Corresponding angles (p. 67) Corresponding angles lie on the same side of the transversal t and in corresponding positions relative to ℓ and m.

Ángulos correspondientes (p. 67) Los ángulos correspondientes están en el mismo lado de la transversal t y en las correspondientes posiciones relativas a ℓ y m.

Example $\angle 1$ and $\angle 2$ are corresponding angles, as are $\angle 3$ and $\angle 4$, $\angle 5$ and $\angle 6$, and $\angle 7$ and $\angle 8$.

Counterexample (p. 14) An example showing that a statement is false

Contraejemplo (p. 14) Ejemplo que demuestra que un enunciado es falso

Example **Statement:** All apples are red. **Counterexample:** A Granny Smith Apple is green.

Cross Products Property (p. 409) The product of the extremes of a proportion is equal to the product of the means.

Propiedad de los productos cruzados (p. 409) El producto de los extremos de una proporción es igual al producto de los medios.

Example If $\frac{x}{3} = \frac{12}{21}$, then $21x = 3 \cdot 12$

Glossary Z17

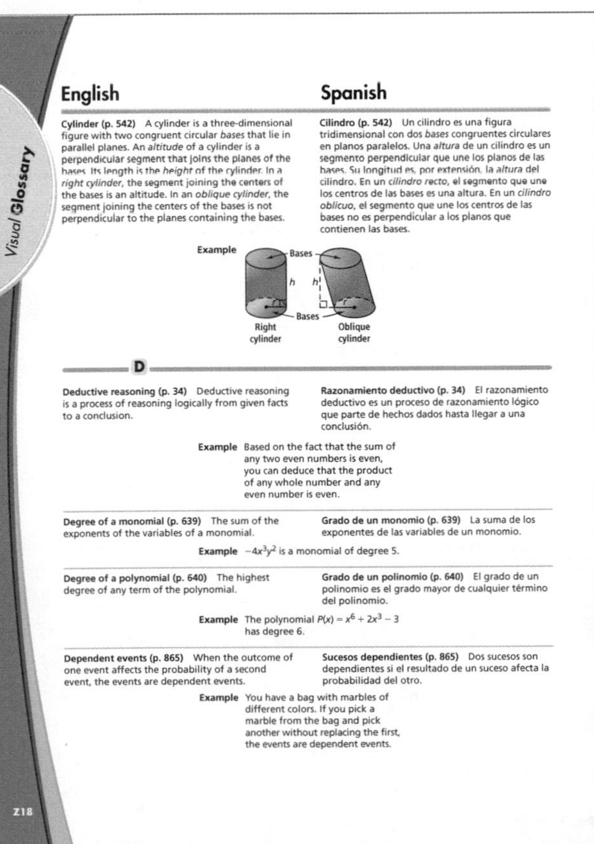

English / Spanish

Cylinder (p. 542) A cylinder is a three-dimensional figure with two congruent circular *bases* that lie in parallel planes. An *altitude* of a cylinder is a perpendicular segment that joins the planes of the bases. Its length is the *height* of the cylinder. In a *right cylinder*, the segment joining the centers of the bases is an altitude. In an *oblique cylinder*, the segment joining the centers of the bases is not perpendicular to the planes containing the bases.

Cilindro (p. 542) Un cilindro es una figura tridimensional con dos *bases* congruentes circulares en planos paralelos. Una *altura* de un cilindro es un segmento perpendicular que une los planos de las bases. Su longitud es, por extensión, la *altura* del cilindro. En un *cilindro recto*, el segmento que une los centros de las bases es una altura. En un *cilindro oblicuo*, el segmento que une los centros de las bases no es perpendicular a los planos que contienen las bases.

Example Right cylinder / Oblique cylinder

D

Deductive reasoning (p. 34) Deductive reasoning is a process of reasoning logically from given facts to a conclusion.

Razonamiento deductivo (p. 34) El razonamiento deductivo es un proceso de razonamiento lógico que parte de hechos dados hasta llegar a una conclusión.

Example Based on the fact that the sum of any two even numbers is even, you can deduce that the product of any whole number and any even number is even.

Degree of a monomial (p. 639) The sum of the exponents of the variables of a monomial.

Grado de un monomio (p. 639) La suma de los exponentes de las variables de un monomio.

Example $-4x^3y^2$ is a monomial of degree 5.

Degree of a polynomial (p. 640) The highest degree of any term of the polynomial.

Grado de un polinomio (p. 640) El grado de un polinomio es el grado mayor de cualquier término del polinomio.

Example The polynomial $P(x) = x^6 + 2x^3 - 3$ has degree 6.

Dependent events (p. 865) When the outcome of one event affects the probability of a second event, the events are dependent events.

Sucesos dependientes (p. 865) Dos sucesos son dependientes si el resultado de un suceso afecta la probabilidad del otro.

Example You have a bag with marbles of different colors. If you pick a marble from the bag and pick another without replacing the first, the events are dependent events.

Z18

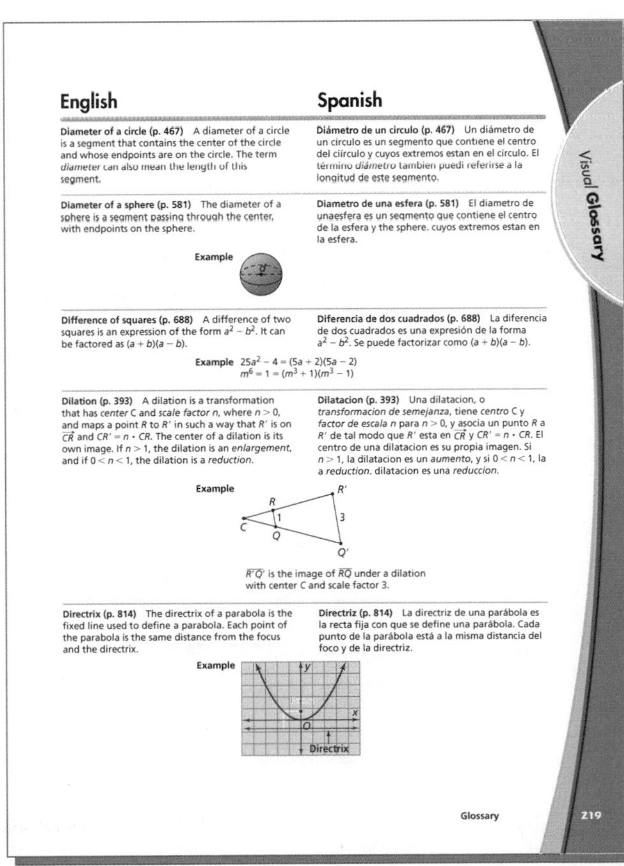

English / Spanish

Diameter of a circle (p. 467) A diameter of a circle is a segment that contains the center of the circle and whose endpoints are on the circle. The term *diameter* can also mean the length of this segment.

Diámetro de un circulo (p. 467) Un diámetro de un circulo es un segmento que contiene el centro del ciírculo y cuyos extremos estan en el círculo. El término *diámetro* tambien puedi referirse a la longitud de este segmento.

Diameter of a sphere (p. 581) The diameter of a sphere is a segment passing through the center, with endpoints on the sphere.

Diametro de una esfera (p. 581) El diametro de unaesfera es un segmento que contiene el centro de la esfera y the sphere. cuyos extremos estan en la esfera.

Example

Difference of squares (p. 688) A difference of two squares is an expression of the form $a^2 - b^2$. It can be factored as $(a + b)(a - b)$.

Diferencia de dos cuadrados (p. 688) La diferencia de dos cuadrados es una expresión de la forma $a^2 - b^2$. Se puede factorizar como $(a + b)(a - b)$.

Example $25a^2 - 4 = (5a + 2)(5a - 2)$
$m^6 = 1 = (m^3 + 1)(m^3 - 1)$

Dilation (p. 393) A dilation is a transformation that has *center* C and *scale factor n*, where $n > 0$, and maps a point R to R' in such a way that R' is on $\overrightarrow{CR}$ and $CR' = n \cdot CR$. The center of a dilation is its own image. If $n > 1$, the dilation is an *enlargement*, and if $0 < n < 1$, the dilation is a *reduction*.

Dilatacion (p. 393) Una dilatacion, o *transformacion de semejanza*, tiene *centro* C y *factor de escala n* para $n > 0$, y asocia un punto R a R' de tal modo que R' esta en $\overrightarrow{CR}$ y $CR' = n \cdot CR$. El centro de una dilatacion es su propia imagen. Si $n > 1$, la dilatacion es un *aumento*, y si $0 < n < 1$, la a *reduction*. dilatacion es una *reduccion*.

Example $\overline{R'Q'}$ is the image of $\overline{RQ}$ under a dilation with center C and scale factor 3.

Directrix (p. 814) The directrix of a parabola is the fixed line used to define a parabola. Each point of the parabola is the same distance from the focus and the directrix.

Directriz (p. 814) La directriz de una parábola es la recta fija con que se define una parábola. Cada punto de la parábola está a la misma distancia del foco y de la directriz.

Example

Glossary Z19

Visual Glossary

Visual **Glossary**

English / Spanish

Discriminant (p. 773) The discriminant of a quadratic equation of the form $ax^2 + bx + c = 0$ is $b^2 - 4ac$. The value of the discriminant determines the number of solutions of the equation.

Discriminante (p. 773) El discriminante de una ecuación cuadrática $ax^2 + bx + c = 0$ es $b^2 - 4ac$. El valor del discriminante determina el número de soluciones de la ecuación.

Example The discriminant of $2x^2 + 9x - 2 = 0$ is 97.

Distance from a point to a line (p. 210) The distance from a point to a line is the length of the perpendicular segment from the point to the line.

Distancia desde un punto hasta una recta (p. 210) La distancia desde un punto hasta una recta es la longitud del segmento perpendicular que va desde el punto hasta la recta.

Example The distance from point P to a line ℓ is PT.

Diverge (p. 993) An infinite series diverges if it does not converge.

Divergir (p. 993) Una serie infinita es divergente si no es convergente.

Example $1 + 2 + 4 + 8 + \dots$ diverges.

E

Enlargement (p. 394) *See* **dilation.**

Aumento (p. 394) *Ver* **dilation.**

Equiangular triangle or polygon (p. 264) An equiangular triangle (polygon) is a triangle (polygon) whose angles are all congruent.

Triángulo o polígono equiángulo (p. 264) Un triángulo (polígono) equiángulo es un triángulo (polígono) cuyos ángulos son todos congruentes.

Example Each angle of the pentagon is a 108° angle.

Equidistant (p. 207) A point is equidistant from two objects if it is the same distance from the objects.

Equidistante (p. 207) Un punto es equidistante de dos objetos si la distancia entre el punto y los objetos es igual.

Example Point B is equidistant from points A and C.

Equilateral triangle or polygon (p. 264) An equilateral triangle (polygon) is a triangle (polygon) whose sides are all congruent.

Triángulo o polígono equilátero (p. 264) Un triángulo (polígono) equilátero es un triángulo (polígono) cuyos lados son todos congruentes.

Example Each side of the quadrilateral is 1.2 cm long.

Z20

English / Spanish

Equivalent statements (p. 22) Equivalent statements are statements with the same truth value.

Enunciados equivalentes (p. 22) Los enunciados equivalentes son enunciados con el mismo valor verdadero.

Example The following statements are equivalent: If a figure is a square, then it is a rectangle. If a figure is not a rectangle, then it is not a square.

Event (p. 841) Any group of outcomes in a situation involving probability.

Suceso (p. 841) En la probabilidad, cualquier grupo de resultados.

Example When rolling a number cube, there are six possible outcomes. Rolling an even number is an event with three possible outcomes, 2, 4, and 6.

Expected value (p. 890) The average value you can expect for a large number of trials of an experiment; the sum of each outcome's value multiplied by its probability.

Valor esperado (p. 890) El valor promedio que se puede esperar para una cantidad grande de pruebas en un experimento; la suma de los valores de los resultados multiplicados cada uno por su probabilidad.

Example In a game, a player has a 25% probability of earning 10 points by spinning an even number and a 75% probability of earning 5 points by spinning an odd number.
expected value =
$0.25(10) + 0.75(5) = 6.25$

Experimental probability (p. 842) The ratio of the number of times an event actually happens to the number of times the experiment is done.

$$P(\text{event}) = \frac{\text{number of times an event happens}}{\text{number of times the experiment is done}}$$

Probabilidad experimental (p. 842) La razón entre el número de veces que un suceso sucede en la realidad y el número de veces que se hace el experimento.

$$P(\text{suceso}) = \frac{\text{número de veces que sucede un suceso}}{\text{número de veces que se hace el experimento}}$$

Example A baseball player's batting average shows how likely it is that a player will get a hit, based on previous times at bat.

Explicit formula (p. 955) An explicit formula expresses the nth term of a sequence in terms of n.

Fórmula explícita (p. 955) Una fórmula explícita expresa el n-ésimo término de una progresión en función de n.

Example Let $a_n = 2n + 5$ for positive integers n. If $n = 7$, then $a_7 = 2(7) + 5 = 19$.

Extended proportion (p. 348) *See* **proportion.**

Proporción extendida (p. 348) *Ver* **proportion.**

Extended ratio (p. 339) *See* **ratio.**

Razón extendida (p. 339) *Ver* **ratio.**

Glossary Z21

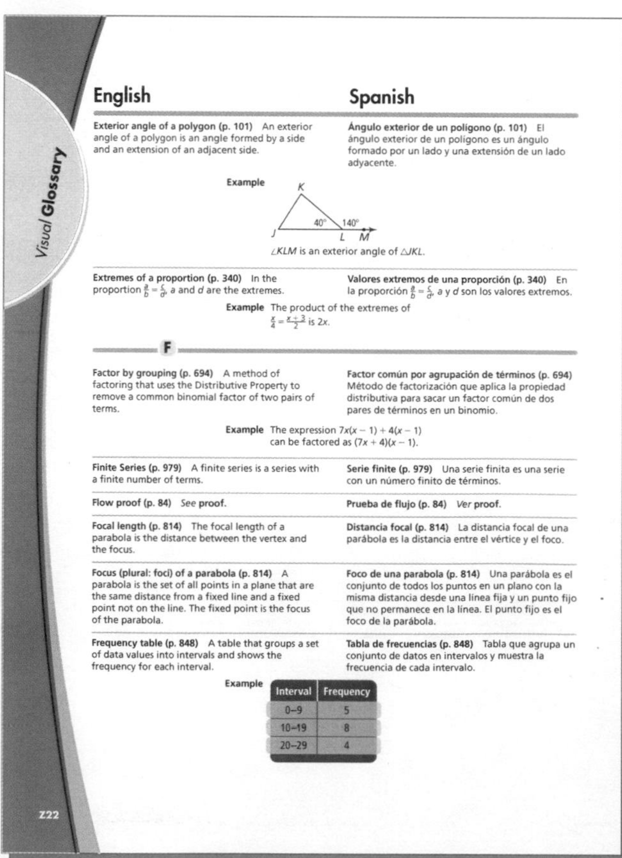

Visual **Glossary**

English / Spanish

Exterior angle of a polygon (p. 101) An exterior angle of a polygon is an angle formed by a side and an extension of an adjacent side.

Ángulo exterior de un polígono (p. 101) El ángulo exterior de un polígono es un ángulo formado por un lado y una extensión de un lado adyacente.

Example $\angle KLM$ is an exterior angle of $\triangle JKL$.

Extremes of a proportion (p. 340) In the proportion $\frac{a}{b} = \frac{c}{d}$, a and d are the extremes.

Valores extremos de una proporción (p. 340) En la proporción $\frac{a}{b} = \frac{c}{d}$, a y d son los valores extremos.

Example The product of the extremes of $\frac{x}{4} = \frac{x+3}{2}$ is $2x$.

F

Factor by grouping (p. 694) A method of factoring that uses the Distributive Property to remove a common binomial factor of two pairs of terms.

Factor común por agrupación de términos (p. 694) Método de factorización que aplica la propiedad distributiva para sacar un factor común de dos pares de términos en un binomio.

Example The expression $7x(x - 1) + 4(x - 1)$ can be factored as $(7x + 4)(x - 1)$.

Finite Series (p. 979) A finite series is a series with a finite number of terms.

Serie finite (p. 979) Una serie finita es una serie con un número finito de términos.

Flow proof (p. 84) *See* **proof.**

Prueba de flujo (p. 84) *Ver* **proof.**

Focal length (p. 814) The focal length of a parabola is the distance between the vertex and the focus.

Distancia focal (p. 814) La distancia focal de una parábola es la distancia entre el vértice y el foco.

Focus (plural: foci) of a parabola (p. 814) A parabola is the set of all points in a plane that are the same distance from a fixed line and a fixed point not on the line. The fixed point is the focus of the parabola.

Foco de una parabola (p. 814) Una parábola es el conjunto de todos los puntos en un plano con la misma distancia desde una línea fija y un punto fijo que no permanece en la línea. El punto fijo es el foco de la parábola.

Frequency table (p. 848) A table that groups a set of data values into intervals and shows the frequency for each interval.

Tabla de frecuencias (p. 848) Tabla que agrupa un conjunto de datos en intervalos y muestra la frecuencia de cada intervalo.

Example

Interval	Frequency
0–9	5
10–19	8
20–29	4

Z22

English / Spanish

Fundamental Counting Principle (p. 855) If there are m ways to make the first selection and n ways to make the second selection, then there are $m \cdot n$ ways to make the two selections.

Principio fundamental de Conteo (p. 855) Si hay m maneras de hacer la primera selección y n maneras de hacer la segunda selección, quiere decir que hay $m \cdot n$ maneras de hacer las dos selecciones.

Example For 5 shirts and 8 pairs of shorts, the number of possible outfits is $5 \cdot 8 = 40$.

G

Geometric mean (p. 371, 975) The geometric mean is the number x such that $\frac{a}{x} = \frac{x}{b}$, where a, b, and x are positive numbers.

Media geométrica (p. 371, 975) La media geométrica es el número x tanto que $\frac{a}{x} = \frac{x}{b}$, donde a, b y x son números positivos.

Example The geometric mean of 6 and 24 is 12.

$$\frac{6}{x} = \frac{x}{24}$$
$$x^2 = 144$$
$$x = 12$$

Geometric sequence (p. 971) A geometric sequence is a sequence with a constant ratio between consecutive terms.

Secuencia geométrica (p. 971) Una secuencia geométrica es una secuencia con una razón constante entre términos consecutivos.

Example The geometric sequence 2.5, 5, 10, 20, 40 ..., has a common ratio of 2.

Geometric series (p. 991) A geometric series is the sum of the terms in a geometric sequence.

Serie geométrica (p. 991) Una serie geométrica es la suma de términos en una progresión geométrica.

Example One geometric series with five terms is $2.5 + 5 + 10 + 20 + 40$.

Great circle (p. 581) A great circle is the intersection of a sphere and a plane containing the center of the sphere. A great circle divides a sphere into two *hemispheres*.

Círculo máximo (p. 581) Un círculo máximo es la intersección de una esfera y un plano que contiene el centro de la esfera. Un círculo máximo divide una esfera en dos *hemisferios*.

Example Hemispheres — Great circle

Greatest integer function (p. 933) The greatest integer function corresponds each input x to the greatest integer less than or equal to x.

Función del entero mayor (p. 933) La función del entero mayor relaciona cada entrada x con el entero mayor que es menor oigual a x.

Glossary Z23

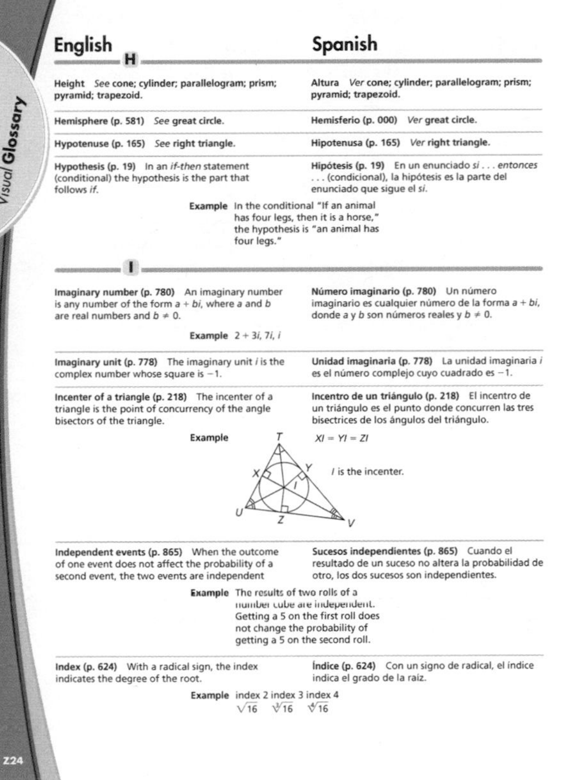

English **Spanish**

H

Height *See* **cone; cylinder; parallelogram; prism; pyramid; trapezoid.** — **Altura** *Ver* **cone; cylinder; parallelogram; prism; pyramid; trapezoid.**

Hemisphere (p. 581) *See* **great circle.** — **Hemisferio (p. 000)** *Ver* **great circle.**

Hypotenuse (p. 165) *See* **right triangle.** — **Hipotenusa (p. 165)** *Ver* **right triangle.**

Hypothesis (p. 19) In an *if-then* statement (conditional) the hypothesis is the part that follows *if*. — **Hipótesis (p. 19)** En un enunciado *si . . . entonces . . .* (condicional), la hipótesis es la parte del enunciado que sigue el *si*.

Example In the conditional "If an animal has four legs, then it is a horse," the hypothesis is "an animal has four legs."

I

Imaginary number (p. 780) An imaginary number is any number of the form $a + bi$, where a and b are real numbers and $b \neq 0$. — **Número imaginario (p. 780)** Un número imaginario es cualquier número de la forma $a + bi$, donde a y b son números reales y $b \neq 0$.

Example $2 + 3i$, $7i$, i

Imaginary unit (p. 778) The imaginary unit i is the complex number whose square is -1. — **Unidad imaginaria (p. 778)** La unidad imaginaria i es el número complejo cuyo cuadrado es -1.

Incenter of a triangle (p. 218) The incenter of a triangle is the point of concurrency of the angle bisectors of the triangle. — **Incentro de un triángulo (p. 218)** El incentro de un triángulo es el punto donde concurren las tres bisectrices de los ángulos del triángulo.

Example $XI = YI = ZI$

I is the incenter.

Independent events (p. 865) When the outcome of one event does not affect the probability of a second event, the two events are independent — **Sucesos independientes (p. 865)** Cuando el resultado de un suceso no altera la probabilidad de otro, los dos sucesos son independientes.

Example The results of two rolls of a number cube are independent. Getting a 5 on the first roll does not change the probability of getting a 5 on the second roll.

Index (p. 624) With a radical sign, the index indicates the degree of the root. — **Índice (p. 624)** Con un signo de radical, el índice indica el grado de la raíz.

Example index 2 index 3 index 4 $\sqrt{16}$ $\sqrt[3]{16}$ $\sqrt[4]{16}$

Z24

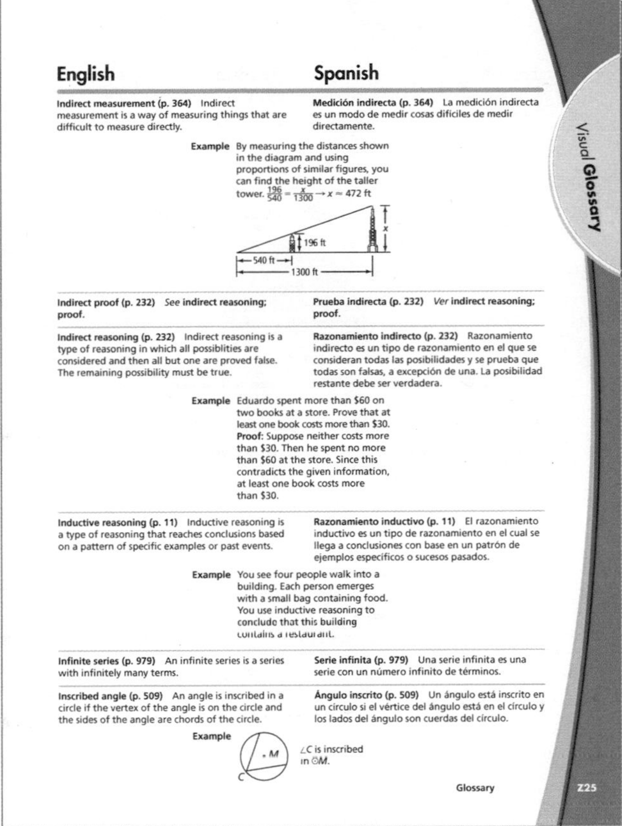

English **Spanish**

Indirect measurement (p. 364) Indirect measurement is a way of measuring things that are difficult to measure directly. — **Medición indirecta (p. 364)** La medición indirecta es un modo de medir cosas difíciles de medir directamente.

Example By measuring the distances shown in the diagram and using proportions of similar figures, you can find the height of the taller tower. $\frac{196}{540} = \frac{x}{1300} \rightarrow x \approx 472$ ft

Indirect proof (p. 232) *See* **indirect reasoning; proof.** — **Prueba indirecta (p. 232)** *Ver* **indirect reasoning; proof.**

Indirect reasoning (p. 232) Indirect reasoning is a type of reasoning in which all possibilities are considered and then all but one are proved false. The remaining possibility must be true. — **Razonamiento indirecto (p. 232)** Razonamiento indirecto es un tipo de razonamiento en el que se consideran todas las posibilidades y se prueba que todas son falsas, a excepción de una. La posibilidad restante debe ser verdadera.

Example Eduardo spent more than \$60 on two books at a store. Prove that at least one book costs more than \$30. **Proof:** Suppose neither costs more than \$30. Then he spent no more than \$60 at the store. Since this contradicts the given information, at least one book costs more than \$30.

Inductive reasoning (p. 11) Inductive reasoning is a type of reasoning that reaches conclusions based on a pattern of specific examples or past events. — **Razonamiento inductivo (p. 11)** El razonamiento inductivo es un tipo de razonamiento en el cual se llega a conclusiones con base en un patrón de ejemplos específicos o sucesos pasados.

Example You see four people walk into a building. Each person emerges with a small bag containing food. You use inductive reasoning to conclude that this building contains a restaurant.

Infinite series (p. 979) An infinite series is a series with infinitely many terms. — **Serie infinita (p. 979)** Una serie infinita es una serie con un número infinito de términos.

Inscribed angle (p. 509) An angle is inscribed in a circle if the vertex of the angle is on the circle and the sides of the angle are chords of the circle. — **Ángulo inscrito (p. 509)** Un ángulo está inscrito en un círculo si el vértice del ángulo está en el círculo y los lados del ángulo son cuerdas del círculo.

Example $\angle C$ is inscribed in $\odot M$.

Glossary Z25

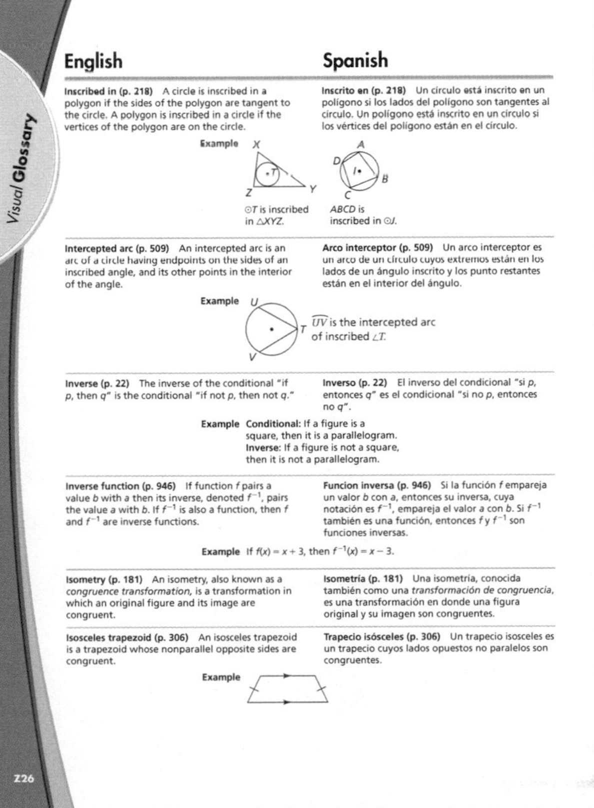

English **Spanish**

Inscribed in (p. 218) A circle is inscribed in a polygon if the sides of the polygon are tangent to the circle. A polygon is inscribed in a circle if the vertices of the polygon are on the circle. — **Inscrito en (p. 218)** Un círculo está inscrito en un polígono si los lados del polígono son tangentes al círculo. Un polígono está inscrito en un círculo si los vértices del polígono están en el círculo.

Example $\odot T$ is inscribed in $\triangle XYZ$. *ABCD* is inscribed in $\odot J$.

Intercepted arc (p. 509) An intercepted arc is an arc of a circle having endpoints on the sides of an inscribed angle, and its other points in the interior of the angle. — **Arco interceptor (p. 509)** Un arco interceptor es un arco de un círculo cuyos extremos están en los lados de un ángulo inscrito y los punto restantes están en el interior del ángulo.

Example $\widehat{UV}$ is the intercepted arc of inscribed $\angle T$.

Inverse (p. 22) The inverse of the conditional "if p, then q" is the conditional "if not p, then not q." — **Inverso (p. 22)** El inverso del condicional "si p, entonces q" es el condicional "si no p, entonces no q".

Example **Conditional:** If a figure is a square, then it is a parallelogram. **Inverse:** If a figure is not a square, then it is not a parallelogram.

Inverse function (p. 946) If function f pairs a value b with a then its inverse, denoted f^{-1}, pairs the value a with b. If f^{-1} is also a function, then f and f^{-1} are inverse functions. — **Funcion inversa (p. 946)** Si la función f empareja un valor b con a, entonces su inversa, cuya notación es f^{-1}, empareja el valor a con b. Si f^{-1} también es una función, entonces f y f^{-1} son funciones inversas.

Example If $f(x) = x + 3$, then $f^{-1}(x) = x - 3$.

Isometry (p. 181) An isometry, also known as a *congruence transformation*, is a transformation in which an original figure and its image are congruent. — **Isometría (p. 181)** Una isometría, conocida también como una *transformación de congruencia*, es una transformación en donde una figura original y su imagen son congruentes.

Isosceles trapezoid (p. 306) An isosceles trapezoid is a trapezoid whose nonparallel opposite sides are congruent. — **Trapecio isósceles (p. 306)** Un trapecio isosceles es un trapecio cuyos lados opuestos no paralelos son congruentes.

Example

Z26

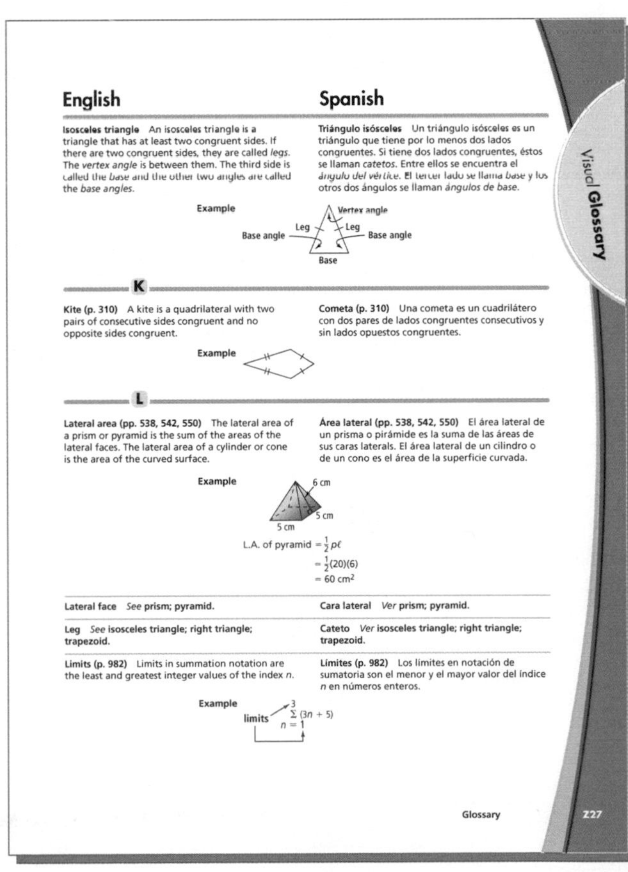

English **Spanish**

Isosceles triangle An isosceles triangle is a triangle that has at least two congruent sides. If there are two congruent sides, they are called *legs*. The *vertex angle* is between them. The third side is called the *base* and the other two angles are called the *base angles*. — **Triángulo isósceles** Un triángulo isósceles es un triángulo que tiene por lo menos dos lados congruentes. Si tiene dos lados congruentes, éstos se llaman *catetos*. Entre ellos se encuentra el *ángulo del vértice*. El tercer lado se llama *base* y los otros dos ángulos se llaman *ángulos de base*.

Example

K

Kite (p. 310) A kite is a quadrilateral with two pairs of consecutive sides congruent and no opposite sides congruent. — **Cometa (p. 310)** Una cometa es un cuadrilátero con dos pares de lados congruentes consecutivos y sin lados opuestos congruentes.

Example

L

Lateral area (pp. 538, 542, 550) The lateral area of a prism or pyramid is the sum of the areas of the lateral faces. The lateral area of a cylinder or cone is the area of the curved surface. — **Área lateral (pp. 538, 542, 550)** El área lateral de un prisma o pirámide es la suma de las áreas de sus caras laterales. El área lateral de un cilindro o de un cono es el área de la superficie curvada.

Example 6 cm, 5 cm, 5 cm

L.A. of pyramid $= \frac{1}{2}p\ell$
$= \frac{1}{2}(20)(6)$
$= 60 \text{ cm}^2$

Lateral face *See* **prism; pyramid.** — **Cara lateral** *Ver* **prism; pyramid.**

Leg *See* **isosceles triangle; right triangle; trapezoid.** — **Cateto** *Ver* **isosceles triangle; right triangle; trapezoid.**

Limits (p. 982) Limits in summation notation are the least and greatest integer values of the index n. — **Límites (p. 982)** Los límites en notación de sumatoria son el menor y el mayor valor del índice n en números enteros.

Example limits $\sum_{n=1}^{3}(3n + 5)$

Glossary Z27

Visual **Glossary**

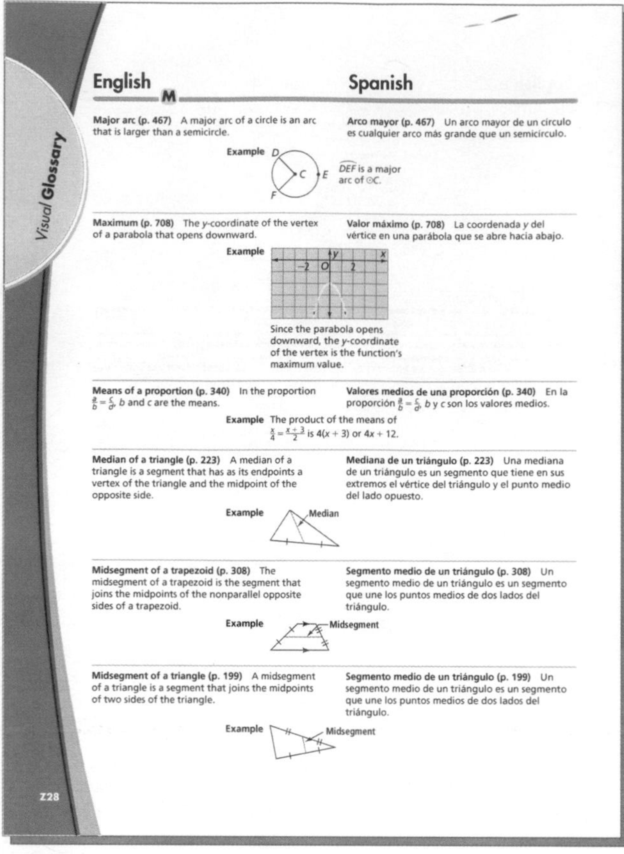

Visual Glossary

English | **Spanish**

M

Major arc (p. 467) A major arc of a circle is an arc that is larger than a semicircle.

Arco mayor (p. 467) Un arco mayor de un círculo es cualquier arco más grande que un semicírculo.

Example $\widehat{DEF}$ is a major arc of ⊙C.

Maximum (p. 708) The *y*-coordinate of the vertex of a parabola that opens downward.

Valor máximo (p. 708) La coordenada *y* del vértice en una parábola que se abre hacia abajo.

Example

Since the parabola opens downward, the *y*-coordinate of the vertex is the function's maximum value.

Means of a proportion (p. 340) In the proportion $\frac{a}{b} = \frac{c}{d}$, *b* and *c* are the means.

Valores medios de una proporción (p. 340) En la proporción $\frac{a}{b} = \frac{c}{d}$, *b* y *c* son los valores medios.

Example The product of the means of $\frac{x}{4} = \frac{x+3}{2}$ is $4(x + 3)$ or $4x + 12$.

Median of a triangle (p. 223) A median of a triangle is a segment that has as its endpoints a vertex of the triangle and the midpoint of the opposite side.

Mediana de un triángulo (p. 223) Una mediana de un triángulo es un segmento que tiene en sus extremos el vértice del triángulo y el punto medio del lado opuesto.

Example

Midsegment of a trapezoid (p. 308) The midsegment of a trapezoid is the segment that joins the midpoints of the nonparallel opposite sides of a trapezoid.

Segmento medio de un triángulo (p. 308) Un segmento medio de un triángulo es un segmento que une los puntos medios de dos lados del triángulo.

Example

Midsegment of a triangle (p. 199) A midsegment of a triangle is a segment that joins the midpoints of two sides of the triangle.

Segmento medio de un triángulo (p. 199) Un segmento medio de un triángulo es un segmento que une los puntos medios de dos lados del triángulo.

Example

Z28

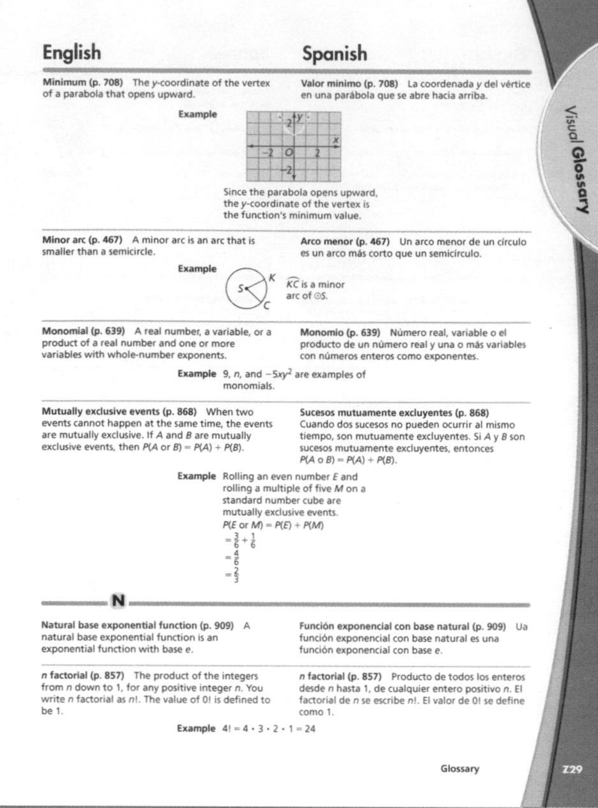

Visual Glossary

English | **Spanish**

Minimum (p. 708) The *y*-coordinate of the vertex of a parabola that opens upward.

Valor mínimo (p. 708) La coordenada *y* del vértice en una parábola que se abre hacia arriba.

Example

Since the parabola opens upward, the *y*-coordinate of the vertex is the function's minimum value.

Minor arc (p. 467) A minor arc is an arc that is smaller than a semicircle.

Arco menor (p. 467) Un arco menor de un círculo es un arco más corto que un semicírculo.

Example $\widehat{KC}$ is a minor arc of ⊙S.

Monomial (p. 639) A real number, a variable, or a product of a real number and one or more variables with whole-number exponents.

Monomio (p. 639) Número real, variable o el producto de un número real y una o más variables con números enteros como exponentes.

Example 9, *n*, and $-5xy^2$ are examples of monomials.

Mutually exclusive events (p. 868) When two events cannot happen at the same time, the events are mutually exclusive. If *A* and *B* are mutually exclusive events, then $P(A \text{ or } B) = P(A) + P(B)$.

Sucesos mutuamente excluyentes (p. 868) Cuando dos sucesos no pueden ocurrir al mismo tiempo, son mutuamente excluyentes. Si *A* y *B* son sucesos mutuamente excluyentes, entonces $P(A \text{ o } B) = P(A) + P(B)$.

Example Rolling an even number *E* and rolling a multiple of five *M* on a standard number cube are mutually exclusive events.

$$P(E \text{ or } M) = P(E) + P(M)$$
$$= \frac{3}{6} + \frac{1}{6}$$
$$= \frac{4}{6}$$
$$= \frac{2}{3}$$

N

Natural base exponential function (p. 909) A natural base exponential function is an exponential function with base *e*.

Función exponencial con base natural (p. 909) Ua función exponencial con base natural es una función exponencial con base *e*.

***n* factorial (p. 857)** The product of the integers from *n* down to 1, for any positive integer *n*. You write *n* factorial as *n*!. The value of 0! is defined to be 1.

***n* factorial (p. 857)** Producto de todos los enteros desde *n* hasta 1, de cualquier entero positivo *n*. El factorial de *n* se escribe *n*!. El valor de 0! se define como 1.

Example $4! = 4 \cdot 3 \cdot 2 \cdot 1 = 24$

Glossary Z29

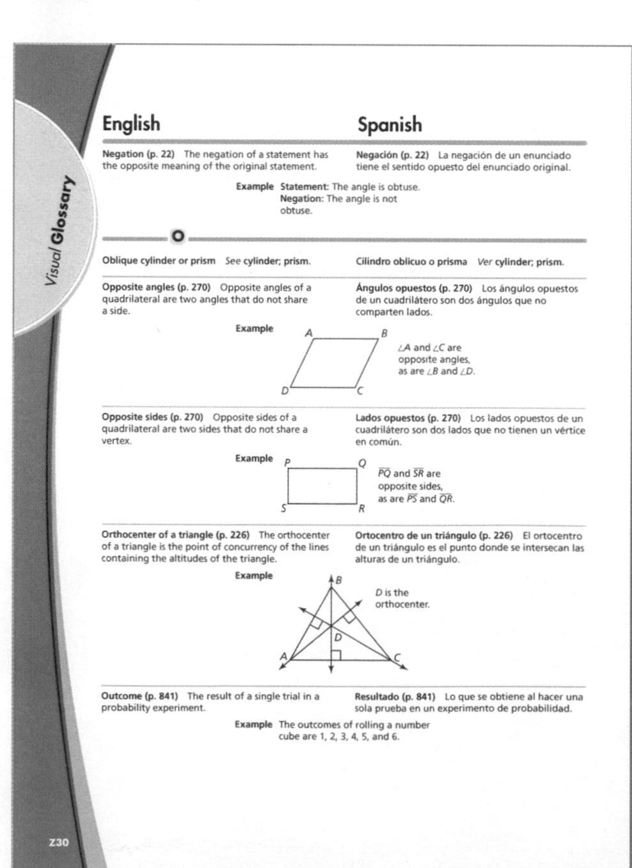

Visual Glossary

English | **Spanish**

Negation (p. 22) The negation of a statement has the opposite meaning of the original statement.

Negación (p. 22) La negación de un enunciado tiene el sentido opuesto del enunciado original.

Example **Statement:** The angle is obtuse.
Negation: The angle is not obtuse.

O

Oblique cylinder or prism *See* **cylinder; prism.**

Cilindro oblicuo o prisma *Ver* **cylinder; prism.**

Opposite angles (p. 270) Opposite angles of a quadrilateral are two angles that do not share a side.

Ángulos opuestos (p. 270) Los ángulos opuestos de un cuadrilátero son dos ángulos que no comparten lados.

Example ∠A and ∠C are opposite angles, as are ∠B and ∠D.

Opposite sides (p. 270) Opposite sides of a quadrilateral are two sides that do not share a vertex.

Lados opuestos (p. 270) Los lados opuestos de un cuadrilátero son dos lados que no tienen un vértice en común.

Example $\overline{PQ}$ and $\overline{SR}$ are opposite sides, as are $\overline{PS}$ and $\overline{QR}$.

Orthocenter of a triangle (p. 226) The orthocenter of a triangle is the point of concurrency of the lines containing the altitudes of the triangle.

Ortocentro de un triángulo (p. 226) El ortocentro de un triángulo es el punto donde se intersecan las alturas de un triángulo.

Example *D* is the orthocenter.

Outcome (p. 841) The result of a single trial in a probability experiment.

Resultado (p. 841) Lo que se obtiene al hacer una sola prueba en un experimento de probabilidad.

Example The outcomes of rolling a number cube are 1, 2, 3, 4, 5, and 6.

Z30

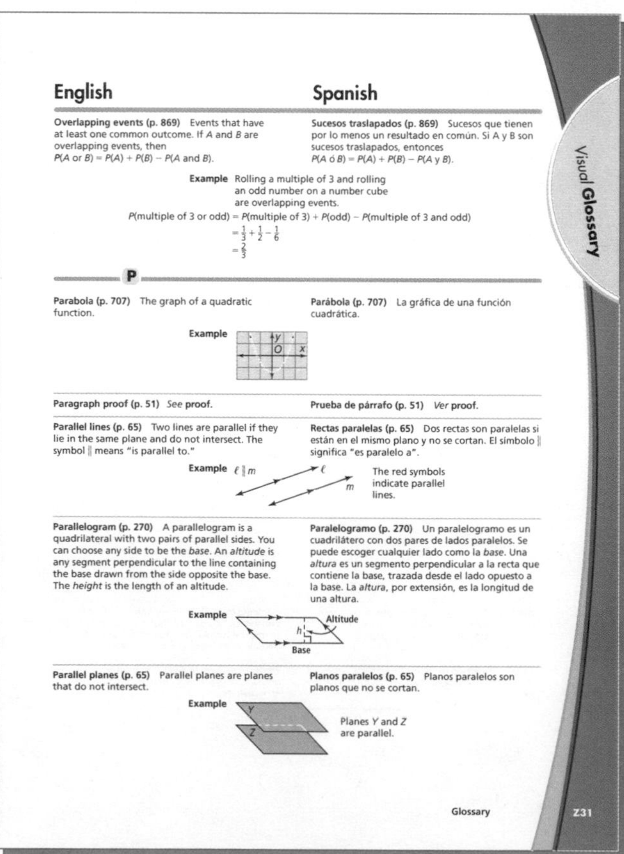

Visual Glossary

English | **Spanish**

Overlapping events (p. 869) Events that have at least one common outcome. If *A* and *B* are overlapping events, then $P(A \text{ or } B) = P(A) + P(B) - P(A \text{ and } B)$.

Sucesos traslapados (p. 869) Sucesos que tienen por lo menos un resultado en común. Si A y B son sucesos traslapados, entonces $P(A \text{ ó } B) = P(A) + P(B) - P(A \text{ y } B)$.

Example Rolling a multiple of 3 and rolling an odd number on a number cube are overlapping events.

$$P(\text{multiple of 3 or odd}) = P(\text{multiple of 3}) + P(\text{odd}) - P(\text{multiple of 3 and odd})$$
$$= \frac{1}{3} + \frac{1}{2} - \frac{1}{6}$$
$$= \frac{2}{3}$$

P

Parabola (p. 707) The graph of a quadratic function.

Parábola (p. 707) La gráfica de una función cuadrática.

Example

Paragraph proof (p. 51) *See* **proof.**

Prueba de párrafo (p. 51) *Ver* **proof.**

Parallel lines (p. 65) Two lines are parallel if they lie in the same plane and do not intersect. The symbol ∥ means "is parallel to."

Rectas paralelas (p. 65) Dos rectas son paralelas si están en el mismo plano y no se cortan. El símbolo ∥ significa "es paralelo a".

Example $\ell \parallel m$ The red symbols indicate parallel lines.

Parallelogram (p. 270) A parallelogram is a quadrilateral with two pairs of parallel sides. You can choose any side to be the *base*. An *altitude* is any segment perpendicular to the line containing the base drawn from the side opposite the base. The *height* is the length of an altitude.

Paralelogramo (p. 270) Un paralelogramo es un cuadrilátero con dos pares de lados paralelos. Se puede escoger cualquier lado como la *base*. Una *altura* es un segmento perpendicular a la recta que contiene la base, trazada desde el lado opuesto a la base. La *altura*, por extensión, es la longitud de una altura.

Example

Parallel planes (p. 65) Parallel planes are planes that do not intersect.

Planos paralelos (p. 65) Planos paralelos son planos que no se cortan.

Example Planes *Y* and *Z* are parallel.

Glossary Z31

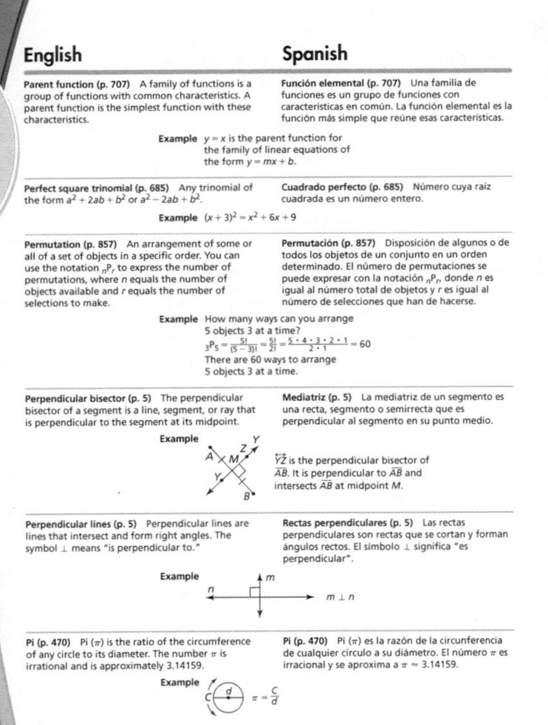

Visual Glossary

English	Spanish
Parent function (p. 707) A family of functions is a group of functions with common characteristics. A parent function is the simplest function with these characteristics.	**Función elemental (p. 707)** Una familia de funciones es un grupo de funciones con características en común. La función elemental es la función más simple que reúne esas características.

Example $y = x$ is the parent function for the family of linear equations of the form $y = mx + b$.

English	Spanish
Perfect square trinomial (p. 685) Any trinomial of the form $a^2 + 2ab + b^2$ or $a^2 - 2ab + b^2$.	**Cuadrado perfecto (p. 685)** Número cuya raíz cuadrada es un número entero.

Example $(x + 3)^2 = x^2 + 6x + 9$

English	Spanish
Permutation (p. 857) An arrangement of some or all of a set of objects in a specific order. You can use the notation ${}_nP_r$ to express the number of permutations, where n equals the number of objects available and r equals the number of selections to make.	**Permutación (p. 857)** Disposición de algunos o de todos los objetos de un conjunto en un orden determinado. El número de permutaciones se puede expresar con la notación ${}_nP_r$, donde n es igual al número total de objetos y r es igual al número de selecciones que han de hacerse.

Example How many ways can you arrange 5 objects 3 at a time?
${}_5P_3 = \frac{5!}{(5-3)!} = \frac{5!}{2!} = \frac{5 \cdot 4 \cdot 3 \cdot 2 \cdot 1}{2 \cdot 1} = 60$
There are 60 ways to arrange 5 objects 3 at a time.

English	Spanish
Perpendicular bisector (p. 5) The perpendicular bisector of a segment is a line, segment, or ray that is perpendicular to the segment at its midpoint.	**Mediatriz (p. 5)** La mediatriz de un segmento es una recta, segmento o semirrecta que es perpendicular al segmento en su punto medio.

Example $\overleftrightarrow{YZ}$ is the perpendicular bisector of $\overline{AB}$. It is perpendicular to $\overline{AB}$ and intersects $\overline{AB}$ at midpoint M.

English	Spanish
Perpendicular lines (p. 5) Perpendicular lines are lines that intersect and form right angles. The symbol $\perp$ means "is perpendicular to."	**Rectas perpendiculares (p. 5)** Las rectas perpendiculares son rectas que se cortan y forman ángulos rectos. El símbolo $\perp$ significa "es perpendicular".

Example $m \perp n$

English	Spanish
Pi (p. 470) Pi (π) is the ratio of the circumference of any circle to its diameter. The number π is irrational and is approximately 3.14159.	**Pi (p. 470)** Pi (π) es la razón de la circunferencia de cualquier círculo a su diámetro. El número π es irracional y se aproxima a $\pi \approx 3.14159$.

Example $\pi = \frac{C}{d}$

Z32

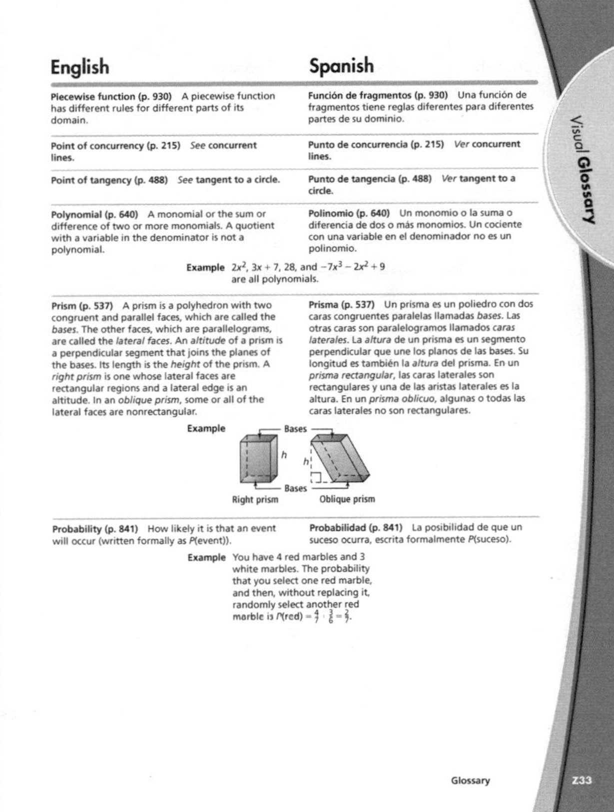

Visual Glossary

English	Spanish
Piecewise function (p. 930) A piecewise function has different rules for different parts of its domain.	**Función de fragmentos (p. 930)** Una función de fragmentos tiene reglas diferentes para diferentes partes de su dominio.
Point of concurrency (p. 215) *See* concurrent lines.	**Punto de concurrencia (p. 215)** *Ver* concurrent lines.
Point of tangency (p. 488) *See* tangent to a circle.	**Punto de tangencia (p. 488)** *Ver* tangent to a circle.
Polynomial (p. 640) A monomial or the sum or difference of two or more monomials. A quotient with a variable in the denominator is not a polynomial.	**Polinomio (p. 640)** Un monomio o la suma o diferencia de dos o más monomios. Un cociente con una variable en el denominador no es un polinomio.

Example $2x^2$, $3x + 7$, 28, and $-7x^3 - 2x^2 + 9$ are all polynomials.

English	Spanish
Prism (p. 537) A prism is a polyhedron with two congruent and parallel faces, which are called the *bases*. The other faces, which are parallelograms, are called the *lateral faces*. An *altitude* of a prism is a perpendicular segment that joins the planes of the bases. Its length is the *height* of the prism. A *right prism* is one whose lateral faces are rectangular regions and a lateral edge is an altitude. In an *oblique prism*, some or all of the lateral faces are nonrectangular.	**Prisma (p. 537)** Un prisma es un poliedro con dos caras congruentes paralelas llamadas *bases*. Las otras caras son paralelogramos llamados *caras laterales*. La *altura* de un prisma es un segmento perpendicular que une los planos de las bases. Su longitud es también la *altura* del prisma. En un *prisma rectangular*, las caras laterales son rectangulares y una de las aristas laterales es la altura. En un *prisma oblicuo*, algunas o todas las caras laterales no son rectangulares.

Example Bases, h, Right prism, Oblique prism

English	Spanish
Probability (p. 841) How likely it is that an event will occur (written formally as P(event)).	**Probabilidad (p. 841)** La posibilidad de que un suceso ocurra, escrita formalmente P(suceso).

Example You have 4 red marbles and 3 white marbles. The probability that you select one red marble, and then, without replacing it, randomly select another red marble is $P(\text{red}) = \frac{4}{7} \cdot \frac{3}{6} = \frac{2}{7}$.

Glossary Z33

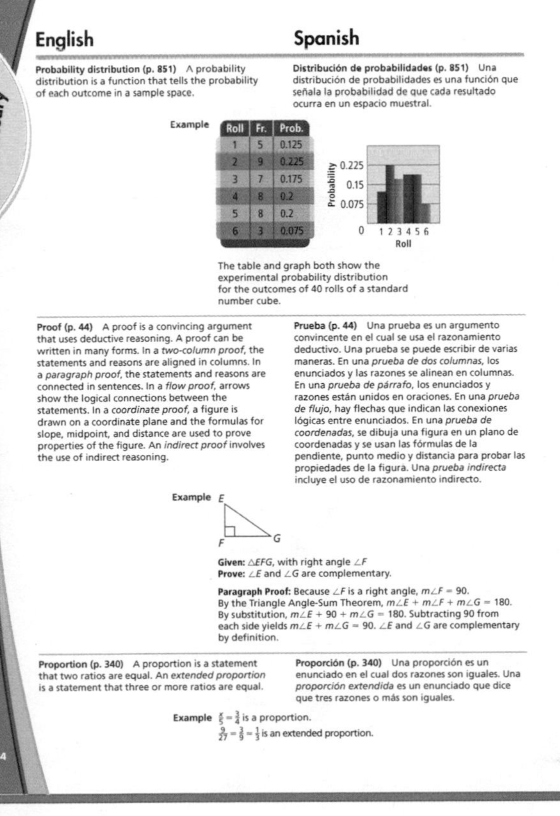

Visual Glossary

English	Spanish
Probability distribution (p. 851) A probability distribution is a function that tells the probability of each outcome in a sample space.	**Distribución de probabilidades (p. 851)** Una distribución de probabilidades es una función que señala la probabilidad de que cada resultado ocurra en un espacio muestral.

Example

Roll	Fr.	Prob.
1	5	0.125
2	9	0.225
3	7	0.175
4	8	0.2
5	8	0.2
6	3	0.075

The table and graph both show the experimental probability distribution for the outcomes of 40 rolls of a standard number cube.

English	Spanish
Proof (p. 44) A proof is a convincing argument that uses deductive reasoning. A proof can be written in many forms. In a *two-column proof*, the statements and reasons are aligned in columns. In a *paragraph proof*, the statements and reasons are connected in sentences. In a *flow proof*, arrows show the logical connections between the statements. In a *coordinate proof*, a figure is drawn on a coordinate plane and the formulas for slope, midpoint, and distance are used to prove properties of the figure. An *indirect proof* involves the use of indirect reasoning.	**Prueba (p. 44)** Una prueba es un argumento convincente en el cual se usa el razonamiento deductivo. Una prueba se puede escribir de varias maneras. En una *prueba de dos columnas*, los enunciados y las razones se alinean en columnas. En una *prueba de párrafo*, los enunciados y razones están unidos en oraciones. En una *prueba de flujo*, hay flechas que indican las conexiones lógicas entre enunciados. En una *prueba de coordenadas*, se dibuja una figura en un plano de coordenadas y se usan las fórmulas de la pendiente, punto medio y distancia para probar las propiedades de la figura. Una *prueba indirecta* incluye el uso de razonamiento indirecto.

Example

Given: $\triangle EFG$, with right angle $\angle F$
Prove: $\angle E$ and $\angle G$ are complementary.

Paragraph Proof: Because $\angle F$ is a right angle, $m\angle F = 90$. By the Triangle Angle-Sum Theorem, $m\angle E + m\angle F + m\angle G = 180$. By substitution, $m\angle E + 90 + m\angle G = 180$. Subtracting 90 from each side yields $m\angle E + m\angle G = 90$. $\angle E$ and $\angle G$ are complementary by definition.

English	Spanish
Proportion (p. 340) A proportion is a statement that two ratios are equal. An *extended proportion* is a statement that three or more ratios are equal.	**Proporción (p. 340)** Una proporción es un enunciado en el cual dos razones son iguales. Una *proporción extendida* es un enunciado que dice que tres razones o más son iguales.

Example $\frac{x}{5} = \frac{3}{4}$ is a proportion.
$\frac{9}{27} = \frac{3}{9} = \frac{1}{3}$ is an extended proportion.

Z34

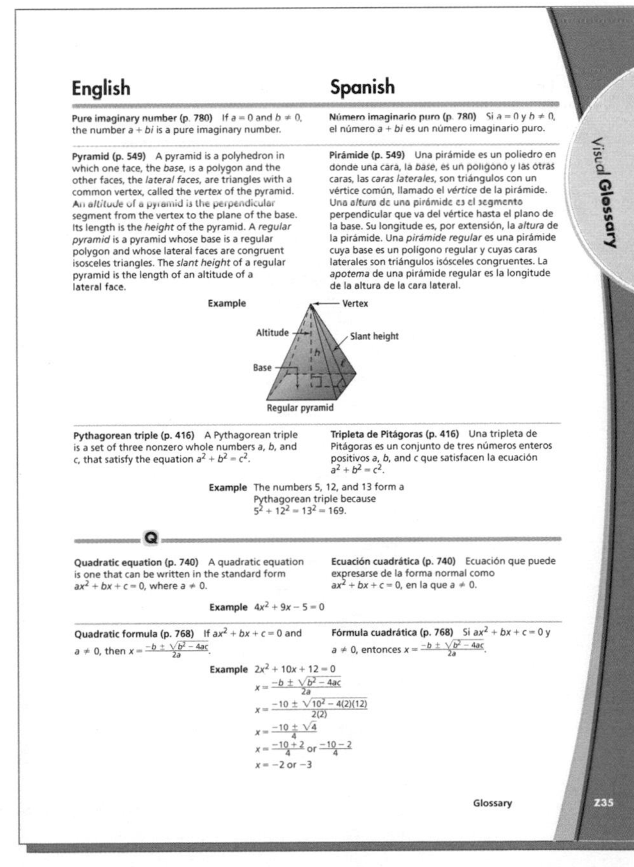

Visual Glossary

English	Spanish
Pure imaginary number (p. 780) If $a = 0$ and $b \neq 0$, the number $a + bi$ is a pure imaginary number.	**Número imaginario puro (p. 780)** Si $a = 0$ y $b \neq 0$, el número $a + bi$ es un número imaginario puro.
Pyramid (p. 549) A pyramid is a polyhedron in which one face, the *base*, is a polygon and the other faces, the *lateral faces*, are triangles with a common vertex, called the *vertex* of the pyramid. An *altitude* of a pyramid is the perpendicular segment from the vertex to the plane of the base. Its length is the *height* of the pyramid. A *regular pyramid* is a pyramid whose base is a regular polygon and whose lateral faces are congruent isosceles triangles. The *slant height* of a regular pyramid is the length of an altitude of a lateral face.	**Pirámide (p. 549)** Una pirámide es un poliedro en donde una cara, la *base*, es un polígono y las otras caras, las *caras laterales*, son triángulos con un vértice común, llamado el *vértice* de la pirámide. Una *altura* de una pirámide es el segmento perpendicular que va del vértice hasta el plano de la base. Su longitud es, por extensión, la *altura* de la pirámide. Una *pirámide regular* es una pirámide cuya base es un polígono regular y cuyas caras laterales son triángulos isósceles congruentes. La *apotema* de una pirámide regular es la longitud de la altura de la cara lateral.

Example Vertex, Altitude, Slant height, Base, Regular pyramid

English	Spanish
Pythagorean triple (p. 416) A Pythagorean triple is a set of three nonzero whole numbers a, b, and c, that satisfy the equation $a^2 + b^2 = c^2$.	**Tripleta de Pitágoras (p. 416)** Una tripleta de Pitágoras es un conjunto de tres números enteros positivos a, b, and c que satisfacen la ecuación $a^2 + b^2 = c^2$.

Example The numbers 5, 12, and 13 form a Pythagorean triple because $5^2 + 12^2 = 13^2 = 169$.

Q

English	Spanish
Quadratic equation (p. 740) A quadratic equation is one that can be written in the standard form $ax^2 + bx + c = 0$, where $a \neq 0$.	**Ecuación cuadrática (p. 740)** Ecuación que puede expresarse de la forma normal como $ax^2 + bx + c = 0$, en la que $a \neq 0$.

Example $4x^2 + 9x - 5 = 0$

English	Spanish
Quadratic formula (p. 768) If $ax^2 + bx + c = 0$ and $a \neq 0$, then $x = \frac{-b \pm \sqrt{b^2 - 4ac}}{2a}$.	**Fórmula cuadrática (p. 768)** Si $ax^2 + bx + c = 0$ y $a \neq 0$, entonces $x = \frac{-b \pm \sqrt{b^2 - 4ac}}{2a}$.

Example $2x^2 + 10x + 12 = 0$

$x = \frac{-b \pm \sqrt{b^2 - 4ac}}{2a}$

$x = \frac{-10 \pm \sqrt{10^2 - 4(2)(12)}}{2(2)}$

$x = \frac{-10 \pm \sqrt{4}}{4}$

$x = \frac{-10 + 2}{4}$ or $\frac{-10 - 2}{4}$

$x = -2$ or -3

Glossary Z35

Visual Glossary

Visual **Glossary**

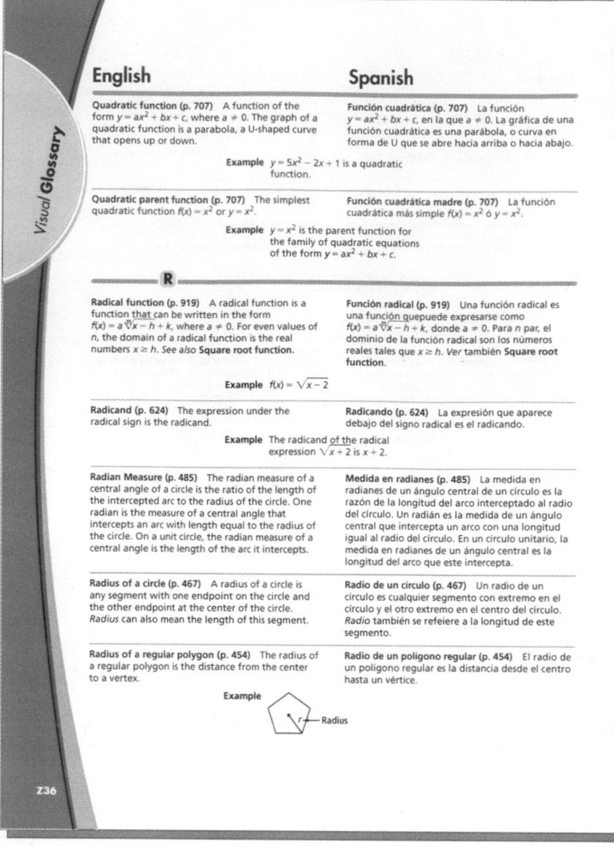

Visual **Glossary**

English	Spanish
Quadratic function (p. 707) A function of the form $y = ax^2 + bx + c$, where $a \neq 0$. The graph of a quadratic function is a parabola, a U-shaped curve that opens up or down.	**Función cuadrática (p. 707)** La función $y = ax^2 + bx + c$, en la que $a \neq 0$. La gráfica de una función cuadrática es una parábola, o curva en forma de U que se abre hacia arriba o hacia abajo.

Example $y = 5x^2 - 2x + 1$ is a quadratic function.

English	Spanish
Quadratic parent function (p. 707) The simplest quadratic function $f(x) = x^2$ or $y = x^2$.	**Función cuadrática madre (p. 707)** La función cuadrática más simple $f(x) = x^2$ ó $y = x^2$.

Example $y = x^2$ is the parent function for the family of quadratic equations of the form $y = ax^2 + bx + c$.

R

English	Spanish
Radical function (p. 919) A radical function is a function that can be written in the form $f(x) = a\sqrt[n]{x - h} + k$, where $a \neq 0$. For even values of *n*, the domain of a radical function is the real numbers $x \geq h$. *See also* **Square root function.**	**Función radical (p. 919)** Una función radical es una función quepuede expresarse como $f(x) = a\sqrt[n]{x - h} + k$, donde $a \neq 0$. Para *n* par, el dominio de la función radical son los números reales tales que $x \geq h$. *Ver* también **Square root function.**

Example $f(x) = \sqrt{x - 2}$

English	Spanish
Radicand (p. 624) The expression under the radical sign is the radicand.	**Radicando (p. 624)** La expresión que aparece debajo del signo radical es el radicando.

Example The radicand of the radical expression $\sqrt{x + 2}$ is $x + 2$.

English	Spanish
Radian Measure (p. 485) The radian measure of a central angle of a circle is the ratio of the length of the intercepted arc to the radius of the circle. One radian is the measure of a central angle that intercepts an arc with length equal to the radius of the circle. On a unit circle, the radian measure of a central angle is the length of the arc it intercepts.	**Medida en radianes (p. 485)** La medida en radianes de un ángulo central de un círculo es la razón de la longitud del arco interceptado al radio del círculo. Un radián es la medida de un ángulo central que intercepta un arco con una longitud igual al radio del círculo. En un círculo unitario, la medida en radianes de un ángulo central es la longitud del arco que este intercepta.
Radius of a circle (p. 467) A radius of a circle is any segment with one endpoint on the circle and the other endpoint at the center of the circle. *Radius* can also mean the length of this segment.	**Radio de un circulo (p. 467)** Un radio de un círculo es cualquier segmento con extremo en el círculo y el otro extremo en el centro del círculo. *Radio* también se refeiere a la longitud de este segmento.
Radius of a regular polygon (p. 454) The radius of a regular polygon is the distance from the center to a vertex.	**Radio de un polígono regular (p. 454)** El radio de un polígono regular es la distancia desde el centro hasta un vértice.

Example

Z36

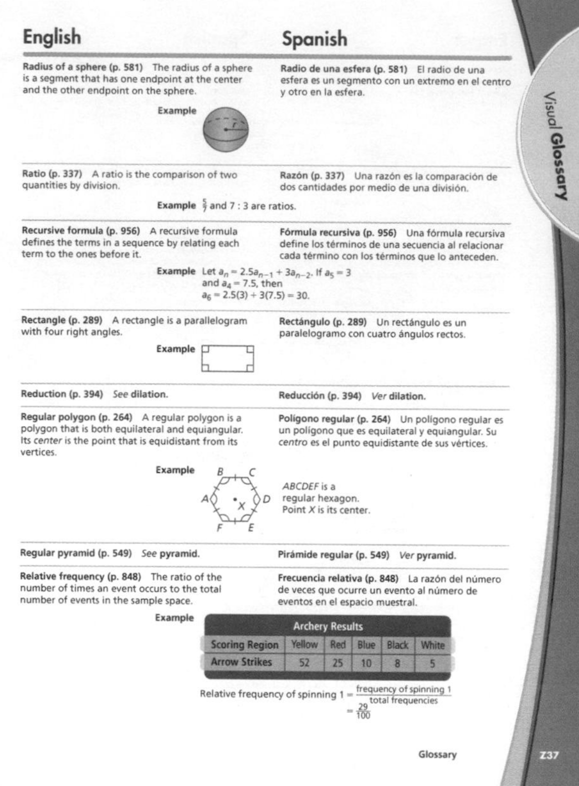

English	Spanish
Radius of a sphere (p. 581) The radius of a sphere is a segment that has one endpoint at the center and the other endpoint on the sphere.	**Radio de una esfera (p. 581)** El radio de una esfera es un segmento con un extremo en el centro y otro en la esfera.

Example

English	Spanish
Ratio (p. 337) A ratio is the comparison of two quantities by division.	**Razón (p. 337)** Una razón es la comparación de dos cantidades por medio de una división.

Example $\frac{5}{7}$ and 7 : 3 are ratios.

English	Spanish
Recursive formula (p. 956) A recursive formula defines the terms in a sequence by relating each term to the ones before it.	**Fórmula recursiva (p. 956)** Una fórmula recursiva define los términos de una secuencia al relacionar cada término con los términos que lo anteceden.

Example Let $a_n = 2.5a_{n-1} + 3a_{n-2}$. If $a_5 = 3$ and $a_4 = 7.5$, then $a_6 = 2.5(3) + 3(7.5) = 30$.

English	Spanish
Rectangle (p. 289) A rectangle is a parallelogram with four right angles.	**Rectángulo (p. 289)** Un rectángulo es un paralelogramo con cuatro ángulos rectos.

Example

English	Spanish
Reduction (p. 394) *See* **dilation.**	**Reducción (p. 394)** *Ver* **dilation.**
Regular polygon (p. 264) A regular polygon is a polygon that is both equilateral and equiangular. Its *center* is the point that is equidistant from its vertices.	**Polígono regular (p. 264)** Un polígono regular es un polígono que es equilateral y equiangular. Su *centro* es el punto equidistante de sus vértices.

Example

ABCDEF is a regular hexagon. Point *X* is its center.

English	Spanish
Regular pyramid (p. 549) *See* **pyramid.**	**Pirámide regular (p. 549)** *Ver* **pyramid.**
Relative frequency (p. 848) The ratio of the number of times an event occurs to the total number of events in the sample space.	**Frecuencia relativa (p. 848)** La razón del número de veces que ocurre un evento al número de eventos en el espacio muestral.

Example

Archery Results

Scoring Region	Yellow	Red	Blue	Black	White
Arrow Strikes	52	25	10	8	5

Relative frequency of spinning 1 $= \frac{\text{frequency of spinning 1}}{\text{total frequencies}} = \frac{29}{100}$

Glossary Z37

Visual **Glossary**

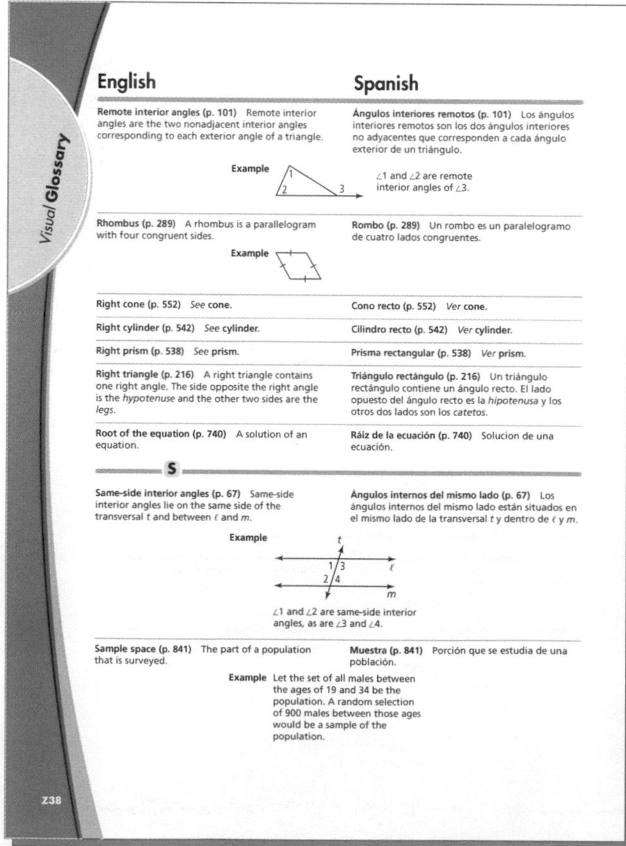

Visual **Glossary**

English	Spanish
Remote interior angles (p. 101) Remote interior angles are the two nonadjacent interior angles corresponding to each exterior angle of a triangle.	**Ángulos interiores remotos (p. 101)** Los ángulos interiores remotos son los dos ángulos interiores no adyacentes que corresponden a cada ángulo exterior de un triángulo.

Example

$\angle 1$ and $\angle 2$ are remote interior angles of $\angle 3$.

English	Spanish
Rhombus (p. 289) A rhombus is a parallelogram with four congruent sides.	**Rombo (p. 289)** Un rombo es un paralelogramo de cuatro lados congruentes.

Example

English	Spanish
Right cone (p. 552) *See* **cone.**	**Cono recto (p. 552)** *Ver* **cone.**
Right cylinder (p. 542) *See* **cylinder.**	**Cilindro recto (p. 542)** *Ver* **cylinder.**
Right prism (p. 538) *See* **prism.**	**Prisma rectangular (p. 538)** *Ver* **prism.**
Right triangle (p. 216) A right triangle contains one right angle. The side opposite the right angle is the *hypotenuse* and the other two sides are the *legs*.	**Triángulo rectángulo (p. 216)** Un triángulo rectángulo contiene un ángulo recto. El lado opuesto del ángulo recto es la *hipotenusa* y los otros dos lados son los *catetos*.
Root of the equation (p. 740) A solution of an equation.	**Ráiz de la ecuación (p. 740)** Solucion de una ecuación.

S

English	Spanish
Same-side interior angles (p. 67) Same-side interior angles lie on the same side of the transversal *t* and between ℓ and *m*.	**Ángulos internos del mismo lado (p. 67)** Los ángulos internos del mismo lado están situados en el mismo lado de la transversal *t* y dentro de ℓ y *m*.

Example

$\angle 1$ and $\angle 2$ are same-side interior angles, as are $\angle 3$ and $\angle 4$.

English	Spanish
Sample space (p. 841) The part of a population that is surveyed.	**Muestra (p. 841)** Porción que se estudia de una población.

Example Let the set of all males between the ages of 19 and 34 be the population. A random selection of 900 males between those ages would be a sample of the population.

Z38

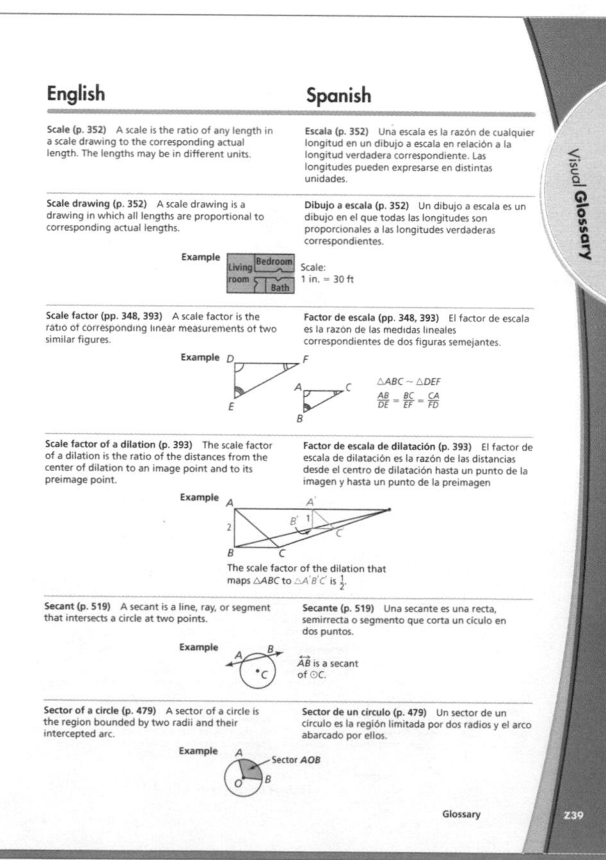

Visual **Glossary**

English	Spanish
Scale (p. 352) A scale is the ratio of any length in a scale drawing to the corresponding actual length. The lengths may be in different units.	**Escala (p. 352)** Una escala es la razón de cualquier longitud en un dibujo a escala en relación a la longitud verdadera correspondiente. Las longitudes pueden expresarse en distintas unidades.
Scale drawing (p. 352) A scale drawing is a drawing in which all lengths are proportional to corresponding actual lengths.	**Dibujo a escala (p. 352)** Un dibujo a escala es un dibujo en el que todas las longitudes son proporcionales a las longitudes verdaderas correspondientes.

Example

Scale: 1 in. = 30 ft

English	Spanish
Scale factor (pp. 348, 393) A scale factor is the ratio of corresponding linear measurements of two similar figures.	**Factor de escala (pp. 348, 393)** El factor de escala es la razon de las medidas lineales correspondientes de dos figuras semejantes.

Example

$\triangle ABC \sim \triangle DEF$

$\frac{AB}{DE} = \frac{BC}{EF} = \frac{CA}{FD}$

English	Spanish
Scale factor of a dilation (p. 393) The scale factor of a dilation is the ratio of the distances from the center of dilation to an image point and to its preimage point.	**Factor de escala de dilatación (p. 393)** El factor de escala de dilatación es la razón de las distancias desde el centro de dilatación hasta un punto de la imagen y hasta un punto de la preimagen

Example

The scale factor of the dilation that maps $\triangle ABC$ to $\triangle A'B'C'$ is $\frac{1}{2}$.

English	Spanish
Secant (p. 519) A secant is a line, ray, or segment that intersects a circle at two points.	**Secante (p. 519)** Una secante es una recta, semirrecta o segmento que corta un cículo en dos puntos.

Example

$\overleftrightarrow{AB}$ is a secant of $\odot C$.

English	Spanish
Sector of a circle (p. 479) A sector of a circle is the region bounded by two radii and their intercepted arc.	**Sector de un círculo (p. 479)** Un sector de un círculo es la región limitada por dos radios y el arco abarcado por ellos.

Example

Glossary Z39

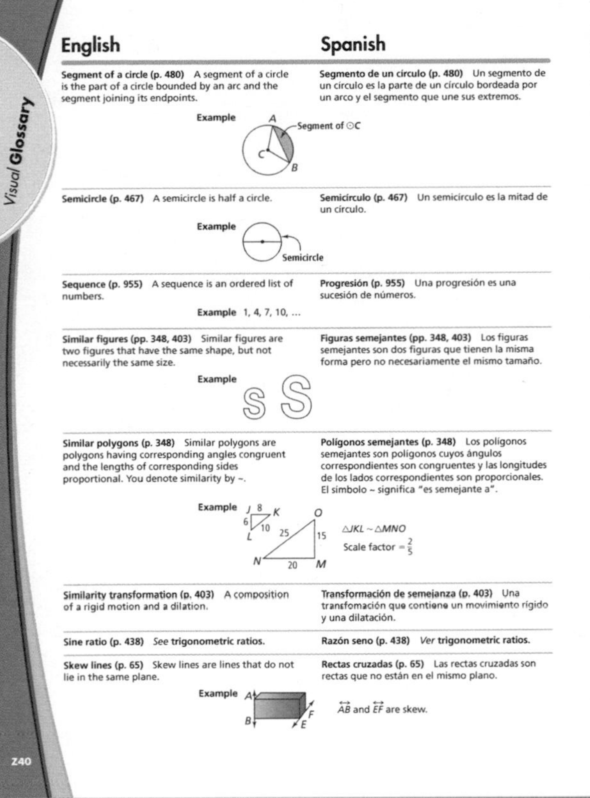

Visual Glossary

English | Spanish

Segment of a circle (p. 480) A segment of a circle is the part of a circle bounded by an arc and the segment joining its endpoints.

Segmento de un círculo (p. 480) Un segmento de un círculo es la parte de un círculo bordeada por un arco y el segmento que une sus extremos.

Example A, B, C, Segment of ⊙C

Semicircle (p. 467) A semicircle is half a circle.

Semicírculo (p. 467) Un semicírculo es la mitad de un círculo.

Example Semicircle

Sequence (p. 955) A sequence is an ordered list of numbers.

Progresión (p. 955) Una progresión es una sucesión de números.

Example 1, 4, 7, 10, ...

Similar figures (pp. 348, 403) Similar figures are two figures that have the same shape, but not necessarily the same size.

Figuras semejantes (pp. 348, 403) Los figuras semejantes son dos figuras que tienen la misma forma pero no necesariamente el mismo tamaño.

Example S S

Similar polygons (p. 348) Similar polygons are polygons having corresponding angles congruent and the lengths of corresponding sides proportional. You denote similarity by ~.

Polígonos semejantes (p. 348) Los polígonos semejantes son polígonos cuyos ángulos correspondientes son congruentes y las longitudes de los lados correspondientes son proporcionales. El símbolo ~ significa "es semejante a".

Example J, K, L, 8, 6, 10; N, O, M, 25, 15, 20

$\triangle JKL \sim \triangle MNO$

Scale factor $= \frac{2}{5}$

Similarity transformation (p. 403) A composition of a rigid motion and a dilation.

Transformación de semejanza (p. 403) Una transfomación que contiene un movimiento rígido y una dilatación.

Sine ratio (p. 438) *See* **trigonometric ratios.**

Razón seno (p. 438) *Ver* **trigonometric ratios.**

Skew lines (p. 65) Skew lines are lines that do not lie in the same plane.

Rectas cruzadas (p. 65) Las rectas cruzadas son rectas que no están en el mismo plano.

Example A, B, E, F

$\overleftrightarrow{AB}$ and $\overleftrightarrow{EF}$ are skew.

Z40

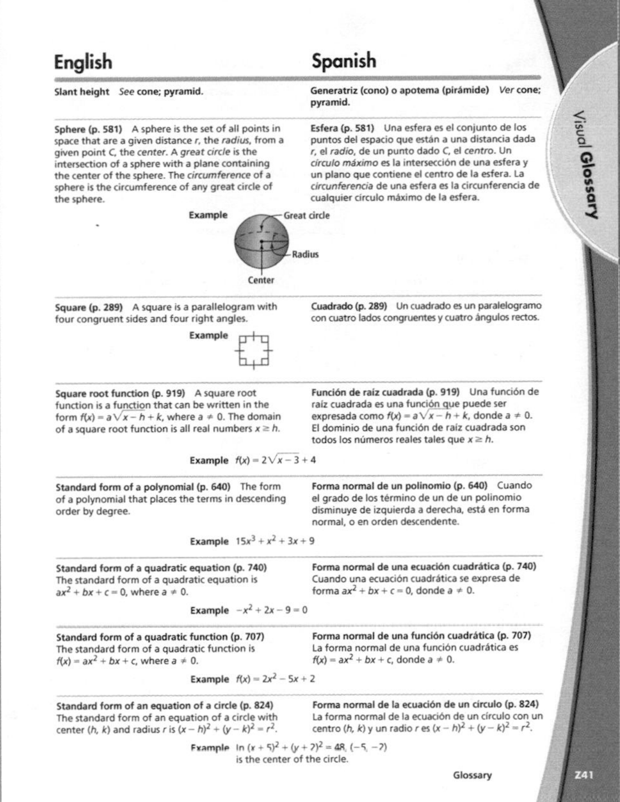

English | Spanish

Slant height *See* **cone; pyramid.**

Generatriz (cono) o apotema (pirámide) *Ver* **cone; pyramid.**

Sphere (p. 581) A sphere is the set of all points in space that are a given distance *r*, the *radius*, from a given point *C*, the *center*. A *great circle* is the intersection of a sphere with a plane containing the center of the sphere. The *circumference* of a sphere is the circumference of any great circle of the sphere.

Esfera (p. 581) Una esfera es el conjunto de los puntos del espacio que están a una distancia dada *r*, el *radio*, de un punto dado *C*, el *centro*. Un *círculo máximo* es la intersección de una esfera y un plano que contiene el centro de la esfera. La *circunferencia* de una esfera es la circunferencia de cualquier círculo máximo de la esfera.

Example Great circle, Radius, Center

Square (p. 289) A square is a parallelogram with four congruent sides and four right angles.

Cuadrado (p. 289) Un cuadrado es un paralelogramo con cuatro lados congruentes y cuatro ángulos rectos.

Example

Square root function (p. 919) A square root function is a function that can be written in the form $f(x) = a\sqrt{x-h} + k$, where $a \neq 0$. The domain of a square root function is all real numbers $x \geq h$.

Función de raíz cuadrada (p. 919) Una función de raíz cuadrada es una función que puede ser expresada como $f(x) = a\sqrt{x-h} + k$, donde $a \neq 0$. El dominio de una función de raíz cuadrada son todos los números reales tales que $x \geq h$.

Example $f(x) = 2\sqrt{x-3} + 4$

Standard form of a polynomial (p. 640) The form of a polynomial that places the terms in descending order by degree.

Forma normal de un polinomio (p. 640) Cuando el grado de los término de un de un polinomio disminuye de izquierda a derecha, está en forma normal, o en orden descendente.

Example $15x^3 + x^2 + 3x + 9$

Standard form of a quadratic equation (p. 740) The standard form of a quadratic equation is $ax^2 + bx + c = 0$, where $a \neq 0$.

Forma normal de una ecuación cuadrática (p. 740) Cuando una ecuación cuadrática se expresa de forma $ax^2 + bx + c = 0$, donde $a \neq 0$.

Example $-x^2 + 2x - 9 = 0$

Standard form of a quadratic function (p. 707) The standard form of a quadratic function is $f(x) = ax^2 + bx + c$, where $a \neq 0$.

Forma normal de una función cuadrática (p. 707) La forma normal de una función cuadrática es $f(x) = ax^2 + bx + c$, donde $a \neq 0$.

Example $f(x) = 2x^2 - 5x + 2$

Standard form of an equation of a circle (p. 824) The standard form of an equation of a circle with center (h, k) and radius r is $(x-h)^2 + (y-k)^2 = r^2$.

Forma normal de la ecuación de un círculo (p. 824) La forma normal de la ecuación de un círculo con un centro (h, k) y un radio r es $(x-h)^2 + (y-k)^2 = r^2$.

Example In $(x+5)^2 + (y+2)^2 = 48$, $(-5, -2)$ is the center of the circle.

Glossary Z41

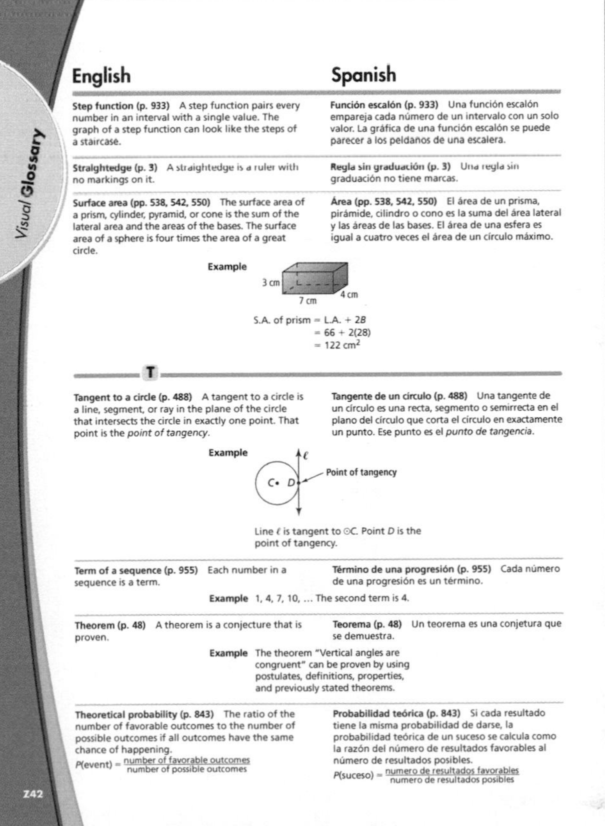

English | Spanish

Step function (p. 933) A step function pairs every number in an interval with a single value. The graph of a step function can look like the steps of a staircase.

Función escalón (p. 933) Una función escalón empareja cada número de un intervalo con un solo valor. La gráfica de una función escalón se puede parecer a los peldaños de una escalera.

Straightedge (p. 3) A straightedge is a ruler with no markings on it.

Regla sin graduación (p. 3) Una regla sin graduación no tiene marcas.

Surface area (pp. 538, 542, 550) The surface area of a prism, cylinder, pyramid, or cone is the sum of the lateral area and the areas of the bases. The surface area of a sphere is four times the area of a great circle.

Área (pp. 538, 542, 550) El área de un prisma, pirámide, cilindro o cono es la suma del área lateral y las áreas de las bases. El área de una esfera es igual a cuatro veces el área de un círculo máximo.

Example 3 cm, 7 cm, 4 cm

S.A. of prism = L.A. + 2*B*
= 66 + 2(28)
= 122 cm²

T

Tangent to a circle (p. 488) A tangent to a circle is a line, segment, or ray in the plane of the circle that intersects the circle in exactly one point. That point is the *point of tangency*.

Tangente de un círculo (p. 488) Una tangente de un círculo es una recta, segmento o semirrecta en el plano del círculo que corta el círculo en exactamente un punto. Ese punto es el *punto de tangencia*.

Example ℓ, C, D, Point of tangency

Line ℓ is tangent to ⊙C. Point *D* is the point of tangency.

Term of a sequence (p. 955) Each number in a sequence is a term.

Término de una progresión (p. 955) Cada número de una progresión es un término.

Example 1, 4, 7, 10, ... The second term is 4.

Theorem (p. 48) A theorem is a conjecture that is proven.

Teorema (p. 48) Un teorema es una conjetura que se demuestra.

Example The theorem "Vertical angles are congruent" can be proven by using postulates, definitions, properties, and previously stated theorems.

Theoretical probability (p. 843) The ratio of the number of favorable outcomes to the number of possible outcomes if all outcomes have the same chance of happening.

$P(\text{event}) = \frac{\text{number of favorable outcomes}}{\text{number of possible outcomes}}$

Probabilidad teórica (p. 843) Si cada resultado tiene la misma probabilidad de darse, la probabilidad teórica de un suceso se calcula como la razón del número de resultados favorables al número de resultados posibles.

$P(\text{suceso}) = \frac{\text{numero de resultados favorables}}{\text{numero de resultados posibles}}$

Z42

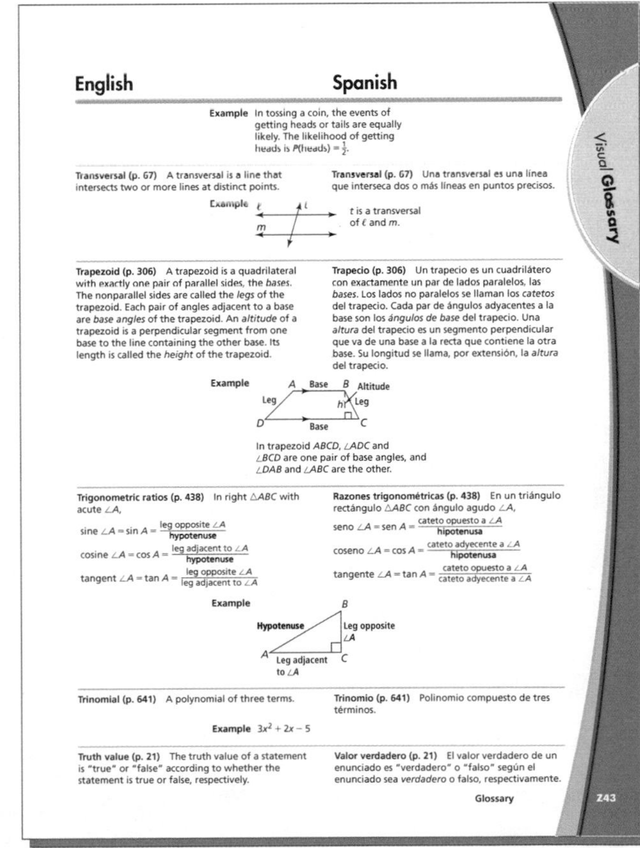

English | Spanish

Example In tossing a coin, the events of getting heads or tails are equally likely. The likelihood of getting heads is $P(\text{heads}) = \frac{1}{2}$.

Transversal (p. 67) A transversal is a line that intersects two or more lines at distinct points.

Transversal (p. 67) Una transversal es una línea que interseca dos o más líneas en puntos precisos.

Example ℓ, *t*, *m*

t is a transversal of ℓ and *m*.

Trapezoid (p. 306) A trapezoid is a quadrilateral with exactly one pair of parallel sides, the *bases*. The nonparallel sides are called the *legs* of the trapezoid. Each pair of angles adjacent to a base are *base angles* of the trapezoid. An *altitude* of a trapezoid is a perpendicular segment from one base to the line containing the other base. Its length is called the *height* of the trapezoid.

Trapecio (p. 306) Un trapecio es un cuadrilátero con exactamente un par de lados paralelos, las *bases*. Los lados no paralelos se llaman los *catetos* del trapecio. Cada par de ángulos adyacentes a la base son los *ángulos de base* del trapecio. Una *altura* del trapecio es un segmento perpendicular que va de una base a la recta que contiene la otra base. Su longitud se llama, por extensión, la *altura* del trapecio.

Example A, B, C, D, Base, Base, Leg, Leg, *h*, Altitude

In trapezoid *ABCD*, ∠*ADC* and ∠*BCD* are one pair of base angles, and ∠*DAB* and ∠*ABC* are the other.

Trigonometric ratios (p. 438) In right $\triangle ABC$ with acute $\angle A$,

sine $\angle A = \sin A = \frac{\text{leg opposite } \angle A}{\text{hypotenuse}}$

cosine $\angle A = \cos A = \frac{\text{leg adjacent to } \angle A}{\text{hypotenuse}}$

tangent $\angle A = \tan A = \frac{\text{leg opposite } \angle A}{\text{leg adjacent to } \angle A}$

Razones trigonométricas (p. 438) En un triángulo rectángulo $\triangle ABC$ con ángulo agudo $\angle A$,

seno $\angle A = \text{sen } A = \frac{\text{cateto opuesto a } \angle A}{\text{hipotenusa}}$

coseno $\angle A = \cos A = \frac{\text{cateto adyecente a } \angle A}{\text{hipotenusa}}$

tangente $\angle A = \tan A = \frac{\text{cateto opuesto a } \angle A}{\text{cateto adyecente a } \angle A}$

Example A, B, C, Hypotenuse, Leg opposite ∠A, Leg adjacent to ∠A

Trinomial (p. 641) A polynomial of three terms.

Trinomio (p. 641) Polinomio compuesto de tres términos.

Example $3x^2 + 2x - 5$

Truth value (p. 21) The truth value of a statement is "true" or "false" according to whether the statement is true or false, respectively.

Valor verdadero (p. 21) El valor verdadero de un enunciado es "verdadero" o "falso" según el enunciado sea *verdadero* o falso, respectivamente.

Glossary Z43

Visual Glossary

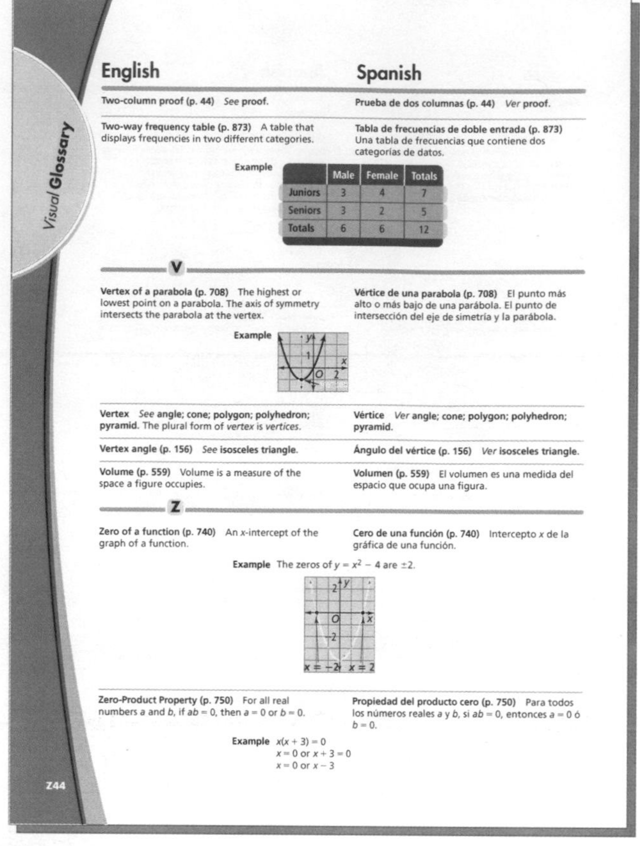

English	Spanish
Two-column proof (p. 44) *See* **proof.**	**Prueba de dos columnas (p. 44)** *Ver* **proof.**
Two-way frequency table (p. 873) A table that displays frequencies in two different categories.	**Tabla de frecuencias de doble entrada (p. 873)** Una tabla de frecuencias que contiene dos categorías de datos.

Example

	Male	Female	Totals
Juniors	3	4	7
Seniors	3	2	5
Totals	6	6	12

V

English	Spanish
Vertex of a parabola (p. 708) The highest or lowest point on a parabola. The axis of symmetry intersects the parabola at the vertex.	**Vértice de una parabola (p. 708)** El punto más alto o más bajo de una parábola. El punto de intersección del eje de simetría y la parábola.

Example

English	Spanish
Vertex *See* **angle; cone; polygon; polyhedron; pyramid.** The plural form of *vertex* is *vertices.*	**Vértice** *Ver* **angle; cone; polygon; polyhedron; pyramid.**
Vertex angle (p. 156) *See* **isosceles triangle.**	**Ángulo del vértice (p. 156)** *Ver* **isosceles triangle.**
Volume (p. 559) Volume is a measure of the space a figure occupies.	**Volumen (p. 559)** El volumen es una medida del espacio que ocupa una figura.

Z

English	Spanish
Zero of a function (p. 740) An *x*-intercept of the graph of a function.	**Cero de una función (p. 740)** Intercepto *x* de la gráfica de una función.

Example The zeros of $y = x^2 - 4$ are ± 2.

English	Spanish
Zero-Product Property (p. 750) For all real numbers a and b, if $ab = 0$, then $a = 0$ or $b = 0$.	**Propiedad del producto cero (p. 750)** Para todos los números reales a y b, si $ab = 0$, entonces $a = 0$ ó $b = 0$.

Example $x(x + 3) = 0$
$x = 0$ or $x + 3 = 0$
$x = 0$ or $x - 3$

Index

A

Index

B

C

D

E

F

G

M

N

O

P

Q

R

Index

S

T

U

V

W

Z

Acknowledgments

Staff Credits

The people who made up the High School Mathematics team—representing composition services, core design digital and multimedia production services, digital product development, editorial, editorial services, manufacturing, marketing, and production management—are listed below.

Patty Fagan, Suzanne Finn, Matt Frueh, Cynthia Harvey, Linda Johnson, Roshni Kutty, Cheryl Mahan, Eve Melnechuk, Cynthia Metallides, Hope Morley, Michael Oster, Wynnette Outland, Brian Reardon, Matthew Rogers, Ann-Marie Sheehan, Kristen Siefers, Richard Sullivan, Susan Tauer, Mark Tricca, Oscar Vera, Paula Vergith

Additional Credits: Emily Bosak, Olivia Gerde, Alyse McGuire, Stephanie Mosely

Illustration

Jeff Grunewald: 13, 14, 21, 27, 29, 36, 39, 41, 44, 52, 57, 278, 280, 293, 306, 309, 314, 316, 324, 336, 355, 357, 363, 364, 366, 370, 371, 384, 386 c, 386 b, 389, 428, 445, 687, 725; **Christopher Wilson:** 623, 643, 719, 790; **Stephen Durke:** 5, 68, 76, 85, 89, 94, 98, 101, 104, 105, 109, 127, 129, 135, 137, 141, 144, 146, 152, 154, 157, 160, 166, 177, 182, 212, 214, 215, 217, 221, 223, 224, 228, 238, 246, 248, 252, 255, 256, 257, 261, 380, 442, 446 t, 446 bl, 446 br, 450 c, 450 b, 473 b, 474, 482, 504, 932; **Phil Guzy:** 419, 425, 437, 443, 467, 470, 471, 473 t, 473 c, 486, 495, 505, 514, 516, 535, 540, 542, 543, 545, 554, 555, 557, 563, 565, 570, 576 cr; **Ted Smykel:** 710; **Rob Schuster:** 790, 884, 921, 923, 924, 927 t, 927 c, 927 b, 929, 936, 943, 952

Technical Illustration

Aptara, Inc.; Datagrafix, Inc.; GGS Book Services

Photography

Every effort has been made to secure permission and provide appropriate credit for photographic material. The publisher deeply regrets any omission and pledges to correct errors called to its attention in subsequent editions.

Unless otherwise acknowledged, all photographs are the property of Pearson Education, Inc.

34, Material courtesy of Bill Vicars and Lifeprint; **58,** Jenny Thompson/Fotolia; **71 c,** Bill Brooks/Alamy Images; **71 b,** Kevin Fleming/Corbis; **82,** Frank Adelstein; **89 t,** Robert Slade/Manor Photography/Alamy Images; **91,** Robert Llewellyn/Corbis; **105,** Peter Cade/Iconica/Getty Images; **136,** Stan Honda/Staff/AFP/Getty Images; **154,** Viktor Kitaykin/iStockphoto; **163, 164,** John Wells/ Photo Researchers, Inc.; **169,** Tony Freeman/PhotoEdit, Inc.; **171 c,** Paul Jones/Iconica/Getty Images; **171 tl,** Veer/Corbis; **174,** Image Source Black/Jupiter Images; **193 l,** M.C. Escher's "Symmetry E56" © 2009 The M.C. Escher Company-Holland. All rights reserved. www.mcescher.com; **193 r,** M.C. Escher's "Symmetry E18" © 2009 The M.C. Escher Company-Holland. All rights reserved. www.mcescher.com; **208,** Momatiuk - Eastcott/Corbis; **209,** Joseph Sohm/Visions of America, LLC/Alamy Images; **257 tr,** Gunter Marx/ Corbis; **275 t,** Anthony Bannister/Gallo Images/Corbis; Robert Harding Picture Library/Alamy Images; **275 br,** Christiana Subekti/ iStockphoto; **bl,** Laurie Strachan/Alamy; **282,** Eric Hood/ iStockphoto; **286,** Esa Hiltula/Alamy Images; **289,** Victor Fraile/ Reuters Media; **298,** Kirsty McLaren/Alamy Images; **299 l,** Claro Cortes IV/Reuters/Landov LLC; **299 r,** Michael Jenner/Alamy Images; **311 cr, 311 r,** Rodney Raschke/Active Photo Service; **320,** Colin Underhill/Alamy Images; **350,** Chuck Eckert/Alamy Images; **361,** Ron Watts/Corbis; **380 r,** ©James L. Amos/Corbis; **386 br,** Victor R. Boswell Jr./Contributor National Geographic/Getty Images; **394,** Martin William Allen/Alamy; **397 tr,** Keith Leighton/Alamy, Reven T.C. Wurman/Alamy Images; **397 bl,** D. Hurst/Alamy, Owaki – Kulla/ Corbis; **421,** Petra Wegner/Alamy Images; **432,** PhotoObjects/ Thinkstock; **439,** Steve Vidler/Imagestate Media; **447,** Dave Reede/ All Canada Photos/Alamy Images; **456,** Dennis Marsico/Corbis; **477,** Matthias Tunger/Photonica/Getty Images; **488 cr,** Marshall Space Flight Center Collection/NASA; **488 c,** T. Pohling/Alamy Images; **492 l, c, r,** Clive Streeter/©DK Images; **499** Cris Bouroncle/Staff/AFP/ Getty Images; **511,** Vario Images GmbH & Co.KG/Alamy Images; **516 tr,** Marshall Space Flight Center Collection/NASA; **516 br,** Melvyn Longhurst/Alamy; **519,** dpa/Corbis; **542 tr,** Ron Chapple Stock/Alamy; **547,** Adam Eastland/Alamy Images; **546,** age fotostock/SuperStock; **566,** John E Marriott/Alamy Images; **571,** D. Hurst/Alamy; **576 tr,** Stephen Sweet/Alamy; **632 cr,** brt PHOTO/ Alamy Images; **632 br,** Paulo Fridman/Corbis; **651,** iStockphoto; **658 tr,** iStockphoto; **658 br,** wingmar/iStockphoto; **666** Brandon Alms/Shutterstock; **728,** Jxpfeer/Dreamstime LLC; **736 b,** ©DK Images; **783,** Hank Morgan/Photo Researchers, Inc.; **793,** George Steinmetz/Corbis, **938,** Thomas J. Peterson/Alamy Images.